Gallagher

S0-BFB-822

HEATH

EARTH SCIENCE

There's no better way to learn about Earth's processes and wonders than with Heath EARTH SCIENCE.

D.C. Heath and Company

Everything you expect from Spaulding/Namowitz— comprehensive, current, manageable.

In the Tenth Edition of **Heath EARTH SCIENCE,** author Nancy Spaulding continues the Spaulding/Namowitz tradition of providing comprehensive treatment of earth science topics: geology, oceanography, astronomy, meteorology, and earth history. You'll find the most current developments in these fields presented with a real understanding of classroom needs. The result? **Heath EARTH SCIENCE** makes teaching and learning earth science more satisfying and successful than ever before. **It's your guidebook to Earth's wonders!**

You can also feel confident that the Tenth Edition of **Heath EARTH SCIENCE** — written and reviewed by experts in all fields of earth science—maintains the integrity of content of past editions. Content consultants hail from the Department of Geology at Boston University, the Scripps Institution of Oceanography, Goddard Space Flight Center, the Department of Atmospheric and Oceanic Sciences at University of Wisconsin, Woods Hole Oceanographic Institution, and the Naval Postgraduate School. (See pages i-ii for a complete listing of authors, contributing writers, content consultants, and teacher reviewers.)

Copyright ©1994 by D.C. Heath and Company

All rights reserved. No part of this publication may be reproduced or transmitted in any form by any means, electronic or mechanical, including photocopy, recording or any information storage or retrieval system, without permission in writing from the publisher.

Published simultaneously in Canada

Printed in the United States of America

International Standard Book Number: 0-669-26184-X

2 3 4 5 6 7 8 9 10 -RRD- 99 98 97 96 95 94 93

What's new in Heath EARTH SCIENCE:

- **Up-to-date treatment** of earth science topics
- **Earth Matters**—a new environmental-awareness feature
- **Current Research**—a new feature that explores current scientific research
- **Lab and Map Activities** in the text
- **Videodisc** option at point of use
- **Environmental Awareness** case studies resource

Where to find it:

Earth science makes Earth's processes understandable to all.

"Why do I have to do this? I'm never going to need to know about rocks or stars or fossils or ocean currents."

Students generally are not impressed when they hear that their day-to-day lives will be enriched by a knowledge of the planet on which they live—even if they don't choose an earth science-related career. Yet earth science is the most fundamental of the sciences, with the greatest number of applications to our lives and our world.

This is a particularly rewarding time to be studying earth science. Our knowledge and understanding of the world is expanding at a truly astonishing rate—from innovative ways to "see" inside Earth to better ways of studying space. How could students not take an interest in the findings of spacecraft flying past another planet, the earthquake potential of their home area, or the search for extraterrestrial life?

There is also growing concern about the future of our planet. Increasing carbon dioxide levels, ozone depletion, decreasing resource and energy supplies, and rapidly expanding world population are just a few of the problems that concern us today and are expected to concern us for many years to come. Our growing understanding of these problems has, in turn, increased our awareness of the need for a scientifically literate citizenry. Citizens who understand the basics of science will be able to make informed, reasoned decisions on scientific and environmental issues of the future.

To become scientifically literate, students need to learn the "language" of science. Mastery of terminology and concepts is key to making reasoned decisions about problems that involve our planet. Just as important is a thorough understanding of basic earth science concepts: Earth's position in space; the enormous duration of geologic time in comparison with human history; changes—massive and minute—Earth has undergone; the behavior of streams, glaciers, winds, waves, and gravity; causes and patterns of day-to-day weather changes. Knowledge of these concepts not only constitutes scientific literacy; it also gives students a deeper appreciation of how our planet works.

From a knowledge of basic facts comes an understanding of basic concepts. Students who have a basic understanding of earth processes and who have learned to think critically are ready to make intelligent, decisions about scientific and environmental problems of the future. Developing informed decision-makers is the overarching goal of **Heath EARTH SCIENCE.**

About the author

As an earth science teacher at the Elmira (New York) Free Academy for over 25 years, Nancy E. Spaulding has been involved in many of the changes that have occurred in earth science education.

Currently, she is a member of the Earth Science Resource Program Innovation Team, a group of New York State earth science teacher-mentors working to develop a new course of study centered on lab activities requiring higher levels of performance and thinking. She is an item writer for the New York State Alternative Assessment Project—a recently funded program to develop new and innovative methods of testing students—and an earth science teacher at Corning Community College.

Contributing writers

Margaret A. LeMone, Ph.D.
Senior Scientist
National Center for Atmospheric Research
Boulder, CO

Thomas Butler
Science Coordinator
Pattonville School District
St. Ann, MO

Janice Arden
Science Teacher
Enka High School
Enka, NC

C. Dale Elifrits, Ph.D.
Professor of Geological Engineering
University of Missouri-Rolla
Rolla, MO

"One of the benefits of having studied earth science is that the course materials are always available. Outcrops along the highways, stars at night, waves on the beach, and even clouds in the sky can be viewed with greater understanding and appreciation every day for a lifetime."

— *Nancy Spaulding, author of Heath EARTH SCIENCE*

Heath EARTH SCIENCE prepares students for a world of changes.

With the Tenth Edition of **Heath EARTH SCIENCE,** students have an authoritative guide to the ever changing physical world around them. This revision is up to date on the most recent geological, environmental, and meteorological events shaping the world. It also reflects recent discoveries that have increased our understanding of how Earth and other planets work.

New content features

- Up-to-date mapping chapter with the latest in satellite-mapping techniques

- Revised, in-depth discussion of mineral crystal systems and structures

- New treatment of environment and natural resources, including discussions of availability versus consumption

- Updated coverage of earthquakes and volcanoes, including the Loma Prieta earthquake and the eruption of Mount Pinatubo

- Revised, up-to-date geologic timetable incorporating the latest figures for the beginnings and endings of eras, periods, and tectonic events

- Extensive revision of earth history chapters based on content review by paleontologists and paleobiologists

- Updated coverage of technologies used in oceanographic and astronomical research

- Up-to-the-minute descriptions of manned and unmanned space exploration missions, including *Magellan* and *Galileo*

- Discussion of the latest findings in astronomy, including the *COBE* evidence for the Big Bang

- Updated coverage and revealing photographs of hurricanes and floods, including hurricanes Andrew and Iniki

- Current information and discussion of the greenhouse effect, global warming, and the threatened ozone layer

- Discussion of current research into global climate change

HURRICANE ANDREW

"Heath EARTH SCIENCE provides a look at science in the '90s. Our knowledge of the causes of climate change, global warming, and ozone depletion has grown markedly over the last decade."

— Margaret LeMone, contributing writer to Heath EARTH SCIENCE

Heath **EARTH SCIENCE** provides up-to-date coverage and photographs of geological, environmental, and meteorological events shaping our world—such as Hurricane Andrew and the eruption of Mount Pinatubo.

"Plate tectonics is one of the most interesting and exciting topics an earth science student can study today. Not only are the basic ideas understandable without an extensive science background, but it involves changes that are occuring on our planet right now!"

— Nancy Spaulding, author of Heath EARTH SCIENCE

Special topics broaden students' understanding of earth science.

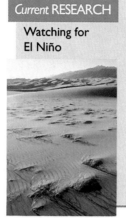

Current RESEARCH

Watching for El Niño

The winter weather of 1992 was far from typical. In Los Angeles, three storms in ten days dumped enough rain to cause killer mudslides and floods. In south-central Texas, severe storms brought over 25 inches of rain in only two months, causing severe flooding and loss of property. Much of the United States had milder temperatures than usual, while half a world away, a drought devastated southern Africa. All of these unusual weather patterns appear to have been caused by El Niño (Topic 15), the warming of the Pacific Ocean near the equator that occurs every three to seven years.

Since an El Niño event causes such dangerous weather conditions worldwide, researchers have been working to find ways to predict when El Niños will occur. The El Niño of 1991–1992 was predicted by a computer model in 1990, almost two years before it arrived. This computer model simulates the winds and currents of the tropical Pacific Ocean and uses that data to project future surface water temperatures and sea levels.

Knowing when an El Niño event will occur can in turn make such unusual weather as occurred in 1992 more predictable. Based on historical data, researchers know that the tropical warmth from El Niño waters can displace the jet streams, steering warmer air to the northern United States and rain to the Gulf Coast. Further refinements of the models will make better predictions possible.

Current Research

To convey the vitality of science today, **Heath EARTH SCIENCE** offers a new feature called Current Research, an exploration of science and scientific discoveries being made today. Current Research explores some of the newest hypotheses being tested and refined by scientists in various earth science disciplines.

EARTHMATTERS

Beach Erosion

Beach erosion by waves and currents has become a serious problem along the Atlantic coast of the United States. As much as a meter of shoreline is being removed from some areas each year. A large storm at high tide can remove ten times that much beach in a single night.

In an effort to protect property and lives, millions of dollars have been spent to rebuild beaches or save them from erosion. Expensive sea walls temporarily stop storm waves from reaching homes but do not help save beaches. In fact, sea walls may speed erosion. The wave crashing against a sea wall carries away far more sand than it would if the wave spent its energy gently rolling up onto a beach.

Some towns losing their beaches to erosion have built structures out into the sea to trap the sand carried by longshore currents. These structures, called jetties, often trap the sand needed at other beaches down the coast, causing these beaches to erode more rapidly.

To date, no method of slowing beach erosion has proved very effective for long. Much of the problem is traceable to rising sea level. Sea level is rising by about a third of a meter every century. The natural response of a beach to rising sea level is to move away from the waves— that is, toward land. As beaches adjust to rising sea level, lines of houses like this one are collapsing into the sea.

There are some ways to naturally slow beach erosion. If you live near the ocean, you may want to help plant dune grass, which stabilizes the dune and makes it more resistant to erosion.

Earth Matters

Another new feature, Earth Matters, promotes environmental awareness by showing how people interact with Earth in the environment. Earth Matters serves as a starting point for students' understanding of the global environment and how it can be protected by a scientifically literate community.

Extensive lab and map activities put concepts into practice.

Heath EARTH SCIENCE gives students valuable practice applying new concepts, with two pages of lab or map activities at the end of each chapter. These 34 activities give students opportunities to practice science process skills. The map activities provide valuable practice in map reading and interpretation. Data Record Sheets for all activities are found in the separate Laboratory Investigations booklet.

Shown are a lab activity, "Dew Point and Relative Humidity," and a map activity, "Folded Mountains." To see these activities at full size, turn to pages 518 and 303.

CHAPTER 27

L A B ACTIVITY

Dew Point and Relative Humidity

For additional activities, see Laboratory Investigations booklet.

Even above the hottest desert areas on Earth, there is water vapor in the air. Water vapor is the source of moisture for clouds and rain. Meteorologists measure both dew point and relative humidity to determine how much water vapor is in the air and to predict chances of precipitation.

Dew point is the temperature at which air is filled or saturated with water vapor. Relative humidity is the extent to which air is saturated with water vapor. When air cools below the dew point, water vapor in the air condenses.

In this lab, you will determine both dew point and relative humidity by using a capacity chart. You will then make and use a psychrometer to find relative humidity.

Lab Skills and Objectives
■ To **observe** dew formation, and **compute** relative humidity, using dew point method
■ To **compute** relative humidity using psychrometer method
■ To **compare** the methods for finding relative humidity

Materials
■ shiny metal cans
■ stirring rod or coffee stirrer
■ ice cubes or crushed ice
■ celsius thermometer
■ cloth strip, 2.5 cm x 10 cm
■ small rubber bands or string
■ spoon
■ piece of paper
■ water at room temperature

27.18 Equipment set up for Part A

27.19 Capacity of Air at 1000mb Pressure

Temp °C	Capacity g/kg	Temp °C	Capacity g/kg
-10	1.8	13	9.5
-9	1.9	14	10.1
-8	2.1	15	10.8
-7	2.3	16	11.6
-6	2.5	17	12.3
-5	2.6	18	13.2
-4	2.9	19	14.0
-3	3.1	20	15.0
-2	3.3	21	15.9
-1	3.6	22	17.0
0	3.8	23	18.1
1	4.1	24	19.2
2	4.4	25	20.4
3	4.8	26	21.7
4	5.1	27	23.1
5	5.5	28	24.6
6	5.9	29	26.1
7	6.3	30	27.7
8	6.8	31	29.4
9	7.3	32	31.2
10	7.8	33	33.1
11	8.3	34	35.1
12	8.9		

Procedure
Part A—Dew Po...
1. Put on sa... goggles.
2. Use a thermo... sure the classr... ature in celsi... temperature i...
3. Look at Figure... capacity of air... vapor for the ... your classroo... capacity.
4. Fill the meta... with water. ...
mometer in t... a small amou...
5. Use a stirring... water slowly.
   CAUTIO... stir with ... meter; it is fra... break.
6. Watch for the ... of dew on the ... container. At ... see dew, reco... temperature i...

CHAPTER 16

M A P ACTIVITY

Folded Mountains

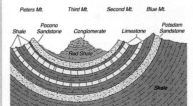

16.10 Cross-section, Harrisburg area

The region around Harrisburg, Pennsylvania displays some of the classic features of folded mountain ranges. Figure 16.10 is a cross-section showing the structure of the rock layers found in the Harrisburg area. In this activity, you will use both this cross-section and a topographic map of the Harrisburg area to study some of the features of folded mountains.

Map Skills and Objectives
■ To **interpret** the structure and geology of an area from map and cross-section data
■ To **infer** the relative resistance to weathering of various rock types

Materials
■ Physical Map of the United States, pages 654–655
■ Topographic Map: Harrisburg, Pennsylvania, page 652
■ tracing paper, 10 cm x 15 cm

Procedure
1. Turn to the Physical Map of the United States on page 654 and 655. Locate Harrisburg on the map. In what mountain range is Harrisburg located?

2. Now turn to the topographic map of the Harrisburg area on page 652. Compare the map with the geologic cross-section shown in Figure 16.10. List the four mountains that occur on both the map and the cross-section. In what general map or compass direction was the cross-section drawn (i.e., N-S, E-W)?

3. Look at the cross-section. Two of the mountains shown on the cross-section are formed from the same rock formation. Identify those two mountains. What is the name of the rock formation?

4. Look at the figures in Chapter 16 between pages 294 and 300. Locate the figure or part of the figure that most resembles the structure shown in the cross-section. What is this structure called?

5. Compare the composition of the ridges in the Harrisburg area with the composition of the valleys. Which rock types form ridges and which rock types form valleys?

6. Lay the tracing paper over the cross-section and trace the

outline of the diagram. Label Third Mountain. Locate Stone Glen on the topographic map. Where would Stone Glen be located on the cross-section? Label the location of Stone Glen on your tracing paper version of the cross-section. Repeat this procedure for the community of Lucknow, the airway beacon, and the WHP TV-tower. Which of these features is either located on or formed by the oldest rocks? Which is located on or formed by the youngest rocks?

7. Answer the questions in *Analysis and Conclusions*.

Analysis and Conclusions
1. Why is it impossible to determine if sedimentary rock layers have been overturned using only a topographic map?

2. Using the Physical Map of the United States, identify at least three eastern states (not including Pennsylvania) where folded rock layers would be expected to occur at Earth's surface. Why would folded rocks not be expected to occur in the Atlantic Coastal Plain?

U.S. Geological Survey Photo by J.D. Griggs

The wonders of Earth on videodisc— a new teaching option.

Short of going on an undersea dive or taking a field trip to the Grand Canyon, you can't find a more appealing way of dramatizing earth science topics than through the use of videodisc. The Teacher's Edition gives you on-page correlations to Optical Data's *The Living Textbook: Earth Science* videodisc series for a fascinating overview of geology, meteorology, and astronomy. Barcodes and frame numbers at point of use let you call up dramatic visual images and video sequences that illustrate and enhance concepts taught in the text.

> "Human activity has a profound effect on Earth's surface and atmosphere. As citizens, we are obligated to understand our impact and make intelligent decisions about the future. Studying earth science is an excellent first step."
> — *Margaret LeMone, contributing writer to* **Heath EARTH SCIENCE**

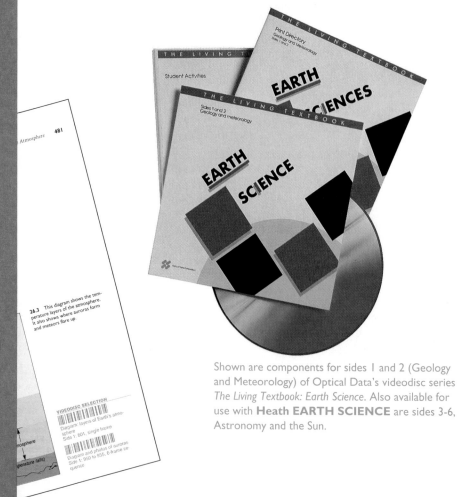

Shown are components for sides 1 and 2 (Geology and Meteorology) of Optical Data's videodisc series *The Living Textbook: Earth Science.* Also available for use with **Heath EARTH SCIENCE** are sides 3-6, Astronomy and the Sun.

Barcodes and frame numbers in the margins of the Teacher's Edition help you call up dramatic video sequences.

New resource promotes environmental awareness.

To further promote awareness of and respect for the environment, **Heath EARTH SCIENCE** offers *Environmental Awareness,* a new resource containing case studies that reflect real-world decision making on environmental issues. Ideal for use in earth science, biology, chemistry, or physics classes, this resource promotes greater environmental awareness and sharpens students' decision-making skills as they learn more about their impact on Earth's complex systems.

With **Heath EARTH SCIENCE**, students learn that even these oil fires, thousands of miles away in Kuwait, have an effect on the environment.

"Earth science is exciting to teach and to learn. It's fun for students because it engages them—with hands-on discovery based on everyday observations and events. Students also enjoy learning about volcanoes, dinosaurs, weather, and environmental concerns and solutions."

— Dale Elifrits, contributing writer to Heath EARTH SCIENCE

Earth science is more accessible than ever—for all students.

The Tenth Edition of **Heath EARTH SCIENCE** provides students with the most up-to-date and comprehensive treatment of the major areas of earth science: geology, oceanography, astronomy, meteorology, and earth history. To make learning earth science more manageable, lessons are divided into short, single-concept topics that students can grasp quickly. Effective illustrations and dramatic photographs—including shots of recent phenomena such as Hurricane Andrew and the eruption of Mount Pinatubo—show Earth's complex processes in concrete, colorful depictions.

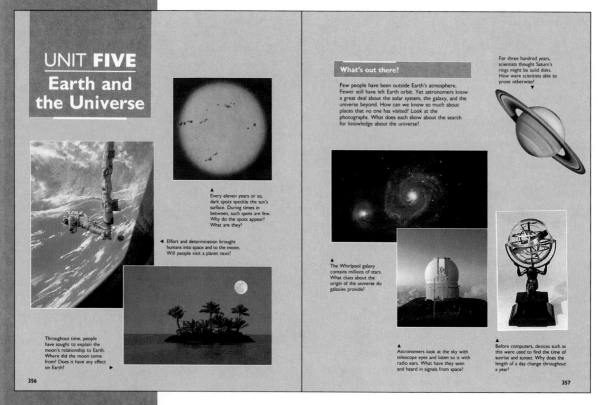

Unit openers show a collage of dramatic photographs that illustrate the unit theme. Thought-provoking questions urge students to think critically, like earth scientists, to determine how the photographs relate to the unit theme.

To help students grasp concepts more easily, lessons are divided into topics that cover one major concept at a time.

Each lesson begins with a set of objectives that give students a quick overview of the major concepts of that lesson.

SCIENCE BACKGROUND
Improvements in navigation have also helped in mapping the seafloor. Surface locations can be determined precisely.

CHAPTER

18

The Ocean Floor and Its Sediments

How Do You Know That . . .

▲
Coral reefs are formations that rise from the ocean floor.

Some islands were formed by tiny sea animals? Even though oceans are the most prominent features of Earth's surface, the structures that are beneath the ocean were unknown until this century. Modern technology and equipment have revealed much about these structures and their formation. For example, oceanographers had wondered how corals, which need light to live, built islands that reach to the surface from the floor of the deep sea thousands of meters below. You will learn how the reefs formed as well as about other topographic features found on the ocean floor.

I Studying the Ocean Floor

Topic 1 Echo Sounding and Satellites

In the days of the first oceanographic surveys, such as the *Challenger* expedition, the distance to the seafloor was measured with a lead weight on a line. The weight was lowered until it touched bottom, the amount of line let out was determined, and the weight was hauled back to the ship. In deep water a single depth reading might take an entire day. The process was tiresome and produced very limited information.

Today ships use a device called the *precision depth recorder* to find the distance to the ocean floor. The device works by sending a sound signal through the water to the seafloor. The length of time needed for the signal to reach the bottom and echo back to the ship measures the depth of the water. The recorder traces a continuous profile of the area over which the ship is sailing. Such profiles are used to make accurate and detailed maps of the seafloor.

A device similar to the precision depth recorder provides information about the sediment layers on the ocean floor. Lower-pitched sound signals are able to penetrate many layers of seafloor sediment. Scientists produce lower-pitched signals using underwater explosives or compressed air blasts and record the way the signals travel through the sediment layers. Such data reveal the structure of each layer of sediment and of the bedrock beneath. Profiles of all but the thickest sediments have been obtained in this way.

In recent years, satellites have come into use in mapping the ocean floor. Satellites can gather far more data more quickly than a seagoing vessel. Signals sent from satellites cannot reach the ocean floor, but they can bounce off the ocean surface. Using ocean surface data for ocean floor mapping works because the level of the ocean surface varies slightly. Ocean water piles up slightly over undersea mountains and dips slightly over undersea trenches. The ocean surface hills and dips are revealed by precise measurements taken from the satellite. The data are processed by computer to produce an image of the ocean floor.

Topic 2 Sampling the Sediments

Although echo soundings provide data about the ocean floor, actual samples of the seafloor yield far more information. Early methods of obtaining samples involved mechanical devices that either grabbed or scooped up sediment and rock. For example, a large

OBJECTIVES

A Describe past and present methods for determining the depth of the seafloor.

B List direct and indirect methods of studying seafloor sediments and identify some kinds of information obtained from direct samples.

C Name some devices used to make direct observations of the seafloor and discuss their advantages and disadvantages.

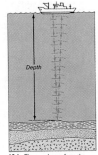

18.1 The sound wave from the ship bounces off the ocean floor and back to the ship. The time it takes to return to the ship indicates the depth of the ocean floor.

322

323

Together with a striking photograph, the introductory question "How do you know that…?" motivates students to read the chapter.

Reliable teaching support gives you a range of teaching options.

Teacher's Annotated Edition

In the **Teacher's Annotated Edition**, you'll find Topic-Referenced Planners that correlate all supplementary materials to text topics. You'll also find many teaching suggestions, rich scientific background information, and answers to all in-text questions.

Teacher's Resource Package

The **Teacher's Resource Package** gives you the materials you need for building skills and testing comprehension—all keyed to text topics.

- Teacher's Edition
- Study Guide (worksheets)
- Chapter Tests
- Answer Key
- Laboratory Investigations

- Laboratory Investigations, Teacher's Annotated Edition
- Overhead Transparencies sampler
- *Environmental Awareness* sampler
- Computer Test Bank Teacher's Guide

Laboratory Investigations

The experiments and activities in the **Laboratory Investigations** booklet develop earth science concepts and skills. The booklet provides in-depth, hands-on experiments, map activities, and student report sheets for in-text lab activities. A Teacher's Annotated Edition is available.

Overhead Transparencies

Overhead Transparencies are full-color reproductions of text illustrations that emphasize earth science processes. The 50 transparencies also include all of the maps that appear in the Map Atlas of the student text.

Computer Test Bank

The **Computer Test Bank** allows you to construct your own testing program with integrated graphics. A Teacher's Guide is also available. (Macintosh, Apple, IBM)

What users of earlier editions say about Heath EARTH SCIENCE.

Up-to-date content

"The content of EARTH SCIENCE is up-to-date and comprehensive. The text is especially strong in its coverage of weather and fossils. As a general resource of earth science information, this text is superior."

Great for students and teachers

"This is an exceptionally strong textbook. For students, each chapter's objectives are clearly stated. As a teacher, I appreciate the teaching resources, the organization of the Teacher's Edition, and the safety guidelines."

Critical thinking

"EARTH SCIENCE gives students lots of chances to think critically with critical-thinking questions at the end of each chapter."

Dynamic photos and illustrations

"The illustrations and diagrams in EARTH SCIENCE are excellent—detailed, colorful, informative, and very professional-looking."

"I appreciate Heath's careful selection of up-to-date photos of the solar system, planets, and moons. One especially good shot is of the continuous daylight effect of the summer sun in the Arctic Circle."

Inspiring careers feature

"I like the careers feature. Seeing real people in diverse occupations shows students that earth science plays an important—and interesting—role in the lives of successful people."

HEATH
Earth Science

Authors

Nancy E. Spaulding
Earth Science Teacher
Elmira Free Academy
Elmira, NY

Samuel N. Namowitz
Former Principal and Earth Science Teacher
Charles Evans Hughes High School
New York, NY

Contributing Writers

Margaret A. LeMone, Ph.D.
Senior Scientist
National Center for Atmospheric Research
Boulder, CO

Thomas Butler
Science Coordinator
Pattonville School District
St. Ann, MO

Janice Arden
Science Teacher
Enka High School
Enka, NC

C. Dale Elifrits, Ph.D.
Professor of Geological Engineering
University of Missouri-Rolla
Rolla, MO

Content Consultants

Duncan FitzGerald, Ph.D.
Geologist
Department of Geology
Boston University
Boston, MA

Reinhard E. Flick, Ph.D.
Staff Oceanographer
California Department of Boating
    and Waterways
Scripps Institution of Oceanography
San Diego, CA

Theodore Gull, Ph.D.
Astrophysicist
Goddard Space Flight Center
Greenbelt, MD

David Houghton, Ph.D.
Chairperson
Department of Atmospheric
    and Oceanic Sciences
University of Wisconsin
Madison, WI

Richard D. Norris, Ph.D.
Paleobiologist
Woods Hole Oceanographic Institution
Woods Hole, MA

Patricia Pauley, Ph.D.
Meterologist
Adjunct Professor
Naval Postgraduate School
Monterey, CA

 D.C. Heath and Company Lexington, Massachusetts/Toronto, Ontario

The Heath Earth Science Program

Pupil's Edition
Teacher's Annotated Edition
Laboratory Investigations
Laboratory Investigations,
  Teacher's Annotated Edition
Study Guide
Environmental Awareness Booklet
Overhead Transparencies
Answer Key
Chapter Tests
Computer Test Bank
Computer Test Bank, Teacher's Guide
Computer Software:
  Mountains and Crustal Movement
  Dating and Geologic Time

Executive Editor:
  Ceanne Tzimopoulos
Supervising Editor:
  Christine H. Wang
Editorial Development:
  Amy R. Pallant, Andrew L. Amster,
  Virginia A. Flook, Edwin M. Schiele
Design Management & Cover Design:
  Lisa Fowler
Design Development:
  Reynolds Design & Management,
  Christine Reynolds; Angela Sciaraffa
Production Coordinator:
  Dorshia Johnson
Writing Assistance:
  Special Features: Andrew L. Amster
Laboratory Safety Consultant:
  Jay A. Young, Ph.D.
Readability:
  J & F Readability Service

Cover Photographs:
  Spider Rock, Canyon de Chelly National
    Monument, Arizona, David Muench
  Earth, © Telegraph Colour Library 199,
    FPG International

Teacher Reviewers

John H. Birkett
Earth Science Teacher
Sycamore High School
Sycamore, IL

J-Petrina Enteles
Earth and Environmental Science Teacher
Robert McQueen High School
Reno, NV

Christine Jakobs
Science Teacher
Santa Fe Preparatory School
Santa Fe, NM

Aline Miller
Earth Science Teacher
Pelham Memorial High School
Pelham, NY

Richard M. Staley
Earth Science Teacher
F.A. Day Jr. High School
Newton, MA

Harvey W. Stick, Jr.
Science Teacher
Eastern High School
Voorhees, NJ

Sharon M. Stroud
Earth Science Teacher
Widefield High School
Colorado Springs, CO

Copyright © 1994 by D.C. Heath and Company
All rights reserved. No part of this publication may be reproduced or transmitted in any form by any means, electronic or mechanical, including photocopy, recording or any information storage or retrieval system, without permission in writing from the publisher.

Published simultaneously in Canada
Printed in the United States of America
International Standard Book Number: 0-669-26183-1
  3 4 5 6 7 8 9 10 -RRD- 99 98 97 96 95 94 93

Why Take Earth Science?
To the Student

At this point in your school career, you may not have much choice about the courses you take. You have a class in each of several subject areas (English, social studies, mathematics, etc.), and the science course offered at your school for your grade level happens to be earth science. But have you ever thought about why an earth science course is offered in the first place?

You live on Earth! Everything you have or use, whether it is this book, your breakfast, your favorite clothes, the bus you rode to school in, or anything else, comes from materials found on Earth. Any place that you are likely to visit or live is on Earth. Everything you see or hear takes place on Earth, in its atmosphere, or in the universe.

Since you will be involved in so many aspects of Earth and the universe in your lifetime, it makes sense that you should know something about them. Also, with an understanding of earth science, you will be able to make more informed choices about how you conserve and use Earth's resources.

Like any worthwhile experience, your earth science course will require some time and effort on your part. For this reason, some suggestions follow to assist you toward a successful, pleasant, and worthwhile experience.

Do the assignments faithfully. Whether the assignment is reading the book, answering questions, or writing a laboratory report, it is important to keep up with the work. Students who keep up with their work find earth science far more enjoyable.

Read your textbook carefully. A textbook cannot be read as quickly as a magazine or novel. Be sure you understand every sentence.

Look at the illustrations. Read the captions that go with them. The illustrations show examples or diagrams of the topics covered in the written part of the text. They will help you to better understand the material in the reading.

Do the Topic Questions at the end of each lesson. These questions help you review the important points in each topic. See whether you can answer them without looking back at the topic, but be sure to look up anything that you do not know.

At the end of every chapter, you will find materials designed to help you review and strengthen your knowledge of the chapter material.

Read the Summary. The summary highlights important points in the chapter. As you read the summary, try to recall the concept described in each item. Think of examples of each concept.

Review the Vocabulary. You should define or give an example of each term in the list. If you find that you are uncertain about a term, look back in the chapter and review the topics in which that term appears.

Do the Review. The Review helps you find out which chapter concepts you know, and which concepts you may need to study more than others.

Try the Interpret and Apply. To answer Interpret and Apply questions, you may need to use ideas and information from more than one topic in the chapter. These questions assess how well you can identify relationships between ideas.

Try the Critical Thinking. Critical Thinking exercises require you to use or analyze new information in light of the concepts you learned. Typically, you will be asked to interpret data in graphs and charts.

Once you know what to look for, you will find examples and applications of earth science all around you. Whether you live in a city or in the country, you can observe changes in the weather, stars, and planets, the effects of rain and snow on rocks and buildings, and many other phenomena that are part of earth science. The knowledge you gain here can give you a lifetime of pleasure in observing and appreciating the world in which you live.

CONTENTS

UNIT ONE: Structure of a Dynamic Earth

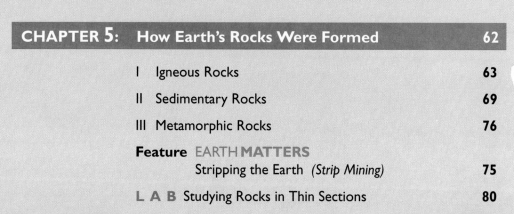

v

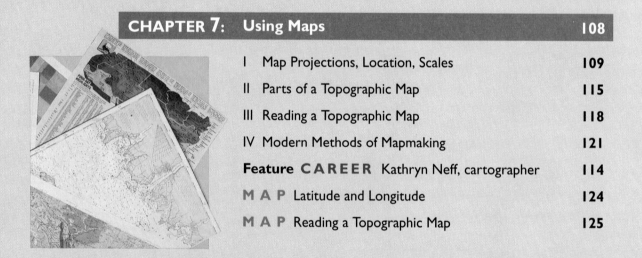
UNIT TWO: Forces That Attack the Surface

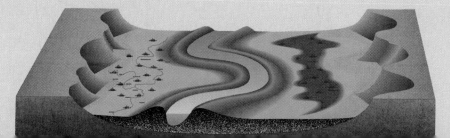

UNIT FOUR: The Ocean

UNIT FIVE: Earth and the Universe

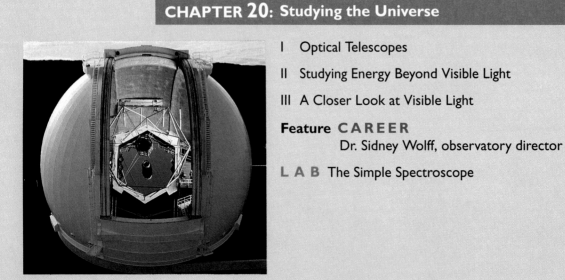

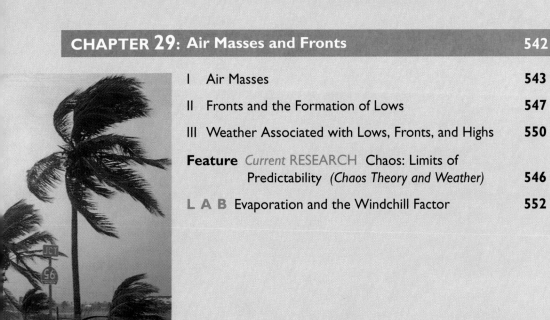

ACTIVITIES

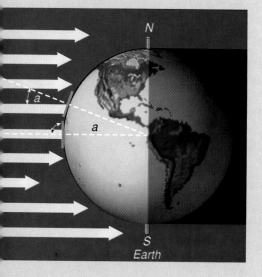

xvi

FEATURES

SAFETY
in the Earth Science Laboratory

The earth science laboratory is a place where discovery leads to knowledge and understanding. It is also a place where caution is essential for your safety and the safety of others. Your knowledge of and adherence to safe laboratory practices are important factors in avoiding accidents. The information below describes some basic rules for safe laboratory work. Your teacher will provide additional rules specific to your laboratory setting. Read the following rules thoroughly and observe them in the laboratory.

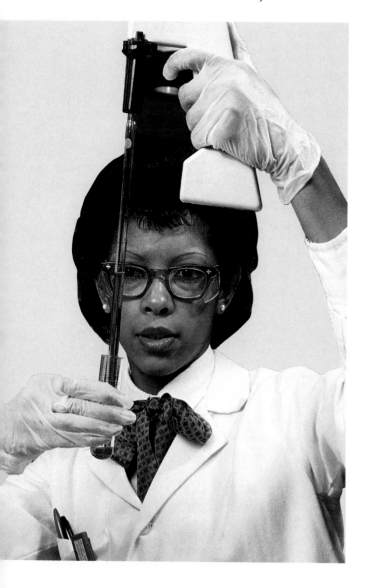

1. Locate and learn to use all laboratory safety equipment.
2. Never eat, drink, chew gum, or apply cosmetics in the laboratory. Do not store food or beverages in the lab area.
3. Never smell a chemical directly; instead, waft the vapor toward your nose by fanning your hand. Never taste a chemical.
4. Never force or twist glass tubing into a stopper. Protect both hands with cloth pads when inserting or removing glass tubing.
5. Never reach over a flame or a heat source. Keep hair and clothing away from flames.
6. Never do an investigation without your teacher's supervision.
7. Read all parts of an investigation before you begin work. Follow your teacher's directions completely.
8. Never run, push, play, or fool around in the laboratory.
9. Keep your work area clean and uncluttered. Store items such as books and purses in designated areas. Keep glassware and containers of chemicals away from the edges of your lab bench.
10. Report all accidents to your teacher immediately. Do not touch broken, cracked, or chipped glassware.
11. Turn off electric equipment, water, and gas when not in use.
12. Pay attention to safety **CAUTIONS.** Wear safety goggles and a lab apron whenever you use heat, chemicals, solutions, glassware, or other dangerous materials.
13. Dress properly for the laboratory. Do not wear loose-fitting sleeves, bulky outerwear, dangling jewelry, or open-toed shoes. Tie back long hair and tuck in ties and scarves when you use heat or chemicals.
14. Never touch a hot object with your bare hands. Use a clamp, tongs, or heat-resistant gloves when handling hot objects.

15. When heating a test tube, point it away from yourself and others. Use sturdy tongs or test-tube holders. Do not reach over a flame.

16. Use care in handling electrical equipment. Do not touch electrical equipment with wet hands or use it near water. Check for frayed cords, loose connections, or broken wires. Use only equipment with three-pronged plugs. Make sure cords do not dangle from work tables. Disconnect electrical appliances from outlets by pulling on the plug, not on the cord.

17. Use flammable chemicals only after ensuring that there are no flames anywhere in the laboratory.

18. Use care when working with chemicals. Keep all chemicals away from your face and off your skin. Keep your hands away from your face while working with chemicals. If a chemical gets in your eyes or on your skin or clothing, wash off the chemical immediately with plenty of water. Tell your teacher what happened.

19. Do not return any unused chemical to its bottle. Follow your teacher's directions for the disposal of chemicals, used matches, filter papers, and other materials. Do not discard solid chemicals, chemical solutions, matches, papers, or any such substances in the sink.

20. Always clean your lab equipment and work space after you finish an investigation. Always wash your hands with soap and water before leaving the laboratory.

Safety in the Laboratory

Throughout the investigations in *Heath Earth Science*, you will see a variety of symbols relating to safe laboratory procedures. These symbols and their meanings are shown below. Study the information and become familiar with all **CAUTIONS** in an investigation before you begin your work.

  Wear safety goggles and a lab apron. Investigation involves chemicals, hot materials, lab burners, or possibility of broken glass.

 Danger of cuts exists. Investigation involves scissors, wire cutters, pins, or other sharp instruments. Handle with care.

 Investigation involves hot plates, lab burners, lighted matches, or flammable liquids with explosive vapors.

 Investigation involves chemicals that are very poisonous. Avoid spills. Avoid touching chemicals directly.

 Investigation involves use of corrosive or irritating chemicals. In case of a spill, wash skin and clothes thoroughly with plenty of water and call your teacher.

 Investigation involves use of electrical equipment, such as electric lamps and hot plates.

 The triangle alerts you to additional, specific safety procedures in an investigation. Always discuss safety CAUTIONS with your teacher before you begin work.

UNIT **ONE**
Structure of a Dynamic Earth

▲ Minerals are part of Earth's structure, yet minerals have structures of their own. What does this mineral's shape tell about its structure?

▲ What do volcanoes reveal about the structure inside Earth?

Oil is found underground within certain kinds of structures. How do geologists on the surface know where to drill for oil? ▶

What is Earth's Structure?

Earth's *structure* refers to the way Earth is put together. Parts of Earth's structure are easily seen. Other parts are hidden from view because they are too small, too large, or are buried underground. Earth scientists strive to understand Earth's structure at many levels, large and small. Look at the photographs. What does each reveal about the structure of a dynamic Earth?

Since early times, people have noticed that ships appear to sink as they sail away. How is this a clue to Earth's overall structure? ▶

How is a steep structure on Earth's surface shown on a flat map? ▼

▲ Rock layers make up the structure of these cliffs. What do layers reveal about the way the rocks formed?

1

Introduction to Earth Science

▲
Rock mounds from a lava
flow cover trees, houses,
and a highway in Hawaii.

How Do You Know That . . .

Earth is changing? The mounds in the photograph were formed
when hot lava flowed over houses, trees, and the highway, then
cooled. The lava flow has closed almost 2 kilometers of highway.
The people living nearby must detour almost 100 kilometers just to
buy groceries and pick up their mail. The lava came from Kilauea, a
volcano in Hawaii that has erupted frequently in recent years.
People living there are used to volcanic eruptions. Eruptions like
this one, however, cause far more damage than most. Lava flows
are just one way Earth's activities affect our lives.

1 What Is Earth Science?

Topic 1 Branches of Earth Science

A volcano erupts in Hawaii, destroying several homes and covering a major highway. An earthquake destroys a city in Central America. A 3-kilogram meteorite travels millions of kilometers through outer space and crashes through the roof of a home in Connecticut. Tornadoes weave erratic paths through the Great Plains, causing loss of life and property. Storms and high waves lash the coast of California, resulting in floods, landslides, and extensive erosion.

All of these occurrences are earth science *events*—that is, each causes a change. However, *Earth* includes more than the solid earth. It also includes Earth's oceans and atmosphere, and the universe of which Earth is a part. To which branch of earth science does each event belong? The volcano and earthquake are part of **geology**, the study of Earth's surface and interior. The meteorite belongs to the branch of earth science called **astronomy**, the study of the universe. Tornadoes belong to **meteorology**, the study of Earth's atmosphere. The Pacific Coast events—like many others—involve more than one branch of earth science. These events involve meteorology, geology, and **oceanography**, the study of the oceans.

OBJECTIVES

A Identify the major branches of earth science and describe events that occur in each branch.

B Define *geology* and list several activities of geologists.

C Explain how astronomers obtain information and list some topics and materials they study.

D Describe the work and activities of meteorologists and oceanographers.

OF INTEREST

The 3-kilogram meteorite went through the roof of a house in Wethersfield, Connecticut, in 1971. Amazingly, the roof of another house in this same town was smashed by another meteorite in 1982.

SCIENCE BACKGROUND

Interrelationships with other sciences are also fundamental to earth science. Geochemistry and astrophysics are just two examples.

VIDEODISC SELECTION

Earth from *Apollo 17*
Side 2: 7048, single frame

1.1 Shoreline phenomena are studied by a variety of earth scientists including meteorologists, oceanographers, and geologists.

1.2 This geologist has donned protective clothing in order to gather data from an active volcano. What are some of the dangers involved?

VIDEODISC SELECTION

Geologist working on Kilauea volcano
Side 2: 1407, single frame

Voyager 1 photograph of Jupiter
Side 2: 7026, single frame

Topic 2 Activities of Today's Geologists

Geologists are scientists who study the origin, history, and structure of Earth and the processes that shape its surface. Like other scientists, geologists are important in today's world. They explore Earth's crust to discover new sources of oil, uranium, and geothermal power. They search for new deposits of important metallic and nonmetallic minerals. They help plan water supply systems for towns and cities. They devise measures for flood control. They do research in forecasting earthquakes and volcanic eruptions. They make topographic maps showing details of Earth's surface and geologic maps to show Earth's rock structure. Using the observations made by spacecraft, geologists can make maps of the moon and nearer planets.

Topic 3 What Astronomers Do

Unlike geologists and most other scientists, astronomers deal mainly with objects and happenings beyond their physical reach. To study the universe beyond the planet Earth, astronomers must use telescopes and other instruments. They study radiations sent out by objects in space and learn about the stars and planets from these radiations. Satellites, lunar explorers, and space probes have been most useful to astronomers.

Many astronomers specialize in studies of the planets and their moons. Some devote their time mainly to comets. Others may be interested in the origin of the universe or the life cycles of stars. Still others work on ways of discovering whether or not life exists anywhere else in the universe.

Do astronomers have any outer-space materials to study? The answer is yes. Meteorites have fallen to Earth from other parts of the solar system. Between 1969 and 1972, *Apollo* astronauts landed on the moon and brought moon rocks back to Earth. In addition, astronauts and space probes—*Mariner, Pioneer, Viking, Voyager,* and others—have provided many photographs and observations of members of the solar system.

1.3 A scientific milestone was reached in 1969 when the first astronauts landed on the moon.

Topic 4 **What Meteorologists Do**

Earth's atmosphere covers Earth's entire surface and reaches a height of hundreds of kilometers. The weather is created in its bottom layer. Today jet planes fly above the weather, and artificial satellites go much higher. Therefore, scientists are very interested in the upper atmosphere too.

The meteorologists known best are the weather forecasters. Standing behind the forecasters are many others. Some study the effects of solar energy in changing the weather. Still others are concerned with the important problems of air pollution. A number of meteorologists are investigating changes in the *climate,* or long-term weather. Then there are those doing research on such problems as hurricane control, thunderstorms, tornadoes, and long-range forecasting.

Topic 5 **What Oceanographers Do**

Oceans cover nearly three fourths of Earth's surface, providing a vast and varied area for scientific research. Oceanographers have many problems to investigate. They work from special research ships to measure the ocean depths and map the ocean floor. They drill into the ocean floor to study its rocks and its history. They locate deposits of valuable minerals.

Oceanographers also track and map ocean currents. They chart the movements of icebergs that break off from the glaciers of Greenland and Antarctica. They study the plant and animal life of the deep sea and of the surface waters. They do research to discover the effects of the ocean on weather and climate. From studying great ocean waves and undersea earthquakes, oceanographers are able to develop warning systems for threatened coastal regions.

1.4 Meteorologists are able to track the dynamic forces within the atmosphere and to make weather predictions based on atmospheric conditions.

VIDEODISC SELECTION

Hurricane Frederic, September, 1979
Side 2: 872, single frame

VIDEODISC SELECTION

Alvin submersible at ocean surface
Side 2: 3048, single frame

1.5 This special diving suit allows oceanographers to dive deep below the surface and to remain below for long periods of time.

ANSWERS

1. (a) geology, astronomy, meteorology, oceanography   (b) in above order: volcano, meteorite, tornado, ocean wave

2. explore for economic materials, plan water supplies, devise flood control, study earthquakes and volcanoes, make topographic maps

3. (a) with telescopes and other instruments, satellites, lunar explorers, space probes   (b) planets and moons, comets, origin of universe, life cycles of stars   (c) meteorites, moon rocks

4. forecast weather; study solar energy, changing weather, climate changes, air pollution, methods of rainmaking, hurricane control, thunderstorms; long-range forecasting

TOPIC QUESTIONS

Each topic question refers to the topic of the same number.

1. (a) What branches of science are included in earth science? **(b)** Name one event that can occur in each of these branches of science.

2. List at least four activities performed by geologists.

3. (a) How can astronomers study space beyond Earth? **(b)** Name three specialized topics studied by astronomers. **(c)** What are some outer-space materials available to astronomers?

4. Name at least three activities carried on by meteorologists.

5. Briefly describe at least four activities of oceanographers.

5. measure ocean depths and map ocean floor, study sea floor history, locate minerals, track and map ocean currents, chart icebergs, study effects of oceans on weather and climate, predict coastal hazards.

CAREERS

Margaret LeMone
Meteorologist

Margaret LeMone is a scientist at the National Center for Atmospheric Research in Boulder, Colorado. She is interested in the structure and evolution of thunderstorms into lines (such as squall lines and hurricane bands) and in how they affect the winds in the atmosphere.

Dr. LeMone's study of thunderstorm lines involves some exciting methods of data collection. She has flown through or directed other research aircraft through numerous thunderstorms, mostly over the central Atlantic Ocean. She has also used data collected from aircraft and tall towers to study air currents heating the lowest few kilometers of the atmosphere. The data help her understanding of how these air currents relate to the organization of cumulus clouds into lines ("cloud streets"). Computer modeling is also a part of her study of clouds and thunderstorms.

Dr. LeMone has been active in the American Meteorological Society, serving as councillor, head of its Board of Women and Minorities, and president of its Denver-Boulder Chapter.

II The Origin of Earth

Topic 6 Where Earth Science Begins: The Solar System

Where should the study of earth science begin — land, oceans, atmosphere, or sky? A good choice seems to be the origin of the planet Earth. Earth, however, is only one member of a whole family of planets circling the sun. So we begin with the origin of the whole family, which is called the solar system.

A **hypothesis** is an informed guess that tries to explain how or why an event occurs. A good hypothesis explains known facts. Every hypothesis about the origin of the solar system has to consider the following six facts:

1. All planets move around the sun (revolve) in the same direction.
2. The paths, or orbits, of the planets around the sun are all nearly circular.
3. Most of the orbits are in nearly the same flat surface (plane).

OBJECTIVES

A Define *hypothesis* and list some facts that a hypothesis of the origin of the solar system must explain.

B Describe the origin of the solar system according to the protoplanet hypothesis.

C Discuss the origin and characteristics of Earth's oceans, atmosphere, internal structure, and continents, and describe Earth's internal structure.

1.6 This artist's conception of the solar system illustrates the orbits of the nine planets revolving around the sun.

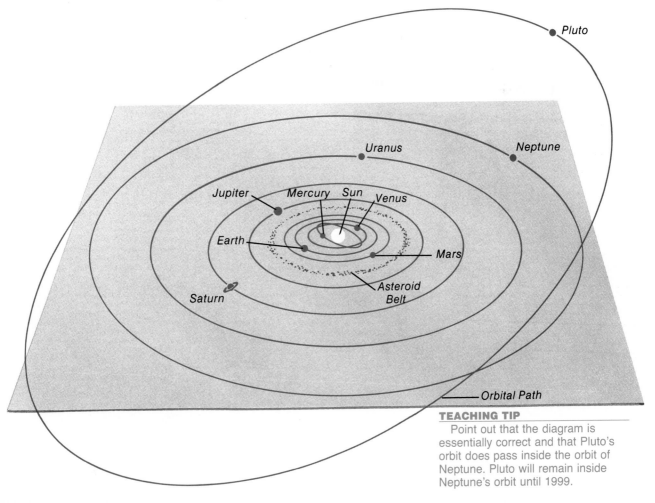

TEACHING TIP

Point out that the diagram is essentially correct and that Pluto's orbit does pass inside the orbit of Neptune. Pluto will remain inside Neptune's orbit until 1999.

OF INTEREST
  Astronomers are observing T-TAURI stars for evidence of how planets form.

VIDEODISC SELECTION

Formation of the solar system
Side 4 movie: 25261 & PLAY

SCIENCE BACKGROUND
  The origin of the solar system did not occur at the same time as the origin of the universe. See Chapter 21, Topic 18, for the Big Bang hypothesis.

1.7 According to the protoplanet hypothesis, a great cloud of gas and dust was gradually transformed into the planets and natural satellites that make up the solar system.

4. The sun turns on its axis (rotates) in almost the same plane as the planets and in the same direction that the planets revolve.
5. Most of the planets rotate in the same direction as the sun.
6. Seven of the nine planets have moons. Most of the moons revolve around the planets in the same direction that the planets revolve around the sun.

The hypothesis that many astronomers favor—because it best explains the facts listed above—is the **protoplanet hypothesis**. It was first proposed about 1944 by a German astronomer, von Weizsacker, and modified by an American astronomer, Kuiper, in 1950.

Topic 7 **The Protoplanet Hypothesis**

The protoplanet hypothesis suggests that about 5 billion years ago a great cloud of gas and dust rotated slowly in space. The cloud was at least 10 billion kilometers in diameter. As time passed, the cloud shrank under the pull of its own gravitation or was made to collapse by the explosion of a passing star. Most of the cloud's material gathered around its own center. Its shrinking made it rotate faster, like a spinning whirlpool. The compression of its material made its interior so hot that a powerful reaction, hydrogen fusion, began and the core of the cloud blazed into a newborn sun.

About 10 percent of the material in the cloud formed a great platelike disk surrounding the sun far into space. Friction within the disk caused most of its mass to collect in a number of huge whirlpools or eddies. These eddies shrank into more compact masses called **protoplanets** and later formed planets and moons. Some uncollected material remains even today as comets, meteoroids, and asteroids.

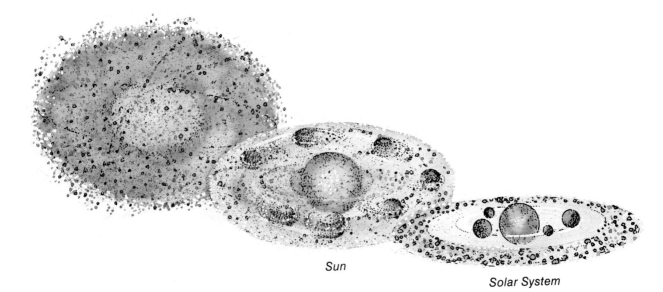

Sun

Solar System

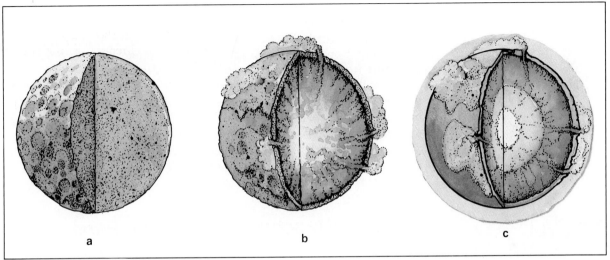

a   b   c

Topic 8   **Origin of the Oceans**

Scientists now agree that when Earth first formed, it had neither oceans nor atmosphere. As the protoplanet changed to the planet Earth, it grew hotter. There were three sources of heat: compression, radioactive minerals, and bombardment by showers of meteorites. Radioactive minerals are natural sources of energy, much of which becomes heat energy. Meteorites produce heat both by friction and by impact.

When Earth became hot enough, the common element iron melted. The molten iron sank toward the center of Earth, forming a dense core. As the molten iron sank, it partially melted other earth materials that it touched (Topic 10). Water and gases that had been trapped in those materials were released. The molten earth materials separated into layers. As the materials separated, the steam and gases that they had held escaped to the surface in volcanic eruptions. The steam that escaped condensed into water that slowly accumulated as oceans.

1.8   According to the model, the protoplanet Earth (a) had no oceans or atmosphere. As the intense heat of Earth's interior built up, volcanic eruptions began to occur (b). Repeated huge eruptions produced volumes of volcanic gases. The steam in these gases condensed upon reaching the surface (c) to form Earth's oceans.

Topic 9   **Origin of the Atmosphere**

The atmosphere that surrounds Earth today includes about 78 percent free nitrogen and 21 percent free oxygen. *Free* means these gases are not combined with other elements. The remaining 1 percent is mostly other gases, such as argon, carbon dioxide, and helium. (Water vapor is in the atmosphere too, but the amount varies with weather and climate.)

This present mixture of gases is very different from what scientists think Earth's original atmosphere must have been. The original atmosphere is thought to have come from volcanoes. It would have been like the mixture of gases that now erupts from volcanoes.

TEACHING TIP

Explain to students that even though the percentage of water vapor in the air is quite small, water is essential for the survival of life forms here on Earth.

This mixture usually is over 50 percent water vapor with large amounts of carbon dioxide and sulfur gases. However, the mixture contains no free oxygen!

Almost all forms of life on Earth need free oxygen. Where, then, did it come from? Scientists think the atmosphere's first free oxygen came from the breakup of water molecules by sunlight in the upper atmosphere. When simple green plants came into existence, they added more free oxygen to the atmosphere by **photosynthesis**. In this process, green plants manufacture sugars and starches from carbon dioxide and water in the presence of sunlight. In photosynthesis, more than half of the oxygen present in the carbon dioxide and water is not used. This excess oxygen is released into the atmosphere as free oxygen.

VIDEODISC SELECTION

Diagram of Earth's inner layers with convection in mantle
Side 2: 724, single frame

Formation of magma, lava, and igneous rock
Side 2 movie: 25860 & PLAY

Topic 10   **Structure of the Solid Earth**

A *model* is a picture that shows a concept, event, or object that cannot be seen in its natural state. For example, no one can directly see the inside of Earth. Yet geologists today have a fairly clear model of Earth's structure from its surface to its very center. Since the center is nearly 6400 kilometers from the surface, most of this model is based on indirect evidence. This indirect evidence will be discussed in the chapter on earthquakes.

For now, consider the Earth model that geologists describe. At its center is a spherical **inner core** 1200 kilometers in diameter. The inner core is made of solid iron and nickel. Surrounding the inner core is an **outer core** about 2250 kilometers thick made of liquid iron and nickel. Then comes a 2900-kilometer-thick layer of heavy rocks rich in compounds of iron, magnesium, and silicon. This layer, called the **mantle**, reaches almost to Earth's surface. The

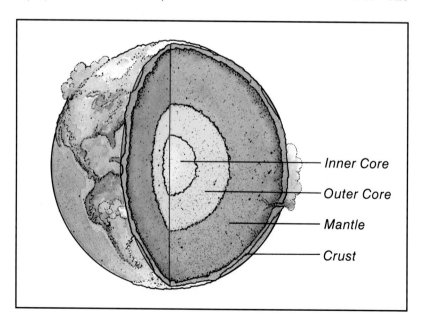

1.9   A simple model of Earth's interior reveals distinct layers between the core and the surface.

mantle is covered by a layer of lighter rocks called the **crust**. The crust ranges in thickness from about 10 kilometers below the ocean basins to about 65 kilometers below the continents. Mines and wells go deep into the crust, but none have reached the mantle.

Was Earth layered like this when it formed more than 4 billion years ago? Probably not. If the protoplanet hypothesis is correct, the original surface of Earth looked much like the moon does today. Below its surface, Earth was probably composed of the same kind of material all the way to its center.

How then did Earth develop its layers of core, mantle, and crust? Many geologists think that as the temperature of the newly formed Earth increased, large quantities of iron and nickel in its rocks melted. Great streams of these hot, heavy liquids flowed toward Earth's center. On their way down they melted lighter rock materials and forced them up to the surface. At the surface the light rock became solid and formed Earth's crust. The mantle formed between the crust and the core.

Topic 11   **How the Continents Formed**

One hypothesis suggests that when the melted iron and nickel sank into Earth's core, it forced out enough light rock to form an immense single continent. Another suggestion is that the continents were formed by great lava flows from erupting volcanoes over hundreds of millions of years. In either case, today's continents are quite different from those that first formed on Earth's surface. In the billions of years following their origin, the continents have undergone many changes. Later chapters will explain the evidence for these changes, how they occurred, and what caused them.

TOPIC QUESTIONS

Each topic question refers to the topic of the same number.

6. (a) What is a hypothesis? (b) What is the solar system? (c) List at least three facts that should be considered by a hypothesis that explains the origin of the solar system.

7. Briefly describe the protoplanet hypothesis.

8. (a) Describe three ways Earth got hotter in its early history. (b) Describe how the oceans formed.

9. (a) How does the present atmosphere differ from Earth's original atmosphere?   (b) How did Earth's atmosphere get its free oxygen?

10. (a) Make a simple labeled diagram showing the model of Earth. (b) Explain how Earth's interior got its layered structure.

11. Briefly describe one hypothesis that explains the forming of continents.

SCIENCE BACKGROUND

There are areas where mantle rocks have been thrust to the surface.

ANSWERS

6. (a) informed guess that explains an event   (b) planets circling sun   (c) planets revolve in same direction, orbits nearly circular, orbits in nearly same plane, sun and planets turn in same direction, moons of planets behave in same way as sun and planets.

7. rotating gas cloud condenses into protoplanets

8. (a) compression, radioactive decay, bombardment   (b) steam brought to surface condensed

9. (a) more oxygen, less carbon dioxide and sulfur   (b) breakup of water molecules by sunlight in upper atmosphere and process of photosynthesis

10. (a) drawing should show crust, mantle, inner and outer cores (b) materials drifted to surface or core by density differences

11. light rock forced to surface, or erupting volcanoes

CHAPTER 1

L A B
ACTIVITY

Collecting and Interpreting Data

Looking at a problem scientifically means you take a close look at the facts involved in a problem. Like many areas of science, earth science answers questions by beginning with facts, such as observations and the recorded data. Interpreting the facts often involves plotting the data on a graph. The shape made by a line on a graph reflects the data used to make the graph. In this lab activity, you will use standard laboratory equipment to collect facts or data. You will then graph and analyze that data. Finally you will use that analysis to compare and contrast graphs while you search for answers to problems.

Lab Skills and Objectives
- To **collect data** using laboratory equipment
- To **graph** and **interpret** data
- To **compare** and **contrast** graphs

Materials
- stopper
- large plastic funnel
- ring stand
- test tube clamp
- 500-mL beaker
- water
- dropper
- washable marking pen or grease pencil
- 50-mL or 100-mL graduated cylinder
- metric ruler
- graph paper

Procedure

1. Use a stopper to seal the small end of a funnel. Be sure the stopper is firmly in place.

2. Attach the funnel to a ring stand by using a test tube clamp. The funnel should be wide side up.

3. Fill a 500-mL beaker with water. Using a dropper, place just enough water in the bottom of the funnel to reach the joint where the funnel starts to expand. With a marking pen, place a mark on the outside of the funnel at this location.

4. Carefully measure 50 mL of water from the beaker into a graduated cylinder. Pour the 50 mL into the funnel. Mark the new water level on the outside of the funnel.

5. Repeat step 4 nine more times. Remember to mark the water level on the outside of the funnel in each case. You should have a total of 11 marks on the funnel when you are through.

6. Without smearing the marks, remove the funnel from the ring stand and pour out the water.

7. With a metric ruler, measure, to the nearest tenth of a centimeter, the distance from the first mark (at the bend of the funnel) to each of the other marks. Record the distances in Data Table A.

8. Draw a graph on a piece of graph paper. Place the pour number from the first column of Data Table A along

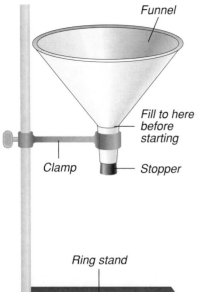

Funnel

Fill to here before starting

Clamp

Stopper

Ring stand

1.10 Equipment set up

the x-axis and distance in centimeters along the y-axis (Figure 1.11). Plot the data from Data Table A on the graph.

9. Answer the questions in *Analysis and Conclusions.*

Data Table A	
Pour #	Distance (cm)
1	3.6
2	5.2
3	6.2
4	7.0
5	7.7
6	8.4
7	9.0
8	9.5
9	9.9
10	10.3

Analysis and Conclusions

1. How did the spacing between the lines on the funnel change as more water was added to the funnel? Why did the change occur in that way?

2. If the funnel was sealed at the wide end, inverted, and filled 50 mL at a time from the narrow end, what would you expect to happen to the spaces between the lines as the funnel was filled?

3. If you lived on a lake with a funnel-shaped bottom, would you be more con-cerned about a heavy rain causing the lake to flood its banks if the funnel was wide side down or wide side up (assuming it could occur either way)? Explain your answer.

4. Locate the graphs on pages 15, 189, 269, and 608 of your textbook. Which is shaped most like your graph? Identify one way in which each of the other graphs is shaped differently from your graph.

5. If the distance between the lines on the funnel had been measured instead of the total distance to each line and then plotted on a graph, which one of the same four graphs would most closely resemble the results? (Plot a new graph by recalculating the new distances.)

6. If instead of a funnel a large beaker had been filled 50 mL at a time and the results plotted on a graph, which of the four graphs above would this graph most closely resemble?

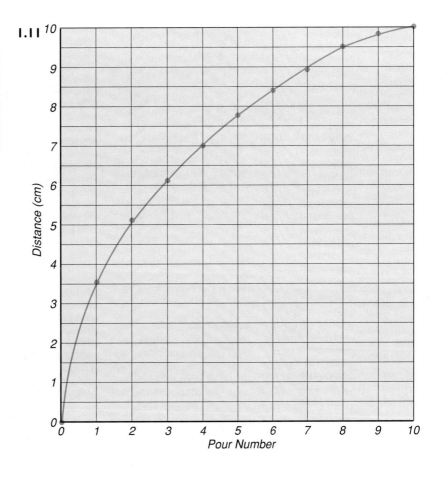

1.11

Distance (cm) vs *Pour Number*

Answers to all questions appear in the Teacher's Guide at the back of this book.

■ Summary

I Geology, astronomy, meteorology, and oceanography are the branches of earth science. Some earth science events are included in more than one branch.

Geologists study and explore Earth's surface and internal structure. Astronomers study the universe beyond Earth.

Meteorologists study Earth's atmosphere to understand the processes that control weather and climate.

Oceanographers study ocean currents and waves, the ocean floor, and other aspects of Earth's oceans.

II A hypothesis is an informed guess that tries to explain how or why an event occurs. The protoplanet hypothesis is an explanation of the origin of the solar system.

According to the protoplanet hypothesis, the solar system originated as a great rotating cloud of dust and gas that shrank into compact masses called protoplanets.

Compression, radioactive decay, and bombardment by showers of meteorites heated the protoplanet Earth. Steam that was released by the heat condensed into water to form oceans. Other gases formed the atmosphere.

The original atmosphere contained large amounts of carbon dioxide and sulfur gases but no free oxygen. Free oxygen was formed later in the process of photosynthesis.

Earth's interior contains an inner core, outer core, and mantle surrounded by a thin rock crust at the surface.

The continents are thought to have formed either from light rock that was forced to Earth's surface or by great lava flows from erupting volcanoes.

■ Vocabulary

astronomy	meteorology
crust	oceanography
geology	outer core
hypothesis	photosynthesis
inner core	protoplanet
mantle	protoplanet hypothesis

■ Review

Match terms in List **A** with phrases in List **B**.

List A

1. astronomers
2. radioactive minerals
3. crust
4. earth science
5. event
6. geologists
7. volcanic eruptions
8. hypothesis
9. inner core
10. mantle
11. space probes
12. oceanographers
13. meteorologists
14. outer core
15. photosynthesis
16. protoplanet

List B

a. scientists who study Earth's oceans
b. process that adds free oxygen to the atmosphere
c. an informed guess that explains an event
d. Earth layer rich in iron, magnesium, and silicon
e. compact masses that became planets and moons
f. an occurrence that causes a change
g. Earth sphere made of solid iron and nickel
h. scientists who study solid Earth
i. layer of lighter rock found at surface
j. a possible heat source for a young Earth
k. scientists who study the universe
l. Earth sphere made of liquid iron and nickel
m. *Mariner, Pioneer, Viking,* and *Voyager*
n. the study of Earth, its oceans, atmosphere, and the universe
o. scientists who study Earth's weather and climate
p. original source of oceans and atmosphere

■ Interpret and Apply

On your paper, answer each question in complete sentences.

1. Describe an earth science event that is related to more than one branch of earth science and explain how it is related to those branches.
2. Information about an object or event that can be obtained by direct observation is called *direct evidence.* For information about objects and events that cannot be observed firsthand, scientists rely on *indirect evidence.* Which branches of earth science are able to use a lot of direct evidence? Which branches use mostly indirect evidence? Explain your answers.
3. Review the protoplanet hypothesis described in Topic 7. Which of the six facts listed in Topic 6 can be explained by the protoplanet hypothesis?
4. Which facts listed in Topic 6 are *not* explained by the protoplanet hypothesis? Explain your answer.
5. A good hypothesis not only explains known facts; it also correctly predicts new facts. Based on the hypotheses about the formation of Earth (Topics 8–11), predict some features that should be true of other planets.

■ Critical Thinking

A skill needed by all earth scientists is graph reading. The graph below shows world population from the population in the year 1750 to the expected population in the year 2000. The straight lines that meet at the lower left corner of the graph are the two *axes* (singular: axis) of the graph. The x-axis is the horizontal line at the bottom of the graph. The y-axis is the vertical line on the left side of the graph.

1. Which axis (x or y) shows population?
2. What was the world population in 1950?
3. What is the population expected to be in the year you graduate from high school?

4. In which year was the world population 1 billion?
5. What was the world population in 1960?
6. In which year was the world population 2 billion?
7. How long did it take world population to increase from 1 billion to 2 billion?
8. In which year was the world population 4 billion?
9. How long did it take world population to increase from 2 billion to 4 billion?
10. What is different about the time it took the world population to double from 1 billion to 2 billion and the time it took to double from 2 billion to 4 billion?
11. According to the graph, will the doubling time from 4 billion to 8 billion be greater or less than the time for the previous doubling?

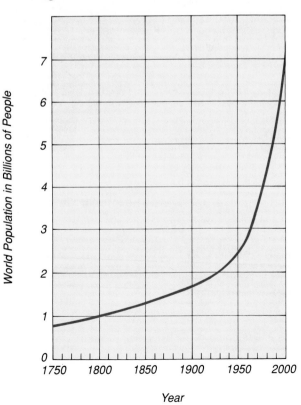

World Population in Billions of People

Year

15

Earth's Shape, Dimensions, and Internal Heat

▲
Even though this vast
area appears to be flat, it
is not. How can you tell
that it is not flat?

OF INTEREST
   The flat area in the photo is the
Bonneville Salt Flats near Salt Lake
City, Utah, site of several land-speed
records.

How Do You Know That . . .

Earth is not flat? This expanse of land has an area of hundreds of
square kilometers. Nearly three hours are required just to drive
across it. This area certainly looks flat, but it is not. Laid out on this
area is a 16-kilometer racetrack used to set land speed records. If
Earth were flat, an observer standing at one end of the track would
be able to see to the other end, but this is impossible. Does this
show that Earth is a sphere? No, it merely shows that Earth is not
flat. We need other evidence to prove that Earth is a sphere.

1 Earth's Shape and Size

Topic 1 Earth Is Spherical

Is Earth flat or round? Because most maps are flat, it is easy to see why someone could think that Earth was flat. However, long before Columbus, many people knew that Earth was not flat but shaped like a sphere. The explorer Magellan provided additional support for a spherical Earth when, in 1522, one of his ships returned to Spain after sailing all the way around Earth.

Early scientists supported a spherical model of Earth based on the following evidence:

1. The mast of a ship was the first part to appear over the horizon. It was the last part to disappear. The traditional cry of the lookout in a sailing vessel is, "I see a mast."
2. When ships sailed north or south, sailors observed that the nighttime sky changed in appearance. The North Star rose higher in the sky as they sailed northward. It sank in the sky as they sailed southward. The position of the North Star changed so gradually and so evenly that it could only be explained in one way. The ship was sailing on a spherical surface. When ships sailed far enough south, constellations such as the Big Dipper could no longer be seen, but new ones such as the Southern Cross appeared in the sky. Would this be true on a flat Earth? Compare Figures 2.1(a) and 2.1(b).
3. An eclipse of the moon occurs when Earth's shadow falls on the moon. During an eclipse of the moon, the edge of Earth's shadow as it moves across the moon is always the arc of a circle. Only a sphere casts a circular shadow, no matter what position it is in.

OBJECTIVES

A List several evidences that Earth is nearly spherical.

B Define *oblate spheroid* and explain the effect of Earth's shape on the weight of an object.

C Describe and use Eratosthenes' method of measuring Earth's circumference.

D Compare Earth's polar and equatorial dimensions and discuss the amount of land and water area on Earth's surface.

2.1 (a) The angle of the North Star above the horizon changes as the latitude of the observer changes. This is evidence that Earth is spherical. (b) If Earth were flat, the North Star would be overhead at all latitudes.

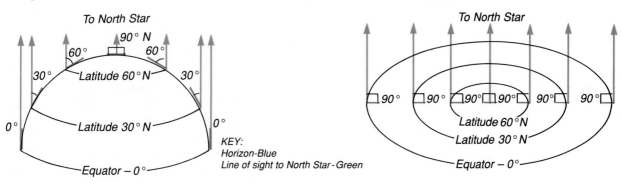

Angular distance of North Star above is the angle between the horizon and the line of sight.
(Because of distance to North Star, all lines of sight are parallel.)

The evidence listed is, of course, still visible today, although a lookout is much more likely to see a smokestack than a mast. But now everyone can see the evidence. Many photographs of Earth have been taken by orbiting spacecraft. Other photographs of Earth have been taken from the moon by the *Apollo* astronauts.

VIDEODISC SELECTION

Data on Earth's size and dimensions
Side 2: 7239, single frame

2.2 A photograph of Earth taken from outer space provides concrete evidence of Earth's spherical shape.

TEACHING TIP

You may wish to discuss the law of gravitation briefly to show the mathematical effect on weight versus distance from Earth's center. The equation to be discussed is the following:

$$F = G \ \frac{m_1 m_2}{r_2}$$

where F is the force between the two objects, G is a constant equal to 6.672×10^{-8} (dyne-cm)^2/g^2, m_1 and m_2 are the masses of the two objects, and r is the distance between the objects.

SCIENCE BACKGROUND

Earth's oblateness is so slight compared to its size that Earth appears to be a perfect sphere when viewed from space. A globe is an accurate model of Earth.

Topic 2 **The Sphere Is Not Perfect**

Further evidence that Earth is a sphere can be obtained by measuring the weight of an object at several places on Earth's surface. The weight of an object, measured in newtons, is simply the force with which gravity pulls the object toward Earth's center. This weight changes with the distance from the center. The farther an object is from Earth's center, the less it weighs. Measurements show that a given object weighs almost the same everywhere on Earth's surface. This means that all of Earth's surface is almost the same distance from Earth's center and that Earth is *almost* a sphere.

Why almost? Careful measurements show that the weight of an object is not exactly the same all over Earth. An object that weighs 195 newtons at sea level at the North Pole or South Pole will weigh 194 newtons at sea level at the equator. This means that the object must be nearer to Earth's center at the poles than at the equator. In other words, Earth is not a perfect sphere. In fact, it is slightly flattened at the poles and slightly bulged at the equator. Such a shape is called an **oblate** (ob'lat) **spheroid.** The polar flattening and equatorial bulge are caused by Earth's rotation.

Topic 3 Measuring Earth's Circumference

How do you measure the distance around Earth?

In principle, the method is simple. Take two points a substantial distance apart on Earth, with one directly north of the other. The line joining these points will be part of a circle that goes around Earth through the North Pole and South Pole. Measure the distance between the two points. Find out what part of the whole circle that part is (you shall see how in a moment). Then multiply the measured distance by the number of parts needed to make the whole circle. This calculation gives the north-south distance around Earth. This distance is called the *circumference* of Earth.

The first scientific measurement of Earth's circumference was probably made by the Greek astronomer Eratosthenes (er uh TOS thuh neez) more than 2000 years ago. Eratosthenes, who lived in Alexandria, heard of a famous well in the city of Syene (sie EE nee) in southern Egypt. Once a year, at noon on the longest day of the year, the sun shone straight down to the bottom of this deep vertical well. This occurrence meant that the sun was directly overhead in Syene at that moment. At noon on the same day in Alexandria, the sun was 7.2° below the overhead point. Since Alexandria was supposed to be directly north of Syene, the two cities must be separated by 7.2° on a circumference of Earth. The whole distance around Earth is 360°, the total number of degrees in a circle, and 7.2° is one-fiftieth of a circle. Eratosthenes multiplied the distance between Syene and Alexandria by 50 and obtained his answer for Earth's circumference.

VIDEODISC SELECTION

Diagram showing how Eratosthenes measured Earth's diameter
Side 2: 7240, single frame

SCIENCE BACKGROUND

Note that even in the time of Eratosthenes, scholars accepted the spherical model of Earth.

OF INTEREST

Eratosthenes measured the shadow of an obelisk. A well is used in the picture to show the comparison better.

2.3 Eratosthenes used the difference in the angle of the sun's rays at two locations in his calculation of Earth's circumference.

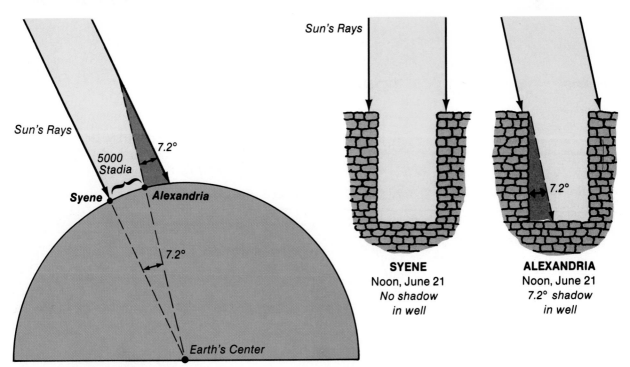

SYENE
Noon, June 21
*No shadow
in well*

ALEXANDRIA
Noon, June 21
*7.2° shadow
in well*

What was Eratosthenes' answer? The distance between the two cities was 5000 stadia (a stadium was about 185 meters). Multiplied by 50, this gave a circumference of 250 000 stadia, or 46 250 kilometers. Despite a number of inaccuracies in his assumptions, Eratosthenes had come remarkably close to the real size of Earth's circumference (about 40 000 kilometers). If you look at a map of Egypt, you may discover one—perhaps two—of Eratosthenes' errors. (Syene is now called Aswan.)

Topic 4 **Earth's Dimensions**

The method used by Eratosthenes is still used today to measure Earth's circumference. Today, however, the data used are gathered by more precise instruments and methods. Modern instruments used to measure Earth include lasers, satellites, and ground-based satellite tracking stations. Here are a few of the important dimensions of Earth. (Remember Earth bulges at the equator and is flattened at the poles.)

Circumference at Equator	40 074 kilometers
Circumference at Poles	40 007 kilometers
Diameter at Equator	12 756 kilometers
Diameter at Poles	12 714 kilometers

The total surface area of Earth is about 510 million square kilometers. Of this, about 149 million square kilometers stand above sea level as continents and islands. The remaining 361 million square kilometers are covered by oceans. Thus, the percentage of land is only about 29 percent, while that of water is about 71 percent.

VIDEODISC SELECTION

Data on Earth's surface area
Side 2: 7250 to 7251, 2-frame
sequence

TEACHING TIP

Students may better grasp Earth's dimensions if they are expressed in more familiar terms. For example, it would take a month of non-stop driving (24 hours a day) at 55 miles per hour to drive around Earth's circumference, if it were possible to do so.

ANSWERS

1. (a) ship's mast appears first and disappears last, changing appearance of nighttime sky over Earth's surface, shadow cast by Earth during an eclipse   (b) photographs of Earth from space
2. (a) weight of an object almost same everywhere   (b) sphere that bulges at equator, flattened at poles (c) weight of object slightly less at equator than at poles
3. (a) difference in angle of sun between Alexandria and Syene, distance between those cities   (b) angle was 1/50 of circumference, multiplied distance by 50
4. (a) equatorial is 42 km greater (b) land is 149 million km^2, or 29%; water is 361 million km^2, or 71%

TOPIC QUESTIONS

Each topic question refers to the topic of the same number.

1. **(a)** Describe two pieces of evidence for Earth's spherical shape that have been known for thousands of years.   **(b)** What modern evidence enables us to see that Earth is spherical?

2. **(a)** How do the effects of gravity show that Earth is almost spherical?   **(b)** What is an oblate spheroid?   **(c)** How do the effects of gravity show that Earth is an oblate spheroid?

3. **(a)** What two measurements did Eratosthenes need to determine Earth's circumference?   **(b)** Explain how he used these measurements to find Earth's circumference.

4. **(a)** Compare Earth's equatorial and polar diameters.   **(b)** Compare the amount and percent of land and water areas on Earth's surface.

II   Earth's Density and Temperature

Topic 5   Earth's Density

Properties of small objects are fairly easy to determine. Properties of the whole Earth must often be measured indirectly. Earth's density is an example. **Density** is a measure of the amount of material (mass) in a given space (volume). The density of an object or substance is determined using the following equation.

$$\text{density} = \frac{\text{mass}}{\text{volume}} \quad \text{or} \quad D = \frac{m}{V}$$

For example, suppose you have a small block of the metal lead. By taking measurements, you find that the block has a mass of 90.4 grams (90.4 g) and a volume of 8 cubic centimeters (8 cm^3). The density of lead is found as follows.

$$D = \frac{m}{V} = \frac{90.4 \text{ g}}{8 \text{ cm}^3} = 11.3 \text{ g/cm}^3$$

The formula $D = m/V$ can also be used to determine Earth's density. The mass of Earth is calculated from its gravitational force, that is, the force with which it attracts objects of known mass to its surface. The volume of Earth can be calculated from its dimensions. Dividing Earth's volume into its mass gives an average density of 5.5 grams per cubic centimeter.

A similar calculation for the rocks of Earth's crust gives an average density of only 2.8 grams per cubic centimeter. How can the density of Earth's rocks (2.8 grams per cubic centimeter) be so much less than its average density (5.5 grams per cubic centimeter)? In order to have an average density value this high, the materials inside Earth must have densities much greater than 5.5 grams per cubic centimeter. The model of Earth's interior is based partly on the difference between Earth's average density and crustal density. Earth's core is thought to be mostly iron and nickel. Iron and nickel are dense enough to account for the difference. The density of iron is just under 8.0 grams per cubic centimeter. The density of nickel is a little more than 8.0 grams per cubic centimeter.

Topic 6   Temperatures Below the Surface

Have you ever visited an underground cave? In summer, caves are pleasantly cool. Deep caves stay at about the same temperature all year. Neither the sun's heat nor winter cold penetrates Earth below about 20 meters. At this depth, the temperature usually remains equal to the average yearly temperature of the particular place — except in areas of hot springs and volcanoes.

OBJECTIVES

A   Define *density* and calculate the density of an object given its mass and volume.

B   Give the values for Earth's average density and the density of its crust; relate these values to the model of Earth's layers.

C   Discuss sources of heat inside Earth; describe the temperatures of Earth's interior and the evidence for these values.

2.4   Density is the mass in a unit volume of a substance. The two objects on the balance have the same volume. Which object is more dense?

VIDEODISC SELECTION

Data on Earth's mass and density
Side 2: 7252 to 7255, 4-frame sequence

Below a depth of 20 meters, however, is a different situation. Beginning at this depth, the temperature of the ground rises. This temperature rise has been measured thousands of times in deep mines, tunnels, water wells, and oil wells. The increase in temperature differs from place to place, but for the outer crust it averages about 1 degree Celsius (1°C) for every 40 meters in depth.

Direct temperature measurements are only available for a few thousand meters down. Temperature is estimated for depths below that. A temperature rise of 1°C in 40 meters is a very high rate. If that rate continued all the way to Earth's center, the inner core would have a temperature of about 150 000°C. Evidence from earthquakes (Chapter 15) indicates that the inner core is solid, which would be very unlikely at such a high temperature. The inner core is probably no hotter than 7000°C. If the model is correct, the rise in temperature must become more gradual somewhere below the first few thousand meters of Earth's crust.

SCIENCE BACKGROUND
Estimates of Earth's interior temperature are frequently revised.

Topic 7 What Makes the Crust Hot?

If Earth's crust gets hotter with increasing depth, there must be some source of heat in the rocks. Most of the heat appears to come from radioactive elements. Radioactive elements give off energy that can be absorbed as heat. Some radioactive elements include uranium, thorium, and a form of potassium. Another possible source of heat is friction between rock masses during movements of Earth's crust. There may also be some heat left over from the original heat of Earth's interior.

Like other planets, Earth loses heat to outer space. The rocks of Earth's crust, however, do not transfer heat very well. Therefore, Earth loses its interior heat slowly. The heat loss is uneven, for several reasons. Some rocks lose heat more quickly than others. The thickness of the rock crust varies. The percentage of radioactive elements is not the same in all rocks. Thus, different amounts of heat loss are measured at different places on Earth's surface.

2.5 Hot springs and geysers at Earth's surface provide evidence that a major heat source exists below the crust.

TOPIC QUESTIONS

Each topic question refers to the topic of the same number.

5. **(a)** A 100-gram rock has a volume of 35 cubic centimeters. Find the density of the rock. **(b)** What is Earth's average density? **(c)** What is the average density of Earth's crust? **(d)** What do these two values indicate about the density of Earth's core?

6. **(a)** Why does an underground cave stay at about the same temperature all year? **(b)** What is the average rate that temperature rises with depth in the outer crust? **(c)** What evidence suggests that this rate does not continue all the way to Earth's core?

7. **(a)** What is thought to be the major source of heat for Earth's crust? **(b)** List some reasons why the heat given off by the crust is different in different places.

ANSWERS

5. (a) D = 100 g / 35 cm^3; D = 2.9 g/cm^3 (b) 5.5 g/cm^3 (c) 2.8 g/cm^3 (d) Core must be very dense.

6. (a) It is not affected by seasonal changes. (b) 1°C per 40 m (c) earthquake evidence suggests solid core

7. (a) radioactive decay (b) different rocks vary in amount of radioactive elements and in rate of heat loss, thickness of crust varies

Current RESEARCH

Investigating with Science

"**L**et's look at the problem scientifically." Exactly what's involved in "doing science?" Having studied science for several years, you know science involves forming hypotheses that can be tested experimentally. Hypotheses that seem to work can — over time — be called theories. A good theory explains why things happen better than other available explanations.

To look at a problem "scientifically" means that you look at data and ask questions. It does not necessarily mean that you find an answer that is totally agreed upon. Open debate is an important part of scientific investigation. There are hundreds of scientific journals in which researchers publish their findings. Data are discussed in the journals or at conferences. New experiments are designed based on those discussions. Work continues on a problem until the scientific community agrees that all data lead to the same conclusions.

Activities in this textbook will ask you to observe, question, think, and explain. Whether it is approaching an experiment in class or the hard choices involved in managing Earth's environment, thinking scientifically can help you find the right questions to ask. Science isn't so much about what is known as it is about what still needs to be known. Without questions, there is no scientific investigation.

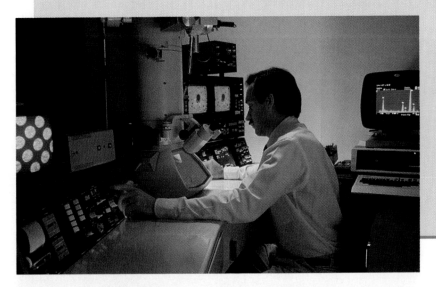

CHAPTER 2
L A B
ACTIVITY

Eratosthenes and Earth's Circumference

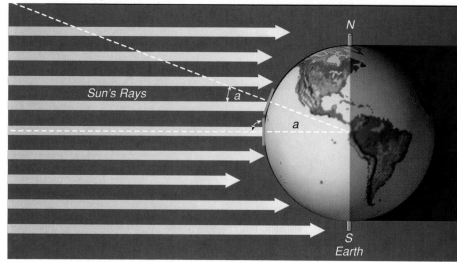

Sun's Rays

N

a

a

S
Earth

More than two thousand years ago, a man named Eratosthenes made a surprisingly accurate estimation of Earth's circumference. He did this by using careful observations of the sun, the shadows the suns rays produced and some simple geometric relationships.

You will use a small circle to demonstrate how Eratosthenes' method for determining circumference works. You will see how the circumference of a circle can be determined using the distance between any two points on the circle and the angle formed by joining those two points with the circle's center. Then you will use this method to determine a value for Earth's circumference.

Lab Skills and Objectives
- To **form** **models** of Eratosthenes' Earth
- To **measure** and **record** data from the model
- To **compute** and **interpret** the data

Materials
- blank sheet of paper
- safety compass
- protractor
- flexible metric ruler

Procedure
Part A
1. Visually locate a point as near the center of a blank sheet of paper as possible. Mark the point and label it point C.
2. With a safety compass, draw a large circle around point C.
3. Use the metric ruler to draw a straight line in any direction from point C to the edge of the paper. Locate the point where the straight line intersects the circle. Label that point A. The line connecting points C and A is called line CA.
4. Place a protractor along line CA so its center is on point C. Mark off an angle equal to any value greater than 15° but less than 50°. Record the angle you select in the space provided in Data Table A.
5. Complete the angle by drawing a straight line from point

C through the point you have marked off with the protractor to the edge of the paper. Locate the point where this straight line intersects the circle and label it point B. The line connecting points C and B is called line CB.

6. Set the flexible metric ruler on edge and bend it to follow the circumference of the circle. Use the curved ruler to measure, to the nearest tenth of a centimeter, the length of the circle from point A to point B (an arc). Record the value in Data Table A.

7. Lay the metric ruler flat on the paper. Measure the length from point C to point A, to the nearest tenth of a centimeter. Line CA is a radius of the circle. Record this value.

8. Answer questions 1–4 under *Analysis and Conclusions.*

Data Table A

Angle used (°)= _____

Length arc AB (cm) =_____
(distance along circle)

Length AC (cm) = _____
(radius of circle)

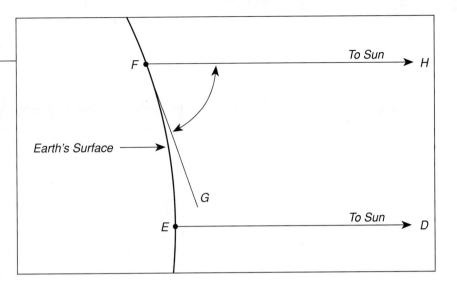

Part B

9. Eratosthenes used the sun's rays to find Earth's circumference. Figure 2.6 shows the sun's rays striking two locations at Earth's surface, E and F. At E the sun is straight overhead, that is, the angle at which the sun's rays strike Earth's surface is 90°. Use a protractor to determine the angle at which the sun's rays strike location F. This is the angle GFH. Record the measured angle in the space provided in Data Table B.

10. Calculate the difference between the angle of the sun's rays at the two locations. Record this value in Data Table B.

11. Use the same curved metric ruler technique you used in Part A to measure, to the nearest tenth of a centimeter, the distance from points E to F along the segment of Earth's surface shown in Figure 2.6. Record the arc length in Data Table B.

12. Use the scale 1 centimeter = 500 kilometers to convert the length of arc EF to kilometers. Record this value in Data Table B.

13. Answer questions 5–7 under *Analysis and Conclusions*.

Data Table B

Angle GFH (°) =_____

Distance for arc E to F (°)

=_____

Measured length of arc EF (cm)

=_____ (distance along circle)

Distance from E to F (km)= ___

Analysis and Conclusions

1. What fractional part of the whole circle is your angle? (Remember that there are 360° in a circle and that 180° is 1/2 circle, 90° is 1/4 circle, and so on.)

2. Use your answer to question 1 and your value for the length of arc AB to determine the circumference of your circle to the nearest tenth of a centimeter. For example, if the angle in question 1 is one tenth of the circle, the circumference will be ten times the length of arc AB. This is the method Eratosthenes used to calculate the circumference of Earth.

3. A standard formula for determining the circumference of a circle is C = 2 π r. Using that formula, determine the circumference of your circle again. (Use π = 3.14.)

4. By what percent do your answers to questions 2 and 3 differ? To calculate the difference, subtract the smaller circumference from the larger circumference, then divide the difference by your circumference value in question 3, and multiply the result by 100.

5. What part of a whole circle is the angular distance from E to F? Use the same method as in question 1.

6. Use your answer to question 5 and the distance in kilometers from E to F to determine the circumference of Earth.

7. Assume Earth's actual circumference is 40 000 kilometers. Determine the percent by which your value from question 6 differs from the actual circumference. Use the same technique as in question 4 but divide by 40 000 before multiplying by 100.

Answers to all questions appear in the Teacher's Guide at the back of this book.

■ Summary

I Evidence that Earth is spherical includes observations of sailing ships, the changing appearance of the nighttime sky over Earth's surface, eclipses of the moon, and photographs of Earth from space.

Earth's diameter is slightly less at the poles, slightly more at the equator. Most of Earth's surface is covered by oceans.

The weight of an object depends on its distance from Earth's center; an object's weight is less the further it is from Earth's center. Because Earth is not a perfect sphere, an object weighs slightly less at the equator than it does at the poles.

Earth's circumference can be calculated if the angle and surface distance between any two points on its surface are known. Eratosthenes is thought to be the first person to calculate Earth's circumference.

Earth's diameter is slightly less at the poles, slightly more at the equator. Most of Earth's surface is covered by oceans.

II The density of an object is found by dividing its mass by its volume $(D = m/V)$.

Earth's average density is 5.5 grams per cubic centimeter. The density of its crust averages 2.8 grams per cubic centimeter. Earth's iron-nickel core is its densest part.

Temperatures increase with depth in Earth's outer crust. Evidence indicates that the temperature does not increase at the same rate all the way to Earth's interior.

Earth's internal heat is mainly from radioactive elements such as uranium and thorium. Earth's original heat and friction between moving rock masses may be other sources of heat. The rate at which Earth loses heat to outer space varies over Earth's crust.

■ Vocabulary

density
oblate spheroid

■ Review

Number your paper from *1* to *18*. On your paper write the word that best completes each sentence.

1. The way a sailing ship gradually appears over the horizon is one evidence that Earth is _____.

2. The North Star rises higher in the sky as an observer travels toward the _____

3. During an eclipse of the moon, Earth's shadow on the moon is always an arc of a _____.

4. Only a _____ casts a circular shadow from every position.

5. Because Earth is almost spherical, an object's _____ is nearly the same anywhere on Earth's surface.

6. An object weighs _____ the further it is from the center of Earth.

7. An object weighs slightly _____ at Earth's poles than at Earth's equator.

8. Eratosthenes used the difference between the angle of the sun at Syene and Alexandria and the distance between those two cities to calculate Earth's _____.

9. An object like Earth that is flattened at the poles and bulges at the equator is said to have the shape of a _____.

10. Earth's diameter at the equator is _____ than its diameter at the poles.

11. Most of Earth's surface is covered by _____.

12. _____ is the measure of the amount of mass in a given volume.

13. The density of Earth's _____ is much less than the average density of Earth.

14. The densest part of Earth is its nickel-iron _____.

15. The temperature of Earth's outer crust _____ 1°C for every 40 meters in depth.

16. If the temperature change were constant all the way to Earth's core, then the core would have to be _____. Earthquake evidence suggests that this is not the case.

For further review, see **Study Guide.**
For assessment, see **Chapter Tests**
and **Computer Test Bank.**

17. The major source of heat inside Earth is _____ elements such as uranium and thorium.

18. Earth's original heat and _____ between moving rock masses may be sources of heat inside Earth.

■ Interpret and Apply

On your paper, answer each question.

1. During a total eclipse of the sun, the moon's shadow falls on Earth. The moon's shadow is always a circle. What does this suggest about the shape of the moon?

2. What should happen to the weight of an object as it is moved from a valley to a nearby mountaintop?

3. Planet X has a spherical shape. Two points on Planet X are 10° of arc apart. The distance between these same two points is 1500 kilometers. **(a)** What is the circumference of Planet X? **(b)** Is Planet X larger or smaller than Earth? (Refer to Topic 3.)

4. Rotating objects experience an apparent force away from the center of rotation. For a rotating sphere, this force is greatest at the equator. Explain how Earth's rotation causes it to have the shape of an oblate spheroid.

5. If Earth did not rotate, would an object at the equator weigh more or less than it does now? Why? (Refer to Interpret and Apply item 4.)

6. What is the density of an object with a mass of 10 grams and a volume of 5 cubic centimeters?

7. An object will float in a liquid if it is less dense than that liquid. The density of water is 1 gram per cubic centimeter. A particular block of wood has a mass of 3.21 grams and a volume of 3 cubic centimeters. Will the wood float in water? Why or why not?

8. **(a)** An object has a mass of 6 grams and a volume of 2 cubic centimeters. Find its density. **(b)** The object described in Part **(a)** is cut in half. What is the density of each half?

■ Critical Thinking

Scientists try to reduce sources of error in their measurements. Eratosthenes did well at measuring Earth's circumference with the information available to him. However, there were several sources of error in the information he used. How many sources of error can you find? Refer to Topic 3, to the map of Egypt, and to the other information listed below. List the errors you find on your paper.

In Eratosthenes' time, travelers had to stay near sources of water.

The sun is overhead at noon on the longest day of the year for locations on the Tropic of Cancer.

Eratosthenes estimated the distance from Alexandria to Syene based on the distance a camel could walk in a day and the number of days it took a camel to walk to Syene from Alexandria.

When size estimates are made by multiplying part of a whole item, using a larger part of the whole leads to more accurate results.

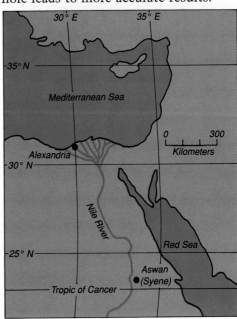

Atoms to Minerals

▲

An amethyst can be cut into many shapes, but amethyst crystals in nature have the same shape.

How Do You Know That . . .

Gemstone shapes are different from natural crystal shapes? The lovely violet mineral shown is amethyst, a kind of quartz. The gemstones surrounding the mineral are also amethyst. The amethyst gems have been artificially cut to have shapes different from the shape of the crystal. Gemstones can be cut to almost any shape. However, the natural crystal shape of a gemstone mineral is always the same. How does the arrangement of mineral particles determine crystal shape?

I Atomic Structure of Matter

Topic 1 Earth's Matter

Amethyst, the gemstone pictured on the opposite page, is just one example of thousands of materials that occur naturally in Earth's crust. Each of these materials has its own unique properties, and each of these materials is made of matter.

What is matter? **Matter** is anything that has mass and volume. *Mass* is the amount of material in an object or a substance. Mass is often discussed in terms of weight, but mass and weight are not the same. Weight is the force of gravity on an object or a substance. If the force of gravity is very weak, as in outer space, an object is weightless but its mass remains the same. *Volume* is the amount of space taken up by an object or a substance. A sample of earth material—for example, amethyst gemstones—has mass and volume and therefore is matter.

Scientists have developed a model to explain observations about matter. According to the model, all matter is made of particles so small that they cannot be seen even with a powerful microscope. There are only about 100 kinds of these tiny particles, which make up the thousands of substances that occur in Earth's crust.

Topic 2 Elements and Atoms

All matter is composed of elements. An **element** is a substance that cannot be broken into simpler substances by ordinary chemical means. The names of many elements are already familiar. Oxygen and nitrogen are elements in the atmosphere; gold, silver, and iron are examples of metallic elements. Each element has a symbol as well as a name. Usually the symbol is the first letter or two of the element's name; for example, the symbol for hydrogen is H, and the symbol for helium is He. Some elements take their symbols from their Latin or Greek name. For example, the symbol for gold is Au, from the Latin name for gold, *aurum*.

What makes up elements? More than 150 years ago the English chemist John Dalton stated his concept of the particle model—that each element is made up of tiny particles called atoms. Dalton defined the **atom** as the smallest part of an element that has all the properties of that element. Today scientists know that the atom itself is made from still smaller particles. Furthermore, all atoms—from every kind of element—contain the same kinds of particles! Let us look closer at the structure of an atom.

OBJECTIVES

A Explain the properties of matter in terms of the particle model.

B Define *element* and *atom*, and describe the particles, structure, and size of the atom.

C Determine the number of protons and neutrons in an atom from its atomic number and atomic mass; define *isotope*.

D Define *compound* and *molecule* and compare the properties of compounds with those of elements and mixtures.

VIDEODISC SELECTION

Data on elements making up Earth's crust
Side 2: 7246 to 7249, 4-frame sequence

3.1   The position of a single propeller blade is difficult to determine while the blades are in motion. The motion of electrons is similar because electrons fill the space in which they move, but the position of one electron is difficult to determine.

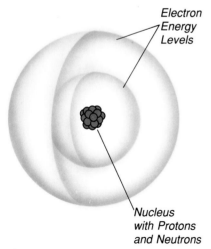

Electron Energy Levels

Nucleus with Protons and Neutrons

3.2   This model of the atom shows a central nucleus surrounded by electrons.

Topic 3   Model of an Atom

How does one imagine an atom? The atom is extremely small and complex. The model of the atom's structure has changed many times since the days of John Dalton. A large part of the atom model of today is based on complex mathematics. The pictures of atoms that you see in this book are used to help you visualize the structure and properties of atoms. However, these pictures do not show how atoms actually look.

Imagine charged particles moving at high speed about a central nucleus (plural, nuclei). The moving charged particles are **electrons**. Their motion creates a cloud of charge surrounding the nucleus. The exact path an electron takes in moving about the nucleus has never been determined. The motion of electrons in the cloud is like the area occupied by the blades of a moving fan. The position of a fan blade cannot be determined while the blades are in motion. The same idea holds for the motion of an electron.

The nucleus of an atom contains **protons** and **neutrons**. Each proton also has an electric charge, but it is unlike that of the electron. The electron's charge is negative and the proton's charge is positive. The amount of the proton's positive charge is exactly equal to the amount of the negative charge of an electron. The neutron carries no charge. An atom has as many electrons in the cloud around the nucleus as it has protons in the nucleus. The atom is electrically neutral, since protons and electrons have equal but opposite charges.

The atom is tiny. An atom of iron, for example, is about 25 ten-millionths of a meter in diameter. Yet most of its volume is empty space! The diameter of the nucleus is, on the average, about one hundred-thousandth of the diameter of the space in which its electrons move. This tiny space contains the more massive atomic particles. The proton is 1836 times heavier than the electron, and the neutron is slightly heavier than the proton. More than 99.9 percent of the mass of an atom is in its nucleus.

Topic 4   Examples of Atomic Structure

The simplest and lightest of all atoms is ordinary hydrogen, the symbol for which is H. Ordinary hydrogen has a nucleus with one proton. It is the only atom without neutrons. A single electron occupies the electron cloud surrounding the nucleus.

The second lightest of the elements is helium, He. The nucleus of a helium atom has two protons. Two electrons in its cloud electrically balance the two positively charged protons in the nucleus. The helium nucleus also contains two neutrons, as shown in Figure 3.3. These neutrons make up about half the mass of a helium atom.

The third lightest element is lithium, Li. The lithium atom has three protons in its nucleus and three electrons in the electron cloud outside the nucleus. The nucleus also includes four neutrons. For atoms that have more than two electrons the electron cloud is divided into energy levels, as the model in Figure 3.2 illustrates. Two of lithium's three electrons move about the nucleus in an energy level like that of the helium atom, but the third electron lies beyond the first two in an energy level of its own.

This scheme of electron structure continues. As the number of electrons increases new energy levels exist, but in every atom the number of electrons equals the number of protons. The largest number of energy levels in any atom is seven. The number of electrons differs from level to level, but the innermost level never holds more than two electrons. Other levels may hold up to 32 electrons.

With each change in the number of protons and electrons, there is a change in the properties of the atoms. The heaviest of the natural elements, uranium, U, has 92 protons in its nucleus. Its 92 electrons are distributed in its seven energy levels as follows: 2, 8, 18, 32, 21, 9, 2.

Topic 5   Atomic Number and Mass Number

The **atomic number** is the number of protons in an atom. This value is 1 for hydrogen; 2 for helium; 3 for lithium; and 92 for uranium. The atomic number of oxygen is 8. The oxygen atom, therefore, has 8 protons in its nucleus and 8 electrons in its electron cloud—2 in the first energy level and 6 in the second.

How many neutrons are there in a nucleus? There is no simple rule relating the number of neutrons to the number of protons. However, the **mass number** of the element gives the average number of protons and neutrons in an atom. To find the number of neutrons in an atom, simply subtract the atomic number (number of protons) from the mass number.

number of neutrons = mass number − atomic number

For example, the atomic number of potassium is 19; its mass number is 39. The potassium nucleus, therefore, contains 19 protons and (subtracting 19 from 39) 20 neutrons. How many electrons move about the nucleus? Since the number of electrons must equal the number of protons, the answer is 19 electrons. Try another example: If uranium, whose atomic number is 92, has a mass number of 238, its atom must include 92 electrons, 92 protons, and 146 neutrons. Check to see if these values are correct.

A periodic table of the elements appears in the Appendix on pages 645–646. Notice that there are more than 100 different elements. No more than 90 of these occur naturally on Earth, although scientists have created synthetic elements in the laboratory. In the periodic table, elements are listed horizontally in order of atomic number and vertically by similar chemical properties. Each element, indicated by its symbol, is in its own box in the periodic table. The box for potassium is shown in Figure 3.4. Each element's box includes information about atoms of the element. Refer to the periodic table when you need information for an element.

3.3   Atoms are three-dimensional. These models of hydrogen, helium, and lithium show the numbers of electrons, protons, and neutrons.

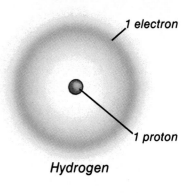

Hydrogen

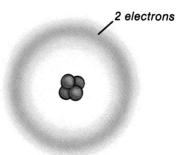

Helium

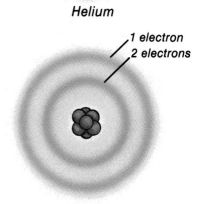

Lithium

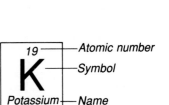

3.4   The box for potassium

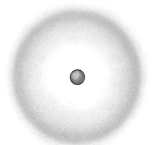

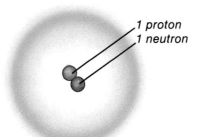

1 proton
1 neutron

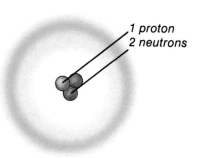

1 proton
2 neutrons

Common Hydrogen
Mass Number = 1
Atomic Number = 1

Deuterium
Mass Number = 2
Atomic Number = 1

Tritium
Mass Number = 3
Atomic Number = 1

3.5 Each hydrogen isotope has the same number of protons and electrons but different numbers of neutrons.

TEACHING TIP
Point out that some isotopes, like U-238 and C-14, are unstable and therefore are radioactive.

3.6 The elements (top) sodium and (bottom) chlorine

Topic 6 Isotopes

The identity of an atom depends only on the number of protons and not on the number of neutrons. Many elements have atoms with the same number of protons but different numbers of neutrons. **Isotopes** are atoms of the same chemical element with different mass numbers.

Hydrogen has three isotopes. Ordinary hydrogen has one proton and no neutrons in its nucleus. Its atomic number is 1; its mass number is also 1. However, hydrogen has a second isotope with 1 proton and 1 neutron in its nucleus. Its atomic number is 1, but its mass number is 2. This isotope is known as "heavy hydrogen" or *deuterium* (doo TEER ee um). It is much less common than ordinary hydrogen. The third isotope of hydrogen is rare. Known as *tritium* (TRIT ee um), it has a mass number of 3 with a nucleus of 1 proton and 2 neutrons.

You may have heard of carbon-14, the heavy isotope of carbon. Each ordinary atom of carbon-12 has a nucleus of 6 protons and 6 neutrons. Carbon-14 atoms (mass number, 14) have nuclei with 6 protons and 8 neutrons.

Uranium has a number of isotopes. Ordinary uranium, described in Topic 5, has a mass number of 238, with 146 neutrons in its nucleus. Uranium-235 (mass number, 235), however, has only 143 neutrons in its nucleus. All isotopes have 92 protons in the nucleus.

Topic 7 Compounds

So far only elements have been discussed. However, most minerals—in fact, most substances—are compounds. A **compound** is a substance that contains two or more elements chemically combined. Dalton said that an atom is the smallest part of an element. The smallest part of a compound that still has all the properties of that compound is a **molecule**. A molecule consists of at least two atoms. In a molecule, each element is present in a definite proportion to the other elements. For example, a molecule of water always contains two atoms of the element hydrogen and one atom of the element oxygen.

A compound can have properties entirely unlike the elements of which it is made. For example, water is certainly different from hydrogen and oxygen. Hydrogen and oxygen are gases, but water is a liquid. Another example is salt, which is a compound of the elements sodium and chlorine. Sodium and chlorine are shown in Figure 3.6; salt is shown in Figure 3.7. Both sodium and chlorine are poisonous by themselves. Yet when these two elements are chemically combined they form salt, a compound most people can eat safely with their food.

Compounds should not be confused with mixtures. In a *mixture* the individual elements or compounds keep their own properties and can be present in any proportions. Most mixtures can be separated easily by physical means—for example, picking them apart, dissolving those that are soluble, or sifting out the different substances by grain size. Salt water is an example of a mixture. It can be separated by evaporating the water. The elements in a compound, however, can only be separated by chemical means. For example, water can be decomposed into hydrogen and oxygen by passing a strong electric current through it.

TOPIC QUESTIONS

Each topic question refers to the topic of the same number.

1. **(a)** What is matter?   **(b)** Describe the particle model of matter.

2. **(a)** What is an element?   **(b)** What is an atom?   **(c)** Who was John Dalton?

3. **(a)** Name and describe the three kinds of particles that make up atoms.   **(b)** Identify where in the atom each kind of particle is located.

4. **(a)** Describe the structure of an atom of each of these elements: hydrogen, helium, and lithium.   **(b)** In what ways are atoms of different elements alike?   **(c)** In what ways are atoms of different elements different?

5. **(a)** Define atomic number.   **(b)** Define mass number.   **(c)** How many protons, neutrons, and electrons are in an ordinary atom of sodium? (Show your work.)

6. **(a)** What is an isotope?   **(b)** List the numbers of protons, neutrons, and electrons for carbon-12, carbon-14, uranium-238, and uranium-235.

7. **(a)** Define compound.   **(b)** What is a molecule?   **(c)** Describe how a compound is different from a mixture and give an example of each.

3.7 The compound sodium chloride, as it occurs in nature

ANSWERS

1. (a) anything with mass and volume   (b) Matter is made up of tiny particles.

2. (a) substance that cannot be chemically broken into simpler substances   (b) smallest part of an element that still has the element's properties   (c) originator of modern atomic theory

3. (a) electron—negative charge, smallest of the three; proton—positive charge, 1836 times heavier than electron; neutron—neutral charge, slightly heavier than proton   (b) electrons—cloud around nucleus; protons and neutrons—nucleus

4. (a) H—1 p, 1 e, no n; He—2 each of p, n, e; Li—3 p, 3 e, 4 n   (b) made of same particles, all have nucleus and electron cloud, number of protons = number of electrons in each   (c) each has different number of protons and electrons from others

5. (a) number of protons   (b) protons plus neutrons   (c) 11 p, 12 n, 11 e

6. (a) atoms of same element with different numbers of neutrons

(b)

Isotope	P	N	E
C-12	6	6	6
C-14	6	8	6
U-238	92	146	92
U-235	92	143	92

7. (a) substance made of two or more chemically combined elements   (b) smallest particle of compound   (c) compound has new properties, elements in mixture keep own properties; compound—water, mixture—salt water

OBJECTIVES

A Identify a substance as a mineral or nonmineral based on its structure and origin.

B Identify the most common elements in Earth's minerals; define *native mineral.*

C Define and describe the formation of ionic and covalent bonds and identify the general element combinations that form each kind of bond.

D Describe some ways minerals form.

SCIENCE BACKGROUND

Synthetic minerals, although identical in chemical composition to natural minerals, do not meet the definition of a mineral because they do not occur naturally. On the other hand, a deposit of calcite in a water pipe could be considered a mineral since it occurred on its own.

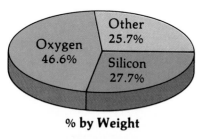

% by Weight

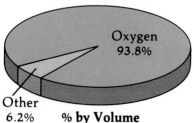

% by Volume

3.8 The percentage of oxygen in Earth's crust is significant in terms of weight and volume.

II Chemical Composition of Minerals

Topic 8 What Is a Mineral?

All matter is made of elements, including the rocks and minerals of Earth's crust. What makes a mineral different from other forms of matter? Several things must be true for a material to be called a mineral. A mineral

1. occurs naturally,
2. is a solid,
3. has a definite chemical composition (that is, its elements are combined in definite proportions),
4. has its atoms arranged in an orderly pattern, and
5. is *inorganic* (it was not formed by any process involving plants, animals, or other organisms).

A substance that fits this description is a **mineral**.

Which earth materials are minerals? Examples of familiar minerals include quartz, halite (rock salt), mica, gold, and diamond. Each of these minerals occur naturally in Earth's crust. Each is a solid at normal surface temperatures. Each has a definite chemical composition. The atoms in each mineral are arranged in orderly patterns. None is made by any process involving plants or animals.

What kinds of earth materials are not minerals? Water is not a mineral because it is not a solid. The glass in a window is not a mineral because window glass does not occur naturally. A pearl is not a mineral because it is formed by an oyster. Coal is not a mineral because it is made from plant remains, it lacks a definite composition, and its atoms are not arranged in an orderly way.

Topic 9 Minerals May Be Elements or Compounds

Of all the elements in Earth's crust, a mere eight make up 98.5 percent of the crust's total mass. These eight elements, which are listed in the table at the top of the next page, are almost always found combined with other elements as chemical compounds. The two most abundant elements, oxygen and silicon, are found in more than 90 percent of the minerals in the crust.

Oxygen is a significantly larger portion of the crust than silicon. By mass, oxygen is nearly 50 percent of Earth's crust while silicon is about 28 percent. By volume, the difference is much more marked. Oxygen, by volume, makes up nearly 94 percent of the crust, while silicon is less than 1 percent. The reason for this difference is that the space taken up by an oxygen atom in a compound is more than the space taken up by a silicon atom.

The Eight Most Common Elements in Earth's Crust

Name	Chemical Symbol	Percent by Mass	Percent by Volume
Oxygen	O	46.6	93.8
Silicon	Si	27.7	0.9
Aluminum	Al	8.1	0.8
Iron	Fe	5.0	0.5
Calcium	Ca	3.6	1.0
Sodium	Na	2.8	1.2
Potassium	K	2.6	1.5
Magnesium	Mg	2.1	0.3

3.9 Native minerals, such as the copper sample shown, are elements that occur uncombined in nature.

Most minerals are compounds. Quartz is a compound of silicon and oxygen. Most sand is composed of quartz. Halite (rock salt) is a compound of sodium and chlorine. The mineral galena, an ore of lead, is a compound of lead and sulfur. A few minerals, however, are made of only one element. Minerals composed of single elements are called **native minerals**, or native elements. Examples of native minerals are gold (Au), silver (Ag), copper (Cu), sulfur (S), and diamond (C).

Topic 10 Ionic Bonds in Minerals

How do atoms of different elements stay together in a mineral that is a compound? For one type of compound, the answer lies in electric attraction. In its normal state each atom has an equal number of protons and electrons. It is electrically neutral. If an atom gains one or more electrons, it becomes negatively charged. If an atom loses one or more electrons, it becomes positively charged. An atom in a charged condition, either negative or positive, is called an **ion**. Groups of atoms may also form ions.

Since opposite charges attract each other, ions of opposite charges may bond together to form compounds. For example, positively charged sodium ions are bonded with negatively charged chlorine ions in the compound sodium chloride, or table salt. Sodium chloride is found in nature as the mineral halite. Many other minerals contain ions.

How do atoms lose or gain electrons to form ions? Consider the element sodium. You can see from the sodium model in Figure 3.10 that its outer energy level contains only one electron. Sodium reacts with many elements in order to lose this outer electron. Chlorine is reactive for the opposite reason. Its outer energy level is short one electron, so it reacts with other elements to gain an electron. When sodium and chlorine react, sodium loses its outer electron, which chlorine gains. Both sodium and chlorine have become charged particles, or ions, and both are now chemically stable. The force of attraction, or **ionic bond,** between the oppositely charged ions holds them together.

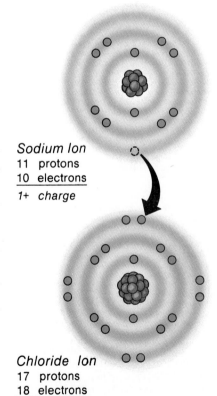

Sodium Ion
11 protons
10 electrons
1+ charge

Chloride Ion
17 protons
18 electrons
1– charge

3.10 Ions are formed when electrons are transferred between atoms. Sodium chloride consists of a positive sodium ion that has transferred one electron to chlorine to form a negative chloride ion.

Nonmetal	**Metal (Metalloid)**
O Atom 0.132 nm	Si Atom 0.234 nm
O²⁻ Ion 0.28 nm	Si⁴⁺ Ion 0.082 nm

Diameters are measured in nanometers (nm). There are 1 billion nanometers in 1 meter.

3.11   Negative ions tend to be larger than the nonmetal atoms from which they formed. Positive ions tend to be smaller than the metal atoms from which they formed.

Oxygen

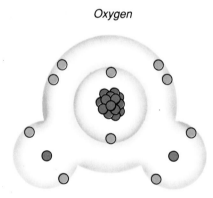

Hydrogen   Hydrogen

3.12   In a water molecule, two hydrogen atoms and one oxygen atom share eight electrons in a covalent bond.

SCIENCE BACKGROUND

  Under different conditions, the same elements can form very different minerals. Conditions for mineral development are the same as those for rock development and are as variable. Conditions for rock formation are covered in Chapter 5.

Elements that lose electrons easily and form positive ions are classed as **metals**. They include gold, silver, iron, copper, lead, aluminum, sodium, potassium, calcium, zinc, and many others. Metals appear on the left side of the periodic table. Notice that most pure elements are metals.

Elements that gain electrons easily and form negative ions are classed as **nonmetals**. They include nitrogen, oxygen, fluorine, chlorine, phosphorus, and sulfur. Nonmetals appear on the right side of the periodic table. The ions of nonmetals are generally much larger than the ions of metals.

Topic 11   **Covalent Bonds in Minerals**

Ionic bonds form easily between metals and nonmetals. How can a compound form from two nonmetals? Compounds also form when elements combine and share electrons. For example, two atoms of hydrogen and one atom of oxygen share electrons in a molecule of water. In a molecule of carbon dioxide, one carbon atom and two oxygen atoms share electrons. The kind of attachment where electrons are shared by atoms is called a **covalent bond**. Covalent bonds are common between nonmetal elements, and many minerals contain covalent bonds. The common mineral quartz contains the elements silicon and oxygen combined by covalent bonds.

Some elements—such as helium, neon, and argon—do not readily gain, lose, or share electrons, and form a limited number of compounds. They are described as *noble gas* elements. Because noble gases do not form compounds easily, they are not found combined in any minerals.

Topic 12   **How Minerals Form**

Minerals can form in several ways. Many minerals form out of molten earth material, or magma. Atoms in magma are free to move around each other. As magma cools, its atoms move closer together. As the atoms move closer together, they are able to combine to form mineral compounds. Many different minerals can form out of one magma mass. The kinds of minerals that form depend in part on which elements are present and in what amount. The rate at which the magma cools determines the size of the mineral grains that form (Topic 13).

Some kinds of minerals form when water containing dissolved ions evaporates. Halite forms when salt water evaporates. As the water molecules evaporate into water vapor, the sodium and chlorine ions arrange themselves into the mineral halite. Other minerals also form by evaporation. Minerals can also be changed into different minerals by heat, pressure, or the chemical action of water.

TOPIC QUESTIONS

Each topic question refers to the topic of the same number.

8. **(a)** List and describe the five factors that determine whether a substance is a mineral.   **(b)** Give several examples of minerals. **(c)** Explain why window glass, pearl, water, and coal are not minerals.

9. **(a)** What are the most common elements in Earth's crust? **(b)** How do the common elements usually occur?   **(c)** Explain why oxygen and silicon are important elements in Earth's crust.   **(d)** What name is given to those few minerals that are composed of only one element? Give examples.

10. **(a)** What is an ion?   **(b)** Describe how ions form.   **(c)** What is an ionic bond?   **(d)** Define metal and nonmetal and give an example of each.

11. **(a)** Describe a covalent bond.   **(b)** What is a noble gas element?

12. Describe two ways minerals can form.

ANSWERS

8. (a) natural, solid, definite chemical composition, orderly atom arrangement, inorganic   (b) quartz, halite, gold, mica   (c) glass—not natural, pearl—organic origin, water—liquid, coal—organic, no definite composition or orderly pattern

9. (a) oxygen, silicon, aluminum, iron, calcium, sodium, potassium, magnesium   (b) in compounds (c) make up 75% of Earth's crustal mass; occur in 90% of minerals (d) native minerals; gold, silver, copper, sulfur, diamond

10. (a) charged atom   (b) atom gains or loses electrons   (c) force of attraction between oppositely charged ions   (d) metal—element that easily forms positive ions. Na, Ca; nonmetal—element that easily forms negative ions, Cl, O.

11. (a) attraction between atoms sharing electrons   (b) element that does not easily bond with other elements

12. by cooling of magma, evaporation of water containing dissolved ions, changing of other minerals

EARTH**MATTERS**

Asbestos and Health

Why is asbestos an environmental concern? *Asbestos* is the name for minerals with thread-like fibers that can be woven or pressed flat into sheets. Until the late 1970s, asbestos was used because it is flame-resistant and does not conduct heat or electricity well. Many schools and theaters had stage curtains made with asbestos fibers to guard against fires. Asbestos also was used in automobile brake linings and to insulate electrical wiring and hot-water pipes.

Asbestos fibers are a hundred times tinier than a human hair. During mining and manufacturing, these fibers break off and float in the air, where they can be inhaled and trapped in workers' lungs. The fibers also break off finished products as the products get old or used. Once inside the human lung, asbestos fibers can cause scarring or cancer.

Because of the dangers, many people feel asbestos should no longer be used. Many towns have called for the removal of asbestos from their schools and other public buildings. The Environmental Protection Agency— the EPA— has tried to phase out asbestos use since the late 1980s.

However, researchers are split on the asbestos issue. Some say that different forms of asbestos act differently and that most asbestos used in the United States is of the least dangerous variety. Other people believe improper asbestos removal releases many more fibers and thereby causes more health problems than leaving the asbestos in place. **Is there asbestos in your local environment?**

OBJECTIVES

A Discuss the origin of mineral crystals and give examples.

B Explain the importance of silicate minerals; describe the silica tetrahedron and the arrangement of silica tetrahedra in several minerals.

C Relate a mineral's atomic arrangement to its crystal shape, hardness, cleavage, and density.

VIDEODISC SELECTION

Diagram of triclinic crystal axes
Side 2: 3203, single frame

Diagram of monoclinic crystal axes
Side 2: 3211, single frame

Diagram of orthorhombic crystal axes
Side 2: 3226, single frame

III Structure of Minerals

Topic 13 Minerals Have Crystalline Structure

All minerals are *crystalline*, that is all minerals are made of atoms arranged in a regular pattern. For example, the mineral halite is composed of sodium ions and chloride ions. The sodium ions are positively charged, while the chloride ions are negatively charged. Each positively charged sodium ion is bonded to a negatively charged chloride ion. In the orderly pattern that results, every sodium ion is surrounded by six chloride ions, and every chloride ion is surrounded by six sodium ions (Figure 3.13). This arrangement is repeated throughout the mineral.

Minerals are often found in the form of beautiful crystals. A **crystal** is a regular geometric solid with smooth surfaces called crystal faces. The orderly arrangement of ions determines the shape of the crystal. Each kind of mineral has its own crystal form. Halite, as a result of its repeating pattern of sodium ions and chloride ions, typically forms a crystal in the shape of a cube. Quartz, a mineral made of silicon and oxygen, may form long, regular, six-sided crystals. All quartz crystals, from microscopic to hand-size or larger, will have this same six-sided shape.

The angle at which crystal faces meet is always the same for each kind of mineral and can be used to help in the identification of the mineral. The cubic shape of halite results in crystal faces that meet at right angles. In quartz, the crystal faces meet at an angle of 120°.

Although there are thousands of different kinds of minerals, only six basic crystal shapes occur. These six shapes are shown in Figure 3.14. To describe these shapes, *crystallographic axes* are used. These axes are drawn perpendicular to crystal faces. Halite, which belongs to the cubic system, has six crystal faces. The crystal faces meet at right angles and form a cube. Each face is opposite another. The axes intersect the center of each pair of opposite faces. Halite, therefore, has three equal axes that intersect at right angles in the center of the cube.

31.3 The crystalline arrangement of sodium chloride shows that each unit consists of one ion surrounded by six ions of opposite charge. Each individual unit has a cubic shape.

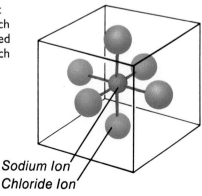

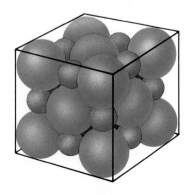

Sodium Ion
Chloride Ion

Six Crystal Systems

CUBIC SYSTEM	**ORTHORHOMBIC SYSTEM**	**TETRAGONAL SYSTEM**
Three axes of equal length that intersect at 90° angles.	Three axes of different length that intersect at 90° angles.	Three axes that intersect at 90° angles.
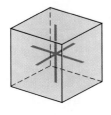	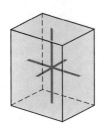	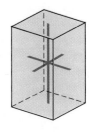
Examples: Halite Sylvite	*Examples:* Sulfur Topaz	*Examples:* Wulfenite Chalcopyrite
TRICLINIC SYSTEM	**HEXAGONAL SYSTEM**	**MONOCLINIC SYSTEM**
Three axes of unequal length that intersect at oblique angles.	Three horizontal axes that are the same length and intersect at 60° angles. A vertical axis that is longer than the horizontal axes.	Three unequal axes, two intersect at 90°, the third is oblique to the other two.
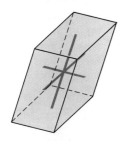		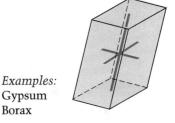
Examples: Turquoise Kyanite	*Examples:* Quartz Graphite	*Examples:* Gypsum Borax

Why don't all crystalline substances have crystal faces? The smooth faces must have room to form. If space is too limited, the atoms of one crystal join to those of another, and the smooth crystal faces are lost. Such a mineral is still crystalline, but it lacks the smooth faces of a crystal.

3.14 Mineral crystal shapes belong to one of six crystal *systems*, or families of related shapes.

Topic 14   The Silica Tetrahedron

More than 90 percent of the minerals in Earth's crust are members of a mineral family called **silicates**. These are compounds of the elements silicon and oxygen, plus one or more metallic element, such as aluminum or iron. In all silicates, the basic building block is four oxygen atoms packed closely around a silicon atom. This unit is held together by covalent bonds between the silicon atom and oxygen atoms. If imaginary lines are drawn to connect the centers of the four oxygen atoms, they make a geometric figure called a tetrahedron. So the basic unit, with the silicon atom in the center, is known as the **silica tetrahedron**. Silicates are classified and named according to the way the tetrahedra are linked as shown in Figure 3.16.

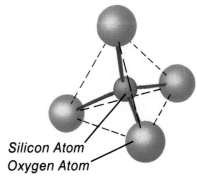

Silicon Atom
Oxygen Atom

3.15 A silica tetrahedron consists of a silicon atom bonded covalently to four oxygen atoms. The oxygen atoms are not drawn to scale.

3.16   Many properties of silicate minerals depend on the arrangement of their silica tetrahedrons.

VIDEODISC SELECTION

Diagram of tetragonal crystal axes
Side 2: 3239, single frame

Diagram of hexagonal crystal axes
Side 2: 3252, single frame

Diagram of isometric crystal axes
Side 2: 3276, single frame

Crystal lattice diagrams
Side 2: 3298 to 3303, 6-frame sequence

Some Bonding Arrangements for Silica Tetrahedrons

IONIC

Silica tetrahedrons with positive iron or magnesium ions attached to negative SiO_4 ions as in the mineral olivine.

SINGLE CHAINS

Silica tetrahedrons sharing electrons to form single chains of tetrahedrons as in pyroxene.

DOUBLE CHAINS

Silica tetrahedrons sharing electrons to form double chains as in amphibole.

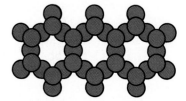

SHEETS

Silica tetrahedrons sharing electrons to form sheets of tetrahedrons as in mica.

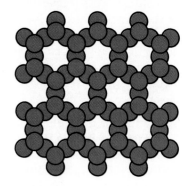

Topic 15   **Crystals and Physical Properties**

The orderly arrangement of the atoms or ions in a mineral helps to explain other properties of the mineral besides its crystal shape.

A mineral is *solid* because of the close packing of its ions or atoms and the strong forces of attraction among them. An increase in temperature weakens the bonds between particles. Therefore, solids melt into the loose groups of particles in a liquid, or they vaporize into a gas in which individual particles are far apart.

The *hardness* of a mineral depends on the arrangement of its ions or atoms and the strength of the electric forces among them. A good example of this property is seen in the element carbon. In one arrangement carbon forms diamond, the hardest natural mineral.

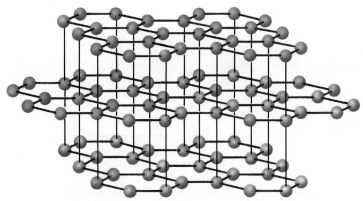

Diamond consists of a tetrahedral network of carbon atoms. In another arrangement, carbon forms graphite, a very soft mineral that flakes easily. Carbon atoms are arranged in layers or sheets in the graphite structure.

The *cleavage* of a mineral is its tendency to split or separate along flat surfaces. The planes along which the mineral splits are directions of weak bonds among the ions or atoms of the mineral. Halite splits into cubes between layers of ions. Quartz, with its strong network of atoms, does not split along any plane.

Remember that the density of a mineral is the ratio of its mass to its volume. This property depends on the mass of the ions or atoms of the mineral, but it also depends on how closely they are packed together. The density of the loosely packed mineral graphite is about 2.3 g/cm^3, but that of closely packed diamond is 3.5 g/cm^3. Both minerals are pure carbon.

Let us now summarize the characteristics of a mineral as described in this chapter.

1. A mineral is an element or compound found in nature.
2. Its ions or atoms usually are arranged in regular patterns that give it a crystalline structure.
3. It has a characteristic chemical composition.
4. It has definite physical properties.
5. It is inorganic.

TOPIC QUESTIONS

Each topic question refers to the topic of the same number.

13. **(a)** Why is halite crystalline?   **(b)** What is a crystal?   **(c)** Why is the angle at which crystal faces meet important?   **(d)** Why aren't all minerals also crystals?

14. **(a)** What are the silicate minerals?   **(b)** How are the atoms arranged in the silica tetrahedron unit?

15. How does the crystalline structure of a mineral explain its **(a)** solid nature,   **(b)** hardness,   **(c)** cleavage, and   **(d)** density? **(e)** Summarize the characteristics of a mineral.

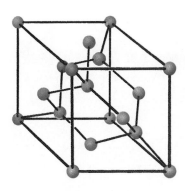

3.17   Graphite (left) consists of layers of carbon atoms bonded in interlocking hexagonal rings. Diamond (right) is a network of carbon atoms. The bonds between the layers of carbon atoms in graphite are weak. The bonds between carbon atoms in diamond are strong. Thus the properties of graphite differ greatly from those of diamond.

VIDEODISC SELECTION

Examples of mineral cleavage
Side 2: 3339 to 3345, 7-frame sequence

ANSWERS

   13. (a) atoms are arranged in an orderly pattern   (b) regular geometric solid with smooth faces (c) same for each mineral, aids in identification   (d) lack of space to grow smooth crystal faces
   14. (a) mineral compounds of oxygen and silicon   (b) 4 oxygens packed closely around 1 silicon
   15. (a) close packing   (b) arrangement of atoms or ions   (c) strength of bonds and atom arrangement (d) packing   (e) naturally occurring element or compound, crystalline structure, definite chemical composition, inorganic

CHAPTER 3

L A B
ACTIVITY

Growing Crystals

If you left a glass of distilled water and a glass of sea water to evaporate, you would obtain quite different results. The glass that held the sea water would contain evidence of previously dissolved salts and minerals.

When solutions containing dissolved solids, such as salt water or sea water, are allowed to evaporate, a solid will slowly come out of solution. The solid that forms often is called a *crystal* and has a definite shape. In this activity, you will observe the formation of a crystal from a simple solution.

Lab Skills and Objectives
- To **observe** the formation of a crystal
- To **identify** variables that affect crystal growth
- To **evaluate** the shape of crystals

Materials
- safety goggles
- lab apron
- two 250-mL beakers
- 150-mL distilled water
- 20 g ammonium alum
- 10 cm of thread
- wood splint
- stirring rod
- balance
- hot plate
- 250-mL graduated cylinder
- wax pencil
- seed crystals of ammonium alum
- funnel, 75 mm diameter
- filter paper for 75 mm funnel
- paper towel
- scissors
- graph paper
- masking tape

Procedure
Part A

1. **Put on your safety goggles and laboratory apron.**

2. Write your name on one of the 250-mL beakers with a wax pencil. Set this beaker aside until Step 7.

3. Place the other 250-mL beaker on the balance. Determine the mass of the empty beaker.

4. Add 20 grams to the mass of the empty beaker by setting the riders on the balance to that mass. Carefully add ammonium alum to the empty beaker until the balance is zeroed again. Remove the beaker from the balance.

5. Measure 150-mL of distilled water into a graduated cylinder. Carefully pour the distilled water into the beaker with the ammonium alum.

6. Place the beaker with the ammonium alum on a hot plate. Set the heat on *low*. Use a stirring rod to stir the solution until it is clear and no ammonium alum remains on the bottom of the beaker. *Do not* try to hurry the process by turning up the hot plate. The ammonium alum must dissolve slowly.

   ▲ **CAUTION: Do not touch the hot plate while heating the solution.**

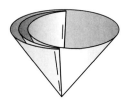

3.18 Folding filter paper.

7. Fold the filter paper and arrange it in a funnel as shown in Figure 3.18. Place the funnel and filter paper in the 250-mL beaker with your name on it.

8. Set this beaker on the hot plate to warm. Carefully pour the solution of ammonium alum into the funnel.

9. Once filtering is completed, remove the beaker from the hot plate and set it in the area designated by your teacher.

10. Use scissors to cut a square of paper towel large enough to cover the top of the beaker. Gently lay the cut towel on the beaker.

11. Use scissors to cut out 1/4 sheet of graph paper. Place the graph paper behind the beaker so that the grid on the paper can be seen through the liquid in the beaker. Tape the graph paper to the beaker.

12. Tie a 10-cm piece of thread around a seed crystal of ammonium alum. Be sure it is tied securely.

13. Tie the other end of the thread to the middle of a wood splint. Be careful to adjust the length of your thread so that when the wood splint is placed on top of the beaker, the crystal will be suspended in the center of the solution. *Do not place your seed crystal in the solution yet.*

14. Set the seed crystal beside your beaker. Do not put it in the beaker until Day 2.

Part B

1. After waiting one day for the solution to reach room temperature, carefully lift the paper towel from the top of the beaker. Lay the wood splint on top of the beaker, suspending the seed crystal in the solution.

2. Observe the suspended crystal each day for 7 class days. Make a sketch of what you see. Use the graph paper grid behind the beaker to help you draw the size and shape of the crystal correctly. Label each sketch with the day of the observation, for example, *Day 1, Day 2,* and so on.

3. After day 7, remove your crystal and clean up all materials.

4. Answer the questions in *Analysis and Conclusions.*

Analysis and Conclusions

1. Why was the piece of paper towel placed over the beaker? Identify at least two functions that it served.

2. What would have happened to the seed crystal if it had been placed in the warm solution the first day?

3. What was the source of material for the crystal?

4. A cube is a six-sided figure in which each of the sides are squares. As your crystal grew, did it resemble a cube on any day?

5. An octahedron is an eight-sided figure in which each side is a triangle. How closely did your final crystal resemble an octahedron?

6. Seed crystals grown in the bottom of a beaker are often only the top half of a crystal. Why wouldn't the other half grow?

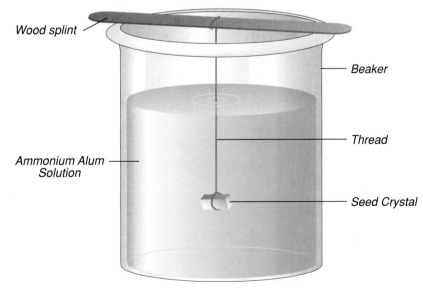

3.19 Equipment setup for Part B.

Answers to all questions appear in the Teacher's Guide at the back of this book.

■ Summary

I Matter is anything that has mass and volume.

An element is a substance that cannot be broken down by ordinary chemical means. An atom is the smallest part of an element that still has all the properties of that element.

Protons and neutrons are particles in the atomic nucleus; electrons occur in a cloud surrounding the nucleus. Protons have a positive charge, electrons have a negative charge, and neutrons have a neutral charge.

Atomic number is the number of protons in an atom. Mass number is the total mass of particles in the nucleus of an atom (protons plus neutrons).

Isotopes are atoms of the same chemical element with different numbers of neutrons in their nuclei and therefore different mass numbers.

In a compound, two or more elements are combined chemically. A compound can have properties different from those of the elements of which it is made.

II A mineral is a naturally occurring inorganic solid with a definite chemical composition and orderly atomic arrangement.

Eight elements make up 98.5 percent of the total mass of Earth's crust. Most elements occur combined with other elements.

Ionic bonds form between metals that lose electrons to form positive ions and nonmetals that gain electrons to form negative ions.

Covalent bonds tend to form between nonmetal atoms that share electrons.

III Some minerals form characteristic crystal shapes.

Silicate minerals make up over 90 percent of Earth's crust. The silicate minerals are built around the silica tetrahedron.

The crystal shape, hardness, cleavage, and density of a mineral are determined by the internal arrangement of its atoms or ions.

■ Vocabulary

atom	ion	molecule
atomic number	ionic bond	native mineral
compound	isotope	neutron
covalent bond	mass number	nonmetal
crystal	matter	proton
electron	metal	silica tetrahedron
element	mineral	silicate

■ Review

Write the letter of your answer on your paper.

1. Matter is defined as anything that has (a) mass and weight, (b) weight and size, (c) mass and volume, (d) molecules.

2. A substance that cannot be broken down by chemical means is a (a) mixture, (b) metal, (c) ion, (d) element.

3. The smallest part of an element that has all the properties of the element is the (a) ion, (b) atom, (c) proton, (d) molecule.

4. Which is NOT part of an atom? (a) electron (b) energy level (c) nucleus (d) mixture

5. The mass number of an element is the sum of its (a) ions and protons, (b) protons and neutrons, (c) protons and electrons, (d) electrons and ions.

6. Isotopes are atoms of the same element that differ in the number of (a) ions, (b) electrons, (c) protons, (d) neutrons.

7. A substance made of two or more elements chemically combined is a (a) mineral, (b) atom, (c) mixture, (d) compound.

8. Which is NOT true of a mineral? (a) solid (b) organic (c) orderly atomic structure (d) definite chemical composition

9. A substance NOT considered a mineral is (a) calcite, (b) diamond, (c) glass, (d) quartz.

10. Which is NOT a native mineral? (a) copper (b) gold (c) halite (d) sulfur

11. Atoms that have lost electrons are (a) metal ions (b) nonmetal ions, (c) noble gases, (d) isotopes.

For further review, see **Study Guide.**
For assessment, see **Chapter Tests**
and **Computer Test Bank.**

12. The two most abundant elements in Earth's crust are (a) aluminum and iron, (b) iron and oxygen, (c) oxygen and silicon, (d) silicon and aluminum.
13. Nonmetal elements share electrons in (a) covalent bonds, (b) mixtures, (c) ionic bonds, (d) atoms.
14. Minerals can form from magma when (a) the magma cools, (b) atoms come closer together, (c) atoms form mineral compounds, (d) all of the above.
15. Which is NOT true of crystals? (a) They are regular shapes. (b) They are always formed from ions. (c) Each mineral has a crystal shape. (d) Atoms are arranged in a pattern.
16. How many oxygen atoms are in a single silica tetrahedron? (a) 1 (b) 2 (c) 3 (d) 4
17. Two minerals composed of carbon but with different atomic structures are (a) quartz and calcite, (b) calcite and graphite (c) graphite and diamond, (d) diamond and quartz.

▪ Interpret and Apply

Answer each question in complete sentences.

1. Would a single atom be considered matter? Would a single electron be considered matter? Explain your answers.
2. Using the periodic table in the Appendix, identify elements a–c. (When using the table, round off atomic masses to the nearest whole number to find the mass number.) (a) atomic number = 7, mass number = 14; (b) atomic number = 26, number of neutrons = 20; (c) number of neutrons = 20, number of electrons = 19.
3. A container holds a mixture of sand, salt, and iron filings. (a) Describe a method for separating the substances in the mixture. (b) The sand is a compound of silicon and oxygen. Could the silicon and oxygen be separated by any of the methods described in part (a)?
4. Is ice in a glacier a mineral? Is the mercury in a thermometer a mineral? Explain.

5. Most minerals that contain metal atoms do not look like metals. Why is this true?

▪ Critical Thinking

Different silicate minerals have different ratios of silicon atoms to oxygen atoms. For example, in quartz there is 1 silicon atom for every 2 oxygen atoms, a silicon to oxygen ratio of 1 to 2 (1:2). The drawings below show the structural models of some silicate minerals. The silicon atoms are shown by dashes because they are hidden by an oxygen atom. Questions 1–3 refer to Model A.

1. How many oxygen atoms are shown?
2. How many silicon atoms are shown?
3. What is the ratio of silicon to oxygen in Model A?

Questions 4–6 refer to Model B.

4. How many oxygen atoms surround the silicon atom indicated by the X?
5. How many of these oxygen atoms are shared with other silicon atoms?
6. Two shared oxygens count as one whole oxygen. What is the ratio of silicon to oxygen in Model B?
7. Compare Models A and B with the models in Figure 3.16. What are the names of the bonding arrangements represented by Models A and B?

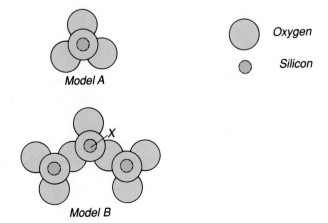

Model A

Model B

Oxygen

Silicon

How to Know the Minerals

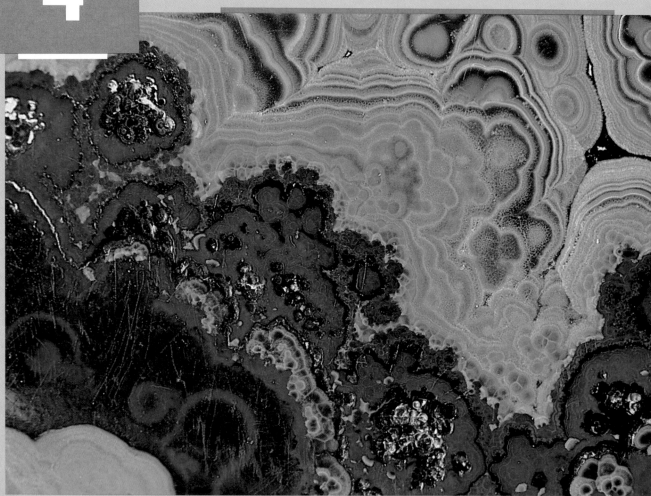

▲
Malachite is easily recognized by its characteristic green color. The blue mineral is azurite, which commonly occurs with malachite.

How Do You Know That . . .

The minerals shown above are azurite and malachite? Some minerals have distinct properties, such as color or crystal shape. Azurite is easily recognized by its blue color; malachite is recognized by its green color. The two minerals often occur together, as they do in this sample. Other minerals are not as easy to recognize. Often, a number of different properties must be observed and tested before a mineral is correctly identified.

I Identifying Minerals

Topic 1 Rock-Forming Minerals

Over 2000 minerals are known. Many of them, such as gold and diamond, are rare. Other minerals, such as quartz, feldspar, mica, and calcite, are common. Common minerals that make up most of the rocks in Earth's crust are called **rock-forming minerals.** Most rock-forming minerals are silicate minerals.

Minerals that occur in rocks are not always large crystals. However, even small mineral grains can be identified, in most cases.

The minerals in rocks are usually identified by their physical properties. Some of these properties can be determined by looking at the mineral with the unaided eye (inspection) and by simple physical tests. Simple chemical tests may also be used. The study of minerals and their properties is called **mineralogy.**

Topic 2 Identification by Inspection

The color, luster, and crystal shape of a mineral may be observed by inspection.

Color is the first and most easily observed mineral property. Some minerals have very characteristic colors that help identify them. For example, cinnabar, an ore of mercury, is red. Malachite (MAL uh kite), an ore of copper, is green.

Color, however, is the least useful property for mineral identification. One reason is that many different minerals have similar colors. For example, orthoclase feldspar, calcite, and other minerals all can have a milky-white color. Also, traces of impurities can turn colorless minerals into colored minerals. For example, pure quartz is colorless or white. A small amount of iron gives quartz a purple color. A small amount of titanium results in pink quartz. A third reason not to rely on color is that some minerals change color when exposed to air. In air, the brass-yellow color of chalcopyrite (kal koe PIE rite) tarnishes to bronze. The brownish-bronze of bornite turns purple. (Both chalcopyrite and bornite are copper ores.)

The **luster** of a mineral is the way the mineral shines in reflected light. Lusters are either metallic or nonmetallic. A mineral with metallic luster shines like polished metal. Examples of minerals with metallic luster are galena and pyrite. A mineral that does not shine like a metal has a nonmetallic luster. Several terms are used to further describe nonmetallic lusters. A vitreous luster, like shining glass, is seen in quartz. Mica has a pearly luster, like a pearl. The

OBJECTIVES

A Name some rock-forming minerals and identify the group to which most belong.

B Discuss the usefulness of color and crystal shape in mineral identification.

C Describe and give examples of mineral luster, streak, cleavage, fracture, and hardness.

D Define *specific gravity*, explain how it is determined, and calculate specific gravity given the necessary data.

E Describe other tests for specific mineral identification.

4.1 The colors of (top) cinnabar and (bottom) malachite can be used to identify these minerals.

a

b

4.2 (a) Galena has metallic luster. (b) Sphalerite is nonmetallic.

TEACHING TIP
  Luster is difficult to show in a photograph. Classroom samples will be needed to show luster well.

4.3 Crystal shape can be used for mineral identification.

VIDEODISC SELECTION

Examples of mineral streak
Side 2: 3346 to 3350, 5-frame sequence

Examples of mineral luster
Side 2: 3351 to 3365, 15-frame sequence

mineral sphalerite (SFAL er ite), an ore of zinc, can have a resinous luster, like wax, or a glassy luster. The hard, brilliant luster of diamond is called adamantine (add uh MAN teen). Other terms that are used to describe luster are greasy, oily, dull, and earthy.

Crystal shape is sometimes helpful in identifying a mineral. When minerals have enough time and room to form, their ions or atoms arrange themselves into patterns. These patterns lead to flat-faced, regularly shaped crystals (Chapter 3, Topic 15). Such crystal faces, however, are rare. More often the mineral grains in rocks lacked room to grow. The mineral grains in most rocks are so small or so imperfect that crystal faces are hard to find.

Crystal Shapes of Some Common Materials

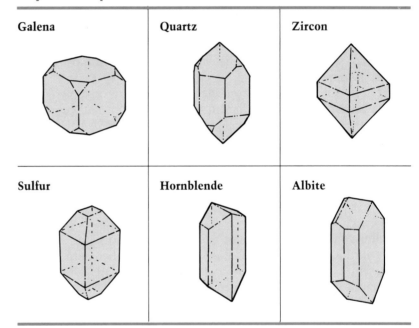

| Galena | Quartz | Zircon |
| Sulfur | Hornblende | Albite |

Topic 3   Identification by Simple Tests

Some mineral properties can be determined by simple tests. The streak, cleavage, and hardness of a mineral, for example, can be tested easily. The **streak** of a mineral is the color of its powder. The streak is obtained by rubbing the mineral on an unglazed white tile, called a streak plate. For many minerals, the streak is not the same color as the mineral. Iron pyrite is brass-yellow. The streak of iron pyrite is always greenish-black. Hematite, another iron-bearing mineral, can be brown, red, or silver. Its streak, however, is always reddish-brown. Although the color of a mineral may vary, its streak rarely does. As a rule, the streak of a metallic mineral is at least as dark as the hand specimen. The streak of a nonmetallic mineral is usually colorless or white.

The **cleavage** of a mineral is its tendency to split easily or to separate along flat surfaces. Cleavage surfaces can be observed even on tiny mineral grains. Therefore, cleavage is a useful property for mineral identification. Mica splits very easily, and always in the same direction (Figure 4.4(a)). Mica is said to have one perfect cleavage. Feldspar splits readily in two different directions, at or near right angles (Figure 4.4(b)). It is said to have two good cleavages. Calcite and galena cleave in three directions. They are said to have three good cleavages.

4.4   Mineral cleavage varies. (a) Mica only cleaves well in one direction. (b) Feldspar cleaves in two directions.

b

a

Not all minerals have cleavage. Some minerals, however, tend to break along non-cleavage surfaces. When minerals break along other than cleavage surfaces, they are said to have **fracture**. *Conchoidal* (kon KOY dul), or shell-like, fracture can be seen in the mineral flint or the rock obsidian (Figure 4.5). The fracture surface is smoothly curved like the inside of a clam shell. Fibrous or splintery fracture leaves a jagged surface with sharp edges, as in native copper. Uneven or irregular fracture leaves a generally rough surface, as in the cinnabar sample in Figure 4.1.

The **hardness** of a mineral is its resistance to being scratched. Diamond is the hardest of all minerals. It will scratch any other mineral against which it is rubbed. On the other hand, talc is the softest of all minerals. All other minerals scratch talc.

In order to give a specific measure to hardness, the mineralogist Friedrich Mohs devised a hardness scale. In this scale, ten well-known minerals are given numbers from one to ten. They are arranged from softest (talc) to hardest (diamond). The differences in hardness between one step in the scale and the next are about the same for all except the last. Diamond, number ten, is several times harder than corundum, number nine.

From *Mohs' scale* you can find the approximate hardness of any common mineral. All you need is a copper penny, a knife blade or metal nail file, and a small glass plate. If a mineral is harder than number 5 but softer than number 6 in the hardness scale, it has a hardness of about 5½.

VIDEODISC SELECTION

Examples of mineral fracture
Side 2: 3366 to 3372, 7-frame
sequence

4.5   This rock, obsidian, shows conchoidal fracture. Many minerals—for example, quartz—also have conchoidal fracture.

TEACHING TIPS
  Mineral sets illustrating Mohs'
scale of hardness could be used
here. (Diamond is not needed in the
sets.)

SCIENCE BACKGROUND
  For any mineral, there will be considerable variation from the hardness
stated in the text and from sample to
sample. For many minerals, differences in composition exist as well.

Mohs' Scale of Hardness

Hardness	Mineral	Simple Test
1	Talc	Fingernail scratches it easily.
2	Gypsum	Fingernail scratches it.
3	Calcite	Copper penny just scratches it.
4	Fluorite	Steel knife scratches it easily.
5	Apatite	Steel knife scratches it.
6	Feldspar	Steel knife does not scratch it easily; it scratches window glass.
7	Quartz	Hardest common mineral; it scratches steel and hard glass easily.
8	Topaz	Harder than any common mineral
9	Corundum	It scratches topaz.
10	Diamond	Hardest of all minerals

Hardness should not be confused with brittleness. Glass is a brittle substance that breaks easily when dropped. Glass, however, is harder (resistant to scratching) than copper and other metals.

In doing a scratch test for hardness, the powder rubbed off the softer mineral may look like a scratch on the harder mineral. For example, when calcite is rubbed against glass, the calcite may appear to have scratched the glass. Rub this "scratch" with your finger. It may prove to be powder that comes off and leaves the glass unscratched. The calcite is obviously softer than the glass. A real scratch can be felt with the fingernail.

Topic 4   Specific Gravity

Specific gravity is another property that is helpful in identifying a mineral. Specific gravity is the ratio of the weight of a mineral to the weight of an equal volume of water. In other words, the specific gravity of a mineral tells you how many times as dense as water the mineral is.

Nearly all minerals are denser than water. Their specific gravities are greater than 1. Typical nonmetallic minerals—such as quartz, feldspar, calcite, and talc—have specific gravities of slightly less than 3. Typical metallic minerals—such as the iron ores hematite and magnetite—have specific gravities of about 5. Other metallic minerals are much denser. Gold has a specific gravity as high as 19.3 when pure.

The specific gravity of a mineral is found as suggested by the definition. The weight of the mineral sample is found by weighing it in air. Then the mineral sample is weighed again while it is underwater. This second weighing indirectly gives the weight of a volume of water that is equal to the volume of the mineral sample. The sample weighs less submerged because of the buoyant effect of the water. *Archimedes' principle* states that this loss in weight is equal to the weight of the displaced water. The displaced water is equal in volume to the mineral sample that displaced it. Thus it can be stated that

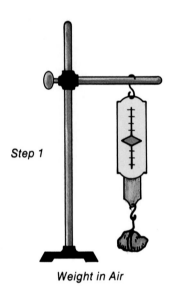

Step 1

Weight in Air

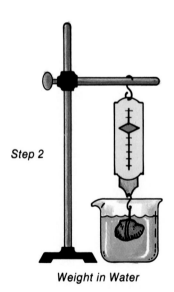

Step 2

Weight in Water

4.6 A mineral's weight in water and in air is used to find specific gravity.

$$\text{Specific gravity} = \frac{\text{weight of sample in air}}{\text{weight of equal volume of water}}$$

$$= \frac{\text{weight of sample in air}}{\text{loss of weight in water}}$$

For example, suppose a specimen weighs 50 newtons in air and 30 newtons in water. (A newton is a unit of weight equal to about 0.25 pounds.) The weight loss is 50 newtons − 30 newtons, or 20 newtons. The specific gravity of the specimen is calculated as follows.

$$\frac{50 \text{ N}}{20 \text{ N}} = 2.5$$

In other words, the specimen is 2.5 times as heavy as an equal volume of water.

Topic 5 **The Acid Test**

Calcite is the principal mineral in limestone and marble. Calcite is easily identified by a simple chemical test. Calcite is calcium carbonate, $CaCO_3$. If a drop of cold, weak hydrochloric acid is placed on calcite, the drop of acid fizzes. The bubbles are carbon dioxide gas. Other minerals also react to acid, but they are not as reactive. They may require using stronger acid, heating the acid, or powdering the mineral.

Topic 6 **Special Properties of Minerals**

There are many other properties that are used to help identify mineral samples. A few particularly interesting ones follow.

Some minerals are magnetic and can be picked up by a magnet. The best example is magnetite, an iron ore. Lodestone, a kind of magnetite, itself acts as a magnet.

Halite (rock salt) can be identified by its taste.

Fluorescence is the state of glowing while under ultraviolet light. It is seen in some samples of fluorite, calcite, and other minerals. Some samples of the minerals willemite (zinc silicate), sphalerite (zinc iron sulfide), and others continue to glow after the ultraviolet light is turned off. They are said to be *phosphorescent.*

Some minerals, such as the uranium minerals carnotite and uraninite, are *radioactive.* They give off subatomic particles that will activate a Geiger counter.

The mineral calcite splits light rays into two parts. One ray travels straight through the mineral. The other ray is bent. This causes two images to be seen when an object is viewed through a transparent specimen of calcite. This property, shown in Figure 4.7, is called *double refraction.*

The topics in Lesson II describe some important rock-forming minerals. The table "Properties of Some Common Minerals" on pages 644–645 lists other minerals.

TEACHING TIP
Make sure students understand the relationship between these two equations.

VIDEODISC SELECTION

Examples of mineral fluorescence
Side 2: 3380 to 3402, 23-frame sequence

VIDEODISC SELECTION

Examples of mineral hardness: minerals in Moh's Scale of Hardness
Side 2: 3325 to 3338, 14-frame sequence

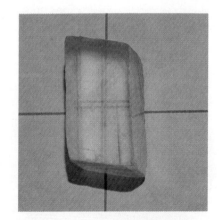

4.7 This mineral is a transparent variety of calcite called Iceland spar. It splits light rays and forms a double image of the red lines. This sample also shows the rhombic shape of calcite.

ANSWERS

1. (a) common minerals found in most rocks; quartz, feldspar, mica, calcite   (b) by properties   (c) study of minerals and their properties

2. (a) many minerals have same color; impurities yield more than 1 color for 1 mineral; tarnish changes color   (b) shine in reflected light; metallic—galena, pyrite; vitreous—quartz; pearly—mica; resinous—sphalerite; adamantine—diamond   (c) rarely seen in hand specimen

3. (a) color of mineral powder; scratch sample on streak plate; metallic—dark, nonmetallic—colorless or white   (b) tendency to split along certain planes; mica, feldspar, calcite, galena   (c) break along other than cleavage planes; conchoidal, fibrous, splintery, irregular   (d) resistance to being scratched; comparison with Mohs' scale

4. (a) ratio of mineral weight to weight of equal volume of water   (b) nonmetals slightly lower than metals   (c)

$$S.G. = \frac{76\ N}{76\ N - 51\ N} = \frac{76\ N}{25\ N} = 3.04$$

5. Drop of weak hydrochloric acid causes calcite to bubble.

6. (a) magnetite   (b) halite   (c) some fluorites and calcites   (d) willemite, sphalerite   (e) carnotite, uraninite   (f) clear calcite

TOPIC QUESTIONS

Each topic question refers to the topic of the same number.

1. **(a)** What are rock-forming minerals? List some examples.
   (b) How are minerals usually identified?   **(c)** What is mineralogy?

2. **(a)** Give three reasons why it is difficult to identify a mineral by its color alone.   **(b)** What is luster? Name different types of luster and give examples of minerals with those lusters.   **(c)** Why is crystal shape not usually helpful in mineral identification?

3. **(a)** Explain what a mineral streak is, how it is obtained, and how the streak of metallic and nonmetallic minerals differ.   **(b)** Define cleavage. Give examples of minerals that can be identified by cleavage.   **(c)** Define mineral fracture and give some examples.   **(d)** What is mineral hardness? How is it determined?

4. **(a)** What is specific gravity?   **(b)** Compare the specific gravity of the average metallic and nonmetallic minerals.   **(c)** A mineral sample weighs 76 newtons in air and 51 newtons in water. Find its specific gravity.

5. Describe the acid test for a mineral.

6. Give examples of minerals that can be identified by   **(a)** magnetism,   **(b)** taste,   **(c)** fluorescence,   **(d)** phosphorescence,   **(e)** radio activity, and   **(f)** double refraction.

CAREERS

Dr. Laurence R. Kittleman
Geologist

Laurence R. Kittleman is a geologist who is interested in volcanic rocks. He began his study at Colorado College, where he earned his B.S. degree in geology. He continued with an M.S. at the University of Colorado and a Ph.D. from the University of Oregon. His professional career has included work with the U.S. Department of Energy and at the University of Oregon's Museum of Natural History. Here he served as curator of geology and as museum director. He has done research on the volcanic rocks of Oregon. Another of his interests is the geology of prehistoric dwelling places. Dr. Kittleman wrote *Canyons Beyond the Sky*, an earth science adventure novel for middle school readers.

II   Descriptions of Rock-Forming Minerals

Topic 7   Silicates: From Silica Tetrahedrons

In Topic 14 of Chapter 3, the silica tetrahedron was discussed as nature's most important building block for minerals. All of the following minerals are made of silica tetrahedrons, either alone or combined with other elements.

(a) *Quartz* is made entirely of silica tetrahedrons bound tightly together. Quartz has the chemical formula SiO_2. Its chemical name is silicon dioxide. The chemical formula and name indicate that there are two oxygen atoms for every silicon atom in quartz.

Several properties help identify quartz. Quartz has a glassy or greasy luster. Its fracture is shell-like or irregular. Quartz is number 7 in Mohs' scale of hardness. It is the hardest of the common minerals. The color of quartz varies. Pure quartz is colorless or white, but many colored varieties exist. Among these are pink rose quartz, purple amethyst, and brown or gray smoky quartz.

Quartz is the second most abundant mineral in Earth's crust. It is an important part of all granites. Sandstone and quartzite are formed almost entirely of quartz. Most sands consist mainly of grains of quartz.

(b) **Feldspar** is the name of the most abundant family of minerals in Earth's crust. Together these minerals make up over 60 percent of the crust. Feldspars are identified by three major properties. All feldspars have two directions of cleavage, a hardness of 6 on Mohs scale, and a pearly luster.

In feldspar, aluminum ions have replaced some of the silicon ions in the basic silica tetrahedron structure. The unequal electrical charge that results is balanced by the addition of ions of potassium, sodium, or calcium. The feldspars are divided into two major groups—the potassium feldspars and the sodium-calcite feldspars—based upon these ions.

OBJECTIVES

A Identify and describe the two most common types of silicate minerals.

B Define and give examples of ferromagnesian silicates.

C Contrast silicate minerals and carbonate minerals, and distinguish between the two principal carbonate minerals.

D Identify and describe some iron-bearing minerals.

4.8   (a) Orthoclase feldspar, (b) pure quartz, (c) rose quartz

a

b

c

a

b

The most common potassium feldspar is *orthoclase.* The color of the mineral varies but is usually a light color such as white, cream, or pink. In orthoclase, the two cleavage surfaces meet at right angles. Like the mineral quartz, orthoclase is most commonly found in granite.

The sodium-calcite feldspars are called *plagioclase* feldspars. Albite and oligoclase are two common varieties. The plagioclase feldspars range in color from white to gray to reddish-brown. The two cleavage surfaces in plagioclase meet at slightly less than a right angle. Unlike orthoclase, one cleavage surface is often marked by fine parallel lines called striations.

(c) Mica minerals are soft silicates found in many rocks. Flat, shiny mica flakes are easily picked out of rocks, such as granite and gneiss. *Muscovite* mica, also known as white mica, is silvery white. *Biotite* mica is dark brown or black. Both are soft—each has a hardness of about 2.5. Each has one perfect cleavage.

(d) *Talc* is the softest mineral—number 1 on Mohs' scale. It is white, gray, or greenish in color. It has one good cleavage and has a soapy feel. Pure talcum powder is ground talc.

(e) Amphiboles are a family of complex silicate minerals. They tend to form long, needlelike crystals. The most common amphibole is *hornblende.* Hornblende is a shiny dark green, brown, or black mineral. It has two good cleavages that meet at oblique angles. (See Figure 4.9(c)). Hornblende has a hardness of 5 to 6.

Hornblende is also an example of a **ferromagnesian silicate.** These silicates can belong to almost any of the silicate families, but they all contain atoms of iron and magnesium. Ferromagnesian silicates are always dark in color.

(f) Pyroxenes have cleavage surfaces that meet nearly at right angles (90°). *Augite* (AW jyte) is the most common member of the pyroxene family. It is also a ferromagnesian silicate. Augite is dark green, brown, or black. It has two good cleavages and has a hardness between 5 and 6. It can be distinguished from hornblende by its poorer luster; its short, stout crystals; its cleavage surfaces that

4.9 (a) Plagioclase feldspar, (b) muscovite mica, (c) hornblende, (d) augite

c

d

a   **b**

meet nearly at right angles.

Both hornblende and augite are common minerals in many dark crystalline rocks.

(**g**) *Olivine* is an olive-green ferromagnesian silicate. It is found in dark crystalline rocks. It belongs to a silicate family in which single silica tetrahedrons are bonded by metal ions. It is glassy, shell-like in fracture, and very hard—about 6.5. It is found in some meteorites.

(**h**) *Garnets* may be dark red, brown, yellow, green, or black. They are very hard (from 6.5 to 7.5) and are used as abrasives. Clear crystals are used as gems. Garnets are found in many crystalline rocks.

(**i**) *Kaolinite* or *kaolin* is an aluminum silicate. It is formed by the weathering of feldspar and other silicate minerals. It is the principal mineral in clay and in shale. Pure kaolin is white, but impurities usually make it yellow. Less often it is red, brown, green, or blue. It has an earthy (crumbly) fracture. Its hardness is between 1 and 2.5. It feels greasy and, when breathed on, it gives off a typical earthy odor.

Summary: There are several main groups of silicate minerals. Only common examples from some of the groups have been described here. The properties and structures of silicate minerals differ. However, all varieties have the silica tetrahedron as their basic building block.

c

4.10   (a) Garnet, (b) kaolinite, (c) olivine

Topic 8   **Carbonate Minerals: Calcite and Dolomite**

While some minerals are built of silica tetrahedrons, others are built of other groups of atoms. The **carbonate** group is made of one carbon atom combined with three oxygen atoms and has a negative charge of two ($-CO_3^{2-}$). A carbonate mineral is made of carbonate groups joined with various metal ions. The rocks limestone and marble are made almost entirely of carbonate minerals.

4.11   Calcite is the most common carbonate mineral.

a

b

4.12   (a) Azurite, (b) dolomite in marble

SCIENCE BACKGROUND

The crystal shape of calcite is not the same as the shape of its cleavage fragments. Both shapes, however, reflect the underlying arrangement of ions in calcite. Both shapes belong to the hexagonal crystal system.

The most common carbonate mineral is *calcite*. Calcite is calcium carbonate, chemical formula $CaCO_3$. Pure calcite is colorless or white. Impurities may make it almost any color. It has a hardness of 3. Calcite has three perfect cleavages that meet at oblique angles. Its cleavages give it a very strong tendency to break into little flat-sided rhombs when dropped or struck. Calcite rhombs are shown in Figures 4.7 and 4.11. Calcite is easily identified by the acid test described in Topic 5.

Colorless transparent calcite is called *Iceland spar*. Iceland spar has the unusual property of double refraction (see Topic 6).

Dolomite is calcium magnesium carbonate. It has a hardness of 3.5 to 4. Like calcite, it cleaves into rhombs. Dolomite is not as reactive to acid as calcite is, and does not easily bubble in the acid test. It must be scratched or powdered, or the acid must be heated or concentrated. Dolomite usually occurs as coarse or fine grains in dolomitic limestones and marbles.

The copper carbonates *malachite* and *azurite* and the iron carbonate *siderite* react to the acid test. They do not react as easily as calcite. These carbonates are best identified by their color. Malachite is always green. Azurite is always blue. Siderite is usually brown or yellow-brown.

Topic 9   Iron Oxides and Sulfides

Some minerals contain large amounts of the metal element iron. These minerals are not as common as the silicate or carbonate minerals. However, they are economically important (Chapter 6, Topic 9). In these minerals, iron tends to be combined with either oxygen or sulfur to form an *oxide* or *sulfide.* An oxide is a mineral consisting of a metal element combined with oxygen. A sulfide is a metal element combined with sulfur. Each iron-bearing mineral has its own identifying properties.

SCIENCE BACKGROUND

While the observed crystal shape of pyrite varies, all pyrite crystals belong to the same crystal system (isometric).

a

b

Hematite is the most common iron oxide mineral. It has a hardness of 5 to 6 on Mohs' scale. Most hematite is red and has an earthy luster and crumbly fracture. Some hematite samples are silvery and have a metallic luster. All hematite samples leave a red-brown streak on a streak plate.

Magnetite is a black magnetic iron oxide. It has a hardness of 5.5 to 6.5. It occurs in many rocks in the form of small grains or crystals. Its name refers to the fact that it is attracted to a magnet. *Lodestone* is a highly magnetic variety of magnetite. It is a natural magnet. The first magnetic compass needles were made from lodestone.

Pyrite is iron sulfide. It is the most common sulfide mineral. Its color ranges from pale brass to golden-yellow. Its hardness is about 6. Pyrite frequently occurs in 6- or 12-sided crystals. Because of its golden color and high metallic luster, it is sometimes mistaken for gold. A common name for pyrite is fool's gold.

TOPIC QUESTIONS

Each topic question refers to the topic of the same number.

7. **(a)** Which of the silicate mineral groups is most abundant? **(b)** Name the two main feldspar groups and describe the general properties of each group. **(c)** Name and describe the two forms of mica. **(d)** What are ferromagnesian silicates? Give three examples. **(e)** Compare and contrast hornblende and augite. To which group does each belong? **(f)** Discuss the properties and importance of quartz, garnet, kaolinite, and talc.

8. **(a)** How are carbonate minerals different from silicate minerals? **(b)** Compare and contrast calcite and dolomite.

9. **(a)** Describe the forms of hematite. What identifying property do all forms of hematite exhibit? **(b)** Describe magnetite. Distinguish between magnetite and lodestone. **(c)** Describe pyrite. How is the composition of pyrite different from that of hematite and magnetite?

4.13   (a) Magnetite, sometimes called lodestone; (b) pyrite, or fool's gold

ANSWERS

7. (a) feldspar   (b) orthoclase—light color, smooth, right-angle cleavages, contain potassium; plagioclase—cleavages at oblique angle, several colors, contain sodium, calcium (c) muscovite—light color, hardness 2.5, perfect 1-way cleavage; biotite—like muscovite but dark   (d) silicates with iron and magnesium; hornblende, olivine, augite   (e) Both are ferromagnesians with 2 good cleavages, H=5–6. Augite—pyroxene, poorer luster, short stout crystals, nearly 90° cleavage angle. Hornblende—amphibole, shiny, oblique cleavage angles, needlelike crystals (f) quartz—hardest of common minerals (H=7), second most common mineral, clear or milky, colorless or colored; garnet—several colors, hardness 6.5, used as abrasive and gem; kaolin—primary clay mineral, white, earthy fracture, soft (H=1–2.5); talc—softest (H=1), white, soapy feel

8. (a) Carbonates are built around carbonate group, not silica tetrahedron.   (b) Both form rhombs and are colorless or white. Acid test—calcite bubbles easily, dolomite with difficulty.

9. (a) reddish and earthy, or silvery and metallic; red streak (b) magnetite—H=5.5–6.5, attracted to magnet; lodestone—acts as magnet   (c) pale brass-yellow color, H=6, metallic luster, 6- or 12-sided crystals; pyrite is sulfide, not oxide.

Answers to all questions appear in the Teacher's Guide at the back of this book.

■ Summary

I Rock-forming minerals make up most of the rocks in Earth's crust. Most rock-forming minerals are silicates.

Minerals are identified by their properties.

Color, luster, and crystal shape can be determined by simple inspection of a mineral.

Color is the most obvious property of a mineral, but it is often the least useful for identification. Crystal shape is sometimes useful.

Minerals have either metallic or nonmetallic luster. Vitreous, pearly, resinous, adamantine, greasy, dull, and earthy are all kinds of nonmetallic luster.

Streak, cleavage, fracture, and hardness of a mineral can be determined with simple tests.

Specific gravity is the ratio of the weight of a mineral to the weight of an equal volume of water.

Other properties used to identify minerals are reaction to acid, magnetism, taste, fluorescence, radioactivity, and double refraction.

II Silicate minerals are made of silica tetrahedrons combined in various structures. Feldspar minerals, quartz, and mica are the most common silicate minerals.

Amphiboles are silicate minerals that form long, needlelike crystals. Pyroxenes are silicates that form shorter, stouter crystals. Hornblende is a common amphibole; augite is a common pyroxene.

Ferromagnesian silicates include any dark silicate mineral containing iron and magnesium. Hornblende, augite, and olivine are examples.

Calcite and dolomite are the two most important carbonate minerals.

Several minerals contain large amounts of iron combined with oxygen (oxides) or sulfur (sulfides). Hematite and magnetite are iron oxides; pyrite is iron sulfide.

■ Vocabulary

amphibole	ferromagnesian	mineralogy
carbonate	silicate	pyroxene
cleavage	fracture	rock-forming
color	hardness	minerals
crystal shape	luster	specific gravity
feldspar	mica	streak

■ Review

Match definitions, List **A**, with terms, List **B**.

List A

1. study of minerals and their properties
2. minerals that make up Earth's crust
3. unreliable for mineral identification
4. vitreous, resinous, pearly, and adamantine
5. tendency of a mineral to split
6. measured by Mohs' scale
7. color of mineral powder
8. ratio of the weight of a mineral to the weight of an equal volume of water
9. bubbles easily in acid
10. state of glowing under ultraviolet light
11. hardest common mineral
12. orthoclase and plagioclase
13. muscovite and biotite
14. hornblende, augite, olivine
15. silicate family that includes hornblende but not augite
16. mineral made mostly of $(-CO_3^{2-})$ groups
17. all samples exhibit red streak

List B

a. amphibole	**j.** hematite
b. calcite	**k.** luster
c. carbonate	**l.** mica
d. cleavage	**m.** mineralogy
e. color	**n.** pyroxene
f. feldspars	**o.** quartz
g. ferromagnesian silicates	**p.** rock-forming minerals
h. fluorescence	**q.** streak
i. hardness	**r.** specific gravity

For further review, see **Study Guide.**
For assessment, see **Chapter Tests**
and **Computer Test Bank.**

■ Interpret and Apply

On your paper, answer each question.

1. Why is color a useful property for identifying malachite, but not quartz?
2. The hardness of a streak plate is about 6. Why would the streak of corundum be difficult to determine?
3. Both calcite and galena have three directions of cleavage. How does the shape of a cleavage fragment of calcite compare with that of a cleavage fragment of galena? (Refer to the table of mineral properties on pages 644–645 in the Appendix.)
4. A specimen of quartz weighs 13.25 newtons in air and 8.25 newtons in water. What is the specific gravity of the quartz specimen?
5. Name one property that would readily distinguish each pair of minerals. (**a**) feldspar and quartz (**b**) magnetite and hornblende (**c**) talc and mica (**d**) calcite and fluorite (**e**) cinnabar and malachite (**f**) pyrite and sphalerite (**g**) halite and calcite (**h**) hematite and pyrite

■ Critical Thinking

Eight rock-forming minerals are shown in the chart. Listed across the top are rocks made up of those minerals. Copy the 0–100% scale from the chart onto the edge of your paper. Use the scale to read the volume percentages of a mineral in a rock. For example, to find the percent volume of quartz in tonalite, slide your scale to the vertical line marked tonalite. Place the zero of your scale at the line between quartz and plagioclase. Read the percentage volume of quartz at the line between quartz and orthoclase. You should read close to 35% quartz.

1. Find the percent of plagioclase feldspar in tonalite.
2. What percentage of the volume of peridotite is pyroxene?
3. Which rock contains 40% orthoclase feldspar, 35% quartz, 12% plagioclase feldspar, 8% biotite, and 5% amphibole?
4. What name would be given to a rock that contained 60% plagioclase feldspar, 20% amphibole, 15% pyroxene, and 5% biotite?
5. Describe the composition of a quartz diorite.

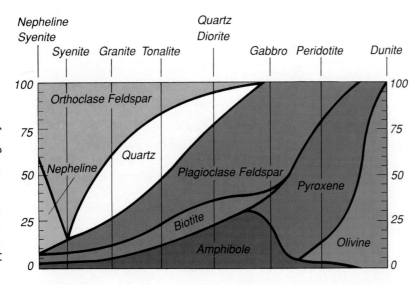

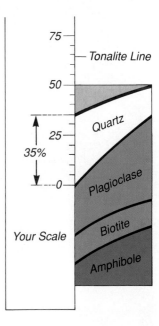

How Earth's Rocks Were Formed

▲
This formation is made of granite, an igneous rock.

How Do You Know That . . .

Rocks are made from minerals? Obtain several different rocks. Examine each with a magnifying glass. Are mineral grains visible in every rock? Can you recognize clear quartz grains, shiny mica flakes, or black bits of hornblende or augite? How hard is each rock? Can you scratch any with a paper clip? Check to see whether layers are visible in any of the rocks. Does the rock appear to have broken along those layers? What else do you notice about the rocks?

I Igneous Rocks

Topic 1 Uniformity of Process

Modern geology is said to have begun in 1795. In that year the Scottish geologist James Hutton described a new concept, called **uniformitarianism.** Before Hutton, most geologists thought that the physical features of Earth had been formed by sudden spectacular events, or catastrophes. In their view, these catastrophes caused the formation of mountains, canyons, waterfalls, and almost all landforms.

James Hutton's ideas were quite different. After years of studying landforms and rocks, he came to the conclusion that "the present is the key to the past." This statement included two concepts. (1) The geologic processes now at work were also active in the past. (2) The present physical features of Earth were formed by these same processes, at work over long periods of time.

According to Hutton, a canyon or a river valley need not be formed by a sudden splitting of Earth's crust. Instead, it can be formed by the slow and steady wearing away of the land. This was done, said Hutton, by the very same river now running in the canyon, doing for thousands and thousands of years what it is still doing today.

Topic 2 Three Groups of Rocks

The study of rocks is an important part of understanding Earth processes. A **rock** can be generally defined as a group of minerals bound together in some way.

Hutton's principles of uniform processes have been used by geologists to explain the origin of rocks. Geologists have noted, for example, that erupting lava hardens into rocks. These rocks are similar to others that have been found in many places on Earth. Geologists have seen that sands and clays sometimes harden into rocklike materials. Such materials resemble present-day sandstone and shale. They have observed that when hot lava flows over other rocks, it changes those rocks. From many studies like these, geologists have concluded that all rocks of the crust form in one of three general ways:

Igneous rocks are formed by the cooling and hardening of hot molten rock from inside Earth. This hot molten rock is called **magma.**

OBJECTIVES

A Explain the principle of uniformitarianism and relate it to the formation of igneous, sedimentary, and metamorphic rocks.

B Discuss differences between plutonic and volcanic igneous rocks.

C Define *rock texture* and list some factors that control the texture of an igneous rock.

D Name and describe members of the granite, diorite, and gabbro igneous rock families.

TEACHING TIP

The standard definition for rock is "an aggregate of minerals." If your students can remember that an aggregate is a group or collection, you may prefer to use that definition.

5.1 James Hutton

63

Sedimentary rocks are formed by the hardening and cementing of layers of sediments. The sediments may consist of rock fragments, plant and animal remains, or chemicals that form on lake and ocean bottoms.

Metamorphic rocks are formed when rocks that already exist are changed by heat and pressure into new kinds of rocks.

Topic 3 Recognizing Igneous Rocks

Granite, a common igneous rock, does not form on Earth's surface. Instead, granite forms from magma that cools deep underground. As magma cools, elements in it form distinct, interlocking mineral grains. Rocks that form underground from cooled magma are called **plutonic,** or *intrusive,* igneous rocks. Such rocks are seen at the surface only after the rock that covers them is worn away.

Magma that pours onto Earth's surface during a volcanic eruption is called *lava.* The rock that forms when the lava cools is called **volcanic,** or *extrusive,* igneous rock. Volcanic rocks also form out of volcanic dust and ash. Volcanic rocks are similar to plutonic rocks in mineral composition. However, they lack distinct mineral grains.

VIDEODISC SELECTION

Formation and classification
of igneous rocks
Side 2 movie: 27713 & PLAY

5.2 After lava flows onto the surface, it begins to cool and harden. It eventually becomes volcanic, or extrusive, igneous rock.

Topic 4 **Kinds of Magma**

From the study of plutonic and volcanic rocks, geologists have learned that there are many kinds of magma. There are two general kinds that are the most common. Both kinds are hot solutions of silicates. Both have temperatures ranging from about 600°C to 1200°C. However, these magmas differ in chemical composition. One kind has a high percentage of silica (SiO_2). It does not have much calcium, iron, or magnesium, which are common in dark-colored minerals. This high-silica magma is thick and slow flowing. When it hardens, it forms rocks that have mainly light-colored minerals. These light-colored, high-silica rocks are called **felsic** (feldspar + silica) rocks. Granite is a common felsic rock. It contains light-colored minerals such as quartz and orthoclase feldspar. Most plutonic rocks are felsic.

The second kind of magma has a much lower percentage of silica. It has a higher percentage of calcium, iron, and magnesium. This low-silica magma is hotter, thinner, and more fluid than the felsic type. When it solidifies, it forms rocks that contain mostly dark ferromagnesian minerals. These dark-colored, low-silica rocks are called **mafic.** They have a high percentage of magnesium and iron (ferric) bearing minerals. Basalt is a mafic rock. It contains a number of dark minerals such as hornblende, augite, and biotite. Most volcanic rocks are mafic.

Topic 5 **Textures of an Igneous Rock**

Rocks are grouped not only by their minerals but also by their textures. A rock's **texture** depends on the size, shape, and arrangement of its mineral crystals. Igneous rock textures range from glassy-smooth, such as obsidian, to coarse-grained, such as granite.

Crystal size is the most important factor affecting texture. The crystal size in an igneous rock depends mostly upon how fast the magma hardens. When rock is in the liquid state, its atoms are free to move around and arrange into crystals. The longer the magma stays liquid, the longer the atoms are free to move, and the larger the crystals become. A second factor that affects crystal size, and thus rock texture, is the amount of gas dissolved in the magma. Dissolved gases help ions move around in the magma. A high percentage of dissolved gases helps crystals to grow faster. Thus the crystals grow large in a relatively short time.

Magmas trapped deep within the crust hardens very slowly. The rocks that form from these magmas have large mineral grains of fairly uniform size. Such plutonic rocks have a granular, or coarse-grained, texture. The most familiar example is granite.

Magmas that reach Earth's surface as lava harden rapidly. The volcanic rock that forms has tiny crystals. The crystals are usually too small to see without a microscope. These rocks have fine-grained textures. A good example is basalt.

VIDEODISC SELECTION

Examples of volcanic igneous rocks
Side 2: 3703 to 3709, 7-frame
sequence

SCIENCE BACKGROUND
Felsic rocks are sometimes called granitic rocks, since granite is the most important felsic rock.

SCIENCE BACKGROUND
Mafic rocks are sometimes called basaltic rocks, since basalt is the most important mafic rock.

SCIENCE BACKGROUND
The relationship between cooling rate and texture is a fundamental concept to the study of igneous rocks.

5.3 In a coarse-grained igneous rock like the granite shown in (a) and (b), the individual mineral grains can easily be seen.

a

b

5.4 A porphyry

TEACHING TIP
  Stress that all members of an igneous family have similar mineral composition, but rocks within the family formed under different conditions and have different textures.

5.5 (top) Rhyolite, (bottom) gabbro

In some cases magma flowing onto the surface hardens so rapidly that there is no time at all for crystals to develop. The rocks that form under these conditions—for example, obsidian—are as smooth as glass. They are said to have a glassy texture.

Topic 6   **Porphyritic Texture**

Some igneous rocks have two distinctly different textures. In these rocks, large crystals are surrounded by a fine-grained mass of rock. Such a rock is called a **porphyry** (POR fur ee).

One explanation of how a porphyry forms involves two stages of cooling. In the first stage the magma is at a great depth. Here it cools slowly enough so that large crystals of one mineral can form. The rest of the magma remains liquid. Then the magma moves upward, possibly melting through overlying rock, until it comes close to the surface. Here the rest of the magma cools into a fine-grained rock around the larger first-stage crystals.

Topic 7   **Families of Igneous Rocks**

Remember that rocks can be described in terms of texture and mineral composition. Igneous rocks are grouped into families according to mineral composition. Each family has coarse-grained, fine-grained, and glassy members.

The *granite family* forms from felsic magmas. All the rocks in this family consist mainly of orthoclase feldspar and quartz. Other minerals likely to be present are plagioclase feldspar, mica, and some hornblende. Orthoclase and quartz are light in color. Thus, the rocks in this family are usually light-colored. In this family granite is coarse-grained, rhyolite is fine-grained, and obsidian and pumice are glassy. These rocks have different textures, but all have similar chemical compositions.

The *gabbro family* forms from mafic magmas. The rocks in this family are made mainly of dark plagioclase feldspar and augite. Other likely minerals are olivine, hornblende, and biotite. These rocks are generally dark in color and more dense than rocks in the granite family. In this family, gabbro is coarse-grained, basalt is fine-grained, and basalt glass is glassy.

The *diorite family* has a composition and color between those of the granite and gabbro families. Diorite, the coarse-grained member, has less quartz than granite. It has less dark plagioclase than gabbro. Andesite is the fine-grained member of the diorite family.

Some igneous rocks do not fit into any of these families. Granodiorite is a coarse-grained rock. It has a composition between those of granite and diorite. Also of interest are three coarse, dark heavy rocks that may be like the rock of Earth's mantle. Pyroxenite is nearly all pyroxene. Dunite is almost all olivine. Peridotite is a mixture of pyroxene and olivine.

Topic 8 **Descriptions of Common Igneous Rocks**

Specific igneous rocks can be recognized by their minerals and textures. *Granite* is made of quartz, orthoclase feldspar, and at least one other mineral, such as mica or hornblende. Quartz grains look like little chips of cloudy or grayish glass. Feldspar often has smooth cleavage surfaces. It is usually white, gray, pink, or orange. Mica, usually black biotite, occurs in shiny little flakes. Hornblende occurs as tiny, dull black chunks or sticks. Granites range in color from light to medium grays and pinks. Feldspar makes up the largest part of granite. Because of this, the color of the feldspar has the greatest effect on the overall color of the rock. Granites have coarse-grained textures.

Granite is the most common continental igneous rock. It occurs in the Rockies, the Adirondacks of New York State, the Black Hills in South Dakota, the White Mountains of New Hampshire, and in many other mountainous areas. Granite is plutonic. Because granite forms far beneath the surface, its presence at the surface shows that erosion removed thousands of meters of overlying rocks since the rock first cooled from magma.

Felsite is the general name for any light-colored, fine-grained rock in the granite family. *Rhyolite* is an example. It is a fine-grained, light gray to pink rock.

Obsidian is volcanic glass of the granite family. Obsidian contains many of the same minerals as granite and other light-colored rocks, so it is grouped with those rocks. However, obsidian is usually dark brown or black. The dark color is due to tiny amounts of dark-colored minerals scattered throughout the rock. Obsidian is hard and brittle. An important property of obsidian is conchoidal, or shell-like, fracture.

Pumice is formed from felsic lava that hardened while steam and other gases were still bubbling out of it. It looks like a sponge with many small holes in it. Because of its many air holes, pumice is sometimes light enough to float on water.

The most common rock of the gabbro family is *basalt.* It is a fine-grained rock that ranges in color from dark green to black. Basalt is the igneous rock of the ocean floor. On land, it is the most common rock formed from flows of lava. Large areas of basalt occur in the lava flows of Iceland, the Hawaiian Islands, and in the Columbia and Snake River Plateaus in the western United States.

Gabbro has about the same composition as basalt. However, because it cooled slowly deep underground, gabbro is coarse-grained. Gabbros are very dark in color. *Diabase* has a composition similar to gabbro. Its texture is finer than gabbro but coarser than basalt.

Basalt glass is like obsidian but has a mafic composition. *Scoria,* like pumice, is full of holes. Scoria, however, is made of denser minerals, so not all scoria floats.

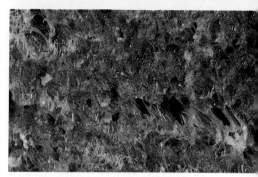

5.6 (top) Pumice, (bottom) close-up of pumice

5.7 (top) Diorite, (bottom) pyroxenite

Summary Table: Common Igneous Rocks

Texture and Origin	Felsic or Light-Colored Rocks		Medium-Colored Rocks	Mafic or Dark-Colored Rocks	
	Colors: white, tan, gray, pink, red *Minerals:* feldspar (mostly orthoclase), quartz; also some mica and hornblende		*Colors:* gray, green *Minerals:* feldspar (mostly plagioclase), hornblende, augite, biotite	*Colors:* dark green, dark gray, black *Minerals:* plagioclase feldspar, augite; also olivine, hornblende, biotite	
	With Quartz	*Almost No Quartz*	*Without Quartz*		
Glassy: cooled quickly at surface of Earth	Obsidian Pumice		Obsidian	Basalt glass Scoria	
Fine-grained: cooled slowly at or near surface	Rhyolite	Trachyte (Felsite)	Andesite	Basalt Diabase	
Coarse-grained: cooled very slowly, usually at great depths	Granite Pegmatite	Syenite Granodiorite	Diorite	Gabbro	*No Feldspar* Peridotite Pyroxenite Dunite

ANSWERS

1. (a) Earth's features formed by sudden events. (b) processes of to-day operated in past, features of Earth formed by these processes

2. (a) Lava forms rocks like existing rocks; sand and clay harden into rocks. (b) igneous—cooling of molten rock; sedimentary—hardening of layers of sediment; metamorphic—changed by heat and pressure

3. (a) magma—molten rock in crust; lava—on surface (b) deep in crust (c) on Earth's surface

4. (a) felsic—light-colored, cooler, silica-rich, granite; mafic—dark-colored, hotter, ferromagnesian minerals, basalt (b) felsic—plutonic; mafic—volcanic

5. (a) time for crystal formation, amount of dissolved gases in magma (b) plutonic—coarse; volcanic—fine-grained; (c) cools very rapidly

6. (a) rock with 2 different textures (b) 2 different cooling rates

7. (a) felsic, orthoclase and quartz, light; in order: granite, rhyolite, obsidian and pumice (b) mafic, plagioclase and ferromag. minerals, dark; in order: gabbro, basalt, basalt glass (c) in between composition color of granite and gabbro

8. granite—quartz, orthoclase, some dark minerals, light-colored; rhyolite—fine-grained granite; obsidian—volcanic glass; pumice—glassy foam; basalt—dark, fine-grained; gabbro, coarse basalt; diorite—in be-

tween basalt and gabbro; scoria—mafic, glassy, many holes

TOPIC QUESTIONS

Each topic question refers to the topic of the same number.

1. (a) Before James Hutton, how had geologists explained the origin of landforms? (b) What two principles make up Hutton's uniformitarianism?

2. (a) Give two examples of the ways in which geologists have applied Hutton's principles to describe the origins of rocks. (b) Identify and describe the three main groups of rocks.

3. (a) What is the difference between magma and lava? (b) Where do plutonic rocks form? (c) Where do volcanic rocks form?

4. (a) How do felsic magmas differ from mafic magmas in color, temperature, mineral composition, and the kind of rock each forms? (b) Which kind of magma is more likely to form a plutonic rock? Which will likely form a volcanic rock?

5. (a) List two factors that affect the texture of an igneous rock. (b) How are textures of plutonic rocks different from textures of volcanic rocks? (c) How does a rock with a glassy texture form?

6. (a) What is a porphyry? (b) How is a porphyry thought to form?

7. (a) Describe the granite family and list its coarse-grained, fine-grained, and glassy members. (b) Describe the gabbro family and list its members. (c) What is the diorite family?

8. List and briefly describe the common igneous rocks.

II Sedimentary Rocks

Topic 9 Kinds of Sediments

Although most of Earth's crust is made of igneous rock, most of its surface is covered by sedimentary rocks. Sedimentary rocks form when sediments harden into rocks. There are three main kinds of sedimentary rock.

Clastic sedimentary rocks are formed from fragments of other rocks. Examples of clastic sedimentary rocks are shale, sandstone, and conglomerate.

Chemical sedimentary rocks are formed from mineral grains that fall out of a solution (precipitate) by evaporation or by chemical action. Rock salt and some limestones are examples of chemical sedimentary rocks.

Organic sedimentary rocks are formed from the remains of plants and animals. Coal is an example. Limestones made of shell fragments are also examples.

Topic 10 How Clastic Rocks Form

Rock fragments that form clastic sedimentary rocks come from the weathering of rocks that already exist. Fragments range in size from large pebbles and gravels down to sand, silt, and microscopic flakes of clay. Winds, waves, and glaciers all can pick up and move these particles. However, running water collects and moves the greatest amount. As particles are moved by running water, they are smoothed and rounded by rubbing against each other and against the stream bed. The farther the particles travel, the more rounded they become. Sediments are deposited when a stream slows down. This occurs when the stream flows into the quiet water of a lake or the ocean. Waves and currents may then spread the sediment over great distances.

How do loose sediments become rock? In coarse sediments such as gravels and sands, the particles do not stick together unless they are cemented. Ocean water, lake water, and groundwater all contain natural cements in the form of dissolved minerals. These natural cements include *silica* (SiO_2), *calcite* ($CaCO_3$), and *iron oxide* (FeO). When these dissolved minerals settle into the spaces between sand grains or pebbles, they bind the fragments together. The cement transforms loose sediments into firm, cemented rock.

The pressure of overlying sediments is sometimes enough to make fine sediments such as clay or silt stick together, even without cement. More often, however, cement is needed to hold the rock together. Cements give their own colors to rocks. Cemented rocks may be gray or white from silica or calcite, or red, brown, or rust-colored from iron cement.

OBJECTIVES

A Describe the three major processes by which sedimentary rocks are formed and give examples of rocks formed by each process.

B Discuss sediment sorting and relate it to rock stratification.

C Explain the origin of fossils, ripple marks, mud cracks, nodules, concretions, and geodes.

TEACHING TIP
You may need to clarify the comparison between the amount of igneous and sedimentary rock in the crust. Ninety-five percent of the crust is igneous rock. Sedimentary rocks are a thin veneer covering most of the crust.

5.8 Most sediments are deposited by running water. Running water also smooths and rounds sediments, such as the rocks in this stream bed.

TEACHING TIP
Stress the fact that particle size decreases as distance from shore increases. The particle size of a sediment can thus be used to interpret the distance of the site from shore at the time of sediment deposition.

5.9 The kinds of sediment deposited on the ocean floor vary with the distance from shore.

Topic 11 Sorting of Sediments

When a river flows into a lake or ocean, it drops its sediment load as it slows down. The first sediments to be dropped are larger pebbles and gravels. These settle to the bottom in the shallow areas near shore. Next to settle are the smaller sands and finally, in calm water, the silts and clays.

The process of sorting does not always produce perfect separation. Sand is sometimes found mixed with pebbles and gravels in shallow water or with silts and clays in deeper water.

In time, the sediments become cemented together into sedimentary rocks. Pebbles and gravels become conglomerate. Sands form sandstones. Silts and clays form shale.

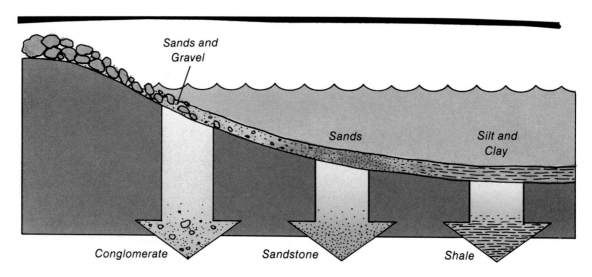

SCIENCE BACKGROUND
The average rock called shale is about ⅔ silt.

5.10 Conglomerate is a cemented rock of pebbles and sand grains.

Topic 12 Conglomerate, Sandstone, and Shale

Conglomerate is the coarsest of the clastic rocks. It is a cemented mixture of rounded pebbles and sand grains that were deposited in rough water. The pebbles in conglomerate may be any rock material. Quartz is most common because it is so durable.

Most *sandstones* are made largely of grains of quartz. The cement in a rock seldom fills all the spaces between the grains. Sandstones may have up to 30 percent air space in them. The air spaces mean that sandstone is both *porous* (filled with small holes) and *permeable* (water is able to pass through it). Sandstones are rough, gritty, and durable if well cemented.

The clays found in *shale* are usually tiny flakes of the mineral kaolin. The spaces between the clay particles in shale are so tiny that water cannot pass through the rock. This makes shale *impermeable*. Shales are smooth, soft, and easily broken.

5.11 (left) Sandstone, (right) shale

Topic 13 **Sedimentary Rocks of Chemical Origin**

Sea, lake, swamp, or underground waters often contain dissolved minerals. Chemical sediments are formed when these minerals fall out of solution. This can occur through evaporation or through chemical action, the combining of dissolved ions to form new minerals. The most common chemical sediments are limestone, rock salt, and rock gypsum.

Limestones of chemical origin are formed from tiny grains of calcite deposited from sea or lake waters. These limestones are often gray to tan in color, compact and dense in appearance, and smooth to the touch.

Rock salt is the natural form of common table salt (sodium chloride). It occurs as a sedimentary rock in thick layers in many parts of the world. Rock salt is almost pure halite.

Rock gypsum, like rock salt, occurs in layers. It also occurs as nearly pure veins of the mineral gypsum.

5.12 (top) Rock salt, (bottom) rock gypsum

Topic 14 **Sedimentary Rocks of Organic Origin**

Organic sediments come from the remains of animals and plants. The most common rocks that come from organic sediments are limestone and coal. Coal will be discussed in Chapter 6.

The "lime" in organic limestones is the mineral calcite. Calcite is dissolved out of rocks on land, carried to the ocean (or lake) by streams, and taken from the water by shell-producing organisms.

Great numbers of animals and plants that use calcite live in the shallow ocean water near shore. These include clams, mussels, oysters, sea snails, corals, microscopic algae, and many others. When

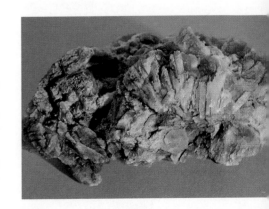

5.13 What sort of rock might these sediments form?

Ans. sandy limestone

5.14 (above) Cross-bedding occurs when sediment is deposited at an angle. (right) The layers of these rocks show stratification. The lines between the layers show bedding planes.

SCIENCE BACKGROUND

Sedimentary rocks are deposited in horizontal layers. The only major exceptions are the cross-bedding of deltas and sand dunes.

VIDEODISC SELECTION

Formation and classification of sedimentary and metamorphic rocks
Side 2 movie: 31258 & PLAY

they die, their calcite shells pile up on the shallow ocean floor. The shells may be whole but are more often broken into fragments by the grinding action of the waves. In time the shells become cemented into limestones. The limestones that form near the shore may contain a good deal of clay. Those that form farther from shore may be almost pure calcite.

Since most limestones are composed of the mineral calcite, they can readily be identified by the acid test (Chapter 4, Topic 5).

Topic 15 **Sedimentary Features: Stratification**

Sedimentary rocks show special features that help to identify them. One of these is **stratification**—arrangement in visible layers. How does stratification develop?

When any change occurs in the kind of sediments being laid down in one place, new rock layers are formed. For example, if a coarse clay is deposited on a fine one, layers of different shale will form, one on top of the other. If sand is deposited on clay, a layer of sandstone will form on a layer of shale. In this way sedimentary rocks become layered. Their beds or layers are separated by bedding planes. Bedding planes are usually horizontal. *Cross-bedding* may develop when beds are deposited by the wind in leaning positions on sand dunes, or deposited by rivers on deltas and sandbars.

The sediment changes that lead to stratification happen for a number of reasons. For example, the river that brings the sediment to the ocean or lake may be wearing away new kinds of rock. It may carry larger amounts and more kinds of pebbles, sand, and clay during flood times. The river may carry its sediments farther out to sea than before. Or, it may drop the sediments closer to shore.

Topic 16 Fossils in Sedimentary Rocks

As sediments pile up, animals and plants that die in the area are buried. The soft parts of the animals and plants usually decay. The hard parts may remain as fossils when the sediments turn to rock. **Fossils** are the remains, impressions, or any other evidence of plants and animals preserved in rock. The shells of clams, mussels, and snails are often found in layers of sandstone, limestone, and shale. More often, the shells themselves have dissolved but were replaced by other minerals that took the shapes of the shells. Other fossils are formed when a shell or a skeleton, such as that of a fish, leaves an impression in the rock layer. These are seen when the rock layers are split apart. Plants can also form impressions in rocks. Plant remains or impressions are usually found in rocks formed from swamp sediments.

5.15 Organic limestone contains fossils of lime-bearing organisms. The fossils in this limestone are easily seen.

VIDEODISC SELECTION

Selected sedimentary rocks
Side 2: 3710 to 3726, 17-frame sequence

Topic 17 Ripple Marks and Mud Cracks

Animals and plants are not the only remains preserved in sedimentary rocks. Many sandstones show *ripple marks* on the surface of a bedding plane. Ripple marks are formed by the action of winds, streams, waves, or currents on sand. Many of them are preserved when the sand becomes sandstone. Fresh ripple marks can be seen today on any sandy beach or stream bed. *Mud cracks* develop when deposits of wet clay dry and contract. If the cracks are later filled with different materials, they are fossilized when the clay becomes shale rock. Fresh mud cracks can be seen wherever muddy roads or puddles of water dry out after a rain.

Topic 18 Nodules, Concretions, Geodes

Limestones often contain lumps of fine-grained silica called *chert.* Geologists call the lumps *nodules.* Round masses of calcium carbonate, called *concretions,* often occur in layers of shale. Both structures were probably deposited from a solution, bit by bit, around a piece of fossil material in the rock. Chert that is dark gray or black is called *flint.* Flint is typically hard and fine-grained.

Limestones sometimes contain small hollow spheres of silica rock. The hollows may be lined with crystals of quartz or calcite. These spheres are called *geodes* (JEE odes). Geodes seem to have been formed by groundwater. First, the water dissolved some of the limestone and formed cavities in it. Then the groundwater deposited quartz or calcite crystals in the cavities.

5.16 Sedimentary features: (top) geode, (bottom left) ripple marks, (bottom right) mud cracks

Summary Table: Common Sedimentary Rocks

	Color	Distinguishing Feature	Origin
breccia	variable	contains angular fragments surrounded by finer grains	clastic
coal	shiny to dull black	found in beds located between other sedimentary rocks	organic
conglomerate	variable	contains rounded pebbles held together by cement	clastic
rock salt	colorless to white	cubic crystals	chemical
gypsum	white, gray, brown, red or green	grains range in size from very fine to very large, can have a very crumbly texture	chemical
limestone	variable—white, gray, yellow, red, brown	found in thick layers on cliffs, may contain fossils	organic
sandstone	white, gray, yellow, red	fine or coarse grains held together by cement	clastic
shale	yellow, red, gray, green, black	dense but soft, breaks easily	clastic

ironstone

TOPIC QUESTIONS

Each topic question refers to the topic of the same number.

9. (a) Compare the total amount of sedimentary rock on Earth's surface with the total amount of sedimentary rock in Earth's crust.   (b) Name, describe the origin, and give examples of the three groups of sedimentary rocks.

10. (a) What substance collects and moves the greatest amount of sediment?   (b) What kinds of materials can act as mineral cement in clastic sedimentary rocks?   (c) How can fine particles be formed into rock without cement?

11. (a) Explain how sediments are sorted when they are deposited in water.   (b) Name the rock that is formed from each kind of sediment.

ANSWERS

9. (a) sedimentary most common surface rock, but only small part of crust   (b) clastic—fragments of other rocks: shale, sandstone, conglomerate; chemical—evaporation or chemical action: rock salt, limestone; organic—remains of organisms: coal, limestone

10. (a) running water   (b) silica, lime, iron   (c) pressure

11. (a) largest dropped first in rough water, smallest dropped last in still water   (b) conglomerate from pebbles and gravels, sandstone from sand, shale from silt and clay

12. (a) Describe conglomerate (b) Explain why sandstone is permeable (c) How does the composition of shale explain the fact that it is impermeable?

13. (a) Describe how chemical sediments are formed (b) Name three examples of chemical sedimentary rocks.

14. Explain the origin of organic limestones.

15. What is stratification? How does it develop in sedimentary rocks?

16. What are fossils? How do they form in sedimentary rock?

17. How do ripple marks and mud cracks form in sedimentary rocks?

18. (a) What is a nodule and how is it thought to form? (b) What is a geode? How is it formed?

ANSWERS (Continued)

12. (a) coarsest clastic, cemented pebbles and sand   (b) Cement never entirely fills space between grains.   (c) Flakes mean little space between grains.

13. (a) minerals formed by evaporation or chemical action   (b) rock salt, rock gypsum, limestone

14. animals with calcite shells die, pile up, become cemented

15. layering of sedimentary rocks, caused by changes in material deposited

16. evidence of past life preserved in rock; Remains pile up with sediments, soft parts decay, hard parts remain, are replaced, or leave impressions.

17. form in sediment, remain when sediment becomes rock

18. (a) silica lump, deposit builds up around fossil bit   (b) small hollow sphere; cavity formed, minerals deposited in it by groundwater

EARTH**MATTERS**

Stripping the Earth

As much as 60 percent of United States coal production comes from strip mining. In strip mining, giant shovels or stripping wheels remove the topsoil and underlying layers of rock to expose coal beds or seams.

Strip mining is the least expensive way to mine shallow coal seams. However, without proper land reclamation efforts, strip mining can leave the land barren, unusable, and subject to erosion.

There is another problem with the strip mining of coal. The rock overlying sulfur-rich coal also contains minerals such as pyrite, which is an iron sulfide. While the coal is being mined, the overburden waste rock is left out in the rain in large piles. The rainwater reacts with the sulfur in the waste rock to form dilute sulfuric acid, which can then flow into nearby ponds, streams, or groundwater. This acid runoff contaminates water supplies and kills aquatic life.

The federal government regulates strip mining. Care must be taken to prevent acid runoff. Coal companies are required to place money in trust, guaranteeing that they will restore the land to its original condition once the coal has been removed. Restoring the land is called land reclamation and involves regrading the surface, replacing the topsoil, and replanting native vegetation.

To date, most strip-mined land is in the eastern United States. However, most of the remaining coal that can be mined by this method is in the West.

What other rocks and minerals are mined using surface mining techniques?

OBJECTIVES

A Explain the difference between dynamic metamorphism and thermal metamorphism.

B Describe the effects of metamorphism on rocks; name and describe some metamorphic rocks and identify the rock from which each formed.

C Describe the rock cycle and discuss different orders of rock-forming events within the cycle.

5.17 The twisted patterns in this metamorphic rock were caused by extreme heat and pressure.

III Metamorphic Rocks

Topic 19 What Metamorphic Rocks Are

Marble, slate, gneiss (NICE), and quartzite are examples of rocks that do not fit into either of the first two classes. These rocks are not formed from either magma or sediment. Yet in many ways they are like members of the first two groups. Marble resembles some limestones. Slate looks similar to shale. Quartzite looks like crystallized sandstone. Gneiss contains minerals like those in granite.

These resemblances are not mere coincidence. The rocks in these pairs are related. One actually is formed from the other through changes produced by natural forces. These metamorphic (*meta*, change; *morph*, form) rocks are formed from existing rock by the action of heat, pressure, and chemicals.

Topic 20 Regional Metamorphism

Most of the metamorphic rock of Earth's crust is formed by the process of **regional metamorphism.** Regional metamorphism occurs when large areas of rock are under intense heat and pressure. This process causes them to change form. This occurs during mountain-building movements. At such times, layers of rock deep in the crust are under high temperature and high pressure. Heat from the friction of the moving rock layers is added to the heat already in the deeply buried rocks. The pressure on the rocks comes from both the great weight of the overlying rocks and the squeezing pressure of the moving rock masses. Hot water, steam, and other liquids and gases in the deep rocks join with the heat and pressure. These forces work together and produce striking changes in the rocks. Regional metamorphism takes place over very large areas.

5.18 (left) Sandstone, (right) quartzite

TEACHING TIP
Point out to students that quartzite and marble are monomineralic rocks, if you introduced this term in Chapter 4.

What happens to rocks that are metamorphosed? Pressure squeezes their grains closer together. The squeezing makes them more dense and less porous. However, pressure alone does not produce all of the changes. Heat and chemicals may rearrange the particles. Minerals may be reformed in the rock, or new minerals may be formed. Two examples of metamorphic rocks are quartzite and marble. Quartzite is metamorphosed sandstone and, like most sandstone, is made of quartz. Marble is metamorphosed limestone and, like limestone, is made of calcite. Both quartzite and marble are dense, crystalline rocks.

Topic 21 **The Metamorphism of Shale**

When shale undergoes regional metamorphism, many changes can occur. The rock becomes more dense and more crystalline. The elements recombine to form new minerals that are not found in shale, such as mica and hornblende. The pressures on the rocks squeeze the flakes of mica or the needles of hornblende into parallel layers. The new rocks split easily along these layers. This new feature in the rocks is called *foliation.*

The first rock formed from shale during regional metamorphism is *slate.* In slate, the foliation layers are microscopically thin. If metamorphism goes further, a shiny rock called *phyllite* (FILL yte) is formed. More intense metamorphism produces a flaky rock called *schist,* in which the foliation layers are easily seen.

Schists can be formed from many different rocks, such as shales, impure sandstones, and basalt. The result is that there are many varieties of schist. These are usually named for their principal mineral. Mica schist, talc schist, and hornblende schist are examples.

Gneiss is another metamorphic rock that is formed from a variety of rocks. It can be formed from shale, granite, conglomerate, and many others. Gneiss has the coarsest foliation of all the metamorphic rocks. Its minerals are arranged in cardboard-thick parallel bands. Bands of light-colored minerals such as quartz and feldspar alternate with dark minerals such as hornblende or biotite.

5.19 Through metamorphism, shale (top) becomes slate (bottom).

5.20 (left) Phyllite, (center) mica schist, (right) gneiss

Topic 22   **Contact Metamorphism**

SCIENCE BACKGROUND
   Contact metamorphism is an example of heat transfer by conduction.

VIDEODISC SELECTION

Selected metamorphic rocks
Side 2: 3727 to 3743, 17-frame sequence

A second kind of metamorphism is **contact metamorphism**. This process occurs when hot magma forces its way into overlying rock. The heat of the magma bakes the rocks that are in contact with it. The width of the affected area depends on the temperature of the intrusion. Hot liquids and gases from the magma also enter the intruded rock and react with its minerals. These effects rarely reach more than a hundred meters into the intruded rock. Much less rock is affected than in regional metamorphism. Changes in the rock are usually less drastic, and foliation is not produced.

Hornfels is a rock formed from shale by contact metamorphism. It is very fine-grained, dense, and very hard.

Relation of Principal Sedimentary Materials, Sedimentary Rocks, and Metamorphic Rocks

Sedimentary Material	Sedimentary Rock	Metamorphic Rock
Pebbles, gravel, sand	Conglomerate	Quartzite conglomerate Gneiss (also from granite and rhyolite)
Sand grains (usually quartz)	Sandstone	Quartzite
Clay (usually kaolin), silt	Shale, mudstone	Slate, phyllite, hornfels, schist
Lime (shells, fragments, or grains)	Limestone	Marble

Topic 23   **The Rock Cycle**

VIDEODISC SELECTION

Explanation of the rock cycle
Side 2 movie: 23939 & PLAY

Classifying the rocks of the crust according to their origin shows how closely related they are. The igneous rocks may be thought of as the primary, or parent, rocks of the crust. As these are attacked by weathering and erosion, sediments form. The sediments are turned into sedimentary rocks. If these rocks are buried beneath other sediments and are involved in movements of Earth's crust, they may become metamorphic rocks.

If crustal movements force rocks deep into Earth's crust, they may reach temperatures so high that they melt into magma. The magma may then harden into igneous rocks to complete the rock cycle.

The rock cycle has many shortcuts and detours. Igneous rocks may be metamorphosed directly. Sedimentary rocks may be weathered without being metamorphosed. Metamorphic rocks may be metamorphosed or weathered a second time. The story of the rock cycle is outlined in Figure 5.21. In brief form, it is a large part of the story of geology.

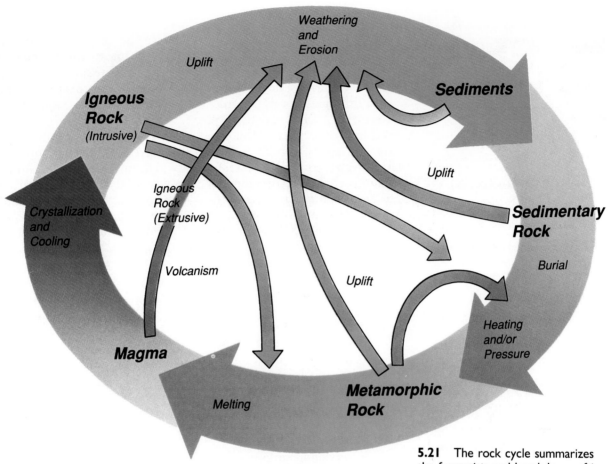

5.21   The rock cycle summarizes the formation and breakdown of igneous, sedimentary, and metamorphic rocks.

TOPIC QUESTIONS

Each topic question refers to the topic of the same number.

19. Define metamorphic rock and list four examples

20. (a) Explain the process of regional metamorphism. (b) What general changes does metamorphism cause in rocks? (c) In what ways does metamorphism change sandstone? Limestone?

21. (a) What changes occur in shale during regional metamorphism? (b) What rocks are formed from shale as metamorphism progresses? (c) Describe schist and gneiss.

22. (a) What causes contact metamorphism? (b) How do the effects of contact metamorphism compare with those of regional metamorphism?

23. (a) List the general steps of the rock cycle. (b) Identify two shortcuts in the rock cycle.

ANSWERS

19. rock formed when existing rock was changed by heat or pressure; marble, slate, gneiss, quartzite

20. (a) Mountain-building exerts heat and pressure on large areas of rock. (b) squeezes grains together, forms new minerals, realigns crystals (c) Both become more dense, highly crystalline.

21. (a) new minerals form, layers become foliated (b) slate, phyllite, schist (c) schist—flaky, foliation easily seen; gneiss—coarsest foliation, alternating mineral bands

22. (a) hot magma in contact with rock (b) smaller area affected, less change to rocks, no foliation

23. (a) weathering of igneous rock into sediment, sediments cemented into rock, burial, metamorphism, melting, magma (b) metamorphism of igneous rocks, weathering of metamorphic rocks

L A B ACTIVITY

Studying Rocks in Thin Sections

For additional activities, see Laboratory Investigations booklet.

Have you ever tried to look through a rock? In addition to looking at hand-held rock samples, sometimes geologists need to see through the rock in order to study it. They do this by making thin sections. Thin sections are slices of rock so thin that light actually passes through them! Thin sections are analyzed by using microscopes. The magnified view in the microscope makes it possible to see minerals that are not large enough to view in the hand-held sample and to more easily identify the larger minerals that can be seen.

In this lab, you will look at some diagrams of rock thin sections. You will study minerals that are found in the rocks as well as identify the rocks containing the minerals.

Lab Skills and Objectives
- To **observe** and **interpret** several diagrams of rock thin sections
- To **classify** and **identify** the minerals and rocks represented by the diagrams

Materials
- metric ruler

Procedure
1. Look at Rock A in Figure 5.23. Use the key to determine the name of each mineral. List the names of the minerals found in Rock A.

2. Use the chart in Figure 5.22 to estimate the percent of each mineral present in Rock A. For example, does the amount of quartz in Rock A look as if it occupies 10% of the diagram? 20%? 40%? 50%? Repeat your estimate for each of the minerals in Rock A. Record the percents. Your values should total 100%. Repeat steps 1 and 2 for Rock B.

3. Using the metric ruler, measure the diameter of the circular diagram for Rock C. Record your measurement.

4. Look at the mineral grains in Rock C. Measure the width in any direction across five different mineral grains. Record your data. Calculate an average width for the grains.

5. Answer the questions in *Analysis and Conclusions.*

Analysis and Conclusions
1. Grain or crystal size can provide clues to rock types. Typically, sedimentary grains are rounded and found in a cement matrix. Igneous grains fit together in a jigsaw puzzle fashion. Metamorphic grains exhibit linear patterns and foliation. (Foliation is a parallel arrangement of minerals such as alternating layers of dark and light minerals) Look at rocks A to D. Which of the rocks shown is sedimentary? Metamorphic? Igneous?

5.22 Chart to aid in visual estimations.

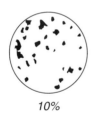

10%

20%

30%

40%

50%

2. Determine the actual size of an average grain of Rock C. The actual diameter of the rock sample shown in each diagram is 0.5 centimeters. Use your average grain diameter data and the magnified diameter you recorded. Show your work.

3. Using your answer to question 2, determine the name of the average grain size in Rock C. The diameter of clay-sized grains ranges from 0.00001 to 0.0004 cm, silt 0.0004 to 0.006 cm, sand 0.006 to 0.2 cm, and pebbles 0.2 to 6.4 cm. Which kind of sedimentary rock is Rock C? Explain your answer.

4. In Rock A, which two minerals did you estimate make up over 50% of the rock? Which minerals make up the remainder of the rock?

5. In Rock B, which two minerals did you estimate make up over 50% of the rock? Which minerals make up the remainder of the rock?

6. Turn to the graph on page 61. Which rock in the graph most nearly matches the mineral composition of Rock A? Which rock most nearly matches the mineral composition of Rock B? Explain your answers.

7. Igneous rocks are commonly grouped into mafic rocks and felsic rocks based on their chemical composition. Mafic rocks are dark in color because they contain a number of dark minerals such as amphibole, pyroxene, olivine, biotite, as well as plagioclase feldspar. Felsic rocks are light in color and contain minerals such as quartz and orthoclase feldspar as well as some dark minerals such as biotite and amphibole. Based on these definitions, which rock, A or B, is mafic? Which rock is felsic? Explain your answer.

8. Compare the diagrams for Rock C and Rock D. Look at each rock's texture (i.e. size, shape, orientation and contact points with other crystals). How does the texture differ in the two rock samples?

9. Look at the diagram of Rock E. Is it sedimentary, metamorphic, or igneous? Explain your answer.

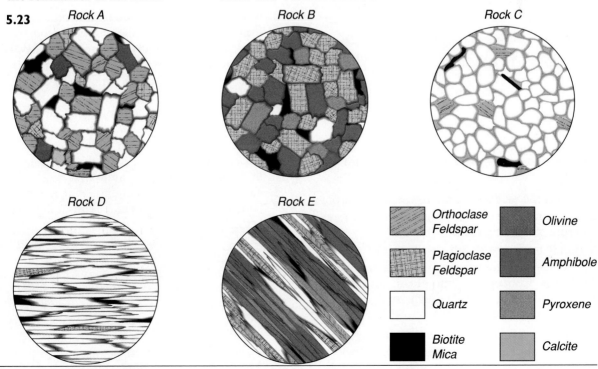

5.23

Rock A

Rock B

Rock C

Rock D

Rock E

Orthoclase Feldspar

Plagioclase Feldspar

Quartz

Biotite Mica

Olivine

Amphibole

Pyroxene

Calcite

CHAPTER

5 REVIEW

Answers to all questions appear in the Teacher's Guide at the back of this book.

■ Summary

I The same processes that form and shape Earth's crust today also formed features in the past. This is the principle of uniformitarianism.

Plutonic igneous rocks form from magma deep in the crust and have distinct mineral grains. Volcanic igneous rocks form from lava at or near the surface and lack distinct grains.

Felsic magmas form light-colored, silica-rich rocks such as granite. Mafic magmas form dark-colored, ferromagnesian-rich rocks such as basalt.

Igneous rock texture depends mainly on the rate at which magma cools. The slower magma cools, the coarser the texture. A porphyry is a rock with two distinct textures.

Igneous rocks are grouped into families by mineral composition. Each family has members with different textures.

II Sedimentary rocks are grouped by the kind of sediment from which they form: clastic, chemical, or organic.

Clastic sediments are often sorted by water action before pressure and mineral cements turn them into rock.

Sedimentary rocks often occur in visible layers. These form when different sediment types are deposited on top of each other.

Fossils, ripple marks, mud cracks, nodules, concretions, and geodes are all features of sedimentary rock layers.

III Metamorphic rocks are formed when heat or pressure or both change the density, minerals, and structure of existing rocks.

Regional metamorphism results from the heat and pressure of mountain-building and affects large areas. Contact metamorphism results when hot magma is in contact with rock; it affects small areas.

The rock cycle shows how the formation of igneous, sedimentary, and metamorphic rocks are interrelated.

■ Vocabulary

chemical	plutonic
clastic	porphyry
contact	regional
metamorphism	metamorphism
felsic	rock
fossils	sedimentary
igneous	stratification
mafic	texture
magma	uniformitarianism
metamorphic	volcanic
organic	

■ Review

On your paper, write the word or words that best complete each sentence.

1. The principle of uniformitarianism states "The present is the _____ to the past."
2. Molten rock underground is called _____.
3. Depending on where they form, igneous rocks are _____ (intrusive) or volcanic (extrusive).
4. Depending on their mineral composition, igneous rocks are felsic (silica-rich) or _____ (ferromagnesian-rich).
5. Igneous rocks that cool slowly in the crust are likely to have a _____ texture.
6. A rock with two different textures is a _____.
7. Quartz and _____ are the two most important minerals in the granite family.
8. The most important member of the gabbro family is the fine-grained rock from lava flows, _____.
9. _____ rocks are classified as clastic, chemical, or organic.
10. Silica, calcite, and iron are natural _____ that bind sediments into sedimentary rocks.
11. When streams drop sediments, heavy pebbles and gravels are left near shore, but _____, silt, and clay are left farther away.
12. A sedimentary rock made of rounded pebbles and sand grains is called _____.

For further review, see **Study Guide.**
For assessment, see **Chapter Tests**
and **Computer Test Bank.**

13. A sedimentary rock made of tiny calcite grains or of fossil shell bits is _____.
14. When different kinds of sediments are laid down on top of each other, _____ results.
15. A _____ is some evidence of a plant or animal, preserved in rock.
16. The bedding planes of some sedimentary rocks show ripple marks and _____ cracks.
17. A lump of silica that forms in limestone is called a _____.
18. If sedimentary or igneous rocks are subjected to heat and pressure, they become _____ rocks.
19. Regional metamorphism affects a large area, while _____ metamorphism affects only a small area.
20. _____ forms when limestone undergoes metamorphism.
21. Three metamorphic rocks that form from shale are _____, phyllite, and schist.
22. In the rock cycle, igneous rocks weather to form _____, which becomes sedimentary rocks.

■ Interpret and Apply

On your paper, answer each question in complete sentences.

1. Using the terms *felsic*, *mafic*, *plutonic*, and *volcanic*, compare each pair of igneous rocks. (a) granite and gabbro (b) granite and rhyolite (c) gabbro and basalt (d) rhyolite and basalt
2. Why are fossils more likely to be formed in shale and sandstone than in conglomerate?
3. Why are fossils less likely to be found in metamorphic rocks than in the sedimentary rocks from which those metamorphic rocks formed?
4. Explain several ways of distinguishing white marble from white quartz.
5. If the heat and pressure of regional metamorphism caused a rock to melt, would the rock that results still be considered a metamorphic rock?

■ Critical Thinking

The graph shows a classification system for sandstones that are made of varying amounts of three minerals: kaolin, feldspar, and quartz. Each corner shows a rock made up of 100% of the named mineral. The side opposite the same corner shows rocks with 0% of that mineral, but 100% of the other two. Determine the composition of a sandstone by finding the amount of each mineral in that sandstone. For example, to find the amount of feldspar at point X, start at the "0% Feldspar" side. Count the red lines from this side to point X. There are 5 lines. Each line is 10%; point X is on the 50% feldspar line. Likewise, it is on the 30% kaolin line, and the 20% quartz line. It also falls within the graywacke area. Thus, point X shows a graywacke with 50% feldspar, 30% kaolin, and 20% quartz.

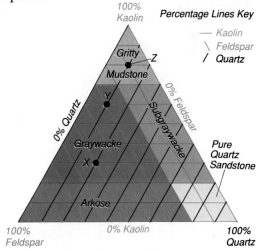

1. What is the composition and name of the sandstone at point Y?
2. What is the composition and name of the sandstone at point Z?
3. A sandstone has 40% quartz, 30% feldspar, and 30% kaolin. What kind is it?
4. Oriskany Sandstone is an oil and gas source in New York and Pennsylvania. It has 95% quartz, 5% other minerals. What kind is it?

83

Resources and Our Environment

▲
The United States is considered a leader in the development of photovoltaic power plants where mirrors focus sunlight onto solar cells.

How Do You Know That . . .

There are many other sources of energy other than fossil fuels? Some of Earth's resources, such as oil and coal, cannot be replaced once they are used. As supplies are dwindling, it has become important to conserve energy and explore alternative sources of energy. For example, research is being done on alternative energy sources such as wind power, water power, and solar power like the Carissa Plains power station above. The power station uses over 10 000 photovoltaic cells to produce electricity for thousands of homes in the area.

I Renewable Environmental Resources

Topic 1 Renewable versus Nonrenewable Resources

A great deal of attention is being given to the protection of the environment. Earth's **environment** includes all of the resources, influences, and conditions at Earth's surface. Some of the most important resources are basic to life on Earth—air, water, land, and sunlight. Other resources have become vital to the world economy since the late nineteenth century. These include energy resources, such as coal and oil, as well as raw materials, such as metal ores.

Earth's resources can be grouped as renewable and nonrenewable. A **renewable resource** is one that can be replaced in nature at a rate close to its rate of use. Examples are oxygen in the air, trees in a forest, food grown in the soil, and solar energy from the sun.

A **nonrenewable resource** is one that exists in a fixed amount or is used up faster than it can be replaced in nature. These resources include metals such as gold, silver, iron, copper, and aluminum; nonmetals such as sand, gravel, limestone, and sulfur; and energy sources such as coal, oil, natural gas, and uranium. Some geological resources can be reused. However, most of them, especially the energy resources, are destroyed by use.

OBJECTIVES

A Compare renewable and nonrenewable resources.

B Identify the sources of solid and gaseous air pollutants.

C Describe factors that affect the usability of land and soil.

D Identify sources of water pollution.

TEACHING TIP

The difference between renewable and nonrenewable resources is fundamental to the chapter.

Topic 2 Air

Air is a renewable resource. Dry air is made up of about 78 percent nitrogen and 21 percent oxygen. The other 1 percent is made up of argon, carbon dioxide, and other gases.

For living organisms, the two most important gases in the air are oxygen and carbon dioxide. Oxygen is used by all plants and animals in respiration. **Respiration** is the process by which oxygen is combined with food molecules to produce energy, water, and carbon dioxide. Carbon dioxide is used by plants in photosynthesis. **Photosynthesis** is the process by which plants use light to convert carbon dioxide and water into sugars and oxygen. Photosynthesis and respiration restore oxygen and carbon dioxide to the atmosphere almost as quickly as they are used.

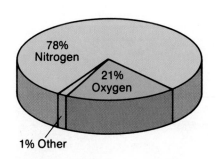

6.1 Nitrogen and oxygen occupy about 99 percent of air by volume. The remaining 1 percent is a mixture of other gases.

VIDEODISC SELECTION

Air pollution
Side 2: 2818, single frame

SCIENCE BACKGROUND
   Sulfur pollutants accelerate the deterioration of iron and steel, zinc, and paint. Sulfur particles are the greatest factor in reduced air visibility. Electric utilities account for about 3/4 of the sulfur dioxide in the eastern United States.

SCIENCE BACKGROUND
   Only 22% of the ice-free land surface is capable of supporting crops without irrigation.

6.2 Cultivation and irrigation are used to increase the productivity of land resources.

Topic 3   Air Pollution

Pollution occurs when some part of the environment is changed in a way that makes it unfit for human, plant, or animal use. As clean air moves across Earth's surface, it picks up materials produced by natural events and human activities. When the concentration of a normal air component or of a new chemical or particulate added to the air builds to the point of causing harm, it is called a *pollutant.* There are hundreds of potential air pollutants, including carbon monoxide, oxides of nitrogen, hydrocarbons, sulfur dioxide, and suspended particulate matter.

Most potential pollutants are the result of human activities. Sulfur dioxide, a poisonous gas that is irritating to the nose and the throat, enter the air when coal and fuel oil are burned. When sulfur dioxide combines with droplets of water in the air, it forms a harmful acid that causes acid rain (Topic 22). The other gas pollutants result mainly from the burning of fuels in car and truck engines. Many gases in the exhaust from such engines are poisonous. The nitrogen oxides and hydrocarbon gases form smog.

Natural sources of air pollutants include forest fires, dust from soil, pollen, volcanic eruptions, and sea spray. Pollutants from these sources, however, rarely reach high enough concentrations to cause serious environmental damage.

Topic 4   Land and Soil

About 29 percent of Earth's surface is land. How humans use land depends on a number of factors. Factors include the land's steepness, the local climate, and whether the soil is suitable for growing food. One use of land is as a foundation for buildings. Not all land is suitable for this purpose. If the land is too soft, too hilly, or in an area with a hostile climate, it will generally not be used to build on.

Soil is a mixture of mineral matter, decaying organic matter, water, air, and living organisms. Together these substances affect soil fertility. **Soil fertility** is the ability of soil to grow plants. The amounts of mineral matter, water, and organic matter in soil determines the kinds of plants that will grow there. Soil that is fertile for potatoes may be less fertile for wheat. In part, this is because potatoes require a different quantity of soil nutrients and water than wheat does. Soil is generally thought to be a renewable resource. In this case, renewable means that the nutrients can be replaced by natural and artificial fertilizers.

Soil is used to grow the rooted plants needed by humans and other animals to live. Cultivated soils provide the grains, fruits, and vegetables needed for human nutrition. Trees, which provide timber for buildings and fuel, also grow on soil. Grasses grown on soil provide food for livestock. However, less than 25 percent of Earth's land can be used to grow crops. Rough terrains, such as mountain regions, often have no soil cover. Temperature and available water also affect how humans use land. Polar regions are too cold to grow crop plants, while desert regions are too hot and dry.

6.3 Severe environmental conditions such as droughts have a serious impact on the renewability of land resources.

Topic 5 Problems in Land and Soil Use

Although soil is generally thought of as renewable, several problems limit its renewability. When the average rate of topsoil erosion exceeds the rate of topsoil formation on a piece of land, the soil becomes a nonrenewable resource that is being depleted. *Erosion* of soil by flowing water or wind (Chapter 8, Topic 11) is most prevalent on steep slopes or where plant cover has been removed by farming or by farm animals. Lost soil is difficult to replace. Topsoil is renewed at a rate of a few inches every thousand years. In many areas, topsoil is eroded at a few inches every decade. If agriculture is to remain productive, soil erosion must be controlled.

A second problem in land and soil use is **soil depletion.** Plants grown as crops use certain nutrients in the soil as does natural vegetation. When vegetation dies, the nutrients are returned to the soil. When crops are harvested, however, the nutrients are removed from the soil. Over time, soil can become so lacking or depleted in nutrients that it will no longer grow a usable crop. The problem of soil depletion can be managed through good farming practices. Fields can be left to rest. A crop can be allowed to return to the soil, or the kind of crop grown on a field can be changed from year to year. These practices are not always followed, however, because they can be very expensive in the short term.

Salinization is a problem in desert areas. With the addition of water, some desert soils are very fertile. However, water brought in to irrigate a desert contains minerals. The dry air of the desert causes the water to evaporate rapidly. When this happens, minerals in the water, such as salt, are left behind on the soil surface. In time, the soil contains so much mineral matter that crops can no longer be grown. Such soil is difficult to reclaim.

Finally land itself is a limited resource. In most cases, using land for one purpose prevents it from being used for any other purpose. Areas with the most fertile soil are often the same areas on which people want to build their houses. In some areas of the world, the conflict between using land for housing and land for crops is a critical problem. In Japan, about 85 percent of the land surface is mountainous. The amount of land suitable for farming and housing is quite limited. Therefore, the bulk of the Japanese population, including farmers, live on the same 15 percent of the country.

SCIENCE BACKGROUND

The population density of New Jersey is 380 people per square kilometer of land, while Wyoming has a density of only 1.9 people per square kilometer. The average population density for all of Japan, including less-populated mountain regions, is 317 people per square kilometer.

TEACHING TIP
Be prepared to explain that salt water is not drinkable and that boiling it does not make it drinkable. Both are common misconceptions among students.

Topic 6 **Water**

Water, essential to all life forms, most clearly distinguishes Earth from other planets. Over 70 percent of Earth's surface is covered by water. About 97 percent of Earth's total water supply is found in the oceans. Ocean water is too salty for drinking, and growing crops, and for most industrial purposes. Most uses of water require fresh water found in lakes, rivers, and in the ground. The supply of fresh water is continually replenished by the natural water cycle (Chapter 9) and therefore is considered a renewable resource.

Water resources are not evenly spread around Earth because of the differences in average annual rainfall. Some areas have too little fresh water and others too much. With varying degrees of success, humans have tried to correct these imbalances by capturing fresh water and redistributing it. In addition, there is also an attempt to reduce water use.

Two problems increasingly plague water supplies. First is the problem of quantity. Supplies are being depleted while demands for industry, agriculture, and expanding populations are increasing. The second problem is quality. Like air, water can be polluted.

Roughly half of the United States receives sufficient rainfall to supply rivers and lakes with drinking water. The other half taps groundwater reserves held in geologic formations called aquifers (Chapter 9). In many regions, domestic, industrial, and agricultural uses are making demands on these supplies that neither the surface water nor the groundwater can supply indefinitely.

Topic 7 **Water Pollution**

Pressure on water supplies is compounded by pollution from both industrial waste and domestic waste. Pesticides, sewage, oil leaks and spills, and contaminated water all find their way into the water supply. Even though soil and wetlands remove some impurities in groundwater, pollutants do remain. It is especially difficult for groundwater to clean itself once it becomes polluted.

6.4 Poisonous waste flows into this polluted river. Notice the strange color of the water.

Phosphates and nitrates from fertilizers and detergents enter lake water and lead to the unusual growth of some algae and other microscopic organisms. Oxygen-using organisms eat the algae and multiply rapidly. The oxygen of the lake is then used up faster than it can be replaced. When this happens, fish and other animals in the lake die from lack of oxygen. This process called **eutrophication** also occurs in some rivers.

Harmful germs from sewage may pollute water and can cause diseases such as cholera and hepatitis. In towns where sewers are connected to storm drains, the sewage also contains toxic metals and oil washed from roads.

Poisonous waste from factories that ends up in lakes and rivers can cause a build-up of poisons in fish that live there. The poisons, pesticides, lead, mercury, and other by-products of industrial processes also can kill birds that feed on the fish.

Not all water pollutants are actual substances. Thermal energy is also a water pollutant. Water from streams and lakes is used to cool electric power plants by absorbing excess thermal energy. Nuclear power plants, in particular, use tremendous amounts of water to cool reactors. When the warmer water is put back into the streams or the lakes, it harms the plants and the animals living there.

6.5 Phosphates can cause water plants like this algae to grow too much.

TOPIC QUESTIONS

Each topic question refers to the topic of the same number.

1. **(a)** What are renewable resources? List some examples. **(b)** What are nonrenewable resources? List some examples.

2. **(a)** How is oxygen used by living things?   **(b)** How is oxygen returned to the air?   **(c)** How is carbon dioxide used by living things?   **(d)** How is carbon dioxide returned to the air?

3. **(a)** When is the environment considered to be polluted? **(b)** Give examples of common air pollutants.   **(c)** What are some natural sources of pollutants?

4. **(a)** List some factors that make land or soil difficult to use. **(b)** What determines soil fertility?

5. **(a)** Why is eroded topsoil so difficult to replace?   **(b)** What is soil depletion? How can it be controlled?   **(c)** How does salinization occur?   **(d)** Describe the conflict between farming and housing.

6. **(a)** List some sources of fresh water.   **(b)** Describe two problems facing the water supply.

7. **(a)** Describe how eutrophication occurs.   **(b)** Describe some ways other than eutrophication that water can become polluted.

ANSWERS

1. (a) can be replaced at reasonable rate; air, trees, food, solar energy   (b) used faster than replaced; mineral and some energy resources

2. (a) in respiration   (b) through photosynthesis   (c) in photosynthesis (d) through respiration

3. (a) when harmful substances make it unfit for life   (b) carbon monoxide, hydrocarbons, sulfur dioxide, and suspended particulates (c) forest fires, soil, pollen

4. (a) rough terrain, poor climate, poor soil   (b) amount of minerals, water, and organic matter it contains

5. (a) takes thousands of years to replace it   (b) loss of soil nutrients; fertilization   (c) water evaporates, leaving salts behind   (d) areas with most fertile soil are often areas with most people

6. (a) lakes, rivers, groundwater (b) quantity due to overuse and quality due to pollution

7. (a) accidental nutrient enrichment   (b) thermal pollution, factory wastes, acid rain

OBJECTIVES

A Define the terms *ore mineral,* *mineral resource,* and *mineral reserve.*

B Identify the ores and uses of various metals.

C Identify various nonmetal resources and their uses.

TEACHING TIP

Remind students that gold, silver, and copper are examples of native minerals, which can occur in an un-combined state in a rock.

6.6 Gold often occurs in association with quartz.

VIDEODISC SELECTION

Strip and open pit mines (described in disc directory)
Side 2: 2746 to 2752, 7-frame sequence

II Nonrenewable Resources: Metals and Nonmetals

Topic 8 Minerals and Ores

All metallic elements and many important nonmetallic elements can be obtained from minerals. Some of the elements are attached to other elements. Since these elements are not chemically bound, they are easily separated. Gold and silver are good examples of such elements. More commonly, the metal or nonmetal is combined with another substance. It must then be chemically separated to be useful. In either case, the needed element is often only a small part of the rock in which it occurs.

If the rock has enough of the element to make the separation profitable, the rock is called an ore. Iron ore and copper ore are examples of rocks from which elements can be removed. The valuable mineral is called the **ore mineral.** The rest of the rock is the **gangue** (gang). Quartz, feldspar, calcite, and dolomite are common gangue minerals.

Mineral resources are nonrenewable. Thus, it is important to know how much of each resource is available for the future. Surveys have been made for this purpose. In these surveys, the amount of a *resource* is an estimate of the total amount of the mineral thought to exist. Mineral **reserves** are the amount of known deposits of a mineral in ores that are worth mining at the present time. Knowing how fast a particular mineral is being used makes it possible to figure out about how long the supply will last.

Ores deep in the ground are usually removed through underground mines reached by tunnels. Ores close to the surface are removed through great holes called open-pit mines.

Topic 9 Mineral Availability

Estimating how much of a particular resource exists on Earth and how much the resource can be used is a complex and controversial process. It is difficult to make reliable estimates of the total available amount of a particular resource because the entire world has not been explored for each resource. Most estimates of the available supply of a particular resource refer to reserves. *Reserves* are resources that have been found and can be extracted at a profit using current technology.

The future availability of a mineral resource depends on its actual supply as well as on how rapidly this supply is being depleted. For large consumers, such as the United States, demands for resources must take into account how costly it is to extract and process the resources for use.

The United States is one of the largest producers and consumers of mineral resources. However, despite its rich resource base, the United States imports a large percentage of its important metals.

Metals are used in a wide variety of ways. Iron is a metal essential to steel production. Steel is used to make large structures such as skyscrapers, bridges, tunnels, ships, planes, and trains. Steel also is used for objects as small as pins and for stainless steel utensils. Copper is used in electrical wiring and in making brass. Aluminum is used for cans, and cookware and in lightweight structural materials. Zinc is combined with copper to make brass. Zinc is also used to coat iron and steel to prevent rusting. Lead is used in storage batteries, solder, and the shielding around radioactive materials.

Figure 6.8 shows the location of the major areas of mineral resources throughout the world. The reserves of many of these minerals could be used up within the next 60 years if present rates of use continue. Some metals are scarce in the United States and must be entirely imported. Examples of such metals include platinum, magnesium, cobalt, chromium, tin, and nickel.

6.7 Gigantic open-pit copper mine in Montana

OF INTEREST

   Economically important metal ores that must be imported by the United States are called strategic metals.

6.8 Major mineral resources occur throughout the world.

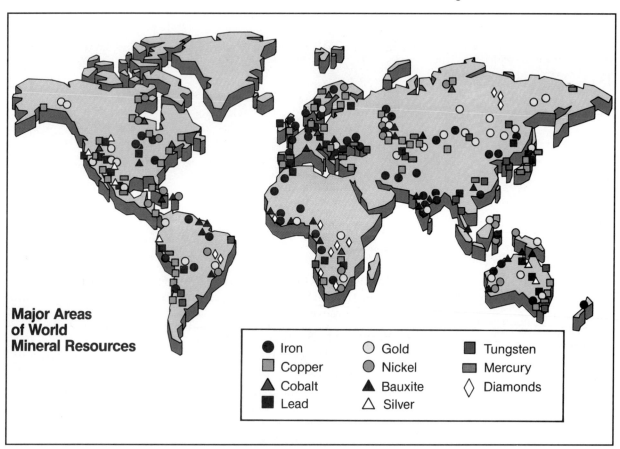

Major Areas of World Mineral Resources

● Iron	○ Gold	■ Tungsten
■ Copper	● Nickel	■ Mercury
▲ Cobalt	▲ Bauxite	◇ Diamonds
■ Lead	△ Silver	

SCIENCE BACKGROUND

One reason that sand and gravel are plentiful in the northern U.S. is because of extensive deposits left by glaciers.

VIDEODISC SELECTION

Sandstone and limestone quarry
Side 2: 2765, single frame

6.9 Salt is a nonmetal mineral resource. Salt can be mined from the earth or extracted from sea water.

Topic 10 **Important Nonmetals**

Unlike most metallic minerals, most nonmetallic mineral resources are used in the form in which they come out of the ground. Little treatment is needed to extract them from other compounds. The main nonmetallic resources are such simple materials as sand, gravel, building stone, rock salt, talc, and graphite.

Sand, gravel, and crushed stone come from quarries. A quarry is a small open-pit mine where these materials occur naturally. The United States has enough of these construction materials.

Materials used as soil fertilizers are also nonmetals. These include phosphate rock, potash, and nitrates. All are mined or produced in the United States.

Salt is plentiful in the United States, with mines in New York, Michigan, Ohio, Texas, and Louisiana. It is an important raw material in the chemical industry. Salt is also used for melting ice from highways and for preserving foods. Gypsum is a common mineral used to make plasterboard and other plaster products.

Sulfur occurs as a native element in the salt mines of Louisiana and Texas. Sulfur is used as a soil conditioner, as a fungicide, and in the manufacture of sulfuric acid. Graphite, a form of carbon, is used in dry cells and as a lubricant. Talc is crushed to make talcum powder and is used as a filler in paints and rubber.

TOPIC QUESTIONS

Each topic question refers to the topic of the same number.

8. **(a)** What is an ore mineral?   **(b)** What is the gangue?   **(c)** What is the difference between mineral reserves and mineral resources?

9. **(a)** Describe what reserves are.   **(b)** What are iron and copper used for?   **(c)** Identify some metals that the United States must import.

10. **(a)** How do most nonmetallic mineral deposits differ from metallic mineral deposits?   **(b)** List some nonmetal materials used in construction.   **(c)** What are phosphate rock, potash, and nitrates used for?

ANSWERS

8. (a) valuable part of ore   (b) rest of rock   (c) reserves—deposits that are economically workable; resources—total known deposits

9. (a) resources that have been found and can be removed for a profit   (b) iron—essential for steel;copper—electrical wiring and brass (c) platinum, magnesium, cobalt, chromium, tin, nickel

10. (a) come from ground ready to use   (b) sand, gravel, crushed stone   (c) fertilizers

III Nonrenewable Energy Resources

Topic 11 Energy Use

Energy is defined as the ability to do work. Water, wind, animals, and even human muscles can supply energy for work. People's use of energy has increased dramatically in the last century. At one time wood, which can be burned for heat, light, and cooking, was the major source of energy in the world.

Today the world's use of energy is greater than ever. Yet only 7 percent of that energy comes from renewable sources like water power and wind. The rest comes from nonrenewable sources of energy such as coal, petroleum, and natural gas.

Coal, petroleum, and natural gas are called **fossil fuels** because they formed from the remains of plants and animals that lived long ago. Burning these fuels releases the energy stored in them. Fossil fuels are nonrenewable because they are burned at rates millions of times faster than they are forming today.

Topic 12 Fossil Fuels: Coal

Coal is an organic sedimentary rock. It is formed from such plant materials as mosses, ferns, and parts of trees. All organic material contains the elements carbon, hydrogen, and oxygen. When plant or animal materials are buried in swamp waters—usually under sand or clay—they slowly decay. They gradually lose most of their hydrogen and oxygen and are left with most of their carbon. As the sediment ages and is compacted over time, it changes. A compressed mass of plant remains in which the mosses, leaves, and twigs can still be seen is called *peat*. During the time that is needed for peat to form, hydrogen and oxygen are lost. This concentrates the carbon that remains. *Lignite,* a soft brown coal that forms when peat is compressed and aged, is about 40 percent carbon. After millions of years of compression, bituminous coal may form. *Bituminous,* or soft coal, may be up to 85 percent carbon. Soft coal burns readily, but it produces a lot of smoke. Regional metamorphism may change bituminous coal to *anthracite,* or hard coal. Anthracite is about 90 to 95 percent carbon. As the percentage of carbon increases, the amount of energy given off by burning the coal increases.

Deep coal deposits are worked in underground mines. Shallow deposits are worked in open-pit mines called strip mines. The main use of coal in the United States today is to run power plants that generate electricity. Coal is also used in making steel and as a raw material in many chemical factories. World reserves of coal could last hundreds of years at the present rate of use.

OBJECTIVES

A Describe the origin, occurrence, and uses of various fossil fuels.

B Describe how uranium is used to generate electricity.

6.10 The carbon content of different kinds of coal depends on the age of the material and on the heat and pressure that affected it.

VIDEODISC SELECTION

Coal mine in Arkansas
Side 2: 2738, single frame

Topic 13 Fossil Fuels: Petroleum and Natural Gas

The word *petroleum* means "rock oil." Petroleum, like coal, is a sedimentary material of organic origin. It is a mixture made mainly of liquid hydrocarbons, which are compounds of hydrogen and carbon. Gasoline and kerosene are hydrocarbons.

Scientists think that petroleum was formed by slow chemical changes in plant and animal materials buried under sand and clay in shallow coastal waters. Some of the hydrocarbons formed were liquids, and some were gases. As the sediments became compacted, the hydrocarbons were squeezed into pores and cracks of nearby sandstones or limestones. These rocks also contained sea water. The lighter, mixed hydrocarbon liquids (petroleum) rose above the water, and the natural gas collected above the petroleum.

Why haven't the petroleum and gas kept rising and escaped from the rock in the millions of years since they formed? Probably a good deal did. The petroleum found today was sealed in by an impermeable rock layer, such as shale. Such rock structures are called *oil traps*. Figure 6.11 shows the most common kind of trap, the anticline, or upfold.

6.11 Oil and natural gas are often found trapped in sedimentary layers that are located beneath a layer of impermeable rock. By drilling through the impermeable layer, the oil and gas can be extracted from the permeable layer.

VIDEODISC SELECTION

Offshore oil drilling platform
Side 2: 2731, single frame

Wells are drilled into oil-bearing rock to release the oil. The pressure of the natural gas helps bring the oil to the surface. Unless the drilling is carefully controlled, the high pressure causes wasteful oil gushers. Even with modern technology, only about 40 percent of the oil is pumped out of a given well.

Natural gas often occurs with petroleum. Yet it may also exist in great deposits of gas alone. It is a mixture of hydrocarbon gases, mostly methane. Natural gas is an efficient fuel for use in heating.

When petroleum is refined, it is separated into many different hydrocarbons. Gasoline is used in automobiles. Kerosene and fuel oil are used for heating. Other oils are used as lubricants. Both petroleum and natural gas are used as the raw material in making such substances as plastics, fertilizers, dyes, and medicines.

The world is extremely dependent on petroleum. While new reserves may be found, petroleum is getting more difficult to locate. Oil companies now drill many wells looking for petroleum beneath the ocean floor.

6.12 (Left) Oil shale contains so much oil that the rock burns. (Right) Offshore wells have produced petroleum and natural gas from beneath the ocean floor.

Topic 14 **Other Fossil Fuels and Gasohol**

Coal and oil are presently the least expensive fossil fuels. In Utah, Colorado, and Wyoming there are vast amounts of oil shale. *Oil shale* contains a high percentage of carbon compounds. When oil shale is heated, oil in vapor form is driven off. The oil vapor can be recovered as liquid oil. At present, this process is too expensive for oil shale to compete with oil from wells.

Another possible source of oil is *tar sand*. Great deposits of tar sands occur in the Athabaska region of Canada. The pore spaces in these sands are filled with tar. This tar seems to be the dried residue of petroleum. Oil can be removed from these sands, but the process is too expensive at present. It is estimated that the amount of oil in the oil shales and tar sands of the world is 50 percent more than the remaining oil resources.

One way to conserve oil resources is to use fuel mixtures that contain smaller amounts of fossil fuel. *Gasohol* is a mixture of gasoline (usually 90 percent) and alcohol from corn or other grain crops (usually 10 percent). Gasohol can be used instead of 100 percent gasoline in auto engines. This reduces the use of gasoline. At present, gasohol costs more than gasoline. However, the mileage an automobile gets per gallon of gasohol is greater than that per gallon of gasoline.

VIDEODISC SELECTION

Sample of oil shale and oil shale outcrop
Side 2: 2724 to 2725, 2-frame sequence

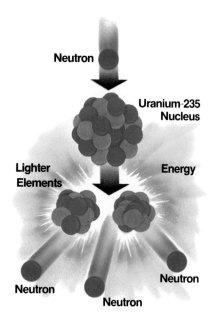

6.13 An atom of a certain isotope of uranium, U-235, can be made to split (fission) by hitting it with neutrons.

6.14 The energy released by fissioned uranium atoms can be used to generate electricity.

Topic 15 Uranium

Although uranium is not a fossil fuel, it is a fuel, that is, a source of energy. It is used in nuclear reactors to generate electricity. Uranium is a metal. Energy is obtained from certain kinds of uranium during a reaction that can be triggered within the nucleus of the uranium atom. Such a reaction is called atomic fission. The chain of events in atomic fission is illustrated in Figure 6.13. The fission of one gram of uranium releases as much energy as the burning of nearly 3 tons of coal or 14 barrels of oil.

A nuclear power plant can be used to produce electricity. In a nuclear power plant, uranium is fissioned in a special vessel called a nuclear reactor. Water under high pressure is pumped through the reactor. The energy given off by the fission reaction heats the water. This hot water is used to heat other water, which becomes steam. The steam is pumped into turbines, which generate electricity. This system is quite similar to the one used when electricity is generated from coal. In both cases, the fuel (either uranium or coal) turns water to steam. The steam then runs a turbine.

The main ores of uranium are the black mineral *uraninite* and the yellow mineral *carnotite.* Both are oxides of uranium. Uranium is the fourth most important source of energy, behind oil, natural gas, and coal, in the world today. At present rates of use, United States uranium reserves will last about 30 years.

There are problems with nuclear energy. Fission creates radioactive waste that must be stored away from living things for thousands of years. The waste must never leak. This means storing the waste in a dry place far from people and in an area free of faults.

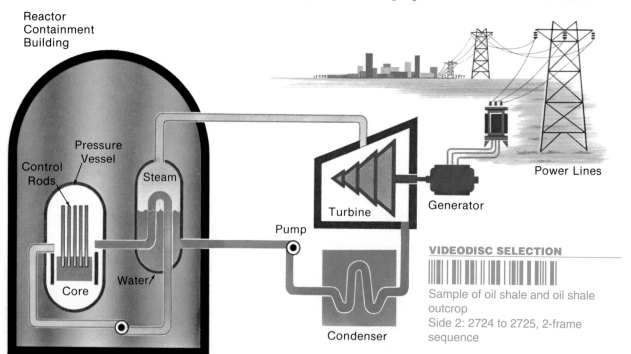

VIDEODISC SELECTION

Sample of oil shale and oil shale outcrop
Side 2: 2724 to 2725, 2-frame sequence

Topic 16 **Energy Conservation**

Currently the world relies on nonrenewable resources for most of its energy needs. As energy needs increase, the worlds supply of fossil fuels will continue to be used at a much faster rate. Dwindling fuel supplies and rising fuel prices make it important for everyone to consider energy conservation and energy alternatives.

There are three general methods of energy conservation. First, reduce energy consumption. This can be done by changing energy-wasting habits. For example, walk or ride a bicycle for short trips, arrange car pools when possible, wear a sweater indoors in cold weather to allow a lower thermostat setting, and turn-off unneeded lights.

Second, use less energy to do the same amount of work. For example, install better insulation in buildings so that less energy is required to maintain temperatures, keep car engines tuned, and switch to more energy-efficient cars, houses, and appliances. Switching lamps to compact fluorescent bulbs can provide the same amount of light while using less energy and saving money.

Finally, use less energy to do more work. Industry and government can make long-term investments in developing new machines that waste less energy or use alternative energy.

Conservation is the largest and cheapest source of energy currently available. By conserving energy, fossil fuel supplies will last longer, and there will be more time to develop alternative energy sources like those discussed in the next lesson.

TOPIC QUESTIONS

Each topic question refers to the topic of the same number.

11. **(a)** Define *energy* and list some sources of energy. **(b)** Define *fossil fuel.* **(c)** Why are fossil fuels considered nonrenewable energy sources?

12. **(a)** Describe the formation of coal. **(b)** What are the main uses of coal in the United States?

13. **(a)** What is petroleum and how does it form? **(b)** What is an oil trap? **(c)** What are some products of refined petroleum?

14. **(a)** How is uranium used as an energy source? **(b)** Explain how a nuclear reactor generates electricity. **(c)** How does uranium rank as an energy source in the world today?

15. **(a)** How is oil removed from oil shale? **(b)** What is tar sand? **(c)** What is gasohol? **(d)** Explain why oil shale, tar sand, and gasohol are not commonly used at present.

16. List three methods of energy conservation.

ANSWERS

11. (a) ability to do work; water, wind, animals, humans, wood, fossil fuels   (b) form from plant and animal remains   (c) used faster than replaced

12. (a) plant remains age, decay, are compressed and/or metamorphosed   (b) electricity, steel making, in chemical factories

13. (a) mixture of compounds of hydrogen and carbon; from plant and animal remains   (b) rock structure containing oil and gas   (c) gasoline, kerosene, fuel oil

14. (a) when fissioned, releases huge amounts of energy to run generator   (b) energy heats coolant water, which turns other water to steam, which runs turbine   (c) fourth behind oil, natural gas, and coal

15. (a) heating and condensing (b) sands with tar-filled pores   (c) mixture of gasoline and alcohol   (d) Gasoline is less expensive.

16. reduce consumption, use less energy for same amount of work, less energy for more work.

OBJECTIVES

A Identify and describe properties of renewable energy sources.

B Describe the advantages and disadvantages of various alternative energy sources.

IV Alternative Energy Sources

Topic 17 Renewable Energy Sources

Some energy resources are replaced in nature almost as fast as they are used, and are said to be renewable resources. Water power, wind power, solar energy, and geothermal energy are examples of renewable energy sources. Water power is renewed by falling rain. Wind power is renewed every time the wind blows. Solar energy is renewed when the sun shines. Geothermal energy comes from rocks that will be hot for many years.

Each of these energy resources is limited in some way. Water power can be used only in areas where dams can be built for water storage. Wind power can be used only in areas with strong, steady winds. Solar energy varies with the time of day, the season, and the location. Geothermal energy is presently useful only in areas with hot bedrock near the surface. Thus, although these energy sources use no fuel and are nonpolluting, none are usable everywhere.

Topic 18 Water Power

The major use of *water power* today is to produce electricity. Water power is the most efficient way to generate electricity. When burning coal or atomic fission is used, the energy must first heat water to change it into steam. The steam then turns the blades of a turbine to generate electricity. With water power, the turbine blades are turned directly by the moving water. Electricity generated in this way is called *hydroelectric power*. Unfortunately, hydroelectric power can only be used in areas with rivers suitable for damming. Today, only 8 percent of the electricity used in the United States comes from hydroelectric power.

Efforts are underway to generate electricity from tides. The water of Earth's oceans rises and falls with the tides. Water levels can differ from 1 to 10 meters in height. When this water is held back and released slowly, its motion can be used to spin a turbine to produce electricity. Currently, a tidal-powered plant exists at the mouth of La Rance River in France.

SCIENCE BACKGROUND
The states of Washington, California, Oregon, New York, and Arizona are the major hydroelectric producers.

SCIENCE BACKGROUND
Another tidal plant at Annapolis Royal in Nova Scotia, Canada, is being tested to see if the famous Bay of Fundy tides can be used to make electricity.

6.15 Hydroelectric plants produce electricity without burning a fuel; therefore, such plants are nonpolluting.

Topic 19 **Wind Power**

Wind power depends on the force of moving air against a windmill. The amount of power produced depends on the speed of the wind, the diameter of the blades on the windmill, and the efficiency of the windmill. In some areas, vast arrays of windmills, called *windmill farms*, produce significant amounts of electrical energy for their local area. There are problems with using wind power, however. Windmills are noisy. They also interfere with television and radio reception. There is also the problem of energy storage. No good method has been found to store the energy produced during strong winds for use during calmer periods.

Topic 20 **Solar Energy**

Solar energy uses the limitless energy of the sun to provide both heat and electricity. When solar energy is used to heat buildings, the system may be passive or active. In *passive solar heating systems*, the building is designed to collect and store solar energy. For example, a special window might let sunshine into the house but not let heat escape. An outside wall might be made of a material that heats easily in the sunshine and then gives up its heat to the inside of the house. For passive heating systems, important factors include the materials used to build the house, the location of the house relative to the sun, and the landscaping around the house.

An *active solar heating system* has three parts. First, a solar collector facing the sun absorbs heat. This heat is transferred to a storage area. Second, the storage area stores the heat energy until it is needed. Third, a system moves the heat throughout the building. The same system can also be used to heat water and to cool the building in summer.

Solar cells, also known as *photovoltaic cells,* have been used to generate electricity for spacecraft since the start of the space age. These cells convert sunlight into electricity. Recent advances in the design of solar cells may lead to power plants that can produce millions of watts of electrical power.

6.16 Wind can be harnessed by wind generators and used as a source of energy in areas where the wind is consistent and high in speed.

VIDEODISC SELECTION

Wind power sites
Side 2: 2802 to 2806, 5-frame sequence

Solar energy installations (described in disc directory)
Side 2: 2793 to 2801, 9-frame sequence

Aerial view of geothermal power plant
Side 2: 2817, single frame

6.17 Rooftop solar panels are a common sight in some areas of the country.

6.18 At the Geysers power plant in California, naturally occurring, high-pressure steam is used to run electricity generators.

OF INTEREST

The first geothermal power plant was built in Italy in 1904. Other countries that have geothermal power plants are New Zealand, Iceland, Japan, and Mexico.

ANSWERS

17. (a) water and wind power, solar and geothermal energy
(b) water requires swift streams or dams; wind needs strong, steady winds; solar needs steady sun; geothermal needs hot bedrock near surface
18. (a) water hits turbine blades directly, no middle step of boiling water involved   (b) trap water at high tide, release slowly
19. (a) wind speed, blade diameter, efficiency   (b) arrays of windmills used to generate commercial amounts of electricity   (c) noisy, interfere with TV and radio, no method to store extra electricity
20. (a) when building itself is designed to collect and store solar energy   (b) collector, storage area, transport system   (c) convert sunlight to electricity
21. (a) heat from Earth, usually in volcano and geyser regions
(b) uses natural steam   (c) method could be useful anywhere   (d) advantages—no fuel, little pollution; disadvantages—far from people, corrosion, equipment replacement

Topic 21   **Geothermal Energy**

Geothermal energy is heat from the interior of Earth. The heat may be brought to the surface by steam or hot water. If the steam or hot water can be piped into a power plant to run a generator, the geothermal energy is changed into electric energy. Hot water from geothermal areas can also be piped into homes for heating and cooking. Only a few countries generate electricity using geothermal energy. The largest geothermal power plant in the world is in an area called the Geysers, located in California. This power plant is driven by superheated, highly pressurized steam. The steam rises naturally out of deep hot rock. Most other geothermal sources, however, are drilled and controlled like oil wells.

Since hot rock can be found in all parts of Earth's crust at some depth, scientists are thinking of ways to use it at any location. One plan underway at Fenton Hill, New Mexico, involves pumping cold water into an underground reservoir hollowed out in the hot rocks. The water is left underground to warm. Then it is pumped back to the surface to generate electricity and heat homes.

Geothermal energy has many advantages. For example, it needs no fuel, and gives off little pollution. It also has disadvantages. Geothermal power plants are usually far from population centers. The energy must be moved a long way to be used. The superheated steam and superheated water is very corrosive. It requires expensive piping and other equipment. Hot water drawn from the ground must be returned to the ground to prevent cave-ins. For these reasons, geothermal energy presently provides much less than one percent of the world's total supply of energy.

TOPIC QUESTIONS

Each topic question refers to the topic of the same number.

17. **(a)** Identify some renewable energy sources.   **(b)** Describe reasons each resource is limited.

18. **(a)** Why is water power a more efficient method of generating electricity than coal or nuclear energy?   **(b)** Describe how energy can be gained from tides.

19. **(a)** List three factors that affect the amount of energy produced by a windmill.   **(b)** What are windmill farms?   **(c)** What are some disadvantages in using windmills?

20. **(a)** What is a passive solar heating system?   **(b)** List the parts of an active solar heating system.   **(c)** What do solar cells do?

21. **(a)** Describe the origin of geothermal energy.   **(b)** Describe the Geysers geothermal power plant in California.   **(c)** What is important about the geothermal energy plant being developed at Fenton Hill, New Mexico?   **(d)** What are the advantages and disadvantages of geothermal energy?

V Environmental Problems and Solutions

Topic 22 **Acid Rain**

A negative result of our modern society is the pollutants emitted into the air by industry. Nitrogen and sulfur oxides are released into the air from the burning of soft coal and from car exhaust. These gases react with water vapor in the air and form drops of nitric acid and sulfuric acid. These polluted drops of rain are quite acidic. This type of precipitation is called **acid rain.**

Acid rain has many harmful effects on the environment. Soils where acid rain falls become so acidic that forest growth is reduced and crops may be harmed. Lakes become too acidic to support fish. Stone buildings and monuments weather rapidly as the fall of acid rain increases.

Acid rain can be lessened by reducing air pollution. Pollution from sulfur dioxide can be cut down by burning low-sulfur fuels. Special equipment can be used to remove particulate and sulfur-bearing gases from the exhaust from factories. Pollution-control devices on cars and trucks can be used to change exhaust gases to harmless substances. In some places where acid rain has already affected the soil and water, lakes and land can be treated with substances to partly neutralize the acid.

OBJECTIVES

A Discuss the causes and effects of acid rain and toxic wastes.

B Identify environmental concerns associated with the use of nuclear reactors.

C Describe several measures that can be taken to conserve nonrenewable resources.

SCIENCE BACKGROUND

Normal rain has a pH of 5.6. The pH of acid rain is about 3.0. It is estimated that about 70% of acid rain is due to sulfur dioxide. Most of the remaining 30% is due to nitrogen oxides.

SCIENCE BACKGROUND

Acid rain has been particularly harmful to lakes in eastern Canada, the northeastern United States, and in Scandinavia. Industrial plants to the west of these locations are the source of the problem.

6.19 Lime is being added to this lake to help neutralize the acid from acid rain.

6.20 Hazardous wastes are extremely dangerous when they are discarded improperly.

Topic 23 **Toxic Wastes**

Toxic wastes are extremely poisonous by-products of some industrial processes. Unlike pollution, these compounds usually do not enter the environment directly but are disposed of at specific locations. Unless disposed of with care, these wastes pollute the soil around them and the water with which they come in contact. For many years, toxic wastes were dumped with little care, and their locations were not recorded. In some cases, houses were on old toxic waste disposal sites. When the toxic waste was later discovered, families had to be moved.

The Environmental Protection Agency (EPA) has identified more than 30 000 places across the United States where toxic wastes have been dumped. All are serious threats to health. Over 1200 of these sites are so bad they have been given priority for action and are scheduled to be cleaned up. Other sites will be added to the priority list as money becomes available. Strict rules now govern the disposal of any toxic wastes.

Topic 24 **Nuclear Waste Disposal**

The use of nuclear reactors leads to two important environmental problems. The first is that nuclear reactors produce by-products that are dangerously radioactive for many years. No satisfactory way has been found for the safe storage or disposal of these nuclear wastes. The second problem is the chance of an accident at a nuclear plant. Such accidents can have awful results. There may be immediate injuries, and the radioactivity may make the area around the plant unfit for people and animals for many years.

Topic 25 **Conserving the Nonrenewables**

At present rates of use, many metallic and nonmetallic minerals are likely to be used up sometime in the next 100 years. The only way to deal with this situation is through conservation. Nonrenewable resources are conserved by cutting down on waste, reusing materials, and coming up with substitutes that use more common materials.

Scrap iron, aluminum cans, and the silver in photographic film are examples of metals that are being reused. Glass is made from sand and other minerals. In many states, bottles are returned for recycling or reuse. Glass fibers are replacing copper wire for lines that carry telephone conversations and computer information. Plastic and fiberglass are used instead of metals in cars, airplanes, and other construction. Research is going on to develop high-technology ceramics for use in automobile engines and industrial applications. These are just a few examples of possible conservation measures.

In the field of energy, conservation of nonrenewable resources depends mostly on more efficient use of fuels. Fuel conservation is discussed in Topic 16.

6.21 Recycling of metals conserves both the metal resources and some of the energy resources that would be needed to process new metals.

Are there any new sources of minerals and fuels that are not yet being used? Oil cannot ever be thought of as a renewable resource. However, new deposits may be found. Most of the present-day search for oil is in areas off the shores of continents. The oceans are also possible sources of many important elements such as manganese, cobalt, copper, nickel, and bromine. Methods still have to be developed to recover these resources in a profitable way.

TOPIC QUESTIONS

Each topic question refers to the topic of the same number.

22. **(a)** How does acid rain form?   **(b)** What effect does acid rain have on the environment?   **(c)** How can acid rain be controlled?

23. **(a)** What are toxic wastes?   **(b)** What agency is responsible for finding and cleaning up toxic waste sites?

24. Identify two problems with the use of nuclear reactors.

25. **(a)** What three things can be done to conserve nonrenewable resources?   **(b)** Give examples of how some resources are being conserved.

ANSWERS
   22. (a) from rainwater dissolving sulfur dioxide and nitrogen gases from air   (b) destroys lakes and forests, affects crops   (c) burn low-sulfur coals, clean industrial and auto exhaust, treat affected lakes and soils
   23. (a) extremely poisonous industrial by-products   (b) EPA
   24. disposal of wastes, nuclear accident
   25. (a) conserve, recycle, develop substitutes   (b) recycling iron, aluminum, glass, silver; using substitutes for metals; more efficient car engines

EARTH**MATTERS**

Using It All Again

Perhaps you've never thought of it this way but the United States being "the richest country on Earth" has a flip-side. The United States is also the country that uses the greatest amount of Earth's resources. In fact, for a country with only 6% of the world's population, the United States accounts for between 40% and 50% of the nonrenewable resources used on Earth each year.

While the United States has made a good start in recycling resources, it has a long way to go to catch up with Japan. The United States recycles about 10% of its trash. Japan recycles over 50%. Why is there such a big difference?

Part of the reason Japan recycles so much is that the Japanese have little land to waste on such things as landfills. If you look at a world map, you will be reminded of how small a land area Japan covers. With no land for dumping, Japan has made it a national priority to reduce the amount of trash and to recycle as much material as possible.

Reducing the space needed for landfills is not the only reason to recycle. Recycling not only conserves nonrenewable mineral resources but also conserves energy. Making a new aluminum can from an old one requires 90% to 95% less energy than making a new can from aluminum ore. Similar energy savings are realized by recycling steel, paper, and glass.

What steps can you take at home and at school to reduce material use or to recycle?

CHAPTER **6**

L A B
ACTIVITY

Measuring Particulate Air Pollution

With each breath you take, not only do you inhale gases such as oxygen and nitrogen, but you also inhale many pollutants. One of the major classes of pollutants are tiny solid and liquid particles that are suspended in the air. These particles are referred to as particulates. Many of these particulates are toxic. Breathing large quantities of these particulates can result in allergies, increased susceptibility to illnesses, and even lung damage.

Some particulates come from natural sources such as pollen, smoke from forest fires, volcanic eruptions, or from dust and debris that is picked up off the ground by the wind. However, many other particulates are a result of human activity. Smoke produced by industry, transportation, and solid waste incinerators place many toxic particulates in the air. Even smoke from wood-burning stoves and cigarettes contain particulates.

Although you often think of high particulate levels as an outdoor problem, particulate levels, can also be a problem indoors. In this exercise, you will compare the levels of particulates around your school. You will compare the particulate levels indoors with the particulate levels outdoors. Once you have measured the particulate levels around the school, you can determine what the likely sources of these particulates are.

Lab Skills and Objectives

■ To **measure** the rate at which solid materials are deposited around your school

■ To **compare** the amount of particulates in the air at different places around your school

■ To **determine** the sources of those particulates

Materials

■ wax pencil
■ 7 microscope slides
■ cellophane tape
■ petri dish
■ compound microscope

Procedure

1. Use a wax pencil to label the slides from 1 to 7. Place a piece of cellophane tape on top of each slide, sticky side up. Fasten the ends of the tape to the slide with two smaller pieces of tape. Do not touch the sticky part of the tape with your fingers.

2. Choose six locations around your school where you think particulate levels may differ. The locations may be indoors or outdoors.

3. Carefully record and describe the location of each slide. Estimate the type and amount of material that you think might be deposited.

4. Use your seventh slide as a control. Place this slide under a fume hood or inside a closed petri dish.

5. Observe slides each day and record any differences. If you place any slide outdoors, cover it when it rains. Record the amount of time each slide is covered.

6. At the end of seven days, retrieve the slides. Be careful not to touch the tape on the slides. Discard any slides that have large objects, such as insects or leaves, on them.

7. Use a microscope to observe the types of particulates that have accumulated on each slide. Briefly describe the size and shape of the particulates.

8. Set the microscope at 100X. Without moving the slide, count all the particulates you see. Record your total count on Data Table A.

9. Move the slide so that you are looking at a second microscope field that does not overlap the first. Count and record that number of particulates. Repeat step 8 two more times and record your data in Data Table A.

10. Calculate the average particulate count on each slide by adding the numbers from your four microscope fields and dividing by four.

11. Subtract the average particulate count on the slide you used as a control, from the average particulate count on each experimental slide. This calculation will give the actual number of particulates deposited on the slides over the seven day period. Record your answer on Data Table A.

12. Calculate the number of particulates deposited per square meter. First multiply the average particulate count for each slide by 62 to give the number of particulates per square centimeter. Multiply the number of particulates per square centimeter by 10 000 to give you the number of particulates per square meter. Record your answer on Data Table A.

13. Calculate the number of particulates deposited per square meter per day by dividing the number of particulates per square meter by the number of days the slides were exposed.

14. Answer the questions in *Analysis and Conclusions.*

Analysis and Conclusions

1. Compare the number of particulates deposited in each area. Where did you find the most particulates? Where did you find the least? How did the numbers compare to your predictions?

2. Based on your description of the particulates, did the types of particulates differ from place to place? Were there significant differences in the particulate levels indoors and outdoors? Explain your answer.

3. What do you think are sources for particulates?

4. What do you think would lead to high particulate levels indoors?

5. The severity of outdoor air pollution often depends on weather conditions. Explain how weather conditions might affect the particulate levels from day to day.

Data Table A							
	Slide 1	Slide 2	Slide 3	Slide 4	Slide 5	Slide 6	Slide 7
Days Exposed							
Field 1							
Field 2							
Field 3							
Field 4							
Average Count							
Average Count – Average Count Control							
Particulates per cm^2							
Particulates Deposited per Day							

Answers to all questions appear in the Teacher's Guide at the back of this book.

■ Summary

I Renewable resources are replaced by nature. Non-renewable resources are not replaced by nature.

Air is a renewable resource, but it also can be polluted.

The usability of land depends on its terrain, climate, and soil. Problems with soil use are erosion, depletion, and salinization.

Fresh water is used for sanitation, farming, and industry. Rain renews the water supply, but water can become polluted.

II Mineral resources are the total amount of a mineral. Mineral reserves are the amount of mineral that can be mined profitably.

Nonmetallic mineral resources are used in the form in which they come out of the ground.

III Fossil fuels form from the remains of plants and animals. Fossil fuels are nonrenewable, yet they are the primary energy source used today.

The atoms of some forms of uranium can be made to fission, releasing energy that can be used to generate electricity.

Oil can be obtained from both oil shales and tar sands, but it is presently too expensive to do so.

IV Renewable energy sources, such as water power, wind power, solar energy, and geothermal energy, use no fuel and do not pollute.

V Acid rain, toxic wastes, and the disposal of nuclear wastes are problems that must be addressed.

Nonrenewable resources need to be conserved and recycled. Alternative energy sources must be developed to slow the use of such resources.

■ Vocabulary

acid rain	ore mineral	salinization
environment	photosynthesis	soil depletion
eutrophication	pollution	soil fertility
fossil fuels	renewable	toxic wastes
gangue	resource	
nonrenewable	reserves	
resource	respiration	

■ Review

Choose the best answer for each question.

1. An example of a renewable resource is (a) gold, (b) oxygen, (c) iron, (d) sulfur.
2. Which substance is returned to the air by photosynthesis? (a) pollen (b) sulfur dioxide (c) carbon dioxide (d) oxygen
3. An example of a solid air pollutant is (a) dust, (b) nitrogen oxide, (c) carbon monoxide, (d) sulfur dioxide.
4. Soil fertility is the ability of the soil to (a) absorb water, (b) release oxygen, (c) support buildings, (d) grow plants.
5. The removal of soil nutrients by crops is (a) salinization, (b) eutrophication, (c) soil depletion, (d) erosion.
6. Which is NOT a source of fresh water? (a) oceans (b) lakes (c) rivers (d) ground
7. Eutrophication results from (a) germs in sewage, (b) phosphate and nitrite enrichment, (c) poisonous wastes, (d) oil spills.
8. The amount of a mineral that can be profitably mined at present is the (a) ore, (b) gangue, (c) resource, (d) reserve.
9. The metal used to make steel is (a) aluminum, (b) copper, (c) iron, (d) lead.
10. A nonmetallic resource used to remove ice is (a) gypsum, (b) salt, (c) sulfur, (d) graphite.
11. Which is NOT a fossil fuel (a) coal (b) oil (c) natural gas (d) uranium
12. Which kind of coal contains the highest percentage of carbon? (a) peat (b) lignite (c) soft coal (d) anthracite
13. Gasoline and kerosene are made from (a) petroleum, (b) natural gas, (c) coal, (d) peat.
14. The energy from fission first (a) turns turbines, (b) cools water, (c) produces electricity, (d) heats water to steam.
15. Which can be removed from tar sands? (a) peat (b) petroleum (c) lignite (d) gas
16. Which is true of renewable energy sources? (a) all use sunlight and water (b) none use up fuels (c) all are usable everywhere (d) all are inexpensive

For further review, see **Study Guide.**
For assessment, see **Chapter Tests**
and **Computer Test Bank.**

17. The most efficient way to produce electricity is by (a) coal, (b) water power, (c) oil, (d) nuclear fission.
18. Wind power depends on (a) splitting atoms, (b) direct sunlight, (c) moving air, (d) heat from Earth.
19. A collector, a storage area, and a transport system are sometimes used in (a) water power, (b) wind power, (c) solar energy, (d) geothermal energy.
20. Geothermal power depends on (a) heat from Earth, (b) direct sunlight, (c) moving air, (d) splitting atoms.
21. Acid rain is NOT (a) a result of air pollution, (b) more acidic than regular rain, (c) good for lakes, (d) reduced by using low-sulfur fuels.
22. The group that watches and cleans up toxic waste sites is the (a) United States Geological Survey, (b) Environmental Protection Agency, (c) Federal Bureau of Investigation, (d) National Science Foundation.
23. Which is NOT a concern with nuclear energy? (a) radioactive wastes (b) chance of accidents (c) storage of wastes (d) poor energy yields
24. Eliminating waste, recycling, and using substitutes are ways of conserving (a) nonrenewable resources, (b) renewable resources, (c) nonrenewable energy sources, (d) renewable energy sources.

■ Interpret and Apply

On your paper, answer each question in complete sentences.

1. Explain why wood is a renewable resource.
2. What kinds of problems would result if everyone heated their homes with wood?
3. The noise level at a pep assembly probably would not be considered noise pollution, but the same noise level in the hallway outside your classroom would. Why?
4. Explain why it is possible to increase reserves of a mineral but not resources of a mineral.

5. Which produces more energy, burning peat or burning an equal volume of anthracite? Why?
6. Each of us can develop an individual plan for saving energy. List some ways that would be easy to save energy. Do any of these things require a change in your daily routine?

■ Critical Thinking

The graph shows the concentration of pollutants per cubic centimeter of air in a city over a two-day period. Use the graph to answer the questions.

1. How does the concentration of pollutants at 6 A.M. Tuesday compare with concentration of pollutants at 6 A.M. Wednesday?
2. At what times does the concentration of pollutants peak on both days?
3. What could be the cause of the pollution peaks on the two days?
4. Falling rain tends to clean pollutants from the air. What evidence is there in the graph that no rain occurred Tuesday?
5. If these trends continue into Thursday, July 12, at what time would the greatest amount of pollutants probably be observed on that day?

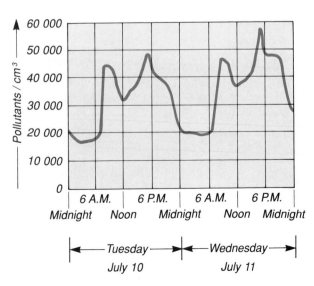

Using Maps

▲
Clockwise from left:
Geologic map, soil types
map, aerial photo,
weather map, navigation
map.

How Do You Know That . . .

Maps are accurate representations? When you use a map, you take
for granted that someone made it carefully. However, there are
problems that mapmakers encounter in producing accurate maps.
See if you can make an accurate map. Try drawing a map to be
used by friends or relatives from another county or state to find
your home for the first time. If you have never done this before,
you may begin to appreciate the work of a mapmaker.

I Map Projections, Location, Scales

Topic 1 Making Accurate Map Projections

A map shows all or part of Earth's surface on a *plane*, or flat surface. Since Earth is a sphere, its surface is like the skin of an orange. Making a map of half of Earth is like making the skin of half an orange fit the flat surface of a table. The orange skin will be distorted, that is, torn or stretched out of shape. Making a single map of the whole Earth is even more difficult and requires more distortion. On the other hand, if a small section of an orange skin is removed, it can be flattened with little distortion. The smaller the area mapped, the less distorted the map will be.

The ideal map would show shapes, distances, and directions correctly, but no map can do all of those things. Still, mapmakers have developed many ways, called **map projections,** for showing the curved Earth on a flat surface. Some map projections show true shapes while distorting distances and directions. Other map projections show true distances and directions but distort shapes. Maps of small areas, however, can be made with very little distortion of any kind.

There are many kinds of map projections. Mercator, gnomonic, and polyconic are three examples. The *Mercator* projection shows the whole world (except the extreme polar regions) on one continuous map. These maps show true directions as straight lines. The

OBJECTIVES

A Describe how three different map projections deal with distortion.

B Describe how longitude and latitude are used to locate points on Earth.

C Define *great circle* and identify a use for great-circle routes.

D Identify three ways map scales are indicated and discuss the differences between a small-scale map and a large-scale map.

SCIENCE BACKGROUND

Maps are also drawn for the planets and their moons as well as for our moon.

SCIENCE BACKGROUND

Some geosciences use maps of Earth's subsurface features.

OF INTEREST

Mercator projections are named for Gerhard Mercator, a sixteenth-century Flemish cartographer and geographer.

7.1 Mapping the entire Earth on a flat surface is difficult because of Earth's spherical shape.

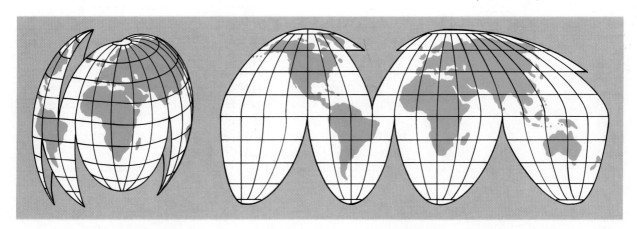

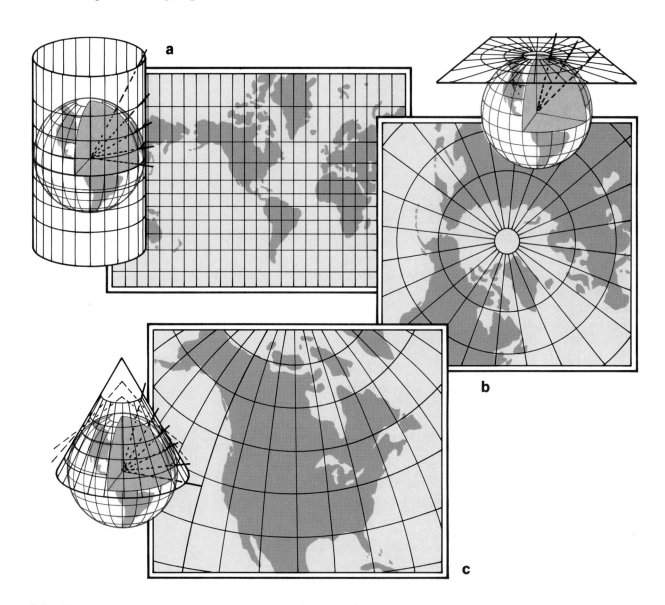

7.2 (a) A Mercator projection shows true direction in straight lines but distorts distance in high latitudes. (b) The gnomonic projection can be used to plot the shortest distance between two points, but direction and distance are distorted. (c) The polyconic projection is a more accurate representation and is useful in making topographic maps.

major problem with a Mercator projection is that high latitudes are enlarged tremendously. For example, a Mercator projection shows the island of Greenland in the North Atlantic Ocean to be nearly the same size as the continent of North America, even though North America is actually about 12 times larger than Greenland.

The *gnomonic* (noe MANH ik) projection is made as if a sheet of paper were laid on a point on Earth's surface. It correctly shows the shortest route between two points on Earth. This projection is useful in planning for long airplane flights and ocean trips. However, directions and distances are distorted.

For small areas, the *polyconic* projection is nearly correct in all respects. This means the lines of latitude and longitude have only a slight curve. Shape and size of landforms are accurate. It is therefore well suited to the making of topographic maps (Topics 6–13).

Usually maps are made with north at the top, south at the bottom, east to the right, and west to the left. In polar view maps, north is toward the center, while east and west are opposite directions around the concentric circles. On any map, however, the location of places on the surface of Earth is shown by means of latitude and longitude (Topics 2 and 3). No matter what projection is used or what distortions a map has, all maps must show the same latitude and longitude for any particular point on Earth's surface.

Topic 2   Latitude: Distance North and South

Latitude is distance in degrees north and south of the equator. Latitude is measured by parallels. **Parallels** are imaginary lines that circle the world from east to west parallel to the equator. The latitude of the equator is zero degrees (0°). The points farthest from the equator are the two poles of Earth, the North Pole and the South Pole. Since the poles are located one quarter of the circular distance around Earth from the equator, their latitudes are 90° N and 90° S, respectively. (One fourth of a circle is 1/4 of 360, or 90.) Latitudes between the equator and the poles have values between 0° and 90°. For example, 30° N and 30° S latitudes mark the locations of parallels that are one third of the way between the equator and each pole. In the same way, 60° N and 60° S latitudes mark the locations of parallels that are two thirds of the way between the equator and the poles.

One degree of latitude is 1/360 of Earth's circumference measured at the poles. The circumference at the poles is about 40 000 kilometers (25 000 miles). Thus, the distance on land of a degree of latitude is about 112 kilometers (70 miles) (40 000 divided by 360 equals about 112 kilometers). Each degree of latitude is divided into minutes, 1 degree latitude (1°) being equal to 60 minutes (60'). Since one minute of latitude is 1/60 of a degree, its length is about 1.85 kilometers (1.16 miles). Notice that the length of degrees and minutes of latitude does not change over Earth's surface.

Topic 3   Longitude: Distance East and West

While the east-west parallels are used to mark off distance north and south on Earth's surface, distances east and west (longitude) are noted with meridians. A **meridian** is a half circle that runs in a north-south direction from the North Pole to the South Pole. The *prime meridian* was declared to be the starting line for the worldwide longitude system. The prime meridian passes through Greenwich (GREN ich) England, as well as through Spain, Algeria, Ghana, Burkina, and Mali. **Longitude** is the distance in degrees east

VIDEODISC SELECTION

Spherical views of Earth and Mercator projection maps
Side 2: 751 to 755, 5-frame sequence

Diagrams of latitude and longitude
Side 2: 3905 to 3906, 2-frame sequence

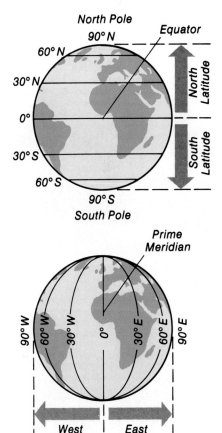

7.3 Latitude is measured in degrees north or south of the equator. Longitude is measured in degrees east or west of the prime meridian.

or west of the prime meridian. The longitude of the prime meridian is 0°. If you move in either direction from the prime meridian, the furthest you can get is 180° away (one half of a full circle of 360°). The 180th meridian (180° east and west) is halfway around Earth from the prime meridian. The half of the world that is west of the prime meridian has west longitude. The half that is east of the prime meridian has east longitude.

Longitude degrees, like latitude degrees, are divided into minutes, and 1 degree of longitude equals 60 minutes of longitude. Unlike parallels, meridians are closer together the farther they are from the equator. There is no set number of kilometers or miles in a degree of longitude. At the equator, 1 degree of longitude is about as long as 1 degree of latitude. Moving toward the poles, the length in kilometers of a degree of longitude gets smaller and smaller, reaching zero at Earth's North and South Poles.

Topic 4   Great Circles

Circles drawn on the surface of any sphere may be either great circles or small circles. A **great circle** is a circle whose plane passes through the center of the sphere. Perhaps it is simpler to say that any circle that divides the sphere in half is a great circle. All other circles drawn on the sphere are called small circles.

On Earth, the equator is a great circle. All other parallels are small circles. Each meridian is half of a great circle. The meridian opposite it in the other hemisphere is the other half of the same great circle. Great circles may also be drawn in slanting positions between the equator and the poles. Think of an orange, which may be cut in half in any direction.

Figure 7.4 shows a *great-circle route* between two points, *A* and *B*, that are on the same small-circle parallel. Great-circle routes are the shortest routes between two points on a sphere. They are almost always the most desirable routes for airplane travel. Great-circle routes between cities at high latitudes pass over or near the poles. To find a great-circle route between any two points on a globe, simply stretch a string between the two points.

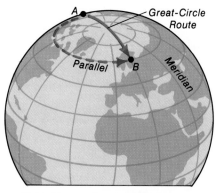

7.4 The great-circle route from *A* to *B* is much shorter than the route along the parallel.

Topic 5   Map Scales

The scale of a map tells how the map compares in size with the piece of Earth's surface that it shows. With many world maps the distortion of distance varies so much over the map that no single scale can be given. Small-scale maps, such as topographic maps, do not have this problem.

A **map scale** is usually defined as the ratio of distance on the map to distance on Earth. This ratio may be shown on the map in three different ways:

1. Verbally as a simple statement, such as "1 centimeter represents 50 kilometers" or "1 inch to 100 miles."

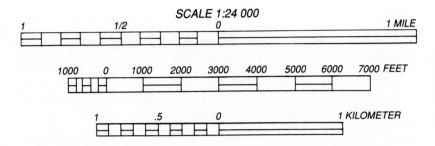

SCALE 1:24 000

| 1 | 1/2 | 0 | 1 MILE |

| 1000 | 0 | 1000 | 2000 | 3000 | 4000 | 5000 | 6000 | 7000 FEET |

| 1 | .5 | 0 | 1 KILOMETER |

7.5 A topographic map has a numerical scale (1:24 000) and three graphic scales (miles, feet, and kilometers).

VIDEODISC SELECTION

Map scales
Side 2: 4077, single frame

2. Graphically by a line divided into equal parts and marked in kilometers, miles, or other units of length.
3. Numerically, usually by writing a fraction to show what part of the true distances the map distances really are. The fraction is known as the representative fraction, or R.F. For example, the scale 1/1 000 000 (also written 1:1 000 000) means that any distance on the map is one millionth of its true length on Earth. This may also be expressed by saying that 1 unit of length on the map represents 1 000 000 of the same units on Earth.

Maps are always much smaller than the pieces of land they show. The more closely the map approaches the land in size, the larger its scale is. A map of the United States on a sheet of paper would have to use a very small scale, such as 1 inch (of paper) to 300 miles (of Earth). On the other hand, a large wall map of the same area would use a larger scale, such as 6 inches (of paper) to 300 miles (of Earth), usually expressed as 1 inch to 50 miles. A still larger scale such as 1 inch to 1 mile would use a sheet of paper 300 feet long (the length of a football field) and almost as wide to show all of the United States.

SCIENCE BACKGROUND

In order to correspond to topographic maps, which use the American system of measurement, the units in this chapter have not been converted to the International system, SI.

7.6 Map scales vary according to the size of the area shown on the map.

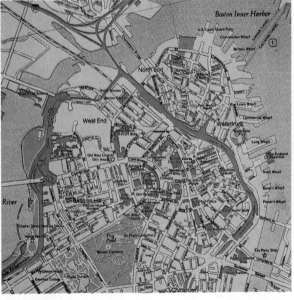

ANSWERS

1. (a) distortion of various values
(b) shape, distance, direction
(c) method of showing curve on a
plane   (d) Mercator—true direction
by straight lines; gnomonic—true distance by straight lines; polyconic—
nearly true shape of small areas
2. (a) N–S distance, by parallels
(b) in order of text: 0°, 90° N, 90° S,
45° N, 45° S   (c) 112 km
3. (a) E–W distance, with meridians   (b) Greenwich, England
(c) opposite prime meridian   (d) Meridians come together at poles.
4. (a) circles that divide Earth in
half   (b) show shortest distances
5. (a) comparison of map size
and Earth size   (b) verbal—1 cm to
50 km; graphic—lines divided into
parts; numerical—1:1 000 000
(c) Large-scale shows more detail of
small area; small-scale shows less
detail of large area.

TOPIC QUESTIONS

Each topic question refers to the topic of the same number.

1. **(a)** What are some problems in making maps? **(b)** What three factors would an ideal map show correctly? **(c)** What is a map projection? **(d)** Name three map projections and identify the features that make each one useful.

2. **(a)** What is latitude and how is it measured? **(b)** State the latitudes of the equator, the North Pole, the South Pole, and the parallels halfway between the equator and the poles. **(c)** How long in kilometers is one degree of latitude?

3. **(a)** What is longitude and how is it measured? **(b)** Where is the starting meridian for the longitude system? **(c)** Where is the 180th meridian? **(d)** Why is there no set distance in kilometers for a degree of longitude?

4. **(a)** What are great circles? **(b)** Why are great circles important in air and ocean travel?

5. **(a)** Explain what a map scale is. **(b)** List three ways of expressing a map scale and give examples of each. **(c)** Distinguish between a large-scale map and small-scale map.

CAREERS

Kathryn Neff
Cartographer

As you have learned, meridians of longitude and parallels of latitude form a system for mapping Earth's surface. Longitude is also used in defining the 24 time zones around the world. According to cartographer Kathryn Neff, the latitude /longi-tude coordinate system is accept-ed worldwide as a means of pin-pointing a unique location on Earth's surface. Ultimately, every-thing that Kathryn Neff and other cartographers do is based on the latitude/longitude system.

As a cartographer in the Office of Research for the U.S. Geological Survey in Virginia, Kathryn Neff is involved with computerizing maps. She works on converting graphic maps into digital maps that can be used by a computer. The use of computer-ized maps represents a new and exciting area of cartography called geographic information systems.

Recently, a county planning department used geographic information systems to help determine the best location for a new school. A cartographer took the existing geographic map of the county and converted it into a digital map. The digital map was fed into a computer along with additional types of information pertinent to the placement of the school. Such data included coun-ty population densities, trans-portation routes, location of waste sites, and industry loca-tions. The computer quickly ana-lyzed all the data and selected the ideal site for the new school. As a result of geographic informa-tion systems, a time-consuming task was completed more quickly and easily!

II   Parts of a Topographic Map

Topic 6   Showing Elevation—Contours

In order to show landforms, maps must show the *relief* (the highs and lows) of Earth's surface. Relief can be shown in many ways, such as shading, coloring, or miniature sketching of landforms. Topographic maps show relief with **contour lines,** that is, lines drawn to connect points at the same elevation (height above sea level). Contour lines show both exact elevations and the shape of the land. Contour lines are best explained by a drawing. Figure 7.7(a) is a sketch of an island in the sea. This island is 6 miles long, 3 miles wide, oval shaped, and 113 feet high at its highest point. In an ordinary map, the island would appear as shown in Figure 7.7(b). The shoreline shows the shape of the island at sea level, and the scale indicates the length and width of the island. However, the map gives no information about the height of the island, how steep it is, or about its shape above sea level.

A mapmaker would survey the island and turn this map into a contour map. The mapmaker would first locate and mark on the map all of the points that were 20 feet above sea level. All points 20 feet above sea level are then joined with a contour line. Every point on this contour line is 20 feet higher than the shoreline. The shoreline is also a contour line—at zero feet above sea level.

Using an interval of 20 feet, a mapmaker then draws contour lines showing where the island reaches the 40-foot, 60-foot, 80-foot, and 100-foot elevations above sea level. The **contour interval** is the difference in elevation between two consecutive contour lines, in this case, 20 feet. Contour intervals differ depending on the relief of the land. If the land is high and steep, a mapmaker uses a large contour interval such as 50 feet or 100 feet. If the land slopes gently or is nearly level, a mapmaker uses a small contour interval such as 10 feet, 5 feet, or even 1 foot. For moderately steep land such as the island, a 20-foot contour interval is used.

Do not confuse the contour interval, which is difference in height, with distance along the ground. The distance along the ground between any two points is found with the map scale. Using the scale in Figure 7.7(d), note that between *A* and *B* the island reached the 20-foot elevation in one mile. Between *C* and *D* the same height is reached in only one third of a mile. Obviously, then, the island is steeper between *C* and *D*. Instead of figuring each time, use the rule that where the contour lines are close, the slope is steep; where the contour lines are far apart, the slope is gentle.

To make the reading of contour lines easier, every fifth line is made heavier and its elevation is marked. The other contour lines are not numbered, but the contour interval is stated at the bottom of the map. Notice that the contour lines show three things—elevation of the land, steepness of its slopes, and the shape of the land at various heights.

OBJECTIVES

A Describe how contour lines show the elevations, shape, and slope of the land.

B Name and compare the two series of topographic maps published by the USGS.

C Identify the meanings of some symbols and colors used on topographic maps.

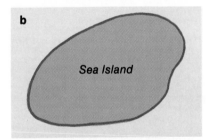

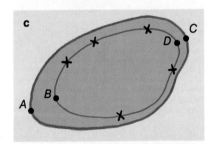

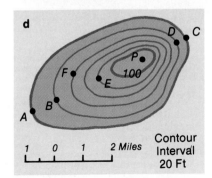

7.7   Mapping a sea island

a   Dead Volcano Island

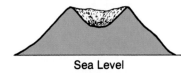

Sea Level

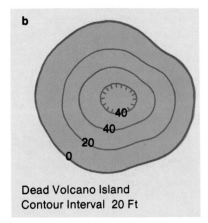

Dead Volcano Island
Contour Interval 20 Ft

7.8 (a) Sketch of an island volcano,
(b) contour map of the same island
with contours showing its crater

7.9 A bench mark is an elevation
reference point for surveyors.

SCIENCE BACKGROUND
   The width in kilometers represented by a topographic map varies
with the latitude of the location
shown by the map.

TEACHING TIP
   Use quadrangle maps from your
own area to show the naming of
sheets as well as the distinction between 15-minute and 7.5-minute
quadrangles.

Topic 7   Depression Contours

Moving inland from sea level does not always result in higher elevations. In climbing a volcano, for example, the highest point is
reached at the rim of the crater. The crater is a lower area, or depression, inside the rim. This lower area is shown on a topographic map
by the use of **depression contours.** These lines are drawn like contour lines but are marked on the inside (Figure 7.8).

   In reading depression contours, the first one is read at the same
elevation as the ordinary contour that comes before it. Thereafter,
each depression contour is lower than the one that comes before it
by an amount equal to the contour interval of the map. If the land
rises in the middle of the depression, this is shown with a regular
contour. In such a case, the first regular contour has the same altitude as the last depression contour that encloses it.

Topic 8   Bench Marks, Spot Elevations

In mapmaking, surveyors find the exact elevation of many points in
the map area. These may be shown on the map in a number of ways.
A **bench mark** point is a location whose exact elevation is known
and is noted on a brass or aluminum plate. This plate is permanently set into the ground at the location surveyed. Bench marks
are shown on the map by the letters *BM*. Numbers give the elevation to the nearest foot. A survey point for which there is no bench
mark is shown on the map by a triangle and the elevation.

   Spot elevations are the elevations of road forks, hilltops, lake
surfaces, and other points of special interest. These points are usually shown on the map by a small cross. Numbers giving elevations
checked by surveyors are printed in black. Unchecked elevations
are printed in brown. Water elevations are shown in blue.

Topic 9   U.S. Geological Survey Maps

The United States Geological Survey (USGS), a branch of the federal government, produces topographic maps of the entire country.
Each map covers a quadrangle area bounded by meridians of longitude and parallels of latitude. Maps with these standard boundaries are called quadrangles. Several series of maps have been
produced. A map series is a family of maps conforming generally
to the same specifications or having a unifying characteristic such
as scale. Adjacent maps of the same quadrangle series can be combined to form a single large map.

   One series of quadrangles is called the 7.5-minute quadrangle
series. This represents quadrangles that cover 7.5 minutes of latitude and 7.5 minutes of longitude. The scale 1:24 000 is most
often used for this series; in this case, 1 inch represents 24 000
inches or 2000 feet. The 1:24 000 scale is fairly large. A large scale
map shows more detail than a small scale map. A map at this
scale provides detailed information about the natural and

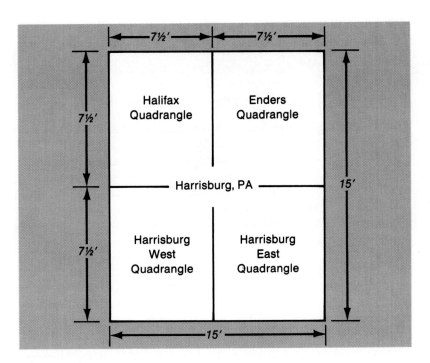

7.10 Four 7.5-minute quadrangles fit into one 15-minute quadrangle of the Harrisburg, Pennsylvania, area.

VIDEODISC SELECTION

Selected USGS topographic contour maps (described in disc directory)
Side 2: 3908 to 3915, 8-frame sequence

human-made features of an area including the locations of places such as campgrounds, caves, and ski lifts.

On topographic maps published by the Geological Survey, the colors in which symbols are printed have been standardized. Contour lines are always printed in brown. Roads, buildings, railroads, and other works built by people are printed in black. Water features—such as rivers, lakes, and swamps—are shown in blue. Many maps show woodland areas in green, highways in red, and densely developed areas such as cities in pink. The features and symbols found on contour maps are detailed in the Appendix on pages 666–667 at the back of this book.

SCIENCE BACKGROUND

The geodetic network on which topographic quadrangles are based was recomputed in 1986 by finding the precise location and elevation of 250 000 points.

TOPIC QUESTIONS

Each topic question refers to the topic of the same number.

6. (a) How are contour lines drawn on maps?   (b) How does a contour map show whether a slope is gentle or steep?   (c) Define *contour interval* and give examples of large and small contour intervals.   (d) Distinguish between the use of the contour interval and the map scale.

7. Explain the meaning, use, and rules for drawing and reading depression contours.

8. (a) What is a bench mark?   (b) How is a bench mark point shown on a map?   (c) What are spot elevations? How are they shown?

9. (a) What are topographic quadrangles?   (b) What is the scale of a 7.5-minute quadrangle sheet?   (c) Describe the use of color on topographic maps.

ANSWERS
  6. (a) by connecting points with same elevation   (b) by distance between contours   (c) difference in elevation between two adjacent contours; large—100 feet; small—5 feet   (d) difference in elevation vs distance on ground
  7. show lower elevation, elevation of first one same as preceding regular contour
  8. (a) permanent plate showing exact elevation of site   (b) BM plus elevation   (c) elevations of special locations; small crosses
  9. (a) maps with standard boundaries described by latitudes and longitudes.   (b) 1:24 000 (c) contours—brown, buildings—black, water—blue, woodlands—green, highways—red, cities—pink

OBJECTIVES

A Use a topographic map to read distances and elevations and calculate the average slope of an area from such information.

B Identify landforms and estimate steepness from contour lines.

C Draw a profile from a contour map.

10°

Magnetic North

True North

Approximate Mean Declination, 1988

7.11 Topographic maps show the magnetic declination of the area they represent.

VIDEODISC SELECTION

Important features of a topographic map

Side 2: 4072 to 4080, 9-frame sequence

III Reading a Topographic Map

Topic 10 Reading the Contour Map

Almost all maps show directions in some way. Most maps show direction with parallels and meridians (Topics 2 and 3). If a map does not show parallels or meridians, the map should have an arrow pointing to the North Pole or true north. Except for a few areas on Earth, a compass points, not to true north, but to the Magnetic North Pole, or magnetic north. The **magnetic declination** is the difference in the angle between true north and magnetic north. This angle is different over Earth's surface. Each topographic map gives the angle of the magnetic declination for the area it shows.

If the scale of a map is given verbally, distances on the map may be measured with a ruler. When a graphic scale is printed on the map, the distance between two points can be marked off with a straightedge, such as the edge of a sheet of paper. A piece of string may also be used. The marked straightedge is held against the scale for reading. Zigzag distances along roads or rivers may be marked off one after the other on the edge of a sheet of paper before measuring against the graphic scale.

When a point is on a contour line, its exact elevation is known. Any point between two contour lines is higher than the last contour line but lower than the next contour line. For example, a point between the 100-foot line and the 120-foot line may be any elevation from 101 feet to 119 feet. The elevation of points between two contour lines can be estimated. For example, a point halfway between the 20-foot and 40-foot contour lines would have an estimated elevation of about 30 feet.

Each elevation given on a contour map represents height above sea level. Only those contour maps that include a seacoast will start from sea level. To figure the elevation of any point, start from the marked contour line that is nearest to that point.

Topic 11 Landforms on Contour Maps

The map distance between contour lines indicates the steepness or levelness of the land. When contour lines are far apart, the land is fairly level. Grassy Terrace in the northwest corner of Figure 7.12, for example, does not have contour lines, so it must be level.

Where contour lines run very close together, the land is very steep. If contour lines coincide, it means that the higher ground is directly above the lower ground. Such contour lines indicate a cliff. An example of this formation is Sheer Cliff in Figure 7.12.

Closed circles or ovals at the end of a rising series of contours show the tops of hills, as at *J, K, L, M,* and *N.* The exact elevation of

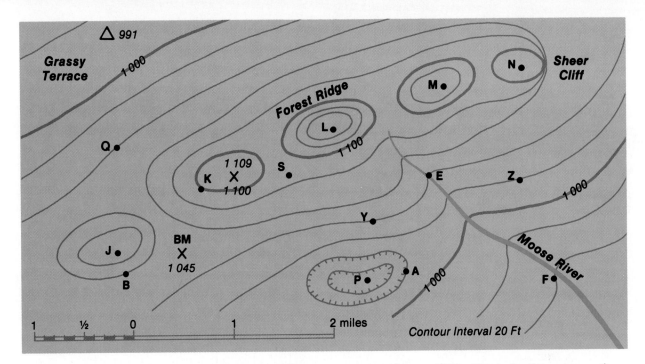

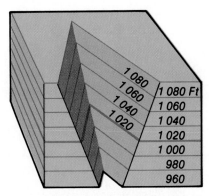

the top of a hill may be indicated, as at *K*. Hills or mountains that are long and narrow are called ridges. These may include a number of peaks. Ridges are shown by long oval contour lines, as at Forest Ridge in Figure 7.12.

Where a river has cut a valley, contour lines plainly show the valley. As each contour line comes near the valley, it can stay at the elevation it represents only by bending in the direction of the high land from which the river flows. This rule may be used to figure out the direction in which a river flows. The direction the river flows can also be figured out by noticing the elevations of marked contour lines. A river flows from higher to lower elevations.

The steepness of a river is shown by the closeness of the contour lines that cross it. The width of a valley is approximately shown by the width of the V made by a contour line where it crosses a river.

Topic 12 **The Average Slope**

The **average slope,** or *gradient,* between any two points of a hill, mountain, river, trail, or road can be determined from a contour map. If you know how many feet the hill drops in a given distance, you can find the average slope using the following equation.

$$\text{Average slope} = \frac{\text{change in elevation (ft)}}{\text{distance (mi)}}$$

Both the drop in elevation and the distance between two points can easily be read from a contour map. For example, a trail is four miles long, as measured by the scale on the map. The beginning of the trail is at the 1060-foot contour, and the end of the trail is at the 960-foot contour. Calculate the average slope of the trail in this way.

$$\text{Average slope} = \frac{1060 \text{ ft} - 960 \text{ ft}}{4 \text{ mi}} = \frac{100 \text{ ft}}{4 \text{ mi}} = 25 \text{ ft/mi}$$

7.12 Simple landforms are easily identified on a contour map.

7.13 Contour lines bend upstream where they cross a river valley.

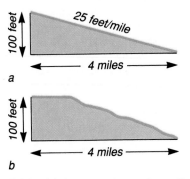

7.14 (a) Average slope of a trail; (b) the actual slope may vary.

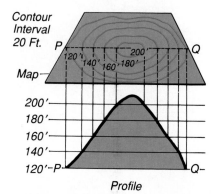

Contour Interval 20 Ft.

Map—

Profile

7.15 A profile—a line showing the changes in elevation across a section of a topographic map—can be made as shown in this sketch.

Topic 13 Profiles from Contour Maps

It is easy to make a **profile** that shows the ups and downs of a line across any part of a contour map. Wherever the line meets a contour, the exact height above sea level is known. Plotting these points on a vertical scale results in a profile.

A profile is done most easily by placing the bottom edge of a sheet of paper on top of the line to be followed. At each point where the line crosses a contour, make a mark on the edge of the paper. Record the height of the contour next to its mark on the paper. When all points are marked, use the vertical scale to raise each point to its proper height. (Plotting is easier if graph paper is used.) Vertical scales are usually stretched out compared to the horizontal scale. This is to make the differences in elevation more visible. An example of a vertical scale is ⅛ inch = 20 feet. Of course, it is important to keep the points the same horizontal distance apart as they were on the map. Once the elevated points have been plotted, they are joined to make the profile.

TOPIC QUESTIONS

Each topic question refers to the topic of the same number.

10. **(a)** How is direction shown on a contour map? **(b)** How is distance measured on a contour map? **(c)** How is the elevation of a point determined on a contour map?

11. How does a contour map show each of the following: **(a)** level areas, **(b)** cliffs, **(c)** hilltops, **(d)** ridges, **(e)** river valleys, **(f)** the steepness of a slope?

12. **(a)** Explain the meaning of the average slope between two points. **(b)** How is average slope determined?

13. **(a)** What does a profile show? **(b)** How is a profile made from a contour map?

Map Skills

The following questions refer to the topographic map of Monadnock, NH, on page 650 in the Appendix.

1. What is the name of the tallest feature on the map?

2. Locate Gap Mountain in the southwest part of the map. Which side of Gap Mountain would be the more gentle climb? How can you tell?

3. Why would a fire lookout be located on top of Monadnock Mountain rather than on top of Gap Mountain?

ANSWERS

10. (a) by north arrow or by meridians and parallels (b) mark straightedge with map scale (c) estimate from nearest contour line
11. (a) contour lines far apart (b) coincident lines (c) closed lines (d) long ovals (e) lines bend toward source (f) closeness of lines
12. (a) steepness; number of feet land drops per horizontal distance (b) change in elevation/distance
13. (a) relief of land (b) on vertical scale, plot points where contours cross profile

ANSWERS

1. Monadnock Mountain
2. west side; contour lines are farther apart, thus slope is not as steep
3. Monadnock is much higher, lookout could see farther

IV   Modern Methods of Mapmaking

Topic 14   **Remote Sensing**

Making an accurate topographic map requires finding the exact location of many points on land. The first topographic maps were made using only *ground survey*. In ground survey, a surveying team collects the necessary data while standing on the ground surface. Each map drawn by ground survey takes a long time to complete. Today, most maps are made by **remote sensing,** that is, by gathering data about the land from above the surface. Remote-sensing data is commonly collected using equipment placed onboard airplanes or satellites. The methods used in remote sensing are quicker, cheaper, and easier than those used in ground surveys. Also, maps made from remote-sensing data are far more detailed and accurate.

The oldest method of remote sensing is **photogrammetry.** This is a method for determining the position and elevation of surface features from aerial photographs. Photogrammetry was used to produce the accurate maps of the moon that made possible the choice of safe landing sites for the *Apollo* missions.

Radar has proven to be a very valuable tool in remote sensing. Unlike aerial photography, radar can be used even when the surface is dark or hidden by clouds. The radar system used to study Earth is called **imaging radar.** Like all radar systems, imaging radar sends out a signal and then "listens" for the signal to echo off Earth's surface. The signal used in imaging radar is aimed, not at the surface beneath the airplane or spacecraft, but off to one side. This scatters the signal and returns many different echoes, instead of just one, to the radar receiver. Called **side-looking radar,** this method provides far more information about the surface than an ordinary radar echo. Computers are used to turn the radar data into images of Earth's surface.

OBJECTIVES

A List and describe some methods of remote sensing.

B Explain the function of a false-color image and identify some uses of computer-drawn images.

VIDEODISC SELECTION

Examples of remote sensing and photogrammetry (described in disc directory)
Side 2: 4251 to 4277, 27-frame sequence

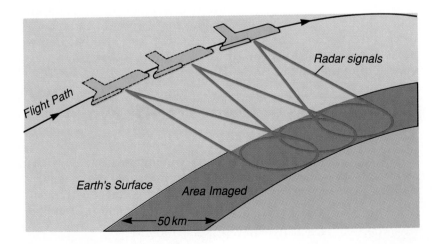

7.16   Side-looking radar involves scattering radar signals from an aircraft. The radar signals bounce back to the craft. Computers process the information into an image.

VIDEODISC SELECTION

Selected *Landsat* images of the
U.S. (described in disc directory)
Side 2: 4279 to 4290, 12-frame
sequence

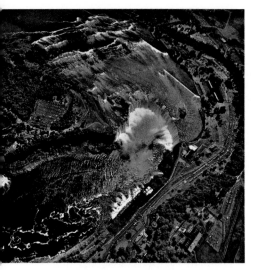

7.17 In this false-color image of
Niagara Falls, calm water is black,
rough water is blue, trees and grass
are red, and buildings are blue-gray.

7.18 This side view of California's
Mount Shasta was generated by a
computer from imaging radar data.

Another method of remote sensing uses optical satellites. These satellites do not take actual photographs of the ground. Instead, they use sensors to detect wavelengths of solar energy reflected from the ground surface. The data collected by the sensors are sent to ground stations as a stream of numbers; then computers turn the data into images of Earth's surface. Once assembled the data can be manipulated. Unique or unusual combinations of reflected light levels can be intensified by computers to reveal features not readily apparent to the human eye. Interesting images have come from a series of satellites called **Landsat.** *Landsat* satellites orbit Earth about 700 kilometers above the surface. Their sensors scan the ground in 185-kilometer wide strips. The location of each strip changes with each orbit of the satellite. In this way, a single *Landsat* can scan all of Earth every 16 days.

Topic 15 **Computer Imaging**

Computer imaging is used to make maps from the data collected by *Landsats* and imaging radar. *Landsat* sensors are designed to detect wavelengths of green, blue, and red visible light and several wavelengths in the infrared spectrum. These wavelengths were chosen so that certain surface features, such as rock structures and kinds of plants, would show more clearly. *Landsat* sensors are more sensitive than the human eye to differences in wavelengths. For example, two wavelengths of light may appear to the eye as the same shade of red. The *Landsat* sensor, however, clearly records the difference. When the image is processed by computer, a different color is assigned to each wavelength. The different colors make each wavelength easier to see on the map. The resulting image is called a **false-color image.** For example, in a *Landsat* false-color image healthy vegetation appears bright red, cities appear blue or blue-gray, and clear water appears black.

False-color images can also be made from radar data. Radar images are made from a signal sent from an airplane or a spacecraft. By processing the radar echo data through a computer, it is possible to draw topographic maps of the surface. Colors are added to the map by the computer to make specific surface features more visible. The radar-imaging data can also be used to make three-dimensional images of features, as if features were viewed from the ground. Such an image is shown in Figure 7.18.

Topic 16 **Uses of Computer-Drawn Maps and Images**

Computer-drawn maps and images have many uses, and new uses are being found all the time. One of the most important is mapmaking. Remote sensing has made it possible to draw highly accurate and detailed maps of even the most remote and inaccessible areas of Earth.

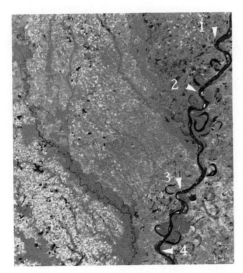 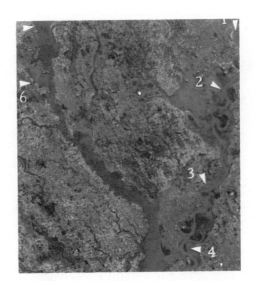

The uses of computer-generated images of Earth go far beyond mapping. In farming and forestry, computer-generated images make it possible to find the health of a particular crop or stand of trees and to estimate the yield of each crop. Remote-sensing methods can help detect hazardous waste-disposal sites, oil slicks, and water and air pollutants. Prospecting for oil and mineral resources is often done using color-enhanced imaging. False-color radar imaging has even detected features below the surface, like ancient riverbeds, that were previously unknown.

Satellite imaging has revolutionized meteorology and oceanography. The weather maps that appear in newspapers and on television are made from data gathered by weather satellites. *Seasat*, a satellite launched in 1978, produced images of underwater mountain ranges and valleys that were previously unknown.

These are just a few of the applications for computer-generated satellite imaging. Remote-sensing data are also used in commercial fishing, wildlife biology, archaeology, military applications, and in monitoring the effects of acid rain. The current uses have only begun to tap the potential information that is available through modern methods of mapmaking.

7.19 Computer images made from satellite data help locate areas of environmental and safety concerns, such as this floodplain area along the Mississippi river. (left) During the dry autumn season, (right) during spring flooding

OF INTEREST

One location where a buried stream channel was discovered was in the desert of Egypt. Later field investigations verified the discovery.

VIDEODISC SELECTION

Computer-generated digital terrain model
Side 2: 4089, single frame

TOPIC QUESTIONS

Each topic question refers to the topic of the same number.

14. (a) How were the first topographic maps made? (b) What is remote sensing? (c) List three methods of remote sensing used today and identify the method by which each collects data.

15. (a) What wavelengths do *Landsat* sensors detect? (b) What are false-color images and why are they used?

16. List some areas of study in which maps and other images generated from remote-sensing data are used.

ANSWERS

14. (a) ground survey (b) data collected from above surface (c) photogrammetry—takes photograph; *Landsat*—reflected solar energy; imaging radar—radar signal

15. (a) red, blue, green, and some infrared (b) computer images in which colors are assigned to various wavelengths; show more detail

16. mapmaking, agriculture, oceanography, geology, pollution control, weather forecasting

CHAPTER 7

M A P
ACTIVITY

Latitude and Longitude

Every point on Earth's surface, including your school, has a unique combination of latitude and longitude. Many cities located east or west of one another share the same latitude. Likewise, there are thousands of locations with the same longitude. Pinpointing a location on Earth's surface requires knowledge of both its latitude and its longitude.

In describing a location, latitude is always stated first followed by longitude. Both are expressed in degrees, minutes, and seconds. For example, the center of Washington, D. C., is located at 38°53′ 51″ N and 77°00′ 33″ W. In practice, readings are rounded to the nearest whole degree. Thus, Washington, D. C., is located at 39°N, 77°W. In this map activity, you will use latitude and longitude to locate cities around the world.

Map Skills and Objectives
- To **interpret** latitude and longitude lines on various maps
- To **identify** cities by their latitude and longitude

Materials
- Earth's Climates map, Appendix B, page 664
- Physical United States map, Appendix B, pages 654–655

Procedure
1. Use the Earth's Climates map on page 664 to identify the city nearest to the following rounded latitudes and longitudes.
   (a) 41°N, 74°W
   (b) 56°N, 38°E
   (c) 12°S, 77°W
   (d) 34°S, 151°E
   (e) 42°N, 12°E
   (f) 26°S, 28°E
   (g) 71°N, 24°E
   (h) 6°S, 107°E
   (i) 40°N, 116°E
   (j) 1°S, 37°E
   (k) 35°S, 59°W
   (l) 61°N, 150°W
2. To the nearest whole degree, estimate the latitude and longitude of the following cities. Be sure to include the correct compass directions (N, S, E, W) in your answer.
   (a) Manaus (South America)
   (b) Tokyo (Asia)
   (c) Barrow (North America)
   (d) Melbourne (Australia)
   (e) Singapore (Asia)
3. Turn to the Physical United States map on pages 654–655. Determine the city nearest to each of the following rounded latitudes and longitudes. Include the state in your answer.
   (a) 37°N, 122°W
   (b) 42°N, 71°W
   (c) 30°N, 95°W
   (d) 30°N, 84°W
   (e) 44°N, 70°W
   (f) 33°N, 117°W
   (g) 46°N, 123°W
   (h) 40°N, 80°W
   (i) 40°N, 105°W
4. Answer the questions in *Analysis and Conclusions*.

Analysis and Conclusions
1. Copenhagen is approximately 13° due north of Rome. Using the conversion given on page 111, determine the distance in kilometers between the two cities.
2. Is it possible for a city to be located at 120°S, 30°W? Explain your answer.
3. How many degrees of latitude separate the cities of New Orleans and Philadelphia? Express your answer in minutes of latitude.
4. Would you travel farther if you drove 2° due east from Bismarck, North Dakota, or from Austin, Texas? Explain your answer.
5. What is the approximate latitude and longitude of your school?
6. The antipode is the location directly on the opposite side of Earth from your location. It is the same distance south of the equator as you are north and on the same north-south great circle. Determine the latitude and longitude of your antipode.

CHAPTER 7

M A P
ACTIVITY

Reading a
Topographic Map

Harrisburg, Pennsylvania, is located in an area of the Appalachian Mountain belt noted for its ridges and valleys. The Susquehanna River cuts through the ridges in the Harrisburg area severing once connected mountain ridges. The Harrisburg Topographic Map that you will use in this activity shows both a section of the river and several ridges. By studying this map, you will learn some fundamental aspects of map reading as well as some interesting features of this scenic area of the Appalachian Mountains.

Map Skills and Objectives

- To **identify** features on a topographic map
- To **interpret** contour lines to determine elevations
- To **evaluate** distance using a map scale

Materials

- Topographic Map: Harrisburg, PA, Appendix B, page 652
- Topographic Map Symbols, Appendix B, page 666
- magnifier (optional)

Procedure

1. Study the Harrisburg map and locate the following features: the Susquehanna River, Peters Mountain (only the letters PETE and the bottom of the letter R appear on the map), Third Mountain, Second Mountain, Cove Mountain, Blue Mountain east of the river, and Blue Mountain west of the river. Based on your observations, which of these mountain ridges appear to have been connected before the Susquehanna cut through them?

2. How does the spacing between contour lines on ridges differ from the spacing between contour lines in valleys? (A magnifier may help.) What does this spacing tell you about the steepness of the land in these areas?

3. The contour interval of the map is 20 feet. What is the elevation of the highest contour line shown on Cove Mountain? Second Mountain? Third Mountain?

4. Locate Fishing Creek on the west side of the Susquehanna River. Look closely at the contour lines along the creek. (A magnifier may help here, also.) How do the contour lines show that Fishing Creek flows into the Susquehanna River?

5. Locate the Rockville Bridge in the lower center of the map. How wide is the Susquehanna River at the Rockville Bridge? (Hint:

Lay the edge of your report sheet along the bridge and mark off both ends of the bridge. Use the map scale on page 650 like a ruler to measure the distance.)

6. Answer the questions in *Analysis and Conclusions.*

Analysis and Conclusions

1. How does color on the map distinguish ridges from valleys? What does this color difference indicate? What is the cause of this difference?

2. If you were standing on the contour line at the base of the Water Gap Observation Tower (upper shore of the Susquehanna River near the left edge of map), could you see the Rockville Bridge on a clear day? Could you see the village of Heckton (east side of the river near the middle of the map)? Explain.

3. (a) Locate the highway that crosses Peters Mountain. Why does the highway jog to the east (toward the Airway Beacon) instead of going straight over the mountain?

   (b) What is the straight line distance, in miles, between the point where the highway crosses Clark Creek and the point where it crosses the Appalachian Trail near the beacon? (Hint: Use the edge of your report sheet as in Procedure step 5.)

   (c) What is the distance along the highway between these same two points? (Hint: Move the edge of your report sheet along the highway.)

Answers to all questions appear in the Teacher's Guide at the back of this book.

■ Summary

I A flat map of a curved surface is distorted. Different map projections are used to minimize distortion of shape, distance, or direction.

Latitude indicates distances north and south of the equator. Longitude indicates distances east and west of the prime meridian.

Map scales compare the size of the map with Earth's surface. Map scales can be verbal, graphic, or numerical, and vary with the size of the area shown by the map.

II Contour lines show the elevations, shape, and slope of the land. Hollows in the land are shown by depression contours.

Some topographic maps are drawn in 7.5-minute series. Colors are used to indicate different kinds of features on topographic maps.

III Direction, distance, elevation, and average slope can be determined from a topographic map.

A map profile shows changes in elevation across a section of a topographic map.

IV The use of remote-sensing methods allows mapmakers to produce accurate maps of many places on Earth.

Computers are used to turn remote-sensing data into detailed maps and false-color images. Satellite images are used in many areas of science and research.

■ Vocabulary

average slope	longitude
bench mark	magnetic declination
contour interval	map projection
contour line	map scale
depression contour	meridians
false-color image	parallels
great circle	photogrammetry
imaging radar	profile
Landsat	remote sensing
latitude	side-looking radar

■ Review

Match the phrases in List **A** with the terms in List **B**.

List A

1. major problem when a flat map is made of spherical Earth
2. map projection used to draw topographic maps
3. distance in degrees north and south of the equator
4. east-west lines used to measure latitude
5. north-south lines used to measure longitude
6. used to locate shortest distance between two points on Earth
7. example of numerical scale
8. line drawn through points with the same elevation
9. used to show craters and hollows on a map
10. places where exact elevations are shown on permanent plates
11. USGS map series
12. angular difference between true north and magnetic north
13. shown by contour lines far apart
14. shown by contour lines close together
15. numerical value for gradient of land surface
16. shows elevation changes across a map section
17. methods include *Landsat* and imaging radar
18. method that enhances different wavelengths

List B

a. average slope	**l.** longitude
b. bench-mark points	**m.** magnetic declination
c. contour	**n.** meridians
d. depression contour	**o.** parallels
e. distortion	**p.** polyconic
f. false-color imaging	**q.** profile
g. gnomonic	**r.** remote sensing
h. great-circle route	**s.** steep land
i. ground survey	**t.** 1:1 000 000
j. latitude	**u.** 7.5-minute
k. level land	quadrangle

For further review, see **Study Guide.**
For assessment, see **Chapter Tests**
and **Computer Test Bank.**

■ Interpret and Apply

On your paper, answer each question in complete
sentences.

1. Globes are true representations of Earth's surface. Why aren't they used instead of maps?
2. Where are north, south, east, and west on a
   gnomonic projection of the Southern Hemisphere? (Figure 7.2 shows map projections.)
3. Why are high-latitude polar regions enlarged
   on a Mercator projection? (Figure 7.2 shows
   map projections.)
4. A map is drawn so that 1 centimeter on the
   map represents 100 meters along the ground.
   What is the numerical scale of this map? Is
   this a large-scale or a small-scale map? (Note:
   There are 100 cm in 1 m.)
5. For places in the Northern Hemisphere, the
   southern edge of a topographic map is slightly
   wider than the northern edge. Explain why
   this is so.
6. What is the average slope between two points
   that are 5 kilometers apart and differ in elevation by 200 meters?
7. Answer questions a through i about Figure
   7.12. (a) What is the maximum elevation of
   hilltops *J*, *L*, *M*, and *N*? (b) How high are
   points *S*, *Y*, *Z*, *A*, and *B*? (c) What is the
   height, from base to top, of Sheer Cliff?
   (d) From *L*, in what directions are *J*, *N*, *Q*, and
   Y? (e) In what direction does Moose River
   flow? (f) At what elevation does Moose
   River start? (g) How many feet on the
   average does Moose River drop per mile?
   (h) How far is it from *Q* to *Y*? (i) What is
   the feature at *P* called? What is the lowest
   possible elevation for *P*?

■ Critical Thinking

The profile below was drawn from a topographic
map. Use the profile to answer questions 1–6.

1. What is the difference in elevation between
   point *B* and point *A*?
2. What is the map distance between point *B* and
   point *A*?
3. Determine the average slope in feet per mile
   between point *A* and point *B*.
4. Determine the average slope in feet per mile
   between point *C* and point *D*.
5. The relief of an area is the difference between
   the highest and lowest point. What is the total
   relief of the profile?
6. The vertical exaggeration of a profile is the
   amount by which the vertical scale is expanded compared to the true scale. The horizontal scale in feet is the true scale. Compare
   the vertical scale with the true scale. What is
   the vertical exaggeration of this profile?

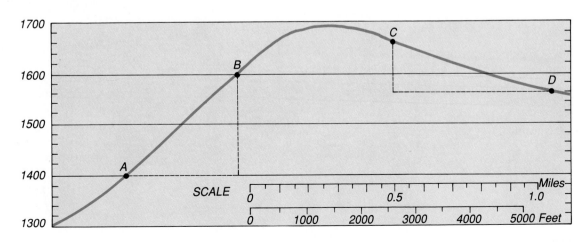

Water cascades over a cliff. How does running water shape the land? ▶

◀ This hole suddenly appeared in Florida. It grew larger for weeks, swallowing cars, swimming pools, and homes. How did it begin?

These houses were built on the ground, well away from the water's edge. What happened to the land beneath them? ▶

What wears away Earth's surface?

Earth's surface is under attack. Hard rains pound the land. Swift streams tear chunks out of mountains. Glaciers grind out valleys. Ocean waves rip up shorelines. Gravity pulls rocks and soil down hillsides, burying roads and damming rivers. What evidence does each photograph show of the constant attack on Earth?

Much of North America was once covered by huge masses of ice. How did the ice affect the landscape?
▼

In moments, this highway was buried under a mass of soil and rock that took days to clear away. What forces cause such a change? Can such changes be predicted? ▶

SLOWER
TRAFFIC
KEEP
RIGHT

129

Weathering, Soils, and Mass Movement

▲
The older photograph shows how Cleopatra's Needle appeared in 1880, when it first arrived in New York. The newer photograph shows the monument as it appears today.

Air and moisture affect rocks? The photographs show a monument called Cleopatra's Needle. It was carved in Egypt around 1450 B.C. The sides of the monument are carved with hieroglyphs, the writing of ancient Egypt. Cleopatra's Needle stood in the dry, hot Egyptian desert for over 3000 years. During all that time, the hieroglyphs remained distinct. In 1880, the monument was moved to New York City. Almost immediately, the hieroglyphs began to fade. In only a few years in the wet and variable climate of New York, the Egyptian writing became indistinct.

I Weathering

Topic 1 **Weathering and Erosion**

Cleopatra's Needle was carved from granite, a hard, tough, crystalline rock. Although it is tough, granite is changed by the atmosphere. Some of the minerals that make up granite change to clay. Chips and flakes of minerals break away from the granite surface. In other rocks, minerals may slowly dissolve. Eventually the surface of all rocks crumbles, or weathers. **Weathering** is the break-up of rock due to exposure to the atmosphere.

Why do rocks weather? Weathering of rocks is due in part to the difference between conditions at depth and conditions at Earth's surface. Rocks like granite form deep underground where pressure is great and temperatures are high. When these rocks are raised to Earth's surface, the pressures and temperatures are much less. Water and oxygen, which are lacking deep within the crust, are present at the surface.

What happens to materials that form by weathering? Typically those materials do not stay in place. For instance, rain or wind can move them from the rock face. Gravity may pull them to lower levels. Finally these materials can wash into a stream and be carried to the ocean. The rain, wind, and stream are all agents of erosion. **Erosion** is the removal and transport of earth materials by natural agents. Other agents of erosion include glaciers (ice in motion) and waves or ocean currents (water in motion).

Topic 2 **Types of Weathering**

Weathering includes many processes. These processes are grouped under two headings—mechanical weathering and chemical weathering. **Mechanical weathering,** or disintegration, takes place when rock is split or broken into smaller pieces of the same material without changing its composition. The breaking of a rock cliff into boulders and pebbles is an example of mechanical weathering.

Chemical weathering, or decomposition, takes place when the rock's minerals are changed into different substances. Water and water vapor are important agents of chemical weathering. The formation of clay minerals from feldspar is an example of chemical weathering.

OBJECTIVES

A Explain why weathering occurs, distinguish between weathering and erosion, and name several agents of erosion.

B Distinguish between mechanical and chemical weathering and identify processes by which each occurs.

C Discuss the effect of weathering on several common minerals and rocks.

D Identify some factors that control the rate at which a rock weathers.

OF INTEREST

Monuments in the shape of Cleopatra's Needle are called obelisks. By definition, an *obelisk* is any four-sided pillar that tapers gradually upward and is topped by a pyramid. The Washington Monument is another example.

VIDEODISC SELECTION

Weathering and erosion
Side 2 movie: 9921 & PLAY

SCIENCE BACKGROUND

Even in a desert, chemical weathering may be more effective than mechanical weathering.

VIDEODISC SELECTION

Mechanical weathering: tree root splitting rock
Side 2: 1956, single frame

SCIENCE BACKGROUND

In some areas, the formation of salt crystals in cracks may break rocks apart. Like ice, salt crystals require room for formation and exert great forces as they form.

OF INTEREST

Alternate wetting and drying is the standard technique for disintegrating fine-grained sedimentary rocks with clay minerals in order to remove tiny fossils unharmed.

SCIENCE BACKGROUND

Burrowing animals also bring rock fragments to the surface, where the fragments weather more rapidly.

8.1 The process of ice wedging was partly responsible for the damaging cracks that formed in the porous rocks shown on the right.

Mechanical weathering processes and chemical weathering processes are often studied separately. However, the two processes seldom occur alone. The fact that water vapor is present in the air almost everywhere means that chemical weathering occurs almost everywhere. In different parts of the world, one process may be more important than the other. However, mechanical and chemical weathering almost always act together.

Topic 3   Types of Mechanical Weathering

Mechanical weathering happens in many ways. Common mechanical weathering processes are frost action, wetting and drying, action of plants and animals, and the loss of overlying rock and soil.

Water takes up about 10 percent more space when it freezes. This expansion puts great pressure on the walls of a container. For example, think about a pail of water left outdoors in freezing weather. The force of freezing water may split the pail. In the same way, water held in the cracks of rocks wedges the rocks apart when it freezes. This process is called **ice wedging,** or frost action. Ice wedging often occurs in places where the temperature varies from below the freezing point of water (0°C) to above the freezing point. In the northern United States and in other places in which there are frequent freezes and thaws, ice wedging is the most damaging of all weathering processes.

Ice wedging occurs mostly in porous rocks and in rocks with cracks in them. Bare mountaintops, especially, are subject to ice wedging. Vast fields of large, sharp-cornered boulders are often found on such mountaintops. Ice wedging also causes potholes on paved streets and highways. Here it is helped by *ice heaving.* Ice heaving happens when water in the ground freezes and lifts the pavement above it. When the ice thaws, the pavement collapses, leaving the pothole.

Repeated *wetting and drying* is especially effective at breaking up rocks that contain clay. Clays swell up when wet and shrink when dry. Constant swelling and shrinking causes rocks that contain clay, such as shale, to fall apart.

Small plants, such as lichens (LIE kens) and mosses, grow on rocks. They wedge their tiny roots into pores and crevices. When

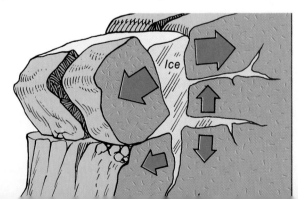

8.2 When lichens grow on rocks, their tiny roots act like wedges to split the rock. Lichens also release acids that dissolve minerals.

VIDEODISC SELECTION

Mechanical weathering: frost heaving
Side 2: 1950, single frame

SCIENCE BACKGROUND

Sheet structures may extend 75 meters down into a rock. This is far too deep for chemical weathering processes to be a factor. At the rock's surface, however, chemical weathering processes probably assist exfoliation.

VIDEODISC SELECTION

Mechanical weathering: exfoliation on Half Dome, Yosemite Park, California
Side 2: 1962, single frame

the roots grow, the rock splits. Larger shrubs and trees may grow through cracks in boulders. Ants, earthworms, rabbits, woodchucks, and other animals dig holes in the soil. These holes allow air and water to reach the bedrock and weather it.

Granite is a rock formed far below Earth's surface. It is exposed when large masses of rock are lifted up to form mountains and the rocks above the granite are worn away. The removal of the rocks reduces the pressure on the granite. When this happens, the relief from pressure lets the granite expand. Upward expansion leads to long curved breaks, or *joints*. The joints are parallel to the surface and occur in exposed peaks or outcrops. This process is *sheet jointing*. From time to time, large sheets of loosened rock break away from the outcrop. This process is called **exfoliation**—the peeling of surface layers. Rounded mountain peaks called exfoliated domes are formed in this way. In the United States spectacular exfoliated domes occur in Yosemite National Park, California. Other famous granite domes are Stone Mountain in Georgia and Sugarloaf Mountain near Rio de Janeiro, Brazil.

a

8.3 **(a)** Sheet jointing on a granite outcrop produces cracks in the rock, thereby exposing more of the rock surface to weathering. **(b)** Half Dome in Yosemite National Park, California, is an exfoliation dome.

b

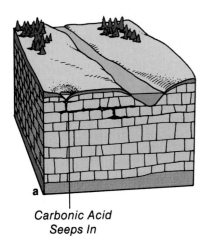

Carbonic Acid
Seeps In

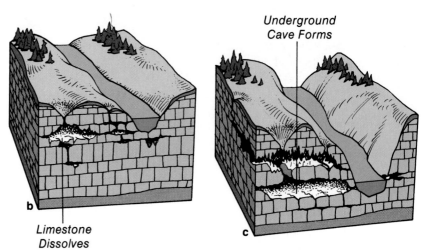

Underground
Cave Forms

Limestone
Dissolves

c

8.4 When carbonic acid seeps into bedrock made of minerals that dissolve easily, such as calcite, the bedrock dissolves and is carried away. The result is an underground cavern.

TEACHING TIP
Remind students that all chemical weathering processes involve water.

8.5 Carbonic acid created this cave by dissolving limestone bedrock. (Luray Caverns, Virginia)

Topic 4 Chemical Weathering

Chemical weathering of rock results mainly from the action of rainwater, oxygen, carbon dioxide, and acids of plant decay. There are several ways in which these chemical agents work.

The chemical reaction of water with other substances is called **hydrolysis.** Common minerals that undergo hydrolysis include feldspar, hornblende, and augite. When these minerals are exposed to water, they slowly unite with it and form clay.

The chemical reaction of oxygen with other substances is called **oxidation.** Iron-bearing minerals are the ones most easily attacked by oxygen. These include magnetite, pyrite, and the dark-colored ferromagnesian silicates—hornblende, augite, and biotite. Oxidation of these minerals results in kinds of rust, or iron oxides. If the iron in these minerals combines with oxygen alone, the rust is the red iron oxide hematite. When water is also present, rusting occurs more quickly, and the brown rust limonite is formed. The hematite and limonite formed by weathering are often the reason for the reddish and brownish colors of soils and rocks at exposed surfaces.

Carbon dioxide dissolves easily in water. When it does, it forms a weak acid called **carbonic acid.** This compound is the acid in carbonated soft drinks. Carbonic acid attacks many common minerals, such as feldspar, hornblende, augite, and biotite mica. The acid dissolves out elements such as potassium, sodium, magnesium, and calcium. When this occurs, the original mineral is changed into a clay mineral.

Carbonic acid has a greater effect on calcite than on the minerals listed above. Carbonic acid dissolves calcite completely. Unless the calcite is impure, no clay is left over. The dissolving action of carbonic acid has hollowed out great underground caverns in limestone bedrock. Gypsum and halite also dissolve, slowly but surely, in carbonic acid.

Acids that are formed by the decay of plants and animals are dissolved by rainwater and carried through the ground to the bedrock. Like carbonic acid, these acids attack minerals.

Carbon dioxide and sulfur compounds released by industries unite with water in the atmosphere to form acid rain (Chapter 6, Topic 21). Increasing amounts of acid rain in the environment increases the rate of chemical weathering.

Chemical weathering occurs most quickly at the corners and edges of rock outcrops and boulders. These areas are more exposed to chemicals. This process rounds the rock and is called *spheroidal* (sfir OY dl) *weathering.* Boulders rounded this way are spheroidal boulders.

Topic 5 **Which Minerals and Rocks Resist Most?**

There are several overall effects of weathering on the major rock-forming minerals and their rocks.

Quartz does not react very much to water, oxygen, or acids. It is almost unchanged by chemical weathering. Because it is hard and does not have cleavage, it also resists mechanical weathering. In time, however, quartz is broken into pebbles and sand grains.

Feldspar, hornblende, biotite mica, augite, calcite, and gypsum are all affected by chemical and mechanical weathering. Mechanical weathering breaks these minerals into small fragments. Chemical weathering turns these fragments into clay minerals. Some minerals, such as calcite, gypsum, and halite, are also dissolved and carried off in solution.

Most igneous rocks and many metamorphic rocks weather more rapidly in wet climates than in dry ones. These rocks often have cracks that are widened by mechanical weathering. They contain minerals that are easily attacked by chemical weathering. The first weathering products from igneous and metamorphic rocks are

8.6 Acids from decaying plant and animal matter dissolve in rainwater and chemically attack minerals.

SCIENCE BACKGROUND
  The decomposition of vegetation forms humic acid.

8.7 Some rocks are more susceptible to mechanical and chemical weathering than others. This can result in strange erosional patterns.

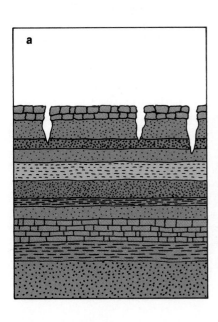

SCIENCE BACKGROUND

Quartz, although very resistant to solution, does dissolve. Chert nodules, geodes, and petrified wood contain quartz that has been dissolved and redeposited.

VIDEODISC SELECTION

Chemical weathering: oxidized basalt
Side 2: 1952, single frame

Butte as example of resistance to weathering
Side 2: 7372, single frame

Bryce Canyon, Utah
Side 2: 2991 to 2996, 6-frame sequence

8.8 Weathering and erosion by rainwater has occurred along weak vertical joints, resulting in this spectacular formation in Bryce Canyon, Utah.

boulders, pebbles, sands, and some clay minerals. In time, even boulders are turned into clay. Pebbles and sands may also be left if the rocks contain quartz or other chemically resistant minerals.

Sandstones, quartzites, and quartz-pebble conglomerates are only as durable as the cements that hold them together. When the cement gives out, the rocks fall apart into the grains that make them up. Rocks cemented with calcite are subject to faster weathering. Rocks that are cemented with silica (quartz that dissolved and reformed as cement) are more durable. Quartzites and silica-cemented sandstones and conglomerates are among the most lasting of all rocks.

Shales, weakest of the sedimentary rocks, split easily between layers. In time they crumble into the clays from which they were formed.

Marbles and limestones are fairly resistant to mechanical weathering. However, the calcite that makes up marble and limestone undergoes slow attack by acids in water. In moist climates there is much dissolved acid, and rocks made of calcite are less durable than quartzites or sandstones. In dry climates there is very little dissolved acid, and limestones may be among the most durable of rocks.

Topic 6 **The Rate of Weathering**

There are several factors that affect the rate of weathering. One is that rocks themselves weather at different rates. Less-resistant rocks, such as shale, are weathered away relatively quickly. More-resistant rocks, such as granite and gneiss, take much longer to weather away. When rocks of different resistance are in the same place, spectacular landscapes are sometimes formed. An example is seen at Bryce Canyon in Utah (Figure 8.8). Each rock layer in Bryce Canyon has its own rate of weathering. In some places, remnants of more-resistant rock have protected the layers of less-resistant rock beneath. The taller formation in Figure 8.8 has a cap of more-resistant rock.

An important factor that affects the rate at which rock weathers is the amount of rock surface that is exposed. When a rock is broken into smaller pieces by mechanical weathering, the rock has more surface area. This means that more surface is exposed to chemical weathering. Thus, breaking a rock into smaller pieces causes the rock to weather away faster.

Climate is also an important factor in rock weathering. In general, warm, wet climates favor chemical weathering processes. Cold or dry climates favor mechanical weathering processes.

Keep in mind the fact that, under average conditions, weathering is a very slow process. For example, it is estimated that limestone dissolves as little as one twentieth of a centimeter in a hundred years. At this rate, it would take 60 million years to dissolve away a 300-meter layer of limestone. During the same time, however, other weathering processes would remove far more rock.

TOPIC QUESTIONS

Each topic question refers to the topic of the same number.

1. **(a)** Why do rocks weather? **(b)** Distinguish between weathering and erosion. **(c)** Identify some agents of erosion.

2. **(a)** Define mechanical weathering and give an example. **(b)** Define chemical weathering and give an example.

3. Explain how rocks are weathered by **(a)** frost action, **(b)** plants and animals, **(c)** wetting and drying, and **(d)** unloading of overlying rock.

4. **(a)** What substances cause chemical weathering? **(b)** Explain how rocks are weathered by hydrolysis, oxidation, and natural acids. **(c)** How do spheroidal boulders form?

5. **(a)** Which rocks and minerals are affected mostly by mechanical weathering? **(b)** Which rocks and minerals are affected mostly by chemical weathering? **(c)** Why do igneous and metamorphic rocks weather rapidly in wet climates? **(d)** What factor determines the resistance of sedimentary rocks?

6. Identify three factors that control the rate at which a rock weathers.

ANSWERS

1. (a) differences between depth and surface conditions (b) weathering—breakup of rocks; erosion—removal and transport of weathered material (c) streams, glaciers, winds, waves and currents, gravity

2. (a) disintegration; breaking cliff into boulders (b) decomposition; formation of clay from feldspar

3. (a) water in cracks expands as it freezes (b) plant roots in cracks grow; burrowing animals help air and water to reach bedrock (c) clays swell when wet, shrink when dry (d) rock expands from pressure release

4. (a) water, oxygen, carbon dioxide, acids of plant decay, and acid rain (b) In order: reaction with water to form clay; reaction with oxygen; dissolves mineral (c) weathering of boulder corners and edges

5. (a) feldspar, hornblende, biotite, augite, quartz; igneous and metamorphic (b) calcite, marble, limestone, weak clastic sedimentary rock (c) cracks subject to mechanical, contain minerals subject to chemical (d) durability of cement

6. kind of rock, particle size/surface area, climate

EARTH**MATTERS**

Acid Weathering

The sculptor who created this statue intended for his design to last for centuries. The rock used should have withstood the normal effects of weathering. Yet it clearly has not. The statue is being dissolved at a rate that has noticeably increased in the last century. The reason for the greater rate of weathering is acid rain.

Rain's natural ability to dissolve materials is boosted by the presence of more acid. Statues and tombstones made of marble dissolve more rapidly in acid rain. Perhaps more importantly, it is possible that acid rain is to blame for the some of the damage being experienced by roads and bridges. It can cause concrete to break apart much faster than expected. Acid rain may also be lead to increased rusting or corrosion of the metals used in bridges and building supports.

The United States Park Service has conducted tests over a period of years, placing sample stones outdoors and then observing the stones to determine how quickly the surfaces weather. Rainwater that runs off the stones is collected and checked for dissolved calcium.

What interest would the National Park Service have in studying ways to prevent acid rain-related weathering of stone and metal surfaces?

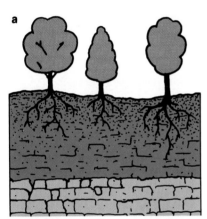

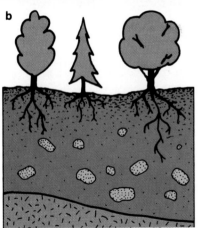

8.9 **(a)** The parent material for residual soil is the underlying bedrock. **(b)** Transported soil is formed from deposits left by wind, water, or a glacier. Notice that it does not resemble underlying bedrock.

II Soils, Mass Movements, and Soil Conservation

Topic 7 Soils: Result of Weathering

Weathering has attacked the rocks of Earth's surface since the beginning of geologic time. It has helped to wear down mountains and to shape countless landforms in this and past ages. Weathering has led to valuable mineral deposits and materials for sedimentary rocks. Most important, it has helped form a priceless resource — Earth's life-supporting soil. Without soil there could be no life on land. **Soil** is made of loose, weathered rock and organic material in which plants with roots can grow. The rock material in soil contains three noticeable parts: sand, clay, and silt.

The material from which a soil is formed is called its **parent material.** Often this material is the bedrock beneath the soil. Soil that has bedrock as its parent material is **residual soil.** The soil of the famous Bluegrass region of Kentucky is an example of a residual soil. The parent material in the Bluegrass region is the underlying limestone bedrock. In other parts of the country, deposits left by winds, rivers, and glaciers have covered over the bedrock. Soils formed from such materials are called **transported soils.** The soils of New England and much of the midwestern United States are transported soils. Their parent material is loose soil, boulders, sands, and gravels left by glaciers after the Ice Age.

Topic 8 A Mature Soil Profile

Scientists who study soil dig through layers of soil until they reach the parent material. The cross section of earth exposed by the digging is called the **soil profile.** In most mature soils, three distinct zones, or horizons, can be seen in the soil profile. These are named the A-, B-, and C-horizons. Beneath them is the parent material.

The A-horizon is **topsoil.** Its color is generally gray to black. Topsoil tends to be darker than soil in other horizons because it has organic material, or humus. Humus forms from decayed plant and animal materials. Although both sand and clay are in topsoil, most of the clay is washed to the B-horizon. The sand that is left tends to make topsoil sandy.

The B-horizon begins with the **subsoil.** Much of the clay in the topsoil is washed to the subsoil. Thus, the B-horizon contains more clay. The color, usually red or brown, is from iron oxides that formed in the A-horizon and then washed down. The B-horizon may contain soluble minerals that were washed into it, such as calcium and magnesium carbonates.

The C-horizon is made of slightly weathered parent material, such as rock fragments. Near the bottom of the C-horizon, these fragments sit on top of the unweathered bedrock.

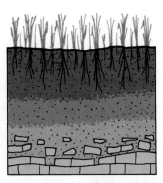

8.10   Mature soil develops from the gradual weathering of parent material.

Topic 9   **Soil Types and Climates**

Soil scientists have learned that the most important factor affecting soil is the climate. Once a soil has matured, the parent material no longer has much effect on soil type. The soil formed from granite in a wet tropical climate is very different from the soil formed from granite in a desert. At the same time, mature soils in a wet tropical climate strongly resemble each other no matter what their parent material is.

A *tropical soil* forms in the areas that have constant high temperature and heavy rainfall. Warm, wet conditions speed up chemical weathering, and soil forms quickly. The soil profile that results may be more than three meters thick. Frequent heavy rains wash nutrients out of the soil. Thus, tropical soils are relatively infertile. They must be fertilized heavily if they are used to grow crops.

Grassland soils form in areas that receive enough rainfall for heavy grass, but not enough for trees. The soil profile is usually less

VIDEODISC SELECTION

Transported soils
Side 2: 1887 to 1891, 5-frame sequence

Diagram of soil layers
Side 2: 2409, single frame

OF INTEREST

The destruction of Earth's rain forests to provide farmland is particularly ironic, since the tropical soil cannot support crops for more than a few growing seasons. Once the nutrients are gone, the farmers have no choice but to clear new land, destroying more valuable forests.

8.11   Note the three distinct horizons in this soil profile.

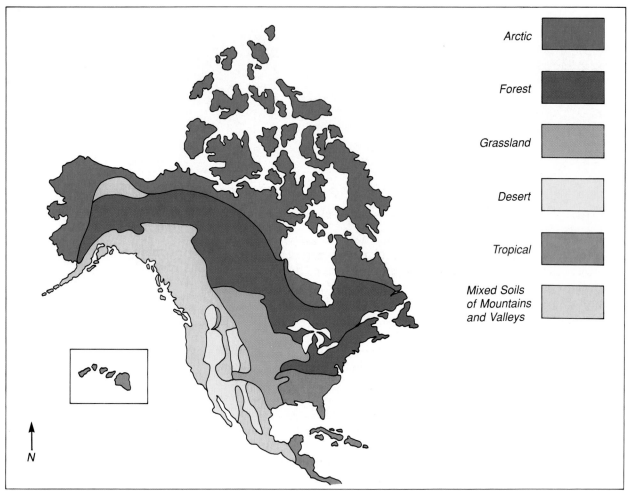

8.12 Map of soil types in North America

than a meter thick. The A-horizons are black or deep-brown. Grassland soils are very rich in organic matter and, as a result, are very fertile soils. Grassland soils are good for growing wheat and similar grains.

Forest soils form in humid regions that have cool seasons and forests of hardwood and evergreen trees. These soils have very well developed A , B , and C-horizons. However, the soil profile in forests is usually less than a meter in total thickness. Forest soils are not very fertile.

Desert soils form in very dry climates. Their profiles are seldom more than a few centimeters from top to bottom. Nutrients that would be washed from the soil in a wet climate stay in a desert soil. Such soils often have a great deal of calcium. These soils can be very fertile when they are watered.

Arctic soils form at high elevations and high latitudes. The surfaces of these soils are poorly drained and boggy. The bottom layers are constantly frozen (permafrost). The soil profile is very shallow, often only a few centimeters thick.

8.13   Talus forms on a slope at the base of a weathered cliff.

Topic 10 **Mass Movements**

Soil partially protects bedrock beneath it from weathering. On steep slopes, however, loose soil is easily removed by erosion and gravity. This removal continually exposes a fresh bedrock surface to weathering. Gravity, then, is an aid to weathering and erosion. Gravity is largely responsible for the fact that steep slopes weather more rapidly than gentle slopes.

Wherever the ground slopes, gravity causes soil and rock fragments to fall, slide, or move at very slow speeds to lower levels. Such movements of loose earth material down a slope are collectively called **mass movement**. There are several important types of mass movement, some of which have a profound effect on people and the landscape.

Creep is a slow, imperceptible downslope movement of the soil. Creep can be noticed by its effects. Creep causes fence posts, poles, and other objects fixed in the soil to lean downhill. Water in the soil probably adds to creep.

Talus is the result of mass movement near steep slopes. *Talus* is a pile of rock fragments at the base of a cliff. The fragments are weathered from the cliff and pulled down by gravity. Talus hides the lower part of the cliff. Talus piles rest against the cliff at angles as steep as 40 degrees. Talus is common wherever there are cliffs.

A **landslide** is the sudden movement of a mass of bedrock or loose rock down the slope of a hill, mountain, or cliff. An *avalanche* is a landslide made from masses of snow, ice, soil, or rock, or mixtures of these materials. Landslides are likely to occur on steep slopes, especially those caused by erosion or by mining. *Slumps* occur when small blocks of land tilt and move downhill. Slumps are common on cliffs, steep hills, and roadcuts next to highways.

VIDEODISC SELECTION

Diagrams of mass movement (described in disc directory)
Side 2: 2662 to 2669, 9-frame sequence

Examples of rock falls, slides, and slumps (described in disc directory)
Side 2: 2677 to 2694, 18-frame sequence

8.14 In 1982, three people died when this mudflow crashed into their house.

A **mudflow** is the rapid movement of a water-saturated mass of clay and silt. A *mud avalanche* is an especially fast and large mudflow. A mud avalanche in Columbia, South America, in 1985, was triggered by a volcanic eruption. The heat from the eruption melted part of the volcanic mountain's ice cap. The mixture of water and volcanic ash buried towns below the volcano and killed 25 000 people. The 1980 eruption of Mount St. Helens in Washington state was also accompanied by a deadly mud avalanche.

Steep slopes, which are common in mountain regions, often experience mass wasting. A road or a house that is built on or into the side of a steep slope is at risk of being damaged by a landslide. The risk is even greater in areas near volcanoes and earthquakes, since eruptions and tremors can trigger landslides.

It is best not to build roads or houses on steep slopes. However, people who live in such places can still avoid injury by knowing when the danger of landslide is greatest. Landslides often happen after very heavy rains or during spring melting of snow. Rain and snowmelt contribute to landslides in two main ways. The first is by adding weight. Water is very heavy. Soil that is soaked with water is more likely to be pulled downslope by gravity than dry soil. The second way water contributes to mass wasting is by reducing friction. Water is a good lubricant. When enough rain has fallen to saturate the soil, a layer of water builds up between the soil and the bedrock beneath it. When this happens, the whole mass of soil may be pulled down the slope, riding on top of a layer of water. People can avoid injury by leaving landside areas during heavy rains and spring melts.

SCIENCE BACKGROUND
   A mud avalanche caused by a volcanic eruption is also called a lahar. The Columbia eruption was a classic lahar.

SCIENCE BACKGROUND
   Soil erosion occurs naturally, but it is greatly accelerated once the land is disturbed by plowing or construction.

OF INTEREST
   Midwestern farm fields are estimated to lose 2.5 centimeters of topsoil every 10 to 20 years.

Topic 11   Soil Conservation

Soil erosion is the removal of topsoil by the action of running water or wind. Each year, the streams and rivers of the United States carry away 4 billion metric tons of sediment. Winds blow away another 1 billion metric tons. This loss of topsoil reduces soil fertility and crop production. Once it is lost, soil cannot easily or quickly be replaced. Overgrazing of livestock removes grasses which hold soil in place, increasing erosion. Soil erosion has become a serious environmental and economic problem.

Soil erosion can be reduced by a number of soil conservation methods. One method is the planting of *windbreaks*, belts of trees along the edges of fields. These trees slow the wind and reduce wind erosion. Windbreaks are important on level plains where strong winds may blow nearly all the time.

A second method of reducing erosion is *contour farming*. Instead of plowing up and down a hillslope, crops are planted in rows parallel to land contours. This prevents water from flowing rapidly downhill and carrying soil with it. Flattening hillslopes into *terraces* also slows stream flow and reduces soil erosion.

8.15 The crop on this hillside has been planted in contours, which reduce the effects of soil erosion.

Another method of reducing soil erosion is *strip cropping*. In this method, a crop that leaves bare ground between rows is alternated with a crop that completely covers the ground. For example, the ground between rows of corn plants is bare. Alfalfa is a crop that covers the ground. By planting alternating strips of a field with corn and alfalfa, soil erosion can be reduced.

Still another method of reducing soil erosion is a technique called *no-till*. In this method, plowing, planting, fertilizing, and weed control are all done at the same time. Once the field is planted, the ground does not need to be disturbed again until harvest. When the soil is left alone, there is less of a chance that it will be carried away by the wind.

TOPIC QUESTIONS

Each topic question refers to the topic of the same number.

7. **(a)** What is soil and why is it important? **(b)** What is parent material? **(c)** How is the parent material of a residual soil different from that of a transported soil?

8. List and briefly describe the three horizons of a mature soil.

9. **(a)** What is the most important factor affecting soil type? **(b)** List and briefly describe five types of soil.

10. **(a)** What is mass movement and what is its cause? **(b)** Identify and describe several kinds of mass movements.

11. **(a)** Why is soil erosion a problem? **(b)** Identify and briefly describe some methods of reducing soil erosion.

ANSWERS

7. (a) loose, weathered rock and organic material able to support rooted plants   (b) source of soil   (c) residual—underlying bedrock; transported—kind of deposit

8. topsoil—dark from humus, sandy; subsoil—red or brown, contains clay, some soluble minerals; C-horizon—barely weathered parent material

9. (a) climate   (b) tropical—very thick, infertile; grassland— < 1 m thick, dark, rich, and fertile; forest—well-developed profile but thin horizons, not very fertile; desert—very thin, many nutrients, high in Ca, fertile when watered; arctic—boggy, lower layers frozen, shallow profile

10. (a) downslope movements of loose earth materials; gravity   (b) creep—slow downslope; landslide—sudden movement of loose rock; mudflow—rapid movement of water-saturated mud

11. (a) reduces soil fertility and crop production   (b) windbreak—trees on edge of field to reduce wind erosion; contour farming—plowing with contours; strip cropping—alternate crops across field; no-till—all steps done at once

CHAPTER 8

L A B
ACTIVITY

Temperature and Chemical Weathering

Whether it's the granite of a New Hampshire mountain breaking down into sand and clay or the limestone of Kentucky decomposing to form rich soil, all chemical weathering processes involve water. What effect does the temperature of the water have on the rate at which chemical weathering occurs?

As you know, carbonic acid is a weak acid that forms when carbon dioxide dissolves naturally in rain, in streams, or in groundwater. A common chemical weathering process is the reaction between carbonate rocks, such as limestone and marble, with carbonic acid. In this lab activity, you will observe a model of this reaction. By changing the temperature of the water, you can model the effect of the temperature on the rate of the reaction between carbonate rocks and carbonic acid.

Lab Skills and Objectives

- To **model** a chemical weathering process
- To **graph** the data from the model and to interpret the graph
- To **predict** what will happen when the model is modified
- To **compare** the observed data with the theoretical data

Materials

- lab apron
- safety goggles
- 5 250 mL beakers
- 5 thermometers
- 5 effervescent antacid tablets
- hot water (40°–50°C)
- ice water
- stopwatch
- graph paper
- map of Earth's Climates, Appendix B, page 664

Procedure

1. **CAUTION: Put on your lab apron and safety goggles.**

2. Arrange 5 beakers in a row. Assign each beaker a number from 1 to 5. Place a thermometer in each beaker. Each beaker should contain about 200 mL of water. The water temperature in each beaker will need to be adjusted to match the following: Beaker 1, 0°–10°C; Beaker 2, 10°–20°C; Beaker 3, 20°–30°C; Beaker 4, 30°–40°C; Beaker 5, 40°–50°C.

3. Begin with Beaker 1. Remove any pieces of ice

from the water. Check to be sure that the water is within the correct temperature range and that the thermometer has stopped changing. Read the temperature of the water in Beaker 1 to the nearest half degree and record it on a copy of Data Table A. Remove the thermometer from the beaker and set it aside in a safe place.

4. Read all of this step before continuing. Drop the antacid tablet into Beaker 1. Start the stop watch at the instant the tablet enters the water. Stop the stopwatch when the last piece of the tablet dissolves. (You do not need to wait for all of the bubbling to stop; wait only for all pieces of the tablet to disappear.) Read the time on the stopwatch. Record the time to the nearest whole second on Data Table A.

5. Repeat steps 3 and 4 for each of the remaining beakers.

6. Plot a graph of the data for the 5 trials. One graph axis will be *Temperature* (in °C) and the other will be *Time* (in seconds). Connect the 5 points with a smooth curve. Label the curve *Observed Data*.

7. Answer *Analysis and Conclusions* questions 1–6.

8. Copy your Beaker 1 data from Data Table A to Data Table B. The remaining values in Data Table B will need to be calculated. For

the temperature values, add 10 to the reading for Beaker 1 and record that as the temperature for Beaker 2. In the same way, continue to add 10 to each temperature reading on the table.

9. For the time values on Data Table B, divide each reading in half to get the next reading. For example, the time for Beaker 2 will be one half the time for Beaker 1 and so on. When you divide the values, round off each result to the nearest whole second.

10. Using the same graph as before, plot the values from Data Table B. Connect the points with a smooth curve. Label the curve *Theoretical Data*.

11. Answer question 7 in *Analysis and Conclusions*.

Analysis and Conclusions

1. In which beaker did the reaction occur most slowly? In which beaker did the reaction occur most rapidly? What do you think is the relationship between the temperature and the rate of a reaction?

2. Based upon your observations, what do you think is the relationship between the temperature and the rate of natural chemical weathering?

3. Look at the temperatures you recorded. Are all of these temperatures likely to occur on Earth's surface? Explain.

Data Table A: Actual Data		
Beaker Number	Temperature (°C)	Time (seconds)
1		
2		
3		
4		
5		

Data Table B: Theoretical Data		
Beaker Number	Temperature (°C)	Time (seconds)
1		
2		
3		
4		
5		

4. Turn to the map of Earth's Climates on page 664. Locate Rio de Janeiro in South America and Seattle in North America. The map key indicates that both cities have climates with abundant moisture. (a) Recall what you know about carbonic acid in rain and in groundwater. Compare the weathering rate of a limestone in Rio de Janeiro with that of a limestone in Seattle. Is there a difference? Explain your answer. (b) Which of the two locations is likely to have thicker soil?

5. Now locate Barrow, Alaska, on the map. Why is a limestone in Barrow likely to weather very slowly?

6. How would the rate of the reaction have been differ-ent if the tablets had been ground into a powder before they were dropped into the water? Why? Would a graph for such a reaction result in a curve above or below the line of your actual data? Why?

7. Look at the calculated values in Data Table B. (a) On your graph, is the line for the theoretical data above, below, or the same as your line for the actual data? (b) What does this mean about the rate of the reaction you observed compared with the theoretical rate of reaction? (c) What change in the procedure might have made your actual results more like the theoretical results?

Answers to all questions appear in the Teacher's Guide at the back of this book.

■ Summary

I Weathering occurs when rocks are exposed at Earth's surface. Agents of erosion transport weathered earth materials.

Mechanical weathering breaks rocks without changing their composition. Chemical weathering changes the composition of the rocks.

The way a rock weathers depends on its mineral content and cement.

Some factors that determine the rate at which rock weathers are mineral composition, particle size, and climate.

II Soil is loose, weathered material capable of supporting rooted plants. Soils may be residual or transported, depending on the parent material.

A soil profile shows the soil layers: A-horizon (topsoil), B-horizon (subsoil), and C-horizon. Each layer has its own characteristics.

The major factor in soil formation is climate. Examples of soil types are tropical, forest, grassland, desert, and arctic soils.

Gravity pulls loose soil and rock downhill in mass movements. Examples of mass movements include creep, landslides, and mudflows.

Soil erosion reduces soil fertility and crop production. Windbreaks, contour plowing, terracing, strip cropping, and no-till planting can be used to conserve soil.

■ Vocabulary

carbonic acid	oxidation
chemical weathering	parent material
creep	residual soil
erosion	soil
exfoliation	soil erosion
hydrolysis	soil profile
ice wedging	subsoil
landslide	topsoil
mass movement	transported soil
mechanical weathering	weathering
mudflow	

■ Review

On your paper, write the term that best completes each sentence.

1. Weathering is due in part to differences between conditions at depth and those at Earth's _____.
2. Streams and rivers, glaciers, wind, and other natural agents that break up and move rocks are called _____.
3. _____ weathering breaks rocks in smaller pieces without changing their composition.
4. _____ weathering changes the minerals in the rock into different minerals.
5. _____ occurs when water enters a crack in a rock and expands as it freezes.
6. In hydrolysis, minerals such as feldspar, hornblende, and augite unite with water and form _____.
7. Rocks like sandstone are only as durable as the _____ that holds them together.
8. Breaking a rock into smaller pieces increases its _____ and, as a result, the rate at which the rock weathers.
9. Warm, wet climates favor _____ weathering, while cold and dry climates favor _____ weathering.
10. The _____ material of a residual soil is the bedrock beneath the soil.
11. _____ soils are formed from deposits left by winds, rivers, or glaciers.
12. The dark, humus-rich A-horizon of a soil profile is also called the _____.
13. Fine materials from the A-horizon are washed to the B-horizon, or _____.
14. _____ soils form in areas that have constant high temperatures and heavy rainfall.
15. _____ soils are especially fertile soils on which wheat and other grains grow well.
16. A _____ is the sudden movement of a mass of loose material down the slope of a hill, mountain, or cliff.
17. Windbreaks, contour plowing, strip cropping, and the no-till method are all ways of reducing _____.

For further review, see **Study Guide**.
For assessment, see **Chapter Tests**
and **Computer Test Bank**.

■ Interpret and Apply

On your paper, answer each question in complete sentences.

1. How is the weathering of a bare mountain peak different from the weathering of bedrock under a forest soil?
2. Why are streets and highways damaged so much more in the winter months than in the summer months in most of the United States? Compare the processes of weathering in the two seasons.
3. Sandstones cemented by calcite usually weather much more rapidly than those cemented by silica. Why?
4. What should be the content of a residual soil that formed in a humid climate from granite composed of quartz, feldspar, and black mica?
5. Which horizon of a soil profile is most weathered? Explain.
6. Using the soil map of the United States in Figure 8.12, determine the soil type for your area.
7. What effect would a long, dry period have on the frequency of landslides and mudslides?
8. Soil erosion is usually the result of human use of the land surface. Are there any ways in which human use has been beneficial to the soil?

■ Critical Thinking

The type of weathering that dominates in an area depends upon the climate in that area. The major factors that control climate are precipitation (rain and snow) and temperature. The graph shows the relationship between precipitation, temperature, and weathering. For example, a climate with an average yearly temperature (AYT) of 5°C and average yearly precipitation (AYP) of 75 centimeters would have moderate chemical weathering with frost action. Use the graph to answer the questions.

1. Determine the major type of weathering that occurs in Washington, D.C., AYT, 23°C; AYP, 104 cm.
2. If the AYT in Washington, D.C., dropped 26°C but the AYP stayed the same, what kind of weathering would dominate?
3. Phoenix, Arizona, has an AYT of 20°C and an AYP of 20 cm. How would the climate in Phoenix have to change for moderate chemical weathering to become dominant?
4. According to the graph, no frost action occurs at a mean annual temperature above 13°C. What is a possible reason?
5. In general, how does a climate with strong chemical weathering differ from a climate with strong mechanical weathering?

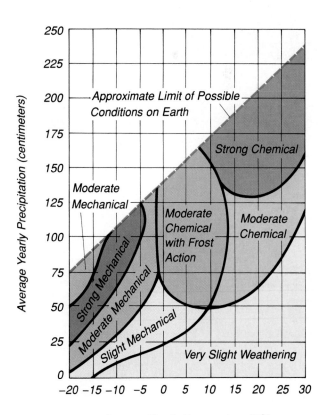

Water Moving Underground

Old Faithful Geyser in Yellowstone National Park, Wyoming

How Do You Know That . . .

Water exists beneath Earth's surface? The following investigation will give you a clue. Fill a plastic container to the top with coarse gravel or marble chips. Is the container really full? Estimate the amount of air space in the container. Check your estimate by filling another container of equal volume with water. Pour the water into the container with the gravel until it can hold no more water. Compare your estimate with your observation. Carefully pour the water off the gravel and back into the water container. Was all the water removed from the gravel?

1 Fresh Water and Water Budgets

Topic 1 All the World's Water

How much water is there on and in the whole Earth? Scientists estimate the answer to be about one and one third billion cubic kilometers. The number is so large that it is difficult to picture. How much of Earth's water is salt water? How much is fresh water? This question is important because most uses of water require fresh water. With the growth of industry and the increase in population, the need for fresh water becomes more and more critical.

More than 97 percent of all Earth's water is in the ocean as salt water. Less than 3 percent is fresh water. Of this 3 percent, more than two thirds is frozen in the ice caps and glaciers of Greenland, Antarctica, and high mountain regions. Therefore, only about one half of one percent of all Earth's water is usable fresh water.

Where is this fresh water located? A tiny part of it flows on the surface in rivers and streams. About 100 times that amount is stored in lakes and swamps. However, most of the fresh water is in the ground. By one estimate, the amount of groundwater is 50 times as much as all the water in rivers and lakes! It is thousands of times as much as in all Earth's rivers at any given moment.

Topic 2 The Water Cycle

The **hydrosphere** is the water of Earth's surface. The hydrosphere includes groundwater, running water, lakes, and oceans. The movement of water from one part of the hydrosphere to another is described by the hydrologic cycle, or **water cycle.** The path of water in the water cycle is shown in Figure 9.2.

Sunlight provides the energy that evaporates water from the surface of Earth. Some of the water vapor comes from the continents, but most comes from the oceans. Winds carry the water vapor from the ocean over the continents. Part of the water vapor condenses into clouds, then falls as rain or snow.

Some of the rain returns to the ocean from rivers and streams as runoff. Some seeps into the ground to become groundwater. Some returns to the air by *evaporation* from the ground or by *transpiration* from plant leaves. Hydrologists (scientists who study the hydrosphere) usually combine evaporation and transpiration in the term **evapotranspiration.**

OBJECTIVES

A Describe the distribution and quantity of fresh water on Earth.

B List the parts of the hydrosphere and describe the movement of water in the water cycle.

C Identify the conditions under which groundwater surplus, usage, deficit, and recharge occur.

D Compare the climates of different areas by comparing their water budgets.

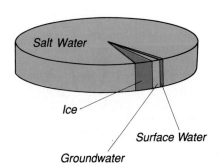

9.1 Less than three percent of Earth's water is fresh water, and less than one third of the fresh water is available as surface or groundwater. The rest is frozen.

149

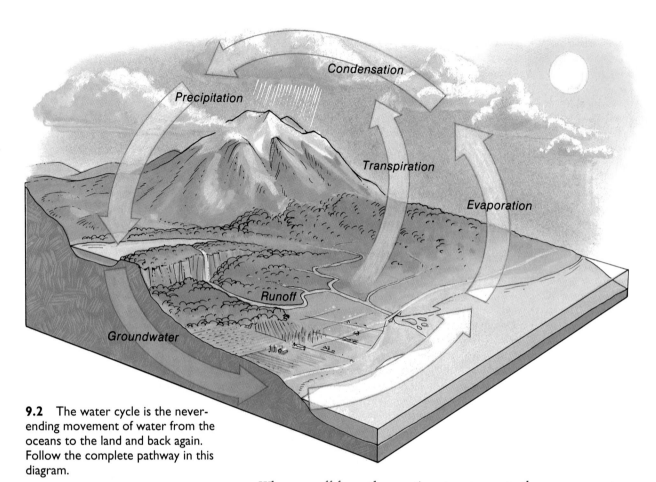

9.2 The water cycle is the never-ending movement of water from the oceans to the land and back again. Follow the complete pathway in this diagram.

VIDEODISC SELECTION

Diagram of the water cycle
Side 2: 2631, single frame

TEACHING TIP
   The parts of the water budget graph will need some discussion and practice. Make the following clear: 1) Usage and deficit occur when need exceeds supply; usage precedes deficit. 2) Recharge and surplus occur when supply exceeds need; recharge must precede surplus.

When runoff from the continents returns to the ocean, one turn of the water cycle is completed. Other routes are possible. For example, water that evaporates from the ocean can return to the ocean as rain. The water cycle never ends. The salt water of the ocean supplies fresh water to the continents over and over again.

Topic 3 **The Water Budget**

A budget is a statement of expected income versus expected spending or expenses. In a balanced budget, income and spending are equal. A **water budget** describes the income and spending of water for a region. In a water budget, the income is rain or snow. The spending includes water lost by use, by runoff, and by evapotranspiration.

The evapotranspiration of an area is controlled by air temperature. When air temperature is high, plants growing in the ground need and use more moisture. At such times, evapotranspiration is high. When air temperature is low, plants do not need or use as much moisture; thus, evapotranspiration is low.

If it rains during a time when the plants need little moisture, the extra moisture soaks into the soil, where it is stored between the

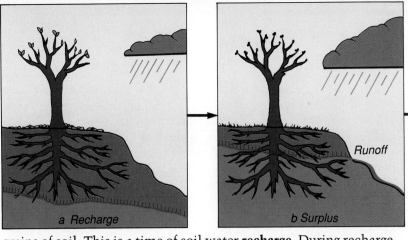

a Recharge   b Surplus   c Usage

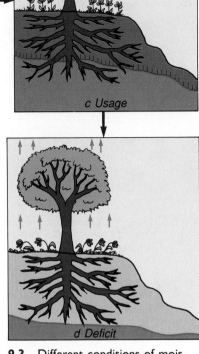

d Deficit

9.3 Different conditions of moisture input and need lead to phases in the yearly water budget cycle of an area.

9.4 Water budget graph for Phoenix, Arizona

grains of soil. This is a time of soil water **recharge.** During recharge, the soil water storage is filling. Figure 9.3(a) illustrates conditions during recharge. If the rain continues so that the soil becomes saturated, the surplus water raises the water table (Topic 7) or becomes part of the stream runoff. Thus, a moisture **surplus** occurs when two conditions are true: the rainfall is greater than the need for moisture and the soil water storage is filled, as in Figure 9.3(b).

If the need for moisture is greater than the rainfall, the plants can draw water from the soil water supply. This is a time of soil water **usage,** Figure 9.3(c). If the need for moisture continues to be greater than the rainfall, all of the water available in the soil may be used up. A water **deficit** occurs when the need for moisture is greater than the rainfall and the soil water storage is gone (Figure 9.3(d)).

Topic 4 Water Budget Graphs

Each location on Earth has its own unique water budget. Water budgets can be summarized by *water budget graphs.* Each water budget graph shows two kinds of information: moisture need and moisture supply. Periods of water usage, deficit, recharge, and surplus can be determined from data on the water budget graph. Three examples of water budget graphs are shown in Figures 9.4 and 9.5, and are discussed in the following paragraphs.

Phoenix, Arizona (Figure 9.4), is located in a dry desert climate in the southwestern United States. The rainfall in Phoenix is very low all year. The need for moisture is great almost all year. Because of these conditions, Phoenix has a moisture deficit nearly all year. The only recharge of water occurs in December and January, but that moisture is used up before April.

Hartford, Connecticut (Figure 9.5(a)), is located in the humid eastern part of the United States. Temperatures in Hartford, even in summer, are not as high as those in Phoenix. Thus, the moisture need in Hartford is never as great as in Phoenix. Rainfall in Hartford is abundant all year long. Plants generally do not use up all of the moisture stored in the ground. As a result, Hartford does not have a moisture deficit. The water usage of summer is quickly recharged in the fall. Thus, Hartford has a moisture surplus more than half the year.

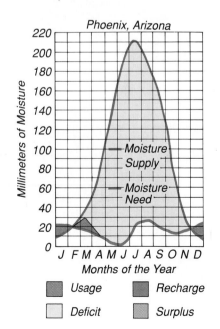

Phoenix, Arizona

Moisture Supply

Moisture Need

Millimeters of Moisture

Months of the Year

■ Usage   ■ Recharge
□ Deficit   ■ Surplus

9.5 Water budget graphs for
(a) Hartford, Connecticut, and
(b) Little Rock, Arkansas

Little Rock, Arkansas (Figure 9.5(b)), has a climate in between those of Phoenix and Hartford. In summer, Little Rock is not as hot as Phoenix nor as cool as Hartford. Summer rainfall at Little Rock is greater than at Phoenix but not as great as at Hartford. The water storage at Little Rock is used up before summer is over, and a period of water deficit occurs. However, the water storage in Little Rock is recharged in the fall. A water surplus starts in December and continues until the next summer.

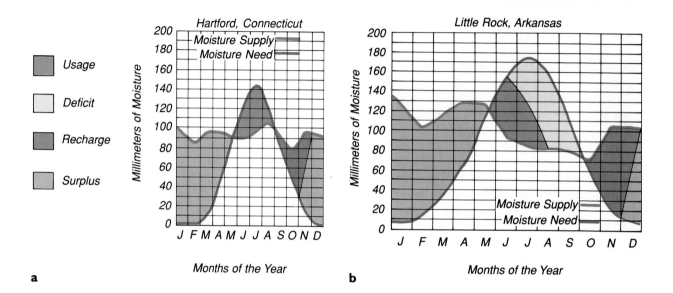

Usage

Deficit

Recharge

Surplus

a

b

TOPIC QUESTIONS

Each topic question refers to the topic of the same number.

ANSWERS
1. (a) 97% salt, 3% fresh (b) ⅔ frozen (c) in the ground
2. (a) groundwater, running water, lakes, oceans (b) sunlight (c) runs off to ocean, seeps into ground, used by plants and returns to air (d) term for evaporation and transpiration
3. (a) describes income and spending of water (b) temperature increase leads to increased moisture need (c) soil water storage fills (d) rainfall greater than need, soil water full (e) moisture is drawn from soil (f) need greater than rainfall, soil water storage empty
4. (a) moisture need and supply: water usage, deficit, recharge, surplus (b) deficit almost all year in Phoenix, surplus most of year in Hartford, deficit and surplus at different times in Little Rock

1. **(a)** Compare the percentage of salt water and fresh water on Earth. **(b)** What portion of Earth's fresh water is frozen into ice caps and glaciers? **(c)** Where is most of Earth's usable fresh water located?

2. **(a)** List the parts of the hydrosphere. **(b)** Identify the energy source for the water cycle. **(c)** What kinds of things can happen to rain that falls on Earth's surface? **(d)** What is evapotranspiration?

3. **(a)** What is a water budget? **(b)** How are temperature and evapotranspiration related in a water budget? **(c)** What occurs during a time of moisture recharge? **(d)** Under what two conditions does a moisture surplus occur? **(e)** What occurs during a time of moisture usage? **(f)** Under what two conditions does a moisture deficit occur?

4. **(a)** Identify the kinds of information shown by a water budget graph. **(b)** Describe the water budgets of Phoenix, Arizona, Hartford, Connecticut, and Little Rock, Arkansas.

II   Water in the Ground

Topic 5   Can Rocks Hold Water?

The amount of water that soil or rock can hold depends upon the amount of space, called pore space, that lies between the grains of the material. **Porosity** is the percentage of a material's volume that is pore space.

The porosity of a material depends upon a number of factors. One factor is particle shape. Rounded particles have a lot of space between them—like picture the space between glass marbles in a jar. Flat or angular particles fit together more closely than rounded particles, and thus have less total pore space. Another factor affecting porosity is sorting. The percentage of pore space is greatest in well-sorted materials—that is, materials in which the particles are all the same size. Where the material is poorly sorted—as in a mixture of gravel, sand, and silt—small particles fill the spaces between the large particles, which greatly reduces the total porosity. Deposits of well-rounded particles of gravel, sand, or silt that have little or no cement between grains may be more than 40 percent pore space. Cement fills pore space and reduces porosity.

OBJECTIVES

A Define porosity and permeability and list some factors that control each.

B Identify and describe underground regions above and below the water table, list factors that determine water table depth, and explain the importance of the water table.

C Describe an artesian formation.

D Identify methods of obtaining groundwater and describe ways to deal with problems in groundwater usage.

SCIENCE BACKGROUND
Clay is not included with gravel, sand, and silt because clay is not a well-rounded particle. Clay is a flake and, as a result, has very little pore space between particles.

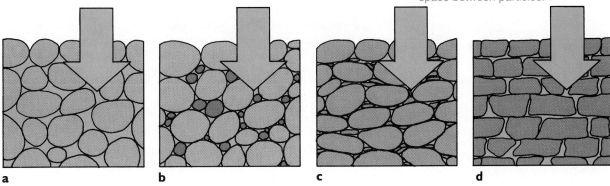

a   b   c   d

Topic 6   Can Rocks Transmit Water?

Porosity describes the pore space in a material, but it does not describe whether water can pass through the material. **Permeability** is the rate at which water or other liquids pass through the pore spaces of a rock. In general, permeability increases with grain size because large-grained materials have large pore spaces. Water passes easily through materials with large pore spaces, such as sand and gravel. It passes slowly through finer materials, such as silt. A material that water cannot pass through is **impermeable**. Clays and shales, which are very fine-grained, are usually impermeable.

It is possible for a material to be highly porous but not at all permeable. An example is pumice. Pumice has many holes, or pores, but the holes are not connected. Thus, water cannot pass

9.6   Different earth materials have different amounts of pore space. (a) All sand with no cement, lots of pore space; (b) sand mixed with silt, less pore space; (c) sandstone, cement reduces pore space; (d) limestone, pore space between crystals and fossil grains and because of cracks and fissures

SCIENCE BACKGROUND
An example of a permeable limestone is the Ocala Limestone in Florida.

through pumice. On the other hand, a nonporous rock such as granite may become permeable if cracks develop in the rock. The cracks transmit the water.

Some of the water that passes through a sediment or rock will stick to the particles. This film of water is *capillary water*. It can be removed only by evapotranspiration. For materials made of small particles, such as shale, capillary water may fill the pore space. When the pore space is filled, the material is impermeable.

Topic 7 Forming the Water Table

When rain falls to the ground, it enters the pores in the soil and sticks to the particles. If enough rain falls, the upper layers of soil will not be able to absorb all the water. When this happens, the water continues downward until it reaches an impermeable material. The water then begins to fill the pore spaces above the impermeable material. As rain continues, the water level in the ground rises higher as more pore spaces are filled. The *zone of saturation* is that part of the ground where all pore spaces are filled. The surface of the zone of saturation is the **water table.**

From the water table to the surface, the ground can still hold more water. This section is called the *zone of aeration* because air can enter this region. It includes three parts. Just above the water table is the *capillary fringe*. In the capillary fringe, water rises from the water table by capillary action. (A familiar example of capillary action occurs when a paper towel is dipped in water. Just as water rises into the towel, water rises into the soil just above the water table.) Above the capillary fringe is a section that is dry except during rains. Just below the soil surface is the soil water, a film of capillary water that sticks to the grains of topsoil.

TEACHING TIP
Use Figure 9.7 to point out that the water table is not a flat surface but follows the land surface. The water table rises where the land surface rises and vice versa.

9.7 The depth of the water table varies, mainly due to the amount of rainfall and the structure of underground formations.

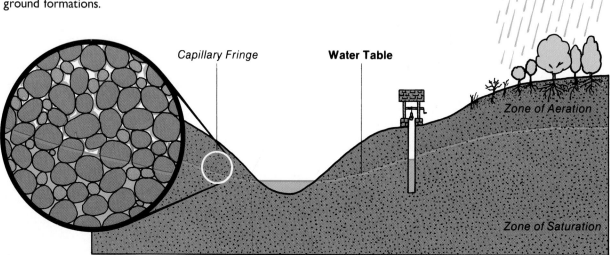

Capillary Fringe

Water Table

Zone of Aeration

Zone of Saturation

Topic 8 Water Table Depth and Use

How far under the surface is the water table? The depth depends upon many things. Some factors include the amount of rainfall, the season, the slope of the ground surface, the thickness of the soil, the climate, and the time between rains.

In places such as swamps, lakes, and rivers, the water table is at the surface. In desert regions, the water table may be hundreds of meters below the surface. In woods, fields, and farmlands, it is likely to be within a few meters of the surface. In hilly country, it is generally nearer the surface in valleys than in hills, but it has its own hills and valleys much like the overlying surface.

The water table is important in several ways. Seepage of water from the water table keeps streams flowing between rains and maintains the water levels of swamps and lakes. The water table also supplies drinking water to springs and wells.

SCIENCE BACKGROUND

The base flow of a stream is that part of the stream flow that is groundwater rather than runoff. During a dry season, the entire stream flow may be base flow.

Topic 9 Ordinary Wells and Springs

In places where the water table does not reach the surface, the groundwater is reached by digging or driving wells into the ground. A well of this type, known as an *ordinary well,* contains water from its bottom up to the level of the water table. Recall that the depth of the water table depends in part on the season. A well must reach below the lowest level to which the water table is likely to fall in dry weather. If it does not, it will not provide water all year. As the water table rises and falls with weather changes, so does the level of the water in the well.

On a hillside where the water table meets the surface, groundwater may flow out as a *hillside spring.* Hillside springs are more common in mountainous areas.

9.8 Wells and springs are fed by the water table. Changes in the water table affect the availability of surface and well water.

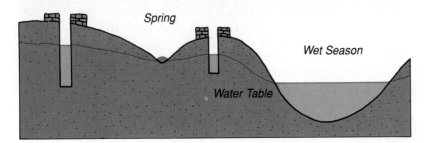

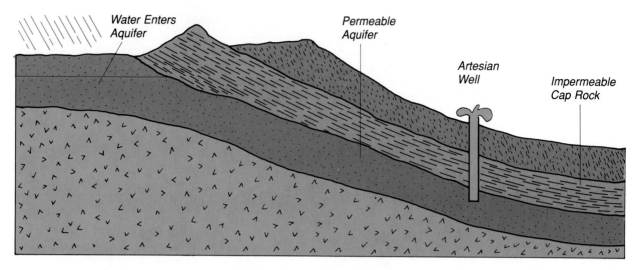

Water Enters Aquifer

Permeable Aquifer

Artesian Well

Impermeable Cap Rock

9.9 The rainwater that enters the aquifer of an artesian formation is trapped between impermeable rock layers. From there it may travel a great distance underground before returning to the surface through an artesian well or spring.

VIDEODISC SELECTION

Diagram of groundwater system
Side 2: 2632, single frame

Topic 10 Artesian Formations

Aquifers are permeable materials that contain and carry groundwater. The best aquifers are uncemented sands and gravels, followed by porous sandstones.

In some parts of the world, aquifers occur near Earth's surface along hillsides and mountainsides. If the aquifer dips underground between impermeable beds, a "sandwich" of permeable and impermeable rocks is formed. This arrangement is called an **artesian formation** (Figure 9.9). The upper impermeable layer of an artesian formation, usually shale, is called the *cap rock.*

Rain that enters this aquifer is trapped by the cap rock and the impermeable bed below. As the water moves downward into the dipping aquifer, it is pushed along by the weight of all the water above and behind it. Gravity pulls the water along this course.

One of the best-known artesian formations in the United States carries water hundreds of kilometers underground from the Rocky Mountains to the Great Plains. Its aquifer, the Dakota Sandstone, is a porous sandstone more than 30 meters thick.

Topic 11 Artesian Wells

Great quantities of water may enter the aquifers of artesian formations where the aquifers are at the surface. Like the water in a great sloping pipe, the water in the aquifer is under pressure. When wells are drilled into the aquifers at lower elevations, water rises in the wells. It may even spout into the air if water pressure is great enough. These are *artesian wells,* that is, wells in which water comes from an aquifer that lies beneath an impermeable layer.

Artesian wells differ greatly in depth. Generally, as the distance from the source of the water increases, the depth of the aquifer increases. On the Great Plains, wells that are hundreds of kilometers from the mountains may go down more than a thousand meters to reach the aquifer.

Artesian formations may be broken by cracks in the cap rock called fissures. Artesian springs, or *fissure springs,* rise through these cracks. Such a spring may form an a desert oasis (Figure 9.10).

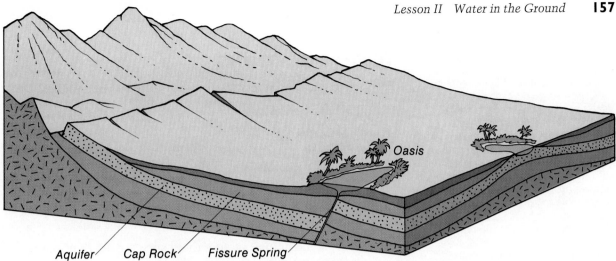

Aquifer　　Cap Rock　　Fissure Spring

Topic 12 Conserving Groundwater

Groundwater supplies are not limitless. The amount of water returned to the ground in a given area must be at least equal to the amount removed by wells and springs. If more groundwater is removed than can be returned, the water table will drop. A drop in the water table lowers the water level of wells and springs. This may cause the wells or springs to go dry. In coastal areas, wells are affected in a different way. Fresh groundwater in these areas rests on top of salt water. As fresh water is used, salt water from the ocean seeps in, replacing the fresh water that has been removed from the ground. When this occurs, wells and springs become salty and unusable.

Pollutants can enter the groundwater. Groundwater is recharged by rain seeping down through the soil. Any polluting agent in the soil becomes part of the groundwater. In agricultural areas, this includes nitrates from fertilizers that are applied to the soil, as well as pesticides applied to plants. Toxic chemicals from accidental spills, careless disposal, or rotting underground storage containers all can become part of the groundwater. Even salt, used to melt ice on highways in the winter, seeps down into the groundwater with the melting snow and spring rains.

What can be done? In areas where heavy groundwater use has lowered the water table, artificial methods of groundwater recharge are used. A former practice was to pour used water into sewers, where it became part of the runoff. Instead, water is pumped back underground through wells, or it is pumped into ponds and allowed to seep back into the groundwater naturally. Many states now require large commercial users of groundwater to purify and return the water they use.

Groundwater pollution is a more difficult problem. As yet, no simple or inexpensive way to purify polluted groundwater is known. However, further pollution can be reduced or prevented. One way is by restricting the use of pesticides and fertilizers. Another is by disposing of toxic wastes in such a way that they cannot enter the environment.

9.10 The oasis on the left is located over a spot where a fissure spring has risen through a crack in the impermeable layer. The oasis on the right occurs where the aquifer intersects the land surface.

TEACHING TIP

Stress that purity and potability of well water and spring water are dependent on the immediate environment. Clear water is not necessarily pure and drinkable.

OF INTEREST

The Long Island aquifer is one area that is experiencing saltwater encroachment.

OF INTEREST

Groundwater used for some purposes—cooling and air conditioning, for example—is essentially uncontaminated and can easily be returned to the ground.

SCIENCE BACKGROUND

One to two percent of groundwater is now thought to be polluted. Groundwater moves so slowly that areas of contamination remain contaminated for very long times, even hundreds of years.

ANSWERS

5. (a) percentage of pore space (b) sorting, particle shape, fractures
6. (a) rate liquid passes through material (b) increased grain size means increased permeability (c) water does not pass through (d) water film on particles; evapotranspiration
7. (a) part of ground where pore spaces are filled with water (b) from water table to surface (c) area where water rises in soil, just above water table (d) top of saturated zone
8. (a) rainfall, season, ground slope, soil thickness, climate, frequency of rain (b) in order: at surface; at surface; hundreds of meters; a few meters
9. (a) hole dug below water table (b) where water table meets surface
10. (a) permeable layer between two impermeable layers (b) permeable layer carrying water
11. (a) well dug to reach artesian aquifer (b) water rising through crack in artesian cap rock
12. (a) It is pumped out faster than returned. (b) brought down from surface by seepage (c) used water pumped back underground or into ponds (d) restrict pesticide and fertilizer use, seal other wastes safely

TOPIC QUESTIONS

Each topic question refers to the topic of the same number.

5. (a) What is porosity? (b) Identify two factors that determine the porosity of a material.

6. (a) What is permeability? (b) What is the relationship between permeability and grain size? (c) Define impermeable. (d) What is capillary water and how is it removed?

7. Locate and describe the (a) zone of saturation, (b) zone of aeration, (c) capillary fringe, and (d) water table.

8. (a) List some natural factors that cause the depth of the water table to vary. (b) How deep is the water table in swamps, lakes, deserts, and farmland?

9. (a) Explain what an ordinary well is. (b) Where do hillside springs occur?

10. (a) Describe the arrangement of rock layers in an artesian formation. (b) What is an aquifer?

11. (a) What is an artesian well? (b) What is a fissure spring?

12. (a) Why is the water table dropping steadily in some areas? (b) How do pollutants enter groundwater? (c) How can groundwater be recharged artificially? (d) How can groundwater pollution be reduced or prevented?

EARTH**MATTERS**

Groundwater Pollution

Where does your community get its drinking water? The drinking water for over half the population of the United States comes from groundwater. That makes the topic of groundwater pollution very important.

Much of the groundwater pollution can be traced to improperly built sanitary landfills or to the illegal dumping of toxic chemicals. Something as seemingly harmless as a car owner changing his or her own oil and dumping the old oil into a ditch can pollute the groundwater. A teaspoon of motor oil can poison hundreds of gallons of groundwater.

The best way to solve the problem of groundwater pollution is to prevent it. Do not dump oil or chemicals into sewers, down sinks, or onto the ground. Return used motor oil to a service station. Find out if your community has a chemical waste clean-up day at which you can turn in your hazardous wastes, such as pesticides, paints, oils, and cleaners. Finally, commit to recycling. With fewer materials going into a landfill, there will be fewer harmful elements leached out of the buried waste and carried into the groundwater.

III Groundwater Characteristics

Topic 13   **Groundwater Is Usually Cool**

At a depth of up to 20 meters under the surface, soil and rock are protected from weather changes. The temperature at that depth remains the same all year. That temperature is the same as the average annual temperature at that location. In most parts of the United States, the average temperature is between 5°C and 15°C. The water of an ordinary well or spring is close to the same temperature as the ground around it. Therefore, the water is relatively cool in summer and does not freeze in winter. In polar regions, where the average temperature is below freezing, there can be no wells or springs, for the water in the ground is always frozen. This permanently frozen ground, which may be hundreds of meters deep, is called *permafrost*.

Topic 14   **Hot Springs, Geysers, and Fumaroles**

Below the 20-meter depth, heat from Earth's interior raises underground temperatures at the rate of about 1°C for every 40 meters of depth. Water from deep artesian wells or springs may therefore be much warmer than water from ordinary wells or springs. Fissure springs that originate a thousand meters below the surface may be warm springs or even hot springs, such as those at Warm Springs, Georgia, or Hot Springs, Arkansas.

Groundwater may be hot without coming from great depth. In many regions of recent volcanic activity, igneous rock near the surface is still hot enough to boil water. In such places the groundwater may come to the surface as boiling hot springs. If the hot water comes up through thick, sticky clays, the result is a sputtering spring called a *paint pot*, or mud volcano.

Geysers are boiling hot springs that periodically erupt as gushers of hot water and steam. There are only a few places in the world where geysers occur. The most familiar may be Yellowstone National Park in Wyoming. Old Faithful in Yellowstone is famous for both its height and its frequency. The average time between its eruptions is about 85 minutes. An eruption lasts several minutes and reaches a height of 45 meters or more.

Why does a geyser erupt violently, instead of simply overflowing as an ordinary hot spring does? The difference seems to be that the ordinary hot spring rises from its source through a wide tube. The geyser's tube, in contrast, has one or more constrictions, such as a partly blocked water pipe, that interfere with the upward flow of heated water. Because of the constriction, the water at the bottom

OBJECTIVES

A Explain why groundwater is nearly the same cool temperature all year.

B Discuss the origin of hot springs, including paint pots, geysers, and fumaroles.

C Discuss the origin of minerals in groundwater and list some factors that control the mineral content of groundwater.

9.11   This paint pot is a hot spring that reaches the surface through sticky clays formed by weathering.

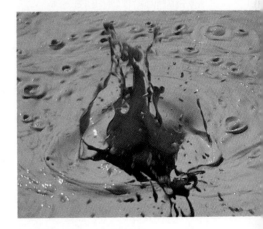

OF INTEREST
The actual time between eruptions at Old Faithful varies between 78 and 100 minutes.

VIDEODISC SELECTION

Old Faithful geyser erupting in Yellowstone Park
Side 2: 1577, single frame

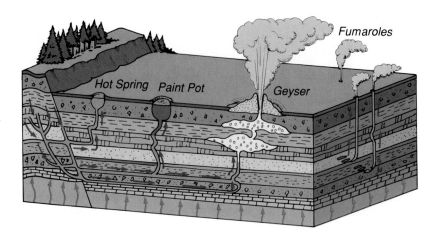

VIDEODISC SELECTION

Paint pots in Yellowstone National
Park, Wyoming
Side 2: 1578 to 1579, 2-frame
sequence

9.12   Heating and pressurization of
groundwater causes geothermal
phenomena, such as geysers, hot
springs, and fumaroles. Red arrows
represent heating. Blue arrows represent pathways for groundwater
and steam.

VIDEODISC SELECTION

Fumarole in Yellowstone Park
Side 2: 1583, single frame

of a geyser's tube is under pressure. It becomes superheated to a
temperature far above its surface boiling point but does not yet turn
into steam because of the pressure. When steam eventually does
form, it forces its way up the tube and pushes some of the superheated water up to the surface. The pressure at the bottom of the
tube is relieved, and the superheated water explodes into steam.
The steam blows out the water above it, and the geyser erupts.

Fumaroles (FEW muh roles) are fissures in the ground from
which steam and hot gases escape. They are found in volcanic
regions where fairly recent eruptions have occurred. A fumarole
field is the source of the geothermal energy at the Geysers in California (Chapter 6, Topic 20). Other commercial fumarole fields are
located in Italy, Japan, Iceland, New Zealand, Mexico, and the Soviet Union.

Topic 15   The Minerals in Groundwater

The water in clouds and in rain comes from water that evaporated
from Earth's oceans and land. When water evaporates, it leaves
impurities behind. Therefore, rainwater contains almost no dissolved mineral matter, although it may contain dissolved gases and
liquids. When rainwater seeps into the ground, however, the situation changes. As groundwater passes through the lower soil layers
or bedrock, it dissolves minerals. Much of the dissolved mineral
matter remains in the groundwater. The kind of rock through
which water passes, the distance the water travels underground,
and the water temperature all affect the kind and amount of mineral matter dissolved in groundwater.

Hard water contains a substantial amount of ions that were dissolved from mineral matter. The ions are usually calcium, magnesium, or iron. Of these ions, calcium (from calcite) is the most common cause of water hardness. The dissolved minerals in hard water
interfere greatly with its use. In laundering, these minerals react
with soap to form scum instead of suds. In boiler tubes and hot-
water pipes, dissolved minerals form deposits called boiler scale.

Artesian water is usually harder than ordinary groundwater. Artesian water travels farther and may be warmer, so it can dissolve more mineral matter than ordinary groundwater. By contrast, ordinary groundwater is almost always harder than river water. Because limestone is largely calcite, almost all the water is hard in regions that have limestone bedrock.

Topic 16 Mineral Springs

A spring containing so much dissolved mineral matter that it cannot be used for ordinary drinking or washing purposes is called a *mineral spring*. The high mineral content of the water may be due to any of the following factors:

1. The water passes through very soluble rock (such as the salt beds in Michigan).
2. The water contains large quantities of gases that form acids when mixed with water, such as carbon dioxide (Saratoga Springs, New York) or hydrogen sulfide (White Sulphur Springs, West Virginia).
3. The water is very hot (Hot Springs, Arkansas). Minerals dissolve better in hot water than in cold water. Therefore, water from hot springs usually has a high mineral content. When the hot water cools at the surface, some of the mineral matter is deposited around the spring. Such deposits are discussed in Topic 19.

Many mineral spring areas have become health resorts. In desert regions, however, alkali (bitter) mineral springs may be poisonous. In the southwestern United States, for example, alkali springs may carry borax, sodium carbonate, and sodium sulfate in solution.

TOPIC QUESTIONS

Each topic question refers to the topic of the same number.

13. **(a)** Why do spring water and well water stay cool in summer? **(b)** Why doesn't well water freeze in winter months? **(c)** What is permafrost?

14. **(a)** Why is the water of very deep artesian wells warmer than ordinary well water? **(b)** Explain the heat source of boiling hot springs and geysers. **(c)** What is a paint pot? **(d)** What causes a geyser? **(e)** What is a fumarole?

15. **(a)** What factors determine the amount and kind of mineral matter dissolved in groundwater? **(b)** What is hard water? **(c)** Compare the hardness of water in ordinary wells, artesian wells, and rivers. **(d)** Why is all the water hard in a limestone region?

16. What three factors cause a high mineral content in a mineral spring?

VIDEODISC SELECTION

Mammoth Hot Springs, Yellowstone National Park, Wyoming
Side 2: 1575, single frame

ANSWERS

13. (a) and (b): water is from depth where temperature is constant and above freezing   (c) permanently frozen ground

14. (a) artesian comes from deeper underground, crust is warmer at depth   (b) recent volcanic activity   (c) hot water erupting through sticky clay   (d) partial blockage of hot spring water pipe   (e) fissure through which steam and hot gases rise

15. (a) kind of rock, distance water travels, temperature   (b) contains a lot of mineral matter   (c) artesian hardest, wells average, rivers softest   (d) limestone is mostly calcite, dissolves easily

16. passage through soluble rock, lots of acid-forming gases, heat

OBJECTIVES

A Describe the formation of several features that result from erosion by groundwater.

B Identify karst topography by its characteristic features.

C List materials that are deposited by groundwater; discuss the role of groundwater in cementing rocks.

VIDEODISC SELECTION

Diagram of cave features
Side 2: 2636, single frame

Aerial photos of karst topography
Side 2: 2640 to 2646, 7-frame sequence

9.13 This 1991 sinkhole in Florida was caused by overpumping groundwater.

IV Caverns and Mineral Deposits

Topic 17 How Caverns Form

Limestone is a common bedrock that dissolves more easily than some other types of rock. Limestone is dissolved by groundwater because groundwater always contains some carbonic acid. Carbonic acid forms when carbon dioxide gas in the air dissolves in falling rainwater. Dissolving the calcite in limestone either creates porosity in limestone or increases the porosity that is already present. Limestone formations are also frequently split by fissures that run down from the surface and by cracks that run horizontally between the beds. As groundwater flows through the limestone, the carbonic acid slowly dissolves the limestone and carries ions away in solution.

After thousands of years, the cracks between beds become so large that they form networks of underground tunnels, sometimes many kilometers long and hundreds of meters deep. The enlarged vertical fissures may form openings at Earth's surface. These tunnels are called *caverns*, or caves. *Sinkholes* form when parts of a cave roof collapses, forming a hole or a depression in Earth's surface. Ponds or lakes form when the sinkhole is deep enough to meet the water table.

Limestone caverns are found in many parts of the world. Some of the best-known caverns in the United States are Carlsbad Caverns in New Mexico, Mammoth Cave in Kentucky, Luray Caverns in Virginia, Howe Caverns in New York, Oregon Caves in Oregon, and Wind Cave in South Dakota.

A natural bridge may form when a surface river disappears into a fissure in the bedrock, runs underground a short distance, and then gushes out of a crack on the face of a cliff. As the fissure and the crack are enlarged, part of the cliff is left as a natural bridge.

Topic 18 Karst Topography

In regions of caverns, most rainwater enters the ground through sinkholes and fissures. Thus there are very few surface rivers. Lost rivers are formed when surface streams disappear underground and flow out of caves many kilometers away. Regions characterized by sinks, sinkhole ponds, lost rivers, and underground drainage are said to have *karst topography*. This name comes from the Kars Plateau region of Yugoslavia. Karst topography forms in areas with bedrock made of calcite, dolomite, or other minerals that dissolve easily. The Mammoth Cave region of Kentucky has karst topography. Other karst regions in the United States are found in Florida, Tennessee, and Indiana.

Topic 19   Mineral Deposits by Groundwater

The minerals dissolved in groundwater are deposited in a variety of ways. Where groundwater drips from the roof of a limestone cave, it slowly deposits some of the calcite. Deposits shaped like icicles hang from the roof along the routes of the dripping water. These slender calcite formations are *stalactites*. On the floor beneath the stalactites, blunt, rounded masses called *stalagmites* are formed. When stalactites and stalagmites meet, columns, or pillars, are made. Stalactites, stalagmites, and pillars are all examples of *dripstone*. Dripstone is a calcite deposit formed from dripping water in caverns. Dripstone can form only when a cave is above the water table, where water can evaporate.

Calcite deposits around mineral springs are called *travertine* (TRAV er teen). Among the most famous travertine deposits are the delicately colored terraces around Mammoth Hot Springs in Yellowstone National Park. Here the hot water pours out of long hillside fissures in limestone bedrock, depositing some of its dissolved calcite as it cools. Algae grow on the moist terraces, producing a variety of beautiful colors.

Around the openings of geysers, a white porous substance called *geyserite* is deposited. Geyserite is silica dissolved from the hot igneous rock through which the geyser waters pass on their way to the surface. Hot groundwater often leaves deposits of minerals in bedrock cracks and fissures. Such mineral veins may contain quartz, calcite, gold, and silver.

Petrified wood is formed when minerals dissolved in groundwater replace the decaying wood of buried trees. As each microscopic particle of wood is replaced by a grain of mineral matter, many details of the wood structure are reproduced. The petrified trees of Arizona, which formed in this way, consist of silica.

Perhaps the most important groundwater deposit is the cement that binds together the sand grains and pebbles of sedimentary deposits to form rocks. While calcite is the most common cementing mineral, silica and iron oxides also serve as natural cements.

TOPIC QUESTIONS

Each topic question refers to the topic of the same number.

17. (a) Explain how groundwater forms sinkholes, caverns, natural bridges, and sinkhole ponds.   (b) Why are limestone caves common?

18. Describe karst topography and give examples.

19. (a) Explain how stalactites and stalagmites are formed. (b) What is dripstone?   (c) Explain the origin of travertine, geyserite, and petrified wood.

9.14 The travertine covering these terraces was deposited when mineral-rich hot spring water evaporated.

VIDEODISC SELECTION

Travertine deposit at Yellowstone Park
Side 2: 1570 to 1575, 6-frame sequence

ANSWERS
   17. (a) Groundwater contains carbonic acid, which dissolves limestone. Formations occur along cracks and fissures.   (b) most limestone occurs at or near surface, dissolves easily
   18. regions of sinks, caverns, sinkhole ponds, lost rivers; Yugoslavia, Kentucky, Florida, Tennessee, Indiana
   19. (a) dripping water in cave evaporates   (b) any calcite deposit formed by dripping   (c) in order: calcite deposit around mineral springs; silica deposit around geysers; wood cells replaced by minerals in groundwater

CHAPTER 9

LAB ACTIVITY

Interpreting Water Budgets

As a renewable natural resource, fresh water is constantly being recycled by the sun. However, not every location receives the same amount of water or has the same amount of groundwater available to use.

Water availability is described in water budgets. In a water budget (Topics 3 and 4), periods of water usage, deficit, recharge, and surplus are controlled by the storage of groundwater. In calculating a water budget, the ground is assumed to hold a certain amount of water. That amount is often 100 millimeters (mm). Thus, a water surplus occurs when a total of 100 millimeters or more of water has been recharged into the soil, and a water deficit occurs when 100 millimeters or more has been taken from the soil (usage).

Lab Skills and Objectives

■ To **describe** how water usage, deficit, recharge, and surplus are shown in both water budget data and graphs

■ To **compare** and **contrast** water budget graphs from different areas

Materials

■ water budget data, Figures 9.15 and 9.16
■ notebook paper
■ water budget graphs for Phoenix, Hartford, and Little Rock, Figures 9.4 and 9.5, pages 151 and 152

Procedure

1. On your paper, make a copy of the table and the data shown in Figure 9.15. Copy the numbers carefully. Include the pluses and minuses where shown.

2. Locate the row for *Supply Minus Need* on the table. Start with the value for May. Because the value in the previous month was positive, the negative value in May shows that this is the first month in which water will need to be drawn from the groundwater. In other words, May is the first month of water usage. On the line labeled *Water Budget Section*, write U for usage in May.

3. Usage will continue until the negative values total 100. The –28 for May and the –50 for June do not add up to –100. Therefore, June is also a usage month. Write a *U* on the table for June.

4. Adding the negative value for July to those for May and June brings the total to –104. This means that the groundwater storage is emptied in July, beginning a period of water deficit. To show the change from usage to deficit, write *U/D* on the table for July.

5. August, September, and October also have negative values. Because the groundwater was drained completely in July, these are deficit months. Write *D* on the table for August, September, and October.

6. November is the first month with a positive value. This means that the groundwater storage will start to fill again in that month. To show this change, write *R* for *recharge* in November.

7. The +34 for November and the +82 for December total more than the storage capacity of 100. Therefore, water surplus begins in December. To show the change from recharge to surplus, write *R/S* for December.

8. The values for January, February, March, and April continue to be positive. Since the storage was filled in December, surplus continues. Write *S* in the space for those four months.

9. Now make three copies of the table in Figure 9.15. Do not include any data or the city name, just the months and row names. Look at

Month	JAN	FEB	MAR	APR	MAY	JUN	JUL	AUG	SEP	OCT	NOV	DEC
Supply	108	131	125	95	96	115	155	142	88	61	60	99
Need	15	19	45	76	124	165	181	166	129	73	26	17
Supply Minus Need	+93	+112	+80	+19	−28	−50	−26	−24	−41	−12	+34	+82
Water Budget Section	S	S	S	S	U	U	U/D	D	D	D	R	R/S

9.15 Water budget data for Albany, Georgia (mm water)

City		JAN	FEB	MAR	APR	MAY	JUN	JUL	AUG	SEP	OCT	NOV	DEC
Cumberland, Maryland	Supply	62	64	75	72	84	102	82	88	69	61	54	64
	Need	0	1	13	48	93	128	145	126	89	48	15	2
Duluth, Minnesota	Supply	27	25	39	54	79	103	95	84	80	53	41	27
	Need	0	0	0	24	66	98	127	113	75	37	0	0
Fresno, California	Supply	44	40	41	24	10	3	0	0	4	13	22	40
	Need	13	20	37	63	99	139	180	165	114	70	31	12

9.16 Water budget data for other United States cities (mm water)

Figure 9.16. Copy the data for Cumberland into one of the new tables. Use the other two tables for the data from Duluth and Fresno.

10. For each city, calculate the difference between supply and need and write the result on the *Supply Minus Need* line. Be sure to indicate if each value is positive or negative.

11. Using the symbols *U*, *U/D*, *D*, *R*, *R/S*, and *S*, label the times of usage, deficit, recharge, surplus, and transitions from usage to deficit and from recharge to surplus for the three additional cities.

12. Answer the *Analysis and Conclusions* questions.

Analysis and Conclusions

1. How are Albany and Cumberland similar in terms of water usage, deficit, recharge, and surplus?

2. Which part of the water budget (usage, deficit, recharge, or surplus,) occurs in Albany but not in Fresno? Which occurs in Albany but not in Duluth?

3. Which city is located in the driest climate? Explain your answer in terms of the duration of periods of deficit and surplus.

4. Which city has the wettest climate? Explain your answer.

5. Compare the water budget data for the four cities in this activity with the three cities in Topic 4 (Figures 9.4 and 9.5, pages 151 and 152). Of the four cities in the activity, which is most like Phoenix? Which is most like Little Rock? Which is most like Hartford? Explain your answers.

Answers to all questions appear in the Teacher's Guide at the back of this book.

■ Summary

I Less than three percent of Earth's water is fresh, and over two thirds of that is frozen. Most usable fresh water is underground.

The hydrosphere includes all of Earth's waters. The movement of water within the hydrosphere is described by the water cycle.

A water budget relates the recharge, surplus, usage, and deficit of soil water to the moisture needs and moisture supply of an area.

II Porosity is the percent of a material's volume that is pore space. Permeability is the rate at which a liquid passes through a porous material.

The water table is the top of the water-saturated region of the ground. The depth of the water table depends on climate, season, and location.

Groundwater can be obtained from natural springs or by making a well that reaches below the water table.

Several methods are used to recharge groundwater. Groundwater pollution can be prevented but it is difficult to clean up.

III Groundwater has nearly the same cool temperature all year. However, in areas of volcanism, groundwater may be very hot and hot springs may result.

Bedrock type, dissolved gases, and water temperature affect the kind and amount of mineral matter in groundwater.

IV Carbonic acid in groundwater dissolves limestone, forming features of karst topography.

Stalactites, stalagmites, travertine, geyserite, petrified wood, and the cement that binds sedimentary rocks are all groundwater deposits.

■ Vocabulary

aquifer	porosity	surplus
artesian formation	recharge	usage
deficit	hydrosphere	water budget
evapotranspiration	impermeable	water cycle
geysers	permeability	water table

■ Review

Number your paper from *1* to *15*. Write the letter of your answer on your paper.

1. Where is most usable fresh water located? (a) oceans (b) glaciers (c) lakes and rivers (d) underground

2. What is the source of energy for the water cycle? (a) solar energy (b) gravity (c) running water (d) ocean tides

3. Rainfall is greater than moisture need, and the soil is saturated. Which will occur? (a) deficit (b) recharge (c) surplus (d) usage

4. Which is the most likely description for a material with high porosity? (a) well-sorted, round grains (b) well-sorted, angular grains (c) unsorted, round grains (d) unsorted, angular grains

5. The rate at which liquids pass through a material is called (a) porosity, (b) permeability, (c) capillarity, (d) rate of recharge.

6. The water table is between (a) zone of aeration and capillary fringe, (b) soil water and capillary fringe, (c) capillary fringe and zone of saturation, (d) capillary fringe and bedrock.

7. A hillside spring occurs in places where the ground surface meets with the (a) zone of aeration, (b) capillary fringe, (c) water table, (d) bedrock.

8. Water often rises on its own in an artesian well because it is (a) under an impermeable layer, (b) under a permeable layer, (c) in a pipe, (d) under pressure.

9. Which is most likely to cause the water table to drop? (a) salt water seeping into wells (b) rainwater seeping into the ground (c) pumping water from the ground (d) pumping used water into the ground

10. The temperature of ordinary well or spring water is usually (a) warm all year, (b) warm in summer and cool in winter, (c) cool in summer and warm in winter, (d) cool all year.

For further review, see **Study Guide.**
For assessment, see **Chapter Tests**
and **Computer Test Bank.**

11. Hot water bubbling up through thick, sticky clay may cause a (a) paint pot, (b) artesian spring, (c) fumarole, (d) sinkhole.

12. Which would probably contain the most dissolved minerals? (a) artesian spring water (b) hillside spring water (c) ordinary well water (d) river water

13. Which does NOT usually affect the mineral content of a spring? (a) acid-forming gases (b) bedrock solubility (c) water temperature (d) local surface temperature

14. Caverns, sinkholes, and other features of karst topography form best in areas where the bedrock is (a) granite, (b) shale, (c) limestone, (d) sandstone.

15. Stalactites, stalagmites, and pillars are most likely to form in (a) artesian formations, (b) limestone caves, (c) hillside springs, (d) areas of impermeable bedrock.

■ Interpret and Apply

On your paper, answer each question in complete sentences.

1. In cold climates less water enters the ground during winter than in any other season. Why?

2. Compare the porosity and permeability of well-sorted sand with a mixture of sand and silt.

3. What is likely to happen to the distance between the ground surface and the water table if rainfall increases but evapotranspiration is unchanged?

4. How is a hillside spring different from a fissure spring?

5. In what ways is the water from a well 10 meters deep likely to be different from the water from a well 1000 meters deep?

6. Why does dripstone form only when a cave is above the water table?

7. In some regions, petrified wood is composed of silica. In other regions, it is composed of calcite. Why?

■ Critical Thinking

The graph shows a water budget for Springfield, Illinois, an area that has four seasons. Use the graph to answer questions 1–4.

1. If moisture need increases with air temperature, what is the warmest month?

2. What is the value for moisture need in January? Why?

3. Which months have the most rainfall?

4. In which month does the water storage finish refilling?

Compare the graph for Springfield with the three graphs in Figures 9.4 and 9.5 and answer questions 5–6.

5. Identify one way in which all four locations are alike.

6. Based on moisture need, how do summer and winter temperatures in Springfield compare with those in Little Rock?

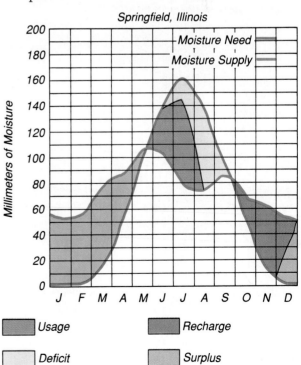

Springfield, Illinois

Millimeters of Moisture

Moisture Need
Moisture Supply

J F M A M J J A S O N D

Usage   Recharge

Deficit   Surplus

Running Water

▲
Running water is a
powerful agent of
erosion.

How Do You Know That . . .

Sediment can be moved by running water? Pour enough clay into a
tall, clear container to form a layer two centimeters deep. Cover
this layer with the same depth of sand and then with two
centimeters of coarse gravel or marble chips. Cover all the layers
with about 15 centimeters of water. With a spoon, mix the
sediment together until the layers have completely disappeared.
Stop stirring and observe the sediments as they settle. Which
materials settle first? Which settle last? Why? Stir the sediment
again. This time, try to keep stirring just fast enough to keep the
sand suspended. Which material was not suspended? What would
happen if you slowed your stirring?

1 Stream Erosion and Transportation

Topic 1 Running Water and Its Energy

Of all the agents of erosion, running water is the most effective in wearing down the surface of Earth. Running water includes all the water that falls on Earth as rain, snow, or other precipitation and then moves downhill under the pull of gravity. It begins with drops of water moving down hillsides. Running water comes together until it forms great rivers such as the Mississippi and the Amazon.

Like the other agents of erosion, running water gets its energy from the sun. The sun lifts water from the oceans by evaporation. Winds created by the sun's heating of the atmosphere carry the water vapor over the continents. When the water falls as rain or snow and runs back to the sea, it is using the sun's energy to erode the lands.

Topic 2 Running Water Attacks Bedrock

Like all agents of erosion, running water wears down the land in two ways. It breaks up bedrock and removes weathered and eroded rock and soil materials.

Running water breaks up the bedrock over which it flows primarily by mechanical means. Using sand, pebbles, and even boulders as its cutting tools, running water grinds and hammers away at its bed. The grinding action is called **abrasion.** Abrasion also causes the cutting tools themselves to be worn down, especially at their edges. In time, abrasion produces the rounded boulders, pebbles, and sand grains that are commonly found in the beds of streams and rivers.

Cutting tools are very important for stream erosion. However, even clear water can break up the rock of a streambed if it runs fast enough. Rapidly flowing water has a lifting effect that splits off and moves rock fragments.

Running water's chemical attack on bedrock consists of dissolving soluble minerals. Limestone, marble, and sandstones that are held together with calcite cements are affected in this way. Rivers flowing over such rocks form pits and holes in the riverbed, and widen existing cracks and holes.

OBJECTIVES

A Explain how running water gets its energy from the sun.

B Describe three ways in which running water breaks up bedrock.

C Describe the three ways running water transports rock material.

D Discuss the relationship between stream speed, discharge, and carrying power.

SCIENCE BACKGROUND

Worldwide, running water is the dominant agent of erosion. Even in a desert, a single rainstorm will make more changes in the landscape than a constant blowing wind. Only areas now covered with ice can escape the effects of falling rain.

TEACHING TIP

Remind students that running water is the surplus moisture of the water budget.

OF INTEREST

The Shoshone River in Wyoming reduces 20- to 30-cm andesite boulders to half their size as it rolls them along its streambed over a distance of only a few tens of kilometers.

TEACHING TIP

The physical grinding caused by windblown sand is also called abrasion. Wind erosion is discussed in Chapter 12.

VIDEODISC SELECTION

Abrasive tools of moving water
Side 2: 1978 to 1979, 2-frame sequence

TEACHING TIP
Be prepared to point out that "brook," "creek," "stream," and "river" are all names for the same thing and are often used interchangeably although "brook" and "creek" imply a smaller stream and "river" a larger one.

SCIENCE BACKGROUND
The relative amount of the stream load carried by each method depends upon the nature of the stream, the climate, the kind of bedrock, and the season.

VIDEODISC SELECTION

A sediment-filled river
Side 2: 2070, single frame

SCIENCE BACKGROUND
Particles that jump or bounce are said to move by saltation; those that roll or slide, by traction.

Topic 3 Water Removes Weathered Rock

When rain runs down even the gentlest of slopes, it carries some weathered rock material with it. Eventually this material reaches a larger and more permanent body of running water such as a tiny brook. The brook is probably part of some river system. The sediment carried by the brook finds its way through larger and larger streams until it reaches the main river. Once in the main river, the water may be carried to a lake or the ocean.

Rivers carry rock material in three ways. Some mineral matter is carried in **solution.** This is material that has dissolved from bedrock. Most of the solution load comes to the river from the groundwater that constantly seeps into streams. The most common minerals carried in solution are compounds of calcium and magnesium.

When river water looks muddy, it is carrying rock material in **suspension.** Suspended material includes clay, silt, and fine sand. Although these materials are heavier than water, they are stirred up and kept from sinking by the turbulence of stream flow. Turbulence includes swirls and eddies that form in water from friction between the stream and its bed and banks. The faster the stream flows, the more turbulent and muddy it becomes. A rough bed also increases turbulence. (See Figure 10.1.)

Sand, pebbles, and boulders that are too heavy to be carried in suspension may be moved along the stream bed, especially during floods. Boulders and pebbles roll or slide along the riverbed. Large sand grains are pushed along the bottom in a series of jumps and bounces. Sediment moved along the stream bed is called the **bed load.**

Geologists estimate that the rivers of the United States carry about 25 percent of their load in solution, about 50 percent in suspension, and about 25 percent as bed load. In general, the suspended load increases with human use of the land. On the other hand, streams flowing from undisturbed areas may have only 25 percent of the load in suspension but 75 percent in solution.

10.1 This diagram shows the rock materials carried by a stream, the name of the carrying process, and the level at which each material is normally found.

Solution:
Dissolved Minerals

Suspension:
Silt, Clay

Bedload:
*Sand, Gravel,
Pebbles, Boulders*

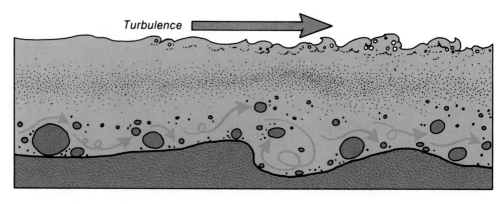

Turbulence

Topic 4 Carrying Power and Load

The **carrying power** of a stream is indicated by both the total amount of sediment in the stream and by the size of the particles being moved by the stream. The carrying power depends upon the speed of the stream and its discharge. Stream **discharge** is the volume of water flowing past a given point in the stream at a given time. Discharge is usually expressed in cubic meters per second or cubic feet per second.

Streams moving at high speed with high discharge can carry both a large amount of sediment and larger sizes of sediment particles than slow-moving streams with small discharge. For example, when the speed of a stream doubles, the ability of the stream to carry larger particles in suspension more than doubles. At normal times the lower Mississippi River may carry nothing larger than silt in suspension. During a flood, the river carries sand and pebbles. The carrying power of a stream increases as the speed and discharge of the stream increases.

The speed of a stream depends mainly upon the steepness, or gradient, of its bed. Speed also increases with increased discharge. During floods the discharge of a river increases tremendously, and its carrying power may be hundreds of times as great. For this reason much of the erosion caused by moving water occurs during floods when the river can erode deeper into its bedrock.

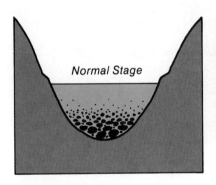

Normal Stage

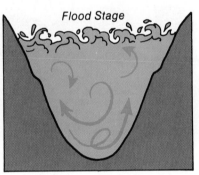

Flood Stage

TOPIC QUESTIONS

Each topic question refers to the topic of the same number.

1. **(a)** Define *running water.*   **(b)** How does running water get its energy from the sun?

2. How does running water break up bedrock?

3. List the three ways rivers carry materials and the most common materials carried by each.

4. **(a)** What two factors indicate the carrying power of a stream? **(b)** What affects the carrying power of a stream?   **(c)** What is a stream's discharge?   **(d)** Why does erosion of a riverbed increase so much during flood times?

SCIENCE BACKGROUND

 Part of a stream's energy is used up in overcoming external friction with its bed and internal friction with water turbulence.

VIDEODISC SELECTION

Aftermath of a flood, Big Thompson River, Colorado, August, 1976
Side 2: 2084, single frame

OF INTEREST

 In April of 1987, a flood on Schoharie Creek in New York State caused the sudden and unpredicted collapse of a four-lane bridge on the New York State Thruway.

10.2 When a river is at flood stage, it flows much faster than normal. It picks up the sediments from the bottom and scours the rock of the riverbed.

ANSWERS

 1. (a) all water that falls as rain or snow and moves downhill by pull of gravity   (b) Sun lifts water into air through evaporation.
 2. Sand, pebbles, etc., in water act as cutting tools—moving water splits off and moves rock fragments.
 3. solution—compounds of Ca and Mg; suspension—clay, silt, fine sand; bed load—sand, pebbles, boulders
 4. (a) total amount of sediment it carries, particle sizes it carries   (b) speed and discharge of the stream (c) volume of water flowing past a given point in a given time   (d) Speed, discharge, and carrying power are greatly increased.

OBJECTIVES

A Explain how rivers form V-shaped valleys and canyons.

B Describe what occurs as a river approaches its base level.

C Define *headward erosion* and identify some features that result from headward erosion.

D Define *stream divide* and *drainage basin* and locate these features for a river system.

SCIENCE BACKGROUND

Youthful valleys are primarily downcutting their beds.

SCIENCE BACKGROUND

V-shaped valleys occur in areas with enough rainfall to wash the sides of the valley into the stream. Canyons occur in dry areas that have little or no erosion of the valley walls.

II The River Valley

Topic 5 V-Shaped Valleys and Canyons

The streams of mountain regions and high plateaus are likely to have formed relatively recently. Such young, or youthful, streams typically have V-shaped valleys. This shape occurs because youthful streams tend to flow at high speeds, which easily scour the streambed. At the same time, the upper valley walls are widened by weathering and erosion.

Valleys with very steep, almost vertical sides are features of scenic interest. Steep valleys are called canyons, gorges, or chasms. The Grand Canyon of the Colorado River, Royal Gorge of the Arkansas River in Colorado, and Ausable Chasm in New York State are examples.

How long does it take a river to make a canyon? The time depends upon the kind of rock the river must erode, the amount of water and sediment in the river, the climate of the area, as well as several other factors. The Colorado River is thought to have taken millions of years to cut the mile-deep canyon into the rocks of the Colorado Plateau. Other rivers in wetter climates may take less time to cut canyons in softer rock.

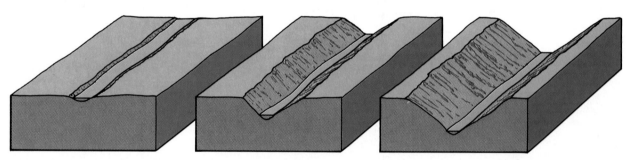

10.3 Young river valleys are V-shaped because while the river is cutting into the valley floor, the valley walls are being worn back by weathering and tributary streams.

VIDEODISC SELECTION

Photo of V-shaped valley
Side 2: 1980, single frame

Topic 6 Base Level: Widening the Valley

A stream cannot cut its bed any lower than the level of the stream, river, or body of water into which it flows. The level is called the **base level** of the stream. For streams that flow into an ocean, the base level is sea level. For streams that flow into lakes or rivers, the base level is the level of the lake or river.

As a stream approaches its base level, the slope of the streambed and the speed of the stream decrease. As a result, the stream cuts into its bed much more slowly. Meanwhile, the valley walls continue to be attacked by weathering, erosion, tributary streams, and the river itself. (See Topic 13.) The result is a wider valley with a broad floor and gentle sloping walls.

b
a

Topic 7 Lengthening the Valley

When a hillside is stripped of its trees and shrubs, it loses its protective covering. A single heavy rain may form a miniature stream valley. This valley is likely to be V-shaped and to have tributaries running into it. When the rain ends, the stream may disappear, but the small valley remains. Such a feature is called a **gully.**

Gullies grow in length, width, and depth every time it rains. The term **headward erosion** means the wearing away of land at the head of the gully or stream valley. Headward erosion makes the gully longer. As a gully grows in length and depth, the stream may cut below the water table. When this occurs, the stream becomes a permanent stream. When the tributary gullies also cut below the water table, a river system is born. Most of the world's river systems probably began in this way.

Even in deserts, water is the main agent of erosion. Desert cloudbursts cause many small streams to flow temporarily. In dry regions of soft clay beds, these temporary streams form many small gullies with steep slopes. Early European explorers in the Americas found some of these badly-eroded regions so difficult to travel through that they called them badlands. Among the best-known badlands in the United States are those in South Dakota, North Dakota, and Nebraska.

10.4 (a) This young river flows fast. Its valley floor is wearing down much faster than its sides. **(b)** This is also a fast-flowing river, but in this valley the walls are also eroding. This V-shaped valley is noticeably different from the nearly vertical walls in (a).

VIDEODISC SELECTION

Gully formation
Side 2: 2002, single frame

SCIENCE BACKGROUND

The South Dakota Badlands consist of soft sedimentary rocks deposited 23 to 27 million years ago (Oligocene Epoch) on a broad, marshy plain crossed by sluggish streams. Later uplift and erosion carved deep gullies into the sedimentary layers. Rapid erosion continues today and prevents plant cover from developing in the area.

a

b

10.5 **(a)** Headward erosion will cause this gully to become deeper and larger. **(b)** The Badlands National Monument contains a giant maze of gullies.

Topic 8 **Divides and Drainage Basins**

TEACHING TIP
Use the streams and watersheds of your own area to help define these terms.

The high land that separates one gully from the next, or one river valley from the next, is called a **divide.** The major divide of the United States, called the Great Continental Divide, is located in the Rocky Mountains. Rain falling east of the Great Continental Divide eventually flows into the Atlantic Ocean. Rain falling west of the Great Continental Divide flows into the Pacific Ocean.

A river and all of its tributaries is called a *river system.* The **drainage basin,** or **watershed,** of a river includes all of the land that drains into the river, either directly or through its tributaries.

The largest single drainage basin in the United States is the Mississippi River system. Its western divide is the Great Continental Divide in the Rocky Mountains. Its eastern divide is a lesser continental divide in the Appalachian Mountains. To the north in Wisconsin and Minnesota, a low divide separates the Mississippi system from land sloping toward the Great Lakes and the Arctic Ocean. Within these three divides lies two fifths of the area of the United States (excluding Alaska and Hawaii).

VIDEODISC SELECTION

Aerial view of a drainage basin
Side 2: 2005. single frame

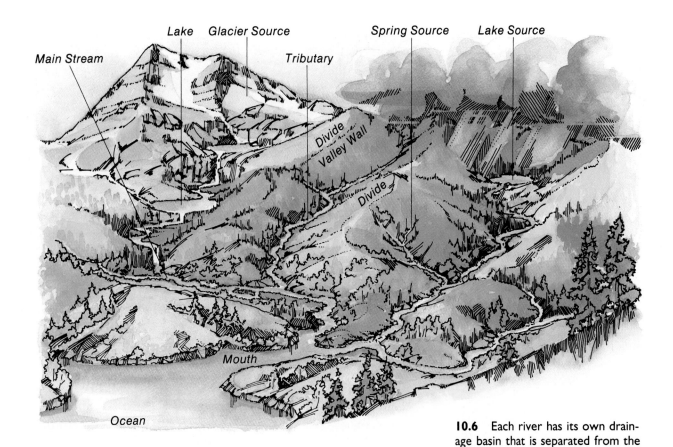

Main Stream
Lake   Glacier Source
Tributary
Spring Source   Lake Source
Divide
Valley Wall
Divide
Mouth
Ocean

10.6   Each river has its own drainage basin that is separated from the next basin by a high ridge called a divide. A river system often has tributaries from different sources.

Topic 9   **Stream Piracy**

Stream piracy, or *stream capture,* is an interesting result of the lengthening of a river by headward erosion. In Figure 10.7, two rivers are separated by a divide. As headward erosion continues, the headwaters of river *A* wear through the divide and capture the headwaters of river *B*. River *A* has grown larger and extended its drainage basin at the expense of its neighbor, river *B*.

Does stream piracy occur often? Geologists think that stream piracy has been an important factor in the early growth of many great river systems.

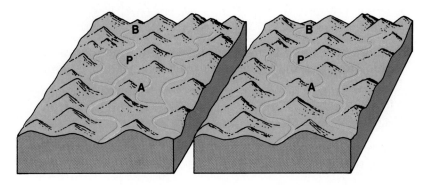

10.7   Stream piracy is illustrated as stream A extends its source by headward erosion until it captures stream B at point P.

10.8 The Delaware Water Gap

VIDEODISC SELECTION

Example of a water gap, Delaware
Side 2: 1975, single frame

Topic 10 Water Gaps and Wind Gaps

As a river cuts into its valley, it may meet an unusually resistant rock formation. As time passes, this rock formation will wear away more slowly than the surrounding rock. A narrow cut called a **water gap** forms in the ridge through which the river runs. An example is the gap in the Delaware River through the Kittatinny Mountain ridge in New Jersey and Pennsylvania.

Occasionally a gap occurs without any river in it. This abandoned water gap is a *wind gap*. These features may have formed when the water of the gap was captured by a neighboring river.

TOPIC QUESTIONS

Each topic question refers to the topic of the same number.

5. **(a)** Why does a youthful river have a V-shaped valley?   **(b)** What is a canyon? Give some examples.   **(c)** What factors determine the time needed for a river to form a canyon?

6. **(a)** What is a river's base level?   **(b)** Describe the changes in a stream as it approaches its base level.

7. **(a)** What is a gully?   **(b)** How are gullies related to rivers?

8. **(a)** What is a divide?   **(b)** What is a drainage basin?

9. What is stream piracy and how does it occur?

10. **(a)** What is a water gap? How does it form?   **(b)** What is a wind gap? How is it thought to form?

Map Skills

Question 1–3 refer to Topographic Map: Harrisburg, PA, which appears on page 652.

1. What is the general direction, or trend, in which the ridges of Blue Mountain and Second Mountain lie?

2. Blue Mountain ridges appear on both sides of the Susquehanna River. What ridge on the west of the river corresponds to the ridge of Second Mountain east of the river?

3. How does the direction of flow of the Susquehanna River compare to the trend of these ridges?

ANSWERS

5. (a) river mainly scours streambed but not walls   (b) steep-sided valley: Grand, Royal Gorge, Ausable Chasm   (c) rock type, water volume, sediment load, climate
6. (a) lowest level of stream erosion   (b) slope decreases, less cutting of streambed, more cutting of sides
7. (a) small, V-shaped valley (b) They are the start of stream systems.
8. (a) high land between drainage systems   (b) all the land that is drained by a river and its tributaries
9. capture of one stream by another through headward erosion
10. (a) cut in resistant rock made by a stream   (b) abandoned water gap, by stream piracy

ANSWERS

1. southwest to northeast
2. Cove Mountain
3. It cuts across the ridges more or less at right angles.

III   Waterfalls and River Deposits

Topic 11   Potholes and Plunge Pools

A stream running over an irregular bed develops small whirlpools in many places. As sand, pebbles, and small boulders swirl around in the whirlpools, they grind deep oval or circular holes. These basins are called **potholes.** The particles responsible for forming a pothole are often found at its bottom.

Potholes occur in any kind of rock. For example, potholes in the James River at Richmond, Virginia, have been ground out of hard granite. Potholes also come in all sizes. Most of the James River potholes are less than 1 meter deep. Some potholes in the Mohawk River valley near Little Falls, New York, are over 3 meters deep. Very large potholes are called *plunge pools.* Such potholes are commonly found at the bases of waterfalls. An example occurs at the base of the Canadian (or Horseshoe) Falls at Niagara Falls.

Topic 12   Waterfalls and Their Recession

Streams running through steep mountain regions flow over ever-changing slopes. The riverbed may be steep enough to form white water rapids. It may level out into a lake or pond, or the stream may plunge over a cliff to form a waterfall.

The steep slopes and cliffs of rapids and waterfalls occur for many reasons. The Great Falls of the Potomac occur where the Potomac River flows over hard igneous rocks onto soft sedimentary rocks. The falls in Yosemite Valley in California were formed when

OBJECTIVES

A Explain the formation of potholes and plunge pools.

B Describe some ways in which a waterfall may occur.

C List some factors that cause streams to deposit their loads.

D Explain the origin of flood plains, meanders, cutoffs, oxbow lakes, entrenched meanders, deltas, and alluvial fans.

SCIENCE BACKGROUND

The Little Falls potholes were formed at the end of the Ice Age when the St. Lawrence drainage was still blocked by ice and the Great Lakes were draining through the Mohawk Valley in a torrent of meltwater.

VIDEODISC SELECTION

Example of a pothole
Side 2: 1985, single frame

10.9   Potholes are small oval or circular basins ground out of a rocky streambed by whirlpool action.

OF INTEREST

The falls on the Potomac are just one of a series of waterfalls along the Atlantic Coast that mark the interface between the Piedmont and the Coastal Plain. Students may know about the "fall line" from their social studies classes.

10.10 The Canadian Falls at Niagara Falls.

VIDEODISC SELECTION

Niagara Falls
Side 2: 2095, single frame

SCIENCE BACKGROUND

The resistant rock at Niagara Falls is the Lockport Dolomite. Beneath it are the soft Rochester Shales. Efforts have been made to reinforce the shales and slow the recession of the falls.

10.11 Whirlpool action at Niagara Falls rapidly erodes the weak shales at the base of the falls. This erosion undermines the tough dolostone layer at the top. From time to time the dolostone breaks off, and the waterfall recedes.

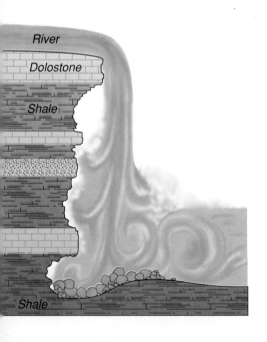

glaciers eroded one valley more deeply than others. The two great falls on the Yellowstone River in Yellowstone National Park are the result of intrusions of igneous rock.

Rapids and waterfalls are temporary features of streams because these are locations where stream erosion is greatest. One way in which streams erode at waterfalls is by *undermining*. The water falling into the plunge pool at the base of the waterfall erodes the rock there, leaving the rocks at the top of the falls to overhang (Figure 10.11). From time to time, pieces break off the top. Each time this breakage occurs, the waterfall recedes farther upstream. The rate of undermining and recession is fastest when the rocks contain fractures or are poorly cemented.

A famous example of a waterfall that recedes by undermining is Niagara Falls. Here the falls are the result of a nearly flat-lying, 20-meter-thick layer of tough dolostone. The rocks underneath the dolostone are almost all thin beds of shale. The rapidly eroding shale undermines the dolostone. The base of the American Falls is littered with huge blocks of fallen dolostone. (Dolostone is a rock similar to limestone, but it is made of dolomite rather than calcite.)

The Niagara Gorge marks the path of recession of Niagara Falls. The gorge extends from the base of the falls to Lake Ontario, a distance of about 11 kilometers. At the end of the Ice Age 11 000 years ago, Niagara Falls was located on or near Lake Ontario. The recession of the falls since that time carved the gorge.

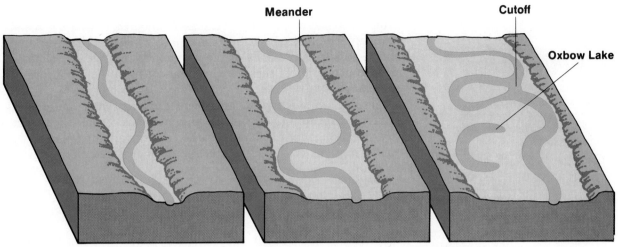

Meander

Cutoff

Oxbow Lake

10.12   Meanders are formed as a riverbed gradually shifts toward the outside of a bend in the river.

Topic 13 **Meanders and Oxbow Lakes**

In times of heavy rains, a river may overflow its banks and cover part of the valley floor. This part of the valley floor is the **flood plain.** At first the flood plain is narrow, but as time passes it becomes wider. Why? As a river cuts its bed lower and lower, its slope and speed decreases. The river is more easily deflected sideward, and its course becomes more winding. The banks and valley walls are eroded, and the valley floor is widened.

When a river swings around a bend, the fastest-moving water is on the outside of the bend. Erosion is most rapid there. The water is shallowest on the inside of the bend. Sediment is often deposited there. In time, the riverbed is shifted toward the outside of its bend. If one bend shifts to the right, the next bend shifts to the left. As this pattern continues, the river eventually forms a series of broad curves across a wide flood plain. The broad curves are called **meanders** (mee AN ders).

VIDEODISC SELECTION

River meanders and oxbows
(described in disc directory)
Side 2: 2043 to 2049, 7-frame sequence

10.13   This aerial view of the Yukon River shows a meandering river with an oxbow in the upper right corner.

VIDEODISC SELECTION

An entrenched meander
Side 2: 2040 to 2042, 3-frame
sequence

SCIENCE BACKGROUND

Meanders are named for the Meander River in Turkey. Entrenched meanders are the result of the rejuvenation of an area by uplift.

There is a limit to how large a meander can become. As it swings wider and wider, the curve becomes a loop that the river breaks through. The breakthrough is called a *cutoff.* Then the river drops mud and silt at the ends of the abandoned meander. In time the deposits completely separate the meander from the river, forming an **oxbow lake.**

Entrenched meanders are deep canyons with meandering courses that are found on some high plateaus. Entrenched meanders are thought to have formed when the surrounding plateau was raised high above sea level after the meanders had already developed on a flood plain.

Topic 14 **Why Rivers Deposit Sediment**

A river may deposit a part of its load of sediment with each decrease in either speed or discharge.

A river's speed decreases when its slope decreases, its bed widens, or it meets an obstruction in the form of a curving bank or a rock outcrop. However, the greatest loss of speed occurs when the river empties into a sea or a lake. At this point all its remaining sediment is deposited.

A river's discharge may decrease if it passes through an arid region where it loses water by evaporation into the air and seepage into the ground. (In humid regions, rivers usually grow larger as they approach a sea and acquire new tributaries.) Discharge may also decrease when people divert water for farmland irrigation or city water supplies.

10.14 **(a)** Three stages in the growth of a river delta **(b)** *Landsat* image of the Mississippi River delta

a

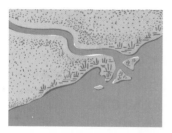

b

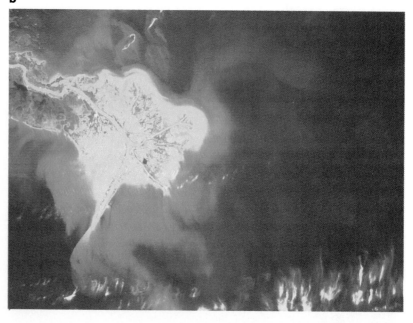

Why does a river leave so much sediment on its valley floor after a flood? As the flooding waters subside, the river's ability to hold its sediment is greatly diminished by losses in both discharge and speed.

Topic 15 **Deltas and Alluvial Fans**

The Mississippi, the Nile, and other great rivers have level, fan-shaped deposits at their mouths. These deposits are called **deltas.** Deltas form when the river flows into a quiet body of water, such as a lake, a gulf, or an inland sea. The river water comes almost to a standstill. Most of its sediment drops at the river's mouth. The river is split into channels by its own deposits and drops more sediment. As the deposit grows in size, it may resemble the shape of the Greek letter Δ (delta). A river flowing over its delta splits into branches called distributaries. Rivers that flow into an open ocean rarely form deltas because strong waves and currents usually carry the sediment away as fast as the river delivers it.

In dry regions, a steep mountain stream may meet dry, level land at the base of the mountain, rather than a lake. When it reaches the land, it slows down greatly. As a result, the stream drops a large part of its sediment load, and a fan-shaped deposit forms. This deposit differs from a delta in several ways. For one, the deposit is formed on land, not in water. Second, the sediments of these deposits are coarse sands and gravels, rather than the fine silts and clays of deltas. Also, their surface is sloping, not flat like a delta. These sloping deposits are called **alluvial fans.** Alluvial fans are most common in desert or semidesert regions. In the United States many of these formations occur at the foot of the Rocky Mountains and the Sierra Nevadas.

SCIENCE BACKGROUND

Other rivers with large deltas are the Rhine, Hwang Ho, Niger, Indus, Irrawaddy, Ganges, Mekong, Danube, Po, Rhône, Ebro, Volga, and Lena.

SCIENCE BACKGROUND

Not all deltas are delta- or fan-shaped. Delta shape is affected by the strength of waves and tides at the river mouth and by the river's discharge and load.

VIDEODISC SELECTION

Stream delta
Side 2: 2118, single frame

Alluvial fans
Side 2: 2127, single frame

10.15 This alluvial fan formed as sediments were washed down from the slopes above.

ANSWERS

11. (a) swirling particles grind them into streambed   (b) large pothole at base of waterfall

12. (a) in order: change in rock hardness, glacial erosion, resistant igneous intrusion   (b) undermines softer rock at base of falls

13. (a) part of valley floor underwater during floods   (b) outside of river bend is eroded more and river channel moves sideways   (c) abandonment of a meander   (d) uplift of land on which meanders have already formed

14. The river's slope decreases, its bed widens, there is an obstruction, excess evaporation, seepage, diversion

15. (a) Loss of velocity causes stream to deposit sediment at its mouth.   (b) those that flow into oceans; waves and currents remove sediment   (c) streams from mountains in dry areas drop sediment on land   (d) forms on land, has coarser particles and steeper slope

TOPIC QUESTIONS

Each topic question refers to the topic of the same number.

11. **(a)** How do potholes form?   **(b)** What is a plunge pool?

12. **(a)** What are the conditions that led to the formation of the Great Falls of the Potomac, the falls of Yosemite Valley, and the falls of the Yellowstone River?   **(b)** How does the action in plunge pools make Niagara Falls recede?

13. **(a)** What is a flood plain?   **(b)** How does a meander develop?   **(c)** How does an oxbow lake form?   **(d)** How do geologists think entrenched meanders form?

14. Name some factors that can cause a river's speed and discharge to decrease, leading to deposition.

15. **(a)** Explain how a delta forms.   **(b)** Which rivers do not form deltas? Why?   **(c)** How is an alluvial fan formed?   **(d)** How does an alluvial fan differ from a delta?

CAREERS

Saundra Duncan
Water Quality Chemist

The water quality of streams and rivers is a growing concern in many areas of the United States. In an effort to determine the present quality of the nation's running water, the U.S. Geological Survey regularly samples and tests streams throughout the country. Saundra Duncan is a chemist at the Denver Central Laboratory, where water samples collected west of the Mississippi River are sent for testing. She says that the samples are tested for many different substances. These include metals such as sodium, potassium, calcium, and aluminum, and ions such as chloride, bicarbonate, sulfate, and bromide.

Tests are also made for dangerous pollutants such as PCB's, dioxin, DDT, and benzene.

Ms. Duncan points out that the function of her lab is not to oversee the cleanup of problem streams but to try to define the conditions as they now exist. Once that is done, her lab may then try to predict what effect additional industries or people will have on the water quality of the watershed tested.

IV The Flood Plain and Floods

Topic 16 Sediment on the Flood Plain

During floods, great rivers like the Mississippi River carry large amounts of sediment. When such a river overflows onto its flood plain, the speed of the river slows and its sediment load is immediately deposited. Thick deposits build up alongside the stream banks. These deposits form elevated ridges called natural **levees.**

Beyond the levees the flood plain is lower, and the sediments are a finer texture. The flood plain slopes away from the river, and swamps, called *back swamps,* may form in the lowest areas. New tributaries may also form and flow through the back swamps. Some may flow for many kilometers parallel to the main stream before breaking through the levee to join the main stream.

Flood plains are among the most fertile agricultural areas in the world. The fertility of a flood plain is due partly to the minerals and soil nutrients that each flood deposits on the valley floor. Flood plains in arid regions, such as that of the Nile River in Egypt, were of great importance in the development of early civilization.

OBJECTIVES

A Describe the origin of levees and back swamps.

B Describe the conditions that lead to normal flooding and conditions that lead to flash flooding.

C Discuss the formation of natural dams.

D Describe methods used to prevent floods.

10.16 (top) The flood plain slopes away from the natural levee toward an area where back swamps form. (bottom) A natural levee along the Mississippi River

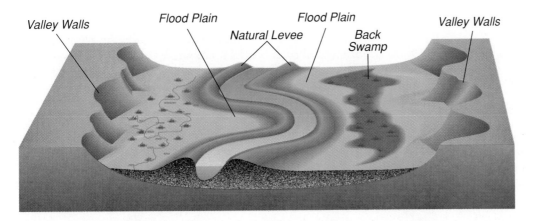

Valley Walls   Flood Plain   Flood Plain   Valley Walls
Natural Levee   Back Swamp

SCIENCE BACKGROUND
Streams that parallel the main stream for considerable distances before joining it are called yazoo streams after the Yazoo River, which parallels the Mississippi River for more than 150 kilometers before joining it at Vicksburg, Mississippi.

OF INTEREST
In addition to the Nile, two other rivers with historically important flood plains are the Tigris and the Euphrates. The regular flooding of the Ganges is important to agriculture in India today.

OF INTEREST
In June 1990, a flash flood tore through Shadyside, Ohio, destroying over 200 houses and trailers and killing over 30 people.

VIDEODISC SELECTION

Flooding after collapse of Teton Dam, Idaho
Side 2: 2113, single frame

10.17 Many cities are located on or near rivers. Flood damage can be a serious threat to those highly populated areas.

Topic 17 **Main Causes of River Floods**

River floods can be destructive as well as constructive. As a result, the causes and control of floods are of great importance.

Most river floods result from heavy or long-lasting rains, the rapid melting of winter snows, or both. A single cloudburst may cause a **flash flood,** especially if the cloudburst occurs over the narrow valley of a young mountain stream. Towns at the bases of such valleys suffer severe damage when hit by flash floods. Such floods are common in many parts of the United States.

Large rivers such as the Ohio, Missouri, and Mississippi do not have flash floods. Their floods result from many days of steady rainfall over large parts of their vast drainage basins. In winter and early spring, thaws (warm spells that melt snow) increase the runoff, especially when the ground is still frozen. Frozen ground is not porous. During a thaw, melted snow cannot soak into the ground.

Topic 18 **Other Causes of River Floods**

When a dam forms across a river, it floods the valley above the river up to the height of the dam. Dams are built to create reservoirs. Dams also form naturally.

A common type of natural dam is the ice jam. An ice jam may form when a frozen river breaks up in winter or spring thaws. Other natural dams may result when a volcano erupts and deposits ash, cinders, or lava across streams. Dams caused by landslides are even more common.

Many bad floods have been caused by the failure of reservoir dams. The famous Johnstown, Pennsylvania flood of 1889 happened when a dam made of earth collapsed after days of heavy rain. The dam had been built to make a reservoir three kilometers above Johnstown. When the dam broke, the water in the reservoir burst down on the sleeping city, drowning more than 2200 people.

In 1963, a massive landslide poured into a reservoir in the Italian Alps. The dam held, but a surge of water swept over the dam and destroyed the town of Longarone, drowning 3000 people.

Topic 19 **Preventing Floods**

Can floods be prevented? The causes of floods are largely natural. The removal of natural vegetation, such as trees, shrubs, and grass, usually increases runoff. In areas where vegetation has been removed, reforestation (the replanting of trees and other vegetation) helps to prevent floods. Replanting is most important in the headwater parts of a river's drainage basin.

If floodwaters are already swelling the river's tributaries, can they be contained before they overflow the main stream? If dams are built across headwaters and tributaries, excess runoff can be stored in reservoirs. An example of this method of flood control is seen in the Tennessee River system, where 26 dams have been built to control the river.

Great rivers such as the Ohio, Missouri, and Mississippi must rise above their natural levees to overflow. Here the usual method of flood control is to build up the levees. Artificial levees are made by placing sandbags or other materials on top of natural levees.

What can be done to control flooding near a river's mouth? On the lower Mississippi, spillways are used. Spillways are channels that run through the 10 to 17 back swamps parallel to the main stream and then flow into the Gulf of Mexico. At certain points on the flood plain, water is guided into these spillways to relieve the flooding in the Mississippi itself. In general, flood problems are becoming more severe because more land is being cleared of vegetation as it is being developed. Land that is covered with buildings and pavement does not absorb water, so development increases problems with runoff. It is essential that lakes, ponds, swamps, and other natural storage areas for rainwater not be filled in or used for building purposes.

TOPIC QUESTIONS

Each topic question refers to the topic of the same number.

16. **(a)** How do natural levees form?   **(b)** Where do back swamps form?   **(c)** Why are flood plains fertile?

17. **(a)** What is a flash flood?   **(b)** What causes floods in large rivers?

18. Name three kinds of natural dams and explain how they form.

19. Explain how each of the following helps to prevent floods: **(a)** reforestation,   **(b)** building of dams,   **(c)** artificial levees, **(d)** spillways.

VIDEODISC SELECTION

Protecting a home from flooding
Side 2: 2080, single frame

10.18 In emergency situations people build artificial levees to control flooding.

SCIENCE BACKGROUND
  Unfortunately, raising levees is only a temporary solution to flooding. The bed of the river is raised in response to higher levees. To continue to prevent floods, either the levees must be raised again between floods or the river must be dredged to lower the bed.

ANSWERS
  16. (a) deposition of sediment at stream bank during flood   (b) in low areas on flood plain   (c) new minerals and nutrients are left by each flood
  17. (a) flood from cloudburst (b) steady rains over large part of basin
  18. ice jam—frozen river breaks up; volcanic eruptions—ash, cinder, lava deposits; landslides
  19. (a) decreases runoff (b) stores excess runoff   (c) prevent overflowing   (d) drain and store excess water

CHAPTER 10

MAP ACTIVITY

Stream Divides and River Systems

Every second, over 500 000 cubic feet of water pour from the Mississippi River into the Gulf of Mexico. All this water originally fell as precipitation in places as far away as Montana and Pennsylvania. Over time, the water flowed through the various rivers and tributaries of the Mississippi River system, working its way to the Gulf.

In this exercise, you will be examining the drainage basins for the Mississippi and other major river systems in the United States.

Map Skills and Objectives
- To **identify** major United States river systems
- To **locate** the drainage divides that form the boundaries of those systems

Materials
- 2 copies of this textbook
- Physical United States map, pages 654–655
- Figure 10.19, outline map of United States showing the major rivers
- tracing paper
- 4 paper clips
- colored pencils

For additional activities, see Laboratory Investigations booklet.

Procedure
1. Work with a partner. Open one of your textbooks to the Physical United States map. Keep the other textbook open to this activity.
2. Use the paper clips to fasten a sheet of tracing paper over Figure 10.19. Trace the outline of the United States coastline.
3. Locate the mouth of the Mississippi River on the river map. Use the Physical United States map as a reference. Use a colored pencil to trace the Mississippi River and all of its tributaries onto the tracing paper.
4. Draw a continuous line around all the rivers you have traced in step 3. The area inside this line should include all of the rivers that flow into the Mississippi River system. The line should not cross any rivers. Label the enclosed area *Mississippi River system.* Use the same colored pencil to lightly shade in the area.
5. Locate the Colorado River. Use a different colored pencil to outline, label, and shade the Colorado River system. (Note: There are two Colorado rivers on your maps. Be sure to use the one that starts in Colorado.)
6. Repeat step 5 for the Columbia River system, the Rio Grande system, and the St. Lawrence River system.
7. Draw a line to show the location of the Great Continental Divide.
8. Answer the questions in *Analysis and Conclusions.*

Analysis and Conclusions
1. In the continental United States, what happens to rain that falls west of the Great Continental Divide? Rain that falls east?
2. The headwaters of three river systems are located in Colorado along the Great Continental Divide. Identify the three systems.
3. Identify the river system in which each of the following rivers are found (a) Snake River, (b) Platte River, (c) Green River, (d) Wabash River, (e) Cumberland River, and (f) Gila River.
4. What is the source of the water in the St. Lawrence River? In what general direction does the river flow?
5. Identify 3 rivers for which the Mississippi River is the base level.
6. Identify the bay, sound, or gulf that serves as base level for (a) the Sacramento and San Joaquin rivers, (b) the Alabama River system, and (c) the Connecticut River system.
7. Locate and label the James, Roanoke, and Savannah rivers. In what topographic feature do these rivers originate?
8. Name the largest river that flows through the area where you live. Where does that river originate and what is its base level? Is the river part of any of the river systems shown on the map? If so, which one?
9. Locate the rivers shown in central Nevada. Why are these rivers not part of a larger river system?

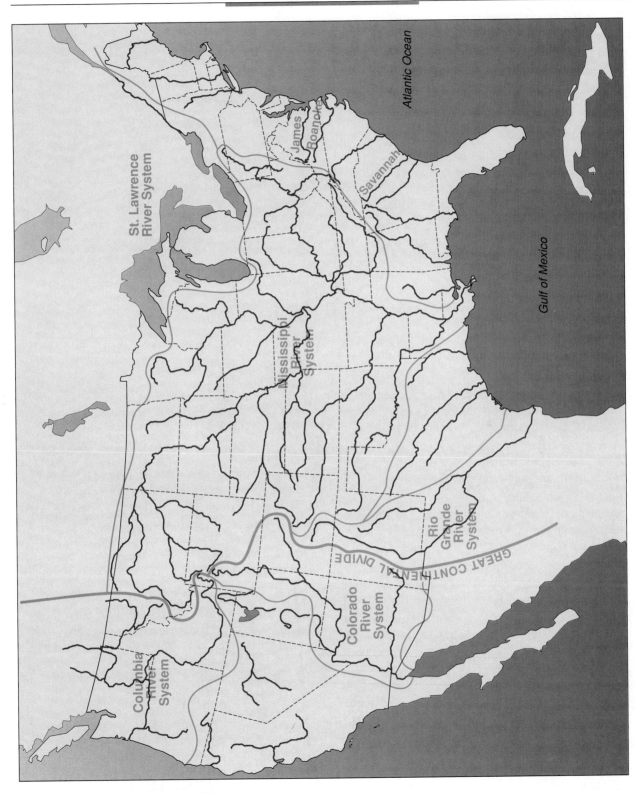

10.19 Major rivers of the United States

Answers to all questions appear in the Teacher's Guide at the back of this book.

■ Summary

I Running water includes all the water that falls on Earth and is moved downhill by gravity. It gets its energy from the sun.

Running water breaks up bedrock by abrasion, by lifting particles, and by dissolving soluble minerals. The particles that result are carried by solution, in suspension, and as bed load.

The carrying power of a stream refers to the amount of sediment it carries and the size of particles it can carry. Carrying power increases as stream speed and discharge increase.

II Youthful streams form V-shaped valleys and steep-sided gorges and canyons.

Base level is the lowest level to which a stream can erode its bed.

Headward erosion is the process by which a stream lengthens its valley. Stream piracy is a result of headward erosion. Gullies can grow into stream systems through headward erosion.

A drainage basin, or watershed, includes the area drained by a river and all of its tributaries. A divide is the high land between drainage basins.

III Features that result from stream erosion include water gaps, wind gaps, waterfalls, potholes, and plunge pools. Some plunge pools are involved in waterfall recession.

Features that occur on flood plains include meanders, cutoffs, oxbow lakes, levees, and back swamps.

A decrease in either speed or discharge causes a river to deposit its load. Deltas and alluvial fans are sediment deposits left by a river when it loses speed at its mouth.

IV Steady rains over large areas of a watershed cause large rivers to flood. Natural damming, or the failure of a dam, also lead to floods. Flash floods result from cloudbursts over small stream valleys.

Flooding can be prevented by reforestation, damming tributary streams, building artificial levees, and using spillways.

■ Vocabulary

abrasion	flood plain
alluvial fan	gully
base level	headward erosion
bed load	levees
carrying power	meanders
delta	oxbow lake
discharge	pothole
divide	solution
drainage basin	stream piracy
or watershed	suspension
flash flood	water gap

■ Review

Match the terms in List **A** with the definitions in List **B**.

List A

1. evaporation
2. abrasion
3. bed load
4. solution
5. carrying power
6. canyon
7. base level
8. gully
9. stream divide
10. drainage basin
11. stream piracy
12. water gap
13. pothole
14. undermining
15. flood plain
16. sediment
17. delta
18. levee
19. flash flood
20. ice jam
21. artificial levee

List B

a. grinding action of particles in a streambed
b. high land between two river systems
c. ridge-shaped deposits formed on riverbanks by flooding streams
d. streambed holes scoured out by particles trapped in whirlpools
e. natural dam resulting from breakup of frozen river
f. small V-shaped valley
g. a rounded river stone
h. method by which streams carry dissolved material

For further review, see **Study Guide**.
For assessment, see **Chapter Tests**
and **Computer Test Bank.**

i. a river, its tributaries, and all land drained by the river

j. whirlpools eroding base of cliff, causing it to overhang

k. deposits at river mouths

l. abandoned water gap

m. measure of total amount of sediment and of particle sizes carried by a stream

n. process by which water is lifted from ocean by sun

o. steep-sided valley

p. capture of one stream by another through headward erosion

q. part of river valley that is underwater during floods

r. broad curves in river on valley floors

s. narrow cut in resistant rock through which a river flows

t. stream deposits at base of steep mountain

u. moves by rolling, sliding, or bouncing

v. materials carried by a river

w. occurs when cloudburst hits narrow valley

x. lowest level to which a stream can erode its bed

y. placing sandbags on top of natural levees

■ Interpret and Apply

On your paper, answer each question in complete sentences.

1. Compare the carrying power of a small, fast-flowing stream in the Rocky Mountains with that of the lower part of the Mississippi River.

2. **(a)** Using the data in Topic 12, determine the average rate of recession of Niagara Falls, in meters per year. **(b)** The rock layers of Niagara are not perfectly horizontal but dip into the ground toward Niagara's source. Explain how continued recession will change the height of Niagara Falls.

3. Why is a meandering river like the Rio Grande an unsatisfactory boundary between the United States and Mexico?

4. Can a tributary form a delta where it enters the main stream of the river system? Explain.

5. Over a 4-day period in spring of 1972, Hurricane Agnes dropped 35 centimeters of rain on the Susquehanna River watershed. Record flooding occurred 36 to 48 hours after the heaviest rain. Why didn't the flooding occur during the rain?

■ Critical Thinking

The graph shows the relationship between particle diameter, in centimeters, and speed of stream flow, in centimeters per second, needed to keep the particle in suspension. The graph also shows the size range for clay, silt, sand, pebbles, cobbles, and boulders. Use the graph to answer questions 1–4.

1. If a particle has a diameter of 0.05 centimeters, what is the particle called?

2. What is the name of the particle that stays in suspension at the slowest stream speed?

3. What is the minimum stream speed needed to carry a boulder in suspension?

4. Name the particles that would be in suspension in a stream moving at 100 cm/s.

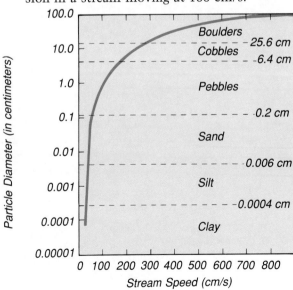

Glaciers

▲
Margerie Glacier, Glacier
Bay, Alaska

How Do You Know That . . .

Glaciers form from snow? To see how solid ice can form from snow, take a handful of snow or crushed ice and squeeze it between your hands. Keep applying pressure until you notice a change in the snow or ice particles. What does squeezing seem to do to the particles of snow or ice? What happens when you stop applying pressure? What would cause the packing of snow to form glaciers?

I Types of Glaciers

Topic 1 The Problem of the Strange Boulders

In the early 1800's, European geologists noted that many rock outcrops in northern regions had polished and scratched surfaces. These were unlike the rock outcrop surfaces of more southern regions. Giant boulders had compositions that differed from the bedrock on which they rested. The boulders could sometimes be traced to outcrops many kilometers north. Pebbles and other sediments were strange to the locality in many places.

Geologists agreed that these materials could not be explained by stream action. Before the late 1800's many geologists hypothesized that all this had happened in one great flood. They thought floodwater had carried the boulders, scoured the bedrock, and deposited sediments over a wide area. Because they thought water had moved the foreign materials, geologists called all such material *drift*, a name still in use.

Meanwhile, another explanation was being offered. A study of existing glaciers in the Alps Mountains of Europe showed how bedrock is attacked by glacial erosion and how boulders and soils are carried downslope. Sometimes deposits were found kilometers down the valley from the glacier front or high above the glacier on the valley walls. In those cases geologists reasoned that the glacier had been longer and thicker. A number of geologists then used this reasoning to explain the drift that covered so much of northern Europe. They concluded that great ice sheets had covered the drift area during a long ice age.

The person who is known for this idea is the famous Swiss naturalist Louis Agassiz (AG ah see). Agassiz did much research to prove his theory, and he worked hard to publicize it.

Topic 2 What Is A Glacier?

Imagine a steep valley high in the Alps Mountains of Switzerland. No river runs in this valley. Instead, the entire valley floor is covered by a mass of snow-covered ice, hundreds of meters thick. This ice mass can be followed up the valley for many kilometers. It begins in huge fields of ice and snow just below the very highest peaks.

Careful study would show that the ice in this valley moves downhill at the rate of several meters a day. At the lower part of the

OBJECTIVES

A Summarize the observations that led Louis Agassiz to propose that glaciers had once covered large parts of Europe.

B Describe how firn becomes a glacier.

C Describe the occurrence and appearance of a valley glacier.

D Identify two kinds of ice sheets.

OF INTEREST

The great flood was assumed to be the one for which Noah built his ark. People who explained the drift with Noah's flood were called diluvialists. The Pleistocene, or Ice Age, is still called the Diluvium in Europe.

VIDEODISC SELECTION

Evidence of glacial activity (described in disc directory)
Side 2: 1694 to 1698, 5-frame sequence

Pebbles and boulders of glacial drift
Side 2: 1826, single frame

Margerie Glacier, Glacier Bay, Alaska
Side 2: 1730, single frame

Diagrams of glacial features
Side 2: 1629 to 1630, 2-frame sequence

11.1   This view of the edge of a glacier shows where a huge chunk of ice broke off. Notice the sizes and kinds of materials left by the ice.

VIDEODISC SELECTION

Valley glacier, Austria
Side 2: 1645, single frame

Antarctic ice sheet
Side 2: 2402, single frame

valley, the ice thins out and suddenly ends. Milky-colored water runs out from beneath the ice and flows down the valley. This long, slow-moving, wedge-shaped stream of ice is a **valley glacier.**

Imagine a great landmass in the polar latitudes of the far north or south. The climate is so cold that only snow falls. For thousands of years snow has been falling, building up, and changing to ice. Almost the whole landmass is covered by the thick mass of ice. Only the highest mountain peaks reach above the ice.

The ice is thousands of meters thick, and it moves outward from its center in all directions toward the seacoasts. In some places it reaches the sea by traveling through low valleys. Here great chunks of ice break off to float away as icebergs. This moving mass of ice, far larger than a valley glacier, is called a **continental glacier.**

Topic 3 **The Snow Line**

Glaciers are born in areas always covered by snow. These are areas where more snow falls than melts each year. Some snow is always left to add to the buildup of previous years. Climates cold enough to cause such conditions may be found in any part of the world. Air temperatures drop with greater height above sea level and with greater distance from the equator.

Even in equatorial areas, then, permanent snows may be found on high mountains. Farther from the equator the mountains need not be so high for snow to exist. In the polar areas permanent snows may be found even at sea level. The lowest level that permanent snows reach in summer is called the **snow line.** A mountain that is completely covered with snow in winter, but from which the snow is all melted by summer, has no snow line.

The snow line is highest near the equator and lowest near the poles. As climates become colder with greater latitude (distance from the equator), less height is needed to reach a snow line. The position of the snow line also changes with the total yearly snowfall and the amount of exposure to the sun. Thus the height of a snow line is not the same for all places in the same latitude.

11.2 The nearly horizontal snow line on these Colorado peaks represents the lowest level that permanent snows reach in the summer.

SCIENCE BACKGROUND

A tropical mountain with a snow line at 4200 meters today had a snow line at about 2000 meters during the Ice Age.

VIDEODISC SELECTION

Visible snowline
Side 2: 1759, single frame

11.3 This diagram shows approximately how the elevation of the snow line varies with latitude.

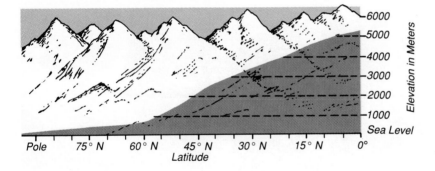

Topic 4 **Birth of a Glacier**

Except for bare rock cliffs, the mountain above the snow line is buried in snow. Great basins below the highest peaks are filled with snow hundreds of meters thick. In the huge snow fields freshly fallen snow becomes compressed and recrystallizes into a rough, granular ice material called **firn,** or *névé* (NAY vay).

The granules of firn start off no larger than fine buckshot. The firn is like the ice of a packed snowball. As the firn becomes thicker, its crystals may grow as large as kernels of corn. The lower layers of firn change to solid ice because they are compressed by the weight of the top layers. This ice begins to flow downward or outward because of the weight of the overlying firn and snow. This moving mass of ice and snow becomes a valley glacier. Figure 11.4 illustrates the development of a valley glacier.

VIDEODISC SELECTION

Photos of glacial ice, Reid Glacier, Alaska
Side 2: 1898 to 1900, 3-frame sequence

Valley Glacier

a

b

c

11.4 Snowfields, such as the one shown at top, may develop into glaciers. Follow the stages in the development of a valley glacier. **(a)** There are great basins and depressions high above the snow line. **(b)** These basins gradually become filled with snow and ice. **(c)** Eventually the huge mass begins to flow downward along the natural path of the valley.

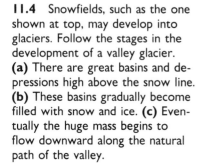

TEACHING TIP
Emphasize that valley glaciers may occur even in equatorial regions if mountains are high enough.

Topic 5 **Where Valley Glaciers Occur**

Valley glaciers are also known as *alpine* glaciers. They occur in all parts of the world where mountains stretch above the snow line. This includes all continents except Australia.

The smallest valley glaciers may be as little as two thousand meters long, a few hundred meters wide, and less than a hundred meters deep. The largest may be over a hundred thousand meters long, several thousand meters wide, and hundreds of meters thick. The world's largest valley glaciers are in southern Alaska. Here mountains with a snow line at about 1500 meters reach to heights above 6000 meters. The world's largest mountains, the Himalayas, also have very large glaciers.

11.5   Two valley glaciers in the Swiss Alps

Topic 6   **Where Continental Glaciers Occur**

Continental glaciers are also called **ice sheets.** They form in polar areas where the snow line is close to sea level and wide areas are above the snow line. These glaciers are roughly circular or oval in shape. Continental glaciers occur today in Greenland and Antarctica. The Greenland glacier is about 1 700 000 square kilometers in area and up to 3 kilometers thick. It covers all of Greenland except a narrow part of the coast.

The Antarctic glacier covers a larger landmass with an area of about 12.5 million square kilometers. Here the ice reaches a thickness of nearly 5 kilometers. Along the coast the ice may descend more than 1.5 kilometers below sea level. Farther inland great mountain peaks called **nunataks** project through the ice.

Small ice sheets called **ice caps** are found in Iceland, Baffin Island, Spitsbergen, and other large islands of the Arctic Ocean. Ice caps may have areas of several thousand square kilometers.

TOPIC QUESTIONS

Each topic question refers to the topic of the same number.

1. **(a)** What is drift?   **(b)** How did Louis Agassiz explain the drift that covered parts of northern Europe?
2. **(a)** Define valley glacier.   **(b)** Define continental glacier.
3. **(a)** Define snow line.   **(b)** How does the snow line change with latitude?
4. **(a)** What is firn?   **(b)** How does firn become a glacier?
5. Where are valley glaciers generally found?
6. What is the difference between ice caps and continental glaciers? Give examples of each.

VIDEODISC SELECTION

Aerial photos of the Antarctic ice sheet
Side 2: 2396 to 2405, 10-frame sequence

SCIENCE BACKGROUND

The richest deposit of cosmic dust on Earth has recently been found in the ice of Greenland. Unlike similar particles obtained from the ocean floor, these particles show little chemical weathering because of their preservation by the ice.

ANSWERS

1. (a) material left by a glacier (b) glaciation
2. (a) slow-moving, wedge-shaped stream of ice   (b) moving mass of ice, much larger than valley glacier
3. (a) lowest level of permanent snow in summer   (b) highest near equator, lowest near poles
4. (a) rough, granular ice (b) firn crystals grow, become ice, flow because of weight of overlying ice and snow
5. in mountains above snow line
6. size; ice caps on arctic islands, continental glaciers on Greenland and Antarctica

OBJECTIVES

A Describe the motion of ice within a glacier and the factors that affect its motion.

B Describe factors that determine the location of the ice front.

C Describe the origin and location of several kinds of moraine.

D Explain several ways in which glaciers erode the land and compare erosion by a continental glacier with erosion by a valley glacier.

TEACHING TIP
Emphasize that a glacier is moving downhill even when the ice front is stationary or retreating.

11.6 Aerial view of huge crevasses in a glacier

II Glacier Movement

Topic 7 How Glaciers Move

A glacier's own weight is an important factor in its movement. The weight of overlying layers of ice and snow push down on lower layers of the glacier. The weight also causes grains of ice to partially melt and refreeze. As this happens, the ice grains slip over each other, and the glacier moves downhill.

Geologists have studied the movement of glaciers by driving rows of stakes into the ice across a valley. They observe the positions of the stakes regularly. They have found that some glaciers move only a few centimeters a day, while others move as much as 3000 centimeters a day. They have learned that glaciers move more rapidly at the surface than at the base and faster in the center than at the sides, where friction with valley walls slows their flow. Geologists have seen that glaciers move more rapidly after winters of heavy snowfall, on steep slopes, and in summer.

Like river valleys, glacial valleys have steep and gentle slopes. When a valley glacier comes to a steep slope, great fissures, or cracks, called **crevasses** form across the width of the glacier. These openings rarely go deeper than about 40 meters. Studies have shown that the glacier ice is brittle to about that depth. Below 40 meters, the ice is more flexible from the pressure of overlying ice.

Topic 8 How Far Glaciers Move

As a valley glacier moves into lower, warmer levels, it thins steadily because of melting and evaporation. Most glaciers extend below the snow line. A glacier is thinnest at the elevation where the ice melts as fast as it moves. Under normal conditions the glacier ends here, at its **ice front.**

A glacier always moves forward. However, as long as the rates of movement and melting are equal, the ice front is stationary. After a winter of heavy snows, which add pressure to the bottom ice, a glacier may move faster than normal and advance beyond its usual limit. On the other hand, in very warm summers, it may melt faster than normal, causing the ice front to move back, or recede.

In regions such as Alaska and Greenland, the snow line is close to sea level. Many glaciers reach the sea. Even here they do not melt as fast as they move. As they extend into the sea, great blocks break off to become icebergs. This process is called **calving.**

In Antarctica, where the snow line is at sea level, the ice sheet reaches the coastline almost everywhere. In a number of places the ice sheet extends beyond the coast far into the sea in huge ice shelves. The largest of these, the Ross Ice Shelf, is hundreds of kilometers wide and about a third of a kilometer thick at its sides. The icebergs that break off from an ice sheet are huge. One such iceberg was about 65 kilometers long.

Topic 9 **Glaciers Transport Loose Rock**

Like rivers, glaciers remove loose rock from the valleys through which they move. There seems to be almost no limit to the size and amount of material carried by a glacier. Particles, ranging in size from fine powder to giant boulders, are picked up by a glacier from its valley floor. Often rocks fall into a glacier from the valley walls. Other material may be brought to it by tributary glaciers.

Large amounts of rock material build up in several areas of a moving glacier. When these materials are deposited, they form **moraines.** Material carried in the bottom of the glacier before it is deposited is called *ground moraine.* The two long lines of rock pieces that pile up along the valley sides of a glacier are called *lateral* (side) *moraines.* Sometimes two glaciers come together to form a single larger glacier. Then their inside lateral moraines are joined to form a single *medial* (middle) *moraine.* At the ice front, rock pieces brought forward by the glacier's motion build up as the ice melts. These pile up as an *end moraine.* An end moraine may grow very large if the ice front does not move for a long time, since glacier movement and melting will constantly add material to it.

Rock flour is a mixture of fine sand and silt formed by the crushing of rock under a glacier. The meltwater pouring out of a glacier is likely to be filled with suspended rock flour. This gives the water a milky white color, so it is called *glacial milk.*

11.7   These icebergs broke off from Portage Glacier near Anchorage, Alaska. Notice the glacier in the background.

SCIENCE BACKGROUND

The lower part of the Variegated Glacier in Alaska has been clocked moving over 60 meters a day. Such rapid glacial movement is called a surge. Surges are thought to be caused by a buildup of water pressure beneath the ice.

VIDEODISC SELECTION

Ice calving at glacial fronts
Side 2: 1913 to 1914, 2-frame sequence

11.8   The material that forms medial and lateral moraines is clearly visible in this glacier as dark parallel bands. (Lamplugh Glacier, Alaska)

11.9   The large parallel scratches on this rock are striations, which were carved by a glacier.

SCIENCE BACKGROUND

Erosional forms are more striking from valley glaciers; depositional forms are more striking from continental glaciers.

VIDEODISC SELECTION

Alaska's Chitna River, made milky by rock flour
Side 2: 1871, single frame

11.10   Glacial erosion of mountain peaks often leaves steep, jagged formations.

Topic 10   **Glaciers Leave Their Mark**

Glaciers erode the bedrock largely by using pieces of rocks as cutting tools. These pieces are dragged over the bedrock by the forward movement of the glacier. Particles of fine sand, acting like sandpaper, smooth and polish the bedrock. Coarse sand, pebbles, and sharp boulders leave long parallel scratches called **striations.** Striations show the general direction of ice movement. If the bedrock is soft, pebbles and small boulders may dig in so deeply as to leave long parallel grooves. The pebbles and boulders carried by the glacier also show signs of wear, becoming flattened and scratched.

Glacial erosion shapes bedrock into many forms. Outcrops of bedrock may become smooth and polished on the side facing a glacier. The opposite side may be left steep and rough where the glacier freezes and plucks away loose blocks of rock. Such outcrops look like resting sheep and are called **roches moutonnées** (rosh moo toe NAY), meaning "sheep rocks." Potholes are ground out beneath glaciers in whirlpools formed by meltwater falling into crevasses.

Frost action and glacial erosion at the head of a glacier wear away the walls of mountain peaks. A semicircular basin called a **cirque** (SERK) is formed at the head of the glacial valley.

When two cirques are formed next to each other on a peak, the divide between them may become narrow and sharp. Such a divide is called an **arête** (ah RET), or knife-edge ridge. When three or more cirques cut into the same peak, they may cut away so much that a spectacular pyramid-shaped peak is left. Such peaks are called **horns,** or *matterhorns,* after the Matterhorn in Switzerland.

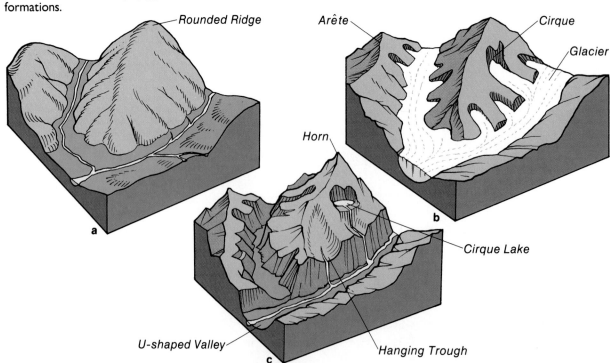

Topic 11 **Recognizing Glacial Valleys**

A river touches only a small part of its valley floor. A valley glacier, on the other hand, touches the entire valley floor and a large part of the valley walls as well. As it moves, a valley glacier scours away the rock until it flattens the entire valley floor and makes the valley walls nearly vertical. The resulting formation is called a **glacial trough**—a glacial valley that is roughly U-shaped.

Main valley glaciers are usually much thicker than their tributary glaciers. Thus, they erode their valleys more powerfully. The effects of this erosion can be seen in regions where a change of climates has caused glaciers to disappear. The main valleys are much deeper than the tributary valleys. The tributary U-shaped valleys are called *hanging troughs*. The rivers that have formed in the hanging troughs plunge over the cliffs, forming *hanging trough waterfalls*. Glacial troughs, hanging troughs, and hanging trough waterfalls are common in all glaciated mountains. A famous hanging trough waterfall is Yosemite Falls in California.

Topic 12 **What Continental Glaciers Do**

Like valley glaciers, continental glaciers remove loose rock and soil. They smooth, striate, and groove bedrock. They form roches moutonnées and other features. However, erosion of mountain areas by continental glaciers differs in several ways from erosion by valley glaciers. A continental glacier deepens and widens valleys that are parallel to its direction of movement. Since a continental glacier covers most mountaintops, it grinds down the peaks and leaves them polished and rounded. Valley glaciers, by contrast, sharpen mountain peaks by grinding away at their sides.

TOPIC QUESTIONS

Each topic question refers to the topic of the same number.

7. **(a)** What causes glaciers to move? **(b)** At what times do glaciers tend to move fastest? **(c)** What are crevasses?

8. **(a)** What determines the location of the ice front of a glacier? **(b)** What causes an ice front to recede? **(c)** How are icebergs formed? What is this process called?

9. **(a)** What are the sources of material that are carried by a glacier? **(b)** Where are ground, lateral, medial, and end moraines located in respect to a glacier? **(c)** Define rock flour.

10. **(a)** Describe the formation of roches moutonnées. **(b)** What is a cirque? **(c)** How are arêtes and horns related to cirques?

11. Describe the shape and origin of glacial troughs, hanging troughs, and hanging trough waterfalls.

12. How does erosion by continental glaciers differ from that by valley glaciers?

11.11 A U-shaped glacial valley, or trough

ANSWERS

7. (a) their own weight; melting and freezing of grains (b) in the summer, after winters of heavy snowfall (c) cracks across ice on steep slopes

8. (a) rate of melting relative to rate of flow (b) melting is faster than its advance (c) blocks of ice break off in ocean; calving

9. (a) valley floor, walls, tributary glaciers (b) in order: bottom, sides, center, ice front (c) mixture of fine sand and silt

10. (a) outcrops polished and smoothed by glacier (b) semicircular basin at head of glacial valley (c) They are sharp ridges and peaks left by action of two or more cirques.

11. in order: valley scoured by glacier; tributary valleys not eroded as deeply as main valleys; river flowing from hanging trough into main trough

12. continental smooths and polishes mountaintops, valley sharpens the tops

OBJECTIVES

A Discuss the origin and properties of till and outwash.

B List some features of glacial deposition and explain how each occurs.

C Name and describe three types of lakes resulting from glaciation.

11.12 End moraines are found in front of glaciers.

11.13 Aerial view of a swarm of drumlins

OF INTEREST

Bunker Hill in Boston is a drumlin.

III   Deposits by Glaciers

Topic 13   Deposition Occurs

Most of the rock material carried by glaciers is deposited by melting. The name *drift* is used for all deposits of glacial origin.

There are two kinds of drift. Unsorted and unstratified rock materials deposited directly by the ice is called **till**. Till deposits may be left under a moving glacier or along its sides. The second kind of drift, called **outwash**, includes deposits made by streams of glacial meltwater. Like all stream deposits these are sorted and stratified.

Topic 14   Glaciers Leave Moraines

When a glacier melts, its rock load remains in nearly the same places as in the glacier. The ground moraine forms a thin, fairly even deposit over the whole area. Lateral and medial moraines form ridges running in almost the same direction as the glacier.

The end moraine forms a ridge along the ice front. The longer the ice front stays in one place, the larger the end moraine becomes. When a receding ice front stops in new places for any length of time, new end moraines are formed behind the main one. These are called *recessional moraines*.

Even a stationary ice front moves back and forth slightly with the seasons. End moraine deposits are spread over a broad belt in front of a glacier. Furthermore, no two parts of the ice front deposit exactly the same amount of material. For these reasons, end and recessional moraines are likely to have irregular hills and hollows, rather than being a single straight ridge. End moraines of continental glaciers may be hundreds of kilometers long, several kilometers wide, and a tenth of a kilometer high. The end moraine marking a glacier's farthest advance is called its *terminal moraine*.

The materials of the moraines range from boulders to clays. They are mixed in widely varying amounts and are unstratified. Large glacial boulders that have been transported into an area are called **erratics.** Erratics differ in composition from the local bedrock.

Topic 15   Drumlins

Drumlins are long, smooth, canoe-shaped hills made of till. They usually are found in swarms. They all point in the direction of glacier movement. A typical drumlin may be 400 meters long, 100 meters wide, and 25 meters high.

Drumlins were probably formed when an advancing glacier ran over an earlier glacial moraine, sweeping it into long strips. Swarms of drumlins are found in southeastern Wisconsin, south of Lake Ontario in New York State, and near Boston, Massachusetts.

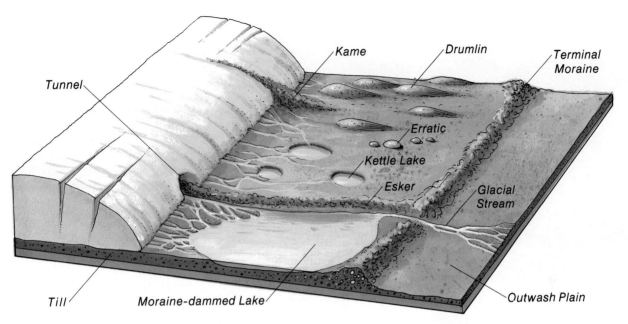

11.14 Notice the different kinds of deposits and formations left by a glacier.

Topic 16 **Outwash Plains and Eskers**

Glacial meltwater pours out at the ice front in streams filled with rock flour, sand, and gravel. These streams form gently sloping stratified deposits that may reach for kilometers beyond the terminal moraine. The deposits look like alluvial fans. In front of large glaciers, they overlap and form broad flat areas called **outwash plains.**

Much of the water of a melting glacier falls to the bottom of the ice through crevasses. Subglacial streams are formed that run in tunnels beneath the ice and come out at the ice front. The winding tunnels of these streams become partly filled with roughly stratified sands and gravel. When the glacier melts, the deposits slump down at the sides and form long, winding ridges called **eskers.**

Eskers are found in the glaciated states of the Mississippi Valley, the north central states, central New York, and Maine. Eskers usually run in about the same general direction as the direction of ice movement.

Topic 17 **Kames, Kettles, and Deltas**

Kames (KAYMS) are small, cone-shaped hills of stratified sand and gravel. They are formed when streams from the top of the glacier deposit their sediments at the ice margin or into lakes on the top of the ice. These pile up in heaps as the ice thins and are finally lowered to the ground surface.

Kettles are circular hollows found on terminal moraines and outwash plains. Kettles are formed in two steps. First, moraine or outwash deposits bury large blocks of ice left as the glacier recedes. Then the ice melts, leaving the kettles.

VIDEODISC SELECTION

Glacial melting and movement
Side 2 movie: 7980 & PLAY

Drumlin in Massachusetts
Side 2: 1705, single frame

Glacial erratics
Side 2: 1727, single frame

VIDEODISC SELECTION

Kettle lakes in outwash plain
Side 2: 1848, single frame

11.15 St. Mary's Lake, Glacier National Park, Montana

When glacial streams empty into lakes or beyond the ice front, *deltas* are formed. These are made up largely of layers of gravel and coarse sand. Fine sands and clays may spread evenly over the whole lake floor.

Topic 18   Lakes Made by Glaciers

Glaciation of an area leaves many new basins or depressions in the land surface. If these basins are permanently filled with water, they form lakes, ponds, or swamps, depending on how large and deep they are. Three important types of lakes that come from glaciation are cirque lakes, kettle lakes, and moraine-dammed lakes.

Cirque lakes are formed when water fills the rock-floored cirque basins left by alpine glaciers. Cirque lakes and rock-basin lakes are also called *tarns.* Examples of cirque lakes are Lake Louise in the Canadian Rockies and St. Mary's Lake in Montana.

Kettle lakes form in large numbers in the kettle holes of moraines and outwash plains. They are common in Minnesota, Wisconsin, New York, and New England.

Moraine-dammed lakes are formed where river valleys are blocked by glacial moraines. The river rises to the height of the moraine dam and floods its valley to form a long, usually narrow lake. Many of the larger lakes of the northern United States came about in this way. Examples are Lake George in New York and Long Lake in Maine.

In many cases, lakes were formed by both glacial erosion that scoured out river valleys and deposition that dammed the rivers. The Finger Lakes of central New York State were formed in this way. Many of their former tributary valleys were left as hanging troughs high above the main troughs. The Great Lakes have a more complicated history. However, they also lie in basins that were deepened and then dammed by glacial moraines.

ANSWERS

13. Till is unsorted, unstratified, and ice-deposited. Outwash is sorted, stratified, and meltwater-deposited.

14. (a) end moraines behind main one   (b) ice front moves back and forth, deposits different amounts of material   (c) one at farthest advance of ice   (d) glacially deposited boulders

15. long, smooth, canoe-shaped hills; may be end moraines swept into this shape by advancing ice

16. (a) broad, flat area beyond terminal moraine   (b) by subglacial streams with long winding ridges

17. (a) by meltwater at ice margin or in lakes on ice surface (b) melting of buried ice blocks (c) when meltwater carries outwash into lakes

18. cirque—in cirque basin; kettle—holes in outwash; moraine-dammed—moraines block drainage

TOPIC QUESTIONS

Each topic question refers to the topic of the same number.

13. How do till deposits differ from outwash deposits?
14. (a) What are recessional moraines?   (b) Why are end moraines usually broad and irregularly hilly?   (c) What is a terminal moraine?   (d) What are erratics?
15. Describe the appearance and possible origin of drumlins.
16. (a) Describe an outwash plain.   (b) How are eskers formed?
17. (a) How are kames formed?   (b) How are kettles formed? (c) How do melting glaciers form deltas?
18. Describe three types of lakes resulting from glaciation.

IV The Ice Age

Topic 19 How It Happened

About a million years ago it was as cold in much of northern North America and northern Europe as it is today in Greenland. Great ice sheets developed over central and eastern Canada and northern Scandinavia. In North America the ice sheets developed over an area that extends as far south as where the Ohio and Mississippi rivers meet and eastward to central Long Island. Much of the north central and northeastern parts of the United States were covered by ice. In Europe the ice sheets covered most of Scandinavia, the British Isles, Denmark, Belgium, northern France, and the Baltic countries and reached far into Germany and Russia.

In North America there were three centers in which the snow and ice were thickest. These centers of accumulation were the Labrador center east of Hudson Bay, the Keewatin center west of Hudson Bay, and the Cordilleran center in the Canadian Rockies.

From the Labrador center came the ice that covered eastern Canada and the northeastern United States. From Keewatin came the ice that covered central Canada and the north central United States. The Cordilleran ice sheet covered the Canadian Rockies down to their foothills but did not move south. At that time there were valley glaciers in the mountains of the western United States, but they were far larger than they are today.

The ice sheets advanced and receded four major times during the million-year period as the climate changed from cold to warm and back again. The last time the ice sheets receded was about 11 000 years ago. Many geologists think we are now in a warm, or *interglacial*, period that will be followed by a return of the ice sheets in perhaps 20 000 years. Others think that this warm period will last millions of years.

OBJECTIVES

A List some evidences for glaciation found in North America.

B List the facts supporting a theory of glacial climate.

C Describe several hypotheses for the occurrence of an ice age.

OF INTEREST

At the height of the last Ice Age, the ice was nearly 2 kilometers thick over Boston and over 3 kilometers thick in parts of Europe.

SCIENCE BACKGROUND

The four classical periods are named Nebraskan, Kansan, Illinoian, and Wisconsin for the states where their deposits are best preserved.

VIDEODISC SELECTION

Animation showing advance of North American ice sheet
Side 1 movie clip: 18646 & PLAY
(STOP at 18880)

11.16 The entire area in white was covered by ice sheets during the Ice Age. Notice the uncovered area south of Lake Superior.

11.17 These smoothly polished rocks provide evidence of glacial erosion.

VIDEODISC SELECTION

Striations and other evidence of a glacier (described in disc directory)
Side 2: 1693 to 1704, 12-frame sequence

Topic 20 Ice Age Evidence

Proof that there was an Ice Age is given in the many glacial features that have been described. The southern limit reached by some advances of ice sheets is marked by terminal moraines. One of these is the Long Island, New York, moraine that extends almost 225 kilometers from Brooklyn to Montauk Point. Other terminal moraines stretch from New Jersey through Pennsylvania, Ohio, Indiana, and westward to Puget Sound in the state of Washington. The edge of the ice sheet illustrated on the map in Figure 11.16 was determined by the location of these terminal moraines. South of the terminal moraines, outwash plains are found in many places.

Much of the northern United States and Canada is covered by drift. There are many glacial boulders in the glacial-till soils. Exposed bedrock is striated and polished, even on mountaintops. North-south valleys are shaped into glacial troughs. East-west valleys are partly filled with drift. Kames, eskers, drumlins, and moraines are found in many places. Lakes and swamps are far more common in glaciated areas than in the unglaciated areas to the south. In the Rockies and the Sierra Nevadas, glacial markings occur high upon the valley walls. This shows that much larger glaciers filled these valleys during the most recent Ice Age.

Topic 21 Causes of Glacial Climates

To explain why Earth was cold enough to have the recent Ice Age, certain facts must be considered:

1. This Ice Age began about 1 million years ago and included four major advances of the ice sheets.
2. Warm interglacial periods came after each advance. Earth may now be in an interglacial period.
3. Other ice ages have occurred from time to time in the past 600 million years.
4. During the last Ice Age, glaciers advanced and receded at the same time in both the Northern and Southern Hemispheres.

Geologists have proposed many hypotheses to account for ice ages. One idea is that the amount of heat energy given off by the sun changes. Ice ages may occur during periods when energy from the sun is less. Or the amount of energy reaching Earth might change due to volcanic dust in the atmosphere. Another possibility is that during periods of mountain building, more of Earth's land area lay above the snow line. More land under snow might change the climate enough for an ice age to begin. A fourth idea concerns the former position of continents on Earth's surface. If continents used to be in the way of currents between oceans, they may have prevented the mixing of cold and warm water. Without mixing between oceans, areas of Earth might become cold enough to start an ice age. Each of these hypotheses has its strong and weak points. Recent research has added to knowledge about the times and durations of the previous Ice Age. Geologists have also discovered evidence of many more ice ages in the distant past.

A hypothesis that explains much of the new evidence being found concerns changes in the motions of Earth itself. Changes in the tilt of Earth's axis and in the shape of its orbit might cause colder climates on some parts of Earth. Changes of this kind do take place over and over again at regular intervals in Earth's history, which might explain why ice ages happen periodically. Also, such changes in Earth's position could cause glacial climates in both hemispheres at the same time. Did the Ice Age occur because of changes in Earth's position and motion? Scientists must study all new evidence to see whether it supports the hypothesis, or to determine whether the hypothesis must be modified.

TOPIC QUESTIONS

Each topic question refers to the topic of the same number.

19. **(a)** What is a center of accumulation?   **(b)** Describe the extent of the ice sheets in North America during the last Ice Age.
20. Identify the kind of evidence for the Ice Age found at the following locations: **(a)** Long Island, New York, to Puget Sound, Washington,   **(b)** northern United States and Canada, and **(c)** Rockies and Sierra Nevadas.
21. **(a)** List four pieces of evidence that must be considered to explain why Earth was cold enough to have an ice age. **(b)** Describe some hypotheses about the cause of ice ages.

ANSWERS

19. (a) place where ice is thickest   (b) from pole to Ohio and Missouri rivers

20. (a) terminal moraine and outwash plain   (b) drift; boulders; striated, polished mountaintops; glacial troughs; kames; kettles; eskers; drumlins; moraines   (c) glacial markings high on valley walls

21. (a) began 1 million years ago and included 4 advances of ice; interglacial periods between advances; many other ice ages in past; advances and retreats occurred at same times in both hemispheres (b) change in sun's energy; volcanic dust in atmosphere; uplift during mountainbuilding; continents blocking ocean mixing; changes in Earth's axis and orbit

EARTH**MATTERS**

Glaciers and Global Warming

In June 1992, the world community met at the Earth Summit in Rio de Janeiro, Brazil, to discuss global environmental issues. The countries pledged to reduce gases released into Earth's atmosphere that might lead to global warming. Is global warming such a simple thing to prevent?

Do glaciers and ice caps affect global temperatures and vice versa? Some scientists believe that as the so-called greenhouse gases increase in Earth's atmosphere so will Earth's temperature increase. As the average yearly temperature rises, the glaciers and the ice caps will

melt. Data from glaciers in Peru, China, and Kenya reveal just such a direct correlation among increased carbon dioxide, rising temperature, and glacial melting.

Some computer simulations predict a more complicated series of events. One scenario predicts that as the glaciers melt, the amount of clouds over the polar regions will increase. The increased cloud cover will reflect much of the incoming energy from the sun, thereby actually decreasing Earth's temperature.

What are the possible risks to life while global warming is being hotly debated?

CHAPTER 11

MAP
ACTIVITY

Glacial Rebound

When a ship is loaded with cargo, the weight of the cargo causes the ship to sink lower into the water. When the cargo is unloaded, the ship rises again in the water. In somewhat the same way, a thick accumulation of ice on a continent causes the crust to sink into the mantle. When the ice melts and disappears, the crust rises again. Large land areas that were pushed down by the weight of glaciers during the Ice Age are still slowly rising today. The eastern part of Canada around Hudson Bay is a good example. This area is said to be undergoing **rebound**. Rebound is when land's elevation rises due to the removal of weight that was on it.

How is it possible to tell if a region is being uplifted? One way is to identify the areas that were ocean beaches in the past.

Because beaches are shoreline features, they must have formed at sea level. Finding a beach at a higher elevation than modern sea level is evidence of crustal uplift. Similarly, finding marine fossils at elevations above sea level also indicates that the land has been uplifted.

In this map activity, you will study a map of an area in eastern Canada that has been rebounding since the Ice Age ended. The map of the area has lines drawn connecting locations with equal amounts of rebound.

Map Skills and Objectives

■ To **interpret** a map showing rebound contours for Canada

■ To **construct** and **interpret** a graph based upon data taken from the map

Materials

■ tracing paper
■ Figure 11.18, glacial rebound map
■ colored pencils
■ graph paper
■ Figure 11.16, page 203

Procedure

1. Place the tracing paper over Figure 11.18 and trace the map border. Trace the contours for 10, 30, 50, 70, and 90 meters of rebound. Use the colored pencils to shade the areas between the rebound contours you have traced. Do not color areas beyond the contours shown on the map. (a)What is the value of the highest rebound contour shown?

Data Table		
Canadian City/Town	Amount of Rebound (meters)	Duration of Rebound (years)
Arctic Bay	20	3700
Cambridge Bay	30	4300
Coral Harbour	89	5800
Baker Lake	100	6000
Churchill	80	5600
Ivujivik	58	5300
Fort George	82	5700
Esker	38	4600
Montreal	13	3100
Quebec	10	2700

(b) Relative to Hudson Bay, where are the areas of greatest rebound located?

2. Locate each of the cities and towns on the map and determine the amount of rebound experienced by each. Record your data on a copy of the data table.

3. The last column of the data table gives data on the number of years the land beneath that city has been rebounding. In other words, this data tells how long ago the city or the town named was at sea level. On a sheet of graph paper, graph the amount of rebound (in meters) you determined from the map versus the duration of rebound (in years). Complete the graph by drawing a smooth curve as near to as many of the points as possible (a "best-fit" curve). Extend the curve to the graph origin (0,0).

4. Answer the questions in *Analysis and Conclusions.*

Analysis and Conclusions

1. The areas on the map with greatest rebound contours are called *rebound centers.* Turn to the map on page 203 and find the locations of the rebound centers identified in *Procedure* question 1. What are these same areas called on the map?

2. What is the probable relationship between the rebound centers and the thickness of ice in Canada?

3. What is the probable relationship between the rebound

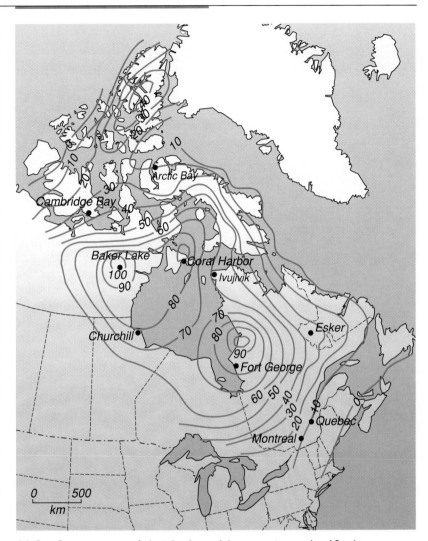

11.8 Contour map of glacial rebound (contour interval = 10 m)

centers and the locations where ice first accumulated?

4. Look at your graph. (a) According to your graph, by what amount did the map area rebound during the first 1000 years shown on the graph (from 6000 to 5000 years ago)? (b) By what amount has the area rebounded in the last 1000 years? (c) Has the rate of uplift been constant? Explain.

5. Which of the following would cause the crust to subside and which to rebound: (a) the formation of a large delta, (b) the erosion of a mountain range, (c) the formation of a large lake behind a dam, (d) the accumulation of sediments in a large sea, (e) the building of a skyscraper?

Answer to all questions appear in the Teacher's Guide at the back of this book.

■ Summary

I Observations of rocks and drift deposits led Agassiz to propose that glaciers had once covered large parts of Europe.

The snow line is the lowest elevation of permanent snow. The snow line is highest near the equator and lowest near the poles.

Glaciers form from compressed snow called firn. A valley glacier is a slow-moving, wedge-shaped stream of ice. Continental glaciers are very large and can entirely cover mountains and valleys.

II Glaciers move most rapidly at the surface of their centers. The location of the ice front of a glacier depends on the rates of glacial movement and melting.

Icebergs form when pieces of glaciers that reach sea level break off in a process called calving.

Glaciers pick up and carry material of all sizes. The material may be carried as ground, lateral, or medial moraines and deposited as end moraines.

Valley glaciers and continental glaciers each leave characteristic landforms and erosional features.

III Till is unsorted, unstratified material deposited directly by the ice. Outwash is sorted, stratified material deposited by meltwater from the ice.

IV Ice accumulated in three areas of North America and extended south to the present Ohio and Missouri rivers.

The features of glacial erosion and deposition are evidence that glaciers once covered large parts of Canada and the northern United States.

There are several hypotheses about the cause of ice ages; a likely one concerns changes in the motion and position of Earth.

■ Vocabulary

arête	crevasses	glacial trough
calving	drumlins	horn
cirque	erratics	ice caps
continental	eskers	ice front
glacier	firn	ice sheet

kames	outwash	snow line
kettles	plains	striations
moraine	roches	till
nunataks	moutonnées	valley glacier
outwash	rock flour	

■ Review

On your paper, write the word or words that best complete each sentence.

1. Before Agassiz, geologists thought that scratched boulders and drift deposits in Europe had been left by a _____.

2. As distance from the equator increases, the elevation of the snow line _____.

3. The rough, granular ice that becomes a glacier is called _____.

4. Slow-moving, wedge-shaped streams of ice found in mountain areas are called alpine, or _____, glaciers.

5. The large ice sheets of Greenland and Antarctica are called _____ glaciers.

6. Glaciers move more rapidly at the _____ than at the base and in the _____ than at the sides.

7. The location of an ice _____ is a balance between the rate of ice movement and the rate of melting.

8. Calving occurs when large blocks of ice break off in the ocean to become _____.

9. Ground, lateral, medial, and end are kinds of _____.

10. Striations are long, parallel _____ in the bedrock that show the general direction of ice movement.

11. An arête is a sharp, narrow ridge between two semicircular basins, called _____.

12. A U-shaped valley carved by a glacier is called a _____.

13. Continental glaciers tend to leave _____, polished mountaintops.

14. Unsorted, unstratified material left by ice is _____, while sorted, stratified material left by meltwater is _____.

For further review, see **Study Guide.**
For assessment, see **Chapter Tests**
and **Computer Test Bank.**

15. The _____ moraine marks the farthest advance of the ice, while the _____ moraine shows where the ice paused as it receded.
16. Long, smooth, canoe-shaped hills that commonly occur in swarms are called _____.
17. The gently sloping, stratified area beyond the farthest glacial front is an outwash _____.
18. _____ are small, cone-shaped hills of stratified sand and gravel that formed at the ice margin.
19. Kettle holes that fill with water become _____.
20. Ice built up at Labrador, Keewatin, and Cordilleran centers on the continent of _____.
21. Striated and polished mountaintops, glacial troughs, kames, eskers, and drumlins are all evidence of _____.
22. One hypothesis is that glacial climates result from changes in the tilt of Earth's _____ and in the shape of Earth's _____ around the sun.

■ Interpret and Apply

On your paper, answer each question in complete sentences.

1. How should the total yearly snowfall and the direction a mountainside faces affect the position of the snow line?
2. Why should glaciers move faster in warm weather than in cold weather?
3. One danger of walking on a glacier is the chance of falling into a hidden crevasse. What should you look for in the surrounding area to tell you when the danger of a crevasse is greater?
4. After the ice sheet retreated from New England, valley glaciers existed for some time in the White Mountains of New Hampshire. What evidence would show this?
5. Compare the amount of sediment carried by the Mississippi River system today with the amount that was probably carried 11 000 years ago.

6. Many eskers go up and down hills. How is that possible?
7. Moraine-dammed lakes often have many irregular inlets and bays. Why?
8. In Wisconsin, fossil evidence of a forest has been preserved between two till layers. What does this indicate about the length of the interglacial period between the formation of the two till layers?

■ Critical Thinking

The graph shows changes in worldwide temperatures over the past 200 000 years. Ice ages occurred when worldwide temperatures were coolest. Interglacial periods occurred when worldwide temperatures were warmer.

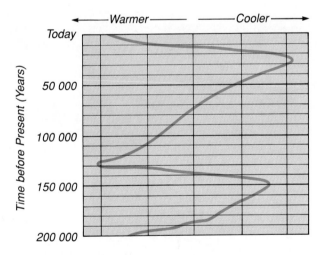

1. How do today's worldwide temperatures compare with those of 150 000 years ago?
2. Compare the temperatures of 20 000 years ago with those of 120 000 years ago.
3. According to the graph, how many ice ages occurred during the past 200 000 years? When did they occur?
4. How does the length of time for an ice age to develop compare with the length of time for an ice age to end?
5. When would the next ice age be expected?

209

Effects of Winds, Waves, and Currents

▲
This toadstool rock was formed by wind action.

OF INTEREST
  Toadstool rocks are also called mushroom rocks, pedestal rocks, and fur-cap rocks. The fact that sand is carried near the ground surface is an additional factor in the more rapid erosion of the stem.

How Do You Know That . . .

Wind causes erosion? Wind erosion is thought to have been a factor in shaping this unusual formation. The formation is called a toadstool rock. It is a flat slab of rock supported by a thin "stem." Although the rock of the slab looks like the rock of the stem, the two must have at least one difference. The slab rock must be slightly harder. It was able to resist wind erosion slightly better than the rock of the stem. The result is that the stem has been worn away faster than the slab above it, leaving the toadstool shape.

I Wind as an Agent of Change

Topic 1 Rock Materials Carried by Winds

Like rivers and glaciers, winds are agents of erosion. Winds act in two basic ways. Winds pick up and move sediment, and they drive sediment against rocks and other materials, causing weathering (Topic 2). Wind erosion and weathering are most effective where sands, silts, and clays lie loose and dry. Conditions for wind erosion are found in great deserts, such as the Sahara in Africa and the Mohave in the southwestern United States. On a smaller scale, these conditions occur on beaches and in semiarid regions.

When strong, steady winds lift great amounts of silt and clay from the topsoil, a **dust storm** occurs. Very destructive dust storms took place on the Great Plains in the 1930's. Long dry spells killed the soil's protective vegetation, leaving the soil exposed to wind erosion. Dust produced during some of the storms was carried high into the atmosphere.

Sand grains are much larger and heavier than clay and silt particles. Experiments with sand grains show that winds of at least 18 kilometers per hour are needed to move them. Sand grains do not move in a steady stream above the ground. Like sand grains in a riverbed, they move in short hops and bounces. Even during strong winds, most sand is carried within one meter of the ground.

Topic 2 Abrasion by Windblown Sediments

Windblown silt and clay particles are too small, and often too soft, to wear away most rocks. Sand grains, however, are larger and tend to be made of more abrasive materials. Sand grains driven by winds grind and scour anything they hit. Quartz sand grains, especially, can wear away many materials. In some desert areas, rocks and telephone poles may be undercut at the base by wind-blown sand. Some poles are even worn through.

Desert sand blasts grind boulders and small rocks into shapes called **ventifacts.** The side of a ventifact that faces the steady wind direction wears into a smooth flat surface, or facet. Figure 12.2 (a) shows how a facet can form. A second facet may form if the wind blows from different directions at different times of the year, or if the boulder is turned so that a new side faces the wind.

A Identify conditions that lead to erosion by wind action and locate areas where such conditions are common.

B Discuss the actions of wind erosion and weathering and identify features resulting from wind action.

C Describe loess and discuss its origin.

D Describe conditions that result in four different sand dune shapes and describe how dune migration occurs.

12.1 Dust storms occur when winds are strong enough to lift and carry dry sand, silt, and clay particles.

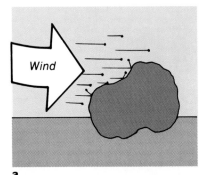 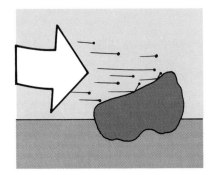 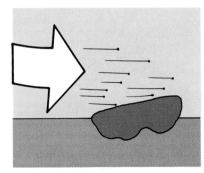

a

b

12.2 **(a)** This series of sketches shows how the abrasive action of windblown sand grinds the face of a boulder into a ventifact. **(b)** The shape of this ventifact gives a clue to the direction of the wind that formed it. The ventifact is surrounded by desert pavement.

SCIENCE BACKGROUND

Silt is more easily removed by wind than clay is, because silt particles do not stick together as well.

SCIENCE BACKGROUND

Loess particles are deposited when wind velocity decreases, but some geologists think that it may be more usual for loess to be washed out of the air by precipitation.

Topic 3 **Deflation: An Erosional Effect**

Deflation is a geological term that describes the removal of loose rock particles by the wind. In many desert areas the sands and clays formed by weathering are blown away by the wind, leaving pebbles and boulders. Such a surface is called **desert pavement.** The surface surrounding the ventifact in Figure 12.2(b) is desert pavement. Desert pavement protects the materials beneath from further deflation. Stony surfaces of this type are common in the deserts of the southwestern United States and in the Sahara in Africa.

In semiarid regions, such as the Great Plains, deflation has formed thousands of hollows called **blowouts.** Most of these are shallow and small. Some are many thousand meters long and perhaps a hundred meters deep. If the bottom of the blowout reaches the water table, the wet ground stops further deflation. The growth of vegetation also stops further deflation. Some desert oases occur in deep blowouts that were probably formed by deflation.

Topic 4 **Loess**

Wind can deposit sediment as well as remove it. Large areas in China, northern Europe, and the north central United States are covered by deposits of material called **loess** (LES or LOW ess). Loess ranges in thickness from about 1 meter to about 100 meters. It is made of unlayered, yellowish particles that are the size of silt. Unlike ordinary silt, loess particles are angular in shape. Loess is made of particles from many different minerals and rocks. Loess holds together so well that when it erodes, it splits off vertically to form clifflike slopes.

Loess appears to be a wind-carried sediment. The particles are light and small enough to be carried by winds in dust storms. The main deposits of loess in the United States are in the upper Mississippi and Missouri river valleys.

The particles that make up loess deposits in the United States and Europe were probably picked up from the outwash left by glaciers. The loess of northern China, however, was probably blown into China from the great deserts of Mongolia.

Topic 5 **Composition and Types of Sand Dunes**

Sand dunes are hills of sand deposited by winds. They form when the sand piles up against shrubs, boulders, or other obstructions.

Sand dunes are found wherever there are strong winds and enough loose sand, such as in the Sahara. Sand dunes also form on sandy river flood plains in semiarid climates and on sandy beaches.

Most sand dunes are made of quartz sands, but there are exceptions. The dunes of White Sands National Monument in New Mexico are made of gypsum sands. Where limestone or coral is common, dunes are calcite sands. Dune sands may contain grains of other minerals, such as feldspar, mica, and magnetite.

If the winds blow steadily from one direction, dunes will have a long, gentle slope on the *windward* side and a shorter, steep slope on the sheltered *leeward* side. For example, winds blowing steadily from the west will form dunes with gentle slopes on their west sides and steep slopes on their east sides. Tiny sand ripples are likely to form on the windward slopes of sand dunes.

Dunes occur in many different shapes. The shape of a dune seems to depend on the supply of sand, the strength and steadiness of the winds, and the amount of vegetation present. Strong, steady winds blowing over a limited supply of sand usually form crescent-shaped dunes called *barchans* (BAR kans). The ends of a barchan point downwind. Where sand is more abundant, long continuous sand ridges called *transverse* dunes form at right angles to the wind. *Parabolic* (U-shaped) dunes often form around blowouts. Unlike barchans, the open ends of parabolic dunes face upwind. Transverse and parabolic dunes are commonly seen on beaches. *Longitudinal*

12.3 Crescent-shaped barchans in Death Valley, California

SCIENCE BACKGROUND

The gypsum sands at White Sands come from the weathering of a gypsum layer in nearby mountains.

12.4 Here are four types of sand dunes: **(a)** barchans, **(b)** parabolic, **(c)** transverse, and **(d)** longitudinal. The arrows represent wind direction.

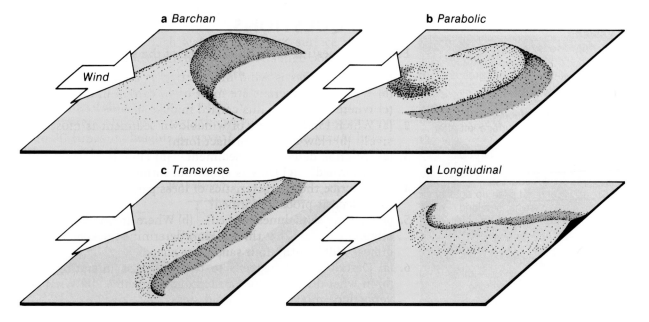

a *Barchan*

Wind

b *Parabolic*

c *Transverse*

d *Longitudinal*

12.7 The size and speed of a tsunami make it an enormously destructive phenomenon.

SCIENCE BACKGROUND

In addition to undersea earthquakes, tsunami may also be caused by landslides, bottomslumping, and volcanic eruptions.

The tsunami caused by the eruption of Krakatau (in the strait between Java and Sumatra) in 1883 reached a height of 130 meters and drowned 36 000 people in nearby coastal areas. The wave was recorded on tide gauges as far away as the English Channel.

VIDEODISC SELECTION

Wave action
Side 2 movie: 14334 & PLAY

12.8 Water particles do not move forward with a wave. Instead, they move in place in a circular path.

The **period** of a wave is the time it takes one wavelength to pass a given point. Most ocean waves have a period that ranges from two seconds to ten seconds. To find the speed of a wave, divide its wavelength by its period.

$$\text{Speed} = \frac{\text{wavelength}}{\text{period}}$$

For example, what is the speed of a wave 24 meters long with a period of 4 seconds? The answer is 6 meters per second.

Waves with periods ranging from 5 to 60 minutes are called long waves. The best-known long wave is the **tsunami,** which can be caused by underwater earthquakes. A typical tsunami may have a wavelength of 150 kilometers and a period of 12 minutes. Dividing 150 kilometers by 12 minutes gives a speed of 12.5 kilometers per minute (or 208 meters per second). When a wave of this speed reaches shore, it can cause great damage.

Water is not carried along with the motion of a wave. Instead, each water particle moves in place in a circular motion (Figure 12.8). (Objects floating in the water have the same kind of motion, which can be seen as objects bob up and down in the water.) As each water particle moves, it bumps into the next one and passes its energy along. In this way, the energy of the wave is passed through the water. The wave travels as far as its energy can carry it.

Wave motion also takes place below the surface. The water molecules move in smaller and smaller circles as depth increases. Motion ceases at a depth equal to about half the wavelength.

Most waves approach a shoreline at an angle. Yet when they reach shallow water, they tend to swing around until they approach the shoreline more or less head on. This bending of the wave is called **refraction.** How does refraction occur? As a wave comes in, the end closest to shore scrapes bottom first and slows down. The end that is still in deep water continues at its normal speed and tends to catch up. The result is that the wave approaches at a gentler angle, one that is more nearly parallel to the shore.

Refraction of ocean waves helps to explain why an uneven shoreline with shallow water is worn away quickly. Headlands are parts of a shore that stick out into the ocean. Coves are areas that are indented. Waves reach shallow water sooner at the headlands.

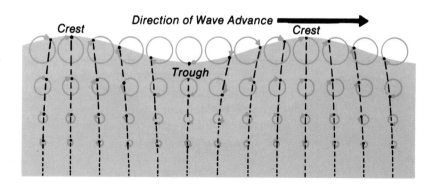

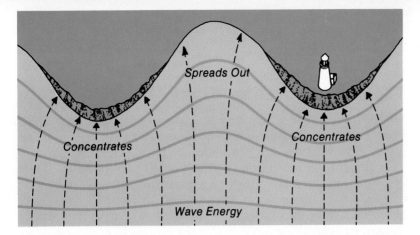

12.9 Refraction causes ocean waves to bend and approach the shoreline at a gentler angle. Because of refraction, wave energy tends to concentrate on headlands and spread out in coves.

VIDEODISC SELECTION

Arrival of a tsunami wave, Oahu, Hawaii, March, 1957
Side 2: 1608 to 1610, 3-frame sequence

Therefore, they slow down sooner in front of the headlands. The wave is bent until it is nearly parallel to, and is striking all three sides of, the headland (Figure 12.9). Wave action, and thus erosion, is reduced in shallow bays and coves.

Topic 9 **Origin of Breakers**

Waves usually approach the shoreline smoothly until they reach water so shallow that they touch the bottom. This happens where water depth is about half the wavelength. Therefore, a wave with a wavelength of 20 meters will scrape bottom at 10 meters of depth.

As the wave scrapes the bottom, the circular motion of the wave is distorted, and the lower part of the wave slows down (Figure 12.10). At the same time the upper part of the wave moves ahead. Finally there is no longer enough water to support the wave. The crest falls over and breaks into surf that washes onto the beach. The next crest will fall over in about the same place. The line along which the crests break is called the *line of breakers.* The depth of water at the line of breakers is one to two times the height of the waves.

The surf formed by breaking waves is a powerful agent of erosion. On rocky shorelines it pounds the rocks and cliffs and wears them down. On beaches it scours the bottom and moves sediments along the shoreline.

12.10 Breakers form when waves reach shallow water—usually where the water depth is one or two times the height of the original wave.

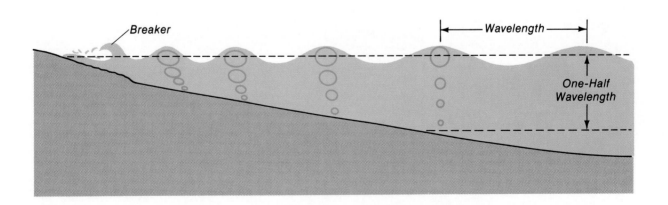

SCIENCE BACKGROUND
Refer to Science Background in the Teacher's Edition for more information about beach profiles.

VIDEODISC SELECTION

Diagram of longshore beach currents
Side 2: 2189, single frame

12.11 **(a)** Swash and backwash carry sand down the beach in a zigzag path. Water beyond the line of breakers is carried in a longshore current. **(b)** An aerial view of waves along the beach

Topic 10 **Shoreline Currents**

Waves, like the winds that form them, may come from any direction. Thus, most waves strike shorelines at angles. When waves break, large amounts of water and sand are pushed up the beach at an angle. The motion of water up the beach is called **swash**. Most of the water runs back down the beach under the next wave in a gentle current called **backwash**. A very strong backwash is sometimes called *undertow*. Backwash drags sand almost straight back toward the sea. Each breaking wave repeats the process of pushing sand up at an angle (during swash) and pulling it straight back (during backwash). The sand drifts down the beach in a zigzag path (Figure 12.11 (a)). The water beyond the line of breakers is also pushed toward shore by waves and pulled back by backwash. This movement forms a **longshore current** that runs almost parallel to shore. Swimmers in the surf often discover that they have been moved along the beach by a longshore current. Longshore currents are important in the movement of sand and in the formation of sandbars.

Rip currents are much more dangerous than backwash. Rip currents are strong surface currents that flow away from the beach. They may form where too much water builds up in the surf zone. This can occur where two longshore currents meet head-on, where breakers bring in more water than backwash can return, or where water is held back by a headland, breakwater, or an underwater sandbar. The piled-up water flows rapidly back to the sea through a gap in the barrier.

Since rip currents can reach speeds of up to five kilometers per hour, they are a serious hazard for swimmers. Swimmers often can avoid rip currents by knowing what to look for. The water in a rip current may carry a lot of sand, which makes the current visible. Waves around a rip current may be steeper than the surrounding waves, or the line of breakers may be further out to sea. For a swimmer who is caught in a rip current, the best thing to do is to swim parallel to shore. Do not try to swim against the rip current.

a

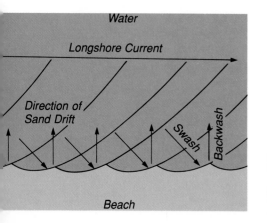

b

TOPIC QUESTIONS

Each topic question refers to the topic of the same number.

7. **(a)** How are most waves produced? **(b)** What two factors affect the height of wind-formed waves? **(c)** What are swells and what is their cause?

8. **(a)** Explain the meaning of wavelength, crest, trough, period. **(b)** Find the speed of a wave that has a length of 12 meters and a period of 3 seconds. **(c)** Describe the motion of water molecules in a wave. **(d)** What is wave refraction and how is it caused? **(e)** What effect does wave refraction have on uneven shorelines and why?

9. **(a)** What causes breakers and surf to form? **(b)** How deep is the water at the line of breakers? **(c)** Why is surf important geologically?

10. **(a)** What are swash and backwash? **(b)** Describe the motion of water and sand in a longshore current. **(c)** What is a rip current? **(d)** How can a rip current be recognized?

ANSWERS

7. (a) by wind (b) fetch and wind duration (c) smooth, steady waves; distant winds

8. (a) in order: distance between crests, high point, low point, time between crests (b) 4 m/s (c) circular, circles become smaller with depth (d) bending of wave, shallow end of wave slows sooner (e) erodes headland faster because wave strikes it on all sides

9. (a) wave touches bottom, slows, crest falls over (b) depth is 1 to 2 times original wave height (c) wears down and undermines rocks and cliffs, moves sediments

10. (a) swash—water running up on beach; backwash—water runs back down beach (b) wave strikes beach at angle, returns straight down, net result is movement along beach (c) large volume of water moving seaward quickly (d) discolored water, breakers further out to sea, steep waves

EARTH**MATTERS**

Beach Erosion

Beach erosion by waves and currents has become a serious problem along the Atlantic coast of the United States. As much as a meter of shoreline is being removed from some areas each year. A large storm at high tide can remove ten times that much beach in a single night.

In an effort to protect property and lives, millions of dollars have been spent to rebuild beaches or save them from erosion. Expensive sea walls temporarily stop storm waves from reaching homes but do not help save beaches. In fact, sea walls may speed erosion. The wave crashing against a sea wall carries away far more sand than it would if the wave spent its energy gently rolling up onto a beach.

Some towns losing their beaches to erosion have built structures out into the sea to trap the sand carried by longshore currents. These structures, called jetties, often trap the sand needed at other beaches down the coast, causing these beaches to erode more rapidly.

To date, no method of slowing beach erosion has proved very effective for long. Much of the problem is traceable to rising sea level. Sea level is rising by about a third of a meter every century. The natural response of a beach to rising sea level is to move away from the waves— that is, toward land. As beaches adjust to rising sea level, lines of houses like this one are collapsing into the sea.

There are some ways to naturally slow beach erosion. If you live near the ocean, you may want to help plant dune grass, which stabilizes the dune and makes it more resistant to erosion.

OBJECTIVES

A Name and describe some features of shoreline erosion and shoreline deposition.

B Define *beach* and discuss factors that affect the kind of materials that make up a beach.

C Describe the formation of coral reef structures.

VIDEODISC SELECTION

Diagram of beach and headland erosion
Side 2: 2190, single frame

Examples of shoreline erosional features (described in disc directory)
Side 2: 2217 to 2228, 10-frame sequence

12.12   Sea stacks on the coast of New Brunswick, Canada

III   Shoreline Features

Topic 11   How Waves Erode Rock Materials

Waves erode the shoreline in a number of ways. Breaking storm waves may strike rock cliffs with a force of thousands of kilograms per square meter. Such breakers easily remove large masses of loose sand and clay. Bedrock is split by water driven into cracks and fissures. The bedrock is also scoured away by the grinding of sands and pebbles. Boulders that fall from rock cliffs are pounded into pebbles and sand. Sea water dissolves minerals from rocks such as limestone.

When waves strike the headlands of a deep-water shoreline, they may cut away the rock up to the high-tide level. If the rock is soft, it is worn away quickly, creating a notch. The materials overhanging the notch collapse. When this happens, a **sea cliff** is formed. These cliffs wear back rapidly, in some cases as fast as a meter a year.

In harder rock materials a notch may deepen until it becomes a *sea cave*. Waves may cut through the walls of sea caves to form *sea arches*. Arches may also form when waves cut through vertical cracks in narrow headlands. If the roof of a sea arch falls in, a tall, narrow rock island called a *stack* remains.

All of these features can be seen on the coasts of California, Oregon, Washington, and Maine, on the Gaspé peninsula of Canada, and in many parts of the Mediterranean Sea.

12.13 A lagoon is an area protected from strong winds and waves, often by a baymouth bar or other sandbar.

Topic 12 Attached and Unattached Sandbars

On irregular shorelines, longshore currents carry away most of the sand and pebbles eroded from the headlands. Where a longshore current passes across the mouth of a bay or cove, some of the sediment is carried inland by waves. There it may form a sand or pebble beach.

Many times, however, the current carries enough sand to form a **sandbar** across the mouth of the bay. The sandbar seems to grow right out of the end of the headland. Such a bar, attached at one end, is called a *spit*. In time it may grow completely across the bay to become a *baymouth bar*. In some places bars form between islands and the mainland.

Waves and crosscurrents may drive the end of a spit toward the shore. A spit with a curved end is called a *hook*. Sandy Hook in New Jersey is a well-known hook. Other famous hooks are Rockaway Beach on Long Island, New York, and the tip of Cape Cod in Massachusetts.

Sandbars usually protect the water behind them from strong winds and waves. The protected areas are called **lagoons.** As time passes, lagoons may fill with sediment and become salt marshes. Jamaica Bay is the lagoon behind the Rockaway Beach hook. It is an important shelter for shorebirds, as are many other lagoons.

Sandbars may also form on coasts with straight shorelines. These bars are not attached to the shoreline. Instead, they run parallel to it at some distance from the shore. They are called **barrier islands.** They are found along the eastern coast of the United States from New York southward to Texas. Some well-known examples of barrier islands include Fire Island in New York, Atlantic City beach in New Jersey, and Hatteras in North Carolina. Galveston, Texas, and Palm Beach and Miami Beach, Florida, are also located on barrier islands. Padre Island, a barrier island in Texas, is about 160 kilometers long.

SCIENCE BACKGROUND

In general, steeper beaches have fewer sandbars. Wide, flat beaches may have as many as three bars. Steep beaches may have only one.

VIDEODISC SELECTION

Sandbar off Chatham, MA
Side 2: 2257, single frame

Aerial photos of sand spits
Side 2: 2325 to 2332, 8-frame sequence

Aerial photo of barrier island
Side 2: 2310, single frame

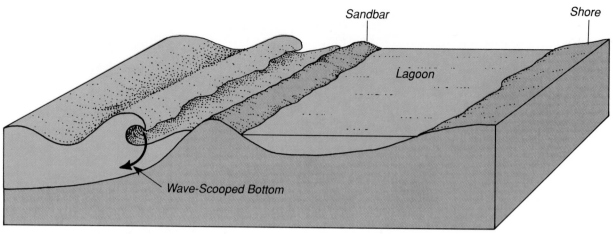

12.14 This diagram shows the relative positions of a sandbar, lagoon, and shore.

Barrier islands, sandbars, and beaches are not permanent features. The sand that makes these features is constantly being removed by waves, storms, and longshore drift. If enough new sand arrives at the beach or island (from rivers or from other beaches), then it remains. However, if the amount of sand removed is greater than the amount that arrives, then the beach or island erodes. In many parts of the country, rock walls have been built to protect houses and other property from beach erosion. Unfortunately, such structures often make the situation worse because they prevent waves from breaking normally. The energy of the waves hits the beach all at once, and the wave removes more sand than it otherwise would have. The best way to avoid property loss due to beach erosion is to avoid building on the beach.

Topic 13   Beach Materials

Geologists define a **beach** as the area between the high-tide level and the low-tide level. The gentler the seafloor, the wider the beach. Beaches may be sandy, pebbly, or even rocky. The makeup of a beach depends on both the material that is available and on the slope of the shoreline. Materials that make up a beach may come from the local area, or they may arrive from other beaches and rivers. Not all materials that arrive are left on the beach. If the seafloor is steep, sands and clays are washed out to sea by backwash, and pebble beaches are left. If the seafloor slopes gently, only clay is washed out, and sand beaches are formed.

Most beach sands are grains of durable minerals, such as quartz and some feldspar. Other materials commonly found in beach sands are grains of magnetite and flakes of muscovite mica. The makeup of beach sand, however, depends not only on the durability of minerals but also on the minerals that are common in the source area. Beach sand that was weathered from granite is mainly quartz and feldspar. Beach sands on coral islands, such as Bermuda, are mainly coral (calcite) fragments.

VIDEODISC SELECTION

Photo of pebbled beach
Side 2: 2289, single frame

Topic 14   **Types of Shorelines**

The shoreline of the Maine coast zigzags from headland to bay, covering a total of nearly 4000 kilometers. The straight-line distance along the coast, however, is about 300 kilometers. The coast of Maine is an example of an irregular shoreline. Other examples of this type of shoreline are the coast of Scotland and the northwest coast of Spain.

Most irregular shorelines appear to have formed when coastal areas were flooded by the sea. This flooding occurred either because the land sank or the sea rose, which the sea did at the end of the Ice Age. After the flooding, the drowned main valleys became short, deep, narrow bays. The divides between the valleys became headlands. The drowned tributary valleys became branches of the bays. Many hills were partly drowned and became islands. Some were completely drowned and became shallow areas called *shoals*. The shallowness of a shoal makes navigation by boat difficult.

The land along the Atlantic coast from New York to Florida is called a *coastal plain*. Much of this area also has an irregular shoreline formed by drowning of the land. However, the river valleys of the coastal plain were wide and gently sloped. Thus, the bays of the coastal plain are wider and longer than those in Maine. The water close to shore is not as deep as in Maine, and there are fewer islands. Chesapeake Bay is the drowned valley of the lower Susquehanna River and its tributaries. New York Bay is the drowned valley of the lower Hudson River. Similarly, San Francisco Bay is the drowned valley of the lower Sacramento River.

VIDEODISC SELECTION

Diagram of coastline features
Side 2: 2187, single frame

12.15 **(a)** The irregular shoreline of the Maine coast formed in a hilly area cut by river valleys. **(b)** The valleys were drowned by a rise in sea level. Valleys became bays, ridges became headlands, and hills became islands. **(c)** Erosion by waves and currents formed sea cliffs and attached sandbars.

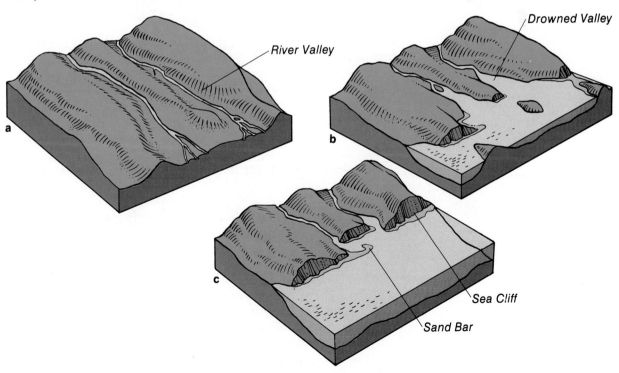

12.16 A deep fiord in Norway

VIDEODISC SELECTION

Alaskan fjord
Side 2: 2826, single frame

During the Ice Age, glaciers in Norway, Alaska, and other near-polar regions reached the oceans. Glacial troughs (Chapter 11, Topic 11) were formed below the present-day sea level. When the Ice Age ended, the sea flooded the parts of the troughs below sea level. This formed long, deep, steep-sided bays called **fiords.** The tributary valleys of glacial troughs are hanging troughs. Where hanging troughs meet the main glacial trough, spectacular waterfalls drop down the walls of the fiord. Fiord shorelines are found in Greenland, Labrador, Chile, New Zealand, Norway, and Alaska.

Almost all of the west coasts of North America and South America—from Oregon to central Chile—have fairly straight or regular shorelines. A regular shoreline does not have many deeply indented inlets or drowned valleys, although it may have a number of shallow, wave-carved coves. The plate tectonic theory (Chapter 13) explains how these regular shorelines were formed. These shorelines are, for the most part, on the boundary line between two sets of plates. As the heavier Pacific Ocean plates meet the continental plates and plunge under them, mountains rise and deep undersea troughs form. Long lines of mountains run parallel to the coasts. The ocean floor slopes steeply to great depths near each shore. Each coast is bordered in many places by sea cliffs and stacks.

Topic 15 Corals, Coral Reefs, and Coral Atolls

Corals are tiny sea animals that live in colonies. They remain fastened to rocky seafloors in warm, clear, fairly shallow water. For corals to survive, the water temperature must be between 18°C and 21°C. The water depth must be no more than about 45 meters.

Since corals do not move, they depend on waves and currents to carry their food supply. They make their shells from the lime in sea water. When corals die, their shells remain, and new corals grow on

them. Large buildups of coral shells are called *coral reefs.* Corals do not grow above the surface of the water. However, as with sandbars, waves may pile coral shells above sea level. When these coral shell fragments are cemented together, they form coral limestone.

Coral colonies growing close to shore form **fringing reefs.** Fringing reefs can be seen in Florida and along many other semitropical and tropical coasts. A coral reef grows mainly on its ocean side, where ocean waves bring food that feeds new corals. When old corals die on the shore side of the reef, their shells are broken and scattered. Thus, a fringing reef slowly moves away from shore.

As a fringing reef grows oceanward, it becomes a **barrier reef.** The Great Barrier Reef of Australia is about 2000 kilometers long and up to 150 kilometers wide. The wide lagoon between the reef and the mainland is called the Inland Waterway.

An **atoll** is a narrow, ring-shaped island or chain of islands. Atolls are found mostly in open waters in the middle of the Pacific Ocean, far away from shores of continents. Most atolls are made of coral limestone, yet coral cannot grow in the deep water far away from shore. Therefore, there must have been a surface on which the coral atoll started to grow. Holes bored through the coral show that each atoll has grown on the slopes of a volcano. The formation of atolls is discussed further in Chapter 18.

TOPIC QUESTIONS

Each topic question refers to the topic of the same number.

11. What features are caused by wave erosion on irregular shorelines?

12. **(a)** How do the following originate: a spit, a baymouth bar, a hook?　**(b)** What is a lagoon?　**(c)** Explain why shoreline features made of sand cannot be considered permanent structures.

13. **(a)** What is a beach?　**(b)** How does a pebble beach form?

14. **(a)** How were most irregular shorelines formed?　**(b)** How do the bays between New York and Florida differ from those of the Maine coast?　**(c)** What are fiord shorelines? Where do they occur?　**(d)** Explain the origin of the regular shorelines of western North America and South America.

15. **(a)** What are corals?　**(b)** How does a coral reef form?　**(c)** What is a fringing reef?　**(d)** Why does a coral reef grow mainly seaward?　**(e)** What is a barrier reef?　**(f)** What is an atoll?

12.17 (left) Corals are tiny marine animals that live in groups. New corals tend to build their shells on top of old coral shells. (right) Over time, the shells of generations of corals build up a coral reef.

VIDEODISC SELECTION

Sea coral
Side 2: 2334 to 2336, 3-frame sequence

Diagrams of reef formation
Side 2: 2191 to 2193, 3-frame sequence

ANSWERS

11. sea cliffs, sea caves, sea arches, stacks

12. (a) in order: sandbar deposited with one end attached to shore; spit that has grown across bay; curved spit off a point　(b) protected water behind a sandbar　(c) Sand is constantly removed; unless it is replaced, feature erodes.

13. (a) area between high and low tide levels　(b) backwash removes sands and clays, leaves pebbles

14. (a) when coastal areas were flooded　(b) wider, longer, shallower, fewer islands　(c) drowned glacial troughs; Greenland, Labrador, Chile, New Zealand, Norway, Alaska　(d) colliding crustal plates

15. (a) tiny shelled animals that build colonies　(b) new corals grow on shells of dead ones　(c) coral colonies close to shore　(d) food source is on ocean side　(e) fringing reef that has grown away from shore　(f) narrow, ring-shaped coral island

CHAPTER 12

L A B
ACTIVITY

Beach Erosion and Deposition

If you visit a beach often enough, you will become familiar with the many features that make a beach unique. For example, you will begin to notice how the beach slope changes as you approach and enter the water. However, if you return to the beach after a major storm, you will see how quickly the beach can change as wind and waves remove or deposit large quantities of sand and other material. In this activity, you will explore how waves influence the development of shorelines through the erosion and deposition of beaches.

Lab Skills and Objectives
- To **compare** the effects of wave speed on beach erosion and deposition
- To **describe** the effect of shoreline slope on the rate of beach erosion

12.18 Cutaway view of model beach with (a) gradual slope and with (b) steep slope

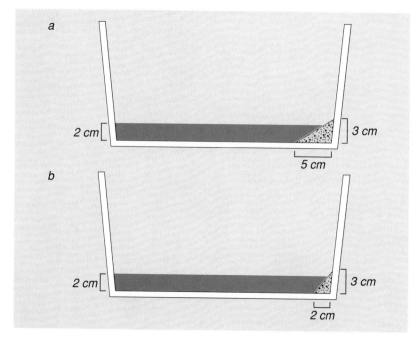

- To **determine** the effects of beach composition on erosion

Materials
- 200 cc Mixture A (75% sand, 25% gravel)
- 200 cc Mixture B (75% gravel, 25% sand)
- clear plastic shoe box
- grease pencil
- metric ruler
- beaker
- water
- small wooden block (5 cm x 10 cm)
- clock or watch

Procedure
1. Use Mixture A to construct a model beach at one end of a clear plastic shoe box. The model beach should extend across the entire end of the shoe box and should slope gradually toward the opposite end of the box. The beach should be 3 cm deep at its deepest point and should extend 5 cm into the box, as shown in Figure 12.18a. You may not need to use the entire 200 cc.

2. Use a grease pencil to place a mark 2 cm from the bottom of the box on the opposite end of the box from the model beach. Use a beaker to fill the shoe box with water to the 2 cm mark. Add the water slowly at the opposite end of the box from the beach so that you do not disturb the model beach.

3. Place the wooden block in the water at the end of the

box opposite the shoreline with the long side of the block parallel to the shoreline (figure 12.19). Without completely removing the block from the water, generate waves by moving the block up and down for two minutes at a rate of one wave per second. Make sure that the rate and size of the waves remain constant.

4. After two minutes, sketch a cutaway view of the slope of the model beach. In your sketch, record the former slope and position of the model beach and indicate the new distribution of both the sand and the gravel.

5. Carefully pour the water from the box into a container provided by your teacher. **Do not pour the water down the sink.**

6. Reconstruct the model beach and refill the shoe box with water as before.

7. Repeat step 3, except this time move the block up and down for two minutes at a rate of two times a second. Sketch a cutaway view of the beach, noting the former position of the shoreline and the new distribution of the sand and gravel.

8. Repeat step 6. Reconstruct the beach, except this time make a steeper slope than in the first two trials. The sand-gravel mixture should extend 2 cm into the box, as shown in Figure 12.18b.

9. Repeat step 3, generating waves at a rate of one wave per second. After two minutes, sketch a cutaway view

of the shoreline. Record the former slope and position of the beach and the current distribution of the sand and gravel.

10. Empty the water and the sand/gravel mixture into the container provided by your teacher.

11. Use Mixture B to construct a beach with the same slope shown in Figure 12.18b.

12. Repeat steps 3–5.

13. Answer the questions in *Analysis and Conclusions.*

Analysis and Conclusions

1. Based on your models, describe how the rate at which waves strike a shoreline affects the erosion of a gradually-sloping model beach.

2. How does the initial slope of the beach affect erosion?

3. Describe the distribution of the sand versus the distribution of the gravel in each of your four trials. Why is there a difference?

4. Explain how the composition of a beach affects beach erosion. Give evidence for your answer.

5. Describe any depositional features formed as a result of wave action on your model beaches. In which trial was deposited material most noticeable?

6. Describe how a large storm could significantly change the features of a beach.

7. Beach erosion is a significant problem for many seaside communities. Suggest ways to stabilize shorelines in order to prevent erosion.

12.19 Waves are generated by moving the block up and down.

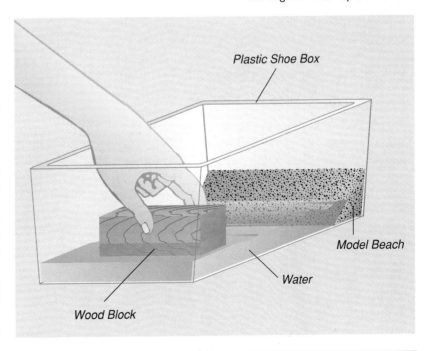

Plastic Shoe Box

Model Beach

Water

Wood Block

Answer to all questions appear in the Teacher's Guide at the back of this book.

■ Summary

I Wind erodes and weathers land by moving loose sediment. Desert pavement and blowouts result from wind erosion.

Loess is a silt-sized, wind-deposited sediment.

Sand supply, wind strength, and vegetation affect sand dune shape. Dunes migrate in the direction toward which the wind blows.

II Most waves result from winds. Fetch and wind duration affect the height of a wind-formed wave.

A wave is described by its height, wavelength, period, and speed. A tsunami is a long, rapidly moving wave often caused by an undersea earthquake.

Water moves in place as a wave passes. Water motion exists to a depth of about one half wavelength, the depth at which a wave begins to slow.

Waves approaching a shoreline at an angle refract and approach the shore at less of an angle.

Swash, backwash, longshore currents, and rip currents move water and sediments on beaches.

III Sea cliffs, sea caves, sea arches, and stacks result from shoreline erosion. Sandbars, spits, baymouth bars, hooks, lagoons, and barrier islands result from shoreline deposition.

Pebble beaches form on steep shorelines, sand beaches on gently sloping shorelines.

Irregular shorelines form when hilly, uneven coastal areas are flooded by the sea. The regular shorelines of western North and South America are the result of crustal plate collisions.

Corals are tiny, shell-building sea animals that build coral reef structures.

■ Vocabulary

atoll	beach	desert pavement
backwash	blowouts	dust storm
barrier island	corals	fetch
barrier reef	deflation	fiord

fringing reef	refraction	tsunami
lagoon	rip current	ventifact
loess	sandbar	wave height
longshore current	sea cliff	wavelength
period	swash	

■ Review

Choose the best answer for each item. Write the letter of the answer on your paper.

1. An area that is LEAST likely to experience wind erosion is a (a) beach, (b) desert, (c) forest, (d) semiarid region.
2. Which material is likely to be the most abrasive in a wind storm? (a) quartz sand (b) calcite sand (c) silt (d) clay
3. A shallow depression formed by deflation is a (a) dune, (b) stack, (c) blowout, (d) spit.
4. Which particle size is closest to that of loess? (a) clay (b) silt (c) sand (d) pebbles
5. Barchan, transverse, parabolic, and longitudinal are kinds of (a) sea arches, (b) offshore sandbars, (c) sand dunes, (d) coral reefs.
6. When sand is blown from the windward side of a dune to the leeward side, the dune will (a) migrate to leeward, (b) weather into clay, (c) stand in vertical cliffs, (d) migrate to windward.
7. The fetch of a wave is the (a) height of the wave, (b) speed of the wave, (c) speed of the wave-forming wind, (d) distance over which the wave-forming wind blows.
8. The distance from the crest of one wave to the crest of the next is (a) wavelength, (b) period, (c) fetch, (d) trough.
9. Wave motion begins to touch bottom at a depth of about (a) ½ wavelength, (b) 1 wavelength, (c) 1½ wavelengths, (d) 2 wavelengths.
10. The process by which waves are turned to be more parallel to the shoreline is called (a) ventifaction, (b) deflation, (c) refraction, (d) erosion.

For further review, see **Study Guide.**
For assessment, see **Chapter Tests**
and **Computer Test Bank.**

11. Longshore currents are (a) strong seaward-flowing currents, (b) gentle seaward-flowing currents, (c) important movers of sand, (d) a kind of tsunami.
12. Which feature results from shoreline erosion? (a) spit (b) stack (c) hook (d) lagoon
13. A beach near a steeply sloping sea floor is likely to be covered with (a) mud, (b) silt, (c) sand, (d) pebbles.
14. Which mineral is most common in beach sands made from coral fragments? (a) quartz (b) calcite (c) gypsum (d) magnetite
15. A glacial trough that was drowned by the sea is a (a) atoll, (b) stack, (c) spit, (d) fiord.
16. A ring-shaped coral island is a(n) (a) atoll, (b) barrier reef, (c) ventifact, (d) tsunami.

■ Interpret and Apply

On your paper, answer each question in complete sentences.

1. How would visibility in a sand storm compare with visibility in a dust storm?
2. Why is quartz sand a better tool of wind erosion than gypsum sand or calcite sand? (The table *Properties of Some Common Minerals* on pages 644–645 may be helpful.)
3. Make sketches showing the windward and leeward sides of sand dunes for winds blowing steadily from (a) north, (b) south, (c) east, and (d) west.
4. How might the sand grains in a sand dune be different from the sand grains in a river delta?
5. Find the speed of a wave that has a wavelength of 300 meters and a period of 25 seconds.
6. At what depth would a 300-meter-long wave first be slowed by the seafloor? At what depth would a 10-meter wave be slowed?
7. Would there be a longshore current in a lagoon behind a long sandbar? Explain your answer.

■ Critical Thinking

Particle sizes in sand dunes and loess vary, as do the amounts of each particle size present. The graph below shows the percent of each particle in a sand dune sample and in a loess sample. Refer to the graph to answer questions 1–5.

1. What is the size range for medium sand?
2. Give the name, size range, and percentage of the most abundant particle in the sand dune sample and in the loess sample.
3. How does the percentage of coarse silt in the sand dune compare with the percentage of coarse silt in the loess?
4. How does the range of sizes for the sand dune compare with those of the loess?
5. Which sample shows better sorting? (Review the term *sorting* from Chapter 5.)

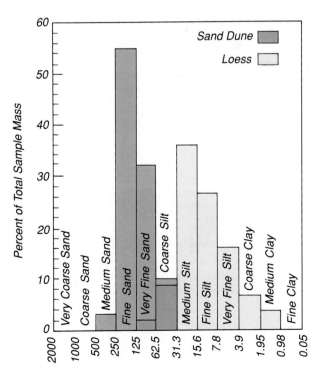

1 micrometer (μm) = 1000 millimeters (mm)

UNIT **THREE**

Forces That Raise the Surface

A movement in Earth's crust made these sediment layers break and shift. Why did Earth's crust move in this particular place?

Rocks and dust explode out of Earth's interior during a volcanic eruption. Can volcanic eruptions be predicted?

Thousands of years ago, these folded rocks lay flat. What Earth forces bend solid rock?

What raises Earth's surface?

Even as Earth's surface is worn away, it is pushed up from within. Unseen forces shift and mold Earth's face, making mountains, adding new material to the crust, raising land out of the sea. Look at the photographs. What evidence does each show of the powerful forces that shape Earth's crust?

Alaska's Mount McKinley, the highest peak in North America, is often shaken by earthquakes. Is there a reason high mountains and earthquakes occur together? ▼

Earthquakes can shatter buildings in a matter of seconds. Here, people in Mexico City look at the damage to their homes following a quake. Why are earthquakes common in some parts of the world, but not in others? ▼

Plate Tectonics

A *Paradoxides* fossil

SCIENCE BACKGROUND

Paradoxides is a trilobite of the Cambrian Period. In addition to Massachusetts, *Paradoxides* has also been found in the Carolina Slate Belt region of the Southern Appalachians.

How Do You Know That . . .

Earth's surface has changed? This fossil, found in an outcrop near Boston, Massachusetts, is called *Paradoxides*. *Paradoxides* is found in similar rocks along the east coast of North America, but nowhere else in North America. However, rocks containing *Paradoxides* are found in the British Isles. *Paradoxides* provides evidence that North America and the British Isles were once part of the same continent. The continent separated as an ocean basin formed between North America and Europe. Some parts of this continent remained on the North American side of the ocean, while other pieces went with the Euopean side.

I What Is Plate Tectonics?

Topic 1 Moving Plates Cover the Globe

The discovery that continents and ocean basins could be separated into parts that can then move about has led to a new understanding of Earth's outer layer. Scientists now know that Earth's surface consists of a number of rigid, but moving, pieces called *plates*. In some areas, the plates are moving away from each other. In other areas, the plates are moving together. The study of the formation and movement of these plates is called **plate tectonics.**

Earth's surface is divided into a dozen major plates and several minor plates. Some of the plates are moving toward each other, and some are moving apart. The South American Plate and the African Plate are moving apart. Other plates are moving together. The Indian Plate is colliding with the Eurasian Plate, and the Nazca Plate is sliding under the South American Plate. In California, the Pacific Plate and the North American Plate are sliding past each other.

OBJECTIVES

A Define *plate tectonics* and describe the relative motions of several plates.

B Locate and describe the lithosphere and the asthenosphere and relate both to plate tectonics.

VIDEODISC SELECTION

Tectonic plate boundaries
Side 1 movie: 21568 & PLAY

13.1 The major plates and some of the minor plates are labeled on the map below. Notice that the large plates include both oceans and landmasses.

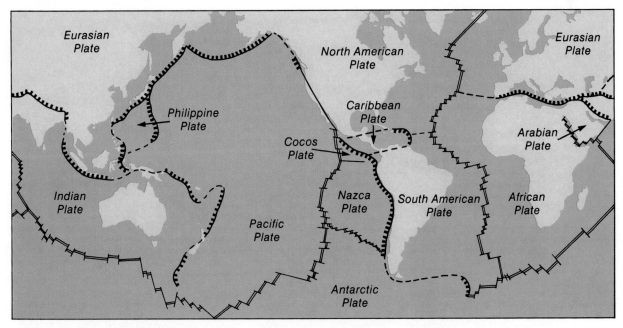

Trenches

Transform Fault

Ridges

Uncertain Boundaries

VIDEODISC SELECTION

Map of Earth's tectonic plates
Side 1: 725, single frame

TEACHING TIP

Point out that the terms "crust" and "mantle" are still used, but the term "lithosphere" has more meaning in plate tectonics.

VIDEODISC SELECTION

Structure of Earth's interior
Side 1: 724, single frame

13.2   The moving lithospheric plates rest upon the asthenosphere. Convection currents within the asthenosphere are the driving force behind lithospheric plate movement.

Topic 2 **How Thick Are the Plates?**

Plate tectonics has expanded the model of Earth's interior as described in Chapter 1. The crust and mantle were originally thought to represent two distinctly different materials. Now it is known that the crust and the uppermost portion of the mantle are very similar in both rock composition and physical properties. Together they make up a single solid layer called the **lithosphere.** The lithosphere is rigid but broken into plates that move with respect to one another. It is about 100 kilometers thick.

The composition of the lithosphere is basically that of the igneous rock basalt. The continents, however, are a major exception. Continental crust has a composition more like that of the igneous rock granite. Because granite is less dense (lighter) than basalt, continents occur as pieces embedded in the more dense (heavier) lithosphere.

Topic 3 **Why Do the Plates Move?**

The Lithospheric plates rest upon a layer within the mantle called the **asthenosphere.** This layer is thought to cause plate movement.

The asthenosphere has a composition similar to the lithosphere above, but it has very different properties. The rock of the asthenosphere is partially melted. As a result, it can flow very slowly. Scientists think that this flow takes the form of very large and slow-

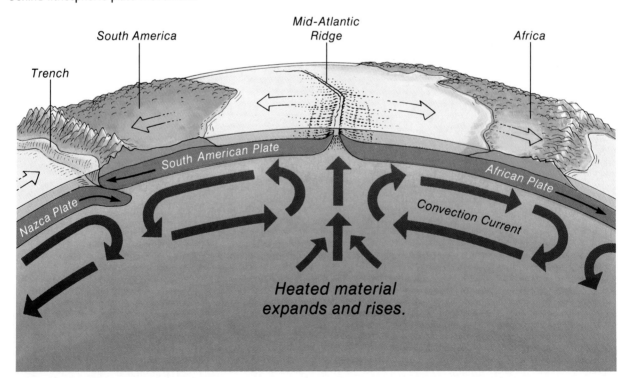

Trench

South America

Mid-Atlantic Ridge

Africa

South American Plate

African Plate

Nazca Plate

Convection Current

Heated material expands and rises.

moving convection currents. Within such currents, material expands and rises upon heating but contracts and sinks upon cooling.

Where the convection currents within the asthenosphere are rising, new material continually arrives at Earth's surface and pushes older material aside. This push drives the lithospheric plates apart. The South American Plate and the African Plate are an example.

Where cooler, denser currents within the asthenosphere seem to be sinking, the plates of the lithosphere are pulled together. This motion is thought to be the reason for the Nazca Plate sliding beneath the South American Plate.

TOPIC QUESTIONS

Each topic question refers to the topic of the same number.

1. **(a)** What is plate tectonics?   **(b)** Identify plates that are moving apart; moving together or colliding; and sliding past each other.

2. **(a)** Describe the structure and properties of the lithosphere. **(b)** How are the composition and density of continental crust different from that of the rest of the lithosphere?

3. **(a)** Where is the asthenosphere?   **(b)** What is the major property of the asthenosphere?   **(c)** How do the lithospheric plates move where convection currents are rising?   **(d)** How do the plates move where convection currents are sinking?

OF INTEREST
The average rate of plate motion is similar to the rate at which the human fingernail grows.

VIDEODISC SELECTION

Convection in Earth's mantle
Side 1: 726, single frame

ANSWERS
1. (a) the study of the formation and movement of lithospheric plates (b) North American and Eurasian, South American and African; Indian and Eurasian, Nazca and South American; Pacific and North American
2. (a) consists of crust and upper mantle; rigid; about 100 km thick (b) granite rather than basalt; less dense
3. (a) below lithosphere   (b) able to flow   (c) apart   (d) together

Current RESEARCH

Seeing Earth's Interior

As you will learn in Chapter 15, most of what is known about Earth's interior is based on the detailed study of earthquake, or seismic waves. These energy waves travel outward from an earthquake's origin. Based on the material they encounter as they travel through Earth's many layers, these waves of energy may speed up, slow down, or be stopped altogether.

Scientists are currently using a technique called seismic tomography to peer inside Earth. Seismic tomography can be compared to a computerized tomography scan (CT) of the human body. A CT scan—called a "cat scan"—gives a three-dimensional view of the inside of the human body by piecing together X ray images from all directions. Various organs and bones absorb X rays differently and show up differently on the CT image.

Using seismic data from stations all over the world, researchers have put together three-dimensional images of what is happening in the mantle. The images show what appear to be hot masses rising up through the asthenosphere at the mid-ocean ridges. Beneath the continents, tomograms reveal cool, thick areas, which may show the thicker continental crust. Current research in seismic tomography centers on the subduction of plates and how deep oceanic plates are carried into the mantle before melting.

OBJECTIVES

A Describe the theory of continental drift and list some evidences that Alfred Wegener used to support the theory.

B Discuss the relationship between earthquakes, volcanoes, and plate boundaries.

C Explain what is meant by normal and reversed polarity, discuss the pattern of magnetic polarity at spreading centers, and relate this pattern to plate tectonics.

D Discuss heat flow and elevation of the seafloor as evidence of seafloor spreading.

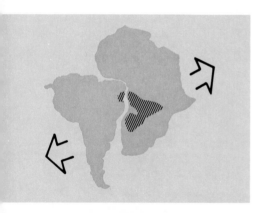

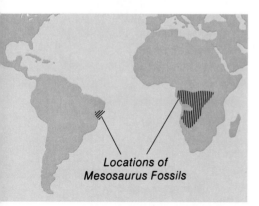

Locations of Mesosaurus Fossils

13.3 The theory of continental drift implies that Africa and South America were once joined. Fossil evidence on both continents seems to back the theory.

II   Evidence for Plate Tectonics

Topic 4   **Africa and South America**

The idea that Earth's solid surface might be moving and changing is not new. When the first reliable world maps were made in the seventeenth century, people noted the remarkable similarities in the shape of the west coast of Africa and the east coast of South America. The suggestion was eventually made that the two continents had once been part of a larger continent that had broken and moved apart. This idea was the start of a theory called *continental drift.*

The most famous version of the theory was proposed in 1912 by Alfred Wegener, a German scientist. In addition to the similarities in continental shape, Wegener found other evidence to show that Africa and South America must have been joined once. He noted that the fossil remains of *Mesosaurus,* a small reptile that lived 270 million years ago, are found in Brazil and in South Africa but are not found anywhere else on Earth. This peculiar distribution is easily explained if the two continents were joined at that time. Wegener also noted that some particularly distinctive rocks are found on both continents. The rocks at these locations would match nicely if the two continents were joined.

Wegener's theory of continental drift was debated for several years after its proposal. It was subjected to ridicule until the 1960's. At that time, new discoveries about such seemingly unrelated phenomena as earthquakes, volcanoes, magnetism, and crustal heat flow added support to Wegener's ideas. The theory of continental drift was expanded and became the theory of plate tectonics.

Topic 5   **Earthquakes and Volcanoes**

Scientists have long observed that earthquakes do not occur randomly throughout the world, but occur in rather limited belts. They have also noted that these same belts contain most of Earth's volcanoes. The locations of the belts became clear with the understanding of plate tectonics. The belts where earthquakes and volcanoes are located mark the location of *plate boundaries.*

It is not hard to understand why plate boundaries are active areas. These boundaries are places where one plate is moving relative to another plate. Stresses build up along the boundary, and when the stress becomes too great, fractures form and earthquakes occur. The boundaries are also areas of high heat flow, where molten rock moves upward to Earth's surface and forms volcanoes.

The largest active belt is the one that nearly surrounds the Pacific Ocean. In an average year, 90 percent of all the world's earthquakes occur there. Many famous volcanoes are found along this belt. Among them are Mount St. Helens in Washington State, Mount Katmai in Alaska, Mount Fujiyama in Japan, and Mount Pinatubo in the Philippine Islands.

SCIENCE BACKGROUND
The active belt around the Pacific
Ocean is often called the "Ring of
Fire" because of all the volcanic
activity there.

Lesson II   Evidence for Plate Tectonics   **237**

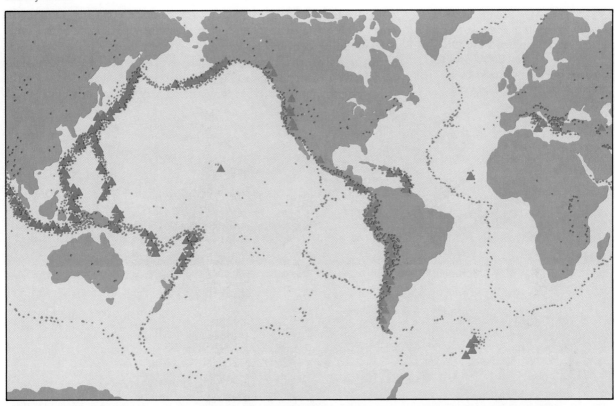

▲▲▲ *Volcanoes*   ⋰⋱⋮ *Earthquakes*

13.4 This map shows the locations
of the world's earthquake and volcano belts. The belts are also the
location of plate boundaries.

Topic 6 **Magnetism**

Some igneous rocks contain minerals that are magnetic. These
minerals provide a record of the direction of Earth's magnetic poles
at the time the rock formed. When this record was studied in igneous rocks on the continents, it was discovered that Earth's crust has
apparently shifted or drifted since the rocks were formed. There is
also evidence that Earth's magnetic poles had often been reversed.
The present north magnetic pole became the south magnetic pole
and the present south magnetic pole became the north magnetic
pole. Scientists found that there have been four major periods of
normal and reversed polarity within the past four million years (see
Figure 13.5).

Magnetic polarity reversals also show in bands in the igneous
rocks on the ocean floor. Where the lithospheric plates are moving
apart, the polarity reversals occur in bands parallel to and on opposite sides of the plate boundaries. Scientists compared the magnetic
bands found in the rock on both sides of the boundary with the
actual age of the rock. They determined that the youngest rocks of
the ocean floor are at the spreading plate boundaries, and that the
ocean floor becomes increasingly older away from the boundaries.

VIDEODISC SELECTION

‖‖‖‖‖‖‖‖‖‖‖‖‖‖‖
Map of worldwide earthquake and
volcano belts
Side 1: 727, single frame

‖‖‖‖‖‖‖‖‖‖‖‖‖‖‖
Diagram of magnetic polarity rever
sals
Side 1: 733, single frame

13.5 There have been four major polarity reversals in the past four million years. Geologists use the knowledge of magnetic polarity to compare the ages of rocks near spreading centers on the ocean floor.

Using this observation, scientists theorize what happens in the areas where the lithospheric plates are moving apart. These areas are **spreading centers.** Lava wells up from deep within Earth and continuously forms new rocks there. At the same time, older rocks move away from the boundary equally in both directions. As the lithospheric plates move apart, they carry their continents with them.

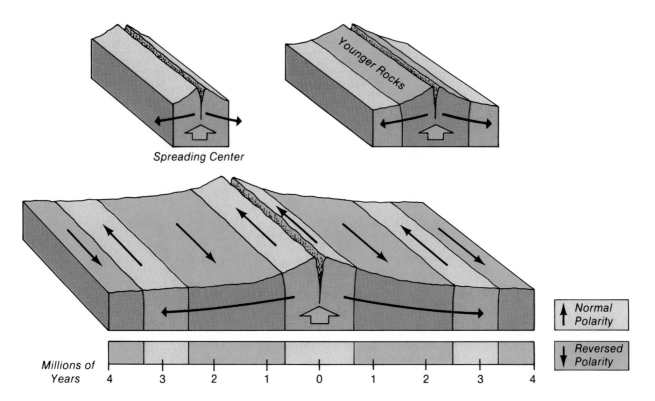

Spreading Center

Younger Rocks

Normal Polarity

Reversed Polarity

Millions of Years 4 3 2 1 0 1 2 3 4

VIDEODISC SELECTION

Diagram of ocean floor spreading center
Side 1: 732, single frame

Topic 7 **Heat Flow and Seafloor Elevation**

If convection currents within the asthenosphere are the driving force behind the movement of the lithospheric plates, some evidence for their existence should be found at spreading centers. Heat flow provides that evidence.

Heat flow is a measure of the amount of heat leaving the rocks of the lithosphere. The values for heat flow are unusually high in the areas of spreading centers and decrease away from the centers. This is exactly what should happen if spreading centers are places where hot convection currents are bringing magma to the surface forming new oceanic crust.

The elevation of the seafloor provides additional evidence of heat flow. Because heated materials expand, spreading centers have higher elevations than the rest of the seafloor. Elevations decrease away from spreading centers as the rocks cool and contract.

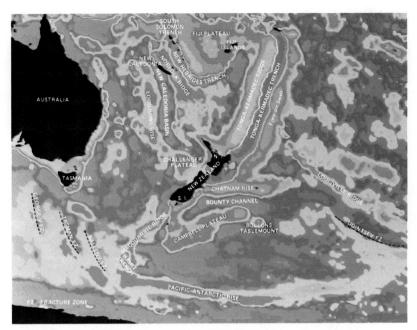

13.6 This *Landsat* photograph of the southeastern portion of the Pacific Ocean emphasizes heat flow on the ocean floor. Warmest areas are red; coolest areas are blue. Notice that the warmer areas are the higher elevations.

VIDEODISC SELECTION

Seasat images of ocean floor topography
Side 1: 775 to 782, 8-frame sequence

TOPIC QUESTIONS

Each topic question refers to the topic of the same number.

4. (a) What is the theory of continental drift?   (b) List three pieces of evidence that Wegener used to support the theory of continental drift.

5. (a) Why do earthquakes and volcanoes occur at plate boundaries? (b) Where is the largest belt of active earthquakes and volcanoes? (c) Name four volcanoes that occur in this belt.

6. (a) Describe Earth's magnetic polarity when the magnetic poles are reversed.   (b) What is the pattern of polarity reversals at spreading plate boundaries?   (c) Describe the age of the rocks of the ocean floor relative to spreading plate boundaries.   (d) What are spreading centers? What occurs there?

7. (a) What is heat flow?   (b) What is the relationship between heat flow and distance from a spreading center?   (c) How does heat flow provide evidence for rising convection currents at spreading centers?   (d) What is the relationship between heat flow and seafloor elevation? Why?

ANSWERS
   4. (a) A large continent made from Africa and South America broke and moved apart.   (b) shape of coastline, fossils, distinctive rocks
   5. (a) Plate movements cause stress.   (b) around the Pacific Ocean   (c) St. Helens, Katmai, Fujiyama, Pinatubo
   6. (a) Present north becomes south, south becomes north.   (b) in bands parallel to and on opposite sides of plate boundaries   (c) older away from boundary   (d) area between spreading plate boundaries; new rocks form, push older rocks away
   7. (a) measure of amount of heat leaving rocks of lithosphere (b) highest at center, decreases away from center   (c) should have highest heat flow at centers   (d) elevation highest at spreading centers because hot materials expanded

OBJECTIVES

A Describe diverging boundaries, identify some features that occur there, and give examples.

B Discuss sliding plate boundaries and give an example.

C Describe collision boundaries and give several examples.

D Define *subduction*, identify and give examples of subduction boundaries, and list features that occur at each.

SCIENCE BACKGROUND

There does not seem to be universal agreement on the terms used to describe plate boundaries. Diverging boundaries are also called *spreading* boundaries; collision boundaries are also called *sutured* boundaries.

III Kinds of Plate Boundaries

Topic 8 Diverging Boundaries

Diverging boundaries, or spreading centers, are places where two lithospheric plates are moving apart. In addition to the pattern of magnetic polarity and heat flow that occurs there, most diverging boundaries have *mid-ocean ridges*. Mid-ocean ridges have deep valleys along their entire length. These valleys, called *rift valleys,* are both the boundary between the lithospheric plates and the place where new rocks form and push older oceanic crust aside.

The rift valleys do not run smoothly along the ridge but are broken into segments, by faults called fracture zones. Movements along the *fracture zones* have been found to be a source of the earthquakes that occur along the ridge.

An example of a mid-ocean ridge is the *mid-Atlantic Ridge.* This ridge is the spreading center that separates the North American Plate from the Eurasian Plate and the South American Plate from the African Plate.

A second example of a mid-ocean ridge is the *East Pacific Rise.* This ridge separates the Nazca Plate from the Pacific Plate. Scientists who studied the East Pacific Rise found hot springs bubbling up from the seafloor along the ridge. Some previously unknown organisms (Figure 13.9) were discovered living in the area around these hot springs. Recently, other hot springs with similar colonies of organisms have been found along other ridge systems including the mid-Atlantic Ridge.

13.7 A mid-ocean ridge forms at a diverging boundary.

VIDEODISC SELECTION

Diagram of diverging plate boundary
Side 1: 734, single frame

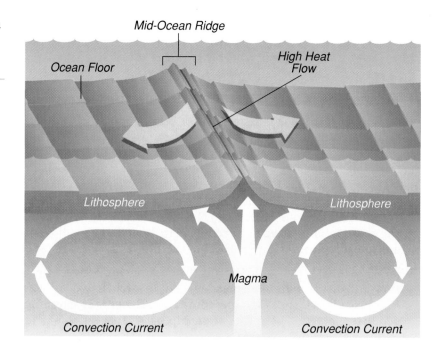

13.8 This rift in Iceland may be an extension of the mid-Atlantic Ridge. It is part of a spreading center.

13.9 (top) Basalt lava forms new ocean lithosphere at spreading boundaries. (bottom) Tubeworms are one kind of organism discovered in the hot-spring areas of the East Pacific Rise.

Topic 9 **Sliding Boundaries**

At the boundaries of some areas, the lithospheric plates are sliding past each other. In California, the North American Plate and the Pacific Plate are sliding past each other along the San Andreas Fault. A **fault** is a break or crack in Earth's crust along which movement has occurred. Southwestern California and the Pacific Plate are moving northwest with respect to the rest of the United States and the North American Plate.

The average rate of movement along the San Andreas Fault is five centimeters per year. However, some areas have not moved for over a century. These are thought to be the most likely places for future earthquakes.

SCIENCE BACKGROUND

Sliding boundaries may not be a separate kind of plate boundary but may be fracture zones of diverging boundaries.

VIDEODISC SELECTION

Formation of pillow lava
Side 1 movie: 36940 & PLAY

242

13.10 The San Andreas Fault is the boundary between two lithospheric plates that are sliding past each other. The arrow represents the direction of plate motion.

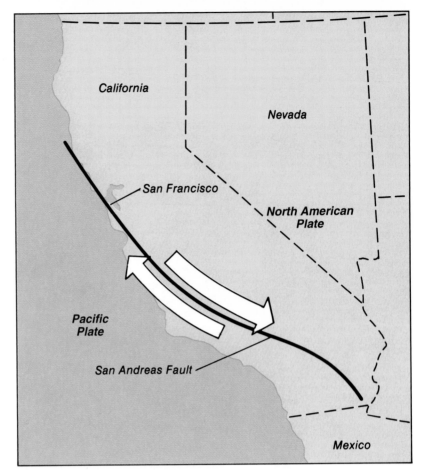

13.11 This orchard in California was offset during an earthquake that occurred in 1940.

VIDEODISC SELECTION

Diagrams of different types of converging plate boundaries
Side 1: 728 to 731, 4-frame sequence

Topic 10   Converging Boundaries: Collision

In addition to moving apart or sliding past each other, lithospheric plates can also move toward each other. A **converging boundary** forms when two plates come together, or converge.

If the converging plates are both carrying continents, the continents may be welded into a single larger continent. This form of converging boundary is known as a **collision boundary.** The collision causes the lithosphere at the boundary to be pushed upward into a mountain range.

The Himalayan Mountains are an example of a collision boundary that is still forming today. Here India is pushing northward into China at a rate of about 5 centimeters each year. The Indian subcontinent is now welded to the Eurasian continent. The result is not only the highest mountain range in the world but large numbers of major earthquakes as well.

Mountain ranges have also formed at other collision boundaries in the past. The Ural Mountains are thought to have formed about 300 million years ago when Europe collided with Siberia to form the Eurasian continent. The Appalachian Mountains formed by the same process during the collision of North America and northern Africa. At a much later time the two continents were rifted apart forming the Atlantic Ocean.

13.12 The converging of two continents at a collision boundary may result in the formation of a mountain range. This photograph is a *Landsat* image of the Great Smoky Mountains. These mountains may have formed when North America and Africa collided.

Topic 11   Converging Boundaries: Subduction

A **subduction boundary** is a form of converging boundary that occurs when one plate plunges down under another overriding plate. The plunging plate is said to be *subducting* beneath the overriding plate. A characteristic feature of a subduction boundary is a *deep-sea trench*. The deepest places in the ocean floor are in such trenches. Subduction boundaries occur in two ways—the convergence of two ocean plates or the convergence of an ocean plate with a continental plate.

When two ocean plates collide, the deep-sea trench that forms between the plates is accompanied by the formation of a chain of volcanic islands on the overriding plate. The Pacific Plate is subducted under the Philippine Plate. In the subduction process the Pacific Plate is pulled down to form the Mariana Trench, the deepest trench in the ocean. The leading edge of the Philippine Plate is marked by a chain of volcanic islands, the Mariana Islands. The rate of subduction here is about one centimeter per year.

When an ocean plate converges with a continental plate, the ocean plate, which is denser than the continental plate, subducts or slides under the continental plate. The deep-sea trench is bordered

TEACHING TIP

Additional material on deep-sea trenches can be found in Chapter 18, Topic 11.

Ocean-Ocean

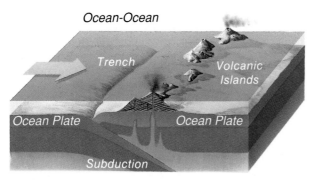

Continent-Ocean

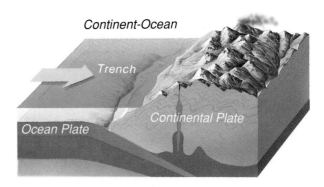

13.13 Two types of subduction: (left) two oceanic plates, and (right) an oceanic and a continental plate

by a mountain chain and volcanoes on the continental plate. For example, on the west coast of South America, the Nazca Plate is subducting under the South American Plate. The Peru-Chile Trench occurs between the plates, and the Andes Mountains and active volcanoes mark the edge of the South American Plate.

Two other facts are important about subduction boundaries. First, some earthquakes that occur with these boundaries originate deeper in the interior of Earth than at any other type of plate boundary. This is because the subducting plate is being pulled down into the asthenosphere. All other plate boundaries involve only the lithosphere and, as a result, have only shallow earthquakes.

The second important fact about subduction boundaries involves the deep-sea trenches that occur there. These trenches are the other half of the story that started at the mid-ocean ridges. The lithosphere that forms at the mid-ocean ridges eventually disappears into the interior by subducting at the deep-sea trenches.

TOPIC QUESTIONS

Each topic question refers to the topic of the same number.

8. **(a)** How are the plates moving at a mid-ocean ridge? **(b)** What two features occur at mid-ocean ridges? **(c)** Name and locate two mid-ocean ridges.

9. **(a)** How are the plates moving at a sliding boundary? **(b)** Give an example of a sliding boundary.

10. **(a)** What is a converging boundary? **(b)** What surface feature occurs at collision boundaries? Give some examples.

11. **(a)** What is happening to the plates at a subduction boundary? **(b)** What features are characteristic of the collision of two oceanic plates? **(c)** Give an example of this kind of plate boundary. **(d)** What features are characteristic of the collision of an oceanic plate and a continental plate? **(e)** Give an example of this kind of plate boundary. **(f)** Why do subduction boundaries have deeper earthquakes than any other type of plate boundary? **(g)** How are subduction boundaries related to mid-ocean ridges?

ANSWERS

8. (a) apart (b) rift valley, fracture zones (c) mid-Atlantic Ridge—between North American and Eurasian Plates and South American and African Plates; East Pacific Rise—between Pacific and South American Plates

9. (a) past each other (b) San Andreas Fault

10. (a) two plates colliding (b) mountains; Himalayas, Urals, Southern Appalachians

11. (a) One plate is plunging down under another. (b) trench, islands (c) Pacific Plate subducting under Philippine Plate and forming Mariana Trench and Islands (d) trench and mountain chain (e) Nazca Plate subducting under South American, forming Peru-Chile Trench and Andes Mountains (f) The subducting plate is pulled deeper than at other boundaries. (g) Lithosphere forms at ridges and disappears at trenches of subduction boundaries.

IV   Continental Growth and Plate Tectonics

Topic 12   **The Craton**

The shapes of the continents have not always been as they exist today. The ancestors of most modern continents were smaller. Through tectonic processes, rock has been added to the margins of the ancient continent cores and the shapes that are currently familiar have gradually formed.

The ancient continent cores are called **cratons.** They are usually the oldest and most altered rock of the continent.

The North American craton is exposed at the surface in most of eastern Canada. Geologists call that part of the craton the *Canadian Shield.* The remainder of the craton lies below the surface from the Rocky Mountain system to the Appalachian Mountain system.

The North American craton shows the approximate shape of the continent 2.5 billion years ago. The remainder of North America has been added to the craton as the continent developed into its present dimensions.

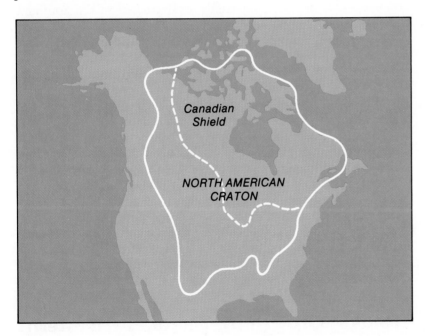

Canadian Shield

NORTH AMERICAN CRATON

Topic 13   **Sources of Growth Material**

Earth material that is added to continents and causes their further development can come from several sources. One source is *deep-sea sediments.* When an oceanic plate plunges under a continental

OBJECTIVES

A Describe the North American craton.

B List some sources of material for continental growth.

C Define *thin-skinned thrusting* and identify a mountain range where thin-skinned thrusting is thought to have occurred.

D Define *terrane* and identify the properties used to identify terranes.

SCIENCE BACKGROUND

The North American craton has been found to be made of four or five mini-continents that collided and welded together starting about 1.9 billion years ago. The Superior craton, the Churchill craton, and the Wyoming craton are pieces.

13.14 The craton of North America is made up of the oldest rocks on the continent. The exposed portion of the craton is called the Canadian Shield.

VIDEODISC SELECTION

Animation of the geomorphic evolution of North America
Side 1 movie: 18235 & PLAY

Computer animation of tectonic movements
Side 1 movie: 7979 & PLAY

TEACHING TIP

Active and passive plate boundaries are discussed in Chapter 16, Topic 1.

plate in a subduction zone, some of the ocean-floor sediments may be scraped off and left behind. These sediments then become part of the continent on the other side of the subduction zone.

A second source of growth material is *volcanic rock.* Chains of volcanic islands are characteristic of many subduction zones. These volcanic chains may also contribute sediment, adding to the further expansion of a continent. There are places where volcanic rocks from former mid-ocean ridges are exposed on land.

A third source of growth material is the *sediments* deposited by rivers that flow across the continent. These sediments build up on continental margins. Unlike ocean-floor sediments and volcanic material, these sediments are not part of an active plate boundary.

Topic 14 Growth by Thin-Skinned Thrusting—The Southern Appalachians

Thin-skinned thrusting is the pushing of thin, horizontal sheets of rock from continental margins over great distances along nearly level fault surfaces. The stacking and shuffling of these thin sheets on the continental margins result in continental growth. Thin-skinned thrusting is thought to occur in many of the world's mountain ranges. It has been especially well studied in the Southern Appalachians.

The Appalachian Mountains are considered by many scientists to represent a typical mountain system. The Southern Appalachians are the part of the system south of Pennsylvania. The history of the Southern Appalachians is complex because it involves periods of both divergence and convergence. Only a general outline of what is thought to have happened is given here.

The ancestors of the continents of North America and Africa were originally part of the same larger continent. About 650 million years ago it split apart, forming an earlier version of the Atlantic Ocean. The closing of this ocean 150 million years later brought North America and Africa together again along with parts of Europe. It also pushed thin pieces of ocean floor, volcanic island, and other features typical of converging boundaries onto the continental margin. The Appalachian Mountains formed at this time as well. At a later date, the continents separated again to form the present Atlantic Ocean.

Topic 15 Growth by Terranes—Western North America

A **terrane** is a large block of lithospheric plate that has been moved, often a distance of thousands of kilometers, and attached to the edge of a continent. The attachment of terranes may have been the primary method of continent growth in western North America.

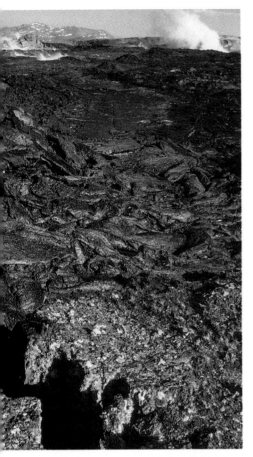

13.15 Volcanic rock is one source of growth material that is added to continents.

13.16 The Appalachian Mountains may have formed during the time North America, Africa, and parts of Europe were converging.

A terrane can be identified by three characteristics. First, each terrane block is bounded on all sides by major faults. Second, the rocks and the fossils found in them do not match those of neighboring terranes. And third, the magnetic polarity found in the terrane does not match that of neighboring terranes. All of the characteristics are strong evidence that the terranes formed in other places and were transported to their present locations.

An example of a terrane is the Cache Creek terrane of British Columbia in Canada. The rocks of this terrane are shallow-water limestones. They were deposited on oceanic crust. More important, the limestones contain fossil shells of tiny ocean animals called *fusulinids.* These shells are totally unlike fusulinid fossils found in rocks of the same age in other parts of North America. Instead, the Cache Creek fusulinids are very similar to shells found in Japan and large parts of Asia. From this evidence, scientists have hypothesized that the Cache Creek terrane had traveled thousands of kilometers across the Pacific Ocean before subduction processes welded it to the North American continent. Many other west coast terranes show evidence of similar histories.

13.17 The Cache Creek terrane contains fossils that resemble fossils found in Japan and other parts of Asia.

OF INTEREST
Do not confuse "terrane" with "terrain." "Terrane" stands for tectonostratigraphic terrane.

TOPIC QUESTIONS

Each topic question refers to the topic of the same number.

12. **(a)** What is a craton?   **(b)** What is the Canadian Shield?

13. List three kinds of material that can become part of a continent.

14. **(a)** What is meant by thin-skinned thrusting?   **(b)** Summarize the history of the Southern Appalachians.

15. **(a)** What are terranes?   **(b)** List three characteristics that identify terranes.   **(c)** What characteristic of the Cache Creek terrane was used to identify the original location of its rocks?

ANSWERS
12. (a) oldest and most altered rocks of continents   (b) exposed part of North American craton
13. deep-sea sediment, volcanic rock, continental sediments
14. (a) pushing of thin sheets from continental margins over nearly level fault surfaces   (b) North America and Africa were together, then split about 650 million years ago forming ancestral Atlantic Ocean. The ocean closed; North America and Africa collided forming Appalachian Mountains, then split to form the present Atlantic Ocean.
15. (a) large blocks of lithosphere that have been moved   (b) faults on all sides, unique fossils, unique polarity   (c) fusulinid fossils

Map Skills

Refer to the map on pages 656–657 to answer these questions.

1. Locate the South American continent on the map. What is the relationship between the Peru–Chile Trench, the Andes Mountains, and the west coast of South America?

2. Compare this map with the map of volcanoes and earthquakes in Figure 13.4. Locate the Atlantic Ocean on both maps. What feature on this map occurs in the same location as the earthquakes in the Atlantic Ocean on the map in Figure 13.4?

3. Locate the Pacific Ocean on both maps. What occurs on the map in Figure 13.4 in the same place as the Aleutian Trench, Kuril Trench, Tonga Trench, and Mariana Trench of the map on pages 656–657.

ANSWERS
Map Skills
1. The trench and the mountains are parallel to the west coast—the trench offshore and the mountains on land.
2. mid-Atlantic Ridge
3. both volcanoes and earthquakes

CHAPTER 13

L A B
ACTIVITY

Convection
Currents

The solid, seemingly fixed ground on which you are standing, is actually a moving lithospheric plate "floating" on top of the partially molten asthenosphere. Earth's lithospheric plates have for eons been slowly sliding past, colliding with, diverging from, and subducting under one another. As a result many of the continents, once thought to be joined, are now separated by vast oceans. The process continues today. Scientists estimate that the United States and Europe, once part of a single larger continent, are moving apart at a rate of 3 centimeters per year!

What causes this continuous motion of the lithospheric plates? *Convection currents* are believed to be the driving force behind plate tectonics. In this activity, you will observe convection currents in a liquid and make connections between your observations and the motions within the asthenosphere.

Lab Skills and Objectives
- To **model** the movement of molten rock material within the asthenosphere
- To **observe** and **describe** the movement of a fluid within a convection current

Materials
- clear plastic shoebox
- 6 foam cups, 6-oz
- 4 cardboard shims, 3-inch square
- white paper
- food coloring
- medicine dropper
- room temperature water
- hot water

Procedure
Part A
1. Place a shoebox on top of four inverted foam cups. The cups may be placed on white paper for better contrast. Put a cardboard shim under each inverted cup, as shown in Figure 13.18.
2. Fill the box half full with room temperature water and allow the water to become still.
3. Collect a small amount of food coloring in a medicine dropper. Slowly lower the dropper into the water and release a drop of food coloring at the bottom center of the box.

13.18 Part A

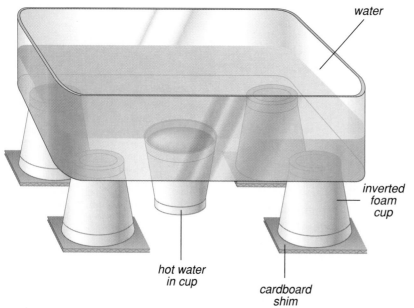

water

inverted
foam
cup

hot water
in cup

cardboard
shim

4. Slowly remove the dropper from the shoebox, trying not to disturb the water.

5. Observe what happens to the food coloring in the water. Sketch a diagram of the path the food coloring followed for the first minute after its addition.

6. Obtain a foam cup full of hot water. Carefully slide the cup under the center of the shoebox.

7. Once again collect a small amount of food coloring in the medicine dropper. After the water in the shoebox becomes still, carefully place a drop of food coloring into the shoebox directly over the cup of hot water.

8. Repeat steps 4 and 5. Sketch a diagram of the path of the food coloring.

9. Answer questions 1–3 in *Analysis and Conclusions.*

Part B

10. Empty the water from the shoe box and repeat procedure steps 1 and 2.

11. Place two cups of hot water, one at either end, under the shoe box, as shown in Figure 13.19.

12. Place a drop of food coloring in the box directly over each cup of hot water.

13. Repeat steps 4 and 5. Sketch a diagram of the path of the food coloring.

14. Answer questions 4–6 in *Analysis and Conclusions.*

Analysis and Conclusions

1. In comparison to Earth's structure, what does each of the following represent in the model: the shoebox? the water? the cup full of hot water?

2. What could be used to represent lithospheric plates in the model?

3. Explain the motion of the food coloring in Part A of this experiment. Use changes in density as the basis of your explanation.

4. In Part B of this experiment, what did you observe occurring in the region between the hot cups?

5. In comparison to Earth's structure, what kind of plate boundary does each of the following represent: the region directly over the cups of hot water? the region between the two cups of hot water?

6. Describe another example of a convection current in a natural system. How does it differ from convection currents in the asthenosphere?

7. What kind of boundary separates the North American Plate from the Eurasian Plate? The Eurasian Plate from the Pacific Plate?

8. If new material is always emerging from a diverging boundary, are the plates continually growing bigger? Explain your answer.

13.19 Part B

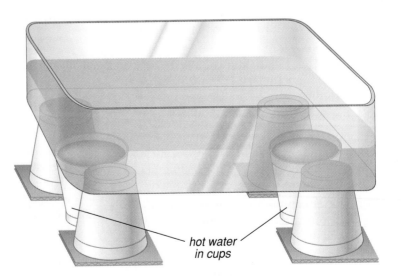

hot water in cups

Answers to all questions appear in the Teacher's Guide at the back of this book.

■ Summary

I Plate tectonics is the study of the formation and movements of the rigid lithospheric plates that cover Earth's surface. Convection currents within the layer below the lithosphere are thought to move the plates.

II Alfred Wegener proposed that the continents of Africa and South America are drifting apart. He used the shapes of the coastlines of the two continents, a reptile fossil, and some distinctive rocks as evidence.

Earthquakes and volcanoes occur at plate boundaries. A belt of earthquakes and volcanoes nearly surrounds the Pacific Ocean.

Minerals preserved in rocks show that Earth's magnetic poles have reversed several times in the past.

The pattern of polarity reversals at spreading centers indicates that new crustal material forms there. Heat-flow values and seafloor elevations provide supporting evidence.

III Lithospheric plates move apart at diverging boundaries. Mid-ocean ridges occur at spreading centers. Rift valleys and fracture zones are features of mid-ocean ridges.

The North American Plate and the Pacific Plate form a sliding plate boundary at the San Andreas Fault in California.

The collision and welding of two continental plates result in a collision boundary.

Subduction boundaries occur when one lithospheric plate plunges beneath an overriding plate. Subduction boundaries have deep earthquakes.

IV The North American craton contains the oldest and most altered rocks of the continent. The Canadian Shield is the exposed part of the craton.

Deep-sea sediments, volcanic rocks, and river-deposited sediments all provide material for continental growth.

The formation of the Southern Appalachians involved thin-skinned thrusting.

Terranes are large blocks of lithosphere that have been moved and attached to continents. Terranes are identified by their faults, fossils, and magnetic polarity.

■ Vocabulary

asthenosphere
collision boundary
converging boundary
craton
diverging boundary
fault

lithosphere
plate tectonics
spreading centers
subduction boundary
terrane
thin-skinned thrusting

■ Review

On your paper, write the word or words that best complete each statement.

1. According to plate _____, Earth's surface consists of a number of rigid, but movable, pieces of lithosphere.
2. The lithosphere is made of the _____ and the upper part of the mantle.
3. Rising convection currents within the asthenosphere drive the lithospheric plate's apart, while _____ convection currents pull the plate's together.
4. Wegener used continent shape, fossils, and rocks to support his theory of _____.
5. Earthquakes and _____ occur at plate boundaries because of stresses that build up there.
6. The pattern of magnetic reversals indicates that the youngest rocks of the ocean floor are found at _____ centers.
7. Values for heat flow are _____ at spreading centers and decrease away from the centers.
8. The mid-Atlantic Ridge and the East Pacific Rise are locations where two lithospheric plates are moving _____.
9. The San Andreas Fault is the result of the Pacific Plate sliding past the North _____ Plate .
10. A collision boundary results when two _____ plates collide and weld together.

For further review, see **Study Guide.**
For assessment, see **Chapter Tests**
and **Computer Test Bank.**

11. The subduction of the Pacific Plate under the Philippine Plate is an example of the convergence of two _____ plates.
12. The deepest earthquakes occur at _____ boundaries as old lithosphere is pulled down into the asthenosphere.
13. The Canadian _____ is the exposed part of the North American _____.
14. Deep-sea sediments, volcanic rocks, and river sediments are all sources of material that increase the size of _____.
15. Thin-skinned thrusting is thought to have been involved in the formation of the _____ Mountains.
16. Terranes can be identified by their faults, fossils, and _____.

■ Interpret and Apply

On your paper, answer each sentence in complete sentences.

1. Coal deposits have been found in Antarctica. How do these deposits provide evidence for plate tectonics?
2. The Great Pyramid of Giza in Egypt was built more than 40 centuries ago. The structure faces slightly east of true north. Did the Egyptian surveyors make a mistake in laying out the foundation for the pyramid or is there some other explanation for this "error"?
3. How do the age of the seafloor, heat flow, and seafloor elevation relate to distance from a spreading center? Why?
4. The oldest rocks of the continents are almost four billion years old, while the oldest rocks of the ocean basin are not even 200 million years old. Explain why this difference in age occurs and how it supports plate tectonics.

■ Critical Thinking

The graph shows a computer model of a slab of lithospheric plate plunging downward into the asthenosphere. The plunging plate is shown in

red, and the plate colliding with the plunging plate is shown in blue. The dots represent earthquakes. The vertical axis of the graph shows depths, in kilometers, inside Earth. The horizontal axis of the graph shows distance, in kilometers, from the location where the plate starts to plunge. Temperatures inside Earth, in degrees Celsius, are indicated also.

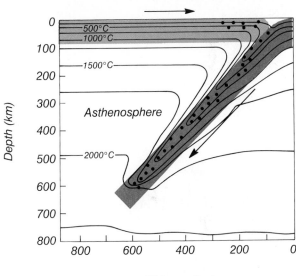

1. Determine the temperature of the asthenosphere at a distance of 600 kilometers and a depth of 100 kilometers.
2. What is the approximate depth of the earthquakes that occur at a distance of 200 kilometers from the point where the plate starts its plunge?
3. State the relationship between distance from the point of plunge and depth of an earthquake.
4. How does the temperature of the asthenosphere compare with the temperature of the plunging plate at a depth of 200 kilometers? At 400 km?
5. What is the approximate depth at which earthquake activity in the plunging plate stops?

251

Volcanism and Plate Tectonics

How Do You Know That . . .

▲

This nighttime view of an erupting volcano in Iceland shows the intense heat and powerful force of an eruption.

OF INTEREST

The 1783 eruption came from a 25-kilometer-long fissure and lasted for 2 years. The dust cloud caused crop failures in Scotland, 965 kilometers away.

Iceland is a volcanically active area? The erupting volcano is just one evidence of activity in Iceland. Craters and lava fields are common sights there. In fact, over one third of the island is volcanically active. Sometimes the volcanic activity causes harm to the people of Iceland. Poisonous gases that erupted from a volcano in 1783 killed two thirds of the island's livestock. During the famine that resulted, a fifth of the population starved to death. On the other hand, Icelanders make use of the volcanic activity. The groundwater is hot enough to heat homes, greenhouses, and even year-round swimming pools. Crops can be planted in hot areas while other areas are still under winter snows.

I Volcanism Releases Magma

Topic 1 Magma

The eruption of molten rock must surely be one of the most spectacular activities that accompanies the movement of lithospheric plates. Where does this molten rock come from and how does it move inside Earth? The answers are not simple because the processes occur deep underground where direct observation is not possible. Even so, several facts are known.

Molten rock underground is called **magma.** It forms wherever temperatures and pressures are high enough to melt rock. One region that meets this requirement is the asthenosphere (Chapter 13, Topic 3). At the asthenosphere, some minerals melt and become magma. Plate boundaries are also areas where rocks can be melted. The movements and stresses there produce enough heat to form magma.

Once the rock is melted, it has greater volume and thus is slightly less dense than the unmelted rock around it. The magma then moves upward, moving through fractures or melting crustal rock as it rises. If the magma reaches the surface, it erupts through an opening called a **volcano.**

The rate at which magma moves is determined primarily by its silica content. Silica is the major ingredient in all magma. Magmas with relatively high silica content are thick, light-colored, and slow moving. These are **felsic** magmas. In contrast, **mafic** magmas have relatively low silica content. They tend to be thinner and darker in color, and they flow more easily.

OBJECTIVES

A Identify some areas where rock underground can be melted.

B Explain the difference between magma and lava and describe the composition, properties, and behavior of mafic and felsic magmas and lavas.

C Name some gases that can occur in magma and discuss the relationship between the amount of gas and the nature of the eruption.

D Define *tephra* and give several examples.

SCIENCE BACKGROUND
There are about 485 active volcanoes worldwide.

SCIENCE BACKGROUND
The term *volcano* also applies to the structure built around the vent by the material ejected from the vent.

SCIENCE BACKGROUND
The term that describes a fluid's resistance to flow is *viscosity.* The more silica the magma contains, the greater its viscosity.

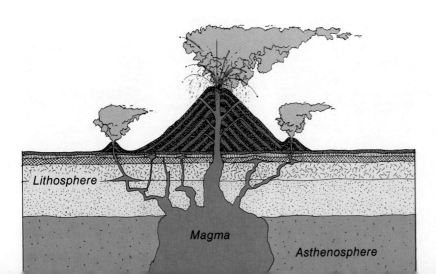

14.1 Magma rises from the asthenosphere through cracks in the lithosphere.

Lithosphere

Magma

Asthenosphere

OF INTEREST

For months after the May 1980 eruption of Mount St. Helens, scientists monitoring the crater had to wear gas masks. The gases emitted by volcano rotted clothing, burned eyes, corroded the finish on radios, etched prism reflectors, and turned the steel rims of eyeglasses green.

TEACHING TIP

Be prepared to explain that *superheated* means that the steam is heated beyond its normal temperature for that particular air pressure.

VIDEODISC SELECTION

Aa lava
Side 1: 1352, single frame

Pahoehoe lava
Side 1: 1212, single frame

14.2 Since there are different types of lava, lava flows have different appearances. **(a)** Aa lava flows are characterized by rough, jagged surfaces. **(b)** Pahoehoe lava flows are smooth with a ropelike surface.

Topic 2   Gases in Magma

Many magmas contain dissolved gases that are given off as the magma erupts. The most important of these gases are water vapor, carbon dioxide, and sulfur. Other gases include hydrogen, which combines with atmospheric oxygen to form additional steam (hot water vapor). Carbon monoxide combines with oxygen to become carbon dioxide. Sulfur combines with both hydrogen and oxygen and forms the gases hydrogen sulfide and sulfur dioxide. Several other gases, such as chlorine and fluorine, are also given off.

The amount of gas dissolved in a magma is a major factor in the kind of eruption that results. As the magma reaches the surface, the pressure on it is greatly reduced. The gases dissolved in the magma come out of solution as bubbles. These bubbles can expand rapidly and even explode. As a result, magmas containing large amounts of dissolved gases tend to produce more explosive eruptions than magmas containing small amounts of gases.

Topic 3   Lava

Magma that reaches the surface is called **lava.** Its composition is somewhat different from that of the original magma because some gases have escaped and some new materials have been added from other rocks the magma has melted. Like magma, lava is classified by its silica content as either felsic or mafic. Like magma, felsic lavas are thick and stiff, while mafic lavas are thin and fluid.

The silica content of the original magma is also important to the type of eruption that occurs. Mafic magmas are more fluid. Thus, gases dissolved within them escape easily. As a result, their lavas pour out smoothly onto the surface. On the other hand, gases cannot move easily in less fluid, felsic magmas. The result is an explosive eruption.

a

b

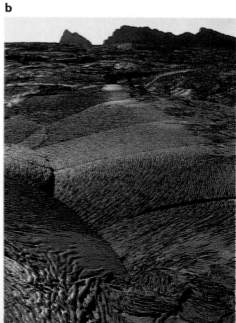

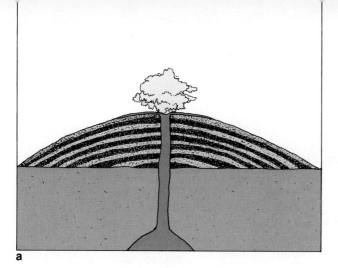

a

b

14.3 **(a)** Mafic magma flows out smoothly over a large area. A gently sloping shield cone results. **(b)** Felsic magma is thicker, containing trapped gases. The resulting explosive eruption forms a steep-sided cone called a cinder cone.

Topic 4 **Lava Fragments**

Explosive eruptions produce solid fragments of lava called **tephra.** The smallest pieces of tephra (less than 2 millimeters in diameter) are called *ash.* Larger pieces (up to 64 millimeters) are called *lapilli.* The largest fragments (more than 64 millimeters) are called *blocks* and *bombs.* Blocks are erupted as solid pieces, while bombs are ejected as liquid and harden as they fall.

In some explosive eruptions, tephra combines with gases to form a dense, superheated cloud that travels downhill with amazing speed. The cloud may follow existing stream valleys and move at more than 100 kilometers per hour. One example of this type of eruption occurred in 1902 when Mount Pelee, a Caribbean volcano, destroyed the city of St. Pierre. The fiery blast shattered stone buildings and burned wooden ones. Within minutes, 30 000 people were smothered or burned to death.

TOPIC QUESTIONS

Each topic question refers to the topic of the same number.

1. **(a)** What is magma?   **(b)** What condition is necessary in order for magma to form?   **(c)** List two places where this condition can be met.   **(d)** What causes magma to rise?   **(e)** What is the major ingredient in magma?   **(f)** List the properties of felsic and mafic magmas.

2. **(a)** List several gases that come from magma.   **(b)** What effect does the amount of gases in a magma have on the kind of eruption that occurs?

3. **(a)** What is lava?   **(b)** Why is the composition of lava different from that of its magma?   **(c)** How are felsic lavas different from mafic lavas?   **(d)** How are their eruptions different?

4. **(a)** What is tephra?   **(b)** How are ash and lapilli different? **(c)** How do blocks form differently than bombs?   **(d)** What kind of eruption destroyed St. Pierre?

14.4 Volcanic ash and cinders

ANSWERS

   1. (a) melted rock underground (b) rock must melt   (c) astheno-sphere, plate boundaries   (d) less dense than surrounding rock   (e) silica (f) felsic: high silica content, thick, light-colored, slow moving; mafic: low silica content, thinner, dark-colored, faster moving

   2. (a) water vapor, CO_2, H_2, CO, H_2S, Cl_2, F_2 (b) eruption more explosive if magma has more gas

   3. (a) magma at surface   (b) lost gases, gained rocks   (c) Felsic are thick and stiff; mafic are thin and fluid.   (d) Mafic are smooth; felsic are explosive.

   4. (a) lava fragments   (b) size (c) blocks solid before ejected, bombs harden in flight   (d) dense, superheated cloud of tephra and gases

OBJECTIVES

A Describe rift eruptions and features associated with them, and tell where they occur.

B Discuss and give examples of subduction zone eruptions, and discuss the features that occur there.

C Discuss the occurrence of hot spots and the features associated with them.

TEACHING TIP
Remind students that spreading centers are places where new crust is forming as two lithospheric plates move away from each other.

OF INTEREST
Famous locations with columnar jointing are Giant's Causeway, Ireland; Devils Postpile, California; and Devils Tower, Wyoming.

II Kinds of Eruptions

Topic 5 Rift Eruptions

Rift eruptions occur at long, narrow fractures in the crust. These fractures may be on the ocean floor or on land. Rift eruptions typically flow out smoothly and fluidly because the lava is basaltic and contains few gases. In some cases layers of lavas build *shield cones.* A shield cone is a volcanic mountain with a broad base and gently sloping sides (Figure 14.3(a)).

Rift eruptions in the oceans occur at spreading centers, such as the mid-Atlantic Ridge and the East Pacific Rise. The lava oozes out and cools rapidly into rounded shapes called *pillow lavas.*

Rift eruptions on land may spread lava evenly over thousands of square kilometers. Lavas from the East African Rift system have covered large areas with basalt, forming a *basalt plateau.* The Columbia Plateau of Washington, Oregon, and Idaho is another example of a basalt plateau. During the past 50 million years, lava from rift eruptions has covered an area of over 200 000 square kilometers with up to 1500 meters of basalt. Other examples are the Karroo Plateau of South Africa, and the Parana Plateau of South America.

When the basalt of plateaus and other thick lava flows on land cool, they may display a unique pattern of closely packed, six-sided columns called *columnar jointing.* These columns are thought to form as cooling lava shrinks and cracks. The columns are as high as the thickness of the basalt flows.

14.5 Columnar jointing is clearly visible in this basaltic sill.

Topic 6 Subduction Boundary Eruptions

Subduction boundary eruptions are the result of magma that forms at subduction boundaries (Chapter 13, Topic 11). Unlike the magma that forms at rifts, this magma tends to be thick and to contain large amounts of gases. As a result, subduction boundary eruptions usually are explosive, and the erupted material is mostly lava fragments (tephra). The volcanic cone that forms usually has very steep sides and is called a *cinder cone* (Figure 14.3(b)).

Most of the world's active volcanoes occur at subduction boundary eruptions. Many form the island chains that are typical of the west side of the Pacific Ocean. The most active volcanic chain is the islands of Indonesia. Other examples of volcanic chains resulting from subduction boundary eruptions are the Philippine Islands, the islands of Japan, and the Aleutian Islands off Alaska.

Subduction boundary volcanoes are also associated with young mountain ranges. The Cascades of Washington and Oregon, the mountains of Central America, and the Andes of South America all have active or recently active volcanoes.

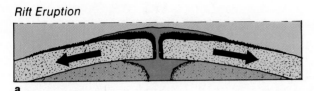

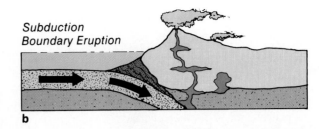

a b

Topic 7 Hot Spots

Not all volcanism occurs at plate boundaries. **Hot spots** are areas of volcanic activity in the middle of lithospheric plates.

The lava erupted at hot spots is similar to that of rift eruptions—it usually flows smoothly over the surface. However, unlike the lava that wells up at rifts, hot spot lavas form cones. These shield cones are usually broad and have gently sloping sides.

The cause of hot spots is not clear, although some kind of concentration of heat from radioactive sources in the asthenosphere is suspected. The hot spot seems to remain in the same location even though the lithospheric plate above it moves. The result is a chain of extinct volcanoes marking former positions of the plate over the hot spot.

The most famous example of hot spot volcanism is the Hawaiian Islands. The island of Hawaii has active volcanoes and is now directly over the hot spot. To the northwest is a chain of extinct volcanic islands (Figure 14.7). The age of the rocks that form each island is increasingly older away from Hawaii. This indicates a steady movement of the Pacific Plate over the hot spot.

14.6 **(a)** Huge amounts of lava flow smoothly from a rift eruption, covering large areas with basalt. **(b)** Subduction boundary eruptions are usually more explosive.

TEACHING TIP
Remind students that subduction boundaries are locations where one lithospheric plate is plunging beneath another.

SCIENCE BACKGROUND
Although a total of 122 hot spots have been active worldwide within the past 10 million years, hot spot eruptions represent less than one percent of the world's volcanic activity.

SCIENCE BACKGROUND
Hot spots are found on every plate. Interestingly enough, the hot spots do not seem to move much relative to each other.

SCIENCE BACKGROUND
There is a new volcano developing off the southeast coast of the island of Hawaii, evidence that the movement of the Pacific Plate over the hot spot is continuing.

VIDEODISC SELECTION

Diagram of subduction boundary eruption
Side 1: 1073, single frame

Diagram of plate movement over a hot spot, forming an island arc
Side 1: 735, single frame

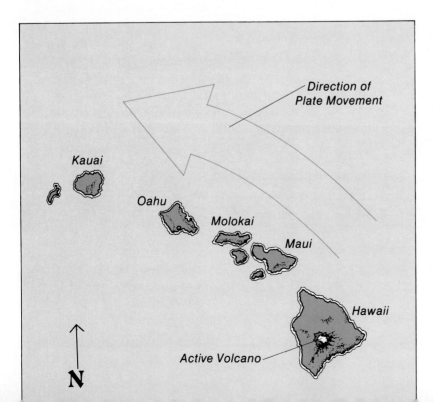

14.7 A chain of extinct volcanoes marks the movement of a lithospheric plate over a hot spot.

TOPIC QUESTIONS

Each topic question refers to the topic of the same number.

5. (a) Where do rift eruptions occur?   **(b)** How does lava behave at rift eruptions?   **(c)** Name two locations where rift eruptions occur in the ocean.   **(d)** Give one example of a rift eruption on land.   **(e)** What is a basalt plateau? Give some examples. **(f)** What is columnar jointing?

6. (a) How are subduction boundary eruptions different from rift eruptions? What causes the difference?   **(b)** What is the shape of the volcanic cone that forms at subduction boundaries? **(c)** Name two landform features that form at subduction boundaries and give one example of each.

7. (a) What are hot spots?   **(b)** How does lava behave at hot spots? **(c)** What is the shape of the volcanic cone that results?   **(d)** What is thought to be the cause of hot spots?   **(e)** How does the lithosphere behave relative to a hot spot?   **(f)** How do the Hawaiian Islands support your answer to **(e)**?

ANSWERS

5. (a) at long, narrow fractures in crust   (b) flows smoothly and fluidly (c) mid-Atlantic Ridge, East Pacific Rise   (d) East African Rift system (e) plateau formed by rift eruptions; Columbia, Karroo, Parana, Deccan (f) six-sided columns in lava flows

6. (a) explosive, mostly tephra because magma thicker and contains more gases   (b) steep-sided (c) volcanic island chains, Philippines, Japan, Aleutians; young mountains, Cascades, Andes

7. (a) volcanic activity in middle of lithospheric plates   (b) flows smoothly   (c) broad, gently sloping (d) possible concentration of radioactive heat   (e) plate moves over hot spot   (f) islands become older away from hot spot

Current RESEARCH

Volcanoes: One Eye on the Giant

Think of a volcano as a sleeping giant. There are over 1300 volcanoes known to have erupted in the last 12 000 years. Recent activity is no indication of a volcano's potential for destruction. A volcano can be inactive for centuries and then suddenly erupt, seemingly without warning. Predicting when a volcano will erupt could save thousands of lives.

In the past, volcanologists monitored changes in a volcano's slope or height, looking for bulges that might indicate a magma buildup. Another warning sign is the increase in the number of small earthquakes beneath the volcano caused by magma moving upward.

New techniques are being used to predict eruptions. In the 1980s, infrared *Landsat* photos revealed a hot spot beneath a volcano in the Andes Mountains of Chile shortly before an eruption. Satellites are also used to measure changes in a volcano's elevation, which may indicate a pre-eruption bulge.

Monitoring volcanoes can be risky. Japan's Mount Unzen had been inactive since 1792 when it started to rumble with earthquakes in 1990. Scientists gathered at the volcano, hoping to predict a catastrophic eruption and warn the 200 000 people living around Mount Unzen. When part of the volcano collapsed on June 3, 1991, thirty-seven people, including three volcanologists, died when a rapidly flowing cloud of hot ash descended on the town of Kamikoba.

III Examples of Volcanic Eruptions

Topic 8   Eldfell

Eldfell is a volcanic mountain on Heimaey, a small island off the south coast of Iceland located near the mid-Atlantic Ridge. Eldfell formed during a five-month period in 1973 from lava and tephra that flowed or was ejected from a newly opened fissure on the island. The tephra covered nearly half the island and burned or buried 50 homes in its only village, Vestmannaeyjar. The roofs of the other homes in the village had to be continually swept clear of tephra to prevent their collapse. The flowing lava added almost three square kilometers to the east side of the island. It also threatened to block the entrance of the village harbor. This was a serious problem because Vestmannaeyjar is Iceland's chief fishing port. The villagers attacked the lava flow by pumping seawater on it in the hope that the water would cool the lava enough to stop its advance. The pumping continued until the volcano fell silent four months later. The lava had stopped 165 meters short of the cliffs on the opposite side of the harbor, and the entrance to the harbor remained open.

Eldfell was an example of a rift eruption. Heimaey, along with the other areas of Iceland, is one of the few places in the world where a mid-ocean ridge is above sea level. Iceland is a part of the mid-Atlantic Ridge.

OBJECTIVES

A Discuss the cause and nature of the 1973 eruption of Eldfell, the 1980 eruption of Mount St. Helens, and the regular eruptions of Kilauea.

B Give the cause and some of the results of some famous volcanic eruptions of the past.

C Discuss the volcanism that occurs on the moon, Mars, and Io.

VIDEODISC SELECTION

1973 Eldfell eruption on Heimaey Island
Side 1 movie: 37633 & PLAY

SCIENCE BACKGROUND

Scientists estimated that the water pumped onto the lava caused it to cool and solidify 50 to 100 times faster than it would have on its own.

14.8 The village of Vestmannaeyjar was nearly buried by tephra from the eruption of Eldfell in 1973.

14.9 Mudflows and ash covered the area near Mount St. Helens after the eruption.

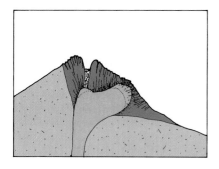

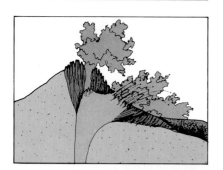

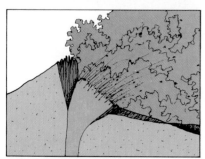

14.10 This was the series of events during the major eruption of Mount St. Helens in 1980.

Topic 9 **Mount St. Helens**

Mount St. Helens, located in Washington, is one of 15 major volcanoes in the Cascade Range. Its eruption in 1980 was the first volcanic activity in that range since 1921.

Signs of renewed activity in Mount St. Helens began in March 1980, two months before the major eruption. During that period, earthquake activity increased, a bulge in the north side of the cone grew larger, and small eruptions of steam and ash occurred. The major eruption involved four separate but related events:

1. An earthquake broke the bulge on the north side of the cone.
2. The bulge became a landslide.
3. An explosion of steam and superheated ash came from the magma, water, and gases that had been trapped under the bulge.
4. Mudflows formed when ash mixed with the melted snow and ice on the mountain.

The explosion blew down trees 25 kilometers away and rattled windows 160 kilometers away. The cloud of steam and ash was shot 20 kilometers into the air and its dust traveled around the world. Ash fall was heavy — 2 to 5 centimeters — over hundreds of square kilometers. Mudflows and landslides accumulated to depths of over 180 meters in some areas.

Mount St. Helens and the other Cascade volcanoes are the result of subduction boundary volcanism. The two converging plates are the Juan de Fuca Plate and the North American Plate. The Juan de Fuca Plate is plunging eastward under the overriding North American Plate. The eruption that resulted at Mount St. Helens was typical of subduction boundary eruptions. It contained very little lava but large amounts of tephra and gases.

14.11 Spectacular lava flows have been a common feature during eruptions of Kilauea.

Topic 10 **Kilauea**

Kilauea is a shield volcano on the island of Hawaii. Kilauea has erupted at least once a year since 1952. Some of the eruptions have featured spectacular lava flows.

Kilauea and the other active Hawaiian volcanoes result from a hot spot under the island (Topic 7). In the case of Kilauea, the magma is thought to come from a depth of at least 50 kilometers below the surface. After rising, it is stored in an irregular reservoir about four kilometers below the top of the volcano.

A unique feature of Kilauea is the lakes of lava that form in depressions in the gently sloping volcanic cone. The lava from the reservoir erupts onto the surface and flows through natural channels to these depressions. When the lava flow stops, the lake starts to harden into rock. Sometimes this takes 25 years. During that time, the lava lake provides volcanologists with great amounts of information on magma and the changes that occur as it hardens.

The lava flows from Kilauea often threaten homes and communities on the island. In 1986, a flow covered a stretch of Kalapana Highway. People who lived beyond the blocked area had to drive as much as 100 extra kilometers to get their mail and groceries.

VIDEODISC SELECTION

Eruption of Mt. St. Helens: diagrams, maps, and photos (described in disc directory)
Side 1: 970 to 995, 26-frame sequence

Selected photos of Kilauea (described in disc directory)
Side 1: 1299 to 1313, 15-frame sequence

Topic 11 **Some Famous Eruptions**

Most volcanoes that become well known occur along subduction boundaries. This is because most subduction boundary eruptions are often dramatic and violent.

Vesuvius and the other volcanoes of the Mediterranean are caused by the subduction of the African Plate beneath the Eurasian Plate. Because their lava is extremely thick and gas-rich, their eruptions are very explosive. The eruption of Vesuvius in A.D. 79 is probably the most famous volcanic eruption in history because it buried and preserved three Roman cities. Pompeii, the largest of the preserved cities, was buried in ash. Vesuvius has been active repeatedly since A.D. 79.

Krakatau, a volcanic island in the Indonesian chain, was

VIDEODISC SELECTION

Mt. Vesuvius and Pompeii, Italy
Side 1 movie: 40651 & PLAY

14.12 An aerial view of Crater Lake shows Wizard Island in the middle of the lake. The island is the top of a volcanic cone that formed inside the original huge caldera.

VIDEODISC SELECTION

Crater Lake caldera
Side 1: 1452, single frame

14.13 The explosive eruption of Mount Pinatubo sent ash and sulfur into the upper atmosphere.

formed by the subduction of the Indian Plate under the Eurasian Plate. On August 27, 1883, an eruption took place that has been described as "the most violent eruption of historic times." More than half of the island was destroyed and blown away in the explosion. The ash cloud reached nearly 30 kilometers into the air.

The compression wave caused by the Krakatau eruption broke windows 150 kilometers away, and the sound was heard 3000 kilometers away in Australia. Great sea waves flooded nearby coasts, and 36 000 people were drowned. The waves even reached the shore of South Africa over 8000 kilometers away. The fine volcanic dust from the eruption was carried completely around the world by upper-air winds. It caused strangely beautiful sunrise and sunset skies for two years after the eruption.

Crater Lake in Oregon is all that remains of a volcano that erupted violently about 7000 years ago. The eruption deposited a blanket of ash as thick as 15 meters over distances of 50 kilometers. The top of the cone collapsed after the lava that had supported it flowed out through cracks in the sides and base. The huge crater, or caldera, that resulted has since filled with rain and melted snow forming the deepest lake in the United States. Crater Lake is 608 meters deep. (Lake Baikal in Russia, at 1706 meters, is the deepest lake in the world.) Crater Lake, like the volcanoes in the Cascade Range, resulted from the subduction of the Juan de Fuca Plate under the North American Plate.

After having been inactive for 635 years, Mount Pinatubo in the Philippines erupted in June 1991. The eruption is ranked as the biggest volcanic eruption of this century. It was caused by the Pacific Plate subducting beneath the Philippine Plate. The eruption of Mount Pinatubo injected more than 20 million tons of sulfur dioxide and ash into the upper atmosphere. During the fall and winter of 1991 and 1992, Pinatubo's spreading ash clouds engulfed much of Earth's atmosphere, causing vivid sunsets. Scientists have been studying the potential effects this eruption may have on Earth's climate and on the Antarctic ozone hole.

Topic 12 **Extraterrestrial Volcanism**

Lava flows on the moon erupted through cracks in the surface of the lunar lithosphere. Both the cracks and the heat needed to form the lava may have been the result of the bombardment by huge rocks from space. The bombardment formed the basins that the lava later filled.

Could the lavas have resulted from lunar plate tectonics? There is no evidence that they did or that such activity exists on the moon today. The moon's lithosphere is too thick to break or move.

The largest known volcanic cone in the solar system is on Mars. It is called *Olympus Mons*. The cone is 26 kilometers high and 500 to 600 kilometers across. The huge size of the Martian volcanoes is one piece of evidence that Mars does not have moving plates near its surface.

Io is a moon of Jupiter that has more than 100 active and inactive volcanoes. It has been proposed that the ejected materials are sulfur and sulfur dioxide. Io is caught in a gravitational tug-of-war between Jupiter and two other moons. As a result, some parts of Io's surface regularly move up and down by as much as 100 meters. The heat produced by the friction of this up-and-down motion is thought to be great enough to cause volcanism.

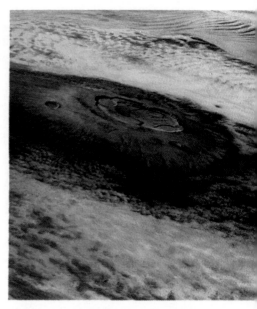

14.14 Olympus Mons is the largest known volcanic cone in the solar system.

TOPIC QUESTIONS

Each topic question refers to the topic of the same number.

8. **(a)** What kinds of materials were ejected from Eldfell? **(b)** What did the residents of Vestmannaeyjar do to save their harbor? **(c)** What kind of eruption was Eldfell?

9. **(a)** What activities preceded the 1980 Mount St. Helens' eruption there? **(b)** List the four major events that occurred with the eruption. **(c)** identify some results of the eruption.

10. **(a)** Where is Kilauea? **(b)** What is the cause of volcanic activity there? **(c)** Why are the lava lakes of Kilauea important?

11. **(a)** What is the cause of the eruptions of Vesuvius? **(b)** Why are the eruptions of Vesuvius so explosive? **(c)** What is the cause of the volcanic activity at Krakatau and the other Indonesian islands? **(d)** List some events that resulted from the eruption of Krakatau. **(e)** What happened at Crater Lake after the volcano erupted? **(f)** Why is the eruption of Mount Pinatubo important?

12. **(a)** What is thought to have caused the lava flows on the moon? **(b)** Why is plate tectonics not likely on the moon? **(c)** What evidence is there that Mars lacks moving lithospheric plates like Earth's? **(d)** What is thought to be the cause of the volcanic activity on Io?

ANSWERS

8. (a) lava and tephra (b) pumped seawater onto advancing lava flow   (c) rift

9. (a) earthquakes, bulge grew, small eruptions of steam and ash (b) bulge broke, landslide, explosion, mudflows   (c) trees blown down, windows rattled, cloud of steam and ash high in air, heavy ash falls

10. (a) Hawaii   (b) hot spot (c) Geologists can study lava as it hardens.

11. (a) subduction of African Plate beneath Eurasian Plate (b) lava extremely thick and gas-rich (c) subduction of Indian Plate under Eurasian Plate   (d) windows broken and explosion heard far away, great ocean waves, dust carried around world   (e) cone collapsed and formed huge caldera   (f) biggest of this century and its potential effect on climate

12. (a) Bombardment made cracks in surface and melted rock. (b) lunar lithosphere too thick to break or move   (c) huge volcanoes, no features of plate movement such as folded mountains   (d) heat from friction caused by gravity of Jupiter and two other moons

OBJECTIVES

A Identify and give examples of the various types of igneous intrusions.

SCIENCE BACKGROUND
"Plutons" can be related to "plutonic," the name for any igneous rock that forms deep underground.

VIDEODISC SELECTION

Diagram of plutonic intrusion
Side 2: 2516, single frame

Photo of small dike and sill
Side 2: 2536, single frame

14.15 There are many volcanic formations below the surface where magma forced its way between existing rock layers. These formations are visible where erosion has removed the surface layer.

14.16 Two basalt dikes

IV Plutonic Activity

Topic 13 Plutons and Volcanism

Volcanoes and lava flows are the surface activities of volcanism. However, much more magma is present below Earth's surface. Magma forces its way into fractures in the bedrock. Magma squeezes between rock layers and pushes up overlying rocks to form domes. Great masses of magma solidify far below the surface to form the cores of mountains.

The rock masses that form when magma cools inside other rocks are called *igneous intrusions,* or **plutons.**

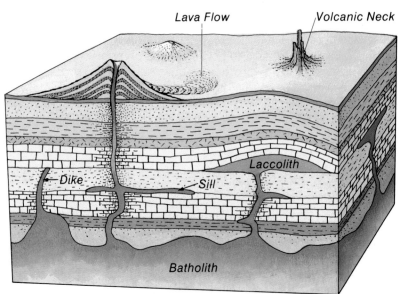

Topic 14 Dikes, Sills, Laccoliths, Necks

Dikes are sheets of igneous rock that cut across the rock layers they intrude. They form when magma is forced into vertical cracks. Dikes come in all lengths and thicknesses. They are common in old volcanic regions. Their rock is usually basalt or diabase.

In contrast to dikes, which cut across layers, are sills. **Sills** are sheets of igneous rock that are parallel to the layers they intrude. They form when magma is forced along bedding planes between rock layers. They too are usually basalt or diabase. They can be hundreds of meters thick and many kilometers long. The Palisades of the Hudson River in New York are the face of a great diabase sill that has been exposed by erosion. It is about 50 kilometers long.

In some places, the magmas that intrude between rock layers are very stiff and unable to flow easily. Instead of spreading to form

sills, these magmas bulge upward to form domelike masses called **laccoliths.** The rock layers above the laccoliths are also pushed up into a dome. Laccoliths can be found in the Henry Mountains of Utah and the Black Hills of South Dakota.

When an extinct volcano is almost completely eroded, a **volcanic neck** may be left. A neck is the plug of hardened magma left in the vent from which lava flowed. One example of a neck is the famous Ship Rock in New Mexico. It is 400 meters high. Volcanic necks form the diamond-bearing rock of the great Kimberley mines of South Africa.

Topic 15 **Batholiths and Stocks**

Batholiths are the largest of all igneous intrusions. They form the cores of many of Earth's mountain ranges. When erosion removes the overlying rock layers, the batholith rocks are exposed. They are usually either granite or granodiorite. The largest batholith in North America forms the core of the Coast Range of British Columbia. Other examples of these plutons are the Idaho batholith in western Idaho and the Sierra Nevada batholith in California.

A small batholith in which less than 100 square kilometers is exposed at the surface is called a **stock.**

TOPIC QUESTIONS

Each topic question refers to the topic of the same number.

13. What are plutons?

14. Describe the origin of a **(a)** dike, **(b)** sill, **(c)** laccolith, and **(d)** volcanic neck. Include examples for **(b)**, **(c)**, and **(d)**.

15. (a) What is a batholith? Give an example. **(b)** What kind of rock is usually found in batholiths?   **(c)** What is a stock?

14.17   (left) An igneous sill intruded between sedimentary layers at Big Bend National Park, Texas (right) A volcanic neck in Monument Valley, Arizona

VIDEODISC SELECTION

Devil's Tower National Monument, Wyoming
Side 2: 2520 to 2521, 2-frame sequence

Volcanic necks in Monument Valley, Arizona
Side 2: 1440, single frame

ANSWERS
   13. igneous rock that cools inside other rocks
   14. (a) intrusion that cuts across rock layers   **(b)** parallels rock layers; Palisades   **(c)** sill that bulges into dome; Henry Mountains, Black Hills **(d)** plug of hardened magma; Ship Rock
   15. (a) largest igneous intrusion; core of Coast Range of British Columbia   **(b)** granite or granodiorite **(c)** small batholith

CHAPTER 14

LAB
ACTIVITY

Patterns of Volcanism

Mount Pinatubo in the Philippines, Mount St. Helens in Washington State, and Redoubt in Alaska are well-known volcanoes These are active, explosive volcanoes whose scenes of destruction and raining ash have been striking images in the news in recent years. The most explosive volcanic eruptions, like the ones mentioned above, occur along subduction plate boundaries. About 45 different subduction volcanic belts have been identified worldwide. In this activity, you will compare the volcanic activity for the past 100 years along 15 subduction volcanic belts.

Lab Skills and Objectives
- To **analyze** data relating to several volcanic belts
- To **describe** volcanic belt properties based on these data

Materials
- graph paper

Procedure
1. Carefully study the data in Figure 14. 17.
2. Determine the number of volcanoes per 100 km (column 4) in the 15 volcanic belts. Divide the total number of volcanoes (column 3) by the length of the belt (column 2) and then multiply by 100. The Italy belt has been done as an example.
3. Volcano years are the total number of years during which volcanoes in a volcanic belt are erupting. For example, if one volcano erupted during 8 different years, a second volcano during 5 different years, and a third volcano during 19 different years, the number in column 5 would be 8 + 5 + 19 = 32 volcano years. Calculate volcano years per 100 km (column 6) by dividing volcano years (column 5) by the number of volcanoes per 100 km (column 4).
4. Determine the number of explosive eruptions per 100 km (column 8) by dividing the total number of explosive eruptions (column 7) by the length of the belt (column 2) and then multiplying by 100.
5. Look at the numbers in column 8. Place a dot (•) in column 9 if the value is between 0 and 0.4. Place a plus sign (+) in column 9 if the value is between 0.5 and 2.0. Place an asterisk (*) in column 9 if the value is greater than 2.0.
6. On a sheet of graph paper, plot volcano-years per 100 km (column 6) on the horizontal axis against the number of volcanoes per 100 km (column 4) on the vertical axis. Use the symbols in column 9 to indicate the number of explosive eruptions at each point of the graph. Next to each point, write the name of the volcano belt.
7. Answer the questions in *Analysis and Conclusions.*

Analysis and Conclusions

1. Of the 15 volcanic belts, which is the longest? How long is it? Does the longest belt have the greatest total number of volcanoes? Explain your answer.

2. If each of the 7 volcanoes in the Taiwan belt had been active every year during the past 100 years, what number would appear in column 5 for the Taiwan belt?

3. During the past 100 years, in which belt have volcanoes been active the greatest number of years? the least number of years?

4. In which belt have the greatest number of explosive eruptions occurred within the past 100 years? How many were there?

5. Based on your graph, what is the relationship between the number of years in which volcanoes in a belt erupted, the number of volcanoes in the belt, and the number of explosive eruptions over the past 100 years that averaged over 100 km?

6. Does the data for the Halmahera belt correspond with your answer to Question 5? What can you

infer about eruptions in the Halmahera belt?

7. The amount of volcanism in a belt is thought to be related to the rate at which the lithospheric plates are coming together. According to your graph, which belt would you expect to have the most rapid rate of convergence? Use Figure 13.1 on page 233 to determine which plates cause the volcanic activity.

14.17   Volcanic belt activity during the past 100 years.

1	2	3	4	5	6	7	8	9
Volcano Belt	Length (km)	Volcanos in Belt	Volcanos per 100 km	Volcano-Years	Volcano years per 100 km	Explosive Eruptions	Explosive Eruptions per 100 km	Symbol
Italy	352	7	2.0	241	68.5	21	6.0	٭
Kermadecs	530	5	0.9	5	0.9	0	0	•
Bismark-West	477	11	2.3	123	25.8	15	3.1	٭
Tonga	686	10	1.5	29	4.2	2	0.3	•
Aleutians	1457	40	2.7	132	9.1	13	0.9	+
Mexico	1043	22	2.1	78	7.5	4	0.4	•
Honshu	732	36	4.9	143	19.5	11	1.5	+
Taiwan	501	7	1.4	1	0.2	0	0	•
Halmahera	162	9	5.6	84	51.9	1	0.6	+
Hikkaido	556	15	2.7	72	12.9	6	1.1	+
Kamchatka	716	47	6.6	203	28.4	26	3.6	٭
Cascades	1152	38	3.3	8	0.7	2	0.2	•
Central America	1254	79	6.3	337	26.9	30	2.4	٭
Peru-Chile-North	1363	63	4.6	43	3.2	1	0.1	•
Sunda	965	30	3.1	112	11.6	6	0.6	+

Answers to all questions appear in the Teacher's Guide at the back of this book.

■ Summary

I Rock is melted in the asthenosphere and at plate boundaries. Molten rock underground is called magma; molten rock that reaches the surface is called lava.

Felsic magmas are rich in silica, thick, light-colored, and slow moving. Gases within this type of magma cannot easily escape, so felsic lavas tend to be associated with explosive eruptions.

Mafic magmas are poor in silica, thin, dark-colored, and fast moving. Gases within the magma escape easily, so mafic lavas pour out onto the surface smoothly.

Ash, lapilli, blocks, and bombs are examples of solid fragments of lava called tephra.

II Lava flows out smoothly at rift eruptions on the seafloor or on land. On land, the eruptions may form shield cones or huge lava plateaus. Columnar jointing is a feature of some of these thick lava flows.

The magma at subduction boundaries tends to result in explosive eruptions of tephra that form cinder cones. Island chains and young mountains are features of subduction boundary eruptions.

Hot spots form a string of volcanoes in the middle of moving lithospheric plates. The Hawaiian Islands are an example.

III Eldfell is an example of a rift eruption; Mount St. Helens is a subduction boundary eruption; Kilauea is an example of a hot spot eruption.

The most famous eruptions, including Vesuvius, Krakatau, Crater Lake, and Mount Pinatubo, occurred at subduction boundaries.

The moon, Mars, and Jupiter's moon Io all show evidence of volcanic activity. The moon has extensive lava flows, Mars has a number of volcanic cones, and Io has over 100 volcanoes. None shows evidence of plate tectonics.

IV Magma that cools underground forms plutons. Examples of plutons, defined by their size and structure, are dikes, sills, laccoliths, volcanic necks, batholiths, and stocks.

■ Vocabulary

batholith	pluton
dike	rift eruption
felsic	sill
hot spot	stock
laccolith	subduction boundary eruption
lava	tephra
mafic	volcanic neck
magma	volcano

■ Review

Number your paper from *1* to *20*. Match the phrases in List **A** with the terms in List **B**.

List A

1. molten rock underground
2. molten rock that reaches Earth's surface
3. molten rock that is silica-rich, thick, light-colored, slow moving, and likely to cause explosive eruptions
4. water vapor, carbon dioxide, sulfur dioxide, and hydrogen sulfide
5. ash, lapilli, blocks, and bombs
6. mid-Atlantic Ridge and East Pacific Rise
7. Columbia, Karroo, Parana, and Deccan
8. closely packed, six-sided columns of some thick lava flows
9. location of island chains, young mountain ranges, and most of the world's volcanoes
10. areas of volcanic activity in the middle of lithospheric plates
11. volcanic mountain on an island near Iceland that erupted lava and tephra in 1973
12. 1980 eruption in the Cascade Range
13. famous explosive eruption of A.D. 79 that buried the city of Pompeii
14. source of "the most violent eruption of historic times"
15. enormous volcano of Mars
16. volcanic moon of Jupiter
17. igneous intrusion between rock layers; Palisades of the Hudson River
18. Henry Mountains and Black Hills

For further review, see **Study Guide.**
For assessment, see **Chapter Tests**
and **Computer Test Bank.**

19. Ship Rock, New Mexico
20. largest igneous intrusion; core of the Coast Range and Sierra Nevadas

List B

a. basalt plateaus
b. batholith
c. columnar jointing
d. dike
e. Eldfell
f. felsic
g. gases in melted rock
h. hot spot
i. Io
j. Krakatau
k. laccolith
l. lava
m. mafic
n. magma
o. Mount St. Helens
p. Olympus Mons
q. rift eruptions
r. silica
s. sill
t. stock
u. subduction boundaries
v. tephra
w. Vesuvius
x. volcanic neck

■ Interpret and Apply

On your paper, answer each question in complete sentences.

1. Earthquake activity often occurs before a volcano erupts but dies out as soon as the eruption starts. Propose a reason.
2. What relationship would be expected between the particle sizes within a tephra deposit and the distance from the volcanic source of the tephra?
3. The rate of movement of subducting plates differs from one subduction zone to another. How would this fact explain why Indonesia usually has one major volcanic eruption each year while the Cascades have only occasional eruptions?
4. At hot spot volcanoes in Africa, lavas of several ages are piled on top of each other. What would this indicate about the movement of the African Plate?
5. A layer of volcanic ash is found paralleling the sedimentary layers of a thick sequence of limestone. Would the ash layer be considered a sill? Explain.

■ Critical Thinking

The graph shows some of the islands of the Hawaiian Island chain (compare with Figure 14.7). The vertical axis of the graph shows the approximate age of the volcanic rocks found on each island, and the horizontal axis shows the distance of each island from Hawaii.

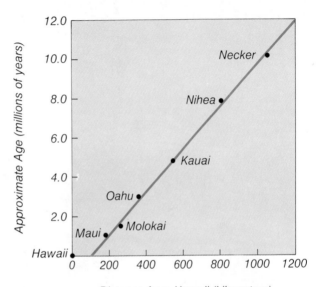

Distance from Hawaii (kilometers)

1. If an island was located 700 kilometers from Hawaii, what would be the expected age of the rocks of the island?
2. How far away from Hawaii would an island be on which the rocks were dated at 4.0 million years?
3. What evidence is there on the graph that Hawaii is currently over the hot spot?
4. Which island was over the hot spot about 5.0 million years ago?
5. According to the graph, which island is the oldest?
6. What is the age difference between the rocks of Oahu and the rocks of Molokai?
7. Assuming an age of 8.0 million years for the rocks of Nihea, determine the rate of motion, in centimeters per year, of the Pacific Plate in this area.

269

CHAPTER

15

Earthquakes and Plate Tectonics

▲
Many buildings in San Francisco's Marina District were damaged during the 1989 Loma Prieta earthquake.

How Do You Know That . . .

An earthquake is a sudden release of stress in Earth's crust? You can demonstrate this. Take a long, thin stick. (A piece of wood about the size of a meterstick or yardstick will work.) Hold one end down firmly at the side of your desk. Allow most of the stick to project beyond the desk. Using your free hand, push down gently on the overhanging end of the stick. Why does the stick bend rather than break? What happens to the stick if you suddenly let go of the overhanging end? A similar release of stress in Earth's crust can cause tremendous damage.

I Earthquakes Result from Stress

Topic 1 What Is an Earthquake?

Earthquakes are very common. More than a million occur each year. That is about one every 30 seconds. Most of these are too small to be noticeable on all but the most sensitive earthquake recording instruments. However, more than 3000 earthquakes strong enough to move sections of Earth's crust are recorded each year. Several hundred earthquakes move Earth's surface significant distances, and about 20 cause severe changes.

An **earthquake** is a shaking of Earth's crust caused by a release of energy. Like volcanoes, earthquakes are a result of the motions of the lithospheric plates. However, the area affected by an earthquake is much larger.

A severe earthquake in a populated area can be especially hazardous. Often the collapse of buildings caused by the ground shaking is only the beginning of the devastation. Explosions and fires start from broken electric wires or broken gas mains. Diseases spread when sewage lines are broken and water supplies become contaminated. Food shortages may occur as normal supply routes—roads, railroads, airport runways—become unusable. Coastal locations long distances from the earthquake may flood under the huge waves called tsunamis (Chapter 12, Topic 8). Earthquakes are the most destructive of natural disasters.

Topic 2 Causes of Earthquakes

Earthquakes can occur for many reasons. The ground can shake from the eruption of a volcano, the collapse of a cavern, or even from the impact of a meteor. However, the major cause of earthquakes is the stress that builds up between two lithospheric plates.

Most of the time, friction between plates prevents movement along the plate boundary. Instead, the stresses cause the plates to deform, or change shape. Eventually, the stresses become great enough to overcome the frictional forces, and the plates suddenly move. This movement causes an earthquake. The plates then snap back to the shapes they had before they were deformed but at new locations relative to each other. This explanation for the cause of an earthquake is called the **elastic-rebound theory** and is fundamental to an understanding of earthquakes.

OBJECTIVES

A Define *earthquake*, list problems caused by earthquakes, and discuss several causes of earthquakes.

B Define *focus* and *epicenter* and identify the significance of the depth of the focus.

C Name and describe the kinds of waves produced by earthquakes.

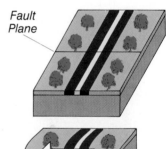
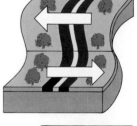

Fault Plane

15.1 Earthquakes occur when the stress along a fault plane overcomes the forces of friction. When friction is finally overcome, the plates move suddenly and release earthquake energy. Then the rocks along the plate boundaries snap back to their original shape.

SCIENCE BACKGROUND
The depth classification of earthquakes is as follows: shallow = 60 km or less, intermediate = 60 to 300 km, deep = over 300 km.

TEACHING TIP
The Critical Thinking for Chapter 13 shows earthquakes at a subduction boundary.

SCIENCE BACKGROUND
The discovery that deep earthquakes occur at some boundaries but not at others was one of the first steps in the development of the plate tectonics concept.

15.2 The focus is the location of the earthquake within Earth. The epicenter is the point on the surface directly above the focus.

VIDEODISC SELECTION

Diagram of earthquake epicenter and focus
Side 2: 1592, single frame

Topic 3 **Depth of Earthquakes**

The depth inside Earth at which an earthquake occurs depends upon the kind of plate boundary involved. At spreading centers and sliding boundaries, such as the mid-Atlantic Ridge and the San Andreas Fault, most earthquakes are less than 30 kilometers deep. At subduction boundaries, however, where one plate is plunging beneath another plate, earthquakes can be as much as 700 kilometers deep. The plate boundary is also plunging downward, often at about a 45-degree angle. Earthquakes can occur along this boundary until such depths are reached where pressures and temperatures transform rigid rocks into a more flexible material.

The point on the fault plane at which the first movement occurs is called the **focus** of the earthquake. The focus is the source of the energy released by the earthquake and can occur at depths of up to 700 kilometers. The point on Earth's surface directly above the focus is the **epicenter** of the earthquake. The epicenter is the location usually given in news reports.

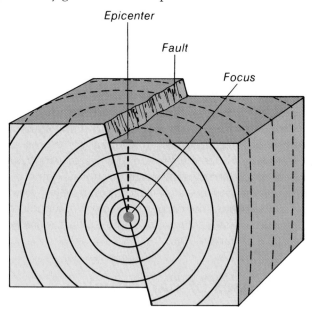

Topic 4 **Earthquake Waves**

Earthquakes produce three basic kinds of wave motions. One motion moves the particles in the rock back and forth, while a second motion moves the particles side-to-side. The third motion resembles waves in water.

The back-and-forth wave motion alternately squeezes and stretches the rock material through which the wave passes. These waves are called *compressional, primary,* or **P waves.** *P* waves can travel through any material—solid rock, magma, ocean water, even through air.

The side-to-side wave causes particles to move at right angles to the direction the waves are traveling. These waves are called *shear, secondary,* or **S waves.** *S* waves can travel through solids but not through liquids or gases. Liquids and gases cannot be sheared apart.

The rate at which *P* waves and *S* waves move through the ground depends upon the type and nature of the rock material. The velocity of these waves is greatest if the rock is rigid and dense but slows as the rock becomes less rigid and less dense. No matter what the material, *P* waves always travel about twice as fast as *S* waves.

Both *P* and *S* waves are called body waves because they travel through the body of Earth. When *P* and *S* waves reach the surface, they set up a third type of wave called *surface waves,* or **L waves.** These waves, which move like ripples on a pond, travel more slowly than either *P* or *S* waves.

15.3 *P* waves and *S* waves travel through Earth. *L* waves travel along the surface.

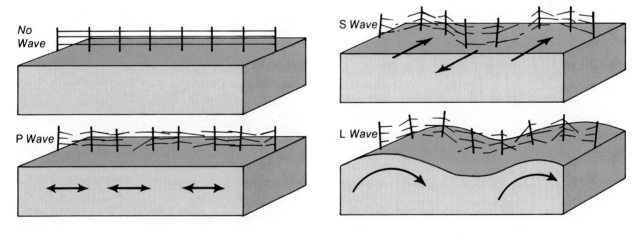

TOPIC QUESTIONS

Each topic question refers to the topic of the same number.

1. **(a)** What is an earthquake?   **(b)** How many earthquakes occur worldwide each year?   **(c)** Name several forms of devastation and hardship that accompany earthquakes.
2. **(a)** List several minor causes of earthquakes.   **(b)** What is the major cause of earthquakes?   **(c)** Describe how earthquakes occur, according to the elastic-rebound theory.
3. **(a)** What type of plate boundary has the deepest earthquakes? Why?   **(b)** What is the focus of an earthquake? What is the range for focal depths?   **(c)** Where is the epicenter of an earthquake?
4. **(a)** How do the particles in a *P* wave move?   **(b)** What kinds of materials can *P* waves travel through?   **(c)** How do the particles move in an *S* wave?   **(d)** What materials can *S* waves *not* travel through?   **(e)** How do the speeds of the *P* and *S* waves compare?   **(f)** What are *L* waves?

ANSWERS

1. (a) shaking of Earth's crust (b) more than 1 million   (c) building collapse, explosions, fires, diseases, starvation, tsunamis

2. (a) volcanic eruption, cavern collapse, meteor impact   (b) stress from plate motions   (c) stresses overcome friction, plates move, snap back

3. (a) subduction; plate is plunging downward   (b) place of actual quake; 0–700km   (c) point on surface directly above focus

4. (a) back and forth   (b) all (c) side-to-side   (d) liquids and gases   (e) *P* is about twice as fast (f) surface waves

OBJECTIVES

A Describe how a seismograph works.

B Discuss the relationship between the arrival time of the *P* and *S* waves at a seismograph station and the distance of the station from the earthquake epicenter.

C Explain how to locate an earthquake epicenter.

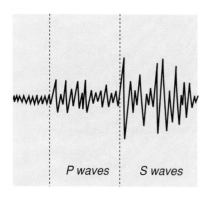

P waves   S waves

15.4 Seismic waves as they would look on a seismogram

15.5 Different kinds of seismographs record earthquakes by tracing earthquake waves.

II   Locating an Earthquake

Topic 5   Seismographs

The instrument that detects and records earthquake waves is called a **seismograph.** Because there are different directions of motion produced by an earthquake—back and forth (horizontal) and up and down (vertical)—there are different kinds of seismographs. Some record horizontal motions and others record vertical motions. The way in which each works is simple.

A heavy weight is attached to a base anchored in bedrock. The weight stays almost perfectly still (due to inertia) even when the bedrock and base are being shaken by an earthquake.

A record sheet, called a **seismogram,** is put on a drum attached to the base. The drum is turned slowly by a clock. A pen attached to the heavy weight rests its point on the drum. As long as the bedrock is quiet, the pen makes a straight line on the turning drum. When the bedrock shakes, the drum shakes slightly. However, the pen does not shake because it is attached to the heavy weight. The result is a zigzag trace that shows an earthquake is taking place.

Since *P* waves travel faster than *S* or *L* waves, the first major zigzag made on the seismogram marks the arrival of the *P* wave at the seismograph station. The distance the pen departs from the center tracing is related to the amount of energy released by the earthquake. The larger the zigzag, the bigger the earthquake. The slower *S* wave arrives next, producing a different pattern. The *L* waves arrive last.

Seismographs are built differently to record different earthquakes. Some are designed to measure small earthquakes that occur near the seismograph station, while others may record moderate earthquakes located thousands of kilometers away.

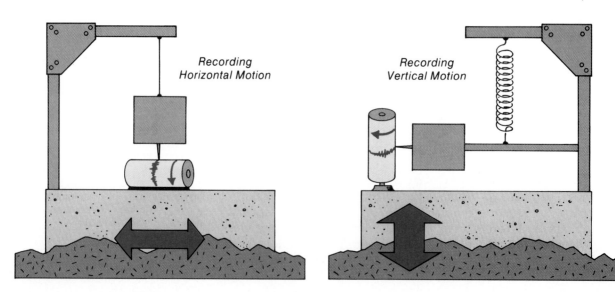

Recording Horizontal Motion

Recording Vertical Motion

Topic 6 **Determining the Distance to the Earthquake Epicenter**

The tracing made by a seismograph can be used to tell how far away the earthquake epicenter is from the seismograph station that recorded the tracing. Since *P* waves travel faster than *S* waves (Topic 4), the *P* waves made by the earthquake always arrive at a seismograph station before the *S* waves. The farther the seismograph station is from the earthquake epicenter, the larger the difference is in the arrival times of the two waves. For example, the difference in arrival times for the *P* and *S* waves for an earthquake that occurs 2000 kilometers from a seismograph station is about 3 minutes 10 seconds. The difference for a station 5000 kilometers away is about 6 minutes 40 seconds.

The relationship between *P* and *S* wave travel times and epicenter distance is shown on a **time-travel graph** (Figure 15.6). If the

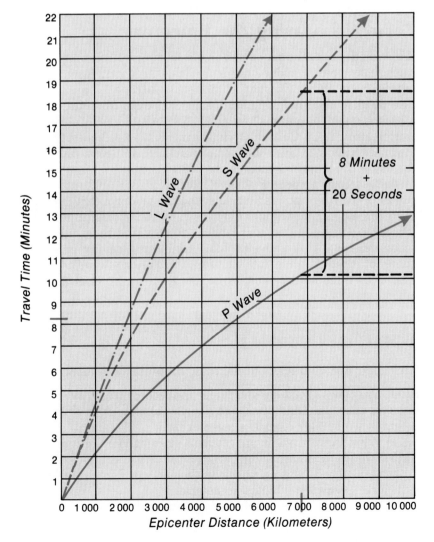

TEACHING TIP

To use the time-travel graph, lay the edge of a sheet of scrap paper on the time scale on the left side of the graph. Place one mark on the paper at the bottom of the graph for time zero and another at the difference between the arrival times of the *P* and *S* waves. Then, keeping the paper straight up and down, slide the bottom mark along the *P* wave curve until the *S* wave curve is the same distance away as the upper mark. Read the distance to the epicenter at the bottom of the graph.

VIDEODISC SELECTION

Seismograph station
Side 2: 1603, single frame

15.6 A time-travel graph can be used to find the distance to an earthquake. For example, if the difference between the arrival times of the *P* and *S* waves is 8 minutes 20 seconds, the earthquake occurred 6800 kilometers from the seismograph station.

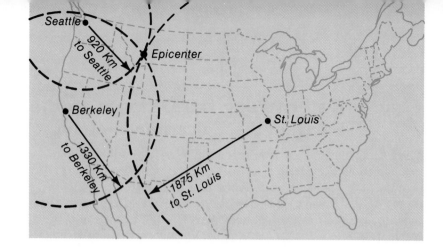

15.7 A single seismograph station can only determine the distance to the epicenter. Three stations are needed to pinpoint the exact location of the epicenter.

difference in the arrival times of the two waves is known, the distance to the epicenter can be read directly from the graph. For example, suppose the time difference between the arrival of the *P* wave and the arrival of the *S* wave is 8 minutes 20 seconds. The distance from the seismograph station to the earthquake epicenter is 6800 kilometers.

Topic 7 Locating the Epicenter

Knowing the distance between a single seismograph station and an earthquake epicenter does not locate the epicenter. Instead, distances from three different stations are needed. For example, assume that a seismograph station at St. Louis, Missouri, determines that the epicenter is located 1875 kilometers away. A second station at Berkeley, California, find that the same epicenter is 1330 kilometers away. A third station at Seattle, Washington, finds that the distance to the epicenter is only 920 kilometers.

To locate the epicenter, three circles are drawn on a map. The center of the first circle is St. Louis, and the radius of that circle is 1875 kilometers. You know that the earthquake's epicenter was located at some point on that circle. Berkeley is at the center of a second circle with a radius of 1330 kilometers. Seattle is at the center of the third circle with a radius of 920 kilometers. The point where all three circles meet is the location of the earthquake's epicenter.

TOPIC QUESTIONS

Each topic question refers to the topic of the same number.

5. **(a)** What does a seismograph detect and record?   **(b)** Why is there more than one kind of seismograph?   **(c)** How does a seismograph work?   **(d)** What is a seismogram?
6. **(a)** What kind of wave arrives at a seismograph station first?   **(b)** What is the relationship between the arrival times of *P* and *S* waves and the distance to the earthquake epicenter?   **(c)** What is a time-travel graph used to determine?
7. **(a)** How many seismograph stations are needed to locate an epicenter?   **(b)** How is the epicenter located?

VIDEODISC SELECTION

Locating an epicenter
Side 2: 1593, single frame

SCIENCE BACKGROUND
  L waves are used to find the depth of the focus.

ANSWERS
  5. (a) earthquake waves   (b) to record both horizontal and vertical motions   (c) nearly stationary pen traces pattern on shaking drum   (d) the wave record
  6. (a) *P* waves   (b) as distance increases, difference in arrival times increases   (c) distance to epicenter
  7. (a) 3   (b) draw 3 circles with radii equal to distance from station to epicenter: point of interception is epicenter

III   Measuring an Earthquake

Topic 8   Earthquake Magnitude

In addition to locating the epicenter, seismograms can be used to determine other facts about an earthquake. For example, seismograms can be used to determine the strength, or magnitude, of the energy produced by the earthquake.

The most widely used scale of earthquake magnitude is the scale developed by Charles F. Richter in the 1940's. The **Richter scale** is designed to be a measure of the amount of energy released by the earthquake itself. Each magnitude number represents an earthquake 32 times stronger than the next lower number. For example, an earthquake with a magnitude of 6 is 32 times stronger than an earthquake with a magnitude of 5 and more than 1000 times stronger than an earthquake with a magnitude of 4.

In recent years, another method of determining earthquake magnitude called **seismic moment** has been developed. The number for the seismic moment is not as easy to measure as Richter magnitude. However, the result is a more accurate indicator of the total energy involved. For example, both the 1906 San Francisco earthquake and the 1964 Alaskan earthquake had Richter magnitudes of 8.3. The Alaskan earthquake, however, released more total energy than the San Francisco earthquake because of larger movements along a much larger fault plane. The seismic moment values reflect these differences. The San Francisco earthquake has a seismic moment of 7.9; the Alaskan earthquake, 9.2. These numbers show that the Alaskan quake was more than 100 times stronger than the San Francisco quake.

The strongest earthquake recorded to date was the Chilean earthquake of 1960. This quake registered 8.3 on the Richter scale and 9.5 on the seismic moment scale.

Topic 9   Earthquake Damage

Even a mild earthquake can cause buildings to collapse. The two major causes of building collapse are ground shaking and foundation failure.

Ground shaking is the result of the waves set in motion by the earthquake. The sudden release of energy in an earthquake causes all of Earth to vibrate in much the same way that a bell vibrates when struck. Some of these vibrations move up and down while others move side to side (Topic 4). Buildings react to these vibrations and begin to shake up and down and sideways too. Most buildings can withstand large up-and-down vibrations. However, the largest motions at Earth's surface are side to side. Few buildings can survive severe side-to-side movements. As a result of these side-to-side movements, they collapse.

OBJECTIVES

A Identify the scales used to describe earthquake magnitude.

B Name the two major causes of building collapse during earthquakes.

C Identify several kinds of data that are being studied for earthquake prediction.

SCIENCE BACKGROUND

Each whole number on the Richter scale represents a tenfold increase in the amplitude of the earthquake waves. In order to obtain this tenfold increase, there must be a 32X increase in released energy. A two-point difference in magnitude is a 1024 times difference in energy released (1024 = 32 × 32).

VIDEODISC SELECTION

Damage from the 1906 San Francisco earthquake
Side 2: 1617 to 1622, 6-frame sequence

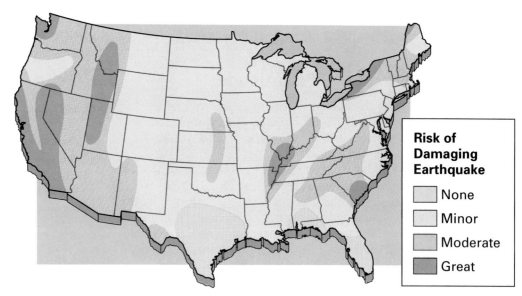

Risk of Damaging Earthquake

- None
- Minor
- Moderate
- Great

15.8 Many parts of the United States have some risk of having an earthquake.

Foundation failure is also a result of ground shaking but in a different way. The soils under a building may settle from severe shaking or even become liquified. In either case, the building is no longer safely supported and may collapse.

The importance of the foundation was first noted in the 1906 San Francisco earthquake. Buildings on solid rock experienced little damage. However, buildings located on bog muds or soft fill suffered severe damage. In fact, almost all of the buildings on soft material collapsed completely.

Similar foundation failures have occurred with other earthquakes. The collapse of buildings located on old lake sediments was a factor in the severe destruction in the Mexico City earthquake of 1985. Liquefaction of sediments was a major cause of the destruction from the 1964 Anchorage, Alaska, earthquake. That same year, an earthquake in Niigata, Japan, caused buildings to sink into the sediment beneath them and collapse. More recently, the destruction of buildings in San Francisco's Marina district during the Loma Prieta earthquake in 1989 was the result of foundation failure. The land in the Marina district was created by filling in part of the bay. In the earthquake, this artificial fill rolled like waves, shaking the buildings off their foundations.

Topic 10 **Earthquake Risk and Prediction**

Where in the United States is the risk of earthquakes the greatest? Almost everyone thinks first of California. But there are many other areas of the United States at risk as well. As shown in Figure 15.8, areas at risk include parts of Washington, South Carolina, Utah, Idaho, and the states bordering the Mississippi River near St. Louis, Missouri. Alaska and Hawaii are also high-risk areas. In fact, almost no location is without some earthquake risk. Any area that has experienced a damaging earthquake at some time in the past is considered to be at risk of having another earthquake some time in the future. Unfortunately many areas of the United States in which the risk of earthquakes is greatest are also areas with large and growing populations.

People in high-risk areas have a serious need for timely earthquake predictions. But is it possible to predict earthquakes? A successful earthquake prediction must correctly forecast three things—*where* the earthquake will occur, *when* the earthquake will occur, and what the *magnitude* of the earthquake will be.

Most prediction efforts in the United States are based on an assumption that earthquakes are periodic events. However, this type of prediction only narrows the time to a decade or a few years. Seismologists in California are attempting to make more accurate predictions using the *seismic gap* method. By plotting the locations of earthquake foci along a branch of the San Andreas fault, the seismologists sometimes find a place where the fault has not moved over a period of time. This gap is thought to be a place where the fault is locked together and has built up stress. The gap may be the place where an earthquake may next occur.

Other types of observable data are also being investigated as methods for predicting earthquakes. Very small tremors called microquakes sometimes occur before a major earthquake. In some areas, a slight increase in the elevation of the land or a decrease in the electrical resistance of the ground has been found to precede an earthquake. An increase in the amount of the radioactive element radon in well water may precede an earthquake. *P* waves slow by 10 to 15 percent for a period of time preceding an earthquake. From these and other observable changes, seismologists are hopeful of learning how to predict correctly Earth's movements and to reduce the loss of life and property.

SCIENCE BACKGROUND

Radon is a radioactive gas that forms during the radioactive decay of uranium.

TOPIC QUESTIONS

Each topic question refers to the topic of the same number.

8. (a) What is meant by the magnitude of an earthquake?
   (b) What is the scale most widely used to find magnitude?
   (c) How is the seismic moment scale different from the scale used to find magnitude?

9. (a) What kind of ground shaking is more likely to cause a building to collapse?   (b) In what two ways can shaking cause foundation failure?   (c) What effect did type of foundation have on building failure in the 1906 San Francisco earthquake?

10. (a) What three facts must an earthquake prediction forecast?
    (b) List four kinds of data that are being used to forecast earthquakes. Identify the change that occurs in each kind of data before an earthquake.

ANSWERS

8. (a) strength   (b) Richter (c) more difficult to determine but more accurate value

9. (a) side-to-side   (b) soils settle or liquify   (c) Buildings on solid rock survived; those on soft material did not.

10. (a) where, when, magnitude (b) *P* wave velocity, slows down; change in elevation, increases; electrical resistance of rock, decreases; radon, increases

OBJECTIVES

A Explain the changes in *P* and *S* wave velocities inside Earth.

B Locate the Mohorovicic discontinuity and explain how it was discovered.

C Describe the shadow zone and explain its significance.

IV Earthquake Waves inside Earth

Topic 11 *P* and *S* Wave Velocities

Most information about the inside of Earth has come from an analysis of seismogram tracings. These tracings record far more than just the arrival times of the *P*, *S*, and *L* waves. In combination with a time-travel graph (Topic 6), the tracings can be used to determine if a wave has been bent, speeded up, slowed down, or reflected as it traveled through the inside of Earth. From these kinds of data, seismologists have been able to determine the velocities of *P* and *S* waves as they travel through the different layers inside Earth and to define the locations and characteristics of those layers.

A graph of *P* and *S* wave velocities shows the result (Figure 15.9). The most obvious feature of the graph is the sharp change in velocities at a depth of 2900 kilometers. *P* waves are greatly slowed there, and *S* waves are stopped. Since *S* waves do not pass through liquids, the material directly below 2900 kilometers must be liquid. In fact, this is the evidence that was used to show that Earth's outer core is liquid. The partial recovery of the *P* wave velocity at 5200 kilometers suggests that the inner core, like the mantle, is a solid.

15.9 This graph shows that at a depth of 2900 kilometers the *P* waves slow down and the *S* waves stop. Geologists consider that depth to be the boundary between the mantle and the liquid outer core.

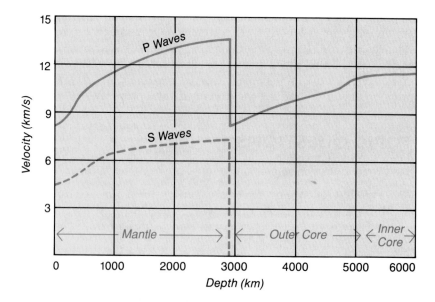

Topic 12 **The Moho**

Another abrupt change in *P* and *S* wave velocities occurs at the boundary between the crust and the mantle. This change was discovered in 1909 by the Yugoslav seismologist Andrija Mohorovicic from a study of many seismograms of minor earthquakes.

Several of the seismograms showed two distinct groups of *P* and *S* waves. One of the groups had traveled at an average velocity of 7 kilometers per second, but the other had speeded up to 8 kilometers per second. Mohorovicic reasoned that the second group had gone through denser material below the crust. He calculated the depth to the denser material to be about 50 kilometers.

The boundary he discovered is considered to be the boundary between the crust and the mantle. In his honor, the boundary is named the **Mohorovicic discontinuity,** or **Moho** for short.

The Moho, however, is not at a depth of 50 kilometers everywhere. The Moho averages 32 kilometers under the continents but only 8 kilometers under the oceans. Thus the continents stand higher on the crust but also sink deeper into the mantle.

Topic 13   **The Shadow Zone**

Even though an earthquake sends waves throughout all of Earth's interior, not all seismograph stations receive information from all earthquakes. Some receive only *P* waves, while others receive no signal at all.

Seismic stations that receive neither *P* nor *S* waves are said to be in the **shadow zone** of that earthquake (Figure 15.11). The shadow zone is a wide belt around Earth on the side opposite the focus of the earthquake. The cause of the shadow zone is Earth's outer core. *P* waves passing through the mantle are refracted (bent) in a smooth arc back to the surface. However, a *P* wave that travels deep enough to enter the outer core is refracted twice, once when it enters the outer core and again when it leaves. The result is that a broad belt around Earth, the shadow zone, receives no *P* wave information. No

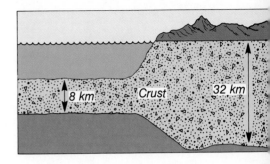

15.10   The Moho is deeper under the continents than under the oceans.

VIDEODISC SELECTION

Diagram showing Moho boundary
Side 2: 740, single frame

SCIENCE BACKGROUND

The shadow zone where it intersects Earth's surface is about 4300 kilometers wide.

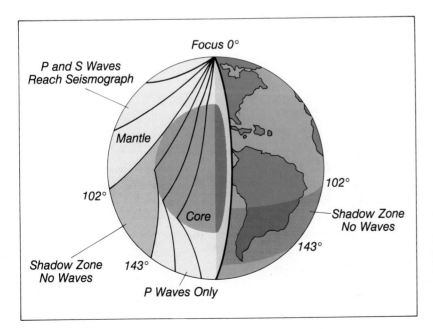

15.11   The shadow zone is caused by Earth's outer core. *S* waves do not reach the shadow zone because they are unable to penetrate the outer core. *P* waves are able to penetrate the outer core, but they are refracted so that none reach the shadow zone.

S wave information arrives in the shadow zone either. *S* waves cannot pass through liquids, and the outer core is a liquid.

Seismograph stations that are between the earthquake epicenter and the shadow zone receive both *P* and *S* waves. Stations within the shadow zone receive neither *P* nor *S* waves. Stations that are beyond the shadow zone on the opposite side of Earth from the earthquake receive only *P* waves. The *S* waves are stopped by the liquid outer core.

TOPIC QUESTIONS

ANSWERS
11. (a) slowed   (b) stopped; *S* waves do not pass through liquids, liquid outer core starts at depth of 2900 km
12. (a) boundary between crust and mantle   (b) seismograms showed two distinct groups of *P* and *S* waves   (c) deeper under continents
13. (a) no *P* or *S* waves return to surface there   (b) outer core   (c) *S* waves do not pass through the outer core.

Each topic question refers to the topic of the same number.

11. **(a)** What happens to *P* wave velocities at a depth of 2900 kilometers inside Earth?   **(b)** What happens to *S* waves at that depth? Why?

12. **(a)** What is the Moho?   **(b)** How did Mohorovicic discover the Moho?   **(c)** How does the Moho's depth vary under the continents as compared with its depth under the oceans?

13. **(a)** What is the shadow zone?   **(b)** What is the cause of the shadow zone?   **(c)** Why do *S* waves not come to the surface beyond the shadow zone?

CAREERS

Dr. Waverly Person
Seismologist

The National Earthquake Information Service (NEIS) in Golden, Colorado, is the most important collector of earthquake information in the world. Dr. Waverly Person is a seismologist there. He says that NEIS regularly computes magnitudes and epicenter locations for between 13 000 and 16 000 earthquakes each year.

The data that Dr. Person and other seismologists use in their work arrive in Golden by satellite transmission, telephone, telegraph, and even by letter. Much of the data arrives as real-time seismic signals sent via satellite from seismic stations throughout the United States, Canada, and other parts of the world. As the data are received, they are recorded on seismograph drums at NEIS.

When large or damaging earthquakes occur, the normal routine of epicenter analysis is interrupted in order to quickly determine the location of the earthquake. This makes it possible to alert agencies responsible for disaster relief, who are then able to begin sending help and supplies. Dr. Person says that for major U.S. earthquakes, the whole staff goes to work, no matter what the hour of the day or night.

V Examples of Earthquakes

Topic 14 **Alaska—1964**

The Alaskan earthquake of 1964 had one of the largest magnitudes of any earthquake in this century. It began as a gentle rocking motion similar to the kind that Alaskans customarily experience. However, unlike the usual tremors that taper off, this one grew worse until the ground was rolling like huge ocean waves. The rolling continued for five minutes. By the time it ended, Alaska had experienced some frightening changes. Whole blocks of houses were moved, buildings collapsed, and huge fissures opened in the ground. More than 260 000 square kilometers of ground were heaved upward 2 meters and then dropped. Another 65 000 square kilometers were moved sideways.

The Alaskan earthquake was caused by movement along a subduction boundary. All along the Aleutian Islands, the Pacific Plate is pushing under the North American Plate. Some subduction boundaries move by long-term steady creep, so severe earthquakes are rare. The subduction of the Pacific Plate at the Mariana Islands is an example. Other subduction boundaries, however, move by horizontal slippage. This kind of slippage causes earthquakes. Both Alaska and Chile are located on such boundaries.

The main reason the Alaskan earthquake was so severe was that the break on the fault that started the earthquake triggered other breaks. In all, over 800 kilometers of fault plane were affected.

The earthquake was so strong that it caused buildings to shake as far away as Seattle, Washington. Even more surprising, many seismograph stations around the world were unable to record the earthquake because it threw tracking pens off their recording drums. Detectable vibrations were recorded for 18 months after the earthquake. Over 10 000 aftershocks were counted.

The earthquake, however, was just the beginning of the devastation. It generated a series of tsunamis, or seismic sea waves. Coastal villages were flooded again and again at intervals of about 30 minutes. One fishing village simply disappeared after a 21-meter wave swept over it. The waves crossed the Pacific Ocean at more than 600 kilometers per hour and caused severe damage as far away as Hawaii and Japan. Amazingly, only 115 people were killed.

OBJECTIVES

A Identify movement along a subduction boundary as the cause of the 1964 Alaskan earthquake.

B Discuss earthquake activity along the San Andreas fault system.

C Explain the cause and significance of midplate earthquakes such as the 1811–1812 New Madrid earthquakes.

OF INTEREST

Many Native American legends tell of ancient devastation and huge sea waves in this same area of Alaska.

15.12 Buildings in downtown Anchorage were severely damaged during the 1964 Alaskan earthquake.

VIDEODISC SELECTION

Damage from the 1964 Alaska earthquake
Side 2: 1604 to 1607, 4-frame sequence

15.13 This map shows the location of the plate boundary that caused the Alaskan earthquake.

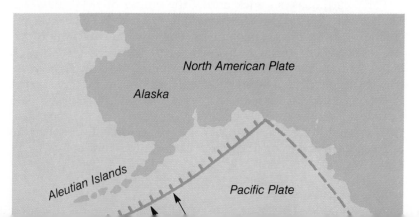

North American Plate

Alaska

Aleutian Islands

Pacific Plate

15.14 An aerial view of the San Andreas Fault

15.15 Seismologists use the latest technology to detect crustal movements. Here a laser beam is used to keep a precise measurement of the distance between two locations on opposite sides of a fault plane in California. Any change in the measurement would indicate seismic activity.

Topic 15 Earthquakes along the San Andreas Fault

The large 1992 earthquake at Landers, California, interested seismologists far more than it did most Californians. The reason few people took note of the earthquake was that Landers is a small town in a relatively isolated area. As a result, the damage caused by the earthquake was relatively light, even though the magnitude was an impressive 7.5.

Seismologists were interested in the Landers earthquake because it was the strongest California earthquake in 40 years. Although other recent earthquakes (San Fernando in 1971, Coalinga in 1983, Rosemead in 1987, Loma Prieta in 1989) caused far more destruction and loss of human life, Landers had a higher magnitude than any of the others. A second reason for seismologists to study the Landers earthquake was that, like the other earthquakes, the Landers earthquake was the result of movement along part of the San Andreas fault system. In 1906, San Francisco was destroyed when the San Andreas fault shifted six meters. Major devastating earthquakes occur along the fault system on the average of once every 160 years.

The San Andreas Fault system marks the boundary between the Pacific Plate and the North American Plate (Chapter 13, Topic 9). An 1100-kilometer piece of California is moving north relative to the rest of the United States. If the two plates would slide smoothly past each other as they do in some areas, Californians would not need to be concerned, but in several places the plates are stuck. Tremendous pressures are building up that will cause major earthquakes when they give way. With 18 million people now living along the fault, the risk of a disaster is very high. This region of the United States has a definite need for reliable earthquake forecasting methods.

Topic 16 New Madrid—1811 and 1812

Three of the largest earthquakes in United States history did not occur in either California or Alaska. in fact, they did not even happen at a plate boundary. Instead, they occurred on the Mississippi River near the town of New Madrid, Missouri.

Three earthquakes struck during the winter of 1811 and 1812. Their estimated magnitudes were 8.6, 8.4, and 8.7. Because the crustal rocks in the area conduct seismic waves well, the earthquakes were felt throughout most of the northeastern United States and are reported to have rung church bells in Boston. At New Madrid, two new waterfalls were formed on the Mississippi River, and its surface was littered with the wreckage of boats. The earthquake activity at New Madrid did not end in 1812. Since then, two large but less severe earthquakes have occurred. Even today the area experiences one small earthquake about every other day.

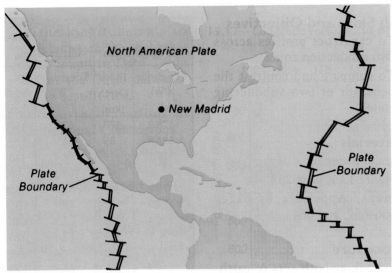

North American Plate

● New Madrid

Plate
Boundary

Plate
Boundary

15.16 The faults at New Madrid are buried near the center of the North American Plate. A major earthquake there would affect a huge geographical area.

VIDEODISC SELECTION

Damage from the 1971 San Fernando, California, earthquake Side 2: 1595 to 1599, 5-frame sequence

SCIENCE BACKGROUND
  Rocks of the eastern United States are cooler and more dense than rocks near the west coast plate boundary. The cooler rocks transmit seismic waves better. Therefore, eastern U.S. earthquakes are felt over a wider area.

If New Madrid is not a plate boundary, why is there so much seismic activity there? The cause of the activity is three faults. These faults cannot be seen at Earth's surface. They are deeply buried by Mississippi River sediments and the thick layers of sedimentary rock beneath them. The faults seem to be related to zones of weakness in the craton, the oldest and strongest rocks of the continental crust (Chapter 13, Topic 12). The faults may have been inactive for millions of years before changes in the stresses on the North American Plate caused them to start moving again.

The activity at New Madrid belongs to a class of earthquakes called midplate earthquakes. On a worldwide scale, the class has little significance. To North America, however, the New Madrid earthquakes have great significance because of the size of the area that would be affected by a major earthquake there.

TOPIC QUESTIONS

Each topic question refers to the topic of the same number.

14. **(a)** List some changes that occurred in Alaska because of the 1964 earthquake there.   **(b)** What was the cause of the Alaskan earthquake?   **(c)** What caused it to be so severe?   **(d)** Name some effects of that severity.   **(e)** What other devastating force accompanied the earthquake?

15. **(a)** Identify two reasons why seismologists were interested in the Landers earthquake.   **(b)** Identify some other recent California earthquakes.   **(c)** How often is the San Andreas fault thought to produce major earthquakes?   **(d)** Why is earthquake prediction important in California?

16. **(a)** Why is the location of the New Madrid earthquake unique? **(b)** How large an area felt the three major earthquakes there? **(c)** Why are the New Madrid earthquakes significant?

ANSWERS
   14. (a) houses moved, buildings collapsed, fissures opened, ground raised and dropped   (b) subduction of Pacific Plate under North American Plate   (c) first break triggered other breaks   (d) shook buildings far away, pens thrown off seismographs worldwide, over 10 000 aftershocks (e) tsunamis
   15. (a) strongest earthquake in 40 years, fault part of San Andreas system   (b) 1971, San Fernando; 1983, Coalinga; 1987, Rosemead; 1989, Loma Prieta   (c) every 160 years   (d) large population lives along the fault
   16. (a) not at plate boundary (b) most of northeastern United States   (c) size of affected area

Mountains and Plate Tectonics

These Himalayan Mountain peaks formed from the mountain-building collision of lithospheric plates.

How Do You Know That . . .

Rock layers of mountainous areas may be squeezed and crumpled into great wavelike folds? A simple model shows how this movement is possible. Use several different colors of modeling clay to make a plateau of four layers of sedimentary rock. Each layer should be about 1 centimeter thick, 15 centimeters long, and 8 centimeters wide. Gently squeeze the two ends of the plateau toward each other so that the clay forms upfolded layers. Now level out the clay again. This time squeeze the ends of the plateau to form downfolded layers.

I Mountains Result from Collisions

Topic 1 Active and Passive Continental Margins

The continental margin is the boundary between continental crust and oceanic crust. This boundary occurs at the continental slope (see Chapter 18), not the shoreline. There are two basic types of continental margins—active and passive. Both are important to the formation of mountains.

Active continental margins occur along plate boundaries. Earthquakes, volcanoes, and mountain building result as the plates move relative to each other. An excellent example of an active continental margin is the west coast of South America. Here the dense, relatively thin, oceanic Nazca Plate is subducting under a less dense, relatively thin, continental South American Plate, forming the Andes Mountains.

Passive continental margins do not occur at plate boundaries. These margins are stable areas of shallow water where the major activity is the buildup of sediment. Some of the sediment comes from rivers flowing off the continents. Other sediment comes from skeletons and shells of marine organisms. An example of a passive continental margin is the Atlantic coast of North America. A wedge of sediment 250 kilometers wide and as much as 10 kilometers thick has accumulated there.

How are passive continental margins related to mountain building? The answer is that these margins are the only places where sediments accumulate in a quantity great enough to make a mountain. The mountains of today were passive continental margins in the past. The active continental margin on the west coast of South America was a passive continental margin until about 200 million years ago. The Andes Mountains contain the sediments that were deposited on that passive margin.

Topic 2 Collisions between Oceans and Continents

The Andes Mountains are an example of one type of mountain-building process—the collision of oceanic crustal material with continental crustal material. In this type of collision, oceanic crust plunges, or subducts, under the continent as rock layers on the

OBJECTIVES

A Describe active and passive continental margins and give examples of each.

B Discuss two ways in which mountains are formed during the collision between an ocean and a continent and give examples of each.

C Describe what happens when two continents collide and name places where such collisions are occurring.

TEACHING TIP

The mountains discussed here are the mountains of continents. The mountains of mid-ocean ridges are excluded. The map on pages 656-657 of Appendix B shows the locations of the plate boundaries and major mountain ranges.

SCIENCE BACKGROUND

Active continental margins are also called Pacific-type or seismic continental margins. Pacific-type margins are further divided into Chilean and Mariana types. Passive continental margins are also called Atlantic-type and aseismic continental margins.

VIDEODISC SELECTION

Aerial view of the Andes Mountains
Side 1: 2835, single frame

SCIENCE BACKGROUND

This second process is called obduction. In a sense, obduction is the reverse of subduction because pieces of oceanic plate are left at the surface rather than being pulled beneath it. The process by which pieces of plate are attached to the edge of another plate is called accretion. The obduction and accretion of large crustal blocks is often called microplate tectonics. The coastal ranges of California are thought to have formed in this manner.

SCIENCE BACKGROUND

In this collision, India does not seem to be deforming very much. Most of the crumpling is Eurasian rock. The reason is thought to be because India consists of denser, tougher igneous rock while Eurasia is composed of sedimentary layers.

VIDEODISC SELECTION

Mt. Everest from *Apollo 7*
Side 1: 2838, single frame

16.1 When an oceanic plate and a continental plate collide, the heavier oceanic plate subducts under the continental plate. Mountains form due to the related volcanism and compression.

continent form mountains. Subduction continues throughout the mountain-building process. Earthquakes are common. Friction from subduction generates magma, some of which rises to the surface to form volcanoes.

In some ocean-continent collisions of the past, another process appears to have accompanied subduction. In these cases, pieces of oceanic plate have ridden over the subduction zone rather than plunge into it. These pieces are found attached to the continents. This type of continental collision is thought to have been important to the formation of the west coast of North America. Like the west coast of South America, this area was a passive plate margin until about 200 million years ago. At that time, the Pacific Plate began to subduct under the North American continent. As it subducted, pieces of the Pacific Plate were scraped off and attached to the edge of the continent. Some of the pieces contained oceanic crust, some were islands, and some were fragments of other continents. These pieces became the mountains of the west coast of North America. They are *terranes*, discussed in Chapter 13.

Topic 3 **Collisions between Two Continents**

A second type of mountain building results when two continents come together at a collision boundary (Chapter 13, Topic 10). The collision of India with Eurasia to form the Himalaya Mountains is an example.

Before two continents can collide, the ocean basin between them must close. This change occurs as the oceanic crust subducts beneath one of the continents. Subduction stops, however, once the ocean is gone and the continents are in contact, because continental crust is too light to subduct. Continued movement causes the rocks of the continental margins to be crumpled into mountains.

The formation of the Himalaya Mountains was preceded by the closing of an ocean between India and Tibet, a part of Eurasia. The oceanic crust is thought to have disappeared into a subduction zone that plunged to the north under Tibet. Once the continental crusts

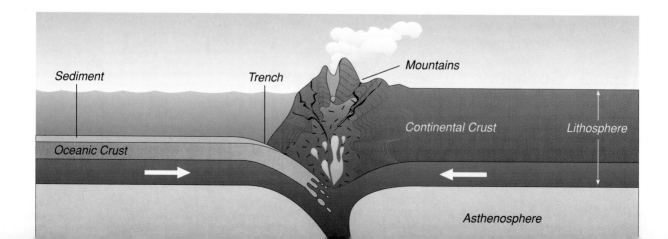

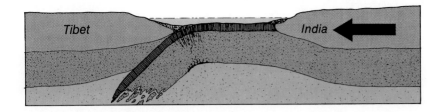

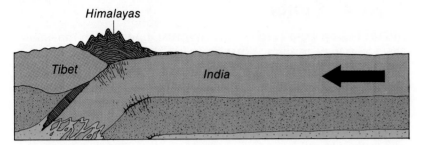

collided, subduction stopped. However, India continued to move north, pushing some rocks aside and crumpling others into mountains. The severe earthquakes that occur in the Himalayas today indicate that the collision is still in progress.

Another example of a mountain range that is forming today by the collision of two continents is the Alps Mountains of Europe. Here the colliding landmass is Italy, which is actually a part of the African Plate. As the African Plate moves toward the Eurasian Plate, crossing the Mediterranean Sea, Italy is colliding with the Eurasian Plate.

16.2 When two continental plates collide, a portion of the crust at the collision boundary is crumpled into a mountain formation. The Himalayas formed in this way as the continental crust of the Indian Plate and the Eurasian Plate collided.

SCIENCE BACKGROUND
The Atlas Mountains of North Africa and the Caucasus Mountains of Turkey are also the result of the collision of Africa with Eurasia.

TOPIC QUESTIONS

Each topic question refers to the topic of the same number.

1. **(a)** What kinds of earth processes occur at active continental margins? **(b)** Where is there an active continental margin today? **(c)** What is the major activity at passive continental margins? **(d)** Give an example of a passive continental margin. **(e)** How are passive continental margins related to mountain building?

2. **(a)** What happens to oceanic crust in most ocean-continent collisions? **(b)** Where do mountains form in an ocean-continent collision? **(c)** What other processes accompany this kind of collision? **(d)** What has happened to oceanic crust in some ocean-continent collisions of the past? **(e)** Where are mountains thought to have formed by this kind of collision?

3. **(a)** When does subduction occur during the collision of two continents? **(b)** Why does subduction stop? **(c)** Where was the subduction zone thought to be for India's collision with Eurasia? **(d)** What evidence indicates that the Indian-Eurasian collision is still in progress? **(e)** What other mountains, in addition to the Himalayas, are forming from the collision of two continents?

ANSWERS
1. (a) earthquakes, volcanoes, mountain building (b) west coast of South America (c) sediment build-up (d) Atlantic coast of North America (e) source of sediments for mountains
2. (a) subducts (b) on continent edge (c) earthquakes, volcanoes (d) pieces of oceanic crust override subduction zone, attach to continents (e) west coast of North America
3. (a) only during the closing of ocean between them (b) continents come into contact (c) under Tibet (d) severe earthquakes (e) Alps

OBJECTIVES

A Name three kinds of faults and give examples of each.

B Identify two kinds of folds, explain how they are described, and name a well-known folded mountain range.

C Discuss the importance of volcanism to the formation of the Himalayas, the Andes, and the Cascades.

SCIENCE BACKGROUND

A downdropped block like the Baikal Rift is called a graben. Lake Tahoe in Nevada also occupies a graben. Many other examples occur around the world.

16.3   Three basic types of faults

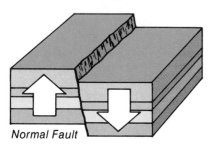

Normal Fault

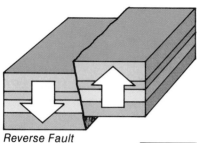

Reverse Fault

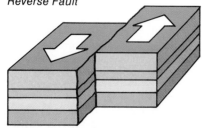

Strike–slip Fault

II Features of Collision Mountains

Topic 4 Faults

A fault is a break or crack in Earth's crust along which movement has occurred. The surface that separates the two moving pieces is the *fault plane*. Movement along fault planes causes the earthquakes that accompany mountain building (Chapter 15, Topic 2). There are three basic kinds of faults.

A **normal fault** occurs when the rocks on one side of the fault plane drop down with respect to the rocks on the other side. Normal faults occur in areas where tension is pulling the crust apart. An example is the Baikal Rift System in southern Russia. Here a piece of crust dropped down between two normal faults. The valley that resulted from the movement now contains Lake Baikal, the deepest lake in the world. Since normal faults are caused by stresses pulling away from each other, they are not common in collision mountains.

A **reverse fault** occurs when one side of the fault plane is driven up over the other side. These faults result from stresses that push toward each other. Reverse faults are important to mountain building because they allow the crust to be shortened as the plates collide. If the fault plane is nearly level, large pieces of crustal material can be moved great distances. This process is the thin-skinned thrusting described in Chapter 13. It is an important feature of most of the world's mountain ranges.

A third kind of fault is a **strike-slip fault.** In this fault, the rocks on opposite sides of the fault plane move horizontally past each other. The San Andreas Fault is a well-known example (Chapter 15, Topic 15).

In the Himalayas, strike-slip faults are more common than reverse faults. These faults result as India pushes rock material aside on its drive into Eurasia. Strike-slip faulting has occurred over a large area. In some cases, the fault planes are over 3000 kilometers away from India. There is even some evidence that earthquakes in China are the result of the Indian-Eurasian collision.

Topic 5 Folds

During plate collisions, the rock layers along the continental margins are crumpled into folds. A number of terms are used to describe these folds.

An **anticline** is an upfold in the rock layers. A **syncline** is a downfold. The sides of the folds are called *limbs.* The steepness, or *dip*, of the limbs reflects the intensity of folding. Limbs may be gently dipping, steeply dipping, straight up and down, or even overturned.

16.4 (a) Normal fault, (b) reverse fault

The compass direction of the fold or of the rock layers exposed at the surface along the fold is called the *strike*.

In some folded mountains the folding is severe, and the rock layers are badly deformed. In others, the layers have been pushed into gentle anticlines and synclines.

A well-known example of folded mountains is the Valley and Ridge Province of the Appalachian Mountains. The rock layers there have not been badly crumpled. Instead, the stress of collision has formed the layers into long, narrow folds. Interestingly, the valleys between the mountains do not correspond to fold synclines nor the ridges to fold anticlines as one might expect. Instead, the locations of the valleys and ridges are controlled primarily by the weathering rates of the rocks in different areas of the folds.

SCIENCE BACKGROUND

The strike and dip are at right angles to each other.

VIDEODISC SELECTION

Diagrams of fault types
Side 1: 2570 to 2573, 4-frame sequence

Diagrams and examples of crustal folding (described in disc directory)
Side 1: 2554 to 2563, 10-frame sequence

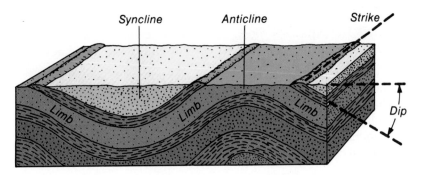

16.5 An anticline is an upfold in rock layers, and a syncline is a downfold. The strike is the direction of the fold, and the dip is the steepness of the fold.

Topic 6 **Volcanoes**

Volcanic rocks are not common in the Himalayas, but some do occur on the northern edge of the range. These rocks may have formed during the time the Indian Plate was still subducting under the Eurasian Plate but before the two continents collided.

Volcanism has been important throughout the history of the Andes. In fact, the core of the Andes is a granite batholith that apparently supplied magma to many surface volcanoes. Erosion removed the volcanoes long ago, but the batholith and the feeder dikes to the volcanoes are still present. These features are now easily visible at the surface. The batholith is exposed over an area of about 3000 square kilometers and, because granite resists erosion, contains the highest peaks of the Andes. These peaks make up the Cordillera Blanca, or White Range, so named because the mountains are always covered with snow. A similar batholith forms the core of the Sierra Nevada in California. Many geologists believe that the Andes of today resemble the Sierra Nevadas of 100 million years ago and the Northern Appalachians of 450 million years ago.

The eruption of Mount St. Helens in 1980 focused attention on volcanism in North America. The Cascade Range, in which Mount St. Helens is located, is a classic example of an active volcanic mountain range.

TEACHING TIP

The Cordillera Blanca is less than 10 degrees south of the equator. You could review snowline and the glacier chapter by asking students how these mountains could have snow so close to the equator.

TOPIC QUESTIONS

Each topic question refers to the topic of the same number.

4. **(a)** Describe the movement of rocks in a normal fault. **(b)** How did Lake Baikal form? **(c)** How are rocks moved in a reverse fault? Explain why reverse faults are important to mountain building. **(d)** Describe the movement in a strike-slip fault and give an example. **(e)** Which type of fault is most important in the Himalayas?

5. **(a)** How do anticlines and synclines differ? **(b)** Where are the limbs of a fold? **(c)** What is meant by the dip of the limbs of a fold? **(d)** What is strike? **(e)** How are the valleys and ridges of the Appalachians related to the anticlines and synclines that occur there?

6. **(a)** When were the volcanic rocks of the Himalayas thought to have formed? **(b)** What is the Cordillera Blanca and how does it relate to volcanism in the Andes? **(c)** How are the Andes thought to be related to the Sierra Nevadas and to the Northern Appalachians? **(d)** What kind of mountain range is the Cascade Range?

ANSWERS

4. (a) One side drops down relative to the other. (b) crust between two normal faults dropped down (c) One side is driven up over the other; the crust shortens as plates collide. (d) sides move horizontally; San Andreas (e) strike-slip

5. (a) anticline—upfold; syncline—downfold (b) the sides (c) steepness (d) compass direction of fold or of rock layers exposed in it (e) The valleys and ridges are controlled by weathering rates, not folding.

6. (a) before continents collided and while subduction was still occurring (b) a granite batholith; magma source for surface volcanoes of past (c) Andes of today are like Sierra of 100 million years ago and Northern Appalachians of 450 million years ago (d) volcanic

III   Other Evidences of Mountain Building

Topic 7   Uplifting

Not all sedimentary rock layers of passive continental margins are crumpled into folds. In some areas the layers are raised to higher levels with little deformation. Such uplifting is also a part of mountain building. Several methods can be used to determine whether uplifting has occurred.

Fossils are one indicator of uplift. Some of the sedimentary rocks of passive continental margins contain the skeletons and shells of organisms that lived in the ocean. The presence of these marine skeletons and shells in rocks now located high above sea level is good evidence that uplifting has occurred.

A second evidence of uplift comes from *raised beaches*. In some coastal areas of the world, old shorelines can be seen at elevations above the modern shoreline. One particularly well-developed area of old shorelines is the coast of California near Los Angeles. Here a series of level terraces can be seen, each above and inland from the previous one. The terraces are old beaches that originally formed at sea level. Each must have been raised above sea level as the area was uplifted. Since the highest is about 400 meters above the present sea level, the area must have been uplifted by at least that amount.

A third evidence of uplift can be obtained by making regular *measurements of the elevation* of an area over a period of time. Using bench marks (Chapter 7, Topic 8), a surveying team can determine whether any changes in elevation have occurred since the last survey. Using this technique, a mountain pass 80 kilometers east of Los Angeles has been found to be uplifting at a rate of about 14 centimeters per century. Another area within 3 kilometers of the San Andreas Fault has been rising at a rate of 78 centimeters per century.

OBJECTIVES

A Name and describe three ways in which uplifting of rock layers can be detected.

B Identify some ways in which rock layers become tilted; describe and give examples of fault-block mountains.

C List and describe several ways to tell if rock layers have been overturned.

16.6 These raised beaches along the California coast are evidence of uplifting.

Topic 8   Tilting

Most sedimentary rocks are formed in level layers. Therefore, the occurrence of tilted layers is an evidence of mountain building.

Layers of rock can become tilted in a number of different ways. The folding of sedimentary rocks into anticlines and synclines is one way. The folded layers of the Valley and Ridge Province of the Appalachian Mountains contain many examples of tilted sedimentary rock layers. Tilting can also result when rocks are pushed upward. The uplift of the Rocky Mountains caused sedimentary layers in Colorado to be steeply inclined.

SCIENCE BACKGROUND

The fact that sediments form in horizontal layers is called Steno's Law, or the Law of Original Horizontality.

16.7 (left) The tilted layers of this sandstone formation indicate that a geologic change has occurred. (right) Fault-block mountains are usually quite steep on the faulted side.

In other areas, tilted layers are the result of whole blocks of crust having been faulted and uplifted at the same time. The raised structures are called **fault-block mountains.** Such mountains are usually steep on the faulted side but gently sloping on the opposite side. Examples of fault-block mountains are the Sierra Nevadas of California, the Wasatch Range of Utah, and the Teton Range of Wyoming. In addition, a series of fault-block mountains can be seen in Nevada and western Utah.

Topic 9 Overturning

In some areas of the world, rock layers are so severely tilted that they may be bottom side up. Geologists have several methods of determining whether rock layers have been overturned.

Ripple marks are features that form on the floor of a quiet body of water when waves are moving gently across the surface. These features consist of miniature valleys between sharply pointed tiny hills. The rock containing ripple marks is right side up if the sharp hills point up.

Cross-bedding is a feature of deltas, sand dunes, and migrating ripples. Although most sediments are deposited in level layers, parts of deltas and sand dunes are not. These parts are deposited at an angle to the other level layers and can sometimes be used to tell if the entire layer has been overturned. The layer is right side up if the cross-bedding curves downward and the top of the cross-bedded layer is cut off by the layers above it.

Mud cracks develop on the surfaces of such areas as mud flats when the mud and ooze dry. Individual cracks are wider at the top than at the bottom. When these cracks are preserved in rocks, they are still wider at the top if the layer is right side up.

Shells with curved surfaces, such as clam shells, are unstable if their open side is up. Currents in the water tend to flip over such shells. These shells, however, are very stable if the open side of the shell is down. A layer in which most of the curved shells have their open sides down is right side up.

VIDEODISC SELECTION

Photo of cross-bedded sandstone
Side 1: 2461, single frame

Mud cracks
Side 1: 2493, single frame

16.8 Some rock layers can become so severely tilted that they are overturned.

TOPIC QUESTIONS

Each topic question refers to the topic of the same number.

7. **(a)** How do the fossils of organisms that lived in the ocean show that uplifting has occurred?   **(b)** How do old beaches on the California coast show uplifting?   **(c)** At what rate have changes in elevation occurred near Los Angeles and near the San Andreas Fault?

8. **(a)** In what position are most sedimentary rocks formed? **(b)** List two ways in which sedimentary rocks can be tilted. **(c)** What are fault-block mountains?   **(d)** Give some examples of fault-block mountains including a large area where many occur.

9. **(a)** What is meant by overturning?   **(b)** List some sedimentary features that indicate whether overturning has occurred and describe the appearance of each feature if overturning has not occurred.

ANSWERS
7. (a) Rocks containing marine fossils must have been raised if they are now high above sea level. **(b)** formed at sea level, now above sea level   **(c)** 14 cm/century; 78 cm/century
8. (a) level layers   **(b)** folding, uplift   **(c)** faulted and uplifted blocks of crust   **(d)** Sierra Nevadas, Wasatch Range, Tetons; Nevada and western Utah
9. (a) rock layers turned bottom side up   **(b)** ripple marks—crests of ripples point up; cross-bedding—cross-bedded layers curve downward and have their tops cut off; mud cracks—wider at top; shells—open side down

Current RESEARCH

Tracking the Moving Plates

Don't panic, but the ground beneath your feet is *moving*. The movement is too slight for you to detect, but Earth's lithospheric plates are slowly moving toward or away from one other, creating the forces that cause earthquakes and build Earth's great mountain chains.

Until recently, scientists had no way to directly measure a plate's movement. Now satellites are being used to track the plates' slow progression. The technique used is called satellite laser ranging (SLR). Scientists direct a laser beam from Earth's surface toward a satellite that is covered with reflecting prisms. These prisms bounce the light directly back to its point of origin. By timing how long it takes the light to make the round trip to and from the satellite, scientists can use the speed of light to calculate the distance to

the satellite. A comparison of measurements taken over several years provides data on how the location of the ground station has changed, which tells how quickly the plate on which the station is located is moving.

For example, direct measurements from the satellite *Lageos 1* show that the Hawaiian island of Maui is moving toward Japan at a rate of about 7 centimeters per year. Maui is moving away from South America at a rate of about 8 centimeters per year. Even this gradual movement of the Pacific Plate will become substantial over the broad expanse of geologic time. Since Pangaea broke apart 180 million years ago, North America and Europe have been moving apart at a rate of about 3 centimeters per year. Now the two continents are separated by a distance of nearly 5000 kilometers!

OBJECTIVES

A Distinguish between a fracture and a fault.

B Explain how dome mountains are different from folded mountains and describe two kinds of dome mountains.

SCIENCE BACKGROUND

Quarry operations in marble, limestone, and granite often use joint patterns in selecting the boundaries of blocks to be removed.

SCIENCE BACKGROUND

These vein minerals are also called hydrothermal deposits. These deposits are the source of much of the world's gold, silver, and mercury ore.

VIDEODISC SELECTION

Fractures in bedrock
Side 1: 2602, single frame

IV   Other Tectonic Features

Topic 10   Joints

Joints are one of the most common rock structures. Like faults, joints are breaks in the bedrock. Unlike faults, joints do not involve motion. Therefore, a **joint** is a crack or break in the bedrock along which no apparent movement has occurred. Joints can be the result of the same stresses that lift, tilt, and fold rock layers into mountains.

The surface of a joint is usually a plane, although curved surfaces sometimes occur. The joint plane appears on the surface of a rock outcrop as a line. These lines can occur in parallel, evenly-spaced groups called *sets*. Often one joint set is crossed at an angle by another joint set.

In addition to their relationship to mountain building, joints provide channels for fluids to enter and move through bedrock. Hot fluids rising through the crust may fill a joint with quartz, calcite, or some other mineral to form a *vein deposit*. Caverns form when groundwater flows through and dissolves limestone along joint planes. In some areas, the land's surface features are controlled by joint patterns. The spectacular spires at Bryce Canyon in Utah are the result of weathering along joints.

Topic 11   Dome Mountains

A **dome mountain** is a nearly circular folded mountain. However, dome mountains have some fundamental differences from folded mountains like the Andes and the Appalachians. Dome mountains do not form mountain chains. Instead, these mountains are individual, isolated structures. Also, dome mountains are the result of uplifting forces. Folded mountains, on the other hand, are the result of the horizontal forces of plate collisions. The relationship of dome mountains to plate tectonics, if any, is not clear.

16.9   (a) The formation of a plutonic dome, **(b)** the formation of a tectonic dome

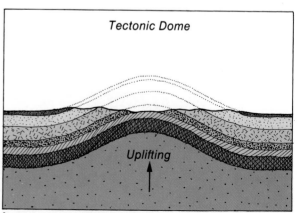

a

b

Dome mountains may occur in areas of essentially flat-lying sedimentary rocks. However, these layers may be bent sharply upward around the dome as a result of the uplifting forces that formed it. If erosion has removed the rocks over the center of the dome, the layers may stand out as sharp ridges around its edge. Dome mountains may be less than 10 kilometers to more than 180 kilometers across.

There are two basic kinds of dome mountains—plutonic and tectonic. *Plutonic* dome mountains are formed when overlying crustal rocks are pushed upward by the intrusion of an igneous mass, such as a laccolith. Because the intrusion occurred after the rocks were formed, the rocks of the exposed core of the mountain are younger than the sedimentary rocks around the core. An example of a plutonic dome mountain can be found in the Henry Mountains of Utah. Many other examples occur on the border of the Colorado Plateau and the Rocky Mountains.

Tectonic dome mountains are the result of uplifting forces that arched the rock layers upward. All of the rocks in the dome were present before the uplift occurred. The rocks at the core extend under the rocks around the dome and, therefore, must be older. Two excellent examples of tectonic domes are the Adirondack Mountains of New York State and the Black Hills of South Dakota. In both cases, the rocks in the core of the dome are older than the rocks around it.

TOPIC QUESTIONS

Each topic question refers to the topic of the same number.

10. **(a)** What is a joint?   **(b)** Describe the pattern or patterns formed by joints in rock outcrops.   **(c)** Identify three features or events that occur along joints.

11. **(a)** What is a dome mountain?   **(b)** Name two ways in which dome mountains differ from folded mountains.   **(c)** What may happen to the rock layers around a dome?   **(d)** How do plutonic domes form?   **(e)** What is the age of the rocks at the center of a plutonic dome compared to the rocks around the dome? **(f)** Give an example of a plutonic dome.   **(g)** How do tectonic domes form?   **(h)** What is the age of the rocks at the center of a tectonic dome compared to the rocks around the dome? **(i)** Give some examples of tectonic domes.

Map Skills

Refer to the map on pages 656–657 to answer these questions.

1. From this map, are the most extensive mountain ranges located on the land or underwater?

2. What type of feature forms the underwater mountain ranges?

SCIENCE BACKGROUND

Dome mountains are not rare. However, they do not form mountain chains.

VIDEODISC SELECTION

Plutonic dome: Half Dome, Yosemite National Park, California
Side 1: 2519, single frame

Eroded tectonic dome near Beaty, Nevada
Side 1: 2436, single frame

ANSWERS
  10. (a) crack without motion (b) parallel, evenly-spaced sets crossed by other sets   (c) mineral veins, caves, weathering of surface features
  11. (a) nearly circular folded mountain   (b) isolated, not chains; result of uplifting forces   (c) bend sharply upward   (d) intrusion of igneous mass   (e) younger (f) Henry Mountains   (g) rock layers arched upward   (h) older   (i) Adirondack Mountains, Black Hills

ANSWERS
  1. underwater
  2. mid-ocean ridges

CHAPTER 16

MAP ACTIVITY

Mountains and Plate Boundaries

For additional activities, see Laboratory Investigations booklet.

Of all the kinds of mountain ranges that occur on continents, the largest and most complex are the folded mountains. Most of these mountains consist of roughly parallel ridges of sedimentary rock. The energy needed to shape, metamorphose, or even melt thousands of meters of sedimentary rock layers into folded mountains comes from the movements of Earth's lithospheric plates. The major mountain chains of today were formed, or are forming, at places where plates meet. The mountains are forming at plate boundaries.

In this activity, you will compare the locations of major mountain ranges with the locations of plate boundaries. You will also make comparisons between mountains that form on land and mountains that form under the ocean.

Map Skills and Objectives

■ To **observe** the locations of the major mountain ranges of the world

■ To **correlate** mountain system locations with types of plate boundaries

■ To **compare** and **contrast** continental and oceanic mountain ranges

Materials

■ Physical World Map, Appendix B, pages 656–657
■ Figure 13.1, page 233

Procedure

1. Use the Physical World Map on pages 656 and 657 to locate the Rocky, Appalachian, Andes, Atlas, Alps, and Himalayan mountains.

2. Turn to Figure 13.1 on page 233. Identify and list the plate (North American, Eurasian, African, etc.) on which each mountain range listed in Question 1 is located.

3. How many of the mountain ranges named in Question 1 are directly on or beside a plate boundary? Name the mountain range and identify the two plates that meet at that plate boundary.

4. Review the definitions of *active continental margin* and *passive continental margin* on page 291. Which of these margin types is associated with each of your answers to Question 3?

5. Use the Physical World Map to locate the mid-Atlantic Ridge, the East Pacific Rise, the Southeast Indian Ocean Ridge, and the Southwest Indian Ocean Ridge. Each of these mid-ocean ridges is an underwater mountain range.

6. Review the definitions of *diverging boundary* and *converging boundary* on pages 240 and 242. Which term applies to the mountains identified in your answer to Question 3? Which term applies to mid-ocean ridge systems? What is the basic difference in plate motions between the formation of mountain chains on continents and the formation of mountain chains on the sea floor?

7. Answer the questions in *Analysis and Conclusions.*

Analysis and Conclusions

1. The Andes Mountains are younger than the Appalachian Mountains. What evidence is there on the physical world map that supports this statement?

2. Would you expect to find extensive mountain building taking place in Australia? Explain your answer.

3. Which mountain range is more likely to have active volcanoes, the Andes or the Rockies? Explain your answer.

4. Active continental margins are also called seismic continental margins while passive continental margins are called aseismic continental margins. To what occurrence does the term seismic usually refer? What must aseismic mean? Explain why these are appropriate terms to apply to their respective plate boundaries.

CHAPTER 16

MAP ACTIVITY

Folded Mountains

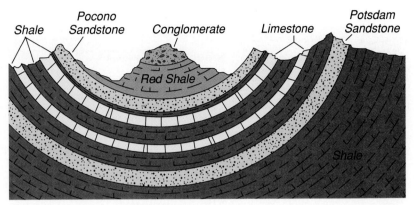

16.10 Cross-section, Harrisburg area

The region around Harrisburg, Pennsylvania displays some of the classic features of folded mountain ranges. Figure 16.10 is a cross-section showing the structure of the rock layers found in the Harrisburg area. In this activity, you will use both this cross-section and a topographic map of the Harrisburg area to study some of the features of folded mountains.

Map Skills and Objectives
■ To **interpret** the structure and geology of an area from map and cross-section data
■ To **infer** the relative resistance to weathering of various rock types

Materials
■ Physical Map of the United States, pages 654–655
■ Topographic Map: Harrisburg, Pennsylvania, page 652
■ tracing paper, 10 cm x 15 cm

Procedure
1. Turn to the Physical Map of the United States on page 654 and 655. Locate Harrisburg on the map. In what mountain range is Harrisburg located?

2. Now turn to the topographic map of the Harrisburg area on page 652. Compare the map with the geologic cross-section shown in Figure 16.10. List the four mountains that occur on both the map and the cross-section. In what general map or compass direction was the cross-section drawn (i.e., N-S, E-W)?

3. Look at the cross-section. Two of the mountains shown on the cross-section are formed from the same rock formation. Identify those two mountains. What is the name of the rock formation?

4. Look at the figures in Chapter 16 between pages 294 and 300. Locate the figure or part of the figure that most resembles the structure shown in the cross-section. What is this structure called?

5. Compare the composition of the ridges in the Harrisburg area with the composition of the valleys. Which rock types form ridges and which rock types form valleys?

6. Lay the tracing paper over the cross-section and trace the

outline of the diagram. Label Third Mountain. Locate Stone Glen on the topographic map. Where would Stone Glen be located on the cross-section? Label the location of Stone Glen on your tracing paper version of the cross-section. Repeat this procedure for the community of Lucknow, the airway beacon, and the WHP TV–tower. Which of these features is either located on or formed by the oldest rocks? Which is located on or formed by the youngest rocks?

7. Answer the questions in *Analysis and Conclusions*.

Analysis and Conclusions
1. Why is it impossible to determine if sedimentary rock layers have been over-turned using only a topographic map?

2. Using the Physical Map of the United States, identify at least three eastern states (not including Pennsylvania) where folded rock layers would be expected to occur at Earth's surface. Why would folded rocks not be expected to occur in the Atlantic Coastal Plain?

Answers to all questions appear in the Teacher's Guide at the back of this book.

■ Summary

I Earthquakes, volcanoes, and mountain building occur at active continental margins. Large quantities of sediments accumulate in the shallow water of passive continental margins.

When an ocean plate collides with a continental plate, the ocean plate usually subducts. Pieces of the oceanic plate may be scraped off and become attached to the continent.

When two continents collide, subduction stops. Mountains form as the collision continues.

II In a normal fault, tension causes rocks on one side to move down relative to the other side. In a reverse fault, compression pushes one side over the other side. In a strike-slip fault, one side moves horizontally past the other side.

Anticlines are upfolds of rock layers; synclines are downfolds. The dip and strike of the fold limbs indicate the shape and orientation of the fold.

III Fossils in mountains, raised beaches, and changes in elevation are evidence of uplifting.

Folded and tilted rocks are evidences of mountain building. Fault-block mountains form where pieces of crust have been faulted and uplifted.

Ripple marks, cross-bedding, mud cracks, and fossil shells can provide evidence of overturning.

IV Joints are breaks in the bedrock along which no movement has occurred. They occur in parallel sets and are often intersected by other sets.

Dome mountains are nearly circular folded mountains that result from uplifting. There are two kinds of dome mountains—plutonic and tectonic.

■ Vocabulary

active continental margin	normal fault
anticline	passive continental margin
dome mountain	reverse fault
fault-block mountain	strike-slip fault
joint	syncline

■ Review

Number your paper from *1* to *13*. Write the letter of your answer on your paper.

1. Which is *least* likely to be a feature of an active continental margin? (a) earthquakes (b) volcanism (c) mountain building (d) sediment buildup

2. In time, passive continental margins may become (a) mid-ocean ridges, (b) mountains, (c) deep-ocean floor, (d) volcanoes.

3. Terranes are thought to form when pieces of (a) continental plate plunge into a subduction zone, (b) continental plate ride over a subduction zone, (c) oceanic plate plunge into a subduction zone, (d) oceanic plate ride over a subduction zone.

4. When two continents collide, subduction (a) does not occur, (b) occurs until the continents are in contact, (c) occurs only when the continents are in contact, (d) occurs throughout the collision.

5. A fault in which one side of the fault plane drops down relative to the other side is a (a) normal fault, (b) strike-slip fault, (c) fault-block mountain, (d) dip-slip fault.

6. Anticlines and synclines are kinds of (a) folds, (b) faults, (c) dome mountains, (d) volcanic cones.

7. The dip of a rock layer indicates the (a) age of the rock layer, (b) source of the particles in the rock, (c) kind of fossils in the rock, (d) steepness of slope of the rock layer.

8. Which mountain range contains active volcanoes? (a) Alps (b) Cascades (c) Himalayas (d) Sierra Nevadas

9. Raised beaches and fossils high in mountains are evidence of (a) volcanism, (b) subduction, (c) uplifting, (d) faulting.

10. Mountains that result from the tilting and uplifting of large pieces of crust are called (a) folded mountains, (b) volcanic mountains, (c) tectonic dome mountains, (d) fault-block mountains.

For further review, see **Study Guide.**
For assessment, see **Chapter Tests**
and **Computer Test Bank.**

11. If a rock layer is right side up, (a) the sharp hills of ripple marks will point down, (b) cross-bedded layers will curve downward, (c) the narrow part of mud cracks will be up, (d) the open side of curved shells will be up.

12. Cracks or breaks in the bedrock that do not involve motion and that always occur in parallel sets are called (a) bench marks, (b) faults, (c) joints, (d) synclines.

13. In what way are dome mountains like folded mountains? (a) Both bend rock layers upward. (b) Both form mountain chains. (c) Both involve uplifting forces. (d) Both involve plate collisions.

■ Interpret and Apply

On your paper, answer each question in complete sentences.

1. Would you expect the west coast of Africa to be an active or a passive continental margin?

2. A geologist standing on a low hill notes that rock layers stand out in sharp ridges all around the edge of the hill and dip gently away in all directions. A study of the rocks shows that the oldest rocks are at the center of the hill, and the rock layers become younger away from the center of the hill. What kind of structure could the geologist be standing on?

3. Both plutonic and tectonic dome mountains can have an igneous rock core. How can thermal, or contact, metamorphism (Chapter 5, Topic 22) be used to distinguish the two kinds of domes?

■ Critical Thinking

The diagram shows a cross section of the sedimentary rock layers in a folded area. The cross section was drawn from west to east along a line about 50 kilometers long. Points A through F are locations along the ground surface. The rock layers have not been overturned.

1. On which side of the anticline do the rock layers have the greater dip? Which side of the syncline?

2. How does the resistance to weathering of the rocks at point B compare to those at point C? Explain.

3. How do the ages of the rocks change from point B to point D? From point E to point D?

4. On the basis of your answer to question 3, how does the age of rocks at the center of an anticline compare with the age of rocks at the center of a syncline?

5. If a normal fault occurs at line XY, what will be the effect on the distance between A and F? What will be the effect on the distance if the fault is a reverse fault?

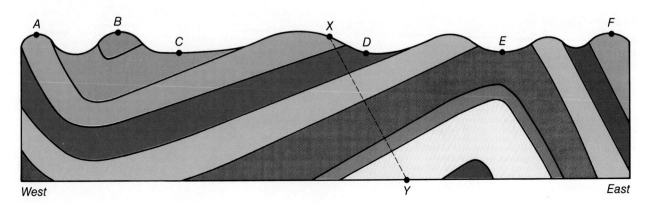

West   East

305

UNIT FOUR
The Ocean

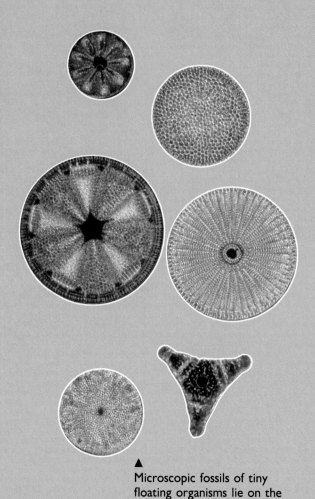

▲ Microscopic fossils of tiny floating organisms lie on the ocean floor worldwide. What do these fossils reveal about the age of the ocean?

◄ People who fish know that parts of the ocean have abundant life, while others have almost none. Why do ocean creatures live where they do?

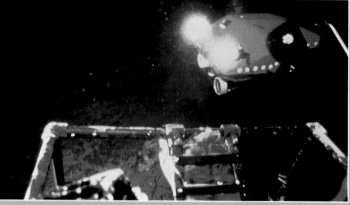

The remote-controlled robot *Jason Jr.* records images in the ocean depths. What features can be observed by using J. J.? ►

What lies in the ocean?

People have sailed the seas for thousands of years, but little was known about the ocean until fairly recently. Since scientists first began to study the ocean, they have solved many of its mysteries, such as the shape of the ocean floor. Yet the ocean still holds some surprises. What does each picture show about the study of the ocean?

This computer-colored satellite image highlights an ocean current. How are satellites helpful in ocean research?
▼

Scientists on research ships can tell when they have entered the Antarctic Ocean, even though it is surrounded by other oceans. How do differences in water properties define ocean areas?
▼

Properties of Ocean Water

▲
A diver explores a coral
reef in the Caribbean Sea.

How Do You Know That . . .

Ocean water is different from fresh water? Swimmers who
accidentally get sea water in their mouths know that it has a
definite salty taste. Fresh water does not taste salty. Ocean water
is also more dense than fresh water. Swimmers can float more
easily in sea water than in fresh water. In addition, the oceans are
home to many animals and plants that do not live in fresh water.
The corals shown with the diver in the photograph are an example.

I Earth—The Water Planet

Topic 1 The World Ocean

When viewed from space, Earth is mostly blue in color because of its oceans. Oceans cover over 70 percent of Earth's surface. For this reason, Earth is sometimes called the water planet. Although all of the oceans are connected, geographers refer to Earth as having four separate oceans. The Pacific Ocean is the largest of the oceans, covering over 30 percent of Earth's surface. The Atlantic Ocean is the second largest and extends the longest distance from north to south. The Indian Ocean is the third largest and is found mostly in the Southern Hemisphere south of Asia. The Arctic Ocean, the smallest ocean, is found in the northern polar region.

How does the depth of the ocean compare with the elevation of the continents? The average depth of the ocean is more than four times greater than the average elevation of the continents. Mount Everest, the highest peak on land, would completely disappear in the Marianas Trench, the deepest place in the ocean.

OBJECTIVES

A Explain why Earth is called the water planet and name and locate the major oceans.

B Discuss the development of the science of oceanography.

C Name some modern research vessels and describe how each is used to explore the oceans.

17.1 The top of Mount Everest is the highest point on Earth's surface. Marianas Trench is the lowest point.

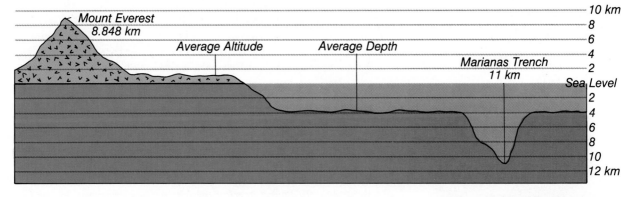

Topic 2 Beginnings of Oceanography

Oceanography is the scientific study of oceans. One of the first modern studies about ocean features was by Matthew Fontaine Maury, a U.S. Navy officer. Because of an injury, Maury was forced to spend most of his career on land. As director of the Navy Department's Depot of Charts and Instruments, he was able to study the logbooks written by the captains of naval vessels. From these records, he compiled worldwide charts of ocean winds and currents.

SCIENCE BACKGROUND

The elevation of Mount Everest is 8848 meters; the depth of the Marianas Trench is 11 040 meters.

VIDEODISC SELECTION

Projections of ocean floor topography Side 2: 751 to 755, 5-frame sequence

17.2 H.M.S. *Challenger* was the first ship designed especially for oceanographic research. It sailed the world's ocean from polar waters to the equator.

OF INTEREST
Challenger had both sails and auxiliary steam power. Steam was used mostly to hold the ship on station and to run the winches that hauled in various lines.

VIDEODISC SELECTION

Alvin research submersible
Side 2: 3039 to 3040, 2-frame sequence

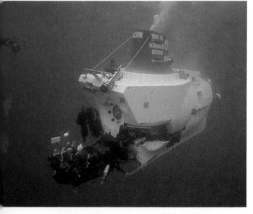

17.3 The minisubmarine *Alvin*

These charts were published in 1855 in his book *The Physical Geography of the Sea.* This was the first scientific book written in English about the physical features of the ocean.

Seventeen years later, in 1872, the British government sponsored the first great study of the oceans. H.M.S. *Challenger* was outfitted as a laboratory and carried a staff of marine scientists. The scientists measured depths, took water and sediment samples, recorded temperatures, collected plant and animal specimens, and studied ocean currents. The expedition lasted nearly four years and resulted in over 50 volumes of reports, some of which are still in use.

The next great advance in oceanographic research occurred during World War II. The military needs of submarines and surface ships led to better ocean charts, sonar, magnetic recorders, and many other new instruments. These instruments became the basic tools of modern oceanographic research.

Topic 3 **Seagoing Ocean Research**

Many countries, including the United States, are involved in oceanographic research. Although there are many oceanographic ships and submarines studying the sea, three vessels have become particularly well known. They are the drillship JOIDES *Resolution*, the minisubmarine *Alvin*, and the deep-towed vehicle *Argo*.

The JOIDES *Resolution* is a seagoing drilling platform and scientific laboratory. The ship is designed to sample the rocks and sediments of the seafloor, a particularly difficult task where the ocean is several kilometers deep. With the help of computers, the JOIDES *Resolution* can remain on an exact spot while drilling into the ocean floor. An on-board six-story laboratory, which includes a scanning electron microscope and other instruments, is used to analyze the cores of sediment and rock samples obtained.

Alvin is a tiny, battery-powered submarine. *Alvin* is designed to descend to depths of more than 4000 meters with a pilot and two passengers and to return safely to the surface. The small submarine can also collect samples and take photographs and television pictures. Its instruments record such factors as the temperature, electric conductivity, and concentration of dissolved oxygen in the water. *Alvin* has been used to explore such deep-sea areas as the mid-Atlantic Ridge and the East Pacific Rise. Recently, *Alvin* was used to explore the wreck of the *Titanic,* the "unsinkable" ocean liner that rammed an iceberg and sank on its first voyage in 1912. A small robot submarine carried by *Alvin,* named *Jason, Jr.,* or *J.J.,* was able to go inside the *Titanic* and photograph decks and rooms inside the wreck. The vehicle *Argo* was also used to explore the *Titanic* wreck. *Argo* is an undersea sled that carries powerful lights, undersea radar, and many cameras. The sled is towed through the water behind a surface vessel.

While the data gathered on seagoing research cruises is important, it does not represent everything that is happening in modern oceanography. Current oceanographic research also uses satellites, supercomputers, and acoustic, electronic, and optical measuring instruments as exploration tools. Research conducted on land can be just as important as a research cruise or piloting *Alvin.*

TOPIC QUESTIONS

Each topic question refers to the topic of the same number.

1. **(a)** What percentage of Earth's surface is covered by oceans? **(b)** Name and describe the four oceans.   **(c)** Compare the average depth of the oceans with the average elevation of the continents.

2. **(a)** What was Maury's contribution to the study of oceanography?   **(b)** Name some kinds of information collected by scientists on the *Challenger* expedition.   **(c)** How did World War II affect oceanographic research?

3. **(a)** What kinds of samples does the JOIDES *Resolution* obtain? **(b)** Describe *Alvin.*   **(c)** What is *Argo?*

OF INTEREST

The *Titanic* was the largest ship of her day and also the most expensive to sail on. A stateroom cost the equivalent of $50 000 in today's money.

ANSWERS

1. (a) 70%   (b) Pacific—largest and deepest, covers over 30% of surface; Atlantic—2nd largest, longest north-south distance; Indian—mostly in Southern Hemisphere; Arctic—smallest, northern polar region (c) average ocean depth more than 4 times land elevation

2. (a) book on ocean winds and currents   (b) water depth, temperature, ocean current, collected water and sediment samples, specimens of plants and animals   (c) spurred ocean research and technology

3. (a) seafloor rocks, sediment cores   (b) tiny, battery-powered submarine   (c) deep-towed sled that carries equipment

CAREERS

Dr. Taro Takahashi
Chemical Oceanographer

For many years, the amount of carbon dioxide in Earth's atmosphere has been steadily increasing. However, the rate of increase is not as great as would be expected. Where is the excess carbon dioxide going?

One aspect of oceanography that makes its study important is the exchange of gases between the ocean and atmosphere. One of these gases is carbon dioxide. Dr. Taro Takahashi studied the exchange of carbon dioxide between ocean and atmosphere during a research cruise that covered the Atlantic Ocean between Greenland and Antarctica.

For much of the late 1980s, scientists thought that the oceans were absorbing most of the excess carbon dioxide. In fact, Dr. Takahashi thought this as well until he and fellow researchers analyzed published data and ran computer simulations. What the researchers found was that the oceans could

only be absorbing less than half of the excess carbon dioxide. That meant the rest is being absorbed by something on land, such as plants.

Many scientists think that the carbon dioxide concentration of the atmosphere is a major control of Earth's climate. Determining both sources and "sinks" of carbon dioxide is a major area of research today as scientists grapple with the possibility of global warming.

Dr. Takahashi has degrees from the University of Tokyo and Columbia University. He is presently associated with the Lamont-Doherty Geological Observatory.

OBJECTIVES

A Define *salinity*, explain how it is determined, and describe some conditions that cause it to vary.

B Explain how electrical conductivity is used to find salinity.

C Name the major ions found in sea water and discuss the relationship between salinity and the relative amounts of these ions.

D Identify some substances that can be removed economically from sea water.

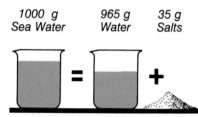

| 1000 g | 965 g | 35 g |
| Sea Water | Water | Salts |

17.4 If you evaporate 1000 grams of sea water, 35 grams of solid minerals (salts) will be left behind.

TEACHING TIP
Note that 35‰ is also 3.5%.

SCIENCE BACKGROUND
On land, 20° to 30° N and S are the latitudes of the greatest desert regions.

SCIENCE BACKGROUND
A water mass is similar in concept to an air mass—both are regions of like properties.

II The Salinity of Sea Water

Topic 4 Salinity

Salinity is a measure of the dissolved solids in sea water. The main solid is common salt, or sodium chloride. Other salts, such as magnesium chloride and calcium sulfate, also occur in sea water. All of these materials contribute to the solids dissolved in sea water.

Salinity can be determined by evaporating a measured quantity of filtered sea water. The white crust that remains in the evaporating dish is made of the salts that were dissolved in the water. The ratio of the mass of this salt crust to the original mass of the water is the salinity. On the average, 1000 grams of sea water contain 35 grams of salts. The salinity of sea water is 35 parts of dissolved salts per 1000 parts of sea water. This is written as 35‰.

Ocean water salinity varies. The figure 35‰ is an average. In deeper ocean waters, the salinity is close to the average figure. Near the surface the salinity can vary between 33‰ and 37‰.

Salinity is below average where large amounts of fresh water enter the oceans. Reduced salinity occurs in areas of heavy rainfall, such as at the equator. It also occurs where glaciers enter the oceans and at the mouths of rivers. The Baltic Sea, for example, has a salinity of only 30‰ because many rivers and glaciers drain into it.

Salinity is above average in areas of hot, dry climates. Here the oceans lose water rapidly by evaporation, leaving the salts behind. These areas lie roughly in latitudes 20° to 30° north and south of the equator. The Mediterranean Sea and the Red Sea are in this dry belt. Their salinity can be as high as 40‰ in some areas.

Salinity may also be above average in polar waters near sea ice. When sea water freezes, only freshwater ice forms at first. This leaves the remaining water saltier than before.

Topic 5 Measuring Salinity

Finding salinity by evaporation is a slow, inaccurate process. Oceanographers have a much quicker method. They measure the *electrical conductivity* of the water. The salt dissolved in sea water makes it possible for an electric current to pass through the water. The greater the quantity of dissolved salts, the more easily current flows. Thus, the conductivity increases as the salinity of the water increases. This fact provides oceanographers with a quick, easy, and accurate method of determining salinity.

Why do oceanographers measure the salinity of the oceans when they already know the approximate value they will obtain? Salinity is an important factor in identifying *water masses*. A water mass is a body of water that has certain properties due to conditions at its place of origin. When oceanographers know salinity and other properties of different water masses, they can trace a water mass as it moves through an ocean. Also, when both salinity and water temperature are known, the water's density can be determined. Knowing ocean water density is important to understanding how water masses move through the ocean and mix together.

Topic 6 The Composition of Sea Water

Salt is present in sea water in the form of dissolved ions. Common salt, for example, consists of a positive sodium ion and a negative chloride ion. Dissolved sodium ions make up 30.61 percent of the salinity of sea water while dissolved chloride ions make up 55.04 percent. The table shows the percentage of dissolved ions, including sodium and chloride, found in sea water.

One of the most amazing facts about the composition of sea water is that the percentages shown in the table are the same for all sea water. The relative amounts of the different dissolved ions do not change even though the salinity does change. The percentages shown are the same for ocean water from anywhere in the world.

Topic 7 Mining Sea Water

At least 55 elements are found in sea water, including such metals as gold, copper, and uranium. These metals occur only in tiny amounts. The percentage of gold, for example, is 4 parts per trillion parts of sea water. Mining these metals from the sea is not profitable. An exception is magnesium. This metal is present in sea water in fairly large percentages. Furthermore, magnesium can be taken from sea water more easily and cheaply than it can be taken from magnesium ore on land.

Salt can also be mined cheaply from sea water. The only energy needed to evaporate the sea water is sunlight. One cubic kilometer of sea water contains about 27 million metric tons of salt.

TOPIC QUESTIONS

Each topic question refers to the topic of the same number.

4. (a) What is salinity?   (b) What does 35‰ mean when applied to sea water?   (c) Identify some factors that cause ocean salinity to fall below 35‰ and to rise above 35‰.

5. (a) How is the electrical conductivity of ocean water related to its salinity?   (b) Why is it important to know the salinity, temperature, and density of a sea water sample?

6. (a) What are the two most abundant ions in sea water?   (b) How are the percentages of each ion in sea water related to the salinity of sea water?

7. (a) Why aren't gold and silver mined from sea water?   (b) Why is magnesium extracted from sea water?   (c) How is salt extracted from sea water?

TEACHING TIP
Ions were introduced in Chapter 3. Be prepared to redefine *ion* here.

SCIENCE BACKGROUND
Ocean waters mix completely every 1500 years or so. This explains the consistency of ion content.

OF INTEREST
Salt lakes, such as the Great Salt Lake in Utah, are also mined for salt because the concentration is so high.

ANSWERS
  4. (a) measure of dissolved solids in sea water   (b) 35 parts solid per 1000 parts of sea water   (c) heavy rain, rivers, glaciers; evaporation, freezing
  5. (a) increases as salinity increases   (b) to identify and follow moving and mixing of water masses
  6. (a) Na^+, Cl^- (b) constant regardless of salinity
  7. (a) amount too small, not economical   (b) easier and cheaper than from ore on land   (c) evaporation leaves salt behind

Composition of Sea Water

Dissolved Ion	Percentage
Chloride (Cl^-)	55.04
Sulfate (SO_4^{2-})	7.68
Bicarbonate (HCO_3^-)	0.41
Bromide (Br^-)	0.19
Sodium (Na^+)	30.61
Magnesium (Mg^{2+})	3.69
Calcium (Ca^{2+})	1.16
Potassium (K^+)	1.10
All others	0.12
	100.00

OBJECTIVES

A Identify three temperature zones found in the ocean.

B Discuss the formation and movement of polar water.

SCIENCE BACKGROUND

By a depth of 1 meter, half the total energy has been absorbed. At 10 meters, only 10% remains. At 100 meters, only 3% remains.

SCIENCE BACKGROUND

These same zones also occur in lakes, but their properties and behavior in lakes are quite different from those in the ocean.

SCIENCE BACKGROUND

Worldwide, the mixed layer can be considered in 3 zones—equatorial water of the mid-tropics, central water of the middle latitudes, and subpolar water of the high latitudes.

III The Temperature of Ocean Water

Topic 8 Heating the Oceans

The oceans do not heat up readily. Almost all the energy that heats the oceans comes from the sun. Light and heat do not penetrate very deeply into the oceans. In fact, most solar radiation is absorbed in the top few meters of ocean water.

Because ocean water does not heat readily, ocean temperature decreases rapidly with depth. A typical set of readings for latitude 40° N might be 20°C at the surface, 11°C at 500 meters, 5°C at 1000 meters, and 2°C at 4000 meters. These data show two facts. First, the decrease in temperature with depth is not uniform. Second, with the exception of the water near the surface, all the water in the ocean is very cold.

Based upon temperature changes like these, oceanographers divide the oceans into three temperature zones—a surface zone of warm water with sunlight, a deep zone of very cold water without light, and a middle region between the two in which temperatures change rapidly and there is little light.

Topic 9 The Mixed Layer

The surface layer is called the **mixed layer** because wind and waves mix heat evenly throughout the zone. This warm-water layer makes up only about two percent of the ocean's volume, but it is very important to life in the ocean. The mixed layer is the only place where light is present in enough quantity to grow the marine plants upon which most other ocean life depends.

How thick is the mixed layer? The answer depends in part upon the latitude. At high latitudes and near the equator, the mixed layer may extend to a depth of about 100 meters. In middle latitudes, the mixed layer may be as thick as 300 meters.

The temperature of the mixed layer also depends upon latitude, although seasonal changes can also be a factor. Near the equator, where air temperatures are always high, the mixed layer may be as

17.5 Most marine life depends, either directly or indirectly, on the tiny phytoplankton in the mixed layer.

warm as 30°C all year. Near the poles, where air temperatures are always cold, the temperature of the mixed layer may remain at about −2°C all year. The largest temperature changes in the mixed layer occur in the middle latitudes because these are areas where the air temperature changes with the seasons. At latitude 40° N, for example, a change of 10°C between summer and winter is not unusual.

Topic 10   **Temperatures under the Mixed Layer**

A thermometer sinking through the mixed layer reads almost the same temperature throughout the layer. However, temperatures drop rapidly below the mixed layer to a depth of about 1000 meters. This water layer in which rapid temperature change occurs is called the **thermocline**.

The water at the bottom of the thermocline is very cold. Even near the equator the temperature may be only about 5°C. The temperature continues to drop, but more slowly, from the bottom of the thermocline to the ocean floor, where temperatures may be only about 2°C.

In polar areas the oceans are cold from top to bottom. Such cold water is denser than other ocean waters and tends to sink beneath them. This cold water moves away from the polar regions along the ocean floor. As a result, polar water is found beneath other ocean water at almost all latitudes. The exceptions are inland seas with high, narrow openings to the ocean. For example, the Straits of Gibraltar prevent polar water from entering the Mediterranean Sea. The temperature at the bottom of the Mediterranean remains warm all year, in some places as high as 12°C.

Ocean Temperature Zones

17.6   The graph shows how water temperature changes according to the depth of ocean water near the equator.

TOPIC QUESTIONS

Each topic question refers to the topic of the same number.

8. Locate and describe the three temperature zones in the ocean.

9. (a) Where is the mixed layer in the oceans?   (b) Why is the mixed layer important?   (c) Describe the thickness or depth of the mixed layer with latitude.   (d) Identify two factors that determine the temperature of the mixed layer.   (e) Compare the temperature of the mixed layer at the equator, the poles, and the middle latitudes.

10. (a) What is the thermocline and where is it located?   (b) How cold is the bottom of the thermocline near the equator?   (c) How does the water temperature change from the bottom of the thermocline to an ocean's floor?   (d) Where is polar water found?

ANSWERS

8. surface—warm; deep—very cold; middle—rapid temperature change

9. (a) surface   (b) only place with enough light to grow marine plants   (c) 100 m at high latitudes and near equator, 300 m at middle latitudes   (d) latitude, season   (e) hot all year at equator, cold all year at poles, changes with seasons in middle latitudes

10. (a) zone of rapid temperature change below mixed layer   (b) 5°C (c) gradually colder with depth (d) at bottom of oceans at all latitudes, except in inland seas

A Discuss the importance of microscopic plants and animals that live in the mixed layer.

B Describe the distribution of oxygen and carbon dioxide in the ocean.

C Discuss the occurrence of ocean-floor vents and the communities of animals that live around them.

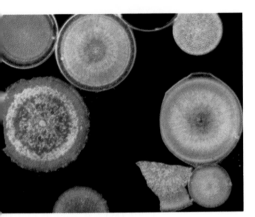

17.7 Diatoms are a common type of phytoplankton. This is a microscopic view.

17.8 Corals can live only in shallow seas where there is sufficient light and oxygen.

IV Life in the Sea

Topic 11 Sunlight and Marine Life

Sunlight is vital in the oceans. Most sea plants, like land plants, need sunlight to grow. However, sunlight penetration decreases rapidly with depth (Topic 8). Only within the mixed layer at the surface is there enough sunlight for plant growth.

The most important group of plants in the mixed layer is the microscopic **phytoplankton.** These tiny plants are floaters and drifters, moving wherever waves and currents carry them.

One of the most abundant kinds of phytoplankton are the **diatoms.** Diatoms are one-celled organisms that build thick shells made of silica. Many diatoms build two shells that fit together like two halves of a tiny pillbox.

The phytoplankton, including the diatoms, are important because they are the basic food source for ocean life. Phytoplankton are able to produce their own food from surrounding materials, using sunlight as their energy source. Nearly all other life in the ocean depends on the making of food by the phytoplankton. Billions and billions of phytoplankton grow in the mixed layer. These tiny organisms are then eaten by microscopic floating animals, called **zooplankton.** The zooplankton, in turn, are eaten by everything from tiny fish to giant whales.

Diatoms are important for another reason. When diatoms die, their shells settle to the bottom and become part of the sediment. Marine geologists use shells preserved in this way to trace changes in diatom populations, to determine the age of the sediment, and even to determine the water temperature at the time the diatoms lived.

Topic 12 Oxygen and Marine Life

All living things need oxygen to convert their food into energy. Oxygen in the ocean comes from two sources. Some of the oxygen mixes into the ocean water from the air above the water. Other oxygen is given off by plants that live in the water. The mixed layer contains plenty of oxygen for the abundant marine life that occurs there. However, the oxygen supply decreases with depth.

Even at the bottom of an ocean's deepest trenches, however, some deep-sea life exists. The oxygen for these depths is provided by the cold, dense water of the polar regions that circulates into all parts of the ocean.

On land, the carbon dioxide produced by animal respiration is consumed by plants in the process of photosynthesis. Although ocean animals also produce carbon dioxide, no plants are found in the deep ocean to consume the carbon dioxide. As a result, deep-ocean waters accumulate carbon dioxide.

17.9 A black smoker at the East Pacific Rise

Topic 13 **Ocean-Floor Vents**

Not all living things in the oceans depend upon sunlight. Researchers aboard *Alvin* discovered some unusual communities of marine animals living two and a half kilometers below the ocean's surface. These animals do not require sunlight for energy or phytoplankton for food. They live near vents, found along mid-ocean ridges, that seep hydrogen sulfide from beneath the ocean floor.

These ocean-floor vents occur in two forms. In one form, hot water gently flows from cracks in the seafloor at temperatures of about 16°C. In other vents, called **black smokers,** water of about 380°C erupts from chimneys (Figure 17.9). In both cases, the hot water begins as cold sea water that seeps into cracks in newly formed basalt at mid-ocean ridges. The water is heated when it comes in contact with hot basalt. The hot water dissolves minerals and gases from the basalt. Then the water moves upward to the seafloor. In the case of the black smokers, the hot water erupts and reacts with surrounding sea water to form clouds of black iron sulfide particles.

The hydrogen sulfide gas is crucial to life near ocean-floor vents. Certain bacteria thrive on the hydrogen sulfide. These bacteria are the food for larvae and other organisms living in the area, which are the food for the barnacles, giant clams, white crabs, giant tube worms, and other unique animals living near the vents.

TOPIC QUESTIONS

Each topic question refers to the topic of the same number.

11. **(a)** What are phytoplankton? **(b)** What are diatoms? **(c)** Why are phytoplankton important to life in the oceans? **(d)** What are zooplankton and how do they relate to phytoplankton? **(e)** Why are diatoms important to marine geologists?

12. **(a)** How do all living things use oxygen? **(b)** What are two sources of oxygen for the upper waters of the ocean? **(c)** How does oxygen reach the deep waters of the ocean? **(d)** Why does carbon dioxide accumulate in the deep ocean?

13. **(a)** How are the animals that live at ocean-floor vents different from other ocean life? **(b)** Describe the two different types of ocean-floor vents. **(c)** What part do bacteria play in life at ocean-floor vents?

SCIENCE BACKGROUND
Diatoms are a kind of protist. Photosynthesis in diatoms is different from the process as it occurs in plants. There are about 10 000 kinds of diatoms. Diatom populations vary with season and nutrient supply.

VIDEODISC SELECTION

Black smokers at rift
Side 2 movie: 23594 & PLAY

Giant tube worms at black smoker
Side 2: 3096, single frame

SCIENCE BACKGROUND
The water emerging from the black smoker is about 380°C. The Plexiglass portholes of *Alvin* soften at 86°C, preventing *Alvin's* occupants from making close observations and measurements of the water.

SCIENCE BACKGROUND
The significance of the hot spring communities is that they do not depend upon photosynthesis. Their energy source is Earth's interior.

ANSWERS
11. (a) microscopic plants (b) most abundant phytoplankton (c) basic food source for ocean life (d) microscopic animals that eat phytoplankton (e) shells in sediments used to trace changes in diatom population, find age of sediment and water temperature at that age
12. (a) to convert food into energy (b) air above water, plants in water (c) water from polar regions (d) no plants there to consume it
13. (a) do not depend upon sunlight for energy or food (b) hot springs flow from cracks at 16°C; water erupts from chimneys of black smokers at 380°C (c) turn hydrogen sulfide into food for other animals

Answers to all questions appear in the Teacher's Guide at the back of this book.

■ Summary

I Seventy percent of Earth's surface is covered by oceans. The average depth of the ocean is more than four times the average elevation of the land.

Oceanography developed through the work of Matthew Fontaine Maury, the voyage of H.M.S. *Challenger*, and the military needs of submarines and surface ships in World War II.

Three vessels now used for oceanography research are the drillship JOIDES *Resolution*, the minisubmarine *Alvin*, and the instrument sled *Argo*.

II Salinity is a measure of the dissolved solids in sea water. The average salinity of sea water is 35‰. Oceanographers measure salinity to locate and trace water masses.

The relative proportions of ions in all sea water is the same. Only a few substances can be mined economically from sea water.

III The surface mixed layer is the only zone with enough light to grow marine plants. The thickness and temperature of the mixed layer depend upon latitude and season.

The thermocline is a zone of rapid temperature change below the mixed layer. The layer below the thermocline is very cold everywhere. Polar water forms in high latitudes and flows along the ocean floor toward the equator.

IV Phytoplankton, such as diatoms, are microscopic organisms that grow in the sea. Zooplankton are microscopic organisms that eat the phytoplankton.

Dissolved oxygen is most abundant near the ocean surface and decreases with depth. Deep water flow from high latitudes supplies the ocean floor with oxygen. The concentration of carbon dioxide is high near the ocean floor.

Unique communities of animals live near hydrogen sulfide vents, such as black smokers, near ocean ridges. Hydrogen sulfide, rather than sunlight, is the energy source for these communities.

■ Vocabulary

black smoker	phytoplankton
diatom	salinity
mixed layer	thermocline
oceanography	zooplankton

■ Review

Match the terms in List *A* with the phrases in List *B*.

List A

1. *Alvin*
2. Atlantic
3. Arctic
4. bacteria
5. black smokers
6. cause of decreased salinity
7. cause of increased salinity
8. chloride
9. electrical conductivity
10. H.M.S. *Challenger*
11. JOIDES *Resolution*
12. magnesium
13. Mediterranean and Red seas
14. mixed layer
15. phytoplankton
16. high latitude oceans
17. salinity
18. thermocline
19. water mass
20. zooplankton

List B

a. hot springs of mid-ocean ridges
b. only region of ocean with enough heat and light to grow marine plants
c. used to measure salinity; increases as water salinity increases
d. tiny, battery-powered, piloted submarine used to explore mid-ocean ridges
e. a region of the ocean with the same temperature and salinity
f. measure of the dissolved solids in sea water; averages 35‰
g. zone of rapid temperature change
h. heavy rainfall, rivers, and melting glaciers
i. ocean that extends longest distance from north to south
j. microscopic organisms, such as diatoms, that are basic food source of ocean life

k. most abundant ion in sea water
l. first seagoing ocean laboratory
m. microscopic organisms that live off food-producing phytoplankton and are eaten by other organisms
n. food source for barnacles, giant clams, white crabs, tube worms, and other unique animals of mid-ocean ridges
o. ocean of the north polar region
p. seagoing drilling platform used to obtain sea-floor sediment and rock samples
q. evaporation and freezing
r. origin of cold, dense water that flows toward equator
s. mineral that can be profitably mined from sea
t. areas of high salinity resulting from high evaporation

■ Interpret and Apply

Answer the following questions on your paper.

1. Why are the bottom waters of the Mediterranean Sea likely to be poor in oxygen?
2. The concentration of silica in rivers flowing into the ocean is more than three times the concentration of silica in the ocean. What could become of the silica that enters the ocean to cause this difference?
3. The percentage of sodium and chloride ions in sea water is much greater than their percentage in Earth's crust. Propose a reason.
4. What relationship would be expected between the amount of dissolved oxygen in a water mass and the "age" of a water mass moving along the bottom of the ocean?

■ Critical Thinking

The graph shows variations in the density of water masses, in g/cm^3, relative to their temperature and salinity. Salinity, in ‰, increases toward the right on the horizontal scale while temperature, in °C, increases upward on the vertical scale.

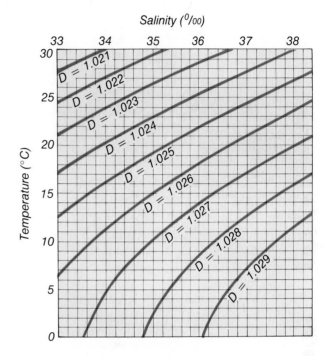

1. The average temperature and salinity of the Atlantic Ocean are 3.7°C and 34.8‰. Water from the Mediterranean Sea that flows into the Atlantic Ocean may have a temperature and salinity of 12°C and 37.2‰. Would this Mediterranean Sea water be expected to rise or to sink when it enters the Atlantic Ocean? Why?
2. The densest water mass in the ocean is the Antarctic Deep Water mass with a temperature of –1.9°C and a salinity of 34.6‰. Extrapolate (extend the information on the graph) to determine the approximate density of this water.
3. When two water masses with the same density but different temperature and salinity mix, the properties of the new water mass are at a point on a straight line joining their original locations on the graph. In general, how does the density of a new water mass compare with the density of the original water masses? (Hint: Lay a straightedge between any two points on the same density line.)

321

The Ocean Floor and Its Sediments

▲
Coral reefs are formations that rise from the ocean floor.

How Do You Know That . . .

Some islands were formed by tiny sea animals? Even though oceans are the most prominent features of Earth's surface, the structures that are beneath the ocean were unknown until this century. Modern technology and equipment have revealed much about these structures and their formation. For example, oceanographers had wondered how corals, which need light to live, built islands that reach to the surface from the floor of the deep sea thousands of meters below. You will learn how the reefs formed as well as about other topographic features found on the ocean floor.

SCIENCE BACKGROUND

Improvements in navigation have also helped in mapping the seafloor. Surface locations can be determined precisely.

I Studying the Ocean Floor

Topic 1 Echo Sounding and Satellites

In the days of the first oceanographic surveys, such as the *Challenger* expedition, the distance to the seafloor was measured with a lead weight on a line. The weight was lowered until it touched bottom, the amount of line let out was determined, and the weight was hauled back to the ship. In deep water a single depth reading might take an entire day. The process was tiresome and produced very limited information.

Today ships use a device called the *precision depth recorder* to find the distance to the ocean floor. The device works by sending a sound signal through the water to the seafloor. The length of time needed for the signal to reach the bottom and echo back to the ship measures the depth of the water. The recorder traces a continuous profile of the area over which the ship is sailing. Such profiles are used to make accurate and detailed maps of the seafloor.

A device similar to the precision depth recorder provides information about the sediment layers on the ocean floor. Lower-pitched sound signals are able to penetrate many layers of seafloor sediment. Scientists produce lower-pitched signals using underwater explosives or compressed air blasts and record the way the signals travel through the sediment layers. Such data reveal the structure of each layer of sediment and of the bedrock beneath. Profiles of all but the thickest sediments have been obtained in this way.

In recent years, satellites have come into use in mapping the ocean floor. Satellites can gather far more data more quickly than a seagoing vessel. Signals sent from satellites cannot reach the ocean floor, but they can bounce off the ocean surface. Using ocean surface data for ocean floor mapping works because the level of the ocean surface varies slightly. Ocean water piles up slightly over undersea mountains and dips slightly over undersea trenches. The ocean surface hills and dips are revealed by precise measurements taken from the satellite. The data are processed by computer to produce an image of the ocean floor.

Topic 2 Sampling the Sediments

Although echo soundings provide data about the ocean floor, actual samples of the seafloor yield far more information. Early methods of obtaining samples involved mechanical devices that either grabbed or scooped up sediment and rock. For example, a large

OBJECTIVES

A Describe past and present methods for determining the depth of the seafloor.

B List direct and indirect methods of studying seafloor sediments and identify some kinds of information obtained from direct samples.

C Name some devices used to make direct observations of the seafloor and discuss their advantages and disadvantages.

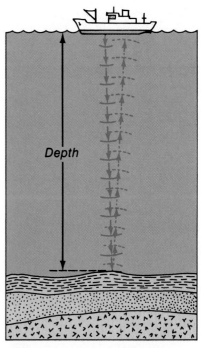

18.1 The sound wave from the ship bounces off the ocean floor and back to the ship. The time it takes to return to the ship indicates the depth of the ocean floor.

323

a

b

18.2 (a) A specially designed camera sled sinks to the ocean floor. (b) Sedimentologists examine a core of sediment split lengthwise.

VIDEODISC SELECTION

Seasat satellite radar images of the ocean
Side 1: 3180 to 3185, 6-frame sequence

Glomar Challenger and coring equipment
Side 1: 3166 to 3170, 5-frame sequence

Coring equipment and cores
Side 1: 3106 to 3110, 5-frame sequence

Alvin research submersible
Side 1: 3039 to 3055, 17-frame sequence

scoop still used today, called a *dredge,* is dragged along the seafloor and is used to sample rocks on seafloor that is bare of sediment.

When a record of the sediment layers on the seafloor is needed, long cylindrical samples called *cores* are taken. Several kinds of coring devices are used. One type is a *gravity corer,* a hollow weighted tube, open at one end and attached to a ship by a cable. The gravity core plummets through the water and pushes into the seafloor under its own weight. In soft sediments, a core of about one meter in length may be obtained. A *piston corer* uses suction to reduce the friction of the tube and draw the mud farther in without disturbing the mud. Cores that result may be 30 meters long. Cores 200 meters or more can be obtained with an *hydraulic piston corer.* All of these coring methods provide relatively undisturbed samples.

The longest cores are obtained by *rotary drilling* techniques in which the corer is a hollow drill. With this method, cores of 1500 meters or more have been obtained. In some cases, these cores have included the total thickness of sediment as well as some underlying bedrock. By examining these cores, we are able to learn about changes in organic productivity, climate, and other ocean phenomena going back more than 150 million years.

Topic 3   Direct Observations

The discoveries made by scientists aboard *Alvin* (Chapter 17, Topic 3) point out the benefit of direct observations of the ocean floor. However, despite its many uses, *Alvin* has one major drawback. While exploring the deep ocean, scientists aboard the minisubmarine must spend half of their research time descending to the ocean bottom and returning to the surface. Only a small part of each dive can be spent actually observing the seafloor.

To overcome this problem, more deep-towed vehicles like *Argo* will be used. These vehicles "fly" above the seafloor as they are towed along by a research ship. Supersensitive television cameras send pictures of the seafloor through a cable to televisions on the surface vessel above. A separate robot vehicle is now being planned. The robot vehicle, using *Argo* or another towed vehicle as a base, will be able to take samples. With these devices, scientists will be able to continuously make direct observations of the seafloor.

Mechanical devices do not need to return to the surface after only a brief time on the seafloor. They can do in a few days the work that might take a submarine carrying scientists, such as *Alvin*, several weeks. *Alvin* is still needed, however, to transport scientists to the ocean depths so they can observe features discovered by the under-sea vehicles.

TOPIC QUESTIONS

Each topic question refers to the topic of the same number.

1. **(a)** How was ocean depth determined in the past?   **(b)** How does a precision depth recorder measure depth?   **(c)** What is constructed from the data obtained by a precision depth recorder? **(d)** Why are ocean surface data collected by satellites helpful in studying the ocean floor?

2. **(a)** Describe how gravity corers work.   **(b)** Compare the core lengths obtained by hydraulic piston corers and rotary drilling. **(c)** What information can you learn from a sediment core?

3. **(a)** What is the major difficulty in the use of research submarines like *Alvin?*   **(b)** How is this problem overcome?

VIDEODISC SELECTION

Argo research sled
Side 1: 3086 to 3087, 2-frame
sequence

ANSWERS
   1. (a) lowering weight to bottom on rope   (b) timing an echo   (c) accurate and detailed maps of the seafloor   (d) ocean surface changes over ocean floor features
   2. (a) hollow weighted tube pushes into the seafloor under its own weight (b) 200 meters or more with hydraulic corer; 1500 meters or more with rotary drilling   (c) changes in organic productivity, climate, and other ocean phenomena over past 150 million years
   3. (a) time needed to get to bottom and return   (b) by the use of deep-towed and robot devices

Current RESEARCH

Alvin in Hot Water

Sometimes you have to be in the right place at the right time. Research carried out by scientists aboard the submersible *Alvin* has taken the vehicle to the rifts of mid-ocean ridges and into the deepest sea trenches. Sometimes, even when they are diving in an area they have studied for years, what the researchers find is far from what they expect.

For instance, three scientists aboard *Alvin* during a 1991 dive southwest of Acapulco, Mexico, never expected to stumble upon the site of a recent lava eruption. While exploring a mid-ocean ridge at a depth of 2.5 kilometers, the crew discovered fresh lava flows covering what was left of a giant tube worm colony. The bodies of the tube worms were scorched but had not yet started to decay. As yet, there were no scavengers feeding on the dead tube worms (although, within four weeks, crabs would move in and start feasting). The water above the lava flow was murky and reached temperatures of 400°C. Even the topography of the seafloor had changed since *Alvin's* last visit to this mid-ocean ridge. *Alvin's* crew had just missed witnessing a rift eruption.

As dangerous as it sounds, scientists hope to get a lot closer next time. By matching the approximate date of the eruption with the dates of earthquakes in the same area, scientists feel they can tell what seismic events accompanied the eruption. With luck, the next time scientists record a similar seismic event, they will be ready to dive again— and this time catch an actual rift eruption as it happens!

OBJECTIVES

A Locate and describe the features of the continental margins.

B Differentiate between passive and active continental margins.

C Discuss the origin and formation of submarine canyons.

SCIENCE BACKGROUND

The widest continental shelves occur in the Arctic Ocean, the deepest off the coast of Antarctica.

TEACHING TIP

Review active and passive continental margins with students.

II The Continental Margins

Topic 4 Continental Shelves

The ocean floor is usually divided into two major regions: the continental margins and the ocean basins (Topics 8–13). The continental margins, in turn, include the continental shelves, the continental slope (Topic 5), and the continental rise (Topic 7).

The **continental shelves** are a part of the continent that is underwater. Continental shelves are extremely flat. They extend from the shoreline of the continent to the *shelf edge,* the boundary between the continental shelf and the continental slope. The shelf edge marks the place where the water depths begin to increase rapidly. Over most of the world, the depth of the shelf edge is about 130 meters.

The characteristics of a continental shelf depend upon the type of continental margin where it occurs. At active continental margins, the continental shelf is very narrow and bordered by an ocean trench. The shoreline is rugged with coastal mountains. The active continental margin on the Pacific coast of South America is an example of this kind of continental shelf.

At passive continental margins, the continental shelf is broad. Some passive continental shelves are more than 300 kilometers wide. On these shelves, no bordering trench or rugged coastal

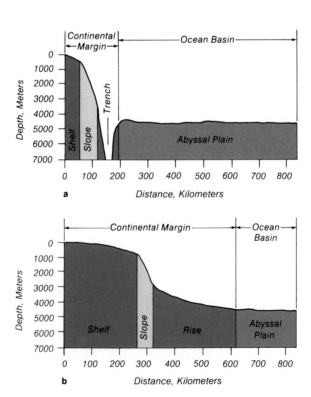

18.3 (a) Ocean floor features at an active continental margin; (b) features at a passive continental margin

mountains are found. Instead, the continental shelf is bordered by a coastal plain. Both the shelf and the coastal plain have generally level surfaces with low hills and shallow depressions. The passive continental margin on the Atlantic coast of North America is a good example of this kind of continental shelf.

Topic 5   Continental Slopes

The **continental slopes** begin at the shelf edge, where water depth starts to increase rapidly. The boundary between the continental shelf and the continental slope is clear and abrupt. Beyond the shelf edge, the seafloor is no longer nearly level but begins to slope toward the deep ocean. The average slope angle is about four degrees, similar to the slope of an aisle in a movie theater. Continental slopes are usually less than 200 kilometers wide and descend to a depth of about 3 kilometers. The change from continental crust to oceanic crust often occurs beneath the continental slope. On an active continental margin, the slope ends in a deep-sea trench. On a passive continental margin, the slope ends in a wide band of sediment, the continental rise.

The continental slopes are cut by many gullies and small valleys. These valleys are probably the results of mudslides. The slopes are also cut in places by gigantic gullies called **submarine canyons.** Some of these canyons rival the Grand Canyon of the Colorado River in size. Submarine canyons often begin on the continental shelf and continue to the end of the slope. Some are extensions of river valleys on the coastal plain.

SCIENCE BACKGROUND

Lagoons, barrier islands, and large deltas are also characteristic of passive continental margins.

SCIENCE BACKGROUND

The base of the continental slope is defined as the point where the gradient drops below 1 in 40.

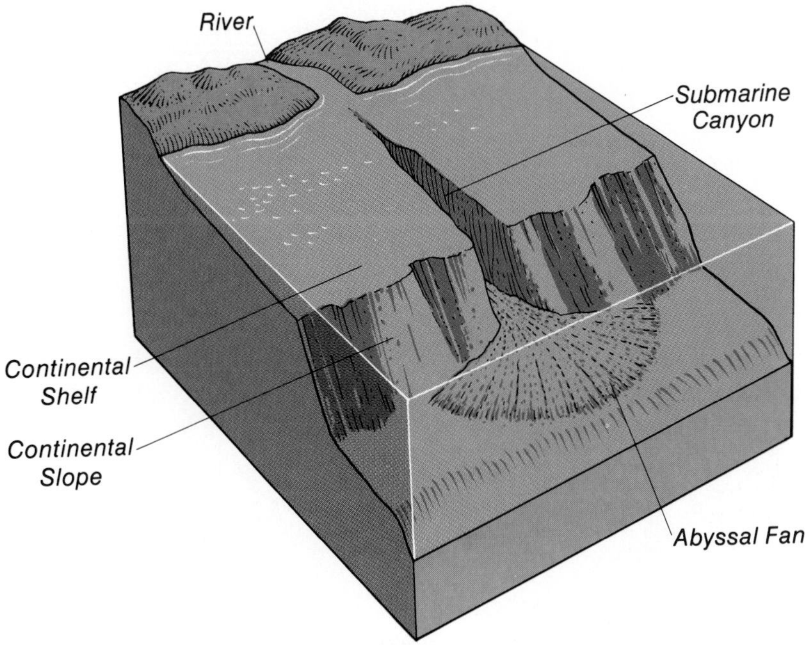

18.4 The upper part of this submarine canyon was formed by a river. The deeper part was formed by undersea currents.

SCIENCE BACKGROUND

There are at least 190 submarine canyons between Labrador and Cape Hatteras.

Many submarine canyons occur off the eastern coast of North America. A well-known example is the Hudson River Canyon. This canyon extends about 300 kilometers out to sea from the mouth of the Hudson River. At the end of the continental slope, the canyon is 3 kilometers deep. Another great submarine canyon is the Monterey Canyon off the California coast.

Topic 6 **The Origin of Submarine Canyons**

SCIENCE BACKGROUND

Submarine canyons that are active today are associated with active continental margins. Canyons on passive continental margins are relatively inactive at this time.

How did submarine canyons form? Some, like the Hudson River Canyon, extend out from coastal plain rivers. The upper part of the canyon is on the continental shelf. The lower part cuts deep into the continental slope. Geologists think the upper parts of submarine canyons were formed during the Ice Age. At that time, sea level was perhaps 100 meters lower than now. Broad areas of the present continental shelves were above sea level. Rivers such as the Hudson River cut valleys to the shelf edge. When the glaciers melted, sea level rose and the valleys were drowned. Many Atlantic coast bays were formed in this way.

What about the lower canyons? These canyons extend thousands of meters into the continental slopes, so they cannot be described as drowned valleys. Furthermore, most canyons show no connection with rivers on the continents.

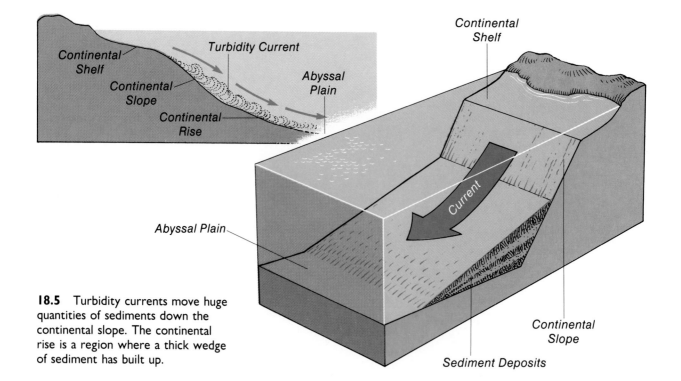

18.5 Turbidity currents move huge quantities of sediments down the continental slope. The continental rise is a region where a thick wedge of sediment has built up.

Geologists think that canyons on the continental slopes have a different origin. They think that these canyons are caused by powerful currents that run like flash floods down the steep continental slopes. Such currents form when great landslides of mud and sand come down the slopes. The landslides may be started by earthquakes or simply by the force of gravity. Such undersea landslides are called **turbidity currents** (*turbid* means "muddy"). The speed of turbidity currents makes these mixtures of water, mud, and sand powerful agents of erosion. Communications cables on the ocean floor are regularly snapped by turbidity currents. The turbidity currents also build great fan-shaped deposits at the mouths of many submarine canyons. These features are called *abyssal fans* shown in Figure 18.4. Some turbidity current deposits can be traced for hundreds of kilometers along the seafloor.

SCIENCE BACKGROUND
A turbidity current is the result of differences in density and is therefore a kind of density current. Dry-snow avalanches and descending clouds of volcanic ash are other examples of density currents.

Topic 7 Continental Rises

The **continental rise** is the gently sloping region between the continental slope and the ocean basin. It was formed by the deposition of masses of sediment several kilometers thick. The sediment originally came from the land and was brought to this region by turbidity currents and gravity flows.

Continental rises are not found at active continental margins because the deep-sea trenches that occur there trap the sediments. They are features of passive continental margins such as the Atlantic coast of North America. Here they may be as much as 1000 kilometers wide with a gentle slope.

TOPIC QUESTIONS

Each topic question refers to the topic of the same number.

4. **(a)** What are the continental shelves?   **(b)** What is the shelf edge? **(c)** List some features of active continental margins and give an example of such a margin.   **(d)** Describe the continental shelf on passive continental margins and give an example.

5. **(a)** Where is the continental slope?   **(b)** How is the slope different from the continental shelf?   **(c)** Where does the slope end on active continental margins?   **(d)** Where does the slope end on passive continental margins?   **(e)** What are submarine canyons? Give an example of a submarine canyon.

6. **(a)** What process may have formed the part of a submarine canyon in a continental shelf?   **(b)** What process may have formed the part of a submarine canyon in a continental slope?

7. **(a)** What is the continental rise?   **(b)** On which type of continental margin are continental rises found? Why are they not found on the other type?

ANSWERS
4. (a) shallow, flat seafloor adjacent to continent   (b) boundary between shelf and slope   (c) narrow shelf, trench, rugged coastal mountains; Pacific coast of South America (d) wide, bordered by coastal plain, level; Atlantic coast of North America
5. (a) beyond shelf edge (b) steeper   (c) in trench   (d) continental rise   (e) gigantic gullies in continental slopes; Hudson River Canyon
6. (a) stream erosion when sea level was lower during last Ice Age (b) erosion by turbidity currents
7. (a) gently sloping region between slope and abyssal plain (b) passive; sediments trapped by trenches at active margins

OBJECTIVES

A Locate and describe the various features of the ocean basins.

B Describe and give examples of deep-sea trenches and mid-ocean ridges.

C Discuss the fracture zones of mid-ocean ridges.

SCIENCE BACKGROUND
Abyssal hills make up 80-85% of the Pacific Ocean floor.

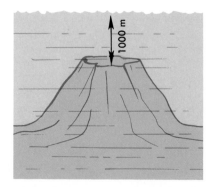

18.6 Seamounts are the peaks of volcanic mountains located on the deep seafloor. Flat-topped peaks are called guyots.

III   The Ocean Basins

Topic 8   Abyssal Plains

The **abyssal plains** are one feature of the floor of the deep sea. These plains range in depth from 3000 to 6000 meters. Their most remarkable feature is their flatness. In fact, abyssal plains are the flattest areas of Earth's surface.

The abyssal plains are composed of sediments. In some areas, these sediments are more than 1 kilometer thick. Most of this material came from the continents. How could material from the continents reach the deep seafloor? The answer is turbidity currents. Continental rivers deposit material on the edges of continental shelves during times of low sea level, such as Ice Ages. Turbidity currents carry sediment down the continental slopes, and spread it evenly over the continental rise and abyssal plain.

Although abyssal plains are found in all oceans, they are particularly well developed and widespread in the Atlantic Ocean. An example there is the Hatteras Abyssal Plain. This plain is 1000 kilometers long and 150 to 300 kilometers wide. The thick sediment layers that cover it are thought to have come from turbidity currents in the Hatteras and Hudson canyons.

Topic 9   Abyssal Hills

The **abyssal hills** are another part of the floor of the ocean basins. They are small, rolling hills that occur, often in groups, next to continental margins and oceanic ridge systems. In the North Atlantic, abyssal hills form two strips parallel to the mid-Atlantic Ridge for almost its entire length.

Individual hills are generally from 1 to 10 kilometers across and usually extend no higher than a few hundred meters above the abyssal plain. Interestingly, the thick sediments of the abyssal plains have been found to hide a surface of abyssal hills that cover much of the deep ocean floor. For this reason, the abyssal hills are thought to represent the original seafloor surface that forms at the mid-ocean ridges. Sediments from turbidity currents bury this surface as it is carried away from the ridges on the lithospheric plate. Thus, abyssal plain sediments merely cover abyssal hills beneath them.

Topic 10   Seamounts, Guyots, and Coral Atolls

Seamounts are cone-shaped mountain peaks that rise high above the deep ocean floor. These peaks may occur alone but more typically are found in clusters or rows, often near plate boundaries. Although they are found on seafloors in all oceans, seamounts are most abundant in the Pacific.

Seamounts are volcanic in origin, and seem to be related to plate boundary activity. However, some seamounts are located away from the edges of lithospheric plates. There is speculation that these isolated groups of seamounts originated over hot spots. In fact, the Hawaiian Islands, a famous chain of hot-spot volcanoes (Chapter 14, Topic 7), are actually a chain of seamounts tall enough to rise above the ocean surface.

Some seamounts look as though they have had their tops sliced off. These flat-topped seamounts are called **guyots** (GHEE ohs). Their tops, thought to have originally been above sea level, were removed by wave action. Later sinking of the oceanic crust lowered the tops of the guyots below the surface. The tops of some guyots are as deep as two kilometers below sea level.

Another result of crustal sinking is the formation of **atolls**, ring-shaped coral islands. An atoll begins to form when a fringing coral reef forms around a volcanic island. Corals are tiny sea animals that live in water less than 80 meters deep (Chapter 12, Topic 15). As the seafloor around the island sinks, the corals sink with it. New corals grow on top of the old, dead corals beneath. As the reef sinks, it "grows" at the top, keeping pace with the lowering of the seafloor. Eventually the mountain is completely below sea level, leaving behind an atoll (circular reef) with a central lagoon.

VIDEODISC SELECTION

Diagrams of coral atoll development
Side 1: 2191 to 2193, 3-frame
sequence

18.7   The three stages in the formation of an atoll

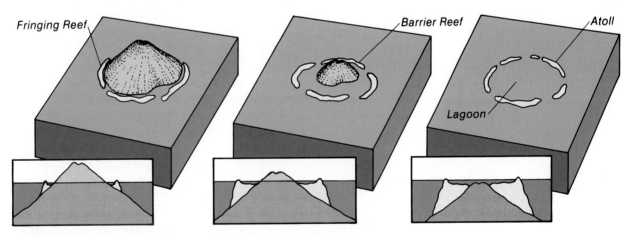

Fringing Reef · Barrier Reef · Atoll · Lagoon

18.8   Kayengel Atoll is located in the South Pacific.

Topic 11 **Trenches**

Deep-sea *trenches* are long, narrow, steep-sided troughs that parallel either continental margins or chains of volcanic islands. Nearly all trenches occur around the margin of the Pacific Ocean. These trenches mark the places where the crust goes beneath the surface as one lithospheric plate subducts beneath another (Chapter 13, Topic 11). On average, deep-sea trenches are 1500 kilometers long but less than 100 kilometers wide. Their depth may be 2 to 4 kilometers below the neighboring ocean floor. The bottoms of the deep-sea trenches are narrow, flat, and filled with sediment.

The longest trench is the Peru-Chile Trench. This trench parallels the coast of South America for 5900 kilometers. The Peru-Chile Trench is the result of the subduction of the oceanic Nazca Plate eastward beneath the continental South American Plate.

The deepest trench is the Marianas Trench on the west side of the Pacific Ocean. Here the Pacific Plate is subducting westward beneath the Indian Plate (Chapter 13). The deepest place in this trench—the deepest place in any ocean—is 11 kilometers below sea level. Four other Pacific trenches are deeper than 10 kilometers. They are the Kurile-Kamchatka Trench, the Philippine Trench, the Tonga Trench, and the Kermadec Trench. Each marks the subduction of the Pacific Plate beneath another plate.

Topic 12 **Mid-Ocean Ridges**

The most obvious feature of the ocean basins is the mid-ocean ridges. These are the diverging boundaries introduced in Chapter 13. They are the locations where new oceanic crust forms as two lithospheric plates move apart.

SCIENCE BACKGROUND

The deepest part of the Marianas Trench is called the Challenger Deep.

SCIENCE BACKGROUND

The convergence of the Indian-Australian Plate with the Pacific Plate produces an ocean trench called the Tonga-Kermadec Trench System. The Tonga Trench is the northern part of the trench. The Kermadec Trench is the southern part of the trench.

1. *Kurile-Kamchatka Trench*
2. *Aleutian Trench*
3. *Philippine Trench*
4. *Marianas Trench*
5. *Tonga-Kermadec Trench System*
6. *Peru-Chile Trench*

18.9 This portion of a computer-generated satellite image shows some of the major trenches in the Pacific Ocean.

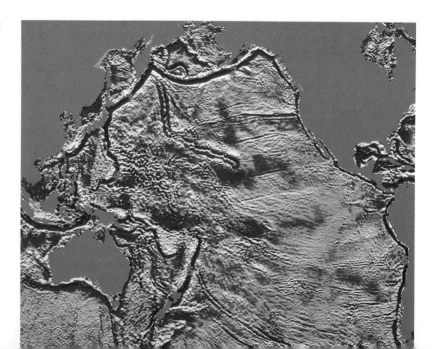

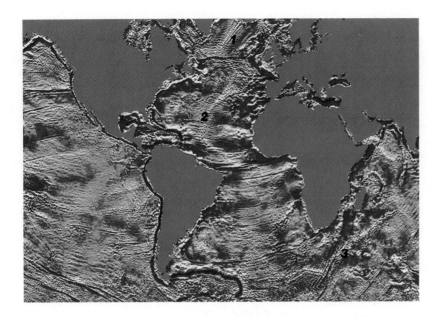

18.10   Another portion of the same satellite image shows the ridge system of the Atlantic Ocean.

1. *Reykjanes Ridge*
2. *Mid–Atlantic Ridge*
3. *Indian Ocean Ridge*

VIDEODISC SELECTION

Satellite images of ocean floor topography
Side 1: 783 to 785, 3-frame sequence

Mid-ocean ridges are great undersea mountain ranges. They form a nearly continuous chain 80 000 kilometers long that crosses every ocean. With the exception of the Pacific, mid-ocean ridges occur in the middle part of each ocean. Their average depth is 2500 meters. In places, however, the highest peaks of mid-ocean ridges reach above sea level as islands. The ridge crest is 1000 to 3000 meters above the neighboring seafloor. Mid-ocean ridges are usually greater than 1000 kilometers wide.

The mid-Atlantic Ridge is the portion of the ridge system in the Atlantic Ocean. This ridge runs roughly parallel to the shoreline of the continents that border the Atlantic. Seamounts rising from the ridge to above sea level include the Azores Islands in the North Atlantic Ocean and Ascension Island in the South Atlantic.

Like some other parts of the ridge system, the mid-Atlantic Ridge has a central rift valley at its crest. This valley is 1 to 2 kilometers deep and tens of kilometers wide. Interestingly, the East Pacific Rise has no rift valley at its crest. The East Pacific Rise is also broader and less rugged than the mid-Atlantic Ridge. The cause of the difference between the two ridge systems is suspected to be their different spreading rates. The mid-Atlantic Ridge is spreading at a rate of about 1 centimeter each year. The rate for the East Pacific Rise is about 6 centimeters each year. In general, ridges with spreading rates of less than 2.5 centimeters per year have rift valleys and rugged profiles. In contrast, ridges with more rapid spreading rates typically lack rift valleys and are less rugged.

Although pieces of ridges may form islands, such as Ascension Island or the Azores, rift valleys rarely appear above sea level. An exception is Iceland. The center of the mid-Atlantic Ridge goes completely across the island of Iceland and is directly responsible for the volcanic activity that occurs there.

18.11 Fracture zones consist of a series of transform faults. Earthquakes occur where the pieces of lithospheric plate are moving in opposite directions.

VIDEODISC SELECTION

Seasat images of ocean floor fracture zones
Side 1: 775 to 782, 8-frame sequence

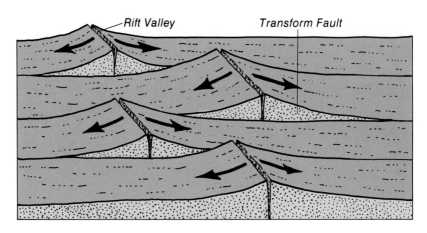

Topic 13 **Fracture Zones**

One more important seafloor feature remains—the hundreds of faults that cut across the mid-ocean ridges. They are a kind of strike-slip fault (Chapter 16, Topic 4) called *transform faults.* The transform faults and the rugged seafloor that occur with them make up oceanic *fracture zones.* Although the mid-ocean ridges together make up the longest mountain range on Earth, the ridge is broken by the fracture zones into separate pieces. These pieces, which are 50 to 100 kilometers long, are offset relative to each other. Some of the offset pieces are only a few kilometers apart, but others have moved several hundred kilometers.

Between the pieces of offset ridge, the crustal plates are moving in opposite directions. The grinding and straining that result from these opposing motions cause earthquakes to occur along these sections of the faults. Beyond the offset ridge, the pieces of plate are moving in the same direction. Earthquakes do not occur in those areas.

18.12 The mid-Atlantic Ridge is broken by a series of fracture zones.

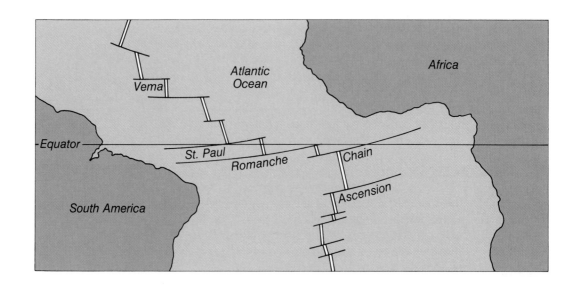

Fracture zones may be as deep as 1500 meters. Some of the fracture zones form high submarine cliffs, and some extend across an ocean basin. An example is the Romanche Fracture Zone, which crosses the mid-Atlantic Ridge near the equator. Here the ridge is offset by almost 1000 kilometers. The fracture zone forms a rift that, in some areas, is more than 7 kilometers below sea level.

TOPIC QUESTIONS

Each topic question refers to the topic of the same number.

8. **(a)** What are abyssal plains? **(b)** Where does the sediment on the abyssal plains come from? How? **(c)** Name one example of an abyssal plain.

9. **(a)** Where are abyssal hills? **(b)** How are they related to abyssal plains?

10. **(a)** What is a seamount? **(b)** Where are most seamounts located? **(c)** How are seamounts in the middle of plates thought to originate? **(d)** What is a guyot? **(e)** How do atolls form?

11. **(a)** Describe the shape of a deep-sea trench. **(b)** What happens to the lithospheric plates at deep-sea trenches? **(c)** Where are most of the world's deep-sea trenches located? **(d)** Identify the longest trench and the deepest trench.

12. **(a)** What happens to the lithospheric plates at mid-ocean ridges? **(b)** Describe the mid-ocean ridges. **(c)** List some ways in which the structure of the East Pacific Rise is different from that of the mid-Atlantic Ridge. **(d)** What is thought to be the cause of these differences?

13. **(a)** What is a fracture zone? **(b)** What effect do fracture zones have on the mid-ocean ridges? **(c)** Where do earthquakes occur at the transform faults? **(d)** Identify a fracture zone on the mid-Atlantic Ridge.

Map Skills

Questions 1 and 2 refer to the physical world map on pages 656–657.

1. Locate the North Atlantic Ocean. Are the deepest places in the North Atlantic Ocean in the middle of the ocean? Explain.

2. **(a)** What color is used to identify areas of the continental shelf? **(b)** Compare the width of the continental shelf off the coasts of California and Florida. **(c)** Based on the width of the continental shelf, does California lie on an active or passive continental margin? Which kind of margin is Florida on?

ANSWERS
8. (a) flat floor of deep sea (b) continents; turbidity currents (c) Hatteras
9. (a) between abyssal plains and mid-ocean ridges (b) many are covered by sediments of abyssal plains
10. (a) cone-shaped peak rising from ocean floor (b) near plate boundaries (c) as volcanoes (d) flat-topped seamount (e) coral reef grows upward as volcanic island sinks
11. (a) long, narrow, steep-sided (b) one plate subducts beneath another (c) around Pacific Ocean (d) Peru-Chile; Marianas
12. (a) move apart as new crust forms between them (b) great undersea mountain ranges, 80 000 km long, 2500 km average depth, 1000–3000 m above seafloor, 1000 km wide (c) no central rift valley, broader, less rugged (d) faster spreading rate
13. (a) transform faults and surrounding seafloor (b) break it into offset pieces (c) between pieces of offset ridges where plates move in opposite direction (d) Romanche

ANSWERS
1. No; the deepest place is the Puerto Rico trench.
2. (a) light blue (b) California—narrow shelf; Florida—wide shelf (c) California—active; Florida—passive

SCIENCE BACKGROUND
A sediment must be 30% organic to be an ooze.

SCIENCE BACKGROUND
Dissolution of $CaCO_3$ at certain depths is the result of low temperature and high pressure.

SCIENCE BACKGROUND
Icebergs also raft large boulders and drop them to the seafloor.

18.13 Icebergs contain rock material that was scoured from the land by the movement of a glacier. When the iceberg melts, this rock material will settle to the ocean floor.

IV Ocean Floor Sediments

Topic 14 Oozes

Oozes are one of four main classes of ocean floor sediments. The other classes are muds and clays, turbidites, and authigenic materials. **Oozes** are sediments made from microscopic shells. These shells are the remains of the tiny floating plants and animals that live in the mixed layer at the ocean surface. When the plants and animals die, their shells settle to the bottom.

There are two kinds of oozes—calcareous ooze and siliceous ooze. *Calcareous* oozes contain calcium carbonate. These oozes cover about half of the entire seafloor. The most common ooze comes from the shells of *Globigerina,* a one-celled animal the size of a pinhead. Calcium carbonate dissolves in sea water at certain depths. In the Atlantic, this depth is about 4500 meters. For this reason, calcareous oozes do not occur below those depths.

Siliceous oozes contain silicon dioxide. The two most common siliceous oozes come from the remains of diatoms and radiolaria, microscopic organisms that build elaborate shells. The major area of siliceous ooze deposition is around Antarctica and near the equator. Diatoms are especially abundant in the ocean water in these places and make up most of the ooze that forms.

Topic 15 Muds and Clays

Muds are mixtures of fine particles of various sizes that have settled to the bottom from the ocean surface. They are soft, plastic materials with a greasy feel. **Clays** also settle to the bottom from the ocean surface. The most important are *red clays.* They are common in deep ocean trenches, where calcium carbonate is dissolved and the supply of diatoms and radiolaria is low. Red clays need not be red in color. Red clays can be brown, yellow, gray, green, or even blue. They are, however, made primarily of flakes of clay-sized (0.004 millimeters) material. As a result of their small size, clay particles may take over 100 years to settle to the bottom. However, some red clay particles are bound together into tiny pellets by zooplankton. These pellets are much larger and denser than individual flakes, and may sink to the seafloor within a week.

Muds and clays of the ocean floor may also come from land. One source is dust blown from deserts. Another source is ash and dust from volcanoes. In both cases, the materials may be carried by the atmosphere many hundreds of kilometers from their source before settling to the ocean surface and then to the seafloor. In some areas, measurable sediment layers may result. Coarser materials may come from icebergs (Chapter 11, Topic 8). Icebergs contain rock material that was ground off the land by a moving glacier. When the iceberg melts, this material settles to the ocean floor to form *glacial-marine* sediments.

Topic 16 Turbidites

Turbidites are deposits made by turbidity currents. These are the currents that sweep material down the submarine canyons and out over the abyssal plains (Topic 6).

The most important feature of turbidites is that they form graded beds. A *graded bed* is a single layer that changes from larger particles at the bottom to smaller particles at the top. For example, a single layer could have pebbles and sand on the bottom and then grade upward into a fine sand at the top. Graded beds form because turbidity currents carry particles of all sizes. Once the current sweeps out over the abyssal plain, the current slows down and these particles settle. The current carries larger particles at a shorter distance above the seafloor. As a result, larger particles reach the bottom first and finer particles are deposited on top of them.

Topic 17 Authigenic Sediments

Authigenic means "formed in place." Authigenic sediments do not settle to the bottom, but form directly on the seafloor.

Probably the best-known example of an authigenic material is **manganese nodules.** These are lumps of material made from minerals rich in manganese and iron oxides, and small amounts of nickel, cobalt, and copper. Originally discovered on the floor of the Pacific Ocean, these nodules have now been found in all of the oceans except the Arctic. Manganese nodules are usually found in areas of red clay deposits where sediments build up slowly. Manganese nodules form, layer by layer, at a rate of 1 millimeter per 1 million years. Most of the material forming the nodule is thought to come from the seafloor sediments around the nodule.

Manganese nodules contain important metals needed in industry. The nodules contain twice the concentration of copper and nickel as do land deposits of these elements. Despite these apparent benefits, manganese nodules are too difficult and expensive to obtain.

TOPIC QUESTIONS

Each topic question refers to the topic of the same number.

14. **(a)** What are oozes? **(b)** Identify the material that makes up most calcareous oozes. **(c)** Why do calcareous oozes not occur below a certain depth? **(d)** Describe siliceous oozes.

15. **(a)** What are muds? **(b)** Describe red clays. **(c)** Name three sources of material for muds.

16. **(a)** What are turbidites? **(b)** What is their most important feature? **(c)** Where and how do these features form?

17. **(a)** Where do authigenic sediments form? **(b)** Why are manganese nodules important?

SCIENCE BACKGROUND

Graded beds can be used to tell if a layer has been overturned (Chapter 16, Topic 9).

OF INTEREST

Each nodule has a nucleus of some other mineral. Shark's teeth are common nuclei.

SCIENCE BACKGROUND

Manganese nodules are 25% manganese, 1.2% copper, 1.5% nickel, and 0.2% cobalt. One of the problems in mining nodules is the question of ownership of the seafloor.

18.14 Manganese nodules

VIDEODISC SELECTION

Manganese nodules
Side 2: 3098 to 3099, 2-frame sequence

ANSWERS

14. (a) sediments made of microscopic shells (b) *Globigerina* (c) CaCO₃ dissolves at depth (d) made of diatoms, radiolaria

15. (a) mixtures of particles that settled from surface (b) most common in deep trenches, can be any color, primarily clay-sized particles (c) floating clays, icebergs, volcanic ash and dust

16. (a) deposits from turbidity currents (b) form graded beds (c) abyssal plain; particles settle out according to size

17. (a) on seafloor (b) materials are used in industry

CHAPTER 18

MAP
ACTIVITY

The Ocean Floor

Until recently no one had any idea of what the ocean floor looked like. That is because no one could see it. There have been significant developments in techniques used to map and study the ocean floor. The result has been a landscape that is hard to imagine! There are massive mountain peaks, ridges, earthquake shattered cliffs, and abyssal plains whose vast sprawling surfaces are flatter than any land on Earth. In this activity you will identify some of the major topographic features found on the ocean floor. You will see how these features may be explained in light of the theory of plate tectonics.

Map Skills and Objectives

- To **identify** and **locate** major topographic features found on the ocean floor
- To **make inferences** about the formation of some of these features

Materials

- Physical World: Continents and Ocean Floor map, Appendix B, pages 656–657

Procedure

1. Deep sea trenches are long linear depressions of the ocean floor. Locate the ocean trenches on the Physical World map, on pages 656–657. Where do most ocean trenches occur in relation to landmasses?

2. Use the map to determine the name of the longest ocean trench. Where is this trench located?

3. Look at the locations of the mid-ocean ridges that appear on the map. Where do most mid-ocean ridges occur in relation to landmasses?

4. On the map, long parallel lines cross the mid-ocean ridges. What do these lines represent?

5. Use your finger to trace the blue line along the mid-ocean ridge. How would you describe the bend of the line? Look at the map. What is causing this shape?

6. Look at Figure 18.15. It is a diagram of a small section of the Pacific Ocean floor. What features appear on the ocean floor in this area? How are these features formed?

7. Answer the questions in *Analysis and Conclusions.*

Analysis and Conclusions

1. How are trenches related to plate boundaries? How are trenches explained by the theory of plate tectonics?

2. Locate the continental shelves on the east and west coasts of South America. Compare the shelves. Use the plate tectonic theory to help explain any differences you see.

3. Compare the shape of ocean trenches to the shape of the mid-ocean ridges. Why are they different?

4. Explain why Japan has numerous severe earthquakes while few occur in Australia.

18.15 Regional features on the ocean floor. There is considerable vertical exaggeration and generalization.

CHAPTER 18

LAB
ACTIVITY

Contour of the Ocean Floor

Some topographic features of the ocean floor are more spectacular than those on land. For example, Mount Everest, at 8840 meters above sea level, is the highest mountain on Earth. However, it is not the tallest. The top of Mauna Kea, a volcano in Hawaii, is only 4205 meters above sea level. If measured from its base on the ocean floor, Mauna Kea is 10 205 meters tall.

By means of echo sounding and sonar, scientists have been able to map the shape and the relief of the ocean floor. Listed in the table are echo soundings giving the Atlantic Ocean's depth along the 39° north parallel. In this activity, you will graph a profile of the ocean floor and identify geologic structures found there.

Lab Skills and Objectives
- To **construct** and **interpret** an ocean floor profile

Materials
- Physical World: Continents and Ocean Floor map, Appendix B, pages 656–657
- ruler
- centimeter graph paper

Procedure
1. Draw a line on the graph paper that is 1 centimeter from the top edge of the paper.
2. On the left side of the paper, draw a vertical line one centimeter from the left edge.
3. Mark the distance every centimeter along the horizontal line.
4. On the line drawn on the left side of the paper, mark the depth every centimeter.
5. Plot the points listed below.
6. There are four points in Data Table A that have superscripts. Mark the corresponding points on your graph with the following labels; 1—Cape May, 2—North Atlantic Ridge, 3—Azores, 4—Cape Roca.

Analysis and Conclusions
1. Approximately how wide is the continental shelf at Cape May, New Jersey, and at Cape Roca, Portugal?
2. Look at the map on pages 656–657. Compare the width of the continental shelf along the east coast of North America with the continental shelf along the west coast of Europe.
3. Continental slope is the steep drop from the edge of the continental shelf. The less-steep portion after the slope is the continental rise. The deepest portions of the ocean are the abyssal plains. Seamounts are peaks rising from the ocean floor that do not rise to the surface. Label all such points on your diagram.
4. Because of the vertical exaggeration of the diagram, the slopes look much greater than they really are. Calculate the actual slope of the continental slope in fathoms per kilometer at Cape May and Cape Roca. (Slope equals change in depth divided by change in distance.)

Data Table A			
Ocean Depths from Cape May, New Jersey, to Cape Roca, Portugal, at 39 ° N			
Distance (km)	Depth (fathom)	Distance (km)	Depth (fathom)
0[1]	0	3560[2]	750
160	100	3720[2]	700
200	1000	3920[2]	550
520	2000	3960[3]	0
760	3000	4040	1000
1440	2900	4320	2000
2080	3125	4480	2800
2280	2900	5040	2700
2360	3000	5280	2300
2560	1600	5440	1000
3040	2500	5480	500
3200	3100	5560	100
3440	1800	5600[4]	0
3520	1150		

Answers to all questions appear in the Teacher's Guide at the back of this book.

■ Summary

I Early methods of measuring ocean depth were slow and difficult. Today, echo devices trace profiles of the seafloor and satellites gather ocean surface data. This information is then used to draw maps.

Seafloor sediments can be studied by echo sounding, coring, and dredging. Core samples can be used to study an ocean's history.

Piloted and robot submarines make direct observations of the seafloor. Each has advantages and disadvantages.

II Continental shelves are the drowned edges of the continents. Continental slopes extend seaward from the shelf edge. Continental rises are found at the base of the slope. Characteristics of each region depend upon the type of continental margin.

Submarine canyons are found on many continental margins. Rivers are thought to have formed the shelf parts of these canyons and turbidity currents the slope parts.

III Abyssal plains are the very level plains of the deep sea, found between continental margins and mid-ocean ridges. The thick sediments found there cover a surface of abyssal hills. The abyssal hills may be the original seafloor that forms at mid-ocean ridges.

Seamounts are volcanic peaks that rise from the seafloor. Guyots are flat-topped seamounts. Atolls form when fringing reefs continue to grow upward as an island sinks.

Deep-sea trenches are the deepest places in the ocean floor. Most are found in the Pacific Ocean.

Mid-ocean ridges form an undersea mountain chain. Ridge features are determined by the rate of formation. The ridges are broken into pieces by fracture zones.

IV The four most important groups of seafloor sediments are oozes, muds and clays, turbidites, and authigenic materials. Each forms in a different way.

■ Vocabulary

abyssal hill	manganese nodules
abyssal plain	muds
atoll	oozes
clays	seamount
continental rise	submarine canyon
continental shelf	turbidites
continental slope	turbidity current
guyot	

■ Review

On your paper, write the word or words that best complete each statement.

1. In the days of the *Challenger* expedition, the depth of the seafloor was found by lowering a lead _____ on a long line.
2. Core samples of ocean sediment contain a record of the _____ of an ocean over the past several million years.
3. While *Alvin* can spend only a limited time underwater, _____ vehicles, like *Argo,* can observe the seafloor continuously.
4. The continental _____ is a part of the continent that is underwater.
5. Narrow continental shelves, deep-sea trenches, and rugged coastal mountains are features of _____ continental margins.
6. On passive continental margins, the continental shelf and continental slope end in a deposit of sediment called the continental _____.
7. Huge gullies, called submarine _____, cut many continental margins.
8. The lower parts of the giant gullies are thought to have been carved by undersea landslides called turbidity _____.
9. The broad, extremely flat areas of the deep seafloor are called abyssal _____.
10. Abyssal hills are thought to form at mid-ocean _____ and to represent the original seafloor.
11. _____ are cone-shaped volcanic mountain peaks that rise above the deep ocean floor.

For further review, see **Study Guide.**
For assessment, see **Chapter Tests**
and **Computer Test Bank.**

12. Guyots are undersea peaks that have had their _____ removed by wave action.
13. Many deep trenches are found on the west side of the _____ Ocean.
14. The mid-ocean ridges are a great undersea _____ range that crosses every ocean.
15. Rapidly forming mid-ocean ridges tend to lack central _____ valleys at their crests.
16. At transform _____, pieces of mid-ocean ridges are offset relative to each other.
17. Oozes are made of microscopic _____ of *Globigerina*, diatoms, and radiolaria.
18. Examples of source material for muds and clays include _____, _____, and _____.
19. Turbidite deposits are called _____ beds because each sediment layer changes from larger particles at the bottom to finer particles at the top.
20. An example of an authigenic sediment is lumps of material called manganese _____.

■ Interpret and Apply

On your paper, answer each question in complete sentences.

1. Why are the mouths of rivers likely sources of turbidity currents?
2. Why is the elevation of an abyssal plain likely to be less than that of abyssal hills, even though the abyssal plains are formed from sediments deposited on top of abyssal hills? (Hint: Review Chapter 13, Topic 7.)
3. Unlike the Atlantic Ocean, the Pacific Ocean has few abyssal plains. Propose a reason for this.
4. The rate of turbidite deposition on the abyssal plains of the North Atlantic Ocean dramatically increased during the Ice Age. Propose at least one reason for this increase.
5. **(a)** Sound travels at 1500 m/s in sea water. Find the depth to the ocean floor at a point where it takes a sound pulse 12 seconds to reach bottom and return.   **(b)** Over what seafloor features can this point be?

■ Critical Thinking

The chart below shows some of the sources of sediment for the abyssal plains. Use the chart to answer the questions that follow.

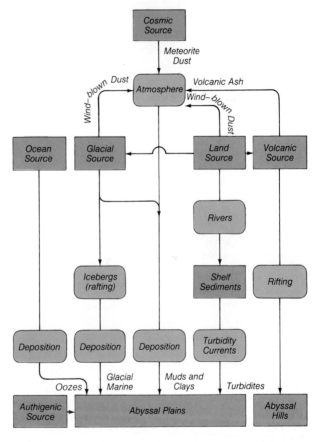

1. What is the process by which oozes, muds, and clays settle from the ocean surface to the seafloor?
2. Which abyssal plain deposit involves ice rafting?
3. List all of the sources shown for the materials that occur in muds and clays.
4. The oozes of the abyssal plain are not likely to be composed of *Globigerina*. Why not?
5. Why are the authigenic sources shown at the bottom of the chart instead of near the top of the chart with the other sources?

341

Ocean Currents

▲
Breaking waves are one
evidence of a moving
ocean.

How Do You Know That . . .

The ocean moves? The waves breaking on this beach are one
evidence of a moving ocean. The rise and fall of the tides is
another. However, there are other ocean movements that are
more difficult to see. These are the great, slow-moving "rivers" of
water that circle each of the ocean basins. These currents carry
enormous amounts of warm water away from the equator and
bring equal amounts of cold water back. Their flow greatly affects
the climates of coastal areas. In this chapter, you will learn about
currents and their effects.

I Surface Currents

Topic 1 Ocean Currents

An **ocean current** can be defined as any continuous flow of water along a broad path in the ocean. The flow may occur at the surface or far below it. The flow may be up, down, or parallel to the surface. Each *water mass* is identifiable because its temperature, salinity, and chemical composition is distinct from water adjacent to it.

The general surface currents of the oceans are shown in the map that appears on page 658 in the Appendix. Several observations can be made from the map. First, both the Atlantic Ocean and the Pacific Ocean have two circles of ocean currents, one in the Northern Hemisphere and another in the Southern Hemisphere. The current circles of the North Atlantic and North Pacific turn clockwise. The current circles of the South Atlantic and South Pacific turn counterclockwise. The directions that the current circles turn are caused by Earth's rotation (Chapter 28).

A second observation that can be made from the map is that the temperature of the water within the circles of current follows a pattern. Currents that flow away from the equator carry warmer water. Currents that flow toward the equator carry colder water. This occurs because areas near the equator have warmer temperatures and areas near the poles have colder temperatures.

The result of these patterns of circulation and temperature is that the western sides of ocean basins have warm ocean currents moving away from the equator, while the eastern sides have cool ocean currents moving toward the equator. The western side of the North Atlantic Ocean has the warm, north-flowing Gulf Stream, while the eastern side has the cool, south-flowing Canary Current. The western side of the North Pacific Ocean has the warm, north-flowing Kuroshio Current, while the eastern side has the cool, south-flowing California Current. Other ocean basins show similar patterns.

Topic 2 Currents and Winds

The driving force of the surface ocean currents is wind. Winds tend to blow in fairly constant directions at different latitudes on Earth's surface. Two sets of constant winds are involved in forming most ocean currents—the trade winds and the westerly winds. Both sets occur in belts around the world.

OBJECTIVES

A Define *ocean currents*, describe the general pattern of surface ocean currents within a basin, and describe the effects of some currents.

B Discuss the relationship between winds and ocean currents.

C Locate and describe the Gulf Stream, its features, and its effects on climate.

D Define and give examples of countercurrents.

SCIENCE BACKGROUND
Current circles are also called gyres.

VIDEODISC SELECTION

Ocean circulation patterns, northern and southern hemispheres
Side 1: 3015 to 3016, 2-frame sequence

TEACHING TIP
Ask students to identify cold and warm currents in Southern Hemisphere ocean basins.

19.1 Winds help drive ocean currents. In the diagram, the black arrows represent winds. The blue arrows represent currents.

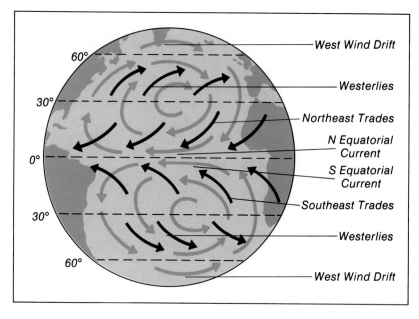

West Wind Drift

Westerlies

Northeast Trades

N Equatorial Current

S Equatorial Current

Southeast Trades

Westerlies

West Wind Drift

SCIENCE BACKGROUND

Winds are named for the direction from which they blow. Ocean currents are named for the direction toward which they flow.

SCIENCE BACKGROUND

These winds are also called prevailing westerlies. They occur between 40° and 65° N and S latitudes. See Chapter 28 for more on Earth's wind systems.

VIDEODISC SELECTION

Earth's wind belts
Side 1: 3014, single frame

SCIENCE BACKGROUND

Warm currents are important to global climates. They transport heat from tropical to polar regions.

SCIENCE BACKGROUND

The Kuroshio is as intense a current as the Gulf Stream. The East Australia and Brazil Currents are less intense.

The *trade winds* affect the part of each current circle that occurs near the equator. The trade winds are very steady winds. They blow from the northeast in the Northern Hemisphere and from the southeast in the Southern Hemisphere. The trade winds push both the North and South Equatorial Current toward the west.

The *westerly* winds, or westerlies, drive the polar portion of the current circles. The westerlies blow from the southwest in the Northern Hemisphere and from the northwest in the Southern Hemisphere. They drive the currents of the polar regions, the West-Wind Drifts, toward the east.

Although seasonal changes in wind direction do not usually change the direction of ocean currents, one ocean area near India is an exception. India is subject to seasonal winds called monsoons. These winds blow from one direction in summer and from the opposite direction in winter. When the winds reverse direction, the surface ocean currents that they cause also reverse direction.

Topic 3 **Warm Currents**

Warm ocean currents flow away from the equatorial region on the west sides of ocean basins. The Gulf Stream in the North Atlantic, the Kuroshio Current in the North Pacific, the Brazil Current in the South Atlantic, and the East Australia Current in the South Pacific are all warm ocean currents on the west sides of ocean basins. Of the four, the Gulf Stream has been studied longest.

The Gulf Stream is a narrow, intense flow of water that begins in the Caribbean Sea. The current follows the east coast of the United States northward to the latitude of Cape Hatteras, North Carolina. Then the Gulf Stream swings northeastward across the Atlantic Ocean. Here it is called the North Atlantic Drift. The current carries warm water to Iceland and the British Isles. Because of the

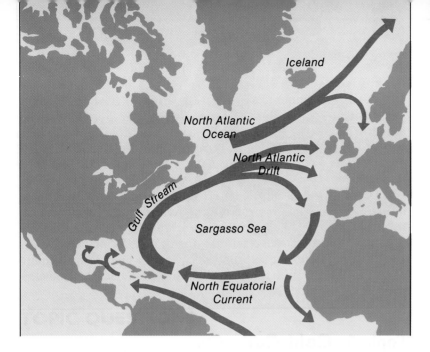

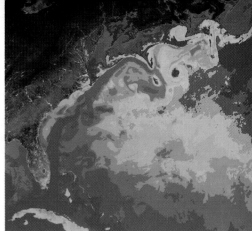

19.2 (left) These currents form a complete circle around the calm waters of the Sargasso Sea. (right) In this infrared satellite image, the warm water of the Gulf Stream appears as red and orange.

Gulf Stream, these places have warmer climates than they would otherwise. On average, the Gulf Stream is 240 kilometers wide and 1.6 kilometers deep and can move 100 000 000 cubic meters of water each second. (As a comparison, the Mississippi River is 0.8 kilometers wide, 0.015 kilometers deep, and discharges 20 000 cubic meters per second.)

The Gulf Stream forms the western and northern boundary of the Sargasso Sea. This is an area of warm water, light winds, and relatively calm seas in the middle of the North Atlantic Ocean. Great amounts of floating brown seaweed called *sargassum* are typical of the surface water there. Similar conditions exist in other oceans, but none is as well developed as in the North Atlantic.

Topic 4 Gulf Stream Rings

Unlike rivers on continents, the Gulf Stream does not flow in the same channel all the time. Instead, the stream wanders, sends out offshoot streams, speeds up in some areas, and slows down in others. Occasionally the Gulf Stream develops eddies or whirlpools that break away from the edge of the current. These eddies become structures called Gulf Stream rings. Figure 19.3 illustrates how Gulf Stream rings form from a bend in the Gulf Stream. As each ring forms, it takes with it a column of water from the opposite side of the Gulf Stream. This column of water becomes the center, or core, of the ring. A ring that forms on the Sargasso Sea side of the Gulf Stream has a core of cold water from the continent side. These rings are called *cold-core rings*. Conversely, a ring that forms on the continent side of the Gulf Stream has a core of warm water from the Sargasso Sea. These are called *warm-core rings*. Cold-core rings may be 300 kilometers in diameter and extend to a depth of 4000–5000 meters. Warm-core rings are smaller and shallower (150 kilometers in diameter, 1500 meters deep). Usually less than 10 rings form each year. Some rings may last as long as two years.

VIDEODISC SELECTION

Nimbus satellite images of Gulf Stream
Side 1: 3193 to 3197, 5-frame sequence

OF INTEREST
   A cold-core ring with a diameter of 300 km has a surface area equal to that of Massachusetts, New Hampshire, Rhode Island, and Vermont combined.

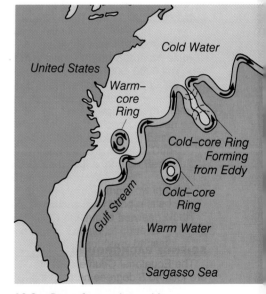

19.3 Rings form when eddies in the Gulf Stream break off. The diagram shows a warm-core ring, a cold-core ring, and an eddy that is becoming a cold-core ring.

CHAPTER 19

MAP ACTIVITY

World Ocean Currents

You probably have heard stories of bottles containing messages being tossed into the ocean only to be found hundreds of kilometers away after drifting for months or even years. Early investigators recognized that a message in a bottle could be the key to understanding the patterns of surface ocean currents. Drift bottles were dropped in ocean water in hopes that their discoverers would follow the instructions on the message and record the date and location of the bottles' recovery. As an incentive, small rewards were offered to those who dutifully returned the information. Today oceanographers rely on instruments and satellites to gather information on the speed, direction, and temperature of ocean currents.

Maps of surface ocean currents are essentially summaries of the vast quantity of data collected from oceans around the world. In this activity, you will use such a map to locate specific ocean currents and identify their properties. You will also use a map of prevailing winds to make connections between wind patterns and ocean circulation patterns.

Map Skills and Objectives
- To **identify** and **describe** the world's major ocean currents
- To **observe** and **interpret** the relationship between winds and ocean currents

Materials
- Surface Ocean Currents map, Appendix B, page 658
- Prevailing World Winds map, Appendix B, page 659
- tracing paper, 12 cm × 12 cm
- sharp pencil
- colored pencils, any two colors

Procedure
Part A—Current Properties
1. Using the Surface Ocean Current map on page 658, locate each of the ocean currents listed in the Data Table. For each current listed, name the ocean basin in which each current occurs, indicate whether the current is located on the east or west side of the ocean basin, identify whether the current is warm or cold, and determine whether the current is flowing toward or away from the equator. The Gulf Stream is completed as an example.

2. Based on your data, what is the relationship between the temperature of the ocean current and the direction of current flow relative to the equator? Explain why this relationship occurs.

3. What is the relationship between current tempera-ture and the side of the ocean on which that current flows?

Part B—Northern Hemisphere
4. Lay a sheet of tracing paper over the Surface Ocean Currents map so that it covers the western half of the map. With a sharp pencil, trace as much of the map border and equator as possible. Using a colored pencil, trace the four arrows showing the flow direction of the North Equatorial current in the Pacific Ocean. In what compass direction do the arrows point?

5. Move the tracing paper to the Prevailing World Winds map on page 659 and align the map border and the equator. With a different colored pencil, trace the three arrows representing the Northeast Trades in the Pacific Ocean. In what compass direction do these arrows point? (Note that winds are named for the direction *from* which they blow not the direction to which they blow.)

6. Turn your tracing paper so that the arrows for the Northeast Trades, in general, point away from you. Do the arrows for the North Equatorial current point to your left or to your right?

7. Based upon your previous answer, what is the general relationship between ocean current direction and the winds that cause them in the Northern Hemisphere?

Data Table				
Name of Current	Ocean Basin	Location in Ocean Basin	General Temperature	Flow Direction Relative to Equator
Gulf Stream	Atlantic	west	warm	away
California	Pacific	east	cold	toward
Canary	Atlantic	east	cold	toward
Peru	Pacific	east	cold	toward
Brazil	Atlantic	west	warm	away
Kuroshio	Pacific	west	warm	away
W. Australia	Indian	east	cold	toward
E. Australia	Pacific	west	warm	away
Benguela	Atlantic	east	cold	toward
Agulhas	Indian	west	warm	away

Part C—Southern Hemisphere

8. Once again, align your tracing paper with the Surface Ocean Currents map and trace the two South Equatorial arrows in the Pacific Ocean. In what compass direction do the arrows point?

9. Move the tracing paper to the Prevailing World Winds map and trace the four Southeast Trades arrows in the Pacific Ocean. In what compass direction do the arrows point?

10. Turn your tracing paper so that the arrows for the Southeast Trades, in general, point away from you. Do the arrows for the South Equatorial current point to your left or to your right?

11. Based upon your previous answer, what is the general relationship between ocean current direction and the winds that cause them in the Southern Hemisphere?

12. Answer the questions in *Analysis and Conclusions.*

Analysis and Conclusions

Refer to the Surface Ocean Currents map on page 658 to answer questions 1–4.

1. Compare the directions (clockwise or counterclockwise) of the major circulation patterns in the oceans of the Northern and Southern Hemispheres.

2. What is the general relationship between current temperature and direction of flow along the east coast of the continents? Along the west coast of the continents?

3. An ocean fog will occur when moist air blowing from a warm ocean current meets cold air over a cold ocean current (Chapter 19, Topic 5). Which Australian coast (N, S, E, or W) is most likely to experience such fogs? Explain your answer.

4. Which ocean current flows around the world without being interrupted by a landmass? Where does it flow?

Answers to all questions appear in the Teacher's Guide at the back of this book.

■ Summary

I An ocean current is any continuous flow of water along a broad path in an ocean.

Ocean currents move clockwise around Northern Hemisphere ocean basins, and counterclockwise around Southern Hemisphere ocean basins.

The western sides of ocean basins have warm currents moving away from the equator. The eastern sides have cool currents moving toward the equator.

Winds are the driving force for surface ocean currents. The trade winds push the equatorial part of each current circle; the westerly winds push the polar part.

The Gulf Stream is a warm, narrow, intense current in the North Atlantic Ocean. It carries a mild climate with it.

Rings form from eddies in the Gulf Stream. Cold-core rings are found on the ocean side of the Gulf Stream, and warm-core rings are found on the continent side.

The Labrador Current carries icebergs to the North Atlantic Ocean.

Countercurrents flow in the opposite direction of wind-related currents. Countercurrents occur both at the surface and beneath the surface of the ocean.

II The density current that flows from the Mediterranean Sea is the result of evaporation.

Density currents that form in polar regions are caused by the cooling and freezing of sea water.

Upwelling occurs where cold currents rise to the surface. Upwelling brings nutrients that support food chains at the surface.

■ Vocabulary

countercurrent
density current
ocean current
upwelling

■ Review

Choose the best answer for each question.

1. In which pair of ocean basins do current circles move clockwise? (a) North Atlantic and North Pacific (b) North Pacific and South Pacific (c) South Pacific and South Atlantic (d) South Atlantic and North Atlantic

2. The western sides of ocean basins have (a) cold currents flowing toward the equator, (b) cold currents flowing away from the equator, (c) warm currents flowing away from the equator, (d) warm currents flowing toward the equator.

3. Which current do the trade winds directly affect? (a) Cromwell (b) West-Wind Drift (c) North Equatorial (d) Labrador

4. An example of a warm ocean current is (a) California, (b) East Greenland, (c) Peru, (d) Gulf Stream.

5. In which ocean is the Sargasso Sea located? (a) North Atlantic (b) South Atlantic (c) North Pacific (d) South Pacific

6. Eddies in the Gulf Stream may break off to form (a) rings, (b) countercurrents, (c) upwelling, (d) deep currents.

7. An example of a countercurrent is the (a) South Equatorial, (b) West-Wind Drift, (c) Canary Current, (d) Cromwell Current.

8. Which would NOT cause a density current? (a) trade winds (b) evaporation (c) freezing (d) cooling

9. The density current flowing from the Mediterranean Sea is the result of (a) rainfall, (b) freezing, (c) cooling, (d) evaporation.

10. The salinity of oceans in polar regions is increased by the (a) melting of ice, (b) freezing of water, (c) arrival of warm currents, (d) heavy yearly snowfall.

11. Deep currents are important to life in the deep sea because they (a) carry carbon dioxide to deep water, (b) carry oxygen to deep water, (c) carry carbon dioxide back to the surface, (d) carry oxygen back to the surface.

For further review, see **Study Guide**.
For assessment, see **Chapter Tests**
and **Computer Test Bank**.

12. Which is true of upwelling? (a) It occurs only near Antarctica. (b) It is caused by evaporation. (c) It brings nutrients to the surface. (d) It forms cold-core rings.

■ Interpret and Apply

On your paper, answer each question in complete sentences.

1. If you were standing on the west coast of a continent in the Southern Hemisphere, what kind of ocean current would you expect offshore? In what direction would the current be flowing?

2. In the Southern Hemisphere, the West-Wind Drift goes completely around the world from west to east. In the Northern Hemisphere it does not. Why is this true?

3. How does the temperature of a south-flowing current in the Northern Hemisphere compare to the temperature of a south-flowing current in the Southern Hemisphere?

4. Laguna Beach, California, and Myrtle Beach, South Carolina, are at nearly the same latitude. How would the water temperature at the two beaches be different? Explain.

5. The Cromwell Current moves 40 million cubic meters of water each second. How does the flow in the Gulf Stream compare to the flow of the Cromwell Current?

6. How are the processes of freezing and evaporation similar in the way they make sea water more dense?

7. Topic 8 states that Mediterranean water entering the Atlantic Ocean sinks to a depth of 1000 meters. At that location, the Atlantic Ocean is 3000 meters deep. Why would Mediterranean water sink only to 1000 meters?

■ Critical Thinking

The graph shows how the average speed of a deep current in the western Atlantic Ocean changes with height above the seafloor. The horizontal axis of the graph shows the average current speed in centimeters per second. The vertical axis shows height above the seafloor in meters. Refer to the graph to answer questions 1–5.

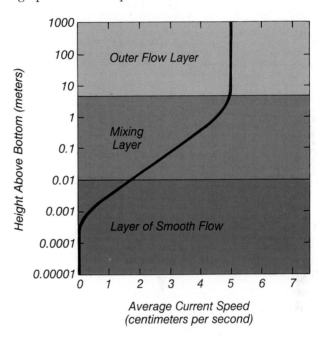

*Average Current Speed
(centimeters per second)*

1. (a) Determine the thickness, in meters, of the mixing layer and the layer of smooth flow. (b) How many times thicker is the mixing layer than the layer of smooth flow?

2. (a) What is the average current speed at 1 m above the seafloor? (b) What is the speed at 0.01 m above the seafloor?

3. In which layer is current speed constant with height above the seafloor?

4. Why is current speed nearly zero at the bottom of the graph?

5. The mixing layer is where seawater properties (salinity, temperature, sediment content, etc.) become thoroughly mixed together. If a deep-sea storm causes the speed of the current to increase, what is likely to happen to the thickness of the mixing layer? (Recall the effect of speed on sediment transport from Chapter 10.)

UNIT FIVE
Earth and the Universe

▲ Every eleven years or so, dark spots speckle the sun's surface. During times in between, such spots are few. Why do the spots appear? What are they?

◄ Effort and determination brought humans into space and to the moon. Will people visit a planet next?

Throughout time, people have sought to explain the moon's relationship to Earth. Where did the moon come from? Does it have any effect on Earth? ▶

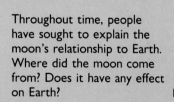

What's out there?

Few people have been outside Earth's atmosphere. Fewer still have left Earth orbit. Yet astronomers know a great deal about the solar system, the galaxy, and the universe beyond. How can we know so much about places that no one has visited? Look at the photographs. What does each show about the search for knowledge about the universe?

For three hundred years, scientists thought Saturn's rings might be solid disks. How were scientists able to prove otherwise?
▼

▲
The Whirlpool galaxy contains millions of stars. What clues about the origin of the universe do galaxies provide?

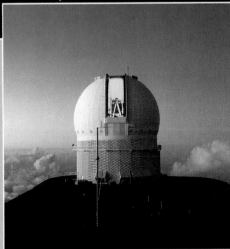

▲
Astronomers look at the sky with telescope eyes and listen to it with radio ears. What have they seen and heard in signals from space?

▲
Before computers, devices such as this were used to find the time of sunrise and sunset. Why does the length of a day change throughout a year?

357

CHAPTER 20

Studying the Universe

▲
This star exploded
thousands of years ago.

How Do You Know That . . .

The stars are really as you see them? When you look at the stars, you are really looking at the past. About 170 000 years ago this star exploded, but no one on Earth knew about it until 1987. It took 170 000 years for the light from the explosion to travel to Earth. Energy from distant objects in space provides astronomers with clues about how the universe changes. Telescopes gather these clues and help astronomers learn about the past, present, and possible future of the ever-changing universe.

I Optical Telescopes

Topic 1 The Functions of a Telescope

Stars are seen best on clear moonless nights at a place well away from the lights of cities. Under these conditions, the sky becomes a breathtaking sight of thousands of stars. What can be seen with the unaided eye, however, is only a small number of the stars in the sky. When powerful telescopes are used, billions of stars are visible.

Telescopes help astronomers in two ways. First, telescopes collect far more light than the unaided eye can gather. Second, telescopes magnify images, enabling astronomers to see detail and to visually separate distant objects from one another. Often, for example, astronomers find that what appears to be a single star is really two or more stars.

The best locations for optical telescopes are on mountain peaks in dry climates. Thinner air at high elevations and dry, clear skies make observing easier. Because city lights overpower starlight, many observations are located in remote areas.

Topic 2 Telescopes and Domes

The earliest telescopes and the ones most used today are optical telescopes. **Optical telescopes** use lenses or mirrors to gather and focus starlight. The light-gathering power of a telescope depends on the area of its lens or mirror. Most lenses or mirrors are circular in shape. The area of a circle varies with the square of its radius. That is, the area of a circle equals πr^2 ($A = \pi r^2$). Doubling the radius of a lens or mirror increases its light-gathering power four times.

Optical telescopes are usually kept in buildings with domed roofs that can be opened for a clear view of the sky. Keeping a telescope in a dome does more than protect it from the weather. Temperature changes, such as those that occur at nightfall, cause the glass of the telescope's lens or mirror to expand or contract. While this is occurring, the image made by the lens or mirror does not focus clearly. Temperature changes around the telescope also lead to air turbulence, another cause of blurred images. Observing time is lost while the telescope adjusts to the new temperature. With a dome the telescope can be kept closer to the nighttime temperature even during the day. It is ready to use as soon as the dome opens.

Telescopes are usually designed such that they can be pointed toward all parts of the sky. This makes it possible to study any

OBJECTIVES

A Describe the functions of an optical telescope.

B Describe the relationship between the diameter of a lens or mirror and its ability to gather starlight.

C Name, describe, and locate an example of each kind of optical telescope.

D Discuss the reasons why refractors are less common than reflectors.

E Identify some devices used to improve the image obtained by optical telescopes.

VIDEODISC SELECTION

Diagrams of lens optics in a basic telescope
Side 3: 538 to 539, 2-frame sequence

20.1 Telescopes are usually kept in buildings with dome-shaped roofs.

TEACHING TIP
Give students more practice with the relationship between light-gathering power and diameter. The chart below could be developed.

Mirror Radius	Light-Gathering Power
1	1 pi
2	4 pi
4	16 pi
8	64 pi

From the chart, emphasize that doubling the radius causes the light-gathering power to increase four times.

OF INTEREST
Two convex lenses, one at arm's length and one closer, can be used to form an image in the same way as a refractor. The image will be upside down, as it is in a refractor.

20.2 (left) In a refracting telescope, light rays are collected and focused by the large objective lens. The image is viewed through the eyepiece. (right) This refracting telescope has one of the world's largest objective lenses—nearly 1 meter in diameter. The telescope is located at the Lick Observatory in California.

object above the horizon. Few objects, however, remain in the same place in the sky all night. Earth's rotation causes the stars to appear to rise and set, just as the sun appears to rise and set. In order to stay pointed at the same star, a telescope must be able to move at the same rate Earth turns. Its dome must also move. Furthermore, movements must be so smooth that the image is not blurred. The location and design of a telescope and its dome are a major engineering project.

Topic 3 **The Refracting Telescope**

The simplest **refracting telescope**, or *refractor*, has two lenses. The *objective lens,* located at the front of the tube, is the larger of the two. The objective lens gathers starlight and bends, or refracts, the rays of light to form an image at the rear of the tube. The smaller eyepiece lens magnifies this image for the observer. The objective lens is like a magnifying glass that is used to focus the sun's rays on a piece of paper. The bright spot of sunlight on the paper is an image of the sun.

The world's largest refractor is located at the Yerkes Observatory in Williams Bay, Wisconsin. Its objective lens is 102 centimeters in diameter. A smaller refractor (diameter of 89.5 centimeters) is

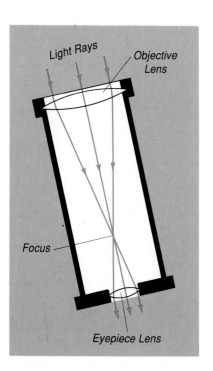

Light Rays

Objective Lens

Focus

Eyepiece Lens

located at the Lick Observatory on Mount Hamilton in southern California.

Almost all major refractors were built before the year 1900. The refractor at the Yerkes Observatory, for example, has been in use since 1897. The refractor at the Lick Observatory has been in use since 1888.

Why aren't large refractors being built today? The primary reason is that telescopes using mirrors are cheaper and easier to build. Why is this the case?

1. Light rays pass through a lens. The glass used to make the lens must be perfect. Mirrors only reflect light, and the glass used does not need to be as pure.
2. Lenses must be ground to a perfectly curved surface on both sides, whereas mirrors need to be ground only on one side.
3. A lens can be supported only at the edges. Over time, a large lens tends to sag under its own weight. This causes the image to blur. A mirror, on the other hand, can be supported over the entire back. It is far less likely to sag and ruin its image.

Topic 4   **The Reflecting Telescope**

The **reflecting telescope**, also known as a *reflector telescope,* uses one large curved mirror to gather and focus starlight. Like the larger lens of a refracting telescope, this mirror is the objective. The mirror is made of glass or a glasslike substance coated with a thin film of a shiny metal, such as aluminum, to reflect light.

VIDEODISC SELECTION

Diagram of refracting telescope
Side 3: 568, single frame

Diagram of reflecting telescope
Side 3: 571, single frame

20.3 (left) The Hale reflector at Mount Palomar is one of the largest conventional reflectors in the world. (right) In a reflecting telescope, light passes through the open top of the tube to the bottom, where it is reflected and focused by the large objective mirror. A small flat mirror reflects the light to the eyepiece. Major reflecting telescopes like Hale have openings in the large mirror for use in photography.

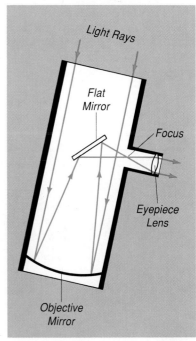

TEACHING TIP

Show how a concave mirror focuses light. If a concave mirror is not available, a piece of aluminum foil shaped into a bowl can be used to concentrate the light from a light bulb in the same way an objective mirror concentrates starlight.

TEACHING TIP

A thick liquid such as glycerine will visibly thin at the center when a shallow dish of it is spun on a turntable. This can be used to demonstrate spin-casting and the curved surface that would result.

VIDEODISC SELECTION

Hale telescope, Mt. Palomar, California
Side 3: 8690 to 8698, 9-frame sequence

The objective mirror is set at the bottom of the telescope tube. When the tube is pointed at a star, a small bright image of the star forms near the top of the tube. This image is reflected to the observer by a smaller mirror. As with the refractor, the observer looks through an eyepiece lens that magnifies the image.

The best-known reflector is the Hale telescope on Palomar Mountain in California. The diameter of its Pyrex mirror is 508 centimeters. It has been in operation since 1948 and, until recently, was the model for all reflecting telescopes built anywhere in the world. Other examples of single-mirror reflectors include a 381-centimeter reflector at Kitt Peak in Arizona and its 400-centimeter twin at Cerro Tololo in Chile. Both were built in the 1970's.

Older methods of making telescope mirrors involved casting a thick flat glass disk. The flat surface disk was then ground until the desired curvature was reached. Using a new technique, scientists at the University of Arizona have melted glass in a large spinning mold. As the glass spins, more glass is pushed toward the outside wall of the mold. The glass cools and hardens in a shape very close to the desired final curve. This method called *spin-casting* saves many months of grinding to reach the proper shape. Several 3.5-meter mirrors have been spin-cast, and progress is being made on casting larger mirrors. To date, one 6.5-meter mirror has been cast.

Topic 5 **Multiple-Mirror Reflectors**

The first major change in the design of large telescopes since the building of the Hale reflector came with the development of the **multiple-mirror telescope,** or **MMT.** In this telescope several mirrors take the place of a single large mirror. The image is formed when the light from each of the individual mirrors is combined and focused on a single point. Such telescopes are less expensive to build than a single large-mirror reflector.

20.4 (left) *Keck Observatory,* a multiple-mirror telescope, built in Hawaii; (right) In a multiple-mirror telescope, several mirrors reflect light to form one image. Computers assist in keeping each mirror in exactly the right location.

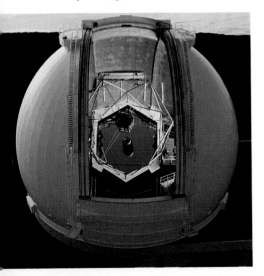

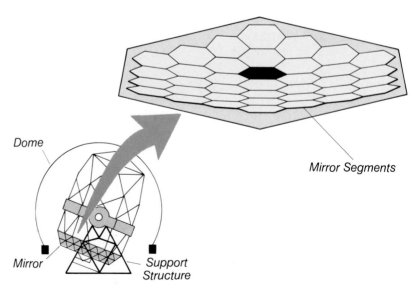

Dome

Mirror

Support Structure

Mirror Segments

The first MMT was built on Mount Hopkins in Arizona, in 1979. It consisted of six 1.8-meter mirrors arranged in a ring around a central axis. The six mirrors together have the light-gathering power of a single 4.5-meter mirror. Another MMT, the *Keck* telescope completed in 1992 has a segmented primary mirror composed of 36 hexagonal pieces. The total diameter of the mirrors is 10 meters. Each of the 36 segments of the *Keck* telescope is controlled by a computer designed to correct for atmospheric conditions. A twin 10-meter telescope, *Keck II*, is being built 85 meters away from the first *Keck* telescope in Hawaii. The two telescopes will be used together resulting in an 85-meter telescope whose light-gathering and resolution capabilities will be unparalleled by other land-based telescopes.

Another MMT under development is the *Very Large Telescope (VLT)*. Four 8.2-meter reflectors have been successfully spin-cast. The four telescopes will operate independently but may be used together, equaling a 16-meter reflector in light-gathering power but a 160-meter reflector in resolution.

SCIENCE BACKGROUND

When the MMT on Mount Hopkins was built in the late 1970's, its equivalent mirror diameter of 4.5 meters was large. The spin-casting method has made large-diameter single mirrors easy to achieve. Because of this, the six mirrors of the MMT at Mount Hopkins are being replaced by one 6.5-meter spin-cast mirror.

SCIENCE BACKGROUND

There are now plans for the *Columbus Project*, known as the "Two-Shooter." It will be two 8-meter telescopes mounted together like binoculars to give the equivalent of an 11.2-meter reflector. It is billed as the largest optical telescope in the Northern Hemisphere.

Topic 6   **Other Optical Telescopes**

Major astronomical observatories have several different kinds of telescopes, each with its own purpose. **Schmidt telescopes** can be found at almost all major observing sites. By using both a reflecting mirror and a refracting lens, these telescopes have an unusually wide field of view. They are used to make wide-angle photographs of the sky. One of the largest Schmidt telescopes in the world is on Palomar Mountain in California.

Earth's atmosphere absorbs and scatters many light waves before they reach any telescope on Earth. From its vantage 610 kilometers above Earth's surface, the *Hubble Space Telescope* was designed to observe the cosmos in unprecedented clarity. However a misshapen main mirror and other mechanical difficulties have degraded the telescope's effectiveness. Thanks to innovative computer techniques and image corrections, astronomers are able to obtain useful data exceeding the resolution of the finest ground-based telescopes. The *Hubble Space Telescope* can also detect ultraviolet rays most of which do not penetrate Earth's atmosphere.

VIDEODISC SELECTION

48" Schmidt telescope, Mt. Palomar
Side 3: 8713, single frame

Absorption of radiation by Earth's atmosphere
Side 3: 461, single frame

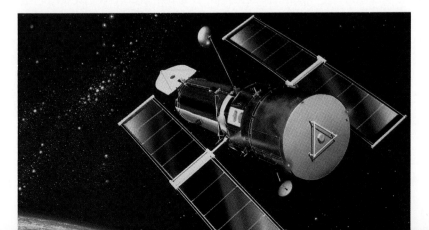

20.5 The *Hubble Space Telescope* is a reflector designed to orbit high above the interference of Earth's atmosphere. The telescope is about the size of a railroad boxcar. The large fins are solar panels to convert sunlight into electricity for the telescope's electrical system.

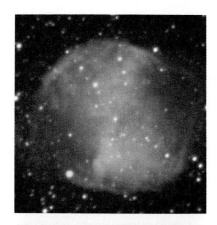

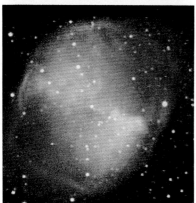

20.6 (top) A photographic image; (bottom) Much more detail is visible in this image, which was made with the assistance of a charge-coupled device.

ANSWERS
1. (a) gathers light, separates distant objects, magnifies image (b) mountaintops in remote, arid regions
2. (a) optical   (b) because power varies with r²   (c) so the telescope can be used immediately without image distortion   (d) to remain pointed at same spot in the sky
3. (a) Objective lens gathers and focuses starlight. Eyepiece lens magnifies image.   (b) Yerkes Observatory, Wisconsin; Lick Observatory, California   (c) cheaper, easier to build reflectors
4. (a) Objective mirror at back focuses light near the top. Small mirror reflects image to eyepiece.   (b) Hale at Palomar Mountain, California; Kitt Peak in Arizona; Cerro Tololo in Chile   (c) Mold spins while glass cools, disk is already curved; less grinding time, cheaper to make
5. (a) a reflecting telescope that uses several mirrors as one (b) Mount Hopkins, *Keck, VLT*
6. (a) has both mirror and lens,

Topic 7 Devices for Improving Images

A simple telescope enables a viewer to see many more stars than with the eye alone. Photographic plates have been used with telescopes for many years and have proved to be of great value. Photographic plates makes it possible to view even more stars. The human eye views incoming light for only a fraction of a second. On plates an image can build up many hours. Plates not only make it possible to detect stars invisible to the eye but also provide a record that can be studied days, weeks, even years later.

Recently an even-better method of collecting data has been developed. The **charge-coupled device,** or **CCD,** is more sensitive to light than photographic plates and reacts to a broader range of light rays. A CCD is a group of photocells, which are cells that react to light. Electrons collect where light strikes the cells. The number of electrons that collect on the cells is directly related to the amount of light striking the cell. Periodically the data in each cell are fed and stored in a computer in numeric form. The image can then be manipulated or enhanced by the computer. CCD images require only minutes to collect the necessary data, allowing telescopes to do many more observations in a night.

TOPIC QUESTIONS

Each topic question refers to the topic of the same number.

1. **(a)** What are the functions of a telescope?   **(b)** Where are optical telescopes best located?
2. **(a)** What is the name for any telescope that uses lenses or mirrors to gather starlight?   **(b)** Why does a lens with a 2-cm diameter have 4 times the light-gathering power of a 1-cm lens?   **(c)** Why is it important to keep the temperature of a telescope's mirror or lens constant?   **(d)** Why must telescopes be able to move at the same rate Earth turns?
3. **(a)** Explain how a refractor works.   **(b)** Name two observatories with refractors.   **(c)** Explain why refractors are not being built today.
4. **(a)** Explain how a single-mirror reflector works.   **(b)** identify the locations of two major single-mirror reflectors.   **(c)** Describe the spin-cast method of making telescope mirrors and the advantages of this method.
5. **(a)** Describe how a multiple-mirror telescope works.   **(b)** Identify two multiple-mirror telescopes (present or planned).
6. **(a)** Describe the design and use of a Schmidt telescope.   **(b)** What advantages does the *Hubble Space Telescope* have over ground-based telescopes?
7. **(a)** What advantages do observations made with photographic film have over observations made by the human eye?   **(b)** What is a charge-coupled device and what does it do?

used for wide-angle photos   **(b)** no atmosphere to interfere
7. (a) More stars are observed by photograph, provides record. (b) CCD: photocells that react to light and record images

II Studying Energy Beyond Visible Light

Topic 8 The Electromagnetic Spectrum

Optical telescopes are used to study visible light from stars, but not all forms of energy are visible. Stars also emit X rays, radio waves, infrared rays, and other kinds of **electromagnetic energy.** All forms of electromagnetic energy travel through space at a speed of 300 000 kilometers per second, but each has different frequencies and wavelengths. Frequency is the number of waves that pass by a point in a second; wavelength is the distance from the crest of one wave to the crest of the next. Frequency and wavelength are inversely proportional, that is, a low frequency means a long wavelength and a high frequency means a short wavelength. Radio waves have the lowest frequencies and the longest wavelengths, up to several kilometers. Gamma rays have very high frequencies and have wavelengths as short as one millionth of a centimeter. The visible light rays that we see range in wavelength from 0.0004 to 0.0007 millimeters. This range of wavelengths, from radio waves to gamma rays, makes up the **electromagnetic spectrum.**

OBJECTIVES

A Identify and compare the wavelengths of the electromagnetic spectrum.

B Discuss the uses and advantages of radio telescopes and radio telescope arrays.

C Identify telescopes used to detect wavelengths other than visible light and radio waves.

VIDEODISC SELECTION

Illustration of the electromagnetic spectrum
Side 3: 459, single frame

20.7 The electromagnetic spectrum includes heat, light, radio waves, and other forms of energy. Only a small portion of the spectrum is visible light.

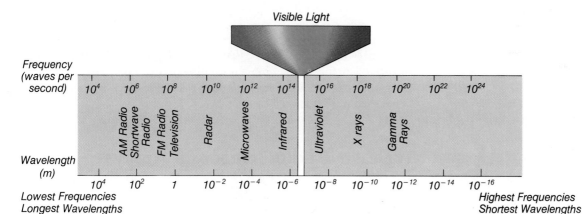

Topic 9 Radio Astronomy

Most objects in space send out several kinds of electromagnetic energy. Astronomers study many of these different energies to learn more about the universe. **Radio astronomy** is the study of radio waves from space. Unlike light rays, radio waves can pass through the clouds of fine dust that lie between stars. Radio waves have been detected from the sun and other stars, from some of the planets, from nebulas within our galaxy, and from other galaxies. More important, radio waves have been received from areas of the sky that appear dark or empty to optical instruments. Some objects can be detected only because of the radio waves they emit.

SCIENCE BACKGROUND
   Atmospheric clouds do not disrupt the collection of radio wave data, but electrical storms do.

20.8 The huge radio telescope at Arecibo, Puerto Rico, has a bowl-shaped antenna over 300 meters in diameter. The metal framework above the antenna is the receiver.

VIDEODISC SELECTION

Diagram of a radio telescope
Side 3: 563, single frame

20.9 The *Very Large Array* radio telescopes near Socorro, New Mexico, work almost as if they were a single telescope with a diameter of 34 kilometers.

In addition to detecting objects that optical telescopes cannot, radio astronomy has other advantages. Most radio waves pass unchanged through clouds in the atmosphere. Radio waves can also be detected during the daytime when stars are not visible in optical instruments. Optical astronomers can only work after dark when stars are visible. Radio astronomers can use their instruments almost any time, day or night.

Topic 10 **The Radio Telescope**

Radio telescopes look something like the dishes used to receive television signals from satellites. The curved antenna may be made of solid metal or wire mesh. It collects the radio waves and feeds them to a receiver. The receiver turns the radio waves into electrical signals that indicate the strength of radio waves and the direction of their source.

Like an optical telescope, the ability of a radio telescope to gather data depends on its size. Radio waves, however, have much longer wavelengths than visible light rays (Topic 8). As a result, radio antennas must be larger than telescope mirrors. For example, the smallest antenna at the National Radio Astronomy Observatory at Greenbank, West Virginia, is 26 meters in diameter. Remember that the large mirror of the Hale telescope is only 5 meters.

The largest single radio telescope in the world is located in Arecibo, Puerto Rico. Its dish is over 300 meters in diameter and occupies a large natural bowl-shaped area in the ground. The dish cannot be moved or pointed, but the receiver can. This, together with Earth's rotation, makes it possible for the telescope to detect radio signals from a wide area of the sky.

Topic 11 **Radio Telescope Arrays**

The construction of a large radio telescope, such as the one at Arecibo, is a complicated and expensive task. It is easier to build several small telescopes than a single large one. Many modern radio telescopes use a combination of small radio dishes to collect radio waves. The antennas are spaced apart; then signals from each are added together. For example, two small radio telescopes 100 meters apart act like a single large radio telescope with a 100-meter dish.

The reason for having more than one radio telescope is the use of **interferometry** to improve the radio image. When two radio telescopes collect data from the same point in space at the same time, the signal that each receives will not be exactly the same. The signals will be slightly "out of phase" and will interfere with one another. This interference between signals can be used to pinpoint locations in the sky with great accuracy—the greater the distance, or **baseline,** between the two radio telescopes the greater the accuracy. Increasing the number of radio telescopes collecting data also improves accuracy.

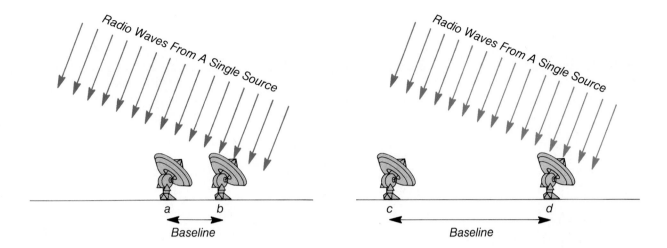

Radio telescopes may be arranged in groups, or **radio telescope arrays.** The *Very Large Array,* or *VLA,* in Socorro, New Mexico, consists of 27 antennas each 25 meters in diameter. Together they work like a single antenna with a diameter of 34 kilometers. The *Very Long Baseline Array,* or *VLBA,* is even larger. It consists of ten radio telescope antennas located throughout the United States. Its baseline is equal to a single antenna with a diameter of 8000 kilometers. The use of an orbiting radio telescope can extend the baseline of *VLBA* to 2.5 Earth diameters, or about 30 000 kilometers!

20.10 Two radio telescopes receive signals from the same object, but the signals do not arrive at exactly the same time and thus are out of phase. The greater the distance between telescopes, the more out of phase the signals are, and the more accurately scientists can pinpoint the object giving off signals.

Topic 12 **Telescopes for Other Wavelengths**

Most ultraviolet light, X rays, gamma rays, and most infrared wavelengths are absorbed by Earth's atmosphere. To collect data on these wavelengths, high flying aircraft, balloons, rockets, and satellites are used. The *Infrared Astronomy Satellite,* or *IRAS,* launched in 1983, detected over 250 000 sources of infrared energy including 10 000 previously unknown galaxies. The *Cosmic Background Explorer,* or *COBE,* launched in 1989, detected fluctuations in the cosmic microwave background that is believed to be energy left over from the creation of the universe. The X ray satellite, *Exosat,* made over 200 observations of X-ray sources between 1983 and 1986. The *Roentgen Satellite,* or *RoSat,* has completed a survey of the entire X-ray sky. NASA's *Gamma Ray Observatory,* or *GRO,* discovered a possible massive black hole in the core of a distant galaxy.

Some infrared wavelengths can be studied from Earth's surface. Several observatories have infrared telescopes, which are similar to optical telescopes. However, there are two problems to consider when building an infrared telescope. The first is that many infrared wavelengths are absorbed by water vapor in Earth's atmosphere. Because of this, infrared telescopes are placed above the clouds on high mountains. Two infrared telescopes are located on Mauna Kea, Hawaii, an extinct volcano over 4200 meters high. The second

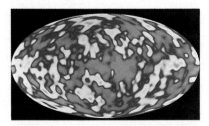

20.11 Instruments on NASA's *COBE* satellite, revealed important fluctuations in the cosmic microwave background.

problem is interference from nearby objects. Infrared energy is heat energy. An infrared telescope must be kept very cool. If it is not, it will "see" all of the warm objects around it, including itself and nearby astronomers, and will never be able to detect the weak infrared sources in space. *IRAS* carried liquid helium to cool itself, but only enough to keep it cool for ten months. When the helium ran out, *IRAS* was unable to detect the very cool stars.

TOPIC QUESTIONS

Each topic question refers to the topic of the same number.

8. **(a)** Identify some forms of electromagnetic energy. **(b)** What property do all forms of electromagnetic radiation have in common? **(c)** How do electromagnetic radiations differ?
9. **(a)** Identify some sources of radio waves from outer space. **(b)** When can radio astronomers collect data? Why?
10. **(a)** How do radio telescopes work? **(b)** Why do radio telescopes have to be much larger than optical telescopes?
11. **(a)** What is the advantage of placing two small radio telescopes 100 meters apart? **(b)** For what purpose is interferometry used? **(c)** Why is the baseline of an array important?
12. **(a)** Why are there no ultraviolet, X-ray, or gamma-ray telescopes on Earth's surface? **(b)** What was *IRAS?* What did astronomers learn from it? **(c)** What was *Exosat?* **(d)** Describe two problems that must be overcome when building an infrared telescope.

ANSWERS

8. (a) visible light, X rays, radio waves, infrared light, UV rays, gamma rays   (b) All travel at 300 000 km/s.   (c) frequency and wavelength

9. (a) sun, moon, stars, planets, nebulas, other galaxies   (b) day or night in most weather; most radio waves not disturbed by clouds or daylight

10. (a) Curved antenna collects radio waves, reflects them to receiver.   (b) because radio waves have much longer wavelengths than visible light

11. (a) The signals can be added together and act like one large telescope.   (b) to pinpoint radio sources with great accuracy, to improve radio image   (c) Longer baselines provide sharper images.

12. (a) These wavelengths are absorbed or scattered by Earth's atmosphere.   (b) an infrared satellite that located 250 000 infrared sources   (c) an X-ray satellite   (d) absorption of infrared by water vapor in air, heat from surrounding objects.

CAREERS

Dr. Sidney Wolff
Observatory Director

As Director of the National Optical Astronomy Observatories (NOAO), Dr. Sidney Wolff rarely gets to use a telescope. Instead, she spends most of her time overseeing the building of new telescopes. She is in charge of a $176 million project to build two telescopes. Each contains a mirror that is 8 meters in diameter. These telescopes will be located in Hawaii and Chile and will be available for use by the year 2000.

Prior to becoming Director at NOAO, Dr. Wolff spent a great deal of time behind the telescope at the University of Hawaii. During her seventeen years there, Dr. Wolff helped to develop the facilities on top of 4300-meter-high Mauna Kea Mountain. It is now the site of the highest astronomical observatory in the world.

How did Dr. Wolff ever become interested in studying the stars? She credits an elementary school spelling lesson on astronomy terms with sparking her interest. Dr. Wolff mastered the spelling and then began to read about the words. She has been reading and studying the heavens ever since.

III   A Closer Look at Visible Light

Topic 13   **The Spectroscope**

Visible light is actually a combination of all colors of light. These are the colors seen in a rainbow or when sunlight passes through a triangular glass prism. Each color has a different wavelength. Red light has the longest wavelength, while violet has the shortest. When light waves pass from air into a glass prism and out again, they are bent, or refracted. Long wavelengths, such as red, are refracted less than short wavelengths, such as violet. The band of colors that forms is called the **visible spectrum**.

Astronomers use the spectrum from distant stars to learn more about those stars. One tool used to separate starlight into its colors is called a **spectroscope**. It is basically a combination of a prism and a tiny viewing telescope. The prism separates the light into the spectrum of different colors. This spectrum is viewed with the tiny telescope. The more common **spectrograph** consists of a prism or diffraction grating, a lens, and a camera. The spectrum is then recorded on a photographic plate or by a CCD.

What do astronomers learn from the spectra of stars? For one, the spectra allows astronomers to determine which chemical elements are present in the star's outer layers. Further study of spectra indicates the temperature, pressure, magnetic field, and condition of the gases in the star. Spectra also allow astronomers to learn if the distance between Earth and the star is increasing or decreasing. The study of the spectra of stars and other objects in the sky is one of the most useful tools that astronomers have for learning about the universe.

OBJECTIVES

A Describe the visible spectrum and discuss how astronomers use spectroscopes to study stars and planets.

B Name and describe the three types of visible spectra.

C Identify the origin of the red shift in stellar spectra and describe it in terms of the Doppler effect.

VIDEODISC SELECTION

Diagrams of the Doppler effect
Side 3: 517 to 519, 3-frame
sequence

Doppler effect for a moving car
Side 3 movie: 44991 & PLAY

Doppler effect and the expansion of
the universe
Side 3 movie: 45169 & PLAY

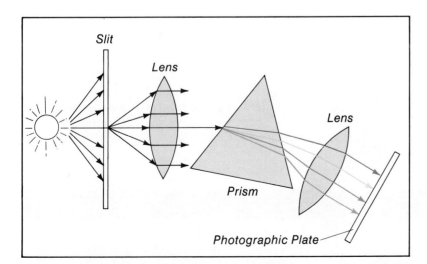

20.12   White light can be separated into different colors by a spectrograph. Each color in white light has a different wavelength. As a result, each color is refracted a different amount.

The lenses bend the light rays to make them parallel to each other. This provides a clearer image.

a

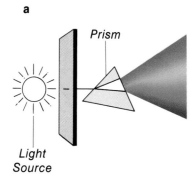

Light Source

b

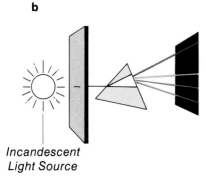

Incandescent Light Source

c

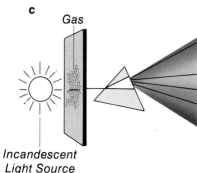

Incandescent Light Source

20.13 **(a)** Continuous spectrum, **(b)** bright-line spectrum, **(c)** dark-line spectrum

20.14 The middle horizontal band is part of the sun's dark-line spectrum. It is being compared with the bright-line spectrum of iron vapor.

Topic 14 **Kinds of Visible Spectra**

Three different types of spectra may be seen in a spectroscope. Each provides information about the source of its light.

A **continuous spectrum** is an unbroken band of colors, which shows that its source is sending out light of all visible wavelengths. Such a spectrum can come from three kinds of materials:

1. a glowing solid, such as the hot filament of an electric light
2. a glowing liquid, such as molten iron
3. the hot, compressed gases deep inside a star

A **bright-line spectrum** is an unevenly spaced series of lines of different colors and brightness. The bright lines show that the source is sending out, or emitting, light in certain wavelengths only. A bright-line spectrum is also called an *emission spectrum*. Bright-line spectra come from chemical elements when they are in the form of a glowing thin gas or vapor. An example is the glowing neon gas in a neon sign. Each element has its own, unique bright-line spectrum. The different wavelengths (seen as colors) appear as bright lines at different places on the spectrum for each element.

A **dark-line spectrum** is a continuous spectrum with dark lines where light is absorbed. The dark lines are in exactly the same place as the bright lines from the same element in a bright-line spectrum. The dark lines form when the light from a continuous spectrum passes through a cooler gas. The gas then absorbs the same wavelengths as it would give off if heated. Since the absorption leaves dark places for these wavelengths in the spectrum, a dark-line spectrum may also be referred to as an *absorption spectrum*. The positions of the dark lines are used to identify the element.

Topic 15 **Dark-Line Spectra and the Solar System**

A dark-line spectrum from a star or planet shows the composition of the star's outer layer or the planet's atmosphere. The sun's spectrum is a dark-line spectrum. The hot compressed gases of its interior radiate a continuous spectrum. When these radiations pass through the sun's own cooler atmosphere, absorption occurs. As a result the sun's spectrum has thousands of dark lines. When the dark lines are matched with bright-line spectra, the elements in the sun's atmosphere can be identified. More than 80 elements have been identified on the sun. Like the sun, almost all stars form absorption spectra.

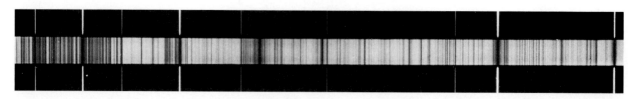

Absorption spectra can be used to determine the composition of a planet's atmosphere for the following reason. A planet shines by reflecting sunlight. If the spectrum of a planet shows dark lines that are not found in the sun's spectrum, then they must be caused by substances in the planet's atmosphere.

Topic 16 **The Doppler Effect**

When the spectrum of a star is compared in a laboratory with the bright-line spectrum of an element, a strange thing is sometimes noted. The black lines of the star's spectrum are shifted to the left or right of the bright lines formed by the element's spectrum as observed in the lab. If the shift is toward the red end of the spectrum, it means that longer wavelengths are coming from the star. If the shift is toward the violet end, it means that shorter wavelengths are coming from the star. Why does the shift occur?

Astronomers explain that these shifts happen because the distance between the star and Earth is increasing or decreasing. If the distance is increasing, the wavelengths the star radiates seem to become longer. This movement causes all of the star's spectral lines to shift toward the red end of the spectrum. The faster the distance between the star and Earth increases, the greater the *red shift* of its spectrum. If a star's spectrum is shifted toward the shorter wavelengths (violet), it means the distance between the star and Earth is decreasing. If a star is moving but the distance is not changing, the spectral lines do not shift.

The principle of the red shift is explained by the **Doppler effect**. It works the same way in sound waves. Think about the sound of a moving train or automobile horn. As it approaches, the wavelengths apparently shorten and the pitch rises. As it recedes, the wavelengths become longer and the pitch becomes lower.

TOPIC QUESTIONS

Each topic question refers to the topic of the same number.

13. (a) Why does light separate into colors when passing through a glass prism? (b) What are the parts of a spectrograph? (c) What can astronomers learn about stars from their spectra?
14. (a) Describe the appearance of each of the three types of spectra. (b) How are elements identified from bright-line spectra? (c) How are elements identified from dark-line spectra?
15. (a) Why does the sun have a dark-line spectrum? (b) How does the spectrum of a planet give data about its atmosphere?
16. (a) How does a star's spectra appear to be changed if the distance between the star and Earth is decreasing? (b) How does a star's spectra appear to be changed if the distance between the star and Earth is increasing? (c) Describe how this effect can be heard in sound.

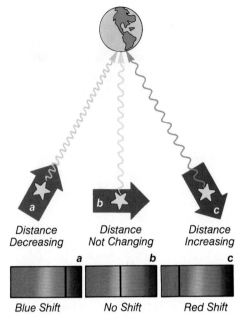

Distance Decreasing | Distance Not Changing | Distance Increasing

a | b | c

Blue Shift | No Shift | Red Shift

20.15 Stars **a**, **b**, and **c** all emit yellow light. The distance between **a** and Earth is decreasing. The light from **a** appears shifted toward the blue end of the spectrum. Star **b** is moving relative to Earth, but the distance is not changing. The light from **b** has no shift. The distance between **c** and Earth is increasing.

ANSWERS

13. (a) Each color is refracted to a different degree. (b) prism, or grating, lens, camera, and recording device: a photographic plate or CCD (c) elements, temperature, pressure, magnetic field, condition of gases, movement

14. (a) continuous: unbroken band of colors; bright-line: unevenly spaced lines, different colors and brightness; dark-line: continuous band with dark lines (b) Each element has its own pattern (c) Positions of dark lines match those of bright-line spectrum.

15. (a) Sun's atmosphere absorbs wavelengths of gases present. (b) Planet is seen by reflected sunlight. Differences between planet's and sun's spectrum identify elements in atmosphere.

16. (a) Spectral lines shift toward shorter wavelengths. (b) Spectral lines shift toward longer wavelengths. (c) Pitch seems higher as sound source approaches, lower as source recedes.

CHAPTER 20

L A B
ACTIVITY

The Simple
Spectroscope

Have you ever wondered how astronomers are able to determine the composition of the sun, other planets, and even distant galaxies from so far a way? One method that astronomers use is to study the light that travel from these distant bodies to Earth. Because different elements emit different wavelengths of light, astronomers can determine a planet's or star's composition based only on the wavelengths of light that reach Earth.

The instrument used to study light is called a spectroscope. A spectroscope separates light into its component wavelengths or colors. In this lab activity, you will make your own spectroscope by using a shoe box and a diffraction grating. A diffraction grating is a transparent piece of film that has been etched with thousands of parallel, evenly spaced lines. These lines cause the light to separate into different colors in much the same way that a prism separates light. You will use your spectroscope to study the spectra of the light sources around you.

Lab Skills and Objectives
- To **make** a simple spectroscope
- To **compare** spectra from different light sources

Materials
- diffraction grating
- shoe box with cover
- metric ruler
- tape
- sharp knife
- notebook paper
- scissors
- index card
- 2 pieces of aluminum foil
- lamp with incandescent bulb
- Bunsen burner
- safety goggles
- sodium chloride
- beaker of water
- nichrome wire with loop in one end
- small cork
- colored pencils
- Chapter 20, topics 14 and 15

Procedure
1. Place a mounted diffraction grating on one end of a shoe box. The grating should be against the left edge and about 1.5 cm from the bottom. (See Figure 20.16.) Trace the outline of the diffraction grating on the box. Remove the grating and mark off a 3-cm square in the center of the outlined space. Carefully cut out the 3-cm square with a knife. **CAUTION: Use knife with care. The blade is sharp.**

2. Hold the diffraction grating to your eye and point it toward a light within the classroom. Turn the grating until it forms a horizontal spectrum. Keeping it in the same position, tape the grating over the 3-cm square opening.

3. Cut a sheet of notebook paper 6 cm × 10 cm. Tape the paper to the inside of the box opposite the grating. This piece of paper will be used as a screen.

4. Carefully use the knife to cut a 3 cm × 3 cm square in the end of the box next to the screen. The square should be located 1 cm from the left edge of the box and halfway between the top and the bottom. (See Figure 20.16.)

5. Cut a 2 cm × 2 cm square in the center of an index card.

6. Take two pieces of aluminum foil and find the straightest edge on each. Place the two pieces of foil side by side over the hole on the index card so that the straightest edges of the foil are next to each other. Separate the two pieces of foil so that there is a one-half millimeter space between them.

7. Tape the pieces of foil to the index card so that the slit between the two pieces crosses the center of the hole in the index card. (See Figure 20.16.) Hold up the index card to the light to make sure that the slit is straight. It is very important that the slit is straight and that the edges are not

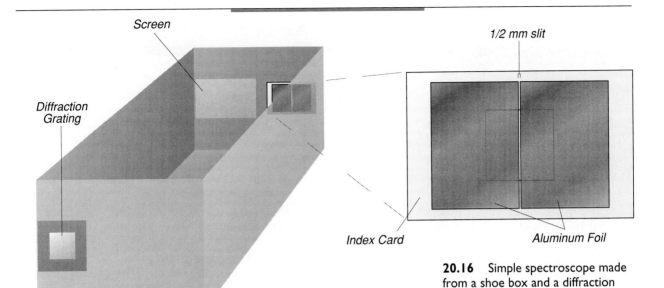

Screen

Diffraction
Grating

1/2 mm slit

Index Card

Aluminum Foil

20.16 Simple spectroscope made from a shoe box and a diffraction grating

ragged.

8. Tape the index card over the hole you cut in the box so that the slit between the two pieces of foil is vertical.

9. Turn on a lamp with an incandescent bulb.

   ![CAUTION icon] **CAUTION: Make sure electric cords do not dangle from tables and that they do not run through any puddles or spills.** Put the cover on the box. Put the grating close to your eye and point the slit to the left of the light. Observe the spectrum that appears on the screen at the rear of the box. Use colored pencils to draw the pattern you see.

10. Repeat step 6 using a fixed fluorescent light source such as the light in the ceiling. Make a sketch of the pattern.

11. Point the spectroscope through a window at the sky away from the sun.

![CAUTION icon] **CAUTION: Do not look directly at the sun.** Make a drawing of the spectrum you see.

12. Take a piece of nichrome wire that has a loop in one end and insert it into a cork so that the loop is sticking up.

13. ![safety goggles icon] **Put on your safety goggles.** Light a Bunsen burner and adjust the air intake until the flame is colorless. Holding the cork, dip the looped end of the wire into water and then into sodium chloride. Place the loop in the flame, and observe the spectrum through the spectroscope. (This step will be easier if you work with someone else. Take turns making and observing the flame.) Make a sketch of the pattern you see.

14. Answer the questions in *Analysis and Conclusions.*

Analysis and Conclusions

1. Describe the spectrum for white light based on your observations of the incandescent bulb. What does the spectrum tell you about the composition of white light?

2. Compare the spectra for the incandescent light, fluorescent light, and daylight. How are all three similar? How do they differ?

3. Describe the spectrum for sodium chloride. What type of spectrum is it? How do the colors differ from the other spectra you have seen?

4. Once again, observe the spectrum of daylight. If you look carefully, you should be able to see that some colors are missing. What do you think accounts for these missing colors?

Answers to all questions appear in the Teacher's Guide at the back of this book.

■ Summary

I Telescopes gather more light than the eye, help visually separate objects, and magnify images.

Optical telescopes gather light by means of lenses (refractors) or mirrors (reflectors). Larger lenses or mirrors gather more light.

The image made by an optical telescope is improved by the use of photographic film and the charge-coupled device (CCD).

II The electromagnetic spectrum includes radio, infrared, visible, ultraviolet, X-ray, and gamma-ray wavelengths. All electromagnetic energy travels at 300 000 km/s.

Radio telescopes concentrate and detect radio waves from space. Arrays of radio telescopes provide more accurate radio images.

Forms of electromagnetic energy other than light and radio waves are observed with telescopes specially designed to detect them.

III Visible light is made of many colors, or wavelengths. Astronomers use spectrographs to study the colors of visible light from stars.

There are three kinds of spectra: continuous, bright-line, and dark-line. Spectra provide information about the temperature and composition of stars and other objects.

The Doppler effect can be used to determine the movement of a star relative to Earth.

■ Vocabulary

baseline	multiple-mirror
bright-line spectrum	telescope (MMT)
charge-coupled device	optical telescope
(CCD)	radio astronomy
continuous spectrum	radio telescope array
dark-line spectrum	reflecting telescope
Doppler effect	refracting telescope
electromagnetic energy	Schmidt telescope
electromagnetic	spectroscope
spectrum	visible spectrum
interferometry	

■ Review

Select the best answer for each item. Write your answer on your paper.

1. Which does a telescope NOT do? (a) speed up the light from distant objects (b) gather more light than the human eye (c) magnify the image (d) show the separation between distant objects

2. Which part of an optical telescope gathers and focuses light? (a) objective lens or mirror (b) eyepiece lens (c) dome (d) telescope tube

3. Compared to a 1-meter lens, what is the light-gathering power of a 2-meter lens? (a) ½ as great (b) 2 times as great (c) ¼ as great (d) 4 times as great

4. Which is true of refracting telescopes? (a) They use mirrors to focus starlight. (b) They are cheaper to build than reflectors. (c) Many are larger than reflectors. (d) Most major ones were built before the year 1900.

5. Which can be made by the process of spin-casting? (a) telescope lenses (b) telescope mirrors (c) radio telescope antenna dish (d) charge-coupled devices

6. Which was the first major change in optical telescope design since the Hale telescope? (a) Schmidt telescope (b) MMT (c) VLA (d) CCD

7. Which is used to make wide-angle sky photographs? (a) Schmidt telescope (b) MMT (c) *Hubble Space Telescope* (d) VLA

8. Which is most sensitive to visible light? (a) human eye (b) photographic plate (c) charge-coupled device (d) Hale's 5-meter telescope mirror

9. Which is NOT true of electromagnetic energy? (a) It includes many wavelengths. (b) Its speed varies with wavelength. (c) Its wavelength varies with its frequency. (d) It includes visible light.

10. Which is observed with optical telescopes? (a) microwaves light (b) visible light (c) X rays (d) ultraviolet rays

For further review, see **Study Guide.**
For assessment, see **Chapter Tests**
and **Computer Test Bank.**

11. Which is true of radio waves? (a) They can pass through clouds. (b) They can be detected only in daytime. (c) They have very short wavelengths. (d) They cannot be reflected.

12. Why must radio telescopes be larger than optical telescopes? (a) Objects in space emit fewer radio waves than light waves. (b) Radio waves are much longer than optical waves. (c) Static interferes with radio waves. (d) Radio telescopes cannot be moved or pointed.

13. Which is NOT a reason for using radio telescope arrays? (a) It is impossible to build a single telescope as large as some arrays. (b) It is easier to build several small dishes. (c) Interferometry improves radio images. (d) Radio signals are more in phase when more than one dish is used.

14. Which form of E-M radiation from space can only be detected outside Earth's atmosphere? (a) visible light (b) infrared light (c) ultraviolet waves (d) radio waves

15. Which color of visible light is refracted most by a prism? (a) green (b) red (c) orange (d) violet

16. Which would form a bright-line spectrum? (a) the hot filament of a light bulb (b) a neon sign (c) the sun (d) hot gases deep inside a star

17. What happens to spectral lines from a star when the distance between the star and Earth is increasing? (a) They are unchanged. (b) They shift toward the red end of the visible spectrum. (c) They shift toward the blue end. (d) They become a bright-line spectrum.

■ Interpret and Apply

On your paper, answer each question in complete sentences.

1. Optical telescopes gather more light than the human eye can. Why is this so?

2. Using math, compare the light-gathering power of a 3-meter reflector with the light-gathering power of the 5-meter Hale telescope and the 4-meter reflector at Cerro Tololo, Chile. Show your calculations.

3. The mirror of the *Hubble Space Telescope* is half the diameter of the mirror of the Hale telescope. How is it that the *Hubble* can gather light from objects 50 times fainter than the faintest object the Hale can detect?

4. How can stars that are invisible to the eye appear on photographs?

5. Why can a radio telescope antenna be made of wire mesh, while an optical telescope needs a smooth, solid lens or mirror?

6. Helium was discovered on the sun 30 years before it was known on Earth. How is this possible?

7. A few stars have bright lines superimposed on their continuous spectra. How can this be explained?

8. Explain why there is no shift in spectral lines of a star moving at right angles to the line of sight.

■ Critical Thinking

On your paper, answer each item in complete sentences.

1. Assume that you have just been made chairperson of a committee that is to find the best location in the United States for a new astronomical observatory. The observatory will have as many kinds of ground-based telescopes as possible. Make a list of the features that the location should have and explain why each is important.

2. One of the most exciting uses of the *Very Large Baseline Array* of radio telescopes has been to make very precise measurements of the distances between certain points on Earth's surface. What kinds of information could these measurements reveal about Earth's surface?

375

Stars and Galaxies

▲
The Big Dipper, part of
the constellation Ursa
Major

How Do You Know That . . .

Stars change position in the sky? Look at the sky on a clear
moonless night. Chart the position of the Big Dipper when
darkness falls and again four hours later. Note how its position
changes in relation to that of Polaris, the North Star.

Early astronomers noticed how different constellations appeared
with the sun at sunrise and sunset through the course of a year.
The movement of the sun crossed 12 constellations during this
time. Do some library research to find the names of these 12
constellations.

SCIENCE BACKGROUND

The North Celestial Pole is moving closer to Polaris and will continue to do so until A.D. 2102. After that, the distance between the two will increase again. By A.D. 10 000, Deneb will be the pole star and by A.D. 14 000, Vega will be located above Earth's North Pole. These changes are part of a 26 000-year cycle caused by the wobble (precession) of Earth's axis.

I Stars and Their Characteristics

Topic 1 Constellations

A **constellation** is a group of stars that appears to form a pattern in the sky. A total of 88 different constellations can be seen from the Northern and Southern Hemispheres. The Big Dipper is probably the best-known example. It is actually a part of a much larger constellation known as Ursa Major, or the Big Bear. The dipper can be used to find other constellations. Think of an imaginary line drawn through the two stars on the front of the dipper. This line through the "pointer stars" points to the last star in the handle of the Little Dipper (part of Ursa Minor, the Small Bear). This star is Polaris, or the North Star. At the same distance on the opposite side of the Little Dipper is a large, lopsided M. This is the chair of Queen Cassiopeia (CASS ee o PEE ya).

Ursa Major, Ursa Minor, and Cassiopeia are examples of *circumpolar constellations*. From some northern latitudes, such constellations never set below the horizon and can be seen all year long. Circumpolar constellations appear to move around Polaris, the star located almost exactly above Earth's North Pole. The number of stars that are seen as circumpolar depends upon the observer's latitude. The farther north the observer lives, the more stars will appear circumpolar.

The apparent movement of the circumpolar constellations is caused by Earth turning on its axis. Earth turns from west to east. As a result the whole sky appears to turn from east to west. That is why the sun, the moon, and the stars are said to rise in the east and set in the west. The part of the sky above Earth's axis, however, does not rise or set. When Earth turns on its axis, Polaris seems stationary in the sky. The stars near Polaris go around in a counterclockwise direction. Their trails can be recorded with ordinary cameras by using time-exposure photography.

Topic 2 Seasonal Changes in Constellations

Although the circumpolar constellations are visible every night, their positions in the sky change with the seasons. Viewed on a fall evening, the Big Dipper is near the northern horizon. On

OBJECTIVES

A Identify and locate some famous constellations and describe their apparent motions in the sky.

B Define and use several units that express distances in space.

C Compare the physical and chemical properties of the sun with those of other stars.

D Discuss the different ways in which star brightness is measured and compare star brightness using these methods.

VIDEODISC SELECTION

Overview of the universe
Side 6 movie: 60 & PLAY (about 30 minutes)

21.1 The circumpolar stars make circular trails around Polaris on a time-exposure photograph. The brightest trail near the center is Polaris.

377

21.7 The Crab Nebula is a source of radio waves.

ANSWERS

  7. (a) cool, large star; Aldebaran, Arcturus   (b) brighter, bigger than giants; Rigel, Canopus, Antares, Betelgeuse   (c) less luminous star, absolute magnitude < 1   (d) very dense dwarf; Atom nuclei are tightly packed.

  8. (a) stars that regularly vary in brightness   (b) Its light varies by expansion and contraction.   (c) can be used to find distance to star   (d) two stars orbiting each other; Algol

  9. (a) It gave off radio pulses. (b) Pulsars are neutron star remnants of a supernova.   (c) beam of radiation and rotation of pulsar

TOPIC QUESTIONS

Each topic question refers to the topic of the same number.

7. **(a)** What is a red giant? Give examples.   **(b)** How are supergiant stars different from red giant stars? Give examples of supergiants.   **(c)** How is a dwarf star defined?   **(d)** What is a white dwarf? Why are they so dense?

8. **(a)** What are variable stars?   **(b)** What is a pulsating star? **(c)** Why are cepheid variables of great importance to astronomy? **(d)** What is an eclipsing binary? Name an example.

9. **(a)** How was the pulsar in the Crab Nebula discovered? **(b)** How are pulsars related to supernovas?   **(c)** What is thought to be the cause of the rapid pulses put out by pulsars?

EARTH**MATTERS**

Light Pollution

If you are like nine out of ten people in the United States, you have probably never been able to see the star-filled area of the night sky that caused our galaxy to be named the Milky Way. For people living in or near large towns or cities in this country, the view of the stars is far different from the view their ancestors had several decades ago. The reason the view has changed so much is the rapid increase in the amount of light given off by buildings and streetlights. This excess light causes the sky near cities to glow, hiding the incoming light of faint stars. Astronomers call this effect *light pollution.*

Light pollution can be reduced. Signs can be directed downward, so that excess light doesn't go off into space. Streetlights can be shielded so that all of their light shines downward where it is needed. City governments can use low pressure sodium (LPS) lighting, which produces a narrow wavelength of light, easily filtered out by astronomers working nearby.

In addition to helping make the nighttime sky more enjoyable to view, reducing light pollution also helps conserve energy. Up to 30 percent of the light from traditional streetlights goes off to the side and is wasted. Shielding the light means that lower wattage LPS bulbs can be used, saving money by reducing the need for electricity and fossil fuels. Maine and Arizona already require lights to be shielded.

III Formation of Stars

Topic 10 Origin of a Star

Huge clouds of gas and dust occur in parts of space between stars. The density of these clouds is very low. Nevertheless, because the clouds are so large, they contain at least as much material as stars. These clouds are usually about 99 percent gas, most of which is hydrogen. The remaining 1 percent of the clouds is a strange kind of dust. The grains of this dust are very tiny, with diameters of about one ten-thousandth of a centimeter or less. Dust grains collected so far consist of silicon carbide, graphite, diamond, and minor amounts of nitrogen and other elements.

Where does this gas and dust come from? One possible source is the explosion of stars that have become novas or supernovas (Topic 13). Such explosions could scatter material over a wide area.

Most of the great **nebulae**, or clouds of gas and dust in space, are invisible. Some are made visible in one of two ways. A nebula near a bright star is made visible by light from the star. Such a nebula is a *diffuse nebula*. The brightest of these is the Great Nebula in the constellation Orion. Close to the middle star in Orion's sword (Figure 21.8(a)), it is visible to the unaided eye under dark skies.

A nebula that is not near a bright star may show up as a dark patch against the more-distant stars. Such a nebula is called a *dark nebula*. The Horsehead Nebula in Orion is a dark nebula.

According to theory, stars form continually wherever dense clouds of gas and dust exist. An average cloud is about 25 light-years in diameter. Each cloud may contain enough material to form many stars. A force from outside the cloud causes the cloud to begin to condense into stars. The force may be a shockwave from a supernova. The outside force triggers the force of gravity that exists between the gas atoms and dust grains. The attraction of gravity causes the particles in the cloud to move toward each other. Huge areas become denser throughout the cloud. The temperature increases as the areas contract. If the cloud is large enough, parts of it will start to glow. These large glowing cloud sections are called *protostars*. They will eventually become stars.

As contraction continues, the protostars become hotter and brighter. Eventually the center is so hot that a fusion reaction begins. During fusion, light hydrogen nuclei unite to form heavier helium nuclei. When fusion begins, the protostar has become a star. Huge amounts of energy are radiated during fusion. When the release of energy counterbalances the force of gravity, the star stops contracting and has reached a *stable state*. In the stable state, more-massive stars are so hot that they glow blue or white. Less-massive stars are cooler and glow yellow or orange. Massive blue stars may reach a stable state in a few hundred thousand years. Less-massive yellow and orange stars contract more slowly and may take millions of years to reach this stable state.

OBJECTIVES

A Name, describe, and give examples of several kinds of nebulae and explain the relationship between nebulae and stars.

B Describe the formation of red giants and dwarfs.

C Describe the formation of novas, supernovas, neutron stars, and black holes.

a

b

21.8   (a) The Great Nebula in Orion is a diffuse nebula. **(b)** Horse head Nebula is a dark nebula.

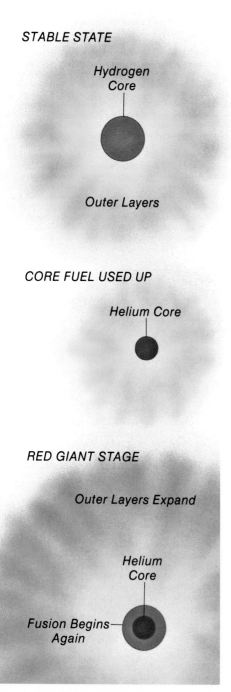

STABLE STATE

Hydrogen
Core

Outer Layers

CORE FUEL USED UP

Helium Core

RED GIANT STAGE

Outer Layers Expand

Helium
Core

Fusion Begins
Again

21.9 The diagram shows how a stable star first shrinks and then expands to become a red giant. Eventually it collapses and becomes a white dwarf.

Topic 11   Formation of Red Giants

In the stable state a star's diameter and radiation remain the same for millions or even billions of years. Eventually, however, so many of the core's light nuclei are used up that the energy of fusion no longer balances the force of gravity. Then the star loses its stability. When this occurs, the center or core of the star contracts again. The core gets so hot that it causes the star's outer layers to expand. This expansion enlarges the star's surface area. The star again radiates more light and appears brighter. In the meantime the fusion reaction starts occurring in the outer layers. The core is now composed mostly of helium formed from the hydrogen fusion reaction. The star expands farther and becomes a red giant or supergiant.

If the star's core gets hot enough, helium nuclei fuse in a reaction that forms still heavier nuclei, such as oxygen and carbon. If the temperature rise continues after the helium nuclei are used up, oxygen, carbon, and other nuclei fuse to form elements as heavy as iron.

Topic 12   Formation of White Dwarfs

Finally the stage comes in a star's life when most of the fuel for the fusion reaction is used up. The temperature and pressure of the core can no longer support the weight of its outer layers. The giant collapses. The nuclei of its atoms are squeezed tightly together. The star becomes a white dwarf and is probably no larger than Earth.

With most of its fuel gone, the white dwarf no longer produces energy and cannot maintain its high temperature. It gives off enough leftover heat to glow faintly for perhaps a billion years. The white dwarf continues to cool until it becomes cold and dark.

Occasionally a white dwarf flares up brilliantly, brightening a hundred to a million times. Astronomers then call it a nova (new star). A nova may be the result of bombardment by a companion star. Novas fade to their former luminosity in a few years at most.

The sun is thought to be at least five billion years old. It is still in its stable stage. The sun is expected to remain stable for another five billion years before it swells to a red giant and eventually collapses to a white dwarf.

Topic 13   Supernovas

White dwarfs form from stars with about the same mass as the sun. Stars with at least seven times the sun's mass become red giants in a relatively short few million years. When fusion has stopped, it leaves a central iron core. As the star starts to cool, this core collapses. With the collapse, the pressures and temperatures within the core rise dramatically. The iron nuclei become fused into heavier elements. In a rush toward further collapse,

21.10 The great supernova of 1987 is the best-studied supernova in history. Data from it are still being analyzed. (left) Before the supernova became visible, (right) after the supernova became visible

the star explodes so violently that half its mass is blown away as a great cloud. The star flares up into an intensely bright object called a **supernova**. For a few weeks to a few months, one star outshines an entire galaxy!

The best record of a supernova before modern times was made by Chinese astronomers in a.d. 1054. The brilliant star faded after a year. Its outer shell was changed into a great expanding cloud of gas, which is now known as the Crab Nebula in the constellation of Taurus the Bull.

The most famous supernova in modern times occurred in the Large Magellanic Cloud and was visible to the unaided eye in 1987. This supernova was the closest observed since the development of modern scientific equipment. Astronomers were able to examine old photographic plates and determine which star had exploded. Many hypotheses about supernovas have been tested by studying data from the 1987 supernova. For example, scientists had predicted that supernovas produce subatomic particles called neutrinos. In fact, instruments did detect a burst of neutrinos just hours before light from the 1987 supernova became visible. Data from the 1987 supernova are still being collected and analyzed. The event will be studied in detail for years to come.

Topic 14 Neutron Stars and Black Holes

Recall that a supernova removes only about half of the exploding star's mass. The mass that remains after the explosion is what astronomers call a **neutron star**. A normal atom is made up of a nucleus, containing protons and neutrons, surrounded by a cloud of spinning electrons. Astronomers think that in the core of a supernova, the forces are so great that every atom's electrons are crushed into its nucleus. The collapsed electrons combine with the protons to form neutrons. All of the core's nuclei merge into a single, dense mass of neutrons. Astronomers calculate that a typical neutron star is only about ten kilometers in diameter and trillions of times more dense than the sun.

Neutron stars may not be the densest objects in the universe. In very massive stars, the nuclear forces between the neutrons become overwhelmed by the gravitational forces and the star collapses into a very small volume. These objects have gravitational

SCIENCE BACKGROUND

Technically, white dwarfs, neutron stars, and black holes are not stars because they no longer produce energy. Astronomers call them compact objects.

SCIENCE BACKGROUND

No white dwarfs are visible to the unaided eye.

SCIENCE BACKGROUND

Novas are discovered once or twice a year on the average. They may flare up in just a few hours. Supernovas are less common.

OF INTEREST

The 1987 supernova actually occurred 170 000 years before. Even at 170 000 light-years away, the Large Magellanic Cloud is close by.

VIDEODISC SELECTION

Diagrams of star formation (described in disc directory)
Side 3: 732 to 753, 22-frame sequence

Relative size of white dwarf and neutron star compared with sun
Side 3: 764 to 765, 2-frame sequence

Diagrams of relative star sizes
Side 3: 769 to 770, 2-frame sequence

forces so powerful that even light cannot escape. Scientists call these invisible objects **black holes.**

If black holes do not release light, how can they be located and identified? The first suspected black hole was a strong X ray source detected in the constellation Cygnus by NASA's *Orbiting Astronomical Observatory-3.* It is known as Cygnus X-1. Upon studying this source of X rays, astronomers found that there was a visible star orbiting a very massive invisible companion. Since X rays cannot escape a black hole, astronomers theorize that matter from the visible star is being drawn into the black hole. Before entering the black hole, atoms are ripped apart and emit powerful X rays. Gathering evidence suggests the central cores of galaxies and globular clusters contain black holes.

21.11 An artist's conception of matter falling into a black hole

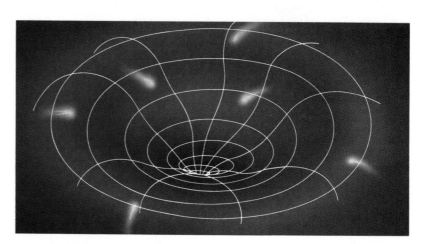

OF INTEREST

Some astronomers suspect that the center of our galaxy is a black hole.

ANSWERS

10. (a) cloud lit by a star; Great in Orion (b) cloud with no nearby star; Horsehead in Orion (c) in gas and dust clouds (d) large glowing cloud that will become stars (e) fusion (f) when the energy released counterbalances gravity

11. (a) when diameter and radiation of star stay the same; when most hydrogen is used up (b) star contracts, core heats, outer layers expand, fusion resumes, star expands more

12. (a) collapses after fuel is gone (b) white dwarf that flares (c) in stable state for past 5 billion years, will swell to red giant and collapse after 5 billion years

13. (a) its mass (b) very dense remains of collapse of massive red giant (c) intensely bright exploding star (d) supernova remnant

14. (a) composed only of neutrons, the heaviest part of atomic nucleus (b) by the collapse of very massive stars (c) gravity too great for even light to escape them

TOPIC QUESTIONS

Each topic question refers to the topic of the same number.

10. (a) What is a diffuse nebula? Give an example. (b) What is a dark nebula? Give an example. (c) Where are stars formed? (d) What is a protostar? (e) What reaction occurs in a protostar that has become very hot? (f) When does a star stop contracting?

11. (a) What is the stable state? Why does it end? (b) Explain how a star becomes a red giant.

12. (a) How does a star become a white dwarf? (b) What is a nova? (c) Summarize our sun's probable past and future.

13. (a) What is the characteristic that determines whether a star becomes a supernova? (b) What is a neutron star? (c) Describe a supernova. (d) What is the Crab Nebula?

14. (a) Explain why a neutron star is very dense. (b) How are black holes thought to form? (c) Why are black holes thought to be even more dense than neutron stars?

IV   Galaxies and the Universe

Topic 15   What Are Galaxies?

Without a telescope you can see several thousand stars. You can also see a few hazy patches of light in the night sky. Small telescopes show thousands more of these patches. Early observers called most of these hazy patches nebulae (clouds).

Today the nebulae described by early observers are studied with powerful telescopes. Modern telescopes show that many of the hazy patches are not nebulae. They are instead systems containing millions or even billions of stars. These systems are **galaxies**. Telescopes show that space contains at least several billion galaxies. Space is so vast that most galaxies are millions of light-years apart.

The galaxy to which the sun belongs is the Milky Way galaxy. In it the sun is one star among 100 billion. Every individual star seen with the unaided eye belongs to the Milky Way.

The Milky Way is shaped like a large, thin magnifying lens with a central bulge. The diameter of the Milky Way is about 140 000 light-years. Its greatest thickness is about 20 000 light-years. The sun is about 23 000 light-years from the galaxy's center.

When looking through the galaxy along its length, so many stars can be seen that the sky looks milky. Observers called this part of the sky the Milky Way long before they actually knew that it was a galaxy.

The Milky Way belongs to a small cluster of 17 galaxies. Astronomers call this cluster the *Local Group.* The nearest neighbors in the Local Group, the two Magellanic Clouds, are in the Southern Hemisphere sky. These galaxies can be seen without a telescope. Another neighbor, the Andromeda Galaxy, is faintly visible to the unaided eye in the Northern Hemisphere sky. The Andromeda Galaxy is larger than the Milky Way and is about two million light-years away.

OBJECTIVES

A Name, describe, and give examples of types of galaxies and quasars that occur in the universe.

B Discuss the big-bang hypothesis and present the evidence for it.

VIDEODISC SELECTION

Milky Way model
Side 3 movie: 19020 & PLAY (no narration)

Classification of galaxies: diagrams and photos
Side 3: 701 to 726, 26-frame sequence

VIDEODISC SELECTION

Depictions of the Big Bang
Side 3: 674 to 678, 5-frame sequence

21.12 Notice the approximate location of Earth's solar system in this side view of the Milky Way Galaxy.

Earth's Solar System

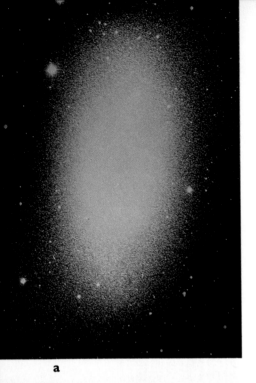

a

b

c

21.13 (a) An elliptical galaxy, (b) an irregular galaxy, (c) a spiral galaxy

Topic 16 Types of Galaxies

There are three main types of galaxies. *Spiral galaxies* have a central lens-shaped, bright nucleus made of millions of stars. Around the nucleus may be a fainter, flat disk of stars. Spiral arms, usually two, come out from opposite sides of the nucleus. The arms trail behind the galaxy as it rotates. There are millions of stars in the arms. The arms also contain great clouds of dust and gas. Few stars and almost no dust or gas occur between the arms. About three fourths of all known galaxies are spirals. The Milky Way and the Andromeda galaxies are spirals.

Elliptical galaxies range from nearly spherical to lens-shaped. Their brightness patterns show that most of their stars are close to the center. They have no arms and almost no gas and dust clouds.

Irregular galaxies are smaller, fainter, and less common than the others. Their stars are spread unevenly. The two Magellanic Clouds are irregular galaxies.

Topic 17 Quasars

Quasars were discovered in 1961. These objects looked like stars, and they emitted radio waves. Yet these objects were different from stars in several ways. Thus, astronomers named them **quasars** for quasi-stellar radio sources (radio sources like stars).

Quasars appear as very faint objects when viewed through a telescope because they are so far away. However, calculations show them to be the most luminous objects in the universe. Quasars are far larger and more massive than any known star. They radiate light and radio waves at very high rates. Scientists think that quasars may be whole galaxies in an early stage of development.

One quasar is called PKS 2000-330. In a powerful telescope it looks like a very faint star. The red shift of PKS 2000-330, however, shows it to be about 12 billion light-years away. At this distance, no known star can be seen even in the most powerful telescopes. For PKS 2000-330 to be seen from that distance, it must be as bright as 100 trillion suns and be billions of times more massive!

Topic 18 Origin of the Universe

How do scientists explain the formation of galaxies? The most widely accepted scientific explanation is the **big-bang hypothesis**. According to the big-bang hypothesis the whole universe was originally packed into one dense sphere of hydrogen. The entire sphere is thought to have been not much larger than the sun is today.

About 15 billion years ago this mass of hydrogen exploded, forming a gigantic expanding cloud. Some parts of the cloud moved faster than others, but all parts moved outward, away from the center. As the cloud parts moved, they condensed into galaxies. Billions of

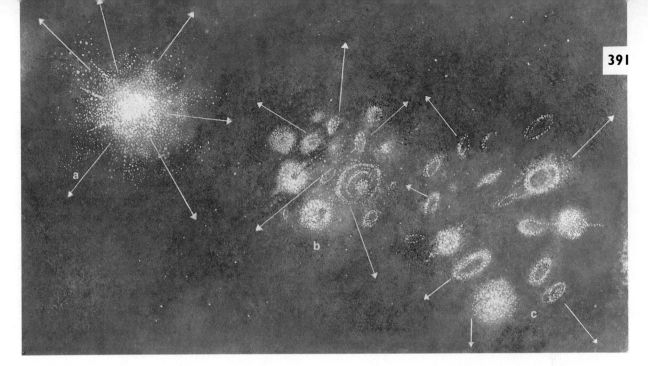

galaxies were formed. All of the galaxies continued moving outward, away from the center and from each other. Those with the highest speeds are now farthest out in space.

Support for this theory takes several forms. In 1929, astronomer Edwin Hubble found red shifts (Chapter 20, Topic 16) in the spectra of galaxies he studied. The red shifts showed that distant galaxies were receding from Earth faster than nearby galaxies. Hubble concluded that the universe was expanding.

In 1964, two physicists, Arno Penzias and Robert Wilson, discovered microwave radiation coming from all directions in space. This "background radiation" is thought to be the echo of the Big Bang. Recently the *COBE* satellite (Chapter 20) measured this background radiation with greater accuracy than previously possible. The new measurements show variations in the background radiation that are thought to be the "echo" of the universe's structure soon after the Big Bang.

TOPIC QUESTIONS

Each topic question refers to the topic of the same number.

15. **(a)** What are galaxies? **(b)** What is the name of our galaxy? Describe its shape and size. **(c)** What is the Local Group? Identify some members.

16. Name and describe the three main types of galaxies. Give examples where possible.

17. **(a)** In what ways do quasars differ from stars? **(b)** What do astronomers think that quasars may be?

18. **(a)** Summarize the Big Bang hypothesis. **(b)** How does the red shift of galaxies provide evidence for the hypothesis?

21.14 How did the universe begin? According to the Big Bang hypothesis, **(a)** a big ball of hydrogen exploded, **(b)** a huge hydrogen cloud moved outward, with cloud parts condensing to form galaxies, and **(c)** the galaxies continued to move outward.

SCIENCE BACKGROUND
Additional information on *COBE* and the structure of the universe can be found in the Teacher's Guide at the back of this book.

ANSWERS
15. (a) systems containing millions or billions of stars (b) Milky Way; lens shape with bulge, 1 billion stars, 120 000 LY diameter, 20 000 LY thick (c) cluster of 17 galaxies; Milky Way, Andromeda, Magellanic Clouds
16. spiral galaxies — lens-shaped with bright center and arms, Milky Way and Andromeda; elliptical — nearly spherical to lens-shaped, no arms; irregular — small, faint, least common, Magellanic Clouds
17. (a) larger and more massive than any known star (b) infant galaxies
18. (a) original sphere of hydrogen exploded into expanding cloud from which galaxies formed (b) shows all galaxies moving away as universe expands

CHAPTER 21

MAP ACTIVITY

Constellations and the Seasons

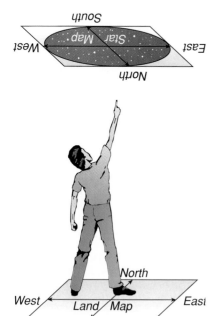

21.15 Notice that east and west are reversed on a star map. Yet, when a star map is held overhead, the direction labels align with those on a land map.

Suppose you sat outside on a clear night gazing up at the stars. Imagine that the sky is a dome touching the ground around you at the horizon. The stars are points of light on the dome's curved surface. If you were to view the dome of stars on a regular basis throughout the year, you would notice that the stars move. Like the sun's motion, the stars' apparent motions in the sky are caused by the daily rotation of Earth on its axis *and* the yearly revolution of Earth in its orbit around the sun.

In this activity, you will use star maps to investigate seasonal changes in the evening sky. The four star maps on pages 660 and 661 represent four views of the dome of stars—snapshots taken every three months at the same time of night in the Northern Hemisphere. To read a star map, hold it directly overhead and turn it until the direction labels are aligned with the compass directions, as shown in Figure 21.15.

Map Skills and Objectives
- To **locate** several stars and constellations on star maps
- To **analyze** the apparent motions of the stars and constellations over the seasons

Materials
- Seasonal Star Maps, Appendix B, pages 660–661
- 3 sheets tracing paper, 13 cm × 13 cm
- sharp pencil

Procedure
Part A—Locating Stars
1. Turn to the star maps on pages 660–661. Locate Polaris on each map. *N* on the map represents the northern horizon. Does the position of Polaris relative to the northern horizon change throughout the year?
2. Locate the Big Dipper on the Winter map. Note that two stars in the Big Dipper are labeled *Pointers*. If a line connecting the Pointers is continued to the right, to which star does the line point? How can the Big Dipper be used to find direction in the Northern Hemisphere?
3. Locate on the Winter map the three closely spaced stars in the middle of Orion. If a line is drawn through these stars and continued to the left, toward which constellation does it point?
4. Name the constellation in which each of the following stars is located:
   (a) Polaris
   (b) Antares
   (c) Vega
   (d) Spica
   (e) Betelgeuse
   (f) Rigel
   (g) Arcturus
5. For each constellation listed in the Data Table, identify its general location (N, E, NE, NW, and so forth) on the Autumn, Winter, Spring, and Summer maps.
6. Answer questions 1–3 in *Analysis and Conclusions*.

Data Table				
Constellation	Autumn	Winter	Spring	Summer
Bootes	not visible	not visible	overhead	W
Lyra	NW	not visible	NE	overhead
Orion	E	overhead	not visible	not visible
Pegasus	overhead	NW	not visible	E

Part B—Apparent Motion

7. Write *Map A* on the bottom of a sheet of tracing paper and trace the circular outline and compass directions from the Autumn map. Trace the outline of Gemini and label it *Autumn*. Move the tracing paper to the Winter map and line up the compass directions. Trace the position of Gemini on this map and label it *Winter*. Repeat for the Spring map. Note that Gemini does not appear on the Summer map. Draw arrows between the seasonal positions of Gemini to show its direction of movement. What is the general compass direction of movement of Gemini across the sky over the three seasons?

8. Write *Map B* on the bottom of a second sheet of tracing paper and trace the outline and compass directions from the Spring map. Mark the locations of the stars Vega, Deneb, and Altair. Connect the stars and label the triangle *Spring*. These three stars make up the Summer Triangle. Repeat this procedure for the Summer and Autumn maps. In what season does the Summer Triangle rise above the horizon, in what direction does it move across the sky, and in what season does it set?

9. Write *Map C* on a third sheet of tracing paper and trace the outline and compass directions from the Spring map. Mark and label Polaris and the constellation Cassiopeia. Label the whole drawing *Position A*. Move Map C to the Summer map. Again trace Cassiopeia. Label this tracing *Position B*. Draw an arrow from Position A pointing toward Position B. In what direction (clockwise or counterclockwise) has Cassiopeia moved relative to Polaris between Position A and Position B? In what direction must other constellations move relative to Polaris from one season to another?

10. Answer questions 4–6 in *Analysis and Conclusions.*

Analysis and Conclusions

1. Explain why the position of Polaris does not change relative to the northern horizon during the year. How does this fact help in finding direction?

2. Explain how stars and constellations can serve as landmarks for other stars and constellations.

3. Look over the data you collected in procedure step 5. Which season provides the best viewing of each constellation? Explain.

4. Based upon the path plotted on Map A, where is Gemini in the summer? Explain why it does not appear on the Summer map.

5. The three closely-spaced stars in the middle of Orion are located almost directly over Earth's equator. Thus, Orion can be seen in the Southern Hemisphere. For an observer at a mid-latitude location in South America, in what compass direction will Orion first appear above the horizon each year? If this observer is looking toward the point in the sky directly above the South Pole, will Orion move clockwise or counterclockwise with the seasons? Explain.

6. Map C shows Cassiopeia at two different times during the year. Cassiopeia will also be in these same two positions at two different times each day. If the four star maps represented the position of the stars during one rotation of Earth on its axis, how much time in hours would have passed between positions A and B? Explain.

Answers to all questions appear in the Teacher's Guide at the back of this book.

■ Summary

I The apparent motion of constellations around Polaris is caused by Earth's turning. Earth's movement around the sun causes visible constellations to change through the year.

Distances in space are measured in astronomical units and light-years.

Stars differ in size, density, and color. Hydrogen and helium are the two most abundant elements in stars.

Apparent magnitude, luminosity, and absolute magnitude all describe the brightness of stars.

II Giants and supergiants are large stars with low densities. Dwarf stars are small, dense stars.

Variable stars change in brightness. Pulsating variables, such as cepheids, and eclipsing binaries are types of variable stars.

Pulsars are neutron stars that produce bursts of both light and radio waves.

III Nebulae are huge clouds of dust and gas in space. Stars are thought to form in nebulae.

A nova is caused by the flare-up of a white dwarf star. Supernovas result from the explosion of a neutron star's outer portions.

Neutron stars are denser than white dwarfs. Black holes are so dense that light cannot escape their gravity. Neutron stars and black holes result from the collapse of massive and very massive stars.

IV Galaxies contain millions or billions of stars. Galaxies may be spiral, elliptical, or irregular.

Quasars are distant objects that may be galaxies in the early stages of formation.

The Big Bang hypothesis is an explanation for the origin of galaxies and the universe.

■ Vocabulary

absolute magnitude	luminosity
apparent magnitude	nebulae
astronomical unit (AU)	neutron star
Big Bang hypothesis	nova

black holes	protostars
cepheid variables	pulsars
constellation	quasars
dwarf stars	red giants
eclipsing binary	supergiants
galaxies	supernova
light-year (LY)	variable stars

■ Review

Write the letter of your answer on your paper.

1. An example of a circumpolar constellation is (a) Ursa Major, (b) Orion, (c) Canis Major, (d) Cygnus.

2. Earth turning on its axis causes (a) stars to rise in the west, (b) stars to appear to move around Polaris, (c) Orion to be seen in winter, (d) Cassiopeia to be overhead in autumn.

3. Which is the greatest distance? (a) 1 astronomical unit (b) 1 kilometer (c) 1 light-year (d) 1 millimeter

4. The two most abundant elements in stars are (a) helium and iron, (b) iron and calcium, (c) calcium and hydrogen, (d) hydrogen and helium.

5. How many times brighter is a first-magnitude star than a third-magnitude star? (a) 2 times (b) 2.5 times (c) 2 x 2.5 times (d) 2.5 x 2.5 times

6. Which object has the brightest apparent magnitude? (a) Sirius, −1.43 (b) Venus, − 4.4 (c) Procyon, +0.37 (d) Barnard's Star, +9.5

7. Which probably describes a blue-white star? (a) massive, hot (b) massive, cool (c) average mass and temperature (d) small mass, cool

8. The variable stars used to calculate star distance are (a) pulsating variables, (b) eclipsing binaries, (c) dwarfs, (d) cepheids.

9. A rapidly spinning neutron star is a (a) nova, (b) quasar, (c) pulsar, (d) nebula.

10. What kind of object is the Horsehead Nebula? (a) diffuse nebula (b) dark nebula (c) black hole (d) supernova

For further review, see **Study Guide.**
For assessment, see **Chapter Tests**
and **Computer Test Bank.**

11. Which stage follows the stable state for most stars? (a) red giant (b) red dwarf (c) nova (d) white dwarf

12. Stars that have used up their nuclear fuel and shrunk to a tiny size are (a) pulsars, (b) white dwarfs, (c) supernovas, (d) binaries.

13. The object located in the same place as a supernova explosion observed in A.D. 1054 is (a) Horsehead Nebula, (b) Orion Nebula, (c) Crab Nebula, (d) Andromeda Galaxy.

14. Cygnus X-1 is thought to be a (a) black hole, (b) pulsar, (c) variable star, (d) quasar.

15. Which may be distant galaxies in the process of formation? (a) black holes (b) neutron stars (c) pulsars (d) quasars

16. To which system does our sun belong? (a) Andromeda Galaxy (b) Milky Way (c) Big Dipper (d) Lesser Magellanic Cloud

17. What kind of galaxy is the Milky Way? (a) diffuse (b) spiral (c) elliptical (d) irregular

18. How long ago is the Big Bang thought to have occurred? (a) 5 billion years (b) 15 billion years (c) 25 billion years (d) 100 billion years

■ Interpret and Apply

Answer each question in complete sentences.

1. How long an exposure would a photographer need to photograph star trails that are complete circles? Why?

2. The star Sirius is 4.3 light-years from Earth. Determine the distance to Sirius in kilometers and in astronomical units.

3. The moon's average distance from Earth is about 380 000 kilometers. How long does it take moonlight to reach Earth?

4. Planets shine by reflected sunlight. How can planets be brighter than stars?

5. Approximately how many times brighter than Mars is Earth's full moon? (Moon's apparent magnitude equals −12.6)

6. Could we see the sun if it were 32.6 light-years from Earth?

■ Critical Thinking

Graph A shows the relationship between the distance to a star in parsecs (1 parsec = 3.26 light-years), and the distance modulus. The distance modulus is the difference between the apparent magnitude (m) of a star and its absolute magnitude (M). Graph B shows the relationship between the period of a cepheid variable and its absolute magnitude.

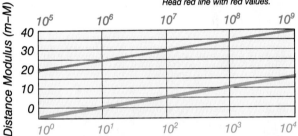

A *Distance (parsecs)* Read blue line with blue values.
Read red line with red values.

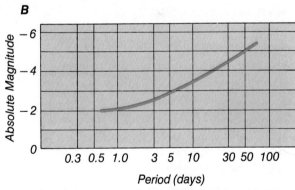

B

1. The distance modulus for a star is 10. How far is the star?

2. What is the distance modulus for a star that is 10^6 parsecs away?

3. How far away is a star if its apparent magnitude (m) is 10 and its absolute magnitude (M) is −10?

4. What is the absolute magnitude (M) of a cepheid variable star with a period of 5 days?

5. A cepheid variable has a period of 50 days. If its apparent magnitude (m) is +0, how far away is the cepheid?

The Sun and Its Solar System

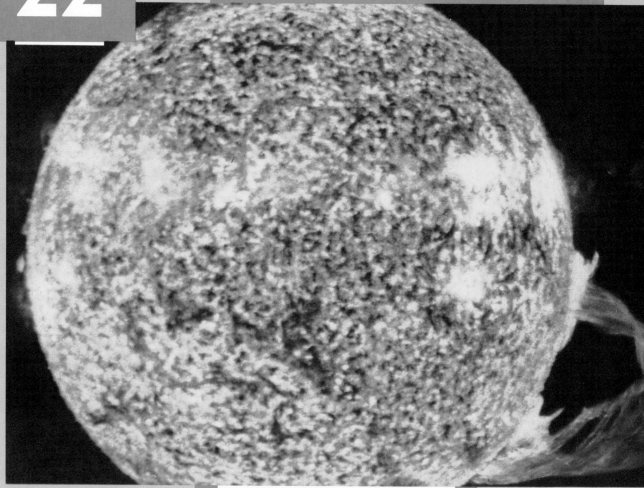

The sun's surface has a mottled, grainy appearance.

SCIENCE BACKGROUND

The pieces on the sun are called granules; the pattern is called granulation. Granulation was discovered in 1748.

How Do You Know That . . .

The sun is constantly changing? To a casual observer, the sun always appears the same. When the sun is observed with special equipment many changes are visible. For example, the surface of the sun appears to be bubbling and boiling. Solar scientists describe the surface of the sun as looking like the surface of a pot of boiling rice in slow motion. When rice boils, individual pieces quickly disappear and others take their place. A similar change appears to occur to the pieces that make up the sun's surface, although the change takes several minutes.

VIDEODISC SELECTION

Kitt Peak solar telescope
Side 5: 2259 to 2267, 9-frame
sequence

I The Sun

Topic 1 Studying the Sun

The sun is a fascinating and dangerous object to study. Observed improperly, the sun can cause blindness. Early Chinese astronomers observed the sun while it was dim and red at sunrise and sunset. They were the first to notice sunspots. Hundreds of years later, Galileo used a telescope to make features on the sun's surface appear larger. He was able to study sunspots continuously over a period of time. Galileo noticed that sunspots move in a regular pattern, and he concluded that the sun rotates. Sadly, Galileo's work viewing the sun probably caused his blindness during the last years of his life.

In 1859, astronomers using a spectroscope were able to demonstrate that lines in the sun's spectra were related to specific chemical elements. Using spectral data, scientists later described the sun's temperature and internal pressures. Modern spectrographs use CCDs (Chapter 20) to record the spectra of the sun. Solar physicists have instruments that create artificial eclipses but still travel to solar eclipse sites to study the corona of the sun under better conditions than the artificial eclipses produce.

Solar physicists have devised special telescopes that make viewing the sun safer. A **solar telescope** projects a large image of the sun into a dark underground room. With special glasses similar to those used by welders, solar physicists can safely watch the sun's image and observe changes that occur on the sun's surface. In 1973, three separate *Skylab* crews took photographs and made observations of the sun using several onboard solar telescopes.

OBJECTIVES

A Identify and describe some methods of studying the sun and discuss the sun's dimensions.

B Name and describe the layers and features of the sun's atmosphere and describe sunspots and the sunspot cycle.

C Define solar wind, identify sources of solar wind, and describe the effects of solar wind on Earth.

D Explain how the sun produces energy.

TEACHING TIP

This is a logical place to do the activity in the Teaching Suggestions about the hazards of looking directly at the sun.

22.1 **(a)** The McMath Telescope is the world's largest solar telescope. It is located at Kitt Peak National Observatory in Arizona. **(b)** A scientist using a solar telescope

a

b

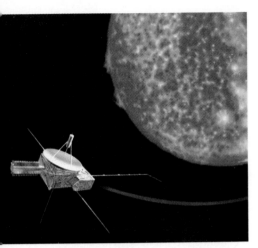

22.2 Data from *Ulysses* will help scientists investigate the sun's magnetic field and other characteristics.

SCIENCE BACKGROUND

Solar Max provided valuable data. Some of the data led to the discovery of several sungrazing comets. *Solar Max* measurements of the sun's energy output showed that the sun is most luminous at sunspot maximum.

SCIENCE BACKGROUND

In early 1992, *Ulysses* used Jupiters gravity to slingshot out of the elliptic plane and back toward the sun. *Ulysses* will pass over the sun's south pole in mid-1994 and the sun's north pole in mid-1995.

OF INTEREST

Ulysses is named for the hero of Homer's *Odyssey*. Homer's Ulysses also journeyed to his goal in a roundabout way.

SCIENCE BACKGROUND

The zone beneath the photosphere in which the columns of gases rise and sink is called the convective zone. This zone brings heat and other radiations from the core to the photosphere.

VIDEODISC SELECTION

Data on the sun: charts and diagrams
Side 5: 722 to 732, 11-frame sequence

Satellites have made it possible to study the sun and its radiation without the interference of Earth's atmosphere. NASA's *Orbiting Solar Observatories* (*OSO–1* through *OSO–8*) returned data from the sun from 1962 through 1979. In 1974 and 1976, *Helios A* and *Helios B* were placed in long, oval orbits that carried them inside the orbit of Mercury. The *Solar Maximum Satellite* (or *Solar Max*) was launched in 1980. During 1984, Space Shuttle astronauts visited *Solar Max* to repair its sun tracking system and replenish its propellant. *Solar Max* functioned until December 1989, when it re-entered Earth's atmosphere and disintegrated. *Ulysses*, a solar satellite launched in 1990, will fly over the sun's poles, an area that cannot be seen from Earth.

Topic 2 **Properties of the Sun**

Even though our sun is just an average-sized star, it is enormous compared to the size of Earth. The sun's diameter, 1 380 000 kilometers, is about 110 times Earth's diameter. The sun's volume could hold more than 1 million Earths. Its mass is 745 times greater than all the planets together.

It is difficult to imagine the huge size of the sun because it is so far away. Even though the sun and the moon appear to be nearly the same size in our sky, the sun is 400 times farther away. The SST (supersonic transport) *Concorde* can fly from Paris to New York in three and one-half hours. If the *Concorde* could fly through space at the same speed, it would take 10 years to reach the sun! Even for a particle traveling at the speed of light (300 000 km/s), it takes 8 minutes and 20 seconds to travel between the sun and Earth.

Temperatures on the sun are extreme. The sun's surface temperature is about 5500°C, about as hot as an electric arc that is used to weld iron. Its interior temperature is even higher, and may be as high as 15 000 000°C.

Topic 3 **The Sun's Atmosphere**

The only parts of the sun that can be studied directly are the three regions of the sun's atmosphere. These regions are the photosphere, the chromosphere, and the corona.

The **photosphere** is the apparent bright yellow surface of the sun. It is about 400 kilometers thick. The photosphere appears to be made of millions of individual cells, called **granules.** Each granule is about 1500 kilometers across with a bright center and dark edges. Granules are the tops of the columns of gases that form in the region below the photosphere. The gases are rising at the center of the granule and sinking back down at the edges. Because the gases are constantly moving, the surface is constantly changing. Individual granules last about eight minutes before disappearing.

The photosphere is the lower, denser part of the sun's atmosphere. It is not at all like Earth's lower atmosphere. The density

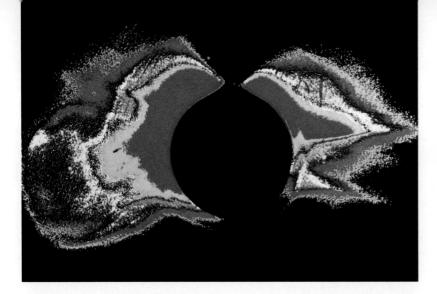

22.3 The sun's corona is visible during a solar eclipse. This image of the corona was taken from *Skylab* by an instrument that masked the sun's disk, creating an artificial eclipse. The image has been colored by a computer to make differences in brightness more visible.

of the photosphere is 28 billionths of a gram per cubic centimeter (2.8×10^{-8} g/cm^3). That is about the same as the density of Earth's outermost atmosphere.

Above the photosphere is the sun's outer, less dense atmosphere. Without special instruments the sun's outer atmosphere can be seen only during a solar eclipse. At the lower part of the outer atmosphere is the **chromosphere**, colored red by glowing hydrogen. The chromosphere extends thousands of kilometers above the photosphere. Above the chromosphere is the **corona**, with so little gas that it would be considered a vacuum on Earth. The corona surrounds the sun to a height of more than 1 million kilometers. It is seen during a total eclipse as a faint, pearly light.

Solar prominences are huge, red, flamelike arches of material that occur in the corona. Although they may look like flames, their light is the result of changes that occur in cooler, denser parts of the corona. Solar prominences may last for many hours. Some extend millions of kilometers above the photosphere.

Topic 4 **Sunspots**

Sunspots are dark spots on the photosphere. Some sunspots are barely visible in telescopes. Others are larger than Earth's diameter. Some last only a few hours before disappearing, while others may remain visible for a few months. Sunspots typically have a dark center, called an umbra, and a lighter rim, the penumbra.

Sunspots occur in pairs. Like the opposite ends of a bar magnet, one of the pair is a north magnetic pole and the other a south magnetic pole. The concentration of magnetic forces at these locations slows down solar activity and causes the photosphere to cool. The gases in a sunspot may be as much as 1500°C cooler than the surrounding photosphere. That temperature is still hotter than many stars, and sunspots would glow on their own if removed from the sun. Sunspots look dark only because the surrounding photosphere is so much hotter and brighter.

Sunspots appear to move from left to right across the sun's surface. This motion is caused by the sun's rotation. Because the sun is not solid like Earth but is made of gases, its rate of rotation is not

SCIENCE BACKGROUND

A density equal to that of water (1 g/cm^3) does not occur until half-way to the sun's center.

SCIENCE BACKGROUND

Another reason the chromosphere and corona are so difficult to see is because they radiate very little visible light. Most of their radiations are in ultraviolet and X ray.

VIDEODISC SELECTION

Cross-section of the solar atmosphere
Side 5: 733 to 734, 2-frame sequence

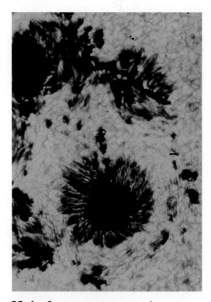

22.4 Sunspots occur on the photosphere. Sunspots appear dark because they are cooler than the surrounding photosphere.

SCIENCE BACKGROUND

Magnetic fields are visible on a spectrogram because radiation emitted by atoms in the presence of a magnetic field modifies the spectral lines by splitting each line into two or more. This pattern is the Zeeman effect. The strength of the magnetic field is read by the spacing between the lines.

SCIENCE BACKGROUND

Solar wind is blocked by Earth's magnetosphere.

SCIENCE BACKGROUND

Solar flares occur at sunspots when the magnetic lines of force become too twisted and snap apart.

SCIENCE BACKGROUND

Auroras are most common at solar cycle maxima.

22.5 Solar flares are outbursts of light from regions of sunspot activity. They usually last a few minutes.

VIDEODISC SELECTION

Sunspots
Side 5: 765 to 772, 8-frame sequence

Solar wind
Side 5: 749 to 750, 2-frame sequence

the same everywhere. At the equator the sun takes about 25 days for one rotation. The rate of rotation near the poles is 27 days.

The number of sunspots visible on the photosphere changes from day to day. At times of peak sunspot activity, over 100 may be counted on the sun's surface. During periods of low sunspot activity, several days may pass when no spots are visible. These changes occur in a *sunspot cycle* that averages about 11 years from one period of peak activity to the next.

Topic 5 **The Solar Wind and Magnetic Storms**

The corona gives off a constant stream of electrically charged particles called **solar wind**. These particles fly into space in all directions, some at an average speed of 400 kilometers per second by the time they reach Earth.

Some solar events produce huge gusts of solar wind. Great tears, called **coronal holes**, sometimes appear in the corona. Some of these holes extend halfway around the sun, and many do not close for several months. Solar wind pours from coronal holes in a great torrent of particles.

Solar flares are another source of solar wind bursts. Solar flares are outbursts of light that rise up suddenly in areas of sunspot activity. Most flare up in a few minutes and then fade rapidly. The number of solar flares increases as the number of sunspots increases.

As the solar wind blows past Earth, some particles interact with Earth's magnetic field and upper atmosphere, causing **auroras**, or northern and southern lights. Auroras are common events in the polar regions near Earth's magnetic poles.

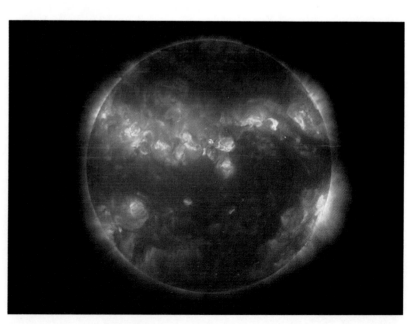

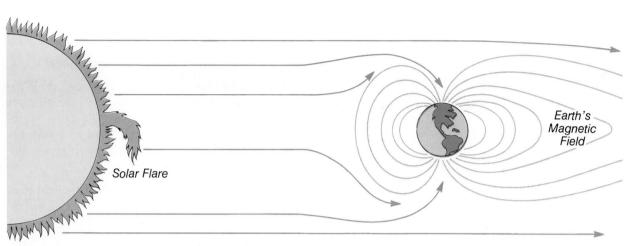

Sun   *Solar Wind*   *Earth*

Magnetic storms occur on Earth when the particles thrown out by coronal holes and solar flares are added to the constant solar wind produced by the corona. At such times auroras may be seen in middle latitudes as well as in polar areas, and compass needles may give inaccurate readings. Electrical surges following large solar flares may disrupt telephone reception and damage unprotected electrical appliances. Other particles in these outbursts affect the ionosphere, a region in Earth's upper atmosphere that reflects certain radio signals back to Earth. Radio reception of AM, citizen's band (CB), and shortwave frequencies may be affected.

22.6   As solar wind passes Earth, some particles are trapped by Earth's magnetic field and are carried to the magnetic poles. When the particles hit the atmosphere, they cause auroras. During periods of intense solar activity, increased solar wind may lead to auroras at latitudes away from the poles.

Topic 6   Source of the Sun's Energy

Remember from Chapter 21 that the fusion of light elements into heavier ones is the source of a star's energy. How does this fusion reaction take place? Why does it provide energy?

Albert Einstein gave the key to the answer in 1905 with his famous $E = mc^2$ equation. It stated that *matter can be converted into energy* and vice versa.

The sun is mostly hydrogen. Four hydrogen nuclei have a mass of about 4.030 atomic mass units. In fusion, four hydrogen nuclei join to form a helium nucleus that has a mass of only about 4.003 atomic mass units. Although some mass seems to disappear in the fusion process, it really does not. The mass changes into energy, which is radiated into space.

Calculations show that the total conversion of 1 kilogram of matter would release enough energy to raise a billion metric tons of matter 10 kilometers above Earth's surface. Astronomers calculate that about 4 million metric tons of matter are being changed to energy every second in the sun. This conversion to energy happens as 564 million metric tons of hydrogen become 560 million tons of helium. The mass of the sun is so great that this process can continue for another 5 billion years.

SCIENCE BACKGROUND

Electrical surges can be caused by currents induced by solar storm particles interacting with Earth's magnetic field. These surges can burn out huge electrical transformers at power stations.

SCIENCE BACKGROUND

The only place on the sun where temperature, density, and pressure are all great enough to sustain a nuclear reaction is in the core.

VIDEODISC SELECTION

Solar energy
Side 5: 735 to 748, 14-frame sequence

TOPIC QUESTIONS

Each topic question refers to the topic of the same number.

1. **(a)** Why is it dangerous to look directly at the sun?   **(b)** What instrument provided astronomers with their first scientific observations of the sun?   **(c)** How does a solar telescope work? **(d)** Identify some satellites that have been used to study the sun.   **(e)** What area of the sun do scientists hope to study during the *Ulysses* mission?

2. **(a)** Compare the sun's dimensions with those of Earth.   **(b)** How hot is the sun?

3. **(a)** Name and briefly describe the three regions of the sun's atmosphere.   **(b)** Describe solar prominences.

4. **(a)** Describe the appearance, size, magnetism, and temperature of sunspots.   **(b)** What do sunspots show about the sun's rotation?   **(c)** What is the sunspot cycle?

5. **(a)** What is solar wind?   **(b)** Name and describe the sources of solar wind bursts.   **(c)** What effects does solar wind have on Earth?

6. **(a)** In the fusion reaction in the sun, what happens to the hydrogen that does not convert to helium?   **(b)** How much longer is this reaction expected to continue in the sun?

ANSWERS
   1. (a) risk of blindness   (b) spectroscope   (c) projects image into a dark room   (d) *Orbiting Solar Observatories, Helios A & B, Solar Max*   (e) polar regions
   2. (a) 110 times diameter, 1 000 000 times volume of Earth (b) 5500°C at surface, 15 000 000°C inside
   3. (a) photosphere—yellow face, granules, low density; chromosphere—less dense, red; corona—almost vacuum, pearly white   (b) huge arches in corona
   4. (a) dark spots, from barely visible to 1/10 diameter of sun, oppositely magnetized pairs, 3500°C (b) rate varies with latitude (c) change in sunspot number over 11-year period
   5. (a) stream of charged particles from corona   (b) coronal holes, solar flares   (c) magnetic storms, auroras
   6. (a) It becomes energy.   (b) 5 billion years

Current RESEARCH

Mission: To Study the Sun

The 370 kg *Ulysses* spacecraft was launched from the space shuttle *Discovery* in October, 1990. Since then, it has taken a circuitous route outward past Jupiter and then back toward the center of the solar system. *Ulysses's* mission is to study the total solar environment. That includes looking at the physical properties of the solar corona, solar wind, the sun's magnetic field, and the wide variety of energy the sun radiates.

What types of data will *Ulysses* be collecting? The spacecraft carries nine data collecting instruments developed in the United States and Europe. One instrument will study variations in the solar wind between the sun's poles and equator. Another instrument will study and record the sun's magnetic field at the poles. Yet another instrument will be looking for the source of gamma rays and tracking the direction of movement of X rays emitted by solar flares.

Another experiment is attempting to record the existence of gravity waves— ripples in space-time caused by mass in motion— that were predicted by Albert Einstein in his theory of general relativity.

II   Observing the Solar System

Topic 7   The Solar System

The sun's family is known as the **solar system**. It includes objects that range in size from tiny sandlike grains to gigantic spheres many thousands of kilometers in diameter. The solar system includes 9 planets, at least 61 natural satellites (also called moons), thousands of asteroids, millions of meteroids, and many comets. All of these objects travel around the sun at high speeds in paths called **orbits**. Some of the orbits are nearly circular, while others are highly elongated. Some of the orbits are near the sun, while others are billions of kilometers away.

Several members of the solar system can be seen with the unaided eye. Five of the planets can be seen without a telescope—Mercury, Venus, Mars, Jupiter, and Saturn. Meteors can be seen regularly with the unaided eye. A telescope is needed to see all asteroids and most comets.

Topic 8   Planets and Stars

To the unaided eye, planets look very much like stars. However, there is one difference that has been noted since earliest times. Over the lifetime of an observer the positions of stars relative to each other, and thus the shapes of constellations, do not noticeably change. The positions of planets among the constellations, however, change constantly. The reason for the difference is the distances to the two kinds of objects—the planets appear to move

OBJECTIVES

A List the members of the solar system and identify those that can be seen with the unaided eye.

B Describe how the motions of the planets across our sky differ from those of stars and explain the cause of this difference.

C Describe the difference between a geocentric and a heliocentric solar system.

VIDEODISC SELECTION

Formation of the solar system
Side 4 movie: 25260 & PLAY

Animated geocentric model of the solar system
Side 4 movie: 21623 & PLAY

22.7 The solar system includes the sun, planets and their moons, asteroids, meteoroids, and comets.

Pluto

Uranus

Neptune

Earth   Mercury

Venus

Sun

Mars

Saturn

Asteroid Belt

Jupiter

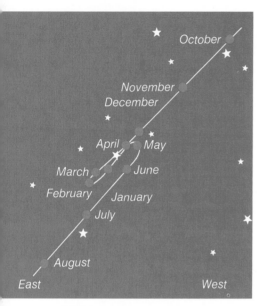

22.8 Planets move eastward against the background of stars but periodically make westward loops called retrograde motion.

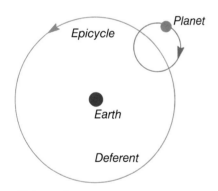

22.9 In Ptolemy's geocentric model of the solar system, the planets traveled on small circles called epicycles, which lay on a larger circle called a deferent.

ANSWERS

7. (a) planets, moons, asteroids, meteroids, comets (b) Mercury, Venus, Mars, Jupiter, Saturn, meteors

8. (a) Planets move eastward through stars. (b) westward loop of a planet, caused by Earth passing the planet

9. (a) earth-centered system (b) Ptolemy; occurred when planet made a loop on an epicycle (c) sun-centered; Copernicus (d) Heliocentric system is simpler.

through the stars because they are so much closer to us than the stars.

Most of the time the planets move eastward in front of the background of constellations, but they periodically make westward loops called **retrograde motion**. These loops occur because each planet travels around the sun at a different speed. Whenever Earth overtakes and passes another planet, that planet appears to move backward, or westward, among the stars. Once the planet has been passed, its eastward motion through the stars continues.

On a single night, a planet will not appear to move significantly. Several days, weeks, or months may be needed to notice a change in the position of a planet. The more distant the planet is from Earth, the more slowly its position changes.

Topic 9 **Solar System Models**

Ancient people did not recognize the cause of retrograde motion. They thought that Earth was the center of the universe and that the sun, planets, and stars moved around it. Such a system is called a **geocentric**, or earth-centered, system. The Greek astronomer Ptolemy, who lived around A.D. 140, developed an earth-centered model that he used to predict the locations of the planets. He imagined the planets on small orbits, called **epicycles**. The center of each small orbit moved around Earth on a larger orbit called a **deferent**. Retrograde motion occurred when the planet made a trip around the epicycle. Ptolemy's model was accepted until the 1600's.

The Polish astronomer Copernicus is credited with proposing the **heliocentric**, or sun-centered, solar system. Copernicus suggested that Earth and the other planets revolved around the sun. Epicycles were no longer needed to explain planetary motion. Retrograde motion would occur whenever Earth passed another planet. The heliocentric system provided a much simpler explanation of the observed motions in the sky. This system marked the beginning of our modern understanding of the structure of the universe.

TOPIC QUESTIONS

Each topic question refers to the topic of the same number.

7. (a) List the kinds of objects that are part of the solar system. (b) Which of these objects are visible to the unaided eye?

8. (a) How do the movements of planets in our sky differ from the movements of stars? (b) What is retrograde motion and why does it occur?

9. (a) What is a geocentric solar system? (b) Who used the geocentric system to explain planetary motions? How did he explain retrograde motion? (c) What is a heliocentric system and who is credited with proposing it? (d) What is the advantage of the heliocentric system over the geocentric system?

III Motion in the Solar System

Topic 10 The Contribution of Tycho

Tycho Brahe (TEE koe BRAH hee) was a Danish nobleman who lived on an island. On the island, Tycho built an astronomical observatory. His observatory did not include a telescope because it had not yet been invented. Tycho's observatory contained several kinds of instruments for measuring the positions of objects in the sky. With these instruments Tycho made very careful measurements of the positions of the stars and planets over a period of 20 years. Tycho's observations were the best ever made before the telescope. They were also the first long-term sky observations.

Topic 11 Johannes Kepler and the Laws of Planetary Motion

After Tycho's death, Johannes Kepler inherited all of Tycho's notebooks of data. Kepler spent many years studying those notebooks, and from their data he developed three **laws of planetary motion**.

Kepler's *first law of planetary motion* states that the planets travel in **elliptical orbits** with the sun at one focus. Instead of having a single center, or focus, as a circle does, an ellipse has two foci (foci = plural of focus). An ellipse was an unfamiliar shape at the time, and Copernicus had thought that the orbits were perfect circles. Because the sun is at one focus of the ellipse, a planet's distance from the sun will change throughout its orbit. The point in a planet's orbit where it is farthest from the sun is called its **aphelion**, while the point nearest the sun is its **perihelion**.

Kepler's *second law of planetary motion* is known as the **equal area law**. It states that each planet moves around the sun in such a way that an imaginary line joining the planet to the sun will sweep over equal areas of space in equal periods of time. Because a planet's orbit is an ellipse with the sun at one focus, the equal area law means that the speed at which a planet travels around the sun is not constant. Kepler determined that planets travel more rapidly when they are closer to the sun. He was not able to explain why they did, but later Isaac Newton discovered the reason (Topic 13).

OBJECTIVES

A Describe the work of Tycho Brahe and explain why his work was important.

B Summarize Kepler's laws of planetary motion and demonstrate their use.

C Identify some objects observed by Galileo with his telescopes and explain why his observations were important.

D Define Newton's law of gravitation and identify some factors that can be determined using the law.

VIDEODISC SELECTION

Heliocentric model of the solar system
Side 4 movie: 23079 & PLAY

SCIENCE BACKGROUND

Kepler's second law explains why, in the Northern Hemisphere, the seasons of fall and winter (around perihelion) are one week shorter than the seasons of spring and summer (around aphelion).

22.10 According to Kepler's law of equal areas, a line connecting Earth to the sun would pass over equal areas of space in equal times. Because Earth's orbit is elliptical, this means that Earth moves faster when it is nearer the sun.

Figure diagram labels: Earth's Orbit · Equal Areas · January 15 · June 15 (30 days) · July 15 · Sun · December 16

Periods of Revolution

Planet	Distance (AU)	Period
Mercury	0.4	88 days
Venus	0.7	225 days
Earth	1.0	365.25 days
Mars	1.5	687 days
Jupiter	5.2	12 years
Saturn	9.5	29.5 years
Uranus	19.2	84 years
Neptune	30.0	165 years
Pluto	39.4	248 years

VIDEODISC SELECTION

Animated diagram of planetary orbits
Side 4 movie: 24435 & PLAY

TEACHING TIP
This is not saying that Galileo invented the telescope.

Kepler's *third law of planetary motion* is the **harmonic law**. The time it takes a planet to travel one orbit around the sun is its *period*. The third law of planetary motion states that the period (P) of a planet squared is equal to the cube of its distance (D) from the sun, or $P^2 = D^3$. The formula is used to find the distance between the sun and a planet if the period is known or to find the period if the distance is known. To use the formula, the period must be in Earth years and the distance from the sun must be in astronomical units (AU, the distance between Earth and the sun). What is the period of Jupiter, if its distance from the sun is about 5.2 AU?

By using Kepler's third law:

$$(\text{Jupiter's period})^2 = (\text{Jupiter's Distance})^3$$

Expressing period in years and distance in AUs:

$$(\text{Jupiter's Period})^2 = (5.2 \text{ AU})^3$$
$$(\text{Jupiter's Period})^2 = 140.6 \text{ years (approx.)}$$
$$\text{Jupiter's Period} = 12 \text{ years (approx.)}$$

Kepler's third law states that the farther a planet is from the sun, the longer is its period of revolution. One reason is that its orbit is larger. Another is that it moves more slowly than nearer planets. The average speed of Earth in its orbit is about 30 kilometers a second. Mercury, nearest to the sun, moves about 49 kilometers a second. Pluto, usually farthest out, travels 5 kilometers a second.

Topic 12 **Galileo and the Telescope**

Galileo is believed to be the first astronomer to have a telescope and to turn it toward the sky. He was amazed at what he saw. In parts of the sky where our eyes can see thousands of stars, his telescope allowed him to see millions of stars that had never been suspected to exist. He could clearly see the craters and mountains on the moon. He observed Venus and discovered that it went through phases like our moon. Most important, he discovered four moons in orbit around Jupiter. In an Earth-centered system, all objects should go around Earth, but these moons clearly did not. Galileo's observation gave support to the heliocentric system.

Topic 13 **Isaac Newton and the Universal Law of Gravitation**

Kepler knew that a force was required to keep the planets in motion around the sun. Isaac Newton identified the force as gravity and determined its mathematical nature. Newton's **universal law of gravitation** shows that the force of gravity between any two objects is directly related to the masses of the two objects but inversely related to the square of the distance between the centers of the two objects. Thus, gravitational force is greater between objects of greater mass, and less between objects of lesser mass. Gravitational attraction also changes in a definite way as the distance between the centers of the two objects changes.

$$\text{change in force} = \frac{1}{\text{distance}^2}$$

The formula indicates that the gravitational attraction between objects changes inversely with the square of the distance between them. For example, if the two objects move to twice their former distance, then the force of attraction between them is one fourth as great. If two objects move to half their original distance, then the force of attraction between them is four times as great.

$$\begin{array}{ll} \dfrac{\text{change}}{\text{in force}} = \dfrac{1}{2^2} = \dfrac{1}{4}; & \dfrac{\text{change}}{\text{in force}} = \dfrac{1}{(1/2)^2} = 4 \end{array}$$

The law of gravitation explains the changing speed of a planet. The speed of a planet increases when it approaches the sun because the gravitational pull between the sun and the planet is greater at that time. The speed of the planet decreases when it is farther from the sun and the gravitational force is less. The law of gravitation also explains why the planet closest to the sun, Mercury, travels at a higher speed in its orbit than any other planet.

From the law of gravitation Newton calculated the masses of the planets from the dimensions of their orbits. He determined that tides are caused by the force of the moon as it revolves around Earth. Gravitational force explained the long orbits of comets and provided proof that they are part of the solar system.

In this century the law of gravitation is used to determine escape velocity. **Escape velocity** is the minimum velocity needed to escape the gravitational pull of a planet, moon, asteroid, or other object. Escape velocity is directly related to the mass of the object. For example, the velocity needed to escape from Earth is 11.2 kilometers per second. Mars, however, has less mass than Earth and its escape velocity is only 5.0 kilometers per second.

TOPIC QUESTIONS

Each topic question refers to the topic of the same number.

10. What was the contribution of Tycho Brahe to astronomy?

11. **(a)** What conclusions did Kepler draw from Tycho's data? **(b)** Define aphelion and perihelion. **(c)** What does the equal area law tell about the speed of a planet? **(d)** What is Kepler's harmonic law used to determine?

12. **(a)** Identify objects Galileo observed with his telescope. **(b)** Which was his most important observation? Why?

13. **(a)** What happens to the force of gravity between two objects if their masses increase? If the distance between them increases? **(b)** Name some phenomena explained by gravitation. **(c)** What is escape velocity?

22.11 Even though the sun is many times more massive than Earth, the force of gravity between Earth and the moon is greater than between the moon and the sun because the distance is so much less. This is why the moon revolves around Earth, rather than revolving around the sun on its own.

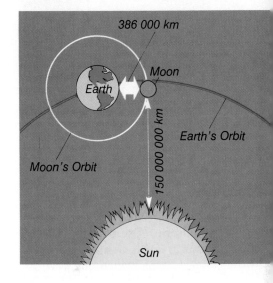

386 000 km

Moon

Earth

150 000 000 km

Earth's Orbit

Moon's Orbit

Sun

ANSWERS

10. He made careful measurements of positions of stars and planets over a 20-year period.

11. (a) developed 3 laws of planetary motion   (b) perihelion–point in planet's orbit closest to sun; aphelion–point farthest from sun (c) Planet moves faster when closer to sun.   (d) distance to planet if period known, period if distance is known

12. (a) moon, phases of Venus, moons of Jupiter   (b) Moons of Jupiter gave support to heliocentric system.

13. (a) gravity increases; decreases   (b) masses of planets, tides caused by moon, comets part of solar system, why speed of orbit changes   (c) minimum velocity needed to escape gravitational pull of an object

L A B
ACTIVITY

Ellipses and Eccentricity

For additional activities, see
Laboratory Investigations booklet.

Lab Skills and Objectives
- To **graph** several ellipses
- To **interpret** graphs to discover relationships between ellipse variables
- To **compare** the ellipse models with orbits of planets

Materials
- graph paper
- colored pencils

Procedure

1. On a sheet of graph paper, draw six sets of axes like the one shown in Figure 22.12. Label the sets of axes from 1 to 6. Use a second sheet of graph paper if you do not have enough room.

2. Look at Data Table A. The top row gives the position for the two foci for each ellipse. Plot the two foci for Ellipse 1. Note that the points for the x-axis are ± 4.5. Therefore, the first point is at +4.5 on the x-axis and the second point is at −4.5 of the x-axis. The y-value for both is 0. Use a + to mark the foci. (You may

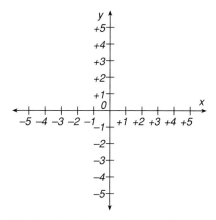

22.12 Axes for graphing an ellipse

want to refer to *Graphing Skills*, page 649, for graphing help.)

3. The remaining rows in Data Table A give points for each ellipse. Plot the points for Ellipse 1.

4. Complete Ellipse 1 by connecting the plotted points with a smooth curve.

5. Repeat steps 2–4 for the other ellipses. Use a different colored pencil for each ellipse.

6. The *major axis* is the line connecting the two farthest ends of the ellipse and passing through the two foci.

Copernicus and his model of the heliocentric solar system were vital in reshaping people's perceptions of the universe. However, Copernicus's model was not any better at predicting the position of the planets than Ptolemy's geocentric model. Kepler solved this problem by proposing that each planet has an elliptical orbit rather than a circular orbit. An ellipse is a closed, oval-shaped curve with two foci (Topic 11). In this exercise, you will draw and compare different ellipses. You will then compare the ellipses you have drawn to the orbits of the planets in the solar system.

Data Table A											
Ellipse 1		Ellipse 2		Ellipse 3		Ellipse 4		Ellipse 5		Ellipse 6	
x	y	x	y	x	y	x	y	x	y	x	y
±4.5	0	±3.0	0	±1.5	0	±3.0	0	±1.5	0	±0.9	0
0	±2.2	0	±4.0	0	±4.8	0	±1.5	0	±2.0	0	±2.9
±1.0	±2.1	±1.0	±3.9	±1.0	±4.7	±1.0	±1.4	±1.0	±1.8	±1.0	±2.7
±2.0	±2.0	±2.0	±3.7	±2.0	±4.4	±2.0	±1.2	±2.0	±1.2	±2.0	±2.1
±3.0	±1.7	±3.0	±3.2	±3.0	±3.8	±2.5	±1.0	±2.5	0	±2.5	±1.6
±4.0	±1.3	±4.0	±2.4	±4.0	±2.9	±3.0	±0.6			±3.0	0
±4.5	±1.0	±4.5	±1.7	±4.5	±2.1	±3.3	0				
±5.0	0	±5.0	0	±5.0	0						

Data Table B						
	Ellipse 1	Ellipse 2	Ellipse 3	Ellipse 4	Ellipse 5	Ellipse 6
distance between foci (d)	9.0	6.0	3.0	6.0	3.0	1.8
length of major axis (L)	10.0	10.0	10.0	6.7	5.0	6.0
eccentricity (e = d/L)	0.9	0.6	0.3	0.9	0.6	0.3

Measure the length of the major axis and the distance between the foci for each ellipse. Record your measurements in Data Table B. Some of the values have already been determined.

7. Use the following formula to calculate the eccentricity of each ellipse:

$$e = \frac{d}{L}$$

where e = eccentricity, d = distance between the two foci, and L = length of the major axis.

8. Answer the questions in *Analysis and Conclusions*.

Analysis and Conclusions

1. Study the shapes of Ellipses 1, 2, and 3. Which ellipse appears to be the most circular? Which ellipse appears to be the least circular? What are the eccentricities of these ellipses?

2. Describe the relationship between how circular an ellipse appears and its eccentricity.

3. Which ellipse has the same eccentricity as Ellipse 1? How do the shapes of these two ellipses compare? Which ellipse has the same eccentricity as Ellipse 3?

How do the shapes of these two ellipses compare?

4. Which factors—distance between foci, length of the major axis, or eccentricity—have to be equal in order for two ellipses to have the same shape? Give evidence for your answer.

5. What geometric shape would result if both foci were located at point (0,0) of the graph? What would be the eccentricity of such an ellipse?

6. Data Table C shows the orbital eccentricity of the planets. Compare the shapes of your ellipses with the shapes of the planets' orbits. Which ellipses are the best models for the shape of the planet orbits? Explain your answer.

7. Which planet has the most circular orbit? Which planet has the least circular orbit? Explain your answer.

8. Many comets have eccentricities of close to 1. Describe the shape of such an orbit. Which of your ellipses is most similar to the orbit of one of these comets?

9. Mars has two moons, Phobos and Deimos. The

Data Table C	
Planet	Orbital Eccentricity
Mercury	0.206
Venus	0.007
Earth	0.017
Mars	0.093
Jupiter	0.048
Saturn	0.056
Uranus	0.046
Neptune	0.010
Pluto	0.248

orbit of Phobos has a major axis length of 18 800 km. The distance between the foci is 281 km. The orbit of Deimos has a major axis length of 46 918 km. The distance between foci is 23.4 km. Which moon has a more circular orbit? Explain your answer.

10. The orbit of Mars has an eccentricity of 0.093. The distance between the two foci is 0.283 AU. The closest Mars gets to the sun during its orbit is 1.38 AU. What is the farthest Mars gets from the sun? (Hint: Remember that the sun is located at one of the foci.)

Answers to all questions appear in the Teacher's Guide at the back of this book.

■ Summary

I The spectroscope, the solar telescope, and satellites are used to study the sun.

The sun is enormous compared to Earth. Its surface temperature is about 5500°C; its interior is even hotter.

The photosphere, chromosphere, and corona are layers of the sun's atmosphere. Granules, solar prominences, sunspots, and solar flares appear on the sun's surface.

The solar wind is a stream of charged particles from the sun's corona. Some solar events cause changes in the solar wind that can affect Earth.

The sun's energy is the result of the conversion of hydrogen to helium in nuclear fusion. The mass that does not convert to helium is not lost, but becomes energy.

II The planets move eastward in front of the stars but periodically make backward loops called retrograde motion.

Ptolemy proposed a complex geocentric solar system to explain planetary motion. Copernicus proposed a simpler heliocentric system.

III Tycho Brahe made careful measurements of the positions of the stars and planets in the sky for a 20-year period.

Kepler used Tycho Brahe's data to develop three laws of planetary motion: the elliptical orbit law, the equal area law, and the harmonic law.

Galileo observed the sky with a telescope. His observations helped to confirm the heliocentric system.

Newton developed the universal law of gravitation, which explained the motions of planets in the solar system.

■ Vocabulary

aphelion	laws of planetary motion
auroras	orbit
chromosphere	perihelion
corona	photosphere

coronal holes
deferent
elliptical orbit
epicycles
equal area law
escape velocity
geocentric system
granules
harmonic law
heliocentric

retrograde motion
solar flares
solar prominences
solar system
solar telescope
solar wind
sunspots
universal law of
    gravitation

■ Review

On your paper write the word or words that best complete each sentence.

1. The instrument that provided the first scientific measurements of the sun was the _____.
2. A solar _____ projects an image of the sun into a darkened room where it can be safely studied.
3. Granules are found on the _____, the apparent bright-yellow face of the sun.
4. Compared to the photosphere, the temperatures of sunspots are _____.
5. Sunspots show that the sun _____ about once every 25 days.
6. The steady stream of the solar wind from the corona causes frequent _____ at polar latitudes on Earth.
7. Solar _____ are sudden outbursts of light that rise up in areas of sunspot activity.
8. Gusts of solar wind cause _____ storms on Earth.
9. The nuclear reaction in the sun changes _____ to helium.
10. Planets, _____, _____, _____, and _____ are all solar system members.
11. The planets travel eastward against the background of stars but periodically make backward loops called _____ motion.
12. Ptolemy used a _____ solar system to describe the motions of planets in the sky.
13. In a heliocentric solar system, the planets travel around the _____.

For further review, see **Study Guide.**
For assessment, see **Chapter Tests**
and **Computer Test Bank.**

14. Kepler used Tycho Brahe's data to show that the orbits of the planets were _____.

15. According to Kepler's equal area law, the speed of a planet _____ when it is nearer to the sun.

16. In Kepler's harmonic law, the period of a planet can be determined if its _____ from the sun is known.

17. Using a _____, Galileo discovered the four largest moons of Jupiter.

18. Increasing the distance between two objects causes the force of gravitation between them to _____.

■ Interpret and Apply

On your paper answer each question in complete sentences. Show any calculations.

1. Using the data in Topic 2, determine how long it would take the SST *Concorde* to fly from Earth to Jupiter. (Distance from the sun to Earth is about 150 000 000 km; from the sun to Jupiter, about 778 000 000 km.)

2. The average speed of the coronal solar wind is 400 km/s. How long does it take a particle in such a wind to reach Earth? (Assume that the distance from Earth to the sun is 150 000 000 km; there are 86 400 seconds in a day.)

3. *Skylab* entered Earth's atmosphere and burned up in 1979. As *Skylab* spiraled toward Earth, its orbital speed increased. Why?

4. Using Kepler's equal area law, explain why the speed of an object in a perfectly circular orbit is constant.

5. Using Kepler's harmonic law, calculate the period of a planet that is four times farther from the sun than Earth.

6. Using the equation given in Topic 13, demonstrate how the gravitational force between two objects changes when they are moved to (**a**) 3 times their original distance, (**b**) 10 times their original distance, (**c**) ½ their original distance, (**d**) 1/10 their original distance.

■ Critical Thinking

When Venus is observed from Earth, it is never more than 45° of arc from the sun. Figure A shows the positions of Earth, the sun, and Venus in a geocentric system. Three *phases*, or lighted portions of Venus visible from Earth, are also shown. In the geocentric system Venus and the sun are always on the same side of Earth. Figure B shows the positions of Venus, Earth, and the sun in a heliocentric system, and shows eight phases of Venus. Study Figures A and B and answer questions 1 – 4.

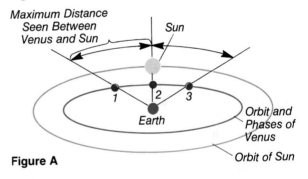

Figure A

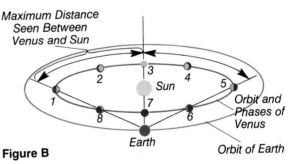

Figure B

1. Which phases in Figure B match phases 1, 2, and 3 shown in Figure A?

2. When Galileo looked at Venus with his telescope, he saw Venus in phases that are impossible in the geocentric system shown in Figure A. What phases did Galileo see?

3. Why did Galileo's observations of Venus help to disprove the geocentric model of the solar system?

4. Are there other planets that would show phases, as Venus does? Explain.

The Planets and the Solar System

▲
The Great Red Spot on Jupiter has long intrigued scientists.

How Do You Know That . . .

Jupiter's atmosphere is stormy and turbulent? A series of close-up photographs taken by the *Voyager* space probes recorded atmospheric movement in swirling bands. A prominent feature of Jupiter's atmosphere is the Great Red Spot, first discovered by telescope over 300 years ago. The large white oval below the Great Red Spot formed only 40 years ago. Over the years, other spots have formed but have later disappeared. Why the Great Red Spot has lasted so long is just one of the many mysteries of the solar system.

VIDEODISC SELECTION

Physical and orbital data on the planets (all sequences in this chapter are more fully described in the disc directory)
Side 4: 10355 to 10366, 12-frame sequence

I The Inner Planets

Topic 1 Two Groups of Planets

Pioneer, Mariner, Voyager, Venera — these are the names of some of the spacecraft launched from Earth to explore the solar system. Spacecraft bearing these names have flown past Mercury, Venus, Mars, Jupiter, Saturn, Uranus, and Neptune and have provided us with a new and exciting view of our neighborhood in space.

Even before the Space Age, scientists knew a great deal about the solar system. The planets are divided into two groups. The four planets nearest the sun — Mercury, Venus, Earth, and Mars — are the **inner planets**, while the other five — Jupiter, Saturn, Uranus, Neptune, and Pluto — are the **outer planets**. The asteroids that orbit between Mars and Jupiter divide the two groups.

The four inner planets are also called the **terrestrial**, or earthlike, **planets**. All have a rocky crust, a denser mantle layer, and a very dense core. All have average densities well above that of water.

Jupiter, Saturn, Uranus, and Neptune are the **Jovian**, or Jupiter-like, **planets**. These planets are huge compared to terrestrial planets. Jovian planets are gaseous and much less dense than the terrestrial planets. Pluto, an outer planet because of its location, is not dense enough to be terrestrial nor large enough to be Jovian.

Topic 2 Planet Mercury

Mercury is the planet nearest the sun. It orbits the sun in the shortest period of time — 88 Earth days. Mercury is the smallest of the four terrestrial planets. Mercury's diameter is one third Earth's, and its gravity is about two fifths of Earth's. Mercury's magnetic field is hundreds of times weaker than Earth's.

Little was known about Mercury until *Mariner 10* photographed it in 1975. These photographs show that craters cover about 75 percent of Mercury's surface. Like the craters on Earth's moon, these **impact craters** probably formed when huge rocks smashed into Mercury. The rest of the surface is smooth plains that may have been formed by lava flowing out of cracks in the surface.

Mercury turns on its axis once every 59 days. This slow rate, combined with Mercury's nearness to the sun, causes a daytime temperature of more than 400°C. In the nighttime, heat radiates away quickly and the temperature may be as low as −200°C.

Mercury has almost no atmosphere. Its weak gravity results in a low escape velocity. High daytime temperatures cause any particles to move at high speeds, allowing gases to escape into space.

OBJECTIVES

A Describe methods for grouping planets and give examples of planets in each group.

B Describe the properties and features of Mercury and Venus.

C Explain why some planets are seen only at sunrise or sunset while others can be seen all night.

D Identify the properties and features of Mars and compare Mars with Earth.

SCIENCE BACKGROUND

There is some question whether the little atmosphere that Mercury has is real or whether it is charged solar particles trapped in a weak magnetic field.

23.1 A close-up shows that the surface of Mercury is cratered.

413

Topic 3 Planet Venus

Venus has been called Earth's twin because the two are near each other and are similar in diameter, mass, and gravity. Unlike Earth, however, Venus has a very weak magnetic field. Unlike the other planets, Venus rotates from east to west.

Thick pale yellow clouds in Venus' atmosphere make its surface impossible to see from Earth. Knowledge of most of Venus' surface comes from radar-mapping done by the *Magellan* spacecraft at Venus, beginning in 1991.

Radar images show that the surface of Venus has some similarities to Earth. *Magellan* revealed a landscape dominated by volcanic features, faulting, and impact craters. Huge areas of the surface show periods of lava flooding, with flows lying on top of previous ones. An elevated region named Ishtar Terra is a lava-filled basin as large as the United States. Lava covers about 80 percent of the surface of Venus. Venus has fault and fracture systems similar to the San Andreas fault system in California. These features indicated that tectonic activity has occurred on Venus in the past. Whether the volcanoes continue to erupt and faulting is still going on is uncertain. The oldest crust on Venus is estimated to be about, 800 million years old; the oldest crust on Earth is about 4.3 billion years old.

In 1985, two balloons carrying weather instruments were placed in the atmosphere of Venus to take measurements. The data showed that the dense atmosphere is mostly carbon dioxide with about three percent nitrogen. Venus' yellow clouds are made of droplets of concentrated sulfuric acid. The surface atmospheric pressure is about 90 times greater than that on Earth.

Despite Venus' thick clouds, its surface gets very hot. Carbon dioxide in the atmosphere acts like the glass roof of a greenhouse. About 25 percent of the sunlight striking Venus reaches the surface and heats the rock. Like a blanket, the carbon dioxide atmosphere

VIDEODISC SELECTION

Data and photos: Mercury
Side 4: 10473 to 10496, 24-frame
sequence

Data and photos: Venus
Side 4: 10762 to 11122, 361-frame
sequence

23.2 (left) The 1.86-mile-high peak Gula Mons looms on the Venusian horizon. It may be the sight of volcanic activity. (right) In 1991–92, *Magellan*, a radar-mapping spacecraft, returned data used to make this image of Venus. An extensive system of faults and fractures can be seen cutting across the planet's surface.

prevents much of this heat from escaping to space. The result of this **greenhouse effect** is a surface temperature of about 482°C. The heating of the atmosphere also leads to strong upper-air winds of over 300 kilometers per hour.

Topic 4   **Evening and Morning Stars**

Venus is visible to observers on Earth at either evening or morning twilight almost all year. Because Venus is nearer the sun than is Earth, it appears only in parts of the sky near the sun. During most of the daytime, the sun is too bright for Venus to be seen. However, when Venus is east of the sun, the sun sets first and Venus is seen in the evening twilight of the western sky. At such times, Venus is called an **evening star**. It may remain visible as long as three hours after sunset. When Venus is west of the sun, it rises before the sun and is seen in the eastern sky as a **morning star**.

Mercury also can be seen only as a morning or evening star. However, Mercury is much more difficult to see because its orbit is closer to the sun. It is also smaller and less bright than Venus.

When Mars, Jupiter, and Saturn appear close to the sun, they are also seen as morning or evening stars. However, these planets have orbits beyond Earth's and can also appear in the nighttime sky.

23.3   When Venus is east of the sun, the sun sets before it. Then Venus is clearly visible in the evening sky.

VIDEODISC SELECTION

Data and photos: Mars
Side 4: 11788 to 12163, 376-frame sequence

23.4   An image of Mars taken from *Viking I*

Topic 5   **Planet Mars**

Mars is the fourth planet from the sun and the first planet outside Earth's orbit. Mars takes 687 days to orbit the sun. Its diameter is about one half that of Earth. The gravity of Mars is two fifths of Earth's. Mars has a very weak magnetic field.

Mars' axis is tilted at almost the same angle and in the same direction as Earth's. This tilt gives Mars four seasons similar to Earth's. However, because a Martian year is about twice as long as an Earth year, each Martian season is also twice as long. Because it is farther from the sun, Mars is colder than Earth. By day, Mars may be as warm as 27°C at the surface, but at night the temperature drops as low as −125°C. The thin Martian atmosphere is about 95 percent carbon dioxide and 5 percent nitrogen and argon with traces of other gases. Because the atmosphere is so thin, atmospheric pressure is about 150 times less than on Earth.

Like Earth, Mars has polar ice caps. Unlike Earth, the polar caps are mostly frozen carbon dioxide and some frozen water. The caps increase in size during each Martian winter and shrink during each summer. The temperature difference between the polar caps and soil warmed by the spring sun leads to strong winds and great swirling dust storms that often cover the entire planet.

The surface of Mars has been photographed by half a dozen spacecraft. The *Viking* spacecraft also sent landers to the surface that took close-up photos, recorded quakes and weather, and tested soil samples. Photographs show that Mars' northern hemisphere is

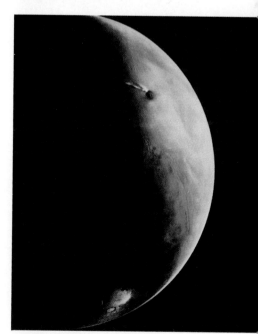

23.5 *Viking* landers photographed the surface of Mars and did tests of its soil and atmosphere. Further exploration of Mars is expected.

SCIENCE BACKGROUND

The next spacecraft to visit Mars, *Mars Observer*, was launched in September 1992.

ANSWERS

1. (a) inside or outside asteroid belt   (b) Mercury, Venus, Earth, Mars; rocky crust, internal structure, high density   (c) Jupiter, Saturn, Uranus, Neptune; large size, gaseous, low density

2. (a) 88 days, ⅓ diameter, ⅖ gravity, weaker magnetic field   (b) craters from impact, smooth plains from lava flows   (c) slow rotation, nearness to sun   (d) high temperature, weak gravity

3. (a) size, mass, gravity; magnetic field   (b) thick clouds; radar   (c) evidence of tectonic activity; surface is much younger   (d) mostly CO_2, 482°C, 90 times Earth's

4. (a) orbits inside Earth's, visible only near sun   (b) Orbits are beyond Earth's.

5. (a) nearly twice as long, ½ diameter and ⅖ gravity, weaker magnetic field   (b) four seasons but twice as long   (c) expand in winter, shrink in summer   (d) winds from temperature differences between ground and polar caps   (e) lowland plain in north, densely cratered highland in south   (f) Valles Marineris looks water-carved.

a smooth lowland plain of volcanic material, with few craters. Its southern hemisphere is a highland fractured by many large craters and cut by small channels.

Rising above the northern plains are several extinct volcanoes. The largest, also the largest known volcano in the solar system, is the shield volcano Olympus Mons (Mount Olympus). It is about 600 kilometers across and 25 kilometers high. Earth's highest volcano, Mauna Loa, rises only 8 kilometers above the Pacific Ocean floor. Unlike many of Earth's volcanoes, Martian volcanoes do not seem to be related to plate motions. The crustal rock of Mars appears thick, strong, and unbroken.

Cutting across the craters of the southern hemisphere is the Valles Marineris, a canyon system nearly as long as the United States is wide. While the canyon system appears to have been carved by water, there is no water on the surface of Mars. Some scientists think that water may have been an agent of erosion in the past. Frozen water reservoirs may lie beneath the surface of Mars.

Is there life on Mars? The *Viking* landers made chemical tests on soil samples to find out. The results were not clear, and while some scientists still hope that evidence of life will be found, many now think it very unlikely.

TOPIC QUESTIONS

Each topic question refers to the topic of the same number.

1. **(a)** How are planets classified as inner and outer?   **(b)** Name the terrestrial planets and identify ways they are alike.   **(c)** Name the Jovian planets and identify ways they are alike.

2. **(a)** Compare Mercury's orbital period, diameter, gravity, and magnetic field with Earth's.   **(b)** Identify the two kinds of surface features on Mercury and name the cause of each.   **(c)** Why is Mercury so hot by day and so cold at night?   **(d)** Why does Mercury have almost no atmosphere?

3. **(a)** How are Venus and Earth alike? Different?   **(b)** Why is the surface of Venus difficult to study? What method has been used to learn about it?   **(c)** How is the surface of Venus like Earth's? Different from Earth's?   **(d)** Describe the composition, temperature, and pressure of Venus' atmosphere.

4. **(a)** Why are Venus and Mercury only seen as evening or morning stars?   **(b)** Why can other planets be seen all night?

5. **(a)** Compare Mars' period of revolution, diameter, gravitation, and magnetic field with Earth's.   **(b)** How are seasons on Mars like seasons on Earth? How are they different?   **(c)** How do polar caps on Mars change with the seasons?   **(d)** What causes dust storms on Mars?   **(e)** How do the surfaces of the northern and southern hemispheres of Mars differ?   **(f)** What is the evidence of water on Mars?

II   The Outer Planets

Topic 6   The Jovian Planets

The Jovian planets—Jupiter, Saturn, Uranus, and Neptune—are unlike the terrestrial planets in several ways. First, Jovian planets are much larger. The smallest Jovian planet, Uranus, is nearly 15 times more massive than the largest terrestrial planet, Earth. Second, Jovian planets are gas planets and their surface is the top of the gas layer. Third, Jovian planets are composed mainly of the light elements hydrogen and helium, while terrestrial planets are made of iron, silicon, oxygen, and other heavy elements.

All Jovian planets have a three-layered structure. A rocky core may lie at the center of each. The rocky core is surrounded by a liquid mantle. For Jupiter and Saturn, this mantle is thought to be liquid hydrogen. Uranus and Neptune are slightly denser than Jupiter and Saturn, and their mantle layers may contain oxygen, nitrogen, and carbon along with liquid hydrogen. The outer layer of all four planets is mainly gaseous hydrogen and helium.

All the Jovian planets have ring systems, although some rings are very faint. The ring systems have three common properties. First, they consist of many particles in independent orbits around the planet. Second, the rings are closer to the planet than its major moons. Third, the rings are centered over the planet's equator. The spectacular rings of Saturn are made of billions of "snowballs" of ice and ice-covered rock. The rings of the other planets are faint and were discovered in the late 1970's by Earth-based telescopes and *Voyagers 1* and *2*. Jupiter's three rings are made of fine bits of dark rock. The 11 rings of Uranus are made of larger rocky chunks. Neptune is surrounded by three narrow rings and one broad sheet of dust.

Topic 7   Planet Jupiter

Jupiter is the fifth planet from the sun. Jupiter, shown in Figure 23.7, takes 11.9 Earth years to complete one orbit. It rotates faster than any other planet—once every ten hours. It is the largest planet in the solar system and has more than twice the total mass of all other planets combined.

Four spacecraft have flown by Jupiter and returned data and photographs of the planet. These show the structure of Jupiter's gaseous surface. It consists of alternating light- and dark-colored bands that run parallel to its equator. The dark bands are areas of sinking gases while the light bands are areas of rising gases. Between the bands, high velocity winds blow parallel to the equator. The winds at the equator travel eastward at an average speed of 400 kilometers per hour. Directly north and south are narrower bands surrounded by westward winds of about 100 kilometers per hour. Jupiter has five or six such bands in each hemisphere.

OBJECTIVES

A Contrast the Jovian planets with the terrestrial planets and describe properties common to Jovian planets.

B Discuss the properties and features of Jupiter and Saturn and compare and contrast these two planets.

C Describe the features of Uranus and identify those which are unusual.

D Describe the features of Neptune and Pluto.

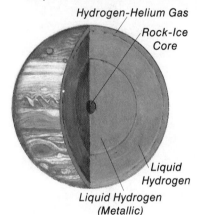

23.6 This diagram shows the possible inner structure of Jupiter. Other Jovian planets have similar inner structures.

SCIENCE BACKGROUND
The Jovian planets are also referred to as gas giants.

SCIENCE BACKGROUND
The cores of Jupiter and Saturn alone are each expected to equal 25 earth masses.

OF INTEREST
The first five rings of Uranus were discovered by accident when they dimmed a star as Uranus passed in front of it.

SCIENCE BACKGROUND
The ring systems of Saturn and Jupiter have a number of tiny moons in or near the rings. These *shepherd moons* prevent particles from leaving the rings.

23.7 Jupiter's surface consists of a series of light and dark bands. The bands are caused by alternating wind belts.

VIDEODISC SELECTION

Data and photos: Jupiter
Side 4: 12916 to 13128, 213-frame
sequence

SCIENCE BACKGROUND
   The *Voyager 2* spacecraft left Earth in August 1977, passed Jupiter in 1979, Saturn in 1981, Uranus in 1986, and Neptune in 1989.

SCIENCE BACKGROUND
   Voyager 2 was designed to explore only Jupiter and Saturn. It was reprogrammed to accommodate for such things as lower light levels, lower power supply, and failed equipment between Saturn and Uranus. The craft was 8 years old when it arrived at Uranus.

OF INTEREST
   Radio signals from *Voyager 2* took 2 hours 44.8 minutes to travel from Uranus to Earth.

23.8 Composite photo of Saturn, the moons are not shown at actual relative size.

The Great Red Spot is the most striking feature of Jupiter's surface, and it rises about 8 kilometers above the cloud tops. However, it is just one of several spots. Some spots appear and disappear quickly, while others remain for decades. Photographs indicate that the spots may be relatively calm areas that rotate slowly within the turbulent atmosphere.

Jupiter has the strongest known magnetic field. As on Earth, the interaction between the solar wind and the magnetic field causes brilliant auroras, colored displays of light (Chapter 26, Topic 6). *Voyager 1* observed these auroras as well as intense lightning storms.

Jupiter radiates between 1.5 and 2.0 times as much heat back to space as it receives from the sun. The extra heat is thought to come from Jupiter's original heat of formation and from contraction due to gravity.

The moons of Jupiter are described in Topic 12.

Topic 8   **Planet Saturn**

Saturn, the sixth planet from the sun, takes nearly 30 Earth years to complete one orbit. Saturn turns on its axis once every 10.7 hours. Most of what is known about Saturn was learned from the flyby flights of *Pioneer 11* in 1979 and *Voyagers 1* and *2* in 1980 and 1981.

Like Jupiter, the surface of Saturn has colored bands, which are areas of rising and sinking gases, parallel to the equator. Saturn, however, has fewer bands than Jupiter, and the wind speed at its equator is faster—about 1800 kilometers per hour. Saturn's density, like Jupiter's, is low—less than 1 gram per cubic centimeter.

Saturn radiates between 1.5 and 2.5 times as much energy as it receives from the sun. Like Jupiter, it apparently has sources of internal heat. Saturn has a weak magnetic field.

The moons of Saturn are described in Topic 13.

Topic 9 **Planet Uranus**

Uranus, the seventh planet from the sun, takes 84 Earth years to complete one orbit. Because Uranus is not easily visible to the unaided eye from Earth, it was not discovered until 1781. Uranus is about 19 times farther from the sun than Earth is. Sunlight there is about 360 times fainter than on Earth, and the average surface temperature is only about −200°C.

Uranus has many unusual features. It turns on its axis once every 17.2 hours, the slowest rate of any Jovian planet. More unusual is its axis of rotation—it is tipped almost completely over, so that Uranus orbits the sun on its side. At the present time, the planet's south pole is pointed almost straight at the sun. Some scientists think that the planet was tipped by a collision with an Earth-sized mass of material early in the history of the solar system.

When *Voyager 2* flew past Uranus in 1986, it discovered something surprising about the planet's magnetic field. Even though the planet is tipped over, the magnetic field is nearly upright. For most planets the axis of rotation and the magnetic field differ by only a few degrees. On Uranus the difference is 60 degrees. This difference causes the planet's magnetic field to trace a spiral pattern in the solar wind as the planet rotates. Scientists used this difference to gain better data about the planet. Usually, rotation rates for Jovian planets are difficult to determine because the movement of the gaseous outer layers may not be the same as the movement of the whole planet. A planet's magnetic field is generated in its core, which does rotate at the same rate as the whole planet. The spiral pattern traced by the magnetic field made it possible to determine Uranus' rate of rotation very accurately.

Voyager scientists were also surprised at the temperatures in the atmosphere of Uranus. The side of the planet facing away from the sun was no cooler than the side facing the sun. In fact, the temperature of the atmosphere is nearly the same over the entire surface of the planet. The reason for this similarity is not yet clear, but some sort of atmospheric currents seem to be at work.

23.9 *Voyager 2* took this photograph of Uranus in 1986.

VIDEODISC SELECTION

Data and photos: Saturn
Side 4: 13131 to 13260, 130-frame sequence

Data and photos: Uranus
Side 4: 13263 to 13289, 27-frame sequence

23.10 For most planets, the angle between the axis of rotation and the magnetic field is small. For Uranus and Neptune, however, the differences are much greater.

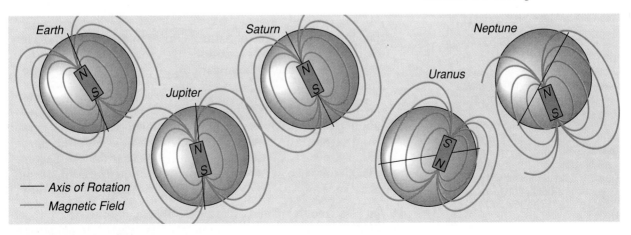

Earth   Saturn   Neptune   Jupiter   Uranus

—— Axis of Rotation
—— Magnetic Field

VIDEODISC SELECTION

Data and photos: Pluto
Side 4: 13312 to 13335, 24-frame
sequence

23.11 Wisps of white clouds accompany the Great Dark Spot on Neptune.

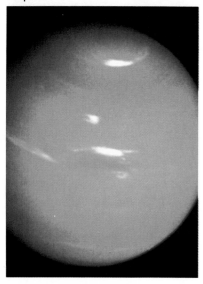

VIDEODISC SELECTION

Data and photos: Neptune
Side 4: 13291 to 13310, 20-frame
sequence

ANSWERS

6. (a) larger, gas surface, hydrogen-helium composition   (b) rocky core, liquid mantle, gaseous outer layer   (c) particles in own orbits, close to planet, on equatorial plane

7. (a) largest planet, shortest day   (b) areas of rising and sinking gases with winds blowing between them   (c) very strong (d) radiates 1.5–2.0 times more

8. (a) alternating wind bands; fewer bands but wind at equator blows much faster   (b) radiates 1.5–2.5 times more away

9. (a) axial tilt, rotation, magnetic field, temperature   (b) axis of rotation on side, magnetic field 60° from axis of rotation   (c) spiral, rotation rate   (d) nearly same all over

10. (a) most distant Jovian, gaseous wind speed 2200 km/hr (b) smallest, coldest, most elongated and inclined orbit   (c) Their orbits cross.

Topic 10   Neptune and Pluto

Neptune, the most distant of the Jovian planets, was discovered in 1846. Its period of rotation is 16.1 Earth hours, and it takes 165 years to orbit the sun. In 1989, *Voyager 2* discovered that the magnetic field of Neptune is tipped 47 degrees in relation to its axis of rotation and is offset from the center of the planet by about 14 000 kilometers. Wind speeds up to 2200 kilometers per hour were recorded on Neptune. Neptune gives off 2.7 times more energy than it receives from the sun. Its temperature was measured at –214°C.

Pluto, discovered in 1930, is the smallest, coldest, and most distant known planet. Its surface temperature is probably below –220°C. At that temperature, most of its atmosphere of methane and helium is frozen solid on the surface. Pluto itself seems to be made of water, ice, and rocks. Pluto orbits the sun in 248 years along a highly elliptical orbit that is inclined 17 degrees in relation to the orbits of the other planets. At one point, the orbit comes closer to the sun than Neptune's orbit. Pluto is currently closer to the sun than Neptune and will remain so until March of 1999.

TOPIC QUESTIONS

Each topic question refers to the topic of the same number.

6. **(a)** List some ways the Jovian planets are different from the terrestrial planets.   **(b)** Describe the internal structure of the Jovian planets.   **(c)** List three properties common to the Jovian ring systems.

7. **(a)** Identify two ways Jupiter is different from all the other planets.   **(b)** Describe Jupiter's winds.   **(c)** Describe Jupiter's magnetic field.   **(d)** How does the amount of heat that Jupiter radiates to space compare with the amount it receives from the sun?

8. **(a)** How is the surface of Saturn similar to that of Jupiter? How is it different?   **(b)** How does the amount of heat Saturn receives from the sun compare to the amount it radiates back to space?

9. **(a)** In what ways is Uranus unusual?   **(b)** What is unusual about Uranus' axis of rotation and magnetic field?   **(c)** What kind of pattern does Uranus' magnetic field make in space? What were scientists able to determine from the pattern? **(d)** Why are scientists puzzled by the temperatures of Uranus' atmosphere?

10. **(a)** Describe the planet Neptune.   **(b)** How are the size, temperature, and orbit of Pluto unique?   **(c)** Why is Pluto sometimes nearer the sun than Neptune is?

III   Planetary Satellites

Topic 11   Satellites of Earth and Mars

Bodies that revolve around planets are called **satellites**, or **moons**. Except for Mercury and Venus, each planet has at least one natural satellite. The moon is Earth's only natural satellite. At 3476 kilometers across, it is about one fourth Earth's diameter and slightly smaller than the planet Mercury. The moon's average distance from Earth is 386 000 kilometers. It circles Earth every 27.3 days. Earth's moon is the subject of Chapter 24.

Mars has two tiny moons, Phobos (FO bus) and Deimos (DIE mus). Both have irregular shapes and are marked with impact craters. Phobos, the larger of the two, is only 27 kilometers across its widest point. It is closer to Mars and circles the planet three times a day.

Topic 12   Jupiter's Moons

Jupiter has at least 16 moons. Only 13 moons were known until *Voyager* discovered 3 more in 1979. The four largest moons—Io, Europa, Ganymede, and Callisto—are known as the *Galilean satellites* in honor of their discoverer, Galileo. Ganymede is the largest moon in the solar system. Callisto is almost as large. Io and Europa are about the size of Earth's moon. Most of what is known about these moons comes from *Voyager* photographs taken in 1979.

Io, nearest of the Galilean satellites to Jupiter, is one of the most exciting moons. Its color varies from bright yellow-orange to red, and it is geologically active! At least 10 active volcanoes have been filmed in eruptions that reach as high as 320 kilometers. The materials that erupt from the volcanoes—sulfur, sulfur dioxide, and other sulfur compounds—cause Io's yellow-orange color. Unlike most bodies in the solar system, Io shows no signs of impact craters. If craters ever existed on Io, they have been completely covered by material erupted from the volcanoes. Io's density is about 3.5 g/cm^3, which is close to that of Earth's moon. Io is thought to have an atmosphere of sulfur dioxide. Its surface is probably covered by layers of sulfur and frozen sulfur dioxide. Its interior may be molten silicate rock. Io may get its internal heat from friction due to the gravitational pull of Jupiter.

Europa, next out from Jupiter, is also a rock-core moon with a density somewhat less than that of Earth's moon. Europa's strangely smooth and shiny white surface appears to be a crust of ice (mostly frozen water) about 100 kilometers thick. The surface is marked by a crisscross pattern of bright and dark lines that are still a mystery. Scientists think there may be deep oceans of water beneath the ice. If so, it is possible that simple forms of life, like those in the lakes of Antarctica, have developed.

OBJECTIVES

A Define *satellite*, identify two planets that have no satellites, and describe the satellites of Mars.

B Name the four Galilean satellites and identify features unique to each.

C Identify and describe the major moons of Saturn, Uranus, Neptune, and Pluto.

VIDEODISC SELECTION

Data and photos: Earth's moon
Side 4: 11593 to 11783, 191-frame sequence

23.12   Two of Jupiter's four Galilean moons: (top) Io, (bottom) Europa

23.13   The Galilean moons (left) Ganymede, (right) Callisto

VIDEODISC SELECTION

Photos of Mars' moons
Side 4: 11811 to 11815, 5-frame
sequence

Data and photos of Jupiter's moons
Side 4: 12944 to 12958, 15-frame
sequence

Ganymede and Callisto, next in order from Jupiter, are very different from Io and Europa. Their densities are less than 2 g/cm³, which suggests that these moons are mainly ice. Both Ganymede and Callisto appear to be covered by thick layers of ice mixed with rock. Their interiors are probably ice with silicate rock cores. Callisto is the most cratered body in the solar system. Its craters were made some 4 billion years ago. Ganymede's surface has dark areas that are cratered like Callisto, but it also has lighter areas. The lighter areas are marked by many grooves that seem to be long parallel ridges and valleys. The grooves are much younger than the impact craters. Geologists think the grooves may have been formed by movements of crustal plates which—if they do exist—are ice.

Topic 13   **Saturn's Moons**

Until the Space Age, Saturn was known to have nine moons, all discovered before 1900. Recently, new moons have been discovered by both telescopes and spacecraft. The latest count is 18 (with 2 more unconfirmed). The largest and most interesting is Titan.

Titan is the second largest moon in the solar system. Its density is just under 2 g/cm³, and it seems to be about half rock and half frozen water. Most of the ice is included in a thick shell reaching nearly halfway to the center. The rest of the interior is rock.

Titan is the only moon known to have a substantial atmosphere. Its atmospheric pressure is about 1.5 times Earth's. Like Earth, its principal gas is nitrogen, which is estimated to be from 90 to 99 percent of the total atmosphere. Most of the remaining gas is methane with traces of hydrogen cyanide and acetylene.

Titan's surface temperature is about −180°C. This is cold enough to turn methane and other gases to liquid. The resulting droplets form a dense orange smog that hides Titan's surface.

VIDEODISC SELECTION

Photos of Saturn's moons
Side 4: 13169 to 13188, 20-frame
sequence

Topic 14   The Moons of Uranus

Only 5 of Uranus' moons were known until *Voyager 2* discovered 10 additional, small moons in 1986. *Voyager 2* also sent back incredible pictures of the five previously known moons.

The five largest moons of Uranus are Titania, Oberon, Umbriel, Ariel, and Miranda. All are alike in that they are dark, lack atmospheres, and have many impact craters on their surfaces. But differences between the moons are visible in the *Voyager* photographs. Titania has huge, faulted valleys. Oberon's impact craters are partly flooded with dark material. Umbriel has an unusual dark surface, and Ariel's cratered surface is crisscrossed by valleys and faults. Miranda (Figure 23.14) proved to be the most startling of all. It has parallel V-shaped grooves over a third of its surface, with jagged, sometimes parallel ridges over the rest. The causes of these features remains unknown.

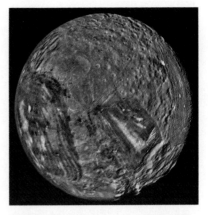

23.14   The Uranian moon Miranda, as imaged by *Voyager 2* in 1986

Topic 15   The Moons of Neptune and Pluto

Neptune has eight moons. Six of those moons, including the second largest, were discovered in 1989 by *Voyager 2*. Triton, the largest of Neptune's moons, is about four fifths the size of Earth's moon. Triton's southern hemisphere ice cap is made of methane and ammonia. Active geysers of nitrogen were erupting from the surface of Triton as *Voyager 2* passed by. Triton has a very thin atmosphere.

Pluto has one known moon, Charon (KARE en), which was discovered in 1978 from Earth-based observations. Its diameter is about half that of Pluto's. Charon orbits the planet in 6.4 days. Pluto has never been visited by spacecraft; however, early planning is now underway to send a spacecraft to reach it in 2015.

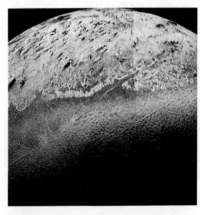

23.15   Triton, the largest moon of Neptune, has nitrogen geysers, which are seen as dark streaks.

TOPIC QUESTIONS

Each topic question refers to the topic of the same number.

11. **(a)** What is a satellite?   **(b)** Which planets have no satellites? **(c)** Describe Mars' satellites.

12. **(a)** Name the Galilean moons of Jupiter. Why are they called Galilean?   **(b)** Identify one unique feature for each of the Galilean moons.

13. Describe Saturn's moons.

14. **(a)** List the five largest moons of Uranus.   **(b)** Name some ways in which all five moons are alike.   **(c)** Identify one unique feature of each.

15. **(a)** Describe Neptune's largest moon.   **(b)** Identify Pluto's moon.

ANSWERS

11. (a) a body that orbits a planet (b) Mercury, Venus   (c) tiny, irregular, many craters

12. (a) Io, Europa, Ganymede, Callisto; discovered by Galileo (b) in above order, geologically active, smooth white surface, largest, heavily cratered

13. At least 18; Titan, second largest in solar system, has atmosphere.

14. (a) Titania, Oberon, Umbriel, Ariel, Miranda   (b) dark, lack atmospheres   (c) in above order, huge faulted valleys, partly flooded impact craters, unusual dark surface, crisscrossed surface, V-shaped grooves

15. (a) Triton—4/5 the size of Earth, ice cap and active geysers (b) Charon

OBJECTIVES

A Describe the appearance of a comet, its orbit, behavior, and composition and identify some comets.

B Describe the sizes, shapes, and orbits of asteroids and discuss their possible origin.

C Define *meteoroid*, *meteor*, *meteorite*, and *meteor shower*, and name and describe the three types of meteorites.

D Explain why meteorite craters are rare on Earth.

IV Comets, Asteroids, and Meteoroids

Topic 16 Comets

What are the parts of a **comet**? A photograph of a comet, Figure 23.15, shows a glowing head and a long, bright tail. The head, or *nucleus,* of the comet glows by reflected sunlight. The nucleus is surrounded by a hazy cloud called a *coma.* Some comets are also surrounded by great clouds of hydrogen. Comets have been observed since earliest times, and many new comets are discovered every year. Most comets, however, can be seen only through telescopes.

Most of the time, a comet is barely visible even through a telescope. Comets spend much of the time out beyond the orbit of Pluto, and only shine by reflected sunlight. When a comet comes near the sun, solar wind drives particles and gases away from the coma and forms the tail. Because the tail is formed by solar wind, it always points away from the sun.

Most comets have very large, elongated orbits. Some come near the sun only once in thousands of years. The closest, Encke's comet, returns every 3.3 years. The most famous, Comet Halley (Halley's comet), returns every 76 years. The comet is named for Edmund Halley, an eighteenth-century English astronomer. In studying records of comets, Halley noticed that bright comets had appeared in 1531, 1607, and 1682. He thought that these were all one comet with an orbital period of about 76 years. He correctly predicted its return sometime in 1758 or 1759. It returned again in 1835, 1910, and 1986.

When Comet Halley returned in 1986, it was studied by six different spacecraft in a truly international effort. *VeGa 1* and *VeGa 2,* launched by the Soviet Union, flew past the comet. *Giotto,* launched by the European Space Agency, came within 605 kilometers of the comet's nucleus. Two Japanese spacecraft, *Suisei* and *Sakigake,* and the American *Pioneer-Venus Orbiter* viewed the comet from greater distances. Shortly before the encounters with Halley, the *International Cometary Explorer (ICE)* flew through the tail of another comet, Giacobini-Zinner.

Much was learned from the data and photographs returned by these spacecraft. The nucleus of Halley's comet was found to be about 16 kilometers long and 8 kilometers wide, a bit larger and more irregular than expected. American astronomer Fred Whipple has long described the nucleus of a comet as a dirty snowball, meaning that it is mostly ice with small pieces of other materials, such as rock, in it. The large size of Halley, however, indicates that a comet nucleus is mostly empty space. Whipple now thinks that "dirty snowdrift" is a better model. The nucleus of Comet Halley was found to contain carbon, nitrogen, oxygen, sulfur, and magnesium, elements common throughout the solar system.

COMA

23.16 (top) Comet Halley as photographed through a telescope in 1986 (bottom) A false-color image of Comet Halley made during the *Giotto* mission in 1986.

Topic 17 **Asteroids**

Early astronomers thought a planet would be found in the great space between Mars and Jupiter. In 1801, the Sicilian clergyman Piazzi discovered the "planet" Ceres. Ceres, however, later proved to be too small to be a planet. It is merely the largest of many small, planetlike bodies called asteroids, of which there are thousands.

Asteroids are solid, rocklike masses. Most seem to have irregular shapes, which explain why their brightness changes as they rotate. Only the two largest, Ceres and Pallas, are spherical. Ceres has a diameter of about 1000 kilometers. Most asteroids are less than 1 kilometer long.

Asteroids revolve around the sun in the same direction as the planets. Most asteroid orbits are nearly circular and lie between Mars and Jupiter. A few, however, have long oval orbits. Some come close to Mercury at perihelion. The most unusual orbit is that of Chiron (KIE ron), discovered in 1977. Its perihelion is inside Saturn's orbit; its aphelion is just inside Uranus' orbit.

How did asteroids originate? Scientists think that some asteroids are left over pieces from the solar system's formation. Others may be extinct or inactive comets.

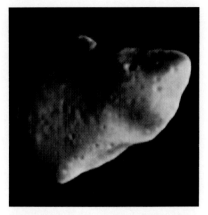

23.17 NASA's *Galileo* spacecraft sent images of Gaspra, a smallish asteroid of the asteroid belt that lies between Mars and Jupiter.

VIDEODISC SELECTION

Comet diagrams and photos·
Side 4: 13347 to 13354, 8-frame sequence

Asteroid diagrams and photos
Side 4: 13338 to 13343, 6-frame sequence

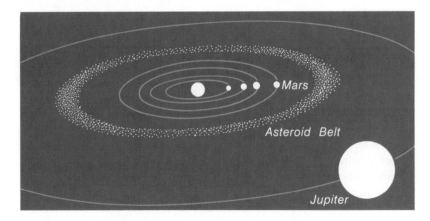

Mars

Asteroid Belt

Jupiter

23.18 Most asteroids orbit in a belt located between the orbits of Mars and Jupiter.

Topic 18 **Meteors and Meteoroids**

A **meteoroid** is a rock or an icy fragment traveling in space. Meteoroids may be as large as boulders or as small as sand grains. A **meteor** is the light made by a meteoroid as it passes through Earth's atmosphere. The light is caused by friction between the rapidly moving meteoroid and the atmosphere. The friction excites the atoms in the atmosphere and causes them to glow. The meteoroid may burn as it enters the atmosphere. An unusually bright meteor is sometimes called a *fireball*.

On a clear, dark night about 5 to 15 meteors can be seen every hour. However, this is a small portion of all meteors. Scientists estimate that about 100 million meteroids enter the atmosphere daily. Most are tiny and burn or vaporize in the air. The dust and gases from meteoroids add a few metric tons to Earth each day.

VIDEODISC SELECTION

Meteor and meteorite photos
Side 4: 13435 to 13444, 10-frame sequence

Meteorite impact craters
Side 1: 2339 to 2350, 12-frame sequence

OF INTEREST

The largest iron meteorite was found in 1920 near Grootfontein, Namibia, South Africa. It weighs 60 tons and measures 2.7 x 2.7 x 1 meters.

OF INTEREST

The Antarctic meteorites are treated in the same way as moon rocks. They are numbered in place next to a scale, teased into Teflon bags without being touched by hand, and shipped frozen to the Johnson Space Center in Houston for analysis in the same nitrogen environment as the lunar rocks.

23.19 This large meteorite has a mass of about 34 metric tons. It is on display at the Hayden Planetarium in New York City.

23.20 Barringer Meteorite Crater in Arizona probably formed when an asteroid crashed into Earth about 25 000 years ago.

Some meteoroids travel through space alone. Others are part of great groups of billions of particles called *meteoroid swarms*, which are associated with the orbits of comets. **Meteor showers** occur when Earth crosses a meteoroid swarm, which happens several times a year. At such times, large numbers of meteors are seen. The meteors of a particular shower appear to come from the same constellation and are named for that constellation. Among the best-known meteor showers are the Perseids about August 12, the Orionids about October 20, the Taurids about November 10, and the Geminids about December 10.

Topic 19 **Meteorites**

A **meteorite** is part of a large meteoroid that survives its trip through the atmosphere and strikes Earth's surface. There are three basic types of meteorites. Ninety-three percent of all meteorites are *stones*. Stones strongly resemble Earth's dark igneous rocks. They are composed primarily of silicates but include 10 to 15 percent iron. The largest known stone weighs about a metric ton. It landed at Norton County, Kansas, in 1948.

The second group of meteorites are called *irons* because they are 85 to 95 percent iron. The remainder is nickel. Iron meteorites are usually black outside and silvery inside. Since they consist largely of iron and nickel, they are much heavier than stones. One of the largest known irons was found in Greenland. It weighs over 30 metric tons. The third group of meteorites are *stony-irons*. These rare meteorites are a mixture of stone and iron.

The most abundant source of meteorites is the Antarctic ice cap. First discovered in 1969, some meteorites had been buried and preserved in the ice for thousands of years. They are exposed at the surface when wind erosion removes the ice around them. Thousands of meteorites have been recovered from Antarctica, providing an enormous increase in the supply of extraterrestrial material available for study. Some Antarctic meteorites appear to have come from the moon or from Mars. They may have been launched into space as particles by meteoroid impact on those bodies.

Topic 20 **Meteorite Craters**

Impact craters are common features of some planets and most moons in the solar system. However, impact craters are rare features on Earth. One reason is that Earth's atmosphere burns up most meteroids before they strike the surface. A second reason is that Earth is geologically active and continually erases the marks made by impacts. However, Earth still has some *meteorite craters* that were formed relatively recently.

The Barringer Meteorite Crater (also called Meteor Crater) in Arizona is thought to have formed 25 000 years ago when an iron meteorite about 20 meters in diameter struck Earth's surface and exploded. The crater is 1300 meters in diameter and nearly 200 meters deep. Fragments of the meteorite were scattered more than a kilometer from the crater. Craters larger than Barringer Meteorite Crater have been found in Australia, Africa, and Canada.

TOPIC QUESTIONS

Each topic question refers to the topic of the same number.

16. (a) Describe the parts of a comet.   (b) What causes a comet to have a tail? Why does the tail always point away from the sun? (c) Describe the orbit and period of most comets.   (d) Describe the comet explorations that took place in 1985–86.   (e) Describe the composition of comets.

17. (a) Describe the general size, shape, and orbit of asteroids. (b) How might asteroids have originated?

18. (a) Distinguish between a meteoroid and a meteor.   (b) Why do meteor showers occur? Name and give the dates of several meteor showers.

19. (a) What is a meteorite?   (b) Name and describe three types of meteorites.   (c) What is unusual about Antarctic meteorites?

20. (a) Why are impact craters rare on Earth?   (b) Describe the shape and possible origin of the Barringer Meteorite Crater.

ANSWERS

16. (a) nucleus inside hazy coma and hydrogen cloud, long bright tail (b) solar wind removing material from coma; follows direction of solar wind   (c) very elongated, long periods   (d) several spacecraft visited and returned data on 2 comets (e) "dirty snowdrift" of ice, carbon, nitrogen, oxygen, sulfur, magnesium

17. (a) < 1 km, irregular, nearly circular between Mars and Jupiter (b) original material, extinct or inactive comets

18. (a) meteor—light from meteoroid in atmosphere; meteoroid—rock fragments in space   (b) Earth encounters meteor swarm; Perseids—Aug. 12; Orionids—Oct. 20; Taurids—Nov. 10; Geminids—Dec. 10

19. (a) meteoroid that strikes Earth   (b) stones—look like dark silicate igneous rocks; irons—black and silvery, iron and nickel; stony-irons—half stone, half iron, rare   (c) abundance, preservation, some from moon and Mars

20. (a) Most meteoroids burn up in the atmosphere.   (b) 1300 m across, 200 m deep, impact of 20-meter iron meteoroid 25 000 years ago

Current RESEARCH

Phobos: Death of a Moon

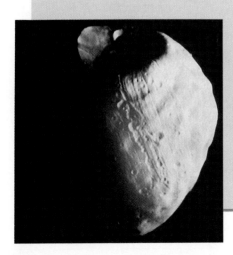

Mars has two small, rocky, irregularly-shaped moons, Phobos and Deimos. However, it now appears that one of those moons is doomed. Recent findings suggest that Phobos is slowly losing altitude. In about 40 million years, scientists believe Phobos will break apart and fall to Mars' surface in a rain of debris.

Phobos orbits Mars once every eight hours. That period of revolution appears to be decreasing a few hundredths of a second each year. Phobos is not traveling faster. Instead, it is traveling a shorter distance— that is, moving down into a Mars orbit that has a smaller circumference. Based on observations from telescopes and space probes, scientists believe Phobos is losing about 4 centimeters of altitude each year.

What is causing Phobos to fall out of its orbit? Even though Mars is not covered with water, the gravitational pull of Phobos on Mars does create a tidal effect. As Phobos orbits, it cause a bulge in the Martian surface. Since Phobos orbits Mars much faster than Mars spins on its axis, Phobos actually outraces the tidal bulge. The bulge pulls Phobos backward, causing it to slip into a lower orbit.

L A B
ACTIVITY

Dimensions of the Solar System

For additional activities, see Laboratory Investigations booklet.

Have you ever considered how long it would take to travel to other planets in the solar system? A voyage to Mars, one of the closest planets to Earth, takes at least five months. However, as you travel beyond Mars, the distances between the orbits of the planets becomes larger and larger. In fact, it took the *Voyager II* spacecraft twelve years to reach Neptune. In this exercise, you will explore the distances between the orbits of the planets as well as the relative sizes of the planets by drawing a scaled model of the solar system.

Lab Skills and Objectives
- To **compute** the orbit distance and sizes of the planets on a scale model
- To **form a model** of the solar system that illustrates the relative orbit distances and sizes of the planets

Materials
- 130 cm adding machine tape
- sharp pencil
- meter stick
- compass
- 150 cm string
- metric ruler

Procedure
1. Obtain a piece of adding machine tape 130 cm long. Draw a line across the tape 10 cm from the end. Write your name and the scales you will be using for the model within the 10 cm space. The scales are 1 cm = 5.0×10^7 km for the orbit distances and 1 cm = 2.2×10^4 km for the planet sizes.

2. The second column in Data Table A shows the distances of each of the planets from the sun. On your model, 1 cm of tape will equal 50 million km of distance in space. Calculate the orbit distance for each planet for your model by dividing each distance found in Column 2 of Data Table A by 50. Round off each value to the nearest 0.1 cm. Write the distance values in Column 3 of Data Table A. The value for Earth already has been calculated.

3. Mark a (+) sign in the center of the line you just drew. This mark represents the sun. On the same side of the line as your name, label the plus sign *Sun*.

4. Use a meter stick to measure the distances you calculated for each planet's orbit from the sun. Mark the position of the planets in the middle of the tape.

5. Place the point of a compass on the mark representing the sun. **CAUTION: The point of the compass is very sharp.** Adjust the compass so that the pencil rests on the mark you made for Mercury. Draw the arc of the orbit for Mercury. Repeat step 5 for the other inner planets and for Jupiter.

6. To draw orbital arcs for the outer planets, tie a pencil to one end of a piece of string. Make sure that the string is tied close to the tip of the pencil. With one hand, hold the pencil tip on the mark

Data Table A					
	Distance from sun		Size of Planet		
Name of Planet	Actual (in million km)	On Model (in cm)	Actual Diameter (in thousand km)	Model Diameter (in cm)	Model Radius (in cm)
Mercury	58	1.2	4.9	0.2	0.1
Venus	108	2.2	12.1	0.6	0.3
Earth	150	3.0	12.8	0.6	0.3
Mars	228	4.6	6.9	0.3	0.2
Jupiter	778	15.6	142.8	6.5	3.3
Saturn	1427	28.5	120.0	5.5	2.8
Uranus	2870	57.4	51.8	2.4	1.2
Neptune	4497	89.9	49.5	2.3	1.2
Pluto	5900	118.0	2.4	0.1	0.1

you made for Saturn. With the other hand, pull the string tight and hold it down on the mark you made for the sun. Keeping the string tight between the sun (+) mark and the mark for Saturn, draw the arc for the orbit of Saturn. Repeat step 6 for the remaining outer planets. You may need a partner to hold the string on the sun as you draw the more distant planet arcs.

7. Calculate the model diameter for each planet by dividing the diameter in Column 4 of Data Table A by 22. Round your answer to the nearest 0.1 cm and record it in Column 5. Remember that the scale for diameters differs from the scale for orbits.

8. Calculate the radius for each planet by dividing each diameter by 2. Record the radius in Column 6 of Data Table A. The values for Earth have been calculated.

9. Starting at the orbit arc, draw the radius for each planet. Because the inner planets will be crowded on your model, you should consider placing at least some of these planets in locations other than the center of their orbit arcs. The outer planets will need to be drawn at the center of their orbital arcs so that they can fit on the tape.

10. Adjust the compass so that the point rests on the orbit arc and the pencil rests on the other end of the radius line. Draw and label each planet.

11. Answer the questions in *Analysis and Conclusions.*

Analysis and Conclusions

1. Based on your model, describe how the sizes of the inner planets compare to the sizes of the outer planets? Which planet is an exception to your answer?

2. Describe how the distances between the orbits of the inner planets compare to the distances between the orbits of the outer planets.

3. How is your model of the orbit of Pluto incorrect? (Refer to Chapter 23.)

4. How many times farther from the sun is the orbit of Pluto than the orbit of Earth?

5. How many times larger than Earth is the planet Uranus?

6. Calculate the orbit distance of Pluto using the same scale you used to calculate its diameter. Multiply Pluto's actual distance from the sun by 1000 and divide the answer by 22. How long a piece of adding machine tape would you need to fit Pluto's orbit?

Answers to all questions appear in the Teacher's Guide at the back of this book.

■ Summary

I The planets are grouped by position as inner or outer and by properties as terrestrial or Jovian.

The terrestrial planets are Mercury, Venus, Earth, and Mars. All are similar in size, all are much more dense than water, and all are thought to have similar inner structures.

Venus and Mercury are seen only at sunrise or sunset; other planets can be seen all night.

II The Jovian planets are Jupiter, Saturn, Uranus, and Neptune. All are large, all are less dense than terrestrial planets, and all have similar structures, such as a gaseous outer layer, and features, such as rings and moons.

III A planetary satellite or moon is a smaller body that revolves around a planet. Except for Venus and Mercury, each planet has at least one satellite. Many satellites have unusual features.

IV A comet has a nucleus of ice and debris, a coma of gas surrounding the nucleus, a bright tail caused by solar wind, and a large, elongated orbit.

Asteroids are small, planetlike bodies. Most orbit the sun between Mars and Jupiter. Ceres is the largest asteroid.

A meteoroid is a rock or icy fragment in space. A meteor is a meteoroid glowing as it enters Earth's atmosphere. Meteor showers are regular events that occur when Earth's orbit crosses the orbit of a meteoroid swarm. A meteorite is a meteoroid that has reached Earth's surface.

■ Vocabulary

asteroid	meteorite
comet	meteoroid
evening star	meteor shower
greenhouse effect	morning star
impact crater	outer planet
inner planet	satellite or moon
jovian planet	terrestrial planet
meteor	

■ Review

Choose the best answer. Write the letter of your answer on your paper.

1. Which planet is not considered terrestrial? (a) Mars (b) Mercury (c) Saturn (d) Venus
2. A planet that has no atmosphere because of its high temperature and low gravity is (a) Mars, (b) Pluto, (c) Venus, (d) Mercury.
3. A planet that can be seen ONLY as a morning star or as an evening star is (a) Jupiter, (b) Uranus, (c) Venus, (d) Mars.
4. Which planet has polar caps of frozen carbon dioxide? (a) Pluto (b) Mars (c) Venus (d) Jupiter
5. The Jovian planets do NOT have (a) rocky surfaces, (b) moons, (c) rings, (d) magnetic fields.
6. Two planets that radiate away more energy than they receive from the sun are (a) Mars and Earth, (b) Jupiter and Saturn, (c) Venus and Mercury, (d) Neptune and Pluto.
7. Which planet orbits the sun on its side, although its magnetic field is nearly upright? (a) Jupiter (b) Venus (c) Neptune (d) Uranus
8. Two planets whose orbits cross are (a) Pluto and Neptune, (b) Uranus and Saturn, (c) Jupiter and Mars, (d) Venus and Earth.
9. Two planets with no satellites are (a) Pluto and Mercury, (b) Mercury and Venus, (c) Venus and Mars, (d) Mars and Pluto.
10. Which is a Galilean satellite? (a) Deimos (b) Titan (c) Io (d) Charon
11. What is unusual about the moon Titan? (a) It is Saturn's only moon. (b) It has a substantial atmosphere. (c) It has V-shaped grooves. (d) It is the largest of all moons.
12. Which Uranian moon has V-shaped grooves over one third of its surface? (a) Titan (b) Ariel (c) Miranda (d) Titania
13. Which is Pluto's moon? (a) Charon (b) Chiron (c) Titan (d) Titania
14. What kind of an object is Ceres? (a) moon (b) comet (c) asteroid (d) meteor crater

15. Which is NOT true about comets? (a) Most orbit between Mars and Jupiter. (b) They have glowing heads and bright tails. (c) They are usually seen only with telescopes. (d) Their tails point away from the sun.

16. How is meteor defined? (a) rock or ice fragment in space (b) rock or ice fragment that reached Earth's surface (c) rock or ice fragment with a large orbit that reappears (d) light made by a rock fragment burning in the atmosphere

17. Why are impact craters rare on Earth? (a) Its surface resists impacts. (b) Its orbit seldom crosses objects that make craters. (c) Most objects are attracted to the moon. (d) Most objects burn up in the atmosphere.

■ Interpret and Apply

On your paper, answer each question.

1. Consider an astronomer with a telescope on Venus and another on Mars. Which would have an easier time learning about Earth and why?

2. Occasionally a planet will pass directly between Earth and the face of the sun. Which planets could do this and why?

3. How many complete orbits has Earth make in your lifetime? How many orbits has Mars made in your lifetime.

4. Neptune was discovered in 1846. Since then, a complete orbit of the sun by Neptune has not yet been observed. Why is this the case?

5. Phobos revolves around Mars from west to east faster than Mars rotates on its axis from west to east. In what direction does Phobos rise and set?

■ Critical Thinking

The straight lines on the graph show the speed (in km/s) needed by several gas molecules to escape a planet relative to the absolute, or kelvin (K), temperature of that planet's atmosphere.* Points representing the planets are also on the graph.

1. If the escape speed of a gas from a planet's atmosphere is directly related to the mass of the planet, then according to the graph which planet has the greatest mass? Is this planet, in fact, the largest planet?

2. According to the graph, which planet has the least mass? Is this planet the smallest?

3. Using the graph, identify two pairs of planets that must have nearly the same masses because gases can escape from their atmospheres at nearly the same speeds.

4. According to the graph, which two planets have no atmosphere? (A gas is not held by a planet if the line for that gas is above the point for the planet.)

5. Which planets have both hydrogen and helium in their atmospheres?

6. According to the graph, how does the atmosphere of Earth differ from that of Mars?

7. The average temperature of the atmosphere of Saturn's moon, Titan, is 100 K. The speed needed for a gas to escape from its atmosphere is 0.5 km/s. Which gases could be held in Titan's atmosphere?

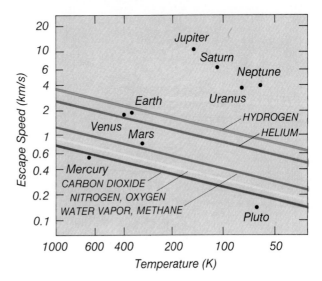

*The speed for a molecule to escape the atmosphere of a planet is not the same as the speed for a spacecraft to escape a planet.

Earth's Moon

▲
The *Apollo* missions were a giant step forward in space exploration.

How Do You Know That . . .

People may someday go back to the moon? Twelve astronauts walked on the moon as part of the *Apollo* program, from 1969–1972. The data and samples that they brought back show that the moon has many potential uses. A lunar mining base could supply materials used up on Earth. A lunar observatory could study the stars without the interference of an atmosphere. A lunar space station could be a stepping stone to other planets. The exploration of the moon has barely begun. Sometime soon, people will return to the moon. Perhaps you will be part of that adventure.

I Lunar Exploration

Topic 1 Getting to the Moon

At 386 000 kilometers away, the moon is Earth's nearest neighbor in space. For more than 350 years, the telescope was the chief instrument for studying the moon. Features on the moon's surface can be observed clearly with a telescope, but such observations are made from a long distance away. The exploration of the moon entered a new phase in 1959 when spacecraft from Earth first flew past the moon and returned data about the lunar surface.

Getting a spacecraft to the moon is a complex task. The rocket used must be large enough to put the spacecraft into Earth orbit before the rocket stops firing (at burnout). Once the spacecraft is in Earth orbit, another rocket fires it out of orbit toward the point where the moon will be when the spacecraft gets there. The aiming and firing of the spacecraft must be precise. If rocket burnout occurs a few seconds too early or too late, or if the spacecraft is not positioned correctly at burnout, the spacecraft will miss the moon and go into orbit around the sun.

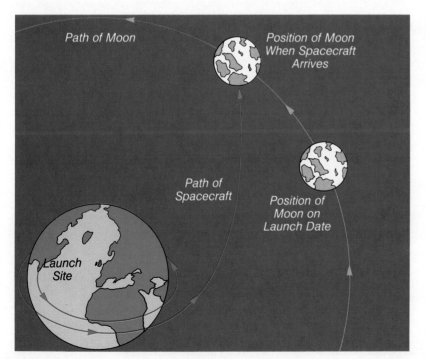

OBJECTIVES

A Discuss the steps involved in landing a spacecraft on the moon.

B Identify the kinds of information needed to land an astronaut on the moon.

C Describe the *Apollo* spacecraft and summarize the accomplishments of the *Apollo* program.

D Identify the parts of a space shuttle and describe the space shuttles' contributions to the space program.

SCIENCE BACKGROUND

Be prepared to explain that the moon does not hold still but is in orbit around Earth. A spacecraft aimed at the moon when it leaves Earth orbit would miss because in the two days needed to travel to the moon, the moon would have moved.

VIDEODISC SELECTION

Movies of *Ranger VIII* impact on lunar surface and *Apollo 17* astronauts on moon's surface
Side 4 movie: 40564 & PLAY

24.1 A lunar spacecraft is aimed at the point where the moon will be when the spacecraft arrives.

Topic 2   **The First Spacecraft to the Moon**

The first spacecraft to leave Earth orbit and reach lunar orbit was part of the **Luna** series of space probes launched by the former Soviet Union. *Luna 1* performed the first successful flyby of the moon before going into orbit around the sun. *Luna 2* crashed into the moon. *Luna 3* orbited the moon and returned the first close-up photos of the moon's surface and the first photos of the moon's far side.

At the same time the *Luna* series was in progress, the United States launched the **Pioneer** space probes. *Pioneers 1, 2,* and *3* were unsuccessful, but *Pioneer 4* reached escape velocity from Earth and returned data as it flew past the moon.

In 1961, President Kennedy made it a national goal to land an astronaut on the moon and return the astronaut safely to Earth. No American had orbited Earth, although Alan Shepard had been in suborbital flight at an altitude of 186 kilometers. While American astronauts were preparing for their first orbital flight, the former Soviet Union had orbited a cosmonaut, and a second cosmonaut Gherman Titov, completed a 17-orbit flight that lasted over 25 hours.

In order to reach the President's goal, the task of researching a safe landing site went to the **Ranger** and **Surveyor** lunar probes. The *Ranger* probes were designed to send back pictures of the lunar surface and then crash into it. The *Surveyor* missions were

VIDEODISC SELECTION

Painting of *Ranger* probe
Side 4: 11655, single frame

Photos from *Surveyor* lunar lander
Side 4: 11660 to 11681, 22-frame sequence

24.2 *Mercury* astronaut Wally Schirra orbited Earth six times in this small capsule. Here, he is being picked up after splashing down in the Pacific Ocean.

able to soft-land on the moon. *Surveyor* probes had small shovels with which to scoop up lunar soil and determine the strength of the lunar crust. Together data from these two programs made the selection of a safe landing place for the astronauts possible.

Topic 3 *Mercury* and *Gemini*

While *Ranger* and *Surveyor* were providing data on the moon's surface, spacecraft were being developed to carry astronauts to the moon. The first American spacecraft to carry astronauts, called **Mercury,** had already flown one successful mission. Alan Shepard's flight in *Mercury 3* was the first of nine *Mercury* flights. John Glenn in *Mercury 6* became the first American to orbit Earth, which he did three times in a flight that lasted nearly five hours. *Mercury 9,* the final flight of the series, completed 22 orbits and lasted over 34 hours.

The **Gemini** spacecraft were designed for two astronauts. Ten missions were flown between March 1965 and November 1966. The missions had two purposes. The first was to find if a human could survive and work in the weightlessness of space for the ten days needed to go to the moon and back. The second was to train astronauts to maneuver the spacecraft.

Topic 4 *Apollo*

The **Apollo** missions accomplished President Kennedy's objectives. In 1969, *Apollo 11* astronauts Neil Armstrong and Edwin Aldrin, Jr., became the first people to walk on the moon. In all, six missions traveled to the moon, collected samples, set up instruments, and returned safely to Earth.

The parts of an *Apollo* spacecraft and launch rockets are shown in Figure 24.3. The *Apollo* spacecraft consisted of a *command module* in which three astronauts were seated, a *service module* that contained the electrical power supply, life-support systems, and small maneuvering rockets, and the *lunar module* that the astronauts used for the trip to the moon's surface and back to the orbiting command module. At lift-off, the spacecraft and its three stages of launch rockets were over 110 meters tall and had a mass of nearly 3 million kilograms.

At the end of each journey, only the command module with the astronauts inside returned to Earth's surface. All other parts of *Apollo* vehicles were jettisoned (thrown away) once they had been used. Of the total mass that was launched, only about 6000 kilograms, including the mass of the astronauts, returned to Earth.

The *Apollo* astronauts brought back a total of 380 kilograms of rock and soil samples. The instruments they left behind measured such things as moonquakes, the moon's magnetic field, solar wind particles, and the gases present at the moon's surface. Some of these instruments continued to send back data long after the *Apollo* program was over.

VIDEODISC SELECTION

Photos from *Apollo* moon landings
Side 4: 11770 to 11774, 5-frame sequence

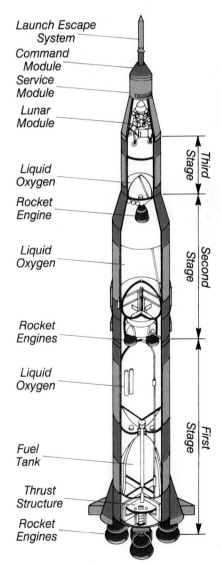

24.3 The *Apollo* command module was only a tiny part of the entire module and rocket assembly.

Topic 5 **The Space Shuttle**

Unlike its predecessors *Mercury, Gemini,* and *Apollo,* the versatile **space shuttle** is designed to be reused. Each shuttle has a short turnaround time. It can make a trip into orbit, return to Earth, and be ready to go into space again within a few months. This flexibility will allow scientists to observe important, but fleeting, astronomical events, drastic weather changes, or other environmental crises.

The space shuttle has three main units: (1) the orbiter, or the airplane body, which is roughly the size of a DC-9; the orbiter has a giant tail, delta-shaped wings, and three main engines; (2) the external tank, which feeds propellants (liquid hydrogen and oxygen) to the engines during the first stage of flight; and (3) two solid rocket boosters that provide the energy for the initial lift-off. During lift-off, the shuttle rides piggyback on the external tank, which is discarded about ten minutes after launch.

An interesting device on the shuttle is the Remote Manipulator System (RMS). This is a fifty-foot-long robot arm that is controlled from the flight deck. The arm has joints that function like an elbow, a wrist, and a hand. It can lift objects out of a shuttle's cargo bay, or it can reach out into space and grasp a satellite as a shuttle is maneuvered alongside. Due to weightlessness in space, the arm can maneuver extremely large and heavy objects.

Space shuttles are now used to launch and maintain a wide variety of scientific and technological instruments. A number of important astronomy payloads have been launched including the *Galileo, Magellan,* the *Hubble Space Telescope, Ulysses,* and the *Gamma Ray Observatory. Spacelab,* a forerunner of laboratories in space, is scheduled to be the main cargo on many space shuttle flights. In 1983, while *Spacelab-1* on the space shuttle *Columbia* circled Earth, more than seventy experiments were performed.

24.4 The two solid rocket boosters operate with main engines to obtain enough thrust for the shuttle to escape gravitational pull of Earth.

ANSWERS

1. mainly unaided eye, telescope
2. (a) flyby, crash, photos
(b) first U.S. flyby and photos
(c) Photographs made selection of a landing site possible.
3. The missions proved humans could work in space; ten 2-person missions trained for rendezvous and docking.
4. (a) traveled to moon and back, collected samples, left instruments
(b) command module—carried astronauts; service module—power, life-support, maneuvering; lunar module —for landing; launch rockets
(c) quakes, magnetism, solar wind, gases
5. (a) the orbiter, external tank, rocket boosters (b) retrieving and launching satellites, scientific research and exploration

TOPIC QUESTIONS

Each topic question refers to the topic of the same number.

1. How was the moon studied before 1959?

2. **(a)** List some accomplishments of the *Luna* space probes. **(b)** What did *Pioneer 4* do? **(c)** How did *Ranger* and *Surveyor* help to meet the President's goal of 1961?

3. Describe the *Mercury* and *Gemini* missions and identify what each accomplished.

4. **(a)** Summarize the *Apollo* missions. **(b)** Name and identify the purposes of the major parts of an *Apollo* spacecraft. **(c)** What kinds of measurements were made by instruments left on the moon?

5. **(a)** Identify the major parts of the space shuttle. **(b)** Describe the primary use(s) for the space shuttle.

II Properties and History of the Moon

Topic 6 Properties of the Moon

Earth's moon may not be the largest satellite in the solar system. However, with the exception of Pluto's Charon, it is closer in size to its planet than any other satellite. The moon's diameter is 3476 kilometers, or more than one fourth Earth's diameter. The moon's density, about 3.3 g/cm³, is less than Earth's, and its mass is only about one eighteenth Earth's. The moon's low gravity (about one sixth Earth's) and low escape velocity (one fifth Earth's) means that it is much easier to launch a spacecraft from the moon than from Earth.

Seismometers left on the moon by *Apollo* astronauts continued to operate for nearly eight years. The moonquakes they recorded were very few and feeble compared to earthquakes. Nevertheless, the data were enough for scientists to develop a model of the moon's interior. The moon, like Earth, has a layered structure. The crust is about 60 kilometers thick and is made of rocks similar to gabbros and anorthosites on Earth. The mantle beneath the crust extends to about 800 kilometers. Seismographs were not able to detect the moon's core, but its central part may consist of iron.

Topic 7 The Moon's Front and Back

The moon turns once on its axis in the same time period it orbits once around Earth. Thus, the same side of the moon always faces Earth. From Earth, we only see the "front side" of the moon. From anywhere else, both sides of the moon can be seen. To the unaided eye, the moon is a pattern of light and dark areas. Modern telescopes reveal details of the pattern. The light areas are lunar highlands, rugged mountains pockmarked with craters. The dark areas are great basins and level plains. Galileo had thought the basins were filled with water and had named them **maria** (MAR ee uh), the Latin word for seas (singular *mare*, MAR ay).

The moon's front side is nearly half highlands and half maria. The back of the moon is very different. Photographs taken by lunar probes show the back half to be mostly highlands and craters. There are only a few small maria.

There are other differences between the front and back of the moon. Lasers carried by the orbiting *Apollo* spacecraft were used to measure precisely the elevations of lunar surface features. From these measurements, scientists determined that the moon is not a perfect sphere but is slightly egg-shaped. The small end of the "egg" points toward Earth. Another difference was discovered from the seismic data. The crust is about 60 kilometers thick on the front

OBJECTIVES

A Compare the properties of the moon with those of Earth and describe the internal structure of the moon.

B Explain why the same side of the moon always faces Earth, and compare the front half of the moon with the back half.

C Outline the moon's geologic history.

D Identify some ways moon rocks are different from Earth rocks and relate the ages of moon rocks to the moon's history.

SCIENCE BACKGROUND
Lunar escape velocity is about 2.4 km/s compared to 11.2 km/s for Earth.

SCIENCE BACKGROUND
Some *Apollo* equipment was deliberately crashed into the moon after it was no longer needed. This practice provided artificial moonquakes for data on the moon's interior.

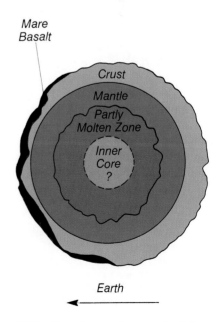

24.5 Data from seismographs left on the moon suggest that it has a layered internal structure.

24.6 This is an *Apollo* photograph of the moon's far side.

side facing Earth. On the side away from Earth the crust is more than 100 kilometers thick. The cause of these differences is unknown but is suspected to be related to Earth's gravitational pull on the moon.

Topic 8 Origin and History of the Moon

The samples of moon rock returned to Earth by *Apollo* astronauts have been thoroughly examined. By studying these rocks, as well as thousands of lunar photographs and other data, scientists have worked out a geologic history of the moon.

One likely theory based on lunar data proposes that the moon formed about 4.6 billion years ago from a collision between Earth and a Mars-sized object. At that time, Earth is thought to have been liquid with a solid crust. In the theory, the collision broke through the solid crust and splashed a huge mass of molten rock into space. This mass cooled and became the moon.

As soon as the lunar crust became solid, a second stage of moon history began. Great showers of rocklike particles bombarded the moon's surface. The largest particles blasted out great basins in many places. Smaller explosions formed smaller craters. Tiny particles ground and pitted the surface. Rock fragments and dust spread over the landscape.

The bombardment lasted for hundreds of millions of years. As it slowed down, a third stage of moon history began. Hot lava poured out of gaps in the great basins. The eruptions continued for nearly a billion years. The basin floors became dark and smooth as the lava hardened. Finally, the moon became geologically inactive.

For 3 billion years the moon's interior has been quiet. No volcanoes have erupted. Few moonquakes have shaken it, and no crustal plates have moved. However, meteoroids have continued to bombard the lunar surface. None of these meteoroids has been large enough to blow out new basins, but smaller ones have dug many new craters in the basins. These basin craters are younger than most of the highland craters. The bombardment going on now is mainly by **micrometeoroids**, tiny objects no larger than sand grains. Micrometeoroids are the major cause of erosion on the moon today.

Topic 9 Lunar Rocks: Evidence of the Moon's History

All lunar rocks differ from Earth rocks in several ways. Lunar rocks contain no water at all. They have greater proportions of elements with high melting points, such as aluminum, titanium, and zirconium. They contain lesser amounts of elements that exist as gases, such as nitrogen and chlorine, and lesser amounts of elements with low melting points, such as sulfur and lead.

VIDEODISC SELECTION

Photos of lunar sample analysis
Side 4: 11776 to 11783, 8-frame
sequence

Lesson II   Properties and History of the Moon   **439**

Radioactive dating has been used to find the age of lunar rocks. Most highland rock specimens are between 4.0 and 4.3 billion years old. However, a few specimens collected by the *Apollo 17* mission have been dated at 4.6 billion years, thought to be the age of the moon itself. These ages support the hypothesis that the lunar highlands are the original lunar crust.

The mare basalts are the youngest lunar rocks. They range in age from 3.1 to 3.8 billion years, which supports the idea that the moon has been inactive for the last 3 billion years.

Lunar maria and highland rocks are further described in Topics 9 and 10.

24.7 The pitted surfaces of these lunar boulders are a result of constant bombardment by micro-meteoroids.

TOPIC QUESTIONS

Each topic question refers to the topic of the same number.

6. **(a)** How does the moon compare in size, mass, surface gravity, and escape velocity to Earth?   **(b)** How are moonquakes different from earthquakes?   **(c)** Describe the moon's interior.

7. **(a)** Explain why one side of the moon always faces Earth. **(b)** What are the light areas of the moon called?   **(c)** What are the dark areas called? Why do they have this name?   **(d)** List some ways in which the front of the moon is different from the back of the moon.

8. **(a)** Summarize the four stages of the moon's history.   **(b)** What is the major cause of erosion on the moon today?

9. **(a)** Name several ways that moon rocks differ from Earth rocks. **(b)** Where are the oldest moon rocks found? The youngest?

ANSWERS

6. (a) 1/4 diameter, 1/80 mass, 1/6 gravity, 1/5 escape velocity (b) fewer, feebler   (c) 3 layers—rock crust, mantle, core, possibly iron

7. (a) Moon turns once on its axis in the same time period it orbits Earth.   (b) highlands   (c) maria; Latin for seas, looked like seas (d) more maria, thinner crust

8. (a) molten splash from collision, cooling crust, bombardment and lava flows, inactivity   (b) micrometeoroid impact

9. (a) no water, more high melting point elements, few gases or low melting point elements   (b) oldest—highlands; youngest—maria

OBJECTIVES

A Discuss the location and probable origin of lunar maria; describe mare rocks, mascons, and rilles.

B Discuss the location and probable origin of lunar highlands; describe the rocks found in lunar highlands.

C Describe lunar craters and give examples; discuss the characteristics and probable origins of rays and of regolith.

III The Moon's Surface Features

Topic 10 The Lunar Maria

Although Galileo thought the dark areas on the moon's surface were seas, the lunar maria contain no water and there is no sign that they ever did. The maria are smooth plains with huge circular basins. Examples are Mare Imbrium (Sea of Rains), Mare Crisium (Sea of Tears), and Mare Serenitatis (Sea of Serenity). The largest mare is the Oceanus Procellarum (Ocean of Storms).

The first three *Apollo* missions to land on the moon explored maria. Rock samples returned by these missions strongly resemble the basalts in lava flows from Hawaiian and Icelandic volcanoes. Like those basalts, the mare basalts are fine-grained crystalline rocks. They are dark gray or black and contain mostly plagioclase feldspar and pyroxene. Some contain olivine and ilmenite (an oxide of iron and titanium).

The first spacecraft to orbit the moon found that the moon's gravity was greater over some of the more circular maria. Gravity readings change if the material beneath the surface has a different density than the surrounding rock. Some lunar geologists suspect that the mass of material that created a mare basin remains buried deep beneath the surface. These areas of higher gravity are called **mascons** for "mass concentrations."

Rilles are long deep clefts or cracks running through maria bedrock. The best known is *Hadley Rille* on the floor of Mare Imbrium, which was explored by *Apollo 15* astronauts. This rille may have formed when the roof of a lava tunnel caved in.

24.8 This lunar rock is a volcanic basalt from one of the maria. What Earth rock does it resemble?

Ans. volcanic scoria

1. Sinus Iridum
2. Plato
3. Alps
4. Aristarchus
5. Mare Imbrium
6. Apennines
7. Kepler
8. Copernicus
9. Mare Humorum
10. Mare Nubium
11. Tycho
12. Mare Serenitatis
13. Mare Crisium
14. Mare Tranquillitatis
15. Mare Foecunditatis
16. Mare Nectaris

24.9 The brighter areas of the moon are mountainous highlands. The darker areas are the level maria. Rays can be seen around the craters Copernicus and Tycho.

Topic 11   **The Lunar Highlands**

The final three *Apollo* flights landed in lunar highlands. These areas appear brighter than the maria because their rocks are lighter in color and they reflect more sunlight. Within the lunar highlands are a few mountain ranges and many craters.

Most lunar mountain ranges are at the edges of maria. One great range forms the western border of Mare Imbrium. This range includes the lunar Alps, Apennines, and Caucasus mountains. These mountains are as high as 5 kilometers above the mare floor.

Lunar scientists think that the Apennines were thrown up by the impact that created Mare Imbrium. Perhaps all lunar mountains that border maria were formed in this way. How could such great masses of rock be thrown so far and high? One reason is that the moon has no atmosphere to slow flying particles. A second reason is the moon's weak gravity.

SCIENCE BACKGROUND

Lunar mountains and Earth mountains are alike in name only. There is no similarity in origin.

SCIENCE BACKGROUND

The highest lunar mountains, the Doerfels, are near the moon's south pole.

24.10 (top) Lunar craters vary in size. (bottom) A close-up of the crater Copernicus shows the rays that extend from it.

24.11 Lunar regolith is a mixture of small rocks and dust.

Two kinds of rock were returned from the lunar highlands. One is a light-colored, coarsely crystalline igneous rock. The composition of this rock lies somewhere between Earth's gabbro and anorthosite. Scientists think that this anorthositic gabbro makes up all the moon's solid crust except where mare basalts cover it.

The other specimens brought back from the lunar highlands are lunar breccias. Breccias are rocks made of angular fragments cemented together with fine material. On Earth, one source of breccia is volcanic eruptions. On the moon, breccias were probably formed by meteoroid impacts that melted the rocks together. Lunar breccias are mostly gray.

Topic 12 **Lunar Craters and Rays**

Lunar **craters** are hollows on the moon's surface. The smallest craters are microscopic pits. The largest, Clavius, is about 240 kilometers across. Most craters were formed by the impact of meteoroids.

Craters are roughly circular. Their rims are rugged cliffs. In large craters the rims may be thousands of meters above the plains, while their floors may be a thousand meters lower than the plains. Most crater floors are themselves dotted with many small peaks and craters. Like the highlands, these peaks reflect enough sunlight to look bright. Lunar craters are named after great scholars and scientists, such as Plato, Aristotle, Archimedes, Kepler, and Copernicus.

Bright streaks, called **rays**, radiate from a number of craters. The rays of the crater Tycho and other large craters are thousands of kilometers long, and cross mountains, plains, and other craters. For a long time the rays were a mystery. Scientists now know that they consist of shattered rock and dust splashed out by the meteoroid impacts that formed the craters.

Topic 13 **Lunar Soil**

Lunar soil is not really soil. Scientists prefer to call it **regolith** which means loose rock materials. Regolith is a grayish-brown mixture of small rock pieces and fine particles that range in size from sand grains to fine dust. Unlike Earth soil, regolith contains no water or organic material. Regolith was made by the smashing impact of meteoroids of all sizes. When large meteoroids explode, they mix rock fragments over broad areas. This stirring of the regolith is called *gardening*.

The regolith ranges in thickness from perhaps 1 to 20 meters. It is likely to consist of chips from many different kinds of rocks and minerals. It also contains tiny beads of glassy material. These formed from rock melted by high-speed meteoroid impacts. Droplets of the melted rock solidified to form glassy beads. Some of the melted rock formed a glaze on other rocks.

TOPIC QUESTIONS

Each topic question refers to the topic of the same number.

10. (a) List some examples of maria.   (b) Describe the mare basalts.
(c) What are mascons and how were they discovered?   (d) What is a rille?

11. (a) Where are most lunar mountains located? Give some examples.   (b) Describe the probable origin of the lunar mountains.
(c) Identify the rocks of the lunar highlands.

12. (a) Describe the lunar craters and explain their origin.
(b) What are lunar rays? How were lunar rays formed?

13. Describe the lunar regolith.

ANSWERS

10. (a) Imbrium, Crisium, Serenitatis   (b) resemble Earth basalts (c) mass concentrations under maria; unusual gravity readings (d) long, deep crack in maria

11. (a) maria edges; Alps, Apennines, Caucasus   (b) impact that formed maria   (c) anorthositic gabbro, breccia

12. (a) circular, any size, rugged rim; meteoroid impact   (b) bright radiating streaks; splashed out from impact

13. loose rock material of all sizes, no water or organics, 1–20 m thick

CAREERS

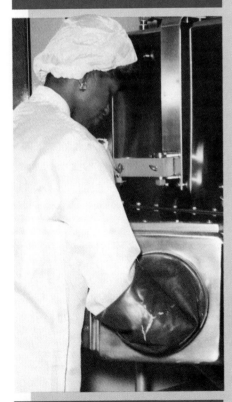

Andrea Mosie
Lunar Geologist

Did you know that geologists and space scientists are still studying the rocks and soil samples collected on the moon by the *Apollo* astronauts? Andrea Mosie is a geologist at the Johnson Space Center in Houston where most of the *Apollo* samples are stored. She is one of several geologists there who continue the detailed analysis of those rocks.

The moon rocks are kept in special cabinets filled with nitrogen gas. Nitrogen is used instead of air to protect the samples from chemical weathering. The oxygen and water vapor in the air would react with minerals in the rocks and change their composition. In addition, the tweezers and other tools Ms. Mosie uses in studying the rocks must be made of stainless steel, aluminum, Teflon, or some other nonreactive substance.

The cabinets themselves are kept in special clean rooms. Before entering, Ms. Mosie must put on white nylon coveralls, booties, gloves, and a cap. She then steps into an air shower to remove all traces of dust and lint, which could contaminate the rooms.

The rocks and other samples stored at the Johnson Space Center are considered a national treasure. Even though these samples have already told scientists a great deal about the moon, much remains to be learned.

OBJECTIVES

A Describe all aspects of the moon's orbit; explain why the sun and moon appear to be about the same size in the sky.

B Explain why the moon rises later each day; describe the moon's cycle of phases; locate the positions of the sun, moon, and Earth at each lunar phase.

C Explain why the period of a lunar month is not equal to the moon's period of revolution.

D Identify and describe the different kinds of eclipses and explain why each occurs.

VIDEODISC SELECTION

Diagrams of the Moon's orbit
Side 4: 11600 to 11602, 3-frame sequence

24.12 The moon's orbit is inclined about five degrees to the plane of Earth's orbit.

TEACHING TIP

Be prepared to explain that Earth turns 15° per hour (students do not learn this until Chapter 25). They should be able to see that Earth needs almost an hour to catch up with the moon.

IV The Moon's Motions and Phases

Topic 14 The Moon's Orbit

The moon revolves around Earth from west to east in an elliptical orbit. Its period of revolution is 27 ⅓ days. Its average distance from Earth is about 386 000 kilometers. When the moon is nearest Earth, it is said to be at **perigee** (peri = near, gee = Earth). When farthest from Earth, it is at **apogee.**

The moon's orbit is not in exactly the same plane as Earth's orbit. The angle between the two orbits is about 5 degrees. This difference is very important in determining how often eclipses occur (Topics 17 and 18).

The sun's diameter is nearly 400 times the moon's diameter, yet both appear to be about the same size in the sky. The reason is that the sun is nearly 400 times farther away from Earth than the moon.

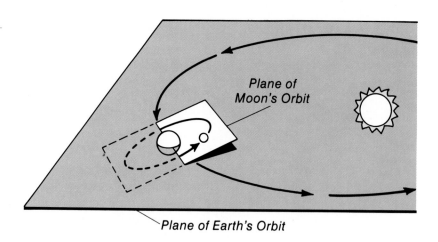

Plane of Moon's Orbit

Plane of Earth's Orbit

Topic 15 Moonrise and Moonset

The moon rises in the east and sets in the west. Like the sun's rising and setting, this is an apparent motion caused by Earth's turning on its axis from west to east. Unlike the sun, the moon is in orbit around Earth.

As the moon moves around Earth, it can be seen rising at a different time each night. Every twenty-four hours the moon moves about 13° eastward along its orbit. Thus, Earth must rotate an extra 13° more than 360° to see the moon rise each night. Turning 13° takes about 50 minutes for Earth. The result is the moon rises about 50 minutes later each day and sets about 50 minutes later as well.

Since the time of moonrise changes each day, the moon can be seen in the sky during day and night. When the moon is opposite the sun, it is seen mostly in the night sky. When it is between Earth and the sun, it is seen mostly in the daytime sky.

Topic 16   **The Moon's Phases**

The **phases** of the moon are the daily changes in the moon's appearance. Moon phases occur for two reasons. One is that the moon is seen by reflected sunlight. The other is that the moon is in orbit around Earth.

The sun lights the half of the moon that is facing it. However, except for a short time each month, the half that always faces Earth is not the half lit by the sun. From Earth, the face of the moon changes from all dark to all light, or from new moon to full moon, in about two weeks. During this time, the moon is said to be **waxing.** During the next two weeks, the face of the moon gradually changes from all light back to all dark, or from full moon back to new moon. During this time, the moon is said to be **waning.**

Figure 24.12 shows the moon at eight points in its orbit. Although the half of the moon facing the sun is always fully lighted, a different portion of the lighted half is visible from Earth during each phase. At the new moon phase, the lighted half faces away from Earth and the moon cannot be seen. At the crescent phases, only one edge of the lighted half faces Earth. At the quarter phases, the half of the moon facing Earth is half lighted and half dark. At the gibbous phases, almost all of the bright half faces Earth. When the moon is full, the entire bright half faces Earth.

OF INTEREST

The time of the new moon or full moon is called syzygy. The term is used more in crossword puzzles than by astronomers.

VIDEODISC SELECTION

Diagrams and photos of the Moon's phases
Side 4: 11605 to 11614, 10-frame sequence

24.13 The left portion of the diagram shows the appearance of the moon at each of the eight phases. The right portion of the diagram shows the actual illumination of the moon at each phase. No matter what the phase, the same side of the moon is always facing Earth.

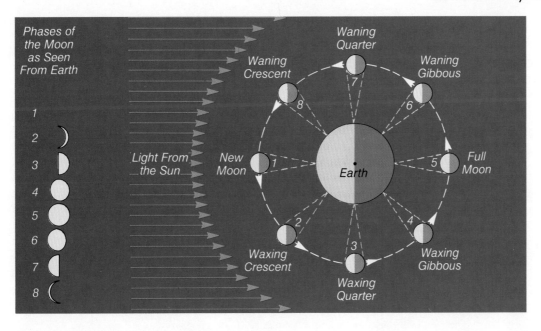

Topic 17 **Lunar Months**

The time from one new moon to the next new moon is not the same as the time for one revolution of the moon around Earth. The time from one new moon to the next is called the **lunar month** and lasts 29.5 days. One revolution only takes 27.3 days.

The reason for the difference in the two values is Earth's revolution around the sun. While the moon travels in its orbit around Earth, Earth moves about 1° each day in its orbit around the sun. During the 27.3 days that the moon takes to complete one revolution, Earth moves about 27.3° along its orbit. The moon must move another 27.3° along its own orbit to return to the same phase. Since the moon moves about 13° along its orbit each day, it takes slightly more than two extra days to arrive at the same position. Thus, the time from one moon phase to the same phase is about two days longer than the time for the moon to orbit Earth once.

24.14 The lunar month, 29½ days, is the time span from one new moon to the next. The diagram shows why the lunar month is longer than the moon's period of revolution, 27⅓ days.

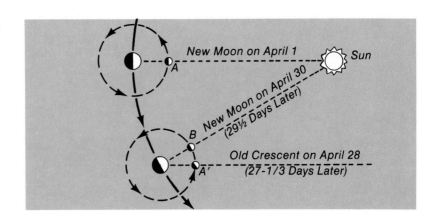

Topic 18 **Lunar Eclipses**

VIDEODISC SELECTION

Diagrams and photos of a lunar eclipse
Side 4: 9956 to 9964, 9-frame sequence

The shadow cast by any opaque object has two parts: The **umbra** is the total shadow and the **penumbra** is the partial shadow surrounding the umbra. Both Earth and the moon cast shadows into space. Earth's umbra is a long, narrow cone. The tip of Earth's umbra is nearly 1 400 000 kilometers beyond Earth. The penumbra is also a cone, but it gets wider and lighter in space. Because the moon is smaller than Earth, the moon's shadows are smaller and shorter.

A **lunar eclipse** occurs when the moon passes into Earth's umbra. A total lunar eclipse occurs when the moon is fully within the umbra. When the moon is only partly in the umbra, that is a partial lunar eclipse.

A lunar eclipse can occur only at the full moon phase. Even though a full moon occurs every month, a lunar eclipse does not occur that often. The reason is that the moon's orbit and Earth's orbit are inclined to each other by about 5 degrees. The full moon is usually above or below Earth's umbra, and no eclipse occurs.

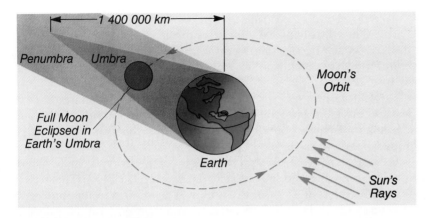

24.15 A lunar eclipse can occur only at the full moon phase. Notice that the umbra is the area of total darkness, while the penumbra is only partially dark. Earth's umbra eclipses the moon.

The moon remains visible during its eclipse, but it has a dusky red or coppery color. This occurs because Earth's atmosphere acts like a lens and bends some sunlight, mostly longer red wavelengths, into the umbra.

On the average, at least one total lunar eclipse occurs every year. With good weather it is visible from the entire nighttime half of Earth. If the moon goes through the center of the umbra, a total lunar eclipse may last for two hours.

Topic 19 **Solar Eclipses**

A **solar eclipse** occurs when the moon's umbra reaches Earth's surface. The moon's umbra is just long enough for its tip to reach Earth at perigee. It is not long enough to reach at apogee. The umbra's greatest width on Earth's surface is about 269 kilometers. The penumbra is much wider and lighter.

Locations on Earth within the umbra experience a total solar eclipse. At that time, the moon blocks the entire photosphere of the sun. The sky is dark. Bright stars and planets can be seen with the unaided eye. The sun's chromosphere and corona glow around the blocked-out disk. A partial solar eclipse is seen at locations within the moon's penumbra shadow. The moon covers only a part of the sun, and often little change in daylight is noticed.

VIDEODISC SELECTION

Diagrams and photos of a solar eclipse
Side 4: 9965 to 9972, 8-frame sequence

Satellite photos showing the path of an annular eclipse shadow
Side 4: 11190 to 11200, 11-frame sequence

24.16 A solar eclipse occurs only at the new moon phase. It is really an eclipse of part of Earth by the moon's shadow. The eclipse is total in the umbra. It is partial in the penumbra.

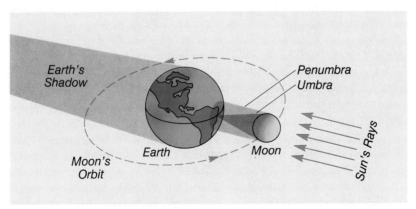

24.17 During a total eclipse of the sun, the sun's corona can be seen extending hundreds of thousands of kilometers into space.

When the moon is at apogee, the umbra shadow fails to reach Earth. When this happens, observers in the center of the umbra see the sun as a thin, bright ring around the moon. This is called an **annular,** or ring, eclipse. Observers in the penumbra see a partial eclipse.

A solar eclipse can occur only at the new moon phase. Like a lunar eclipse, a solar eclipse does not occur every month because of the angle of the moon's orbit. The moon's shadow usually falls above or below Earth.

Although at least one solar eclipse occurs every year, a given location can expect to see one only once every 300 years! This rarity is mainly due to the size of the umbra. The moon's umbra on Earth is usually much less than its maximum possible width. Nor does a total solar eclipse last very long. The moon's revolution makes the narrow shadow race across Earth at over 1600 kilometers per hour. The shadow's track on Earth is called the eclipse path. The eclipse path may be thousands of kilometers, but at any one place a total solar eclipse can last only 7.5 minutes. A few minutes is more usual.

TOPIC QUESTIONS

Each topic question refers to the topic of the same number.

14. **(a)** What is the direction of the moon's revolution? **(b)** Define perigee and apogee. **(c)** How is the plane of the moon's orbit related to the plane of Earth's orbit? **(d)** Why do the sun and moon look equally large in the sky?

15. Why does the moon rise about 50 minutes later each day?

16. **(a)** Why is the moon not full all of the time? **(b)** List the eight moon phases in order. **(c)** During which phases is the moon said to be waxing? **(d)** During which phases is the moon said to be waning?

17. **(a)** How long is a lunar month? **(b)** Explain why a lunar month is longer than the moon's period of revolution.

18. **(a)** Identify the two parts of a shadow. **(b)** How does a total eclipse of the moon occur? Partial eclipse? **(c)** At what phase does a lunar eclipse occur? Why doesn't it occur every month? **(d)** How much of the world can see each lunar eclipse?

19. **(a)** Describe the moon's shadow and its relation to total, partial, and annular eclipses of the sun. **(b)** At what lunar phase does a solar eclipse occur? Why doesn't it occur every month? **(c)** Why are total solar eclipses seldom seen even though one occurs almost every year? **(d)** What is the eclipse path? **(e)** How long can a total solar eclipse last?

ANSWERS
14. (a) west to east (b) nearest Earth; farthest from Earth (c) 5° difference (d) sun 400 times larger but 400 times farther away
15. moon revolves, Earth must rotate to catch up
16. (a) cannot always see whole lighted side (b) new, waxing crescent, waxing quarter, waxing gibbous, full, waning gibbous, waning quarter, waning crescent (c) new to full (d) full to new
17. (a) 29.5 days (b) Earth has moved, moon must revolve 2 days more
18. (a) Umbra, penumbra (b) moon in Earth's umbra is total, moon partly in umbra is partial (c) full; orbital planes inclined (d) entire nighttime half
19. (a) cone-shaped, length about equals distance from moon to Earth; total eclipse in umbra, partial in penumbra, annular when umbra does not reach Earth (b) new; orbital planes inclined (c) moon's umbra very tiny, covers only small area of Earth's surface (d) track of shadow on Earth (e) 7.5 min.

V Sun, Moon, and Tides

Topic 20 The Moon and Tides

The daily rise and fall of the ocean waters are called **tides**. Like the moon, tides rise 50 minutes later each day (on the average). Tides are unusually large during the new moon and full moon phases. They are unusually small during quarter moon phases. Because of these observations, people have known for many years that the moon and the tides are related.

Sir Isaac Newton first explained how the gravity of the moon causes tides. Recall that gravity is stronger when objects are closer together. Because of this, the water on the side of Earth nearest the moon is pulled by the moon more strongly than Earth itself is pulled by the moon. This difference in force causes a bulge in the ocean on the side of Earth near the moon. This bulge is the *direct high tide.* At the same time, Earth's center is nearer to the moon than the water on the side of Earth opposite the moon. Earth itself, therefore, is pulled more strongly by the moon than is the water on the far side of Earth. Earth is pulled away from the water on the far side, leaving a bulge of water behind, which is the *indirect high tide.* Water has been pulled away from the areas that lie between the two high tides. These areas experience low tides.

OBJECTIVES

A List the evidences that relate tides to the moon and explain how the moon causes high and low tides.

B Describe and explain spring tides and neap tides; define tidal range and identify several factors that influence it.

VIDEODISC SELECTION

Diagrams and photos of ocean tides
Side 4: 9951 to 9954, 4-frame sequence

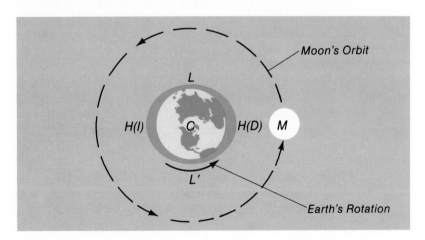

24.18 The moon causes a direct high tide at H(D) and an indirect high tide at H(I). Low tides occur at L and L'.

Topic 21 Rise and Fall of Tides

If Earth and the moon stood still, tides would be in the same places all the time. Earth, however, turns on its axis, and the moon moves around Earth. As Earth rotates, all parts of the oceans pass under the moon in 24 hours and 50 minutes. In one fourth of this time—about 6 hours and 12.5 minutes—the tides change. Each high-tide area gradually rotates to low tide. Each low-tide area gradually rotates to high tide. Six hours and 12.5 minutes later the tides change again.

24.19 (top) At new and full moon phases, sun and moon pull together, causing very high and very low tides called spring tides. (bottom) At quarter moon phases, sun and moon pull against each other, causing a small tidal range, the neap tides.

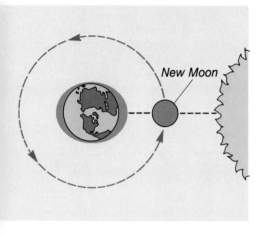

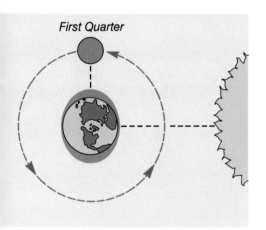

As Earth and the moon move, the tides continue their regular rise and fall. Each day the cycle starts over again, about 50 minutes later than the previous day. The model timetable that follows gives average times for a day of high and low tides. Actual tides are often much more irregular because the shapes of the ocean basins and ocean floors also influence the tides.

Sample Timetable

Tide	Date	Time	Interval Since First High Tide
High	July 4	1:00 A.M.	
Low	July 4	7:13 A.M.	6 h 13 m
High	July 4	1:25 P.M.	12 h 25 m
Low	July 4	7:38 P.M.	18 h 38 m
High	July 5	1:50 A.M.	24 h 50 m

Topic 22   Spring and Neap Tides

The sun has the same kind of effect on Earth's waters as does the moon. However, because it is so much farther away, the sun's tide-making effect is only about half that of the moon. The sun, however, can strengthen or weaken the moon's effects.

Tides are always high in line with the moon and low midway between the high-tide points. When the sun is in line with the moon and Earth, as shown in Figure 24.18 (top), the sun's entire tide-making effect is added to the moon's. When the sun is 90° away from the moon, as in Figure 24.18 (bottom), the entire effect is subtracted from the moon's effect. At new moon and full moon phases, the effects of the sun and moon add together. During these times, high tides are especially high and low tides are especially low. These tides occur twice a month and are called **spring tides**.

At quarter phases the sun is opposing the moon, resulting in high tides that are not very high and low tides that are not very low. These tides also occur twice a month and are called **neap tides**. One other factor that adds to the tidal effect is the moon's nearness to Earth. When the moon is at perigee, the tidal effect is greater, especially if perigee occurs during the new or full moon phases.

Topic 23   Ocean Basins, Shorelines, and Tidal Range

The **tidal range** is the difference in level between high tide and low tide. Tidal ranges vary widely between bodies of water and tend to be more noticeable near the ocean than near lakes. Small lakes show no tides at all. The largest of the Great Lakes, Lake Superior, has a tidal range of only a few centimeters. In the open ocean the tidal range averages less than one meter.

Tidal ranges on ocean shores are most noticeable, but they also vary greatly. In the Gulf of Mexico, the tidal range may be only half a meter. In the Bay of Fundy on the coast of Nova Scotia, the range can be as great as 20 meters.

What causes these differences? The Bay of Fundy is a long, V-shaped bay. Water from the ocean tide is funneled into the wide end of the V. When the water reaches the narrow end of the V, it piles up high. In the Gulf of Mexico, the opposite occurs. The Gulf has a shoreline much broader than its mouth. As the ocean tide enters the Gulf, its water spreads out over the long shoreline.

24.20 Because it is long and V-shaped, the Bay of Fundy has a very large tidal range.

VIDEODISC SELECTION

Bay of Fundy tide
Side 2 movie: 16620 & PLAY

ANSWERS

20. (a) daily tide lag matches moonrise lag; tidal range varies with moon phase   (b) lunar gravity on water and on Earth   (c) direct high tide; indirect high tide   (d) halfway between high tides

21. (a) time of Earth's rotation combined with moon's revolution (b) moon's revolution

22. (a) can pull with or against moon, strengthens or weakens tidal effect   (b) large range in high and low tide from moon and sun pulling together; new and full phases (c) small range between high and low tide from sun and moon pulling against each other; quarter phases

23. (a) difference in level between high and low tides   (b) zero to a few cm; <1 meter   (c) V-shaped bay, funnels water higher (d) shoreline broader than mouth, waters spread out

TOPIC QUESTIONS

Each topic question refers to the topic of the same number.

20. (a) What observations indicate a connection between the moon and tides?   **(b)** Explain how the moon causes tides.   **(c)** What is the bulge of water toward the moon called? The one away from the moon?   **(d)** Where do low tides occur?

21. (a) Explain why tides rise or fall every 6 hours and 12.5 minutes, on the average.   **(b)** Explain why the tides occur 50 minutes later each day.

22. (a) How does the sun affect tides? Explain.   **(b)** What are spring tides? How and when do they occur?   **(c)** What are neap tides? How and when do they occur?

23. (a) Define tidal range.   **(b)** What is the tidal range of lakes? Of the open ocean?   **(c)** Explain the large tidal range of the Bay of Fundy.   **(d)** Explain the small tidal range of the Gulf of Mexico.

L A B

ACTIVITY

Moon, Sun, and Seasons

For additional activities, see
Laboratory Investigations booklet.

You have probably noticed that as the seasons change, the height of the sun in the sky changes. The height of the sun in the sky is its angular distance above the horizon, or altitude. (See page 468, Figure 25.14.) During the long days of summer, the sun's altitude is high for most locations in the United States. As winter approaches, however, not only do the days get shorter but the sun's midday altitude becomes lower and lower. Seasonal changes in the sun's position in the sky are noticeable because of their obvious effect on our weather. Less noticeable are the monthly and yearly variations that the moon experiences in its maximum altitude. These variations result from the sun's position, the seasons, and the phase of the moon. In this activity, you will use the data provided to investigate the relationship between the monthly and seasonal changes in both the sun's and the moon's maximum altitudes.

DATA TABLE

Date	Moon Phase	Maximum Altitude of Moon (°)	Noon Altitude of Sun (°)	Date	Moon Phase	Maximum Altitude of Moon (°)	Noon Altitude of Sun (°)
Jan 4	New Moon	25.9		Jul 7	Waxing Quarter	39.9	
Jan 13	Waxing Quarter	62.9		Jul 14	Full Moon	28.3	71.7
Jan 19	Full Moon	72.0	29.5	Jul 22	Waning Quarter	61.9	
Jan 26	Waning Quarter	34.8		Jul 29	New Moon	69.1	
Feb 3	New Moon	33.1		Aug 5	Waxing Quarter	32.2	
Feb 11	Waxing Quarter	69.9		Aug 13	Full Moon	37.4	64.7
Feb 18	Full Moon	60.2	38.0	Aug 21	Waning Quarter	71.4	
Feb 25	Waning Quarter	26.5		Aug 28	New Moon	56.0	
Mar 4	New Moon	45.3		Sep 3	Waxing Quarter	27.6	
Mar 12	Waxing Quarter	74.5		Sep 12	Full Moon	50.0	54.2
Mar 18	Full Moon	50.7	48.8	Sep 19	Waning Quarter	73.6	
Mar 26	Waning Quarter	26.6		Sep 26	New Moon	46.6	
Apr 3	New Moon	58.9		Oct 3	Waxing Quarter	27.4	
Apr 10	Waxing Quarter	71.6		Oct 11	Full Moon	58.2	43.0
Apr 17	Full Moon	36.1	60.5	Oct 19	Waning Quarter	68.8	
Apr 24	Waning Quarter	30.6		Oct 25	New Moon	37.9	
May 2	New Moon	66.5		Nov 2	Waxing Quarter	34.6	
May 9	Waxing Quarter	64.6		Nov 10	Full Moon	68.9	32.8
May 16	Full Moon	29.6	69.1	Nov 17	Waning Quarter	61.1	
May 24	Waning Quarter	41.1		Nov 24	New Moon	28.4	
Jun 1	New Moon	73.7		Dec 2	Waxing Quarter	45.9	
Jun 7	Waxing Quarter	55.2		Dec 9	Full Moon	72.6	27.2
Jun 15	Full Moon	26.0	73.3	Dec 16	Waning Quarter	51.6	
Jun 23	Waning Quarter	54.0		Dec 22	New Moon	27.3	
Jun 30	New Moon	73.4					

Lab Skills and Objectives

■ To **construct a graph** of the altitudes of the sun and the moon over a one year period

■ To **interpret** the patterns on the graph

■ To **draw conclusions** about the relationship between the sun's noon altitude and the moon's maximum altitude

Materials

■ sheet of graph paper
■ sharp pencil

Procedure

1. Review the Data Table on page 452.

2. To start your graph, take a sheet of graph paper and turn it so that its longest dimension is horizontal. Draw and label the axes, as shown in Figure 24.21. The vertical axis should extend from 0° to 90°. Label the horizontal axis with each of the dates listed in the Data Table.

3. Label the seasons on your graph, as shown in Figure 24.21. Refer to Figure 25.2 on page 457 for the dates of the start of the season.

4. On your graph paper, plot the altitude of the sun using an asterisk (*) for each of the dates given. Connect the asterisks to form a smooth curve.

5. On the same graph paper, plot the maximum altitude of the moon for each of the dates in the Data Table. Use a plus sign (+) for a new moon, a dot (·) for either

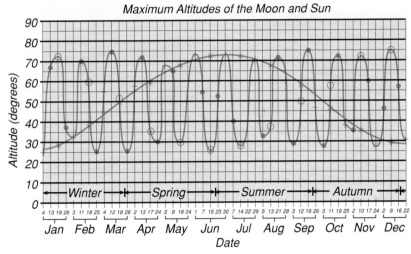

Figure 24.21

quarter phase, and a circled dot (⊙) for each full moon. Connect all of the plotted moon data sequentially to form a smooth, wavelike curve.

6. Answer the questions in *Analysis and Conclusions*.

Analysis and Conclusions

1. Based upon the pattern on your graph, what is the most likely date of the first full moon in the next year? Explain your answer.

2. On your graph, compare the new moon altitudes throughout the year to the curve connecting the sun's altitudes. Why do the new moon altitudes parallel the path of the sun all year?

3. (a) In which month is the sun highest in the sky? Lowest in the sky? (b) During which month is the full moon highest in the sky? Lowest in the sky? (c) From your obser-

vations, what is the relationship between the sun's noon altitude and the maximum altitude of the full moon?

4. Recall that the full moon is always on the opposite side of Earth from the sun. In June, Earth's Northern Hemisphere is tipped toward the sun and away from the full moon. What effect does Earth's tip have on the altitudes of the sun and the full moon? How is this shown on your graph? What season begins in the Northern Hemisphere in June?

5. Compare the altitudes of the sun and the full moon in December. Based on your results, predict how Earth's Northern Hemisphere is tipped relative to the sun and the full moon in December. What season begins in the Northern Hemisphere in December?

Answers to all questions appear in the Teacher's Guide at the back of this book.

■ Summary

I Sending spacecraft to the moon requires enough power to escape Earth's gravity, precise aiming and timing, knowledge of a safe landing site, and the ability to prevent the craft from crashing.

The *Apollo* program brought back lunar material and photos and left equipment on the moon.

The space shuttle is used to launch and maintain a wide variety of scientific and technological instruments.

II The same side of the moon always faces Earth. The front of the moon has smooth plains and a thin crust, while the back has cratered highlands over a thick crust.

One theory of the moon's formation involves a collision between Earth and another object.

Lunar rocks have textures similar to Earth rocks but have differences in composition. Lunar highland rocks are older than mare rocks.

III Lunar maria may have formed when large objects hit the surface, broke through the crust, and caused lava to flow, forming smooth circular basins.

Lunar highlands surrounding lunar maria may have been thrown up by impacts that created maria.

Most lunar craters were caused by the impact of meteoroids; rays were splashed out by the impacts. Regolith is the loose rock material covering the moon's surface.

IV The lunar orbit is tilted 5°. The moon's movement around Earth causes it to rise later each day and to go through phases.

A lunar eclipse occurs when the moon passes through Earth's shadow. A solar eclipse occurs when the moon's shadow falls on Earth.

Tides are caused by the gravitational pull of the moon. The pull of the sun is added to or subtracted from that of the moon.

Tidal range is affected by the size of the body of water, and the shape of coastlines.

■ Vocabulary

annular eclipse	*Mercury*	rilles
apogee	micro meteoroid	solar eclipse
Apollo	neap tide	space shuttle
crater	penumbra	spring tide
Gemini	perigee	*Surveyor*
Luna	phases	tidal range
lunar eclipse	*Pioneer*	tides
lunar month	*Ranger*	umbra
maria	rays	waning
mascon	regolith	waxing

■ Review

Match the descriptions in List **A** with the terms in List **B**.

List A

1. Designed to go back and forth from Earth to low orbit
2. First American lunar probes
3. First American craft to carry astronauts
4. Astronaut's location during *Apollo* moon trips
5. Lunar missions that returned rocks
6. Launch from moon easier because this is less
7. More common on near side of moon
8. Agent of lunar erosion
9. Location of oldest moon rocks
10. Lunar mass concentration
11. Made of cemented angular fragments
12. Lunar soil
13. Bright streaks radiating from craters
14. Point in moon's orbit farthest from Earth
15. Moon rises about this much later each day
16. Full moon to new moon phases
17. Time from one new moon to the next
18. Total shadow of an eclipse
19. Partial eclipse is seen from here
20. Track of moon's umbra on Earth
21. Caused by moon pulling Earth away from water
22. Average time from one high tide to another
23. Tides of new and full moon phases
24. Difference between high and low tide

For further review, see **Study Guide**.
For assessment, see **Chapter Tests**
and **Computer Test Bank**.

List B

a. apogee
b. *Apollo*
c. breccia
d. command module
e. eclipse path
f. escape velocity
g. 50 minutes
h. highlands
i. indirect high tide
j. lunar month
k. maria
l. mascon
m. *Mercury*

n. micro meteoroids
o. penumbra
p. perigee
q. *Pioneer*
r. rays
s. regolith
t. space shuttle
u. spring tide
v. tidal range
w. 12 hours 25 minutes
x. umbra
y. waning
z. waxing

■ Interpret and Apply

On your paper, answer each question in complete
sentences.

1. Could astronauts on the moon observe a meteor shower? Explain.
2. If both the moon and Earth formed at the
   same time, why have no 4.6 billion-year-old
   rocks been found on Earth?
3. If you lived on the moon instead of Earth, how
   often would the sun rise?
4. For each moon phase, identify the phase that
   Earth is in as seen from the moon.
5. What effect would there be on the lunar
   month if the moon revolved east to west
   rather than west to east?
6. If the moon and Earth kept their present sizes
   and separation but were at the distance of
   Jupiter from the sun, how would solar
   eclipses differ?
7. Direct and indirect high tides measured in the
   same location are about the same height
   when the moon is in the plane of Earth's equator. However, these high tides may be very
   unequal when the moon is above or below the
   plane of Earth's equator. Using a diagram,
   explain why this difference occurs.

■ Critical Thinking

Each moon phase is visible only at a particular
time of day or night. For example, a full moon cannot be seen at 12 noon because it is on the side of
Earth opposite the sun. The approximate times
each phase is visible can be determined. The figure below is similar to Figure 24.12 except that
times are shown—12 noon toward the sun, 12
midnight away from the sun, 6 A.M. at sunrise,
and so on. Use a piece of paper to cover the daytime side of Earth and the moon phases on that
side. The full moon is at its highest point in the
sky about midnight. It rises 6 hours earlier, at
6 P.M., and sets 6 hours later, at 6 A.M.

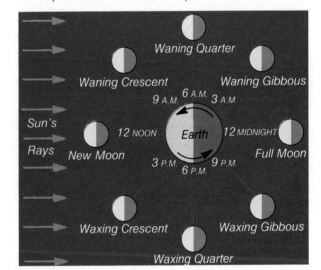

1. Cover the times when the waxing quarter
   phase CANNOT be seen. At what time is the
   waxing quarter at its highest point? What
   time does it rise? What time does it set?
2. Determine the time of moonrise and moonset
   for the waning gibbous phase.
3. If the waning crescent phase is at its highest
   point, what time is it?
4. Which phases could never be seen at 3 P.M.?
5. If the waning quarter phase is midway between moonrise and its highest point, what
   time is it?
6. Which phase rises about 9 A.M.?

455

Earth's Motions

How Do You Know That . . .

▲
This unusual photo shows the altitude of the sun at the same time of day throughout the year. The photo was taken at 42° N latitude.

Earth changes its position in space throughout the year? One clue is the changing position of the sun in the sky. At latitudes away from the equator, the lengths of day and night change as the seasons change. The times and positions of sunrise and sunset also change. The photo above shows the position of the sun at the same time of day over the course of a year. Can you tell which position was photographed around the first day of summer? You will be able to tell by the end of this chapter.

TEACHING TIP

Students often have difficulty remembering that rotation is turning and revolution is the movement in orbit around the sun. These terms may need to be redefined and reviewed frequently.

I Earth's Rotation

Topic 1 **The Axis of Rotation**

Like the other planets in our solar system, Earth turns as it travels around the sun. This turning motion is called **rotation**. The **axis of rotation** is an imaginary straight line through Earth between the North Pole and the South Pole. Earth turns around this axis. Earth's orbit lies within an imaginary flat surface called the *plane of Earth's orbit*. The axis of rotation is not straight up and down when compared to the plane of Earth's orbit, but is slightly tipped. The axis makes an angle of 23.5° from a perpendicular to the plane of Earth's orbit.

The angle that the axis is tilted does not change as Earth moves on its path around the sun. The north axis is always aimed toward the same point in the sky near where Polaris, the North Star, is located. Even though Earth's position in its orbit changes each day, the axis always points toward Polaris. To illustrate this change, try this simple experiment. Hold your left fist in front of you to represent the sun. Grasp a pencil in your right hand. Your right hand will represent Earth; the pencil will be its axis. Place "Earth" to the left of the "sun," with its "North Pole" pointing about 23.5° toward the "sun." Keeping the axis parallel to its first position, move "Earth" around the "sun." Notice how the "North Pole" leans away from the "sun" at the opposite (right) end of the orbit. Notice also that neither pole leans toward the "sun" at the two midway points. Every position of Earth's axis is parallel to every other position of the axis. This behavior is called **parallelism of the axis.** Parallelism of the axis is one of the causes of seasons on Earth.

OBJECTIVES

A Define rotation and discuss the evidences for and effects of Earth's rotation.

B Describe Earth's axis of rotation and explain its rate of rotation and speed of rotation.

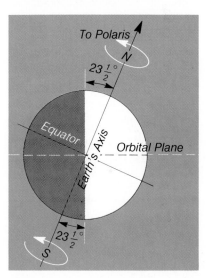

25.1 Earth's axis is inclined by 23½° from a perpendicular to the plane of Earth's orbit.

TEACHING TIP

In Figure 25.2, you may need to remind students that the axis points to Polaris in each position because the lines of sight from a star are parallel due to distance.

25.2 Throughout the year, Earth's axis always has the same tilt and points in the same direction. This parallelism of the axis is important in the change of seasons and in the length of daylight and night.

To Polaris

Spring March 21

To Polaris

To Polaris

Summer
June 21

Winter
Dec. 21

To Polaris

Autumn Sept. 23

457

25.3 The Foucault pendulum can be used to demonstrate Earth's rotation.

VIDEODISC SELECTION

Photos of a Foucault pendulum
Side 4: 9916 to 9917, 2-frame
sequence

SCIENCE BACKGROUND

The rate of rotation in degrees per hour of a Foucault pendulum depends on latitude. As the latitude increases, the rate of rotation increases.

TEACHING TIP

Be careful to teach deflection to the winds' right, not *the* right, in the Northern Hemisphere.

VIDEODISC SELECTION

The Coriolis effect
Side 1 movie: 22001 & PLAY

Topic 2 Evidences for Earth's Rotation

How do we know that Earth rotates? Early evidence of rotation was provided by the French physicist Jean Foucault (FOO koe) in 1851. He constructed a pendulum by hanging a large iron sphere on a long wire. Scientists of the time knew that once a pendulum is set in motion, its direction of swing will not change. Foucault, however, observed that the direction of swing of his pendulum did change. Each hour it shifted about 11° in a clockwise direction. After eight hours it was swinging at a right angle to the starting direction. Because the pendulum could not have changed its direction of swing, Foucault concluded that the shift he saw was caused by Earth turning beneath his pendulum. The *Foucault pendulum* is now a famous demonstration of Earth's rotation.

A second evidence of Earth's rotation can be seen by moving air, or wind. Winds blow from areas of high air pressure to areas of low air pressure. If Earth did not rotate, these winds would blow directly from high-pressure areas to low-pressure areas. Because of Earth's rotation, the winds appear to be turned, or deflected. In the Northern Hemisphere, winds are deflected to their right. In the Southern Hemisphere, the direction of deflection is to the winds' left. This apparent deflection is caused by the **Coriolis effect**. Any substance or object that moves freely over Earth's surface, such as ocean currents, winds, and rockets, will be turned when compared to Earth's surface as a result of the Coriolis effect.

What about the rising and setting of the sun? Doesn't that show that Earth rotates? No, it could also result from the sun moving around a stationary Earth. However, the motions of the sun, as well as those of the stars, are much easier to explain with a rotating Earth rather than with a rotating sky.

Topic 3 Effects of Earth's Rotation

The Coriolis effect and the behavior of a Foucault pendulum occur because Earth rotates. Another result of rotation is the length of a day. One day is defined as the time needed for Earth to turn once on its axis. One day is divided into 24 parts, or hours.

The daily change from daylight to nighttime also results from Earth's rotation. Only half of Earth can be lighted by the sun at any time. If Earth did not rotate, the half facing the sun would have constant daylight while the other half would have constant nighttime. Earth's rotation causes daylight and nighttime to alternate. Its tilted axis results in unequal sunlight on its Northern and Southern Hemispheres. For all but two days each year either the Northern Hemisphere or the Southern Hemisphere leans more toward the sun. The hemisphere that leans toward the sun has longer daylight periods than nighttime periods, while the one that leans away from the sun has shorter daylight periods.

Yet another result of Earth's rotation is the direction of sunrise and of sunset. Seen from above the North Pole, Earth rotates in a counterclockwise direction, that is, it turns from west to east. This causes the sun to appear to rise in the east and set in the west.

TEACHING TIP

Be careful in the use of the terms *day* and *daylight*. Daylight refers to the sunlit part of each 24-hour day.

VIDEODISC SELECTION

Diagram of Earth's orbit, seasons, solstices
Side 4: 9923 to 9924, 2-frame sequence

Topic 4 **Rate of Earth's Rotation**

How fast does Earth turn on its axis? One complete turn occurs every 24 hours. One complete turn is equal to a circle of 360°. Therefore, Earth turns at a rate of 360° in 24 hours, or 15° each hour. The apparent motion of the sun, moon, and stars is caused by Earth's rotation. Thus, these objects move across our sky at the rate at which Earth rotates—15° each hour.

While every location on Earth's surface moves at a rate of 15° per hour, the speed of rotation in kilometers per hour is not the same everywhere. Speed of rotation depends upon latitude. The greatest speed of rotation occurs at the equator. Here, one rotation is the distance of the equatorial circumference, or 40 074 kilometers. Locations on the equator travel 40 074 kilometers in 24 hours, a speed of nearly 1670 kilometers per hour! The distance required to travel around Earth, and thus the speed of rotation, decreases as the distance from the equator increases. At the latitude of Salt Lake City, Utah, the speed of rotation is only about 1300 kilometers per hour. At the poles, the speed of rotation is almost zero.

TEACHING TIP

You may need to explain the term *apparent*. The stars *appear* to move because of Earth's rotation.

SCIENCE BACKGROUND

The rate of rotation of the stars is actually slightly greater than 15° per hour, due to Earth's revolution around ths sun. A star returns to the same location in the sky after 23 hours 56 minutes. This period of time is called a *sidereal day* (star day).

VIDEODISC SELECTION

Satellite photos of Earth's rotation
Side 4: 11156 to 11188, 34-frame sequence

Diagram of Earth's rate of rotation
Side 4: 9919, single frame

North Pole
Distance Around = 0 km
Speed of Rotation = 0 km/h

Distance Around = 31 200 km
Speed of Rotation = 1300 km/h

Distance Around = 40 074 km
Speed of Rotation = 1670 km/h

42° N Latitude

Equator

25.4 As distance from the equator increases, the distance around Earth decreases. As a result, Earth's speed of rotation decreases away from the equator.

ANSWERS
1. (a) the turning of Earth on its axis (b) an imaginary straight line between the North and South Poles around which Earth rotates (c) 23.5° to a perpendicular to the plane of Earth's orbit (d) Polaris (e) Every axis position is parallel to every other axis position.
2. (a) pendulum swing appears to change direction. (b) to their right (c) the Coriolis effect
3. (a) length of day, daily change from light to dark, direction of sunrise and sunset (b) counterclockwise as viewed from North Pole, or from west toward east
4. (a) 15° per hour (b) 15° per hour; apparent motion is caused by Earth's rotation (c) the equator; the greatest distance around Earth. (d) the poles

TOPIC QUESTIONS

Each topic question refers to the topic of the same number.

1. **(a)** What is rotation? **(b)** Describe Earth's axis of rotation. **(c)** What is the angle of tilt of Earth's axis? **(d)** Near what object in space does the axis always point? **(e)** What is parallelism of the axis?

2. **(a)** How does a Foucault pendulum show that Earth rotates? **(b)** In what direction are winds deflected in the Northern Hemisphere? **(c)** What name is given to the cause of this deflection?

3. **(a)** Identify three results of Earth's rotation other than the Coriolis effect and the behavior of a Foucault pendulum. **(b)** In what direction does Earth rotate?

4. **(a)** What is Earth's rate of rotation? **(b)** At what rate do the sun, moon, and stars appear to move across our sky? Why? **(c)** Where on Earth's surface is the speed of rotation greatest? Why? **(d)** Where is the speed of rotation least?

EARTH**MATTERS**

Space Trash

*H*ubble Telescope destroyed in collision with orbiting trash! This isn't such an unlikely headline. Space is not as empty as it once was. In addition to thousands of satellites, there are billions of pieces of space debris in Earth's orbit. This space trash includes everything from pieces of old boosters and satellites that have broken up or been exploded to hand tools lost by astronauts working in space.

Unbelievably, orbiting satellites and debris travel at speeds of up to 10 kilometers per second. That's roughly 100 times the speed of a bullet. The impact of even a small piece of debris moving at that speed can cause incredible damage. In 1983, what is thought to have been a paint chip, smaller than a postage stamp, struck the orbiting space shuttle *Challenger*. The resulting collision dug a deep pit in the shuttle's windshield. A larger piece of debris might have punctured the windshield.

Using a worldwide system of telescopes, radar, and radio receivers, the United States Space Surveillance Network tracks over 7000 known pieces of space debris. Approximately every other shuttle mission has to make unscheduled maneuvers to avoid risking a collision with debris tracked by the network.

Unfortunately the network is only able to track objects larger than a grapefruit. Tens of thousands of smaller, plum-sized objects and billions of objects as small as grains of sand cannot be tracked. Depending on the height of their orbit, these objects can remain in orbit for a few months or as long as 300 years. For space to remain safe and useful, world governments must cooperate to control the rapidly growing threat of space trash.

SCIENCE BACKGROUND
  The rate of shift of solar noon is calculated as follows: 1 hour = 60 minutes. 60 minutes divided by 15° = 4 minutes per degree.

II   Time Measurement and Earth's Rotation

Topic 5   Solar Time

The length of a day, 24 hours, is the result of Earth's rotation. How is time determined within that 24-hour period?

For many years, the position of the sun in the sky was the standard for determining the time of day. During a single day, the sun appears on the eastern horizon, seems to move in an arc across the sky, and disappears below the western horizon. **Solar noon** occurs when the sun is at the highest position on this arc. **Solar time** is time by the sun.

Solar noon does not occur at the same time for everyone. Earth's rotation causes solar noon to move westward at a rate of 15° each hour, or 4 minutes of time for each degree of longitude. For example, New York City is located at 74° W longitude, while Philadelphia is at approximately 75° W longitude. Because of this 1° difference, solar noon occurs at New York City about 4 minutes before it occurs in Philadelphia.

Topic 6   Standard Time

The problem of different solar times at nearby communities was solved by developing worldwide **standard time zones**. There are 24 time zones, each 15° of longitude wide. The basis for the time zone is the rate at which the sun appears to move across the sky. Each

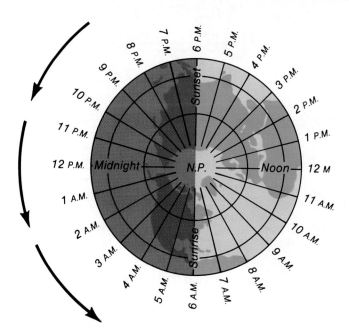

OBJECTIVES

A Describe the nature of solar time and explain the basis for Earth's standard and daylight time systems.

B Determine the time and day in various locations in the world, given the time and day in one location.

C Locate the international date line and describe the changes that occur there.

25.5 A sundial is a device that indicates local solar time. Because of Earth's tilt and orbit, solar time is the same as clock time only a few days each year.

SCIENCE BACKGROUND
  Solar time is the same as clock time only four times each year. During the spring and fall the sun is ahead of the clock, and solar noon occurs before clock noon. During summer and winter sun time is behind clock time. The exact dates when solar time and clock time match up are variable. One reference for this is *Exploring the Universe* by George Abell.

25.6 A map of Earth looking down from above the North Pole, showing Earth's 24 standard time zones; The sun's rays are striking Earth from the right.

25.10 The level surface in which Earth revolves around the sun is called the plane of Earth's orbit.

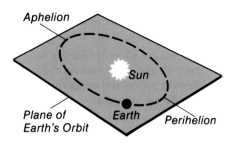

Aphelion

Sun

Plane of
Earth's Orbit   Earth   Perihelion

SCIENCE BACKGROUND

Earth's speed of revolution is 30 kilometers per second.

of the orbit. Earth is about 147 600 000 km from the sun at perihelion, on or about January 2. At aphelion, on or about July 4, Earth is about 152 400 000 km from the sun.

Earth makes one revolution around the sun every 365.24 days. This defines a duration of one year. Since Earth travels 360° (one orbit) in about 365 days, its rate of revolution around the sun is very close to 1° each day.

Topic 11   **Effects of Earth's Revolution**

Earth's axis is not straight up and down but is inclined at an angle of 23.5° (Topic 1). This tilt, together with Earth's revolution, has a profound effect on Earth. For all but two days a year, either the Northern Hemisphere or Southern Hemisphere leans more toward the sun. The hemisphere that leans toward the sun has a longer period of daylight than the one that leans away from the sun.

The hemisphere that leans toward the sun also has warmer temperatures. The closer to vertical the sun's rays strike a surface, the higher the temperature of the surface becomes. The sun's rays strike Earth closer to vertical in the hemisphere leaning toward the sun. The hemisphere leaning away from the sun has cooler temperatures because the sun's rays are less direct.

The changes in daylight and temperature caused by revolution and tilt lead to the yearly change of seasons at middle latitudes. If the axis were perpendicular to the plane of the orbit, seasons would not occur. Every place on Earth's surface would have 12 hours of daylight and 12 hours of nighttime every day. The average temperature at each location would be the result of its distance from the equator. If Earth's axis were tilted more than 23.5°, each hemisphere would lean more toward the sun in summer and more away from the sun in winter. The result would be warmer summers and colder winters. Thus, increasing the tilt of the axis would make seasons more severe, while decreasing the tilt would make seasons milder. No tilt would result in no seasonal changes.

TOPIC QUESTIONS

Each topic question refers to the topic of the same number.

9. **(a)** What is Earth's revolution?   **(b)** Give two evidences for Earth's revolution.

10. **(a)** What are the shape and dimensions of Earth's orbit? **(b)** What is Earth's rate of revolution?

11. **(a)** What effect does the tilt of Earth's axis have on the daylight period and temperature of the hemisphere that leans toward the sun?   **(b)** What would seasons on Earth be like if the axis were not tilted at all?   **(c)** What would be the effect on seasons if Earth's axis were tilted more?

ANSWERS

9. (a) movement of Earth around sun   (b) parallax shift of nearby stars and seasonal change in constellations

10. (a) elliptical orbit, average distance 150 million km from sun (b) 1° per day

11. (a) longer daylight, warmer temperatures   (b) no seasons (c) more extreme seasons

IV   Seasons on Earth

Topic 12   **Summer in the Northern Hemisphere**

The first day of summer in the Northern Hemisphere occurs on or about June 21 each year. This day has the longest daylight period. Because the daily increase in the sun's noon altitude stops on this date, June 21 is the **summer solstice** (sol = sun; stice = stop). On the summer solstice the Northern Hemisphere is at its maximum tip toward the sun. Because this tip is equal to 23.5°, the sun is straight overhead at 23.5° N latitude. The circle around Earth at 23.5° N latitude is called the *Tropic of Cancer.*

On the same date, every point on Earth within 23.5° of the North Pole is having 24 hours of daylight. This latitude, 66.5° N, is the *Arctic Circle* (the latitude of the North Pole is 90° N; 90° minus 23.5° equals 66.5°). On June 21 in the Southern Hemisphere, every point south of the *Antarctic Circle* (66.5° S latitude) is experiencing 24 hours of darkness. Like the Arctic Circle, the location of the Antarctic Circle is a result of the tilt of Earth's axis.

After June 21 the tilt of the Northern Hemisphere toward the sun decreases as Earth continues on its path around the sun. As the tilt decreases, daylight periods in the Northern Hemisphere decrease while those in the Southern Hemisphere increase.

Topic 13   **Winter in the Northern Hemisphere**

Winter begins in the Northern Hemisphere on or about December 21. This is the **winter solstice**, the shortest day of the year. On that date the Northern Hemisphere is at its maximum tip away from the sun, while the Southern Hemisphere is at its maximum tip toward the sun. The sun is straight overhead at the *Tropic of Capricorn,* which is at 23.5° S latitude. Like the Tropic of Cancer, the location of the Tropic of Capricorn results from the tilt of Earth's axis.

Daylight and nighttime conditions on December 21 are the opposite of those on June 21. On December 21, every point north of the Arctic Circle is experiencing constant darkness while every point

OBJECTIVES

A Identify the dates, conditions, and positions of the sun at different latitudes on the solstices and equinoxes.

B Describe the daylight and nighttime conditions that occur at each seasonal date worldwide.

C Describe the apparent path of the sun across the sky on the seasonal dates.

D Identify the causes of seasons on Earth.

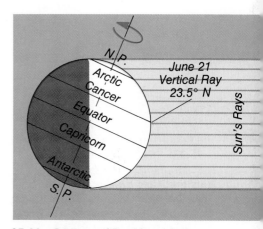

25.11   Because of Earth's axial tilt, latitudes away from the equator experience seasonal temperature differences. On June 21, Earth's Northern Hemisphere is at its greatest tilt toward the sun. June 21 has the longest daylight period in the Northern Hemisphere.

25.12   Bylot Island in Baffin Bay, Canada, is far enough north of the Arctic Circle to have many weeks of continuous daylight in summer. This picture shows the island's midnight sun photographed every fifteen minutes from 11:15 P.M. to 1:00 A.M. on July 25–26.

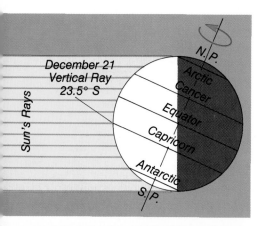

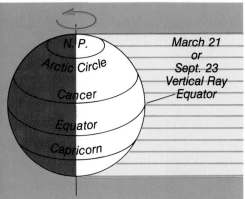

25.13 (top) On December 21, Earth's Northern Hemisphere is at its maximum tilt away from the sun and has its shortest daylight period. (bottom) Daylight and nighttime are equal in length everywhere on Earth only on the two equinoxes.

south of the Antarctic Circle is in constant daylight. A traveler moving north on this date will observe that the daylight period becomes shorter, while one moving south will observe increasing daylight periods.

Topic 14 **The Equinoxes**

There are two days each year when neither hemisphere leans toward the sun. These days occur midway between the solstices. On these dates daylight and nighttime are equal in length all over the world. Each date, therefore, is known as an *equinox* (equi = equal; nox = night). The **spring equinox** occurs on or around March 21. The **autumn equinox** is on or around September 23. The sun is directly overhead at the equator at noon on these dates.

The spring and autumn equinoxes are also the dates when daylight and nighttime reverse at the poles. On March 21, the sun rises above the horizon at the North Pole for the first time in six months. It remains visible at the North Pole for the next six months, while the South Pole begins a six-month period of nighttime. When Earth revolves so the Southern Hemisphere is tipped toward the sun (after September 23) the nighttime period begins at the North Pole and ends at the South Pole.

Topic 15 **Sun and the Dome of the Sky**

How do the changing positions of the sun appear to an observer on Earth? Think of the sky as a huge bowl over head. The horizon is the circular rim of the bowl. The observer is at the center of the circle. The point straight overhead is the **zenith**. The vertical angle between the horizon and the sun's position is the sun's **altitude**. When the sun is at the zenith, its altitude is 90°. When it is on the horizon, its altitude is 0°. For locations in the United States (except Hawaii) the sun is always below the zenith.

On the first day of summer the sun rises 23.5° north of due east, travels across the dome of the sky to its highest noon position of the year, and sets 23.5° north of due west. This arc is longer and higher than any other path throughout the year. That is why the first day of summer has the longest daylight period of the year. On the first day of winter the sun rises 23.5° south of due east, follows its lowest and shortest path across the dome of the sky, and sets 23.5° south of due west. On equinoxes, the path of the sun is halfway between these two extremes, rising due east and setting due west.

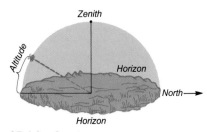

25.14 On the imaginary dome of the sky, the horizon is the rim of the dome and the zenith is the point straight overhead. The altitude of the sun is the vertical angle between the horizon and the sun.

Topic 16 **Summary: Causes of Seasons**

There are three basic causes of seasons: (1) the revolution of Earth around the sun, (2) the tilt of Earth's axis, and (3) the parallelism of Earth's axis. Because the axis always points in the same direction as

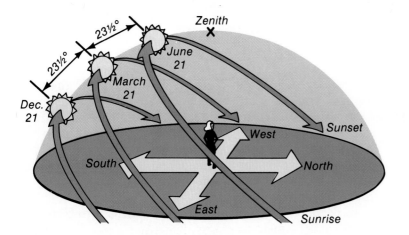

25.15   This diagram shows the path of the sun's apparent motion at latitude 41° N on the solstices and the equinoxes.

VIDEODISC SELECTION

Analemma: sun's declination versus time of day for a year
Side 4: 9929, single frame

Earth travels around the sun, first one hemisphere and then the other hemisphere is tipped toward the sun. The hemisphere tipped toward the sun has longer periods of daylight, more direct sunlight, and thus experiences summer. The hemisphere tipped away from the sun has winter, due to shorter days and less direct sunlight. Areas near the equator do not experience dramatic changes in daylight periods or angle of sunlight, and thus do not have seasons.

Is Earth's varying distance from the sun a cause of the seasons? Try to form an hypothesis based on Earth's dates of perihelion and aphelion. Then try the activity on pages 470–471 which provides data to help you determine if Earth's distance from the sun affects the seasons.

TOPIC QUESTIONS

Each topic question refers to the topic of the same number.

12. **(a)** What happens in the Northern Hemisphere on June 21? **(b)** Where is the Tropic of Cancer? Why? **(c)** Where is the Arctic Circle? Why? **(d)** Where is daylight constant on June 21?

13. **(a)** What happens in the Northern Hemisphere on December 21? **(b)** Where is the Tropic of Capricorn? Why? **(c)** Where on Earth is daylight constant on December 21? **(d)** What happens to the daylight period in the Northern Hemisphere after December 21? Why?

14. **(a)** Why are daylight and nighttime of equal length on an equinox? **(b)** Give the names and dates of the equinoxes. **(c)** Where is the sun straight overhead at an equinox? **(d)** Describe what happens at the North Pole and at the South Pole at each equinox.

15. **(a)** What is the zenith? **(b)** What is meant by the altitude of the sun? **(c)** How does the path of the sun across the sky differ on the first day of summer from the first day of winter?

16. **(a)** List the three basic causes of seasons. **(b)** What evidence is there that distance from the sun is not a cause of seasons?

TEACHING TIP
You may have to explain that *due east* means *directly east*.

ANSWERS
  12. (a) first day of summer, longest day, summer solstice (b) 23.5° N; 23.5° farthest north sun can be overhead (c) 66.5° N, 23.5° from the North Pole, axial tilt (d) north of Arctic Circle
  13. (a) first day of winter, shortest day, winter solstice (b) 23.5° S; as far south as sun can be overhead (c) south of Antarctic Circle (d) becomes longer as Northern Hemisphere is tilted more toward sun
  14. (a) Neither hemisphere leans toward the sun. (b) Spring equinox March 21; autumn equinox September 23 (c) equator (d) spring equinox North Pole begins 6-month period of daylight, South Pole begins 6-month darkness; opposite true at autumn equinox.
  15. (a) point in sky straight overhead (b) vertical angle between horizon and location of sun (c) Summer: sun rises 23.5° north, rises to highest position, sets 23.5° north; Winter: sun rises 23.5° south, rises to lowest noontime position, sets 23.5° south.
  16. (a) revolution of Earth about the sun, tilt and parallelism of axis (b) Our winter is when we are closest.

L A B
ACTIVITY

Apparent Size
of the Sun

For additional activities, see
Laboratory Investigations booklet.

Hold your fist out at arm's length in front of you. How big does your fist appear? Does its apparent size increase, decrease, or stay the same as you pull your fist in closer to you? The apparent size or diameter of an object in the sky, like your outstretched fist, depends on your distance from them. Apparent diameters are measured in degrees. For example, the width of your fist viewed at arm's length has an apparent diameter of about 10°. The apparent diameter of the sun, while in reality a much larger object than your fist, is less than 1°.

As Earth revolves in its elliptical orbit, its distance from the sun, and consequently the sun's apparent diameter, varies. Is distance from the sun a cause of seasons? Is summer warmer because we are closer to the sun and winter colder because we are farther away? In this activity, you will use data on the apparent size of the sun to determine whether distance from the sun can be a cause of seasons.

Lab Skills and Objectives

- To **construct a graph** of solar apparent diameter data
- To **interpret** the graph in terms of Earth's distance from the sun
- To **compare** the graph with Earth's seasonal changes

Materials

- sharp pencil
- sheet of graph paper

Procedure

1. Review the Data Table on this page. The data given is the apparent diameter of the sun as it appears from Earth. Since the apparent diameter of the sun is less than 1° it is measured in minutes (') and seconds ("). There are 60 minutes in a degree and 60 seconds in a minute.

   ▲ **CAUTION: Never look directly at the sun.** The data for this activity was collected using *indirect* measurements.

2. To begin your graph, take a sheet of graph paper and turn it so that its longest dimension is horizontal. Draw and label the axes, as shown in Figure 25.16. The vertical axis should extend from 31 minutes, 20 sec-

Data Table				
Date	Apparent Diameter		Date	Apparent Diameter
Jan 1	32'	32"	Jul 10	31' 28"
Jan 10	32'	32"	Jul 20	31' 29"
Jan 20	32'	31"	Jul 30	31' 31"
Jan 30	32'	28"	Aug 10	31' 34"
Feb 10	32'	25"	Aug 20	31' 37"
Feb 20	32'	21"	Aug 30	31' 41"
Mar 1	32'	17"	Sep 10	31' 46"
Mar 10	32'	12"	Sep 20	31' 51"
Mar 20	32'	07"	Sep 30	31' 57"
Mar 30	32'	02"	Oct 10	32' 02"
Apr 10	31'	56"	Oct 20	32' 08"
Apr 20	31'	50"	Oct 30	32' 13"
Apr 30	31'	45"	Nov 10	32' 18"
May 10	31'	41"	Nov 20	32' 23"
May 20	31'	37"	Nov 30	32' 26"
May 30	31'	33"	Dec 10	32' 29"
Jun 10	31'	30"	Dec 20	32' 31"
Jun 20	31'	29"	Dec 30	32' 32"
Jun 30	31'	28"		

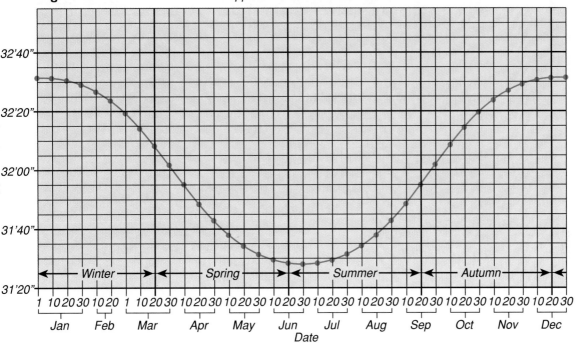

Figure 25.16   *Apparent Diameter of the Sun*

32'40"
32'20"
32'00"
31'40"
31'20"

←— Winter —→ ←— Spring —→ ←— Summer —→ ←— Autumn —→

1 10 20 30 10 20 | 1 10 20 30 10 20 30 10 20 30 10 20 30 10 20 30 10 20 30 10 20 30 10 20 30 10 20 30
Jan   Feb   Mar   Apr   May   Jun   Jul   Aug   Sep   Oct   Nov   Dec
Date

onds to 32 minutes, 40 seconds. Label the horizontal axis with the dates listed in the Data Table. For a review of graphing skills, see Appendix A, page 649.

3. Label the seasons on your graph, as shown in Figure 25.16. Refer to Figure 25.2 on page 457 for the dates of the start of the seasons.

4. Using the data in the table, plot the apparent diameter of the sun for each of the dates listed. Draw a smooth curve through the plotted points.

5. Answer the questions in *Analysis and Conclusions*.

Analysis and Conclusions

1. In general, how is the apparent size of an object affected by its distance from an observer? Does an object appear larger when the observer is closer or farther away from it?

2. From your graph, in which season is the sun's apparent diameter largest? Will Earth be closer to or farther from the sun at that time?

3. In which season is the sun's apparent diameter smallest? Will Earth be closer to or farther from the sun at that time?

4. Based upon your answers to questions 1–3, explain how you know that distance from the sun is not a cause of seasons.

5. What is aphelion? From your graph, determine between which dates Earth is at aphelion?

6. What is perihelion? From your graph, determine between which dates Earth is at perihelion?

7. Compare your answers to questions 5 and 6 with the dates of aphelion and perihelion given on page 466. How do they compare?

8. Using the values in the Data Table for the maximum and minimum apparent diameters, calculate the average apparent diameter of the sun. Show your work. Remember that 60 seconds is equivalent to 1 minute.

9. Use the formula below to calculate the percent variation in the apparent size of the sun throughout the year. Based on your answer, what is the percent variation in Earth's distance from the sun?

$$\% \text{ variation} = \frac{\text{average} - \text{mininimum}}{\text{average value}} \times 100$$

Answers to all questions appear in the Teacher's Guide at the back of this book.

■ Summary

I Rotation is the turning of Earth on its axis. The axis is tilted at an angle of 23.5° from a perpendicular to the plane of Earth's orbit.

The behavior of a Foucault pendulum, the Coriolis effect, the length of a day, the daily change from daylight to nighttime, and the direction of sunrise and sunset are all results of Earth's rotation.

The rate of Earth's rotation is 15° each hour and is the basis for the standard time zones. The speed of Earth's rotation is greatest at the equator and least at the poles.

II Solar noon occurs when the sun is at its highest position. Earth's rotation causes solar noon to move 15° W each hour.

There are 24 standard time zones around the world. Each is 15° of longitude wide. The international date line marks where the calendar date changes for world travelers.

III Revolution is the movement of Earth in its orbit around the sun. Earth's revolution determines the length of a year.

The tilt of Earth's axis causes the hemispheres to receive different amounts of daylight during the course of a year. The angle at which sunlight strikes Earth affects the temperature.

IV The Northern Hemisphere is at maximum tip toward the sun on the summer solstice and at maximum tip away from the sun on the winter solstice. Neither hemisphere is tipped toward the sun on the spring and autumn equinoxes.

Seasons are caused by the combined effects of Earth's revolution, the tilt of Earth's axis, and the parallelism of Earth's axis.

■ Vocabulary

altitude	rotation
autumn equinox	solar noon
axis of rotation	solar time
Coriolis effect	spring equinox

daylight saving time	standard time zones
international date line	summer solstice
parallax	time meridian
parallelism of the axis	winter solstice
prime meridian	zenith
revolution	

■ Review

For each item, select the best answer. Write the letter of your answer on your paper.

1. Toward which star does Earth's north end of axis always point? (a) Sirius (b) Betelgeuse (c) Polaris (d) Vega

2. Which of the following Earth motions is demonstrated by the Foucault pendulum? (a) rotation (b) revolution (c) parallelism (d) perigee

3. Which is NOT caused by Earth's rotation? (a) length of a day (b) direction of sunrise (c) change from day to night (d) location of Arctic Circle

4. What is Earth's rate of rotation? (a) 1° per hour (b) 15° per hour (c) 24° per hour (d) 90° per hour

5. As distance from the equator increases, speed of rotation (a) increases, (b) increases, then decreases, (c) decreases, (d) does not change.

6. Solar noon occurs (a) when the sun is directly overhead, (b) when the sun reaches its highest point for the day, (c) at 12 noon standard time, (d) at 1 P.M. daylight saving time.

7. How many standard time zones are there worldwide? (a) 1 (b) 15 (c) 24 (d) 30

8. What time is it in Chicago if it is 2 P.M. in Los Angeles? (a) 12 noon (b) 1 P.M. (c) 3 P.M. (d) 4 P.M.

9. During daylight saving time, (a) clocks are set 1 hour ahead of standard time, (b) sun does not rise until 8 A.M., (c) clocks are set 1 hour behind standard time, (d) electricity savings are slight.

10. Which is NOT true of the international date line? (a) It is at 0° longitude. (b) It lies within the ocean. (c) People moving west across it lose a day. (d) Areas to its west are one day ahead of areas to its east.

11. Which is NOT true of Earth's revolution? (a) Its path is elliptical. (b) Its rate is 15° per hour. (c) It takes a year to be completed. (d) It occurs in the same direction as revolutions of other planets.

12. Which does NOT occur in the hemisphere that is leaning toward the sun? (a) warmer temperatures (b) longer daylight (c) higher solar altitudes (d) due east point of sunrise

13. Where in the sky is the sun when it is at the zenith? (a) on the horizon, rising (b) directly overhead (c) on the horizon, setting (d) over the prime meridian

14. Which is NOT a cause of seasons? (a) Earth's revolution (b) Earth's distance from sun (c) tilt of axis (d) parallelism of axis

Use the KEY to identify the date when each of the following occurs.

KEY

(a) March 21   (c) September 23
(b) June 21   (d) December 21

15. Moving northward from the equator causes the daylight period to decrease.

16. The sun is overhead at the equator but will be overhead south of the equator the next day.

17. Shortest day of the year in the Northern Hemisphere

18. Every location north of the Arctic Circle is experiencing a 24-hour daylight period.

■ Interpret and Apply

On your paper, answer each question in complete sentences.

1. Suppose Earth rotated from east to west and at twice its present rate. How would a day be different?

2. What time is it in each United States standard time zone when the new date is beginning at the international date line?

3. If Earth's axis were tilted at 33.5° instead of 23.5°, where would the Tropics of Cancer and Capricorn and the Arctic and Antarctic Circles be located?

4. How would increasing the tilt of Earth's axis change the length of daylight and nighttime throughout the year?

5. Compare the length of daylight and nighttime on June 21 and December 21 in your city or town with that in Mexico City, Mexico; Montreal, Canada; and Buenos Aires, Argentina.

■ Critical Thinking

The noon altitude of the sun on the solstices can be calculated for any location if the difference in degrees latitude from that location to the Tropic of Cancer is known. The latitude of Sioux Falls, South Dakota is 43.5° N. Answer questions 1–4. (Refer to information in Lesson IV as needed.)

1. What is the difference in latitude between Sioux Falls and the Tropic of Cancer?

The difference between the zenith and the noon solar altitude on the summer solstice equals the difference in latitude between Sioux Falls and the Tropic of Cancer.

2. Find the altitude of the sun at noon on the summer solstice in Sioux Falls.

The distance of the noon sun from the zenith on the winter solstice is equal to the difference in latitude between Sioux Falls and the Tropic of Capricorn.

3. Find the difference in latitude between Sioux Falls and the Tropic of Capricorn. (Remember that the Tropic of Capricorn is south of the equator.)

4. Find the altitude of the sun at noon in Sioux Falls on the winter solstice.

UNIT **SIX**
Atmospheric Science

Strong winds are evidence of the forces that move water through the atmosphere. How do winds begin?

▲

Water may occur as vapor, as liquid droplets, or as solid ice crystals. What determines the form water takes in the atmosphere?

▼

▲
A satellite photo shows atmospheric water in the form of clouds. What do the patterns show about movement in the atmosphere?

How does water affect the weather?

Earth's atmosphere holds more water than all the lakes and streams combined. You can see some of this water as clouds, but even on clear days water in the air surrounds you. How does this water affect the weather? What drives the water from place to place? Look at the photographs. What does each show about water in the atmosphere?

Changes in the atmosphere lead to changes in the weather. How do meteorologists predict the weather?
▼

The once-fertile African pastureland that these people depend upon is becoming dry desert. With satellites, computers, and ground surveys, climatologists keep a close watch on these changes. How can modern technology help predict and improve conditions in areas of climate change?
▼

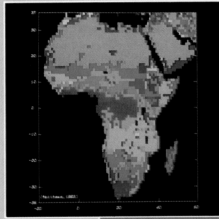

Weather and the Atmosphere

▲
Thunderstorm clouds
seen from a jet aircraft
flying at a height of 10
kilometers

How Do You Know That . . .

Weather occurs close to Earth's surface? From an airplane, you can look down on the weather. Jet aircraft fly at altitudes greater than 10 kilometers. Passengers looking out the windows can sometimes see the lightning from thunderclouds, whose flat tops are near the level of the aircraft. Smaller, fluffy fair-weather clouds lie around the base of the thunderstorm clouds. Outside the aircraft, the pilot announces, the temperature is about −65°F.

Unlike temperatures near Earth's surface, the temperature 10 kilometers up does not change very much. What causes the temperature changes that are a part of what is called weather?

I Composition and Structure of the Atmosphere

Topic 1 What Is Weather?

Anyone looking outside notices right away whether it is cloudy or clear. From personal experience, people know that cloudy skies bring cooler temperatures. Dark clouds often bring rain. Strong winds and blowing snow mean either heavy coats and boots or a day spent indoors.

Weather is the state of the atmosphere at a given time and place. A complete description of the weather includes the amount and type of clouds. Rain, snow, thunderstorms, lightning, and even dust storms are part of the weather. Measurements of temperature, pressure, wind speed and direction, and the amount of moisture in the air are also included in a description of the weather.

Weather is studied and predicted by scientists called meteorologists. The science of **meteorology** is the study of the entire atmosphere, including its weather. To understand and predict the weather, meteorologists must first understand how the atmosphere heats and cools, how clouds form and produce rain, and what makes the wind blow. Meteorologists also study subjects not obviously related to weather. Such subjects include the composition of the atmosphere, the atmospheres of other planets, and the causes of past and present climates. To study these topics, meteorologists measure the state of the atmosphere using many different kinds of instruments. They also perform laboratory experiments and make mathematical models of the atmosphere using computers.

Topic 2 Observing the Weather

Much can be learned about the weather without numerous instruments. Direct observation tells whether it is cloudy or raining. Wind direction and speed can be estimated with a little practice. It is easy to tell whether the air is warm or cold. Even humidity and pressure have observable effects. Certain clouds come with fair weather and other clouds foretell rain. Farmers, sailors, and others dependent on weather become quite skilled at predicting weather from watching the clouds. For example, in the verse

> Mackerel scales and mares' tails
> Make lofty ships carry low sails,

a cloud formation predicts a coming storm.

A Identify a number of things meteorologists do in their study of the atmosphere and show how to observe the weather.

B Describe the composition and temperature structure of the atmosphere.

C Discuss the ozone layer, its importance, and its possible reduction by CFCs.

D Explain the origin and variations of the ionosphere.

26.1 Sailors knew that mares' tails like those pictured here often precede storms.

477

The wind is also related to weather changes. For example, folk wisdom says that winds blowing out of the east bring rain.

Wind direction is shown by flags or blowing dust. The actual wind speed can be estimated by observing its effects. The **Beaufort scale,** named for Sir Francis Beaufort, relates the wind speed to its effects.

The Beaufort Scale

Beaufort Number	MPH	Knots	Wind Effects Observed on Land	Wind Effects Observed at Sea
0	Less than 1	Less than 1	Calm; smoke rises vertically	Sea like a mirror
1	1–3	1–3	Direction of wind shown by smoke drift but not by vanes	Scalelike ripples; no crests
2	4–7	4–6	Wind felt on face; leaves rustle; vanes moved by wind	Small wavelets; glassy crests, do not break
3	8–12	7–10	Leaves, small twigs in constant motion; wind extends light flag	Large wavelets; crests breaking; foam glassy; scattered whitecaps
4	13–18	11–16	Raises dust, loose paper; small branches moved	Small waves become larger; fairly frequent whitecaps
5	19–24	17–21	Small trees in leaf begin to sway; crested wavelets form on inland waters	Moderate waves form many whitecaps; spray
6	25–31	22–27	Large branches in motion; whistling heard in wires; umbrellas used with difficulty	Large waves form; foam crests more extensive; some spray
7	32–38	28–33	Whole trees in motion; inconvenient walking against wind	Sea heaps up; some foam from waves blows streaks
8	39–46	34–40	Breaks twigs off trees; impedes progress	Moderately high waves; well-marked streaks of foam
9	47–54	41–47	Slight structural damage occurs	High waves; dense foam streaks; spray may affect visibility
10	55–63	48–55	Trees uprooted; considerable damage occurs	Very high waves; long overhanging crests; white foam; has white appearance
11	64–72	56–63	Widespread damage	Exceptionally high waves; sea covered with foam patches; edges of wave crests blow into froth everywhere
12	73–82	64–71	Widespread damage	Air filled with foam and spray; sea completely white with driving spray; visibility very seriously affected

The temperature cannot be guessed accurately, but people feel heat and cold. In the winter, people feel colder when the wind is blowing. The actual temperature can be converted into the temperature the body feels using a chart for the *windchill* factor. This adjusted temperature describes the danger of frostbite. In the winter, weather broadcasts often include temperatures adjusted for windchill.

Increased humidity makes wavy and curly hair curlier. High temperatures seem hotter and low temperatures colder when the air is more humid.

Air pressure cannot be felt, but changes in air pressure can. The most common effect of pressure change is the "popping" of the ears. Ear popping occurs during the takeoff or landing of an airplane, a ride in a rapid elevator, or even a ride in a car over a high mountain pass. In all cases, the ears pop because the air pressure falls with height.

To try to predict weather, you need to observe the clouds, wind, temperature, humidity, air pressure, and precipitation over a period of time. Look for patterns in how these factors change relative to one another. For example, is one sequence of events usually followed by rain? See if you can develop your skills at observing and predicting as you study this Unit.

SCIENCE BACKGROUND

U.S. Weather Service maps still show surface air temperatures in degrees Fahrenheit. Temperatures at higher levels are reported in Celsius. Winds at all levels are reported in knots (nautical miles per hour).

OF INTEREST

Experiencing sudden decompression—sudden pressure loss—caused by loss in aircraft cabin pressure is part of the training of aircrews.

26.2 Use this table to find the windchill, or cooling effect of the wind. The combined effect of temperature and wind is called the windchill factor.

Wind Velocity (MPH)

Temp. °F	0	5	10	15	20	25	30	35	40	45	50
−10	−10	−15	−31	−45	−52	−58	−63	−67	−69	−70	70
−5	−5	−11	−27	−40	−46	−52	−56	−60	−62	−63	−63
0	0	−6	−22	−33	−40	−45	−49	−52	−54	−54	−56
5	5	1	−15	−25	−32	−37	−41	−43	−45	−46	−47
10	10	7	−9	−18	−24	−29	−33	−35	−36	−38	−38
15	15	12	−2	−11	−17	−22	−26	−27	−29	−31	−31
20	20	16	2	−6	−9	−15	−18	−20	−22	−24	−24
25	25	21	9	1	−4	−7	−11	−13	−15	−17	−17
30	30	27	16	11	3	0	−2	−4	−4	−6	−7
35	35	33	21	16	12	7	5	3	1	1	0
40	40	37	28	22	18	16	13	11	10	9	8

	Little danger		Increasing danger		Great danger that exposed flesh will freeze

Topic 3 Composition of the Atmosphere

Earth's lower atmosphere is a mixture of many gases called *air*. The two main gases in air are nitrogen and oxygen. Together they form about 99 percent of dry air by volume. The remaining 1 percent is mostly argon and carbon dioxide. The atmosphere also contains tiny amounts of helium, hydrogen, neon, ozone, krypton, and other gases. The approximate percentages by volume are nitrogen, 78; oxygen, 21; argon, almost 1; carbon dioxide, 0.03; all others, 0.01.

The air thins out quickly at altitudes high above Earth's surface. Its composition (by percent) remains the same, however, to an altitude of about 80 kilometers. Above this level the air is so thin that it would be considered a vacuum at sea level. Also, above this level the atmosphere changes to layers of different gases. A layer of oxygen reaches to about 1000 kilometers. Above it is a layer of helium to about 2400 kilometers. Above this a layer of hydrogen thins out into space.

Gas molecules at the bottom of the atmosphere are squeezed together by the gases above them. As a result, 99 percent of the atmosphere's weight is found within about 32 kilometers of Earth's surface. Half the atmosphere's weight is within 5.5 kilometers.

Topic 4 Water Vapor, Ozone, and Dust

Air always contains some water vapor. Water vapor enters the air by evaporation from the oceans and from water or plants on land. The amount of water vapor varies with location, season, and time of day. Most of the water vapor is near the surface, and the percentage decreases with height.

Ozone is a form of oxygen gas. A molecule of ozone contains three oxygen atoms; a molecule of oxygen contains two oxygen atoms. Ozone forms when ultraviolet rays from the sun act on oxygen in the upper atmosphere. It is concentrated at heights of about 10 to 50 kilometers in a region called the ozone layer. Ozone is important because it absorbs 99 percent of the harmful ultraviolet rays. If the atmosphere has less ozone, more ultraviolet rays reach Earth's surface, causing more sunburns, skin cancer, and plant damage.

SCIENCE BACKGROUND

Ozone is formed by the action of sunlight. Thus, the concentration of ozone varies with the latitude, season, and time of day.

Ozone thinning results from the release of gases called **chlorofluorocarbons (CFC's)** into the atmosphere. These gases contain chlorine, fluorine, and carbon. CFC's are used as coolants in air conditioners, to clean electronic components and in making foam products. CFC's do not break apart easily. Eventually they can rise into the ozone layer. The chlorine atoms from the CFC's break down ozone in the presence of sunlight.

Ozone measurements since the late 1970's show a hole in the ozone layer over Antarctica during September and October. From the late 1970's to the early 1990's, the hole grew larger and more intense. In 1990, the ozone decreased by as much as 50 percent. Extreme thinning of the ozone layer in Antarctica results from the isolated climate and extremely cold winters and early springs. The cold allows clouds to form in the atmosphere containing the ozone layer. Ice particles in these clouds provide places for ozone destruction. The ozone hole is filled when warmer winds from the north mix in ozone-rich air.

A similar hole occurs over the Arctic. Winter and spring ozone values over the northern middle latitudes decreased 6 to 8 percent from 1979 to 1990. Smaller decreases have occurred at lower latitudes.

Dust, another part of air, includes tiny grains of rock, dirt, pollen, salt crystals from sea spray, soot from fires, chemicals from factories, and bacteria. Dust helps form fog and rain. Water vapor condenses around some dust grains, forming tiny water droplets.

Topic 5 **Structure of the Atmosphere**

Scientists divide the atmosphere into four layers that are based on temperature changes. The lowest layer is called the **troposphere**. The troposphere starts at Earth's surface. Its thickness depends on the latitude. At the equator the troposphere is about 18 kilometers thick; at the poles it is only about 8 kilometers thick. The gases of the troposphere are essential to life on Earth. Earth's weather occurs in the troposphere.

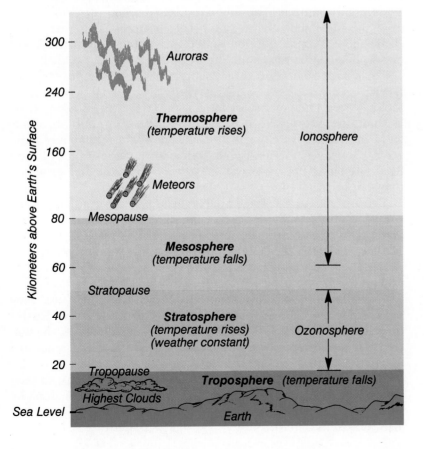

26.3 This diagram shows the temperature layers of the atmosphere. It also shows where auroras form and meteors flare up.

VIDEODISC SELECTION

Diagram: layers of Earth's atmosphere
Side 1: 801, single frame

Diagram and photos of auroras
Side 1: 950 to 955, 6-frame sequence

26.4 Reflection of radio waves by the ionosphere extends the range of radio reception.

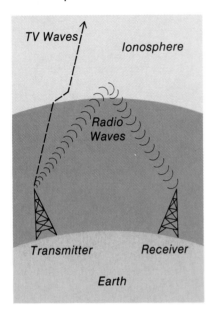

VIDEODISC SELECTION

Aurora Borealis imaged by *Dynamics Explorer* satellite
Side 1 movie: 35291 & PLAY

Aurora Australis as seen from the space shuttle
Side 1 movie: 35732 & PLAY

26.5 An aurora seen from Alaska

Temperatures gradually decrease with altitude in the troposphere. The top of the troposphere is called the *tropopause*. There the decrease in temperature stops. At the poles the tropopause temperature is about −55°C.

The second layer is the **stratosphere**. It reaches from the tropopause to a height of about 50 kilometers from Earth. The stratosphere is clear and dry. It has strong, steady winds and few weather changes. Because of its steady weather conditions, jet aircraft fly in the stratosphere.

The lower part of the stratosphere is as cold as the tropopause. Then it warms up steadily to its top, or *stratopause*. The absorbing or *absorption* of sunlight by ozone is what makes the stratosphere's temperatures increase with height.

The third and fourth layers are the **mesosphere**, in which temperatures drop again, and the **thermosphere**, in which temperatures rise again. The top of the thermosphere is around 500 kilometers from Earth. In the thermosphere, nitrogen and oxygen atoms absorb solar energy, causing the temperature to rise.

Topic 6 **The Ionosphere**

At heights between about 65 and 500 kilometers above Earth, the air is highly ionized. The ions are formed when ultraviolet rays from the sun knock electrons off oxygen atoms. This part of the atmosphere is called the **ionosphere.** It stretches from the lower mesosphere to the top of the thermosphere.

The ions and electrons are concentrated in layers at four different levels. Each layer reflects radio waves of different wavelengths. Radio waves from broadcasting stations travel in straight lines. Without the ionosphere, the waves would mostly go out into space. Only locations very close to the station would receive any radio waves. However, the ionosphere reflects the radio waves back to Earth. Reflection of the waves greatly increases the area in which they can be received.

The ionosphere is affected by solar events. Huge eruptions on the sun send out large amounts of very short-wave radiation, which disrupts radio communications. Solar eruptions reach a peak each 11 years. Scientists see a relationship between solar eruptions and sunspots, since the number of sunspots also reaches a maximum every 11 years.

The solar eruptions also send out ionized particles. Since they are electrically charged, these particles are deflected by Earth's magnetic field to the North and South Poles. At the poles, the ionized particles interact with air molecules to form *auroras*, colored displays of light in the nighttime sky.

The ionosphere does not reflect the waves used to transmit television. These waves, however, can be picked up and rebroadcast by special satellites orbiting high above Earth. Some radio signals are also relayed by satellite.

TOPIC QUESTIONS

Each topic question refers to the topic of the same number.

1. (a) Define weather.   **(b)** What is meteorology?

2. (a) Explain how weather can be observed without the use of instruments.   **(b)** What two factors make the temperature hard to estimate?

3. (a) What is air?   **(b)** List the names and the percentages of the main gases for dry air in the lower atmosphere.

4. (a) Explain where water vapor comes from. At what altitude is the most water vapor found?   **(b)** Why is ozone important? At what altitude is the most ozone found? What gases destroy ozone? When does most ozone destruction occur?   **(c)** How do salt and chemical grains help to make fog and rain?

5. (a) On what basis is the atmosphere divided into four layers?   **(b)** Name the four layers.

6. (a) On what basis is the ionosphere named?   **(b)** How does it help radio communication?   **(c)** Explain how radio communication can be disrupted.   **(d)** Describe what causes auroras.

ANSWERS

1. (a) state of atmosphere at a time and place   (b) study of entire atmosphere, including weather

2. (a) watch clouds, weather events; observe wind direction from flags or blowing dust; estimate speed from comparing wind's effects to Beaufort scale; feel temperature; observe curlier hair in humid weather (b) humidity and wind speed

3. (a) a mixture of gases (b) nitrogen, 78; oxygen, 21 ; argon, almost 1; carbon dioxide, 0.03; all others, 0.01

4. (a) oceans, water and plants on land; near the surface (b) absorbs ultraviolet rays, which can cause cancer; 10 – 50 kilometers; CFC's; during winter and spring months (c) Water vapor condenses on them.

5. (a) temperature   (b) troposphere, stratosphere, mesosphere, thermosphere

6. (a) ionized air   (b) reflects radio waves back to Earth   (c) Very short waves from solar eruptions ionize gases more.   (d) Particles from solar eruptions are deflected by magnetic field to poles, where particles interact with air.

EARTH**MATTERS**

Gulf War, Burning Sky

From the air, it looked like the sands were breathing fire. Indeed temperatures were so great near the burning oil wells that the sand melted, turning into black glass. Thick, dark clouds blocked the sun. The landscape was an ecological nightmare.

When Iraqi troops set fire to over 700 Kuwaiti oil wells during the 1991 Gulf War, they set in motion what could have been an environmental catastrophe. Would burning hundreds of millions of barrels of oil put so much dirty smoke into the atmosphere that global temperatures would cool? Would the soot stay in the atmosphere for years or wash out with precipitation?

Computer models tracked the oil fire smoke from Kuwait eastward. Black rain fell in Pakistan, and black snow fell in the Himalayas. In April of 1991, a large typhoon struck Bangladesh, killing more than 100 000 people. The storm had record-breaking rains and flooding. Smoke was also tracked over China, which also experienced flooding. It is thought that salt particles put into the air by the Kuwaiti oil well fires may have seeded the clouds, causing the torrential rains in Bangladesh and China.

Scientists may never know exactly what impact the Kuwaiti fires had on the global environment. The eruption of Mount Pinatubo and the presence of an El Niño event in the Pacific Ocean make it difficult to determine which event caused which change in the global weather patterns.

SCIENCE BACKGROUND

The wavelengths of the kinds of radiation mentioned so far are radio waves, 10–1000 meters; television waves, about 1 meter; infrared radiation, millimeters to 0.00009 cm; visible radiation, 0.00005–0.00009 cm; ultraviolet radiation, 0.000001–0.00005 cm.

SCIENCE BACKGROUND

Advection also applies to quantities other than heat. For example, meteorologists talk of moisture advection.

II Heating of the Atmosphere

Topic 7 How Heat Moves

Changes in weather involve air movements, formation of clouds, and precipitation. Energy is needed to make all these things happen. That energy comes from the sun. Heat energy enters and moves through the atmosphere in three different ways.

One way that heat energy is transferred is **radiation**. Hot bodies such as the sun radiate their energy mainly in the form of short waves. These short waves are seen as visible light. Cooler bodies such as Earth radiate their energy as longer waves. These longer waves are called infrared waves. They are longer than the longest visible light waves, which are red.

Another way is **conduction**. An object receives heat when it comes into contact with a hotter object. A pan on a hot stove is heated mainly by conduction. The air touching a hot radiator is heated mainly by conduction. So is the air that touches warm ground or a warm ocean.

A third way is **convection**. Convection is the most effective form of heat transfer in liquids and gases. A kettle of water on a hot stove is an example of heating by convection. The bottom of the kettle is heated by conduction. The water near the bottom then heats also by conduction. Heating makes the water expand and become less dense. The denser cold water above it sinks, forcing up the warm water. A steady flow called a *convection current* forms. In time, all the water in the kettle is heated. If water is heated from the top, why wouldn't convection occur?

Convection is very important in moving heat through the atmosphere. It transfers heat from one place to another. For example, convection removes heat from hot beaches. Winds from the tropics carry heat away and into middle latitudes. The transfer of warm or cold air by horizontal winds is called *advection*.

Topic 8 The Heat Balance of Earth and Atmosphere

Ideally just as much energy enters Earth as leaves. When this is true, Earth's heat budget is in balance. If Earth's heat budget was out of balance, Earth would gradually heat up or cool down. The only way energy can enter or leave Earth is by radiation. There are not enough molecules in space for conduction or convection.

The sun radiates energy into space in all directions. Earth, tiny by comparison and far away from the sun, receives only about one two-billionth of the sun's rays. This *incoming solar radiation* is called **insolation**.

Suppose 100 units of solar radiation reach the atmosphere. Of these, 30 are reflected back to space, with only about 70 units

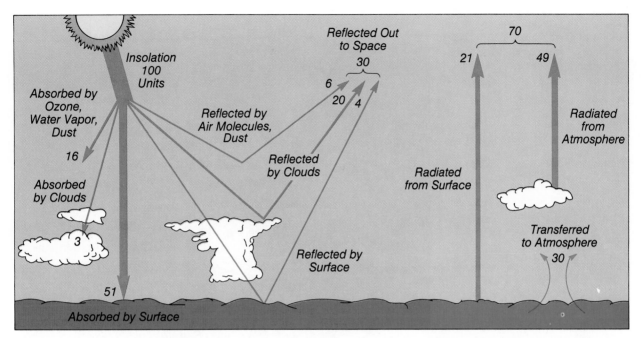

26.6 This diagram shows what happens to 100 units of sunlight entering Earth's atmosphere. Only 51 units are absorbed by the surface.

absorbed. This heat is not absorbed evenly. In the atmosphere, 19 units of sunlight are absorbed by water vapor and clouds, ozone, and dust. Earth's surface absorbs the remaining 51 units of sunlight.

In order to keep Earth's heat budget balanced, 70 units of energy are radiated to space as infrared radiation. The atmosphere and surface also have heat budgets that balance. Of the 51 units of heat absorbed in the form of solar radiation, 21 are radiated back as infrared radiation and 30 are left over. Adding up the complicated radiation budget of the atmosphere, one finds a deficit of 30 units. The 30 units at the surface are transferred from the surface to the atmosphere, so the heat budget balances. How is this done? It is done through the two remaining means of heat transfer, conduction and convection. Conduction from the heated ground heats the very lowest layer of air. Convection currents carry the heat into the atmosphere.

TEACHING TIP

The surface also loses large amounts of excess heat through evaporation. Evaporation as a cooling process is discussed in Chapter 27.

SCIENCE BACKGROUND

This "heat" is in both the form of warm-air currents ("sensible heat") and moisture transported away from the surface ("latent heat," so called because the heat is released when the vapor condenses).

Topic 9 **Absorption and the Greenhouse Effect**

Earth's surface radiates infrared waves. These infrared waves warm the atmosphere because they are absorbed mainly by the water vapor and carbon dioxide in the air.

In a greenhouse, the glass roof acts like the carbon dioxide and water vapor in the air. It lets in the sun's light to heat the soil. However, it does not allow the longer-wave infrared radiation from the warm soil to escape. Scientists call this trapping of the sun's energy by the atmosphere the **greenhouse effect**. The gases that create this effect are known as greenhouse gases.

VIDEODISC SELECTION

Energy absorption by Earth's atmosphere
Side 1: 799, single frame

26.7 Water vapor and carbon dioxide in Earth's atmosphere trap solar energy much as the glass roof of a greenhouse does.

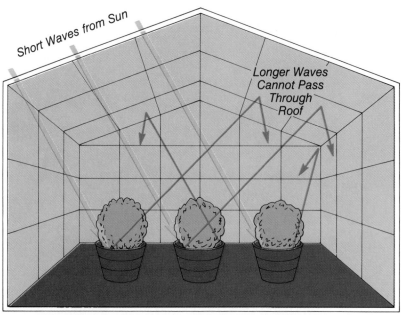

Soil Absorbs Sun's Rays; Radiates Longer Waves

SCIENCE BACKGROUND
Another major reason for the increase in carbon dioxide is deforestation. CFCs are used in aerosol cans, foams, and refrigerators. Nitrous oxides and methane have natural as well as industrial sources.

ANSWERS
7. radiation: electromagnetic waves from warm or hot bodies; conduction: by contact; convection: by moving warmer or colder currents
8. (a) As much energy enters as leaves.   (b) of 100 units, 30 reflected to space, 19 absorbed in atmosphere, 51 absorbed by surface (c) conduction and convection
9. (a) Certain gases let in sunlight but do not let Earth's infrared radiation escape to space.   (b) carbon dioxide and water vapor (c) Resulting warming would melt glaciers and flood coastal areas; shift deserts.

The greenhouse effect of Earth's atmosphere is increasing. The burning of fossil fuels—coal, oil, and natural gas—is constantly adding carbon dioxide into the air. There is too much carbon dioxide to be used by green plants or dissolved in the ocean waters. Scientists estimate that if the present rate of burning continues, the percentage of carbon dioxide in the atmosphere will double in about 100 years. Industry is also producing more CFCs, nitrous oxide, and methane, which are also greenhouse gases. The resulting warming of the atmosphere could have serious effects. The glaciers of Greenland and Antarctica could melt enough to raise sea levels all over the world. Such melting would flood low coastal areas such as Miami and New York City. Rainfall patterns could change in ways that would shift desert areas. Obviously, this problem needs serious attention and study.

TOPIC QUESTIONS

Each question refers to the topic of the same number.

7. Name and describe the three ways that heat is transferred through the atmosphere.

8. (a) Explain why Earth's heat budget is in balance.   **(b)** Describe what happens to sunlight entering Earth's atmosphere. **(c)** What processes balance the heat budget of Earth's surface?

9. (a) Describe the greenhouse effect.   **(b)** Name the two most important greenhouse gases.   **(c)** Why are increased greenhouse gases in the atmosphere a cause for worry?

III How and Why the Temperature Varies

Topic 10 **Temperature Drops with Altitude**

In summertime some people go to the mountains to escape the heat. The higher they go, the cooler it gets. Scientists have measured the rate of cooling with altitude. It averages about 1°C for every 160 meters. This change is called the **normal lapse rate**.

Why is the troposphere warmest near Earth's surface? Most of the sun's radiation is absorbed at the surface. Heat is transferred from the surface to the air just above by conduction and carried aloft by convection. The rising air in the convection currents cools.

The rising air cools from expansion. Rising air expands because it meets lower pressure at higher altitudes. The lower pressure allows the air molecules to move farther apart. As molecules mover farther apart, they collide less often and transfer less energy to each other. Less energy means lower temperatures. (See Topic 16.) Outside of clouds, rising air cools at a rate of 1°C for every 100 meters. When air sinks, its molecules are squeezed closer together by the increased pressure. The molecules gain energy. The temperature rises at a rate of 1°C for every 100 meters in clean air. The word *adiabatic* (a-dee-uh-BAT-ic) describes the temperature change caused by expansion or compression.

The rate of temperature change of rising or sinking air outside of clouds is called the *dry-adiabatic lapse rate*. In contrast, the normal lapse rate is the average temperature change with height. This average includes all air—clear or cloudy, moving or still.

Topic 11 **Temperature Inversions**

Normally the air gets colder with height in the troposphere. Sometimes, however, the air at the surface is colder than the air above it. This upside-down temperature condition is called a **temperature inversion**.

OBJECTIVES

A Explain why the temperature in the troposphere decreases with height.

B Discuss the formation and destruction of temperature inversions near the ground.

C Show how the angle of the sun's rays affects the temperature changes with season, latitude, and hour of day.

D Identify and explain the occurrence of the warmest and coldest hours and the warmest and coldest months.

E Compare the heating and cooling of land and water.

26.8 This diagram shows three reasons why the troposphere is warmest near the ground. (At night, the air nearest the ground cools, but it quickly warms during the day.)

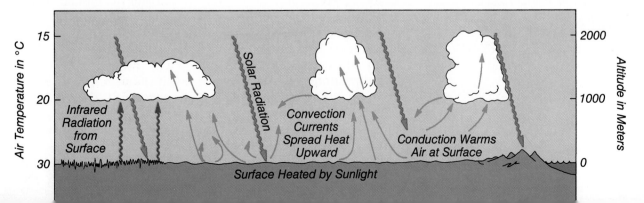

SCIENCE BACKGROUND
Inversions are particularly harmful to cities in basins (Los Angeles) and beside mountain ranges (Denver) because horizontal winds cannot easily carry the pollution away.

26.9 (a) Normal conditions, and (b) a temperature inversion

No Inversion Near Surface

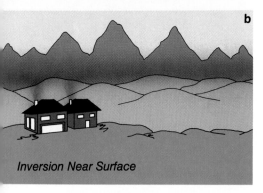

Inversion Near Surface

SCIENCE BACKGROUND
The sunlight is nearly perpendicular to south-facing mountainsides in the Northern Hemisphere much of the year, giving them a warmer "microclimate" than nearby level areas at the same elevation.

SCIENCE BACKGROUND
Sunlight entering the atmosphere at a small angle to the ground also has less total energy because it has to pass through more air before it reaches the surface.

VIDEODISC SELECTION

Earth's orbit versus the seasons
Side 1: 7263, single frame

Temperature inversions form during clear, dry nights. On these nights, the ground and the air near the ground cool rapidly by radiation from the surface. Since the ground cools faster than the air, the air near the ground cools still more due to contact with the cooler ground. The wind mixes the cold air upward in a layer a few hundred meters deep. This bottom layer is cooler than the air above it. Cold air is heavier than warmer air, so smoke and other pollution are trapped beneath the inversion. If the sky remains clear, sunlight soon warms the ground and lower atmosphere. The low-level inversion is destroyed by late morning. Mixing of the air by strong winds can also destroy low-level inversions or prevent their formation.

Topic 12 **Seasons and the Sun's Rays**

The temperature varies with the seasons because the sun's rays do not heat Earth's surface evenly. Because Earth is round, the sun's rays strike the surface at angles ranging from 0° to 90°. When the sun is directly overhead, the angle of insolation is 90°. The sun's rays are vertical, and Earth's surface gets all the energy possible. As the angle of insolation decreases, the energy of the rays is spread out over a larger area. Also, the distance that sunlight travels through the atmosphere increases. More sunlight is absorbed or reflected before it reaches the surface. Both factors reduce the amount of solar energy reaching the surface.

Places near the equator get nearly vertical rays all through the year. Thus, these areas have hot climates. Places in middle latitudes (like most of the United States) get near-vertical rays in summer. Their summers are hot. The angle of the rays is less vertical in winter, so winters in middle latitudes are cold. Places in high latitudes (near the poles, for example) never get rays striking the surface at near-vertical angles. These areas may even have no sun at all for part of the year. They are cold all year round.

Topic 13 **Warmest and Coldest Hours**

Varying insolation also changes the temperature during the day. The highest temperature is not at noon, however, when the sunlight is strongest. Instead, the warmest hour of a sunny day is usually in the afternoon. For several hours after noon, the lower air still receives more heat from the sun and the ground than it loses. Thus, its temperature keeps rising until well into the afternoon. The coldest hour usually comes just before sunrise because the lower air loses heat all through the night.

The difference between the highest and lowest temperatures is the temperature range. For any one day, it is the daily temperature range. For example, a high of 35°C and a low of 10°C give a range of 25°C. The daily temperature range is variable. It is usually large when skies are clear. The clear skies allow strong heating by day. At night they allow rapid loss of heat by radiation.

The daily temperature range is small on cloudy days. The clouds keep out sunshine by day, so the air hardly warms up. At night the clouds keep the air from radiating its heat out into space. This blanket effect keeps the air from cooling much at night.

The average temperature of a day is the sum of the high and low temperatures divided by two. This daily average is then used to compute the average, or mean, temperatures for months, years, or other periods of time.

Topic 14   Warmest and Coldest Months

Like the day's highest temperature, the year's highest temperature occurs after the time of strongest sunlight. In middle latitudes of the Northern Hemisphere, June 21 is the time of strongest sunlight. However, July is usually the warmest month. Similarly, December 21 is the time of weakest sunlight, but January is usually the coldest month. In the Southern Hemisphere, the warmest and coldest months are the reverse.

The annual temperature range for an area is the difference between the average temperatures of the warmest and coldest months. Oceans have small annual temperature ranges. They are relatively cool in summer and warm in winter. Continents and large landmasses have large annual temperature ranges. They are relatively hot in summer and cool in winter.

Topic 15   Heating of Land and Water

Why are the daily and annual temperature ranges larger over continents than over oceans? The reason is water and land warm up and cool off at different rates. Water warms much more slowly than land for many reasons.

1. In water, the sun's rays go to a depth of many meters. On land, the sun's rays heat only the top few centimeters of soil.
2. Water can spread heat easily because it is a fluid.
3. Water needs more energy than land to raise its temperature the same amount.
4. Some solar energy is used in the process of evaporation. Thus, less solar energy is available to raise the temperature of the water.

Water cools more slowly than land because it is a slower conductor of heat. It must lose more energy for the same temperature drop. Also, its heat is spread through a greater depth.

Water and land in the same latitude reach very different temperatures. On a sunny day in summer, dry beach sand is much warmer than the nearby water. At night the same sand cools faster than the water and becomes much colder. On a larger scale, continents are warmer than nearby ocean waters in summer. In winter the same continents become much colder than the nearby waters.

26.10 The vertical rays of sunlight and the slanted rays are of the same width. They carry equal amounts of energy. However, the vertical rays are concentrated between points A and B, and the slanted rays are spread out between A and C.

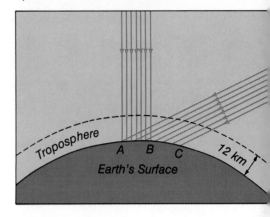

Troposphere
A B C
Earth's Surface
12 km

VIDEODISC SELECTION

Inclination of Earth's axis
Side 1: 7264, single frame

Satellite images showing global temperatures
Side 1: 894 to 895, 2-frame sequence

490

26.11 Satellite image of infrared radiation over the southeastern United States. Lighter shades show colder temperatures. Note the warm (darker) water and cooler (lighter) land.

SCIENCE BACKGROUND

Snow is particularly hard to heat up. It reflects visible light and also loses energy by efficiently emitting infrared radiation. Furthermore, energy is used in melting or evaporating it.

ANSWERS

10. (a) most sunlight absorbed at surface; rising convection currents cool   (b) troposphere's normal cooling rate with height   (c) rate of cooling of rising air outside of clouds

11. (a) Air gets warmer with height. Air near ground cools faster than air higher up, from radiation and from conduction to colder ground, which radiates efficiently to space.   (b) Sun heats surface; surface warms air.

12. (a) more heating with angles closer to vertical   (b) warm temperatures from high sun angles at low latitudes; cold temperatures from low sun angle near poles; middle latitudes in between

13. (a) Air near ground receives more heat from sun and ground than it loses.   (b) Lower air cools all night.   (c) Clouds reduce temperature range by blocking out sunlight during day and keeping air from radiating to space at night.

14. (a) July and January; January and July   (b) difference between the average temperatures of warmest and coldest months

15. (a) sun heats deeper layer of water; fluids spread heat better, water needs more energy to raise temperature; evaporation uses up some heat   (b) water slower conductor; must lose more energy per drop in temperature; deeper layer heated; much heated water below surface   (c) because of many different surface materials

Unlike water, land has many kinds of surface materials. Some of these absorb the sun's rays better than others. Dark soils and rocks absorb more energy than light-colored ones. Rough surfaces absorb more energy than smooth ones. The temperature of dry ground increases faster than wet ground. Meadows warm up more quickly than forests. Pavements get warm long before grassy lawns. Snow and ice reflect sunlight and remain cold.

Surfaces that warm up faster usually also cool off faster. They are warmer in sunshine and cooler at night.

TOPIC QUESTIONS

Each topic question refers to the topic of the same number.

10. **(a)** Explain why the temperature normally drops with altitude in the troposphere.   **(b)** Define normal lapse rate.   **(c)** Define dry-adiabatic lapse rate.

11. **(a)** What is a temperature inversion? Explain how temperature inversions form at night.   **(b)** How are they destroyed in the morning?

12. **(a)** Describe the relationship between the angle of the sun's rays and the heating effect.   **(b)** How is this angle related to climates of the low, middle, and high latitudes?

13. **(a)** Explain why the warmest hour of the day is usually in the afternoon.   **(b)** Why is the coldest hour just before sunrise? **(c)** Why is the temperature range larger on clear days than on cloudy ones?

14. **(a)** List the warmest and coldest months in the Northern Hemisphere; in the Southern Hemisphere.   **(b)** Define annual temperature range.

15. **(a)** List the reasons sunlight warms water more slowly than land.   **(b)** Explain why water holds heat longer than land. **(c)** Why does land heat unevenly?

IV   Measuring Air Temperature

Topic 16   Temperature and Thermometers

Temperature is a measure of the energy of molecules. The more energy the molecules in air have, the hotter it feels. **Thermometers** are the instruments that measure temperature. Common thermometers work on the principle that a rise in temperature causes molecules to move farther apart. Therefore, most materials expand when heated.

Some thermometers contain a liquid such as mercury or alcohol as the expanding material. Mercury is silver in color. Alcohol is clear, so it is usually dyed red or blue to be more visible. The liquid fills the relatively broad bulb end of a long, narrow glass tube. When the temperature rises, the liquid expands into the tube's narrow stem.

Mercury thermometers are more accurate than alcohol thermometers because mercury expands more evenly. However, mercury cannot be used at temperatures below about −40°C, where it freezes. Alcohol freezes at about −129°C.

Metal thermometers have two equally long strips of different metals. Brass and iron are a common pair. The two strips are bonded together, one on top of the other. This forms a device called a *bimetal bar*. Because the metals expand at different rates, a rise in temperature makes the bar curl. A drop in temperature curls it the other way. Usually the bar is shaped into a coil and fastened at one end. As the temperature changes, the coil winds or unwinds.

A *thermograph* is a self-recording thermometer. A *maximum thermometer* shows the highest temperature reached. A *fever thermometer* is a maximum thermometer that has a tiny constriction to keep the mercury from flowing back into the bulb. A *minimum thermometer* indicates the lowest temperature reached.

Topic 17   Temperature Scales

Temperatures are measured in degrees. A **degree** of temperature is a definite fraction of the difference between two fixed temperatures. Usually these points are the temperatures assigned to the melting of ice and the boiling of water at sea level pressure.

On the Celsius scale, the fixed points are labeled as 0 and 100. One degree Celsius is therefore $\frac{1}{100}$ of their difference. On the Fahrenheit scale, the fixed points are labeled 32 and 212. One degree Fahrenheit is therefore $\frac{1}{180}$ of their difference $(212 - 32 = 180)$.

Note that a Celsius degree is almost twice as large as a Fahrenheit degree. To be exact,

$$1°C = 1.8°F, \text{ or } 1°F = \frac{5}{9}°C.$$

OBJECTIVES

A Explain how temperature is measured and identify the Celsius temperature scale.

B Describe and explain the pattern of the world's isotherms.

26.12   The hygrothermograph records temperature and humidity. As the temperature and humidity rise and fall, the pens trace lines on the scale.

26.13   A comparison of the Celsius and Fahrenheit temperature scales

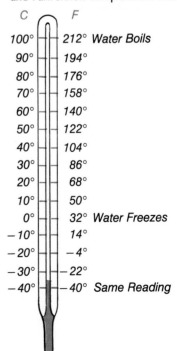

C	F
100°	212° *Water Boils*
90°	194°
80°	176°
70°	158°
60°	140°
50°	122°
40°	104°
30°	86°
20°	68°
10°	50°
0°	32° *Water Freezes*
−10°	14°
−20°	−4°
−30°	−22°
−40°	−40° *Same Reading*

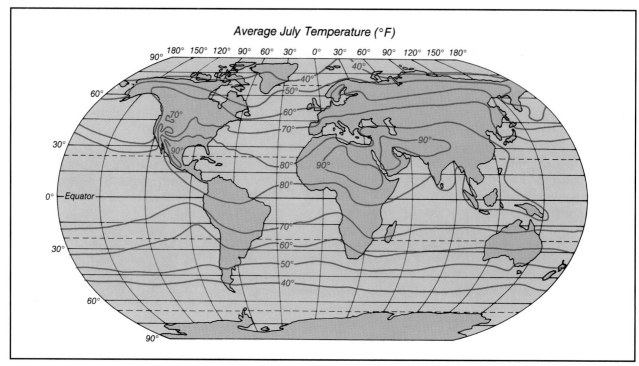

Average July Temperature (°F)

26.14 This map shows isotherms for July.

SCIENCE BACKGROUND

"Iso" means equal. Thus, contour lines on a topographic map are iso-lines of elevation above sea level.

Topic 18 Isotherms

Isotherms are lines drawn on maps that connect places with the same temperature. Usually isotherms are spaced 5 or 10 degrees apart.

The maps in Figures 26.14 and 26.15 show average world temperatures for January and July. Notice that the warmest temperatures are to the north of the equator in July. The sun's rays are more vertical north of the equator in July. If Earth were all water, the isotherms would be east-west, following the parallels of latitude. However, land heats and cools more easily than water, so the continents are warmer in summer and colder in winter. This makes the isotherms more irregular in the Northern Hemisphere, where there is more land.

Topic 19 Why Isotherms Shift

July is the warmest month in the Northern Hemisphere, and January is the coldest month. Thus, the isotherms shift their positions from January to July.

What else do the temperature maps show?

OF INTEREST

The surface of the Southern Hemisphere is 90 percent water, while the surface of the Northern Hemisphere is 50 percent water.

1. The isotherms shift more over the Northern Hemisphere than over the Southern Hemisphere.
2. The isotherms shift more over continents than over oceans.

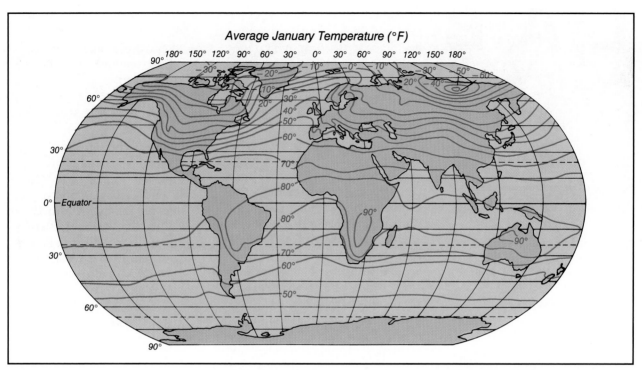

Average January Temperature (°F)

26.15 This map shows isotherms for January.

3. The hottest and coldest places are on land.
4. The coldest spot in the Northern Hemisphere is far south of the North Pole.

What is the explanation of these facts?

SCIENCE BACKGROUND
The temperature range is larger over land because land heats and cools more readily than water.

TOPIC QUESTIONS

Each topic question refers to the topic of the same number.

16. (a) What is the principle used to measure temperature? (b) Describe how a liquid thermometer works. (c) Describe how a metal thermometer works.

17. (a) How are temperature scales determined? (b) Express the freezing and boiling temperatures of water in degrees Celsius. (c) How do the sizes of a Fahrenheit and Celsius degree compare?

18. (a) Explain how isotherms show temperature. (b) Why are the hottest temperatures north of the equator in July? (c) Why are the isotherms more east-west in the Southern Hemisphere?

19. (a) Why do world isotherms shift? (b) Compare the shift of isotherms over land and ocean and explain the differences.

ANSWERS
16. (a) Most materials expand with higher temperatures. (b) Liquid in bulb expands into relatively thin tube. (c) Two metals that expand at different rates with temperature are bonded together in a coil. Heating or cooling tightens or loosens coil.
17. (a) temperature difference between two fixed points (e.g., boiling and freezing of water) divided into equal fractions, called degrees (b) 0°C, 100°C (c) one Fahrenheit degree = 5/9 Celsius degree
18. (a) by connecting points with equal temperature (b) sun's rays more vertical north of equator (c) more ocean, which heats more evenly
19. (a) Temperatures change with season. (b) Isotherms shift more over land because land heats and cools more readily.

CHAPTER 26

L A B
ACTIVITY

Temperature Inversion

In Denver, Colorado, weather reports occasionally inform people that they are experiencing a high pollution day. On these days, people are asked not to drive unless it is absolutely necessary and are told not to light any fires or barbecues. In this investigation, you will determine how temperature inversions in the atmosphere can affect air quality near the ground. Under normal conditions, rising air cools at a rate of 1°C every 160 meters. In a temperature inversion, however, warm air is above cold air, therefore, the temperature increases with altitude. You will graph a normal temperature pattern and a temperature inversion and then analyze how a temperature inversion can trap pollution close to the ground.

Lab Skills and Objectives
- To **graph data** associated with a temperature inversion and with normal conditions, and to **compare** these two graphs.
- To **predict** the effects of a temperature inversion on the levels of air pollution near the ground
- To **predict** changes in temperature conditions in the early morning.

Materials
- 2 sheets graph paper
- ruler

Procedure
1. On a sheet of graph paper, plot Temperature (°C) versus Elevation (m) for the data shown in Data Table A. Plot temperature on the horizontal axis and elevation on the vertical axis, as shown in Figure 26.16. Label this graph Graph 1, leaving space for a graph title.

2. Connect the data points on Graph 1, using a ruler to draw a straight line. On a second sheet of graph paper, plot the data shown in Data Table B. Plot temperature on the horizontal axis and elevation on the vertical axis, as you did in Step 1. Label this graph Graph 2. Leave space for a graph title.

3. Connect the data points on Graph 2. Use a ruler to draw a series of straight line segments.

4. Answer the questions in *Analysis and Conclusions*.

Analysis and Conclusions
1. In Graph 1, does the temperature increase or decrease as altitude increases?

2. In Graph 1, how many meters of elevation does it take for the temperature to change by 1°C? Does the rate at which the temperature decreases change as altitude increases?

3. How does the rate of temperature change from 0–200 meters shown in Graph 1 compare with the rate of temperature change from 0–200 meters shown in Graph 2?

4. Describe the changes in temperature above 200 meters in Graph 2.

5. Determine which of your graphs represents normal conditions and which represents a temperature inversion. Write these terms as titles on the appropriate graphs. Based on your graphs, explain what a temperature inversion is.

6. Since the addition of heat increases the distance between particles, volume also changes. Any slight changes in volume affect density because density is the mass of a substance divided by its volume. In Graph 2, how would the density of air from 200–500 meters compare with the density of air above 500 meters?

7. How would the density difference implied in Graph 2 affect the movement of air pollutants that are released at the surface? Why is it important to be aware of this effect?

8. Strong winds can destroy or prevent temperature inversions from forming. Which city, Des Moines, Iowa or Denver, Colorado is more likely to experience frequent temperature inversions? Explain your answer.

Data Table A	
Elevation (m)	Temperature (°C)
(0)	20.0
100	19.5
200	18.7
300	18.0
400	17.5
500	16.9
600	16.0
700	15.5

Data Table B	
Elevation (m)	Temperature (°C)
(0)	20.0
100	19.3
200	18.8
300	18.0
400	19.0
500	19.5
600	19.4
700	18.8

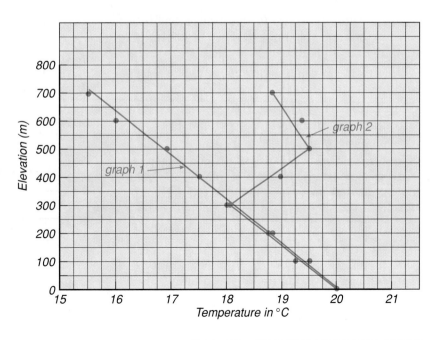

26.16 Setup for Graph I and Graph 2

Answers to all questions appear in the Teacher's Guide at the back of this book.

■ Summary

I Much can be learned about the weather by direct observation without the use of complicated weather instruments.

Earth's atmosphere is a mixture of gases that thin out with height. It contains mainly nitrogen and oxygen, with small amounts of other gases.

The ozone layer protects life from ultraviolet radiation. CFC's threaten to reduce the amount of ozone.

The atmosphere is divided into layers based on temperature. The ionosphere contains ionized air.

II Heat moves in three ways: by radiation, convection, and conduction.

Earth's heat budget is in balance. Most solar radiation is absorbed at the surface, which warms the air above.

Greenhouse gases trap heat in Earth's atmosphere. An increase in carbon dioxide and other greenhouse gases may cause global warming.

III Temperature inversions form on clear nights as the ground and the air just above it cool more rapidly than air higher up.

Climates are warmer at lower latitudes, where the sun is more directly overhead.

The warmest temperatures are generally in the afternoon, and the coldest temperatures just before sunrise.

The warmest month is about a month past the time of maximum sunlight; similarly, the coldest month is about a month past the time of minimum sunlight.

Land heats and cools more readily than water.

IV Temperature is measured using the principle that materials expand when heated. Celsius and Fahrenheit are two commonly used temperature scales.

Isotherms shift with the seasons, more dramatically over land than over water.

■ Vocabulary

Beaufort scale	mesosphere
chlorofluorocarbon (CFC)	meteorology
	normal lapse rate
conduction	radiation
convection	stratosphere
degree	temperature inversion
greenhouse effect	thermometer
insolation	thermosphere
ionosphere	troposphere
isotherm	weather

■ Review

Number your paper from 1 to 20. Match the terms in list **A** with the phrases in list **B**.

List A

1. ionosphere
2. greenhouse effect
3. windchill
4. air
5. annual temperature range
6. water
7. isotherm
8. conduction
9. normal lapse rate
10. meteorology
11. thermometer
12. ozone
13. daily temperature range
14. radiation
15. insolation
16. troposphere
17. temperature inversion
18. angle of insolation
19. carbon dioxide
20. convection

List B

a. difference between the average temperatures of the warmest and coldest months
b. heat transfer by currents within the heated material
c. varies due to Earth's roundness
d. temperature the body actually feels when the wind is blowing
e. condition in which the bottom layer of air is colder than the air above it
f. heat transfer in the form of infrared waves
g. based on the principle that a rise in temperature causes most materials to expand

h. the energy Earth receives from the sun
i. reflects radio waves, but not television waves
j. smaller on cloudy days
k. added to the air by the burning of fossil fuels
l. trapping of the sun's energy by the atmosphere
m. a slow conductor of heat
n. line on a map connecting places with the same temperature
o. study of the atmosphere
p. composed mainly of nitrogen and oxygen
q. heat transfer by direct contact
r. layer of the atmosphere where weather occurs
s. absorbs the sun's ultraviolet rays
t. rate at which the troposphere cools with altitude

■ Interpret and Apply

On your paper, answer each question in complete sentences.

1. Approximately how fast, in miles per hour, is the wind blowing under each of the following conditions? (a) Walking in the wind is difficult and small twigs are breaking off the trees. (b) Pieces of a newspaper are blowing down the street and dust is blown into your eyes. (c) The trees are motionless and smoke is going straight up.
2. The temperature outside is 0°F. How cold does it feel if the wind is blowing (a) 10 mph, (b) 15 mph, (c) 20 mph? (d) Restate these three temperatures in degrees Celsius.
3. How do convection currents help to cool the waters of a lake in autumn?
4. (a) Why are temperature inversions near Earth's surface unlikely on cloudy nights? (b) Under what weather conditions might a temperature inversion NOT disappear in the morning?

5. Why is there very little variation in the time of the warmest and coldest hours of the day at the equator?

■ Critical Thinking

A student performed an experiment to compare the heating and cooling rates of soil and water. She placed identical containers, one filled with soil and the other filled with water, at equal distances from a light source. A thermometer was placed in each container to record the temperatures. She turned the light on and recorded the temperatures each minute for 10 minutes. Then she turned the light off and again recorded the temperatures each minute for 10 minutes. A graph of her data is shown below. Study the graph and then answer the questions that follow.

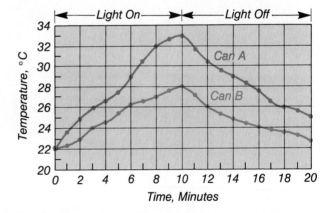

1. In which container did the material warm faster?
2. In which container did the material cool faster?
3. Which container held the water?
4. Did the soil and water both warm the same amount? Why or why not?
5. The smallest daily temperature ranges at Earth's surface are less than 1°C. Where are they and why? What sort of location would usually have the largest temperature range? Why?

Evaporation, Condensation, and Precipitation

CHAPTER 27

Feathery cirrus clouds and fluffy cumulus clouds look very different, but both are made of forms of water.

How Do You Know That . . .

There is water in the atmosphere? You can observe evidence in the sky. Suppose it is a hot, humid spring day. The morning starts out clear, with some patches of fog that disappear early. By noon, small puffy clouds have formed. By afternoon, the puffy clouds have grown deeper. Their dark, flat bases suggest possible rain showers. The puffy clouds are joined by higher, feathery clouds to make a beautiful sky.

Why do the puffy clouds have such flat bases and tops that look so much like cauliflowers? Why do the high, feathery clouds look so different from the puffy clouds? And what keeps the clouds from falling to the ground?

498

I Evaporation and Humidity

Topic 1 States of Water

Water exists in the atmosphere in all of the three states of matter—solid, as snow, hail, and ice particles; liquid, as rain or cloud droplets; and gas, as invisible water vapor.

Water may change from one state to another. The change from solid ice to liquid water is called melting; the reverse process is freezing. The change from liquid water to water vapor is called **evaporation**. The change from water vapor to liquid water is called **condensation**.

Most water vapor in the atmosphere comes from oceans, lakes, marshes, and glaciers. Some water vapor also comes from moist ground, from the leaves of plants, and from erupting volcanoes.

Water vapor is spread throughout the troposphere by convection currents and winds. Since rising air currents stop at the tropopause, there is little water vapor above the troposphere.

Topic 2 Evaporation

The molecules of liquid water are always in motion. Molecules with sufficient energy to escape the water's surface into the atmosphere are said to evaporate. At ordinary temperatures, evaporation is slow because few molecules have enough energy to escape the liquid's surface. As water molecules absorb heat energy, they speed up. Then more molecules have sufficient energy to escape the water's surface. With increasing temperatures the evaporation rate increases. When water evaporates, it enters the atmosphere in the form of water vapor.

Water and other liquids absorb heat energy from their surroundings when they evaporate. Since the high-energy molecules leave the liquid's surface, the remaining liquid molecules have less average energy. This makes evaporation a cooling process.

OBJECTIVES

A Specify the changes in state involved in evaporation and condensation and explain why evaporation is a cooling process.

B Show that warmer air can hold more water vapor.

C Define relative humidity and show how it is measured.

SCIENCE BACKGROUND

The change from solid to gas is called sublimation or evaporation. There is no universally accepted word for the change of phase from vapor to solid. Sublimation, crystallization, deposition, and even condensation are used.

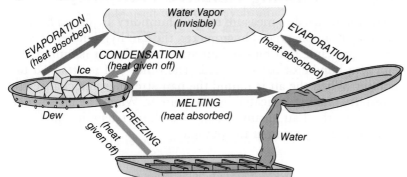

27.1 When water changes from one state to another, it either loses or gains heat.

499

ANSWERS
1. (a) solid—snow, hail, ice; liquid—rain and cloud droplets; gas—water vapor (b) evaporation—change from liquid to gas; condensation—change from gas to liquid (c) oceans, lakes, marshes, glaciers, moist ground, plants, volcanoes (d) rising air stops at tropopause

ANSWERS (continued)
2. (a) Molecules need energy to escape liquid; remaining molecules have less energy. (b) More molecules have enough energy to evaporate.
3. (a) Capacity is greater with higher temperatures. (b) the amount of water vapor in air, in grams of water vapor per kilogram of air (c) when specific humidity equals the air's capacity for water vapor
4. (a) the amount of water vapor in the air compared to the amount of water vapor the air can hold (b) 100 times specific humidity divided by water vapor capacity
5. (a) a relative humidity measuring instrument (b) Human hair stretches with higher humidity. (c) An instrument consisting of two thermometers, one with its bulb in a wetted wick. The wet bulb is cooled more by evaporation when the air is drier. (d) A table gives relative humidity for wet- and dry-bulb readings.

TOPIC QUESTIONS

Each topic question refers to the topic of the same number.
1. (a) In what forms does water exist in the atmosphere? Give examples. (b) Define evaporation and condensation. (c) What are the sources of water vapor in the atmosphere? (d) Why is there so little water vapor above the troposphere?
2. (a) Explain why evaporation is a cooling process. (b) What causes water to evaporate more rapidly when the temperature is warmer?
3. (a) How are the temperature and the water vapor capacity related? (b) Define specific humidity. (c) When is air saturated?
4. (a) What is relative humidity? (b) Explain how relative humidity is calculated.
5. (a) What is a hygrometer? (b) On what principle is a hair hygrometer based? (c) What is a psychrometer? What is the principle of its operation? (d) How is the psychrometer used to find relative humidity?

EARTH**MATTERS**

Rain Forests and Global Environment

Earth's tropical rain forests are disappearing. Each year enough rain forest is chopped down and burned to equal an area the size of Washington state.

In addition to destroying the home of half the world's plant and animal species, destruction of the rain forest affects global warming. Large forests absorb carbon dioxide from the atmosphere. Carbon dioxide (CO_2) is a "greenhouse gas" that contributes to global warming. When trees are burned, not only does the burning remove a CO_2 sink but it actually releases CO_2. The burning of the rain forests may release as much as 2.5 billion tons of CO_2 into the atmosphere each year.

Global warming is also likely to change Earth's precipitation patterns. The planet may receive an average of 7 more inches of rain per year. However, that rain would not fall equally. Parts of North America and Europe would receive more rain while Africa's Sahara Desert would expand. Areas suitable for farming would shift to higher latitudes.

So far computer models have failed to adequately predict the effects of continued rain forest destruction. It is not known how much water might enter the atmosphere and in what form. Different types of clouds would produce different effects on global weather patterns. Some clouds trap heat near Earth's surface; other clouds reflect sunlight back into space.

II Forms of Condensation

Topic 6 Condensation and Dew Point

How does condensation — the change from vapor to liquid — usually happen in the atmosphere? Consider this example. On a sunny spring afternoon the air temperature is 15.5°C and the specific humidity is 8 grams. The air's capacity at this temperature is 11 grams, so it is not saturated. That night the air cools rapidly. When its temperature reaches 10°C, its capacity is only 8 grams. Since the specific humidity of the air is already 8 grams, the air is saturated.

What happens if the temperature drops below 10°C? All the water vapor above its capacity condenses. If the temperature drops to 4.5°C, the air's capacity is 6 grams. Each kilogram of air releases 2 grams of water vapor, which then condenses. If the water vapor condenses on surfaces such as grass, in the form of a liquid, it is called **dew.** The water vapor could also condense into droplets, forming a cloud or fog.

The temperature at which saturation occurs is called the **dew point.** In the example just given, the dew point before condensation was 10°C. Dew point may be higher or lower, depending on the amount of water vapor in the air. The more water vapor the air starts with, the higher its dew point. When air cools to slightly below the dew point, water vapor begins to condense. In fact, when water vapor condenses in cooling air, air temperature and dew point are so close that they are considered equal. In the example, the temperature and dew point fall together until both equal 4.5°C.

Evaporating water molecules absorb heat energy from their surroundings. Condensing water molecules release the same amount of heat energy to their surroundings. Because of this, the process of condensation slows down the rate at which air cools. Thus, the temperature of cooling air drops more slowly after the dew point has been reached.

Topic 7 Condensation Requires Cooling and Nuclei

For water vapor to condense, air must be cooled below its dew point. This cooling can happen in four different ways. Air may lose heat by:

1. contacting a colder surface;
2. radiating heat;
3. mixing with colder air; or
4. expanding when it rises.

The last process is most important in producing clouds, rain, or snow. These processes will be discussed further in the next lesson.

OBJECTIVES

A Demonstrate how cooling produces condensation and list some of the ways in which air becomes cooler.

B Explain why condensation is a warming process.

C Describe how dew, frost, and fog form.

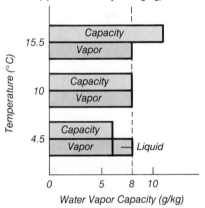

Condensation for Air with 10°C Dew Point
(specific humidity = 8 g/kg)

27.5 When a kilogram of unsaturated air (top) is cooled to 10°C, it becomes saturated (middle). Its dew point is therefore 10°C. When further cooling occurs, any excess water condenses as dew, fog, or cloud particles (bottom).

SCIENCE BACKGROUND

Ice crystals form even without nuclei at temperatures at or below −40°C.

Even when air is cooled below its dew point, condensation may not occur. The air is then said to be supersaturated. Water vapor needs to condense on something. The tiny particles on which water vapor condenses are called **condensation nuclei**. If there are no condensation nuclei, condensation cannot occur.

Condensation nuclei are usually substances such as salt, sulfate particles, or nitrate particles. Salt enters the air when fine sea spray evaporates. The sulfates and nitrates come from natural sources and from the burning of fuels. Condensation nuclei are so tiny that a puff of smoke contains millions of them. Similarly, water vapor requires ice nuclei to form ice crystals. Some types of bacteria and clay particles contaminated with organic material are good ice nuclei.

Topic 8   **Dew and Frost from Contact**

Condensation usually happens when air is cooled below its dew point. If cooling occurs by contact with a colder surface, water vapor condenses directly on that surface. If the temperature is above 0°C, dew forms. The drops of water that form on the outside of a glass of ice water are an often-seen example of dew. Dew may form on the ground, on leaves and grass, and on other surfaces. At night these surfaces become cooler than the air because they lose heat more rapidly. The air reaches its dew point where it touches the cooler objects. Clear nights show greater cooling and heavier dew.

If the temperature at the surface is below 0°C, the water vapor condenses on surfaces as a solid, called **frost**. When the temperatures near the ground drop below −2°C, liquid in the cells of some plants may freeze. This freezing bursts the cell walls and kills the plants. Killing frosts are caused not by atmospheric moisture but by the temperature of the plants themselves.

27.6 Dew forms on a cold surface when the surface temperature falls below the dew point of the air touching it but not below 0°C. Frost forms on a surface when the surface temperature at condensation is below 0°C.

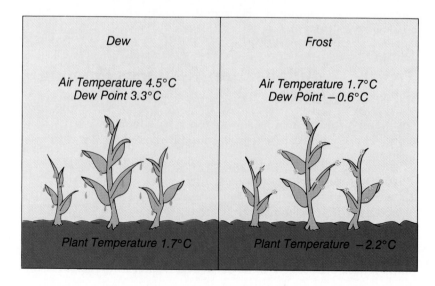

Dew

Air Temperature 4.5°C
Dew Point 3.3°C

Plant Temperature 1.7°C

Frost

Air Temperature 1.7°C
Dew Point −0.6°C

Plant Temperature −2.2°C

Topic 9   **Fogs from Radiation and Advection**

Often a surface layer of air a few hundred meters thick is cooled below the dew point. As water vapor condenses throughout the entire layer, tiny droplets fill the air and form fog. (If the temperature is well below 0°C the fog droplets will be ice.) Each droplet is centered about a condensation nucleus. The droplets are so tiny that they fall slowly. The lightest air movement keeps them suspended in the air.

Radiation fogs, or *ground fogs,* form under conditions similar to those that form dew. The nighttime sky is clear and the ground loses heat rapidly by radiation. Light winds mix the cold bottom air with the air a short distance from the surface. A whole layer of air is cooled below the dew point, and fog forms.

Radiation fogs are common in humid valleys near rivers or lakes. They are most frequent in the fall of the year. These fogs are thickest in the early morning and are "burned away" by the morning rays of the sun. The surface air in this fog is colder than the air above it. This arrangement of warmer air above cool fog is called a temperature inversion.

Advection fogs result when warm, moist air blows over cool surfaces. In the northern United States or southern Canada, advection fogs form when warm, moist southerly winds blow over snow-covered ground. The famous fogs of Newfoundland form when warm, moist air over the Gulf Stream blows over the cold Labrador Current. Summer fogs in coastal California form when warm ocean air strikes cold coastal waters. Winter fogs form along parts of the Gulf Coast when cold Mississippi River waters chill the warm gulf air at the river's mouth.

TOPIC QUESTIONS

Each topic question refers to the topic of the same number.

6. **(a)** Explain how condensation usually occurs in the atmosphere. **(b)** Define dew point. **(c)** When does condensation occur? **(d)** What does the dew point depend on? **(e)** How does condensation slow down the rate at which air cools?

7. **(a)** Name four ways the air can lose heat. **(b)** What are condensation nuclei? Give examples. Where do they come from? **(c)** What are ice nuclei? Give examples.

8. Explain how dew and frost form.

9. **(a)** Explain how fog forms and how it stays in the air. **(b)** How do radiation fogs form? **(c)** How do advection fogs form? Name some places advection fogs occur.

VIDEODISC SELECTION

Fog in San Francisco
Side 1: 877 to 881, 5-frame sequence

SCIENCE BACKGROUND

Since thick fogs prevent the sun from heating the ground, inversions over fog can be very persistent.

ANSWERS

6. (a) The temperature falls, and cooler air cannot hold as much water vapor; condensation begins when there is more water vapor than the air can hold. (b) temperature at which saturation occurs (c) when the temperature drops below the dew point (d) the amount of water vapor (e) Condensing water molecules release heat energy to their surroundings.

7. (a) contact with colder surface, radiation, mixing with colder air, expanding as it rises (b) particles upon which water vapor condenses, examples: salt from sea spray, sulfates and nitrates from the burning of fuels and natural sources (c) particles required to form ice crystals; examples: bacteria, clay contaminated with organic material

8. Dew: temperature of surface drops below dew point, cools air to same temperature, water vapor condenses as dew. Temperature is above 0°C. Frost: same process as dew, except surface temperature is below 0°C.

9. (a) The surface layer of air cools below the dew point; water vapor condenses on condensation nuclei. Smallest air currents keep tiny droplets aloft. (b) On clear nights, air cools by radiation; winds mix cool air upward. Fog forms when the temperature of the air layer drops below the dew point. (c) Warm moist air blows over cool surfaces cooled below dew point; Newfoundland, California coast, mouth of Mississippi.

OBJECTIVES

A Summarize the main types of clouds.

B Describe the conditions under which clouds with vertical development form.

C Show how to predict the base and highest possible top of cumulus clouds.

D Describe the conditions under which layer clouds form.

SCIENCE BACKGROUND

It is thought that the rare nacreas (mother-of-pearl) clouds, from 20–30 km above the surface, and noctilucent clouds, from 70–90 km above the surface, are made up of ice crystals.

OF INTEREST

The tops of some cumulonimbus clouds may penetrate the tropopause.

III Clouds

Topic 10 The Origin of Clouds

Clouds are simply high fogs, mist, or haze. They form when air above the surface cools below its dew point. The shape of a cloud depends on the air movement that forms it. If air movement is mainly horizontal, clouds form in layers. They are called *stratiform clouds.* If air movement is mainly vertical, clouds grow upward in great piles. These are called *cumuliform clouds.*

At temperatures above freezing, clouds are made entirely of water droplets. Below freezing, clouds are usually mixtures of snow crystals and supercooled water. **Supercooled water** is water that has cooled below 0°C without freezing. When supercooled droplets encounter something to freeze on, such as an airplane or ice nuclei, they form snow and ice crystals. Below a temperature of about −18°C, clouds are almost entirely snow and ice crystals.

Figure 27.7 and the table below show the four families of clouds. The average height range given in the table is for middle latitudes. The heights are measured above the surface, not above sea level. Clouds reach higher altitudes in equatorial areas and lower altitudes in polar areas.

Classification of Clouds

Family	Average Height Range	Types	Symbol
High clouds	7000 to 13 000 meters	Cirrus	Ci
		Cirrostratus	Cs
		Cirrocumulus	Cc
Middle clouds	2000 to 7000 meters	Altostratus	As
		Altocumulus	Ac
Low clouds	500 to 2000 meters	Stratocumulus	Sc
		Stratus	St
		Nimbostratus	Ns
Vertical development	500 to 13 000 meters	Cumulus	Cu
		Cumulonimbus	Cb

Topic 11 Cloud Names and Their Meanings

The table includes three simple cloud names—cirrus, stratus, and cumulus. These three names represent the three main cloud types. All the other clouds are combinations or variations of these types.

Cirrus clouds are thin, feathery, or tufted. They are so high that they are always made of ice crystals. All of the high family of clouds

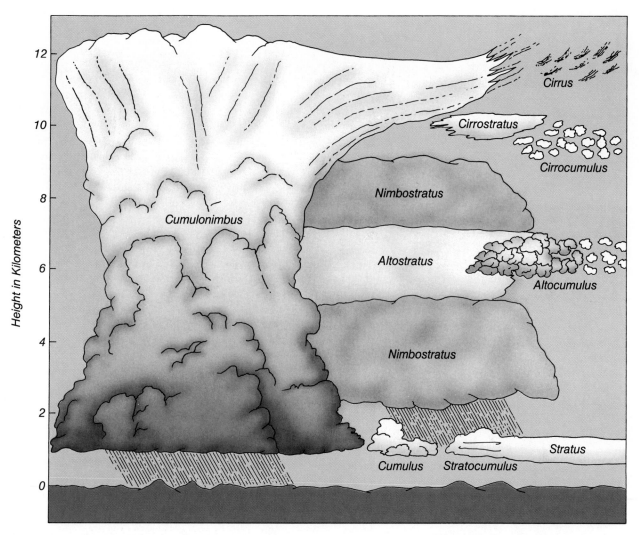

27.7 Cloud types. Cumulus and cumulonimbus belong to the family of clouds of vertical development.

are of the cirrus type. **Stratus** clouds are low sheets or layers of cloud. **Cumulus** clouds are formed by vertically rising air currents. They are piled in thick, puffy masses.

Cirrostratus are high, thin, smooth or fibrous sheets of ice-crystal clouds. They sometimes cause halos, or rings, around the sun or moon. Cirrostratus clouds often mean the approach of rain or snow. *Stratocumulus* clouds are layers made up of round puffs. They often cover the whole sky, especially in the winter. *Cirrocumulus* clouds are small globular patches of cloud made of ice crystals.

The prefix *alto* (high) and the word *nimbus* (rain cloud) are used in cloud names. *Altocumulus* clouds are like stratocumulus clouds. Their puffs look smaller because they are farther away (higher). *Altostratus* clouds are stratus clouds that occur at a higher level. They are gray or bluish and produce no halo around the sun or moon. *Nimbostratus* clouds are dark, gray layers of cloud that produce steady rain.

VIDEODISC SELECTION

Cloud types (described in disc directory)
Side 1: 806 to 843, 38-frame sequence

27.8 Variety of cloud types:
(a) cirrus, (b) cumulus,
(c) altocumulus, (d) cirrostratus,
(e) stratocumulus

Topic 12 **Dry- and Moist-Adiabatic Lapse Rates**

The shapes of clouds show how the air is moving through them. For example, the air in stratiform clouds flows mostly horizontally. Air in a growing cumulus cloud moves upward because it is buoyant. The air is buoyant because its temperature is warmer than the surrounding air. To what height will the cumulus cloud be warmer and more buoyant? To answer this question, it is necessary to know how temperature changes as air rises in a cloud.

Rising dry air cools at a rate of 1°C for every 100 meters (see Chapter 26, Topic 10). This is the dry-adiabatic lapse rate. The cooling is caused only by the air expanding. The air expands as it rises because it is surrounded by lower pressure. Similarly, sinking air is compressed as it encounters higher pressure. This raises the temperature at the same rate, 1°C for every 100 meters. Thus, if an air parcel rises 100 meters and then sinks 100 meters its final temperature will be the same as its starting temperature.

Air rising in a cloud does not cool as fast as rising dry air does. On the average, it cools at 0.6°C for every 100 meters. Why does it cool at a slower rate? The condensing water releases heat to the air, which makes the air cool more slowly. In the same way, sinking air in clouds warms 0.6°C for every 100 meters because the evaporation of cloud droplets slows its warming. Meteorologists call the rate of temperature change of a rising or sinking saturated parcel the **moist-adiabatic lapse rate**.

SCIENCE BACKGROUND

The average moist-adiabatic lapse rate is 0.6°C per 100 meters. It is less for hot air because hot air's capacity for water vapor changes rapidly, leading to a larger release of heat from condensation as air rises. Similarly, it is greater for cold air.

Topic 13   Clouds with Vertical Development

Cumulus clouds and other clouds with vertical development form when rising air currents are buoyant, or lighter than the surrounding air. How can this happen when air cools as it rises? It can, if the temperature of the surrounding air decreases even faster with height. Suppose a cloud is rising through a layer of air with a lapse rate of 1°C for each hundred meters. Since the air in the cloud is cooling at only 0.6°C for each 100 meters, it will be 0.4°C warmer than the surrounding air after rising 100 meters, 0.8°C warmer after rising 200 meters, and so on. The rising air in the cloud is warmer than the surrounding air even though it gets cooler as it rises. Since the cloud is warmer, it is also lighter or less dense. That is, the air in the cloud is buoyant. The cloud can continue to grow. Meteorologists say that the air surrounding the cloud is *unstable*.

If a shallow layer of air is unstable, cumulus clouds can form. If a deep layer of air is unstable, thunderclouds, or **cumulonimbus** clouds, might form. From these come lightning, thunder, and heavy showers. Violent thunderstorms can have hail, strong winds, and even tornadoes.

27.9   Cumulonimbus cloud

Topic 14   Cumulus and Cumulonimbus Clouds

Rising buoyant air currents form cumulus clouds. These clouds often appear in the late morning or early afternoon on bright sunny days. They have flat bases and billowy tops. Their shape reveals how these clouds form and grow.

Cumulus clouds form over heated ground. The ground is warm enough so that rising air remains bouyant even though it is cooling at the dry-adiabatic lapse rate. The flat cloud base shows where the water vapor began to condense. This height is called the **condensation level.** Here the temperature is about equal to the dew point (Topic 6).

Suppose the temperature and dew point of the air at the ground are known. Then the condensation level can be found. For dry air

OF INTEREST

Although it is easy to understand how the updraft feeding a cumulus cloud can form over a hot plowed field, scientists are still not sure how the giant updrafts feeding cumulonimbus clouds get started.

510

27.10 The condensation level of rising air can be predicted if its temperature and dew point are known. Rising air cools at a rate of 1°C per 100 meters. At the same time, however, its dew point changes, dropping 0.2°C per 100 meters. Where air temperature and dew point meet, condensation begins.

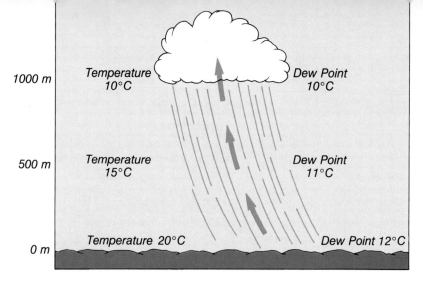

Temperature 10°C   Dew Point 10°C   (1000 m)

Temperature 15°C   Dew Point 11°C   (500 m)

Temperature 20°C   Dew Point 12°C   (0 m)

the rate of cooling by expansion is 1°C for every 100 meters. As the air rises, its dew point falls at a rate of 0.2°C for every 100 meters.

Here is an example: At the surface the air temperature is 20°C, the dew point is 12°C, and the difference between these temperatures is 8°C. However, 100 meters higher the air temperature is 19°C and the dew point is 11.8°C. The difference is only 7.2°C. The two temperatures continue to approach each other at a rate of 0.8°C for each 100-meter rise in altitude.

To find where the dew point will reach the air temperature, divide 8°C (the difference between the air temperature at ground level and the dew point) by 0.8°C (the amount per 100 meters at which the dew point approaches the air temperature).

$$\frac{8°C}{0.8°C} = 10$$

VIDEODISC SELECTION

Visibly lifting condensation level
Side 1: 820, single frame

SCIENCE BACKGROUND
The rising air usually still has some upward momentum at this point, but the deceleration past the neutral-buoyancy point rapidly brings the cloudy updraft to a stop. Typically, the rising air then spreads horizontally, giving the cloud a flat top.

SCIENCE BACKGROUND
Layer clouds have mainly horizontal motions, but there are convection currents between cloud top and cloud bottom.

Thus, 10 multiplied by 100 is the rise necessary in meters (1000 meters) for the beginning of condensation. This level is known as the *lifting condensation level*. It is of great importance in forecasting changes in the weather. A typical value over land in summer is around 1000 meters.

Meteorologists can also estimate the highest possible cloud top. They know that the temperature of the rising air in the cloud starts at the cloud-base temperature and falls with height at the moist-adiabatic lapse rate. They have measurements of the temperature of the surrounding air. The height of the cloud top will be close to the height where the cloud temperature and air temperature are equal. Here, the cloud is no longer buoyant. The rising air spreads out, forming the flat anvil-shaped top characteristic of cumulonimbus clouds.

Topic 15   Layer Clouds

Layer clouds form in stable air, where motions are mainly horizontal. The atmosphere is *stable* when the lapse rate of the air surrounding the clouds is smaller than the moist-adiabatic lapse rate. For example, suppose the temperature of the surrounding air is uniform throughout a thick layer. A cloudy rising current would be

Symbols Showing Percentage of Sky Covered										
Tenths of Sky covered	0	1	2–3	4	5	6	7–8	9	10	Sky Obscured
National Weather Service Weather Maps	○	◒	◔	◑	◐	◕	◖	◉	●	⊗
Newspaper Maps		○			◐			●		

cooler than the surrounding air as soon as it started rising and cooling. Being colder and therefore heavier than the surrounding air, the air current would sink back down to where it started. In this case, the air cannot easily move up or down and tends to spread out in layers.

Clouds can form in stable air in two ways. First, the air can be forced slowly upward to its condensation level. Air is forced upward when it moves up rising terrain, such as a mountainside, or over a layer of colder, denser air. And second, layer clouds form if radiation or mixing cools a layer of air to its dew point.

TOPIC QUESTIONS

Each topic question refers to the topic of the same number.

10. (a) How are clouds formed?   (b) What kind of air motions occur in stratiform clouds? Cumuliform clouds?   (c) At what temperatures do clouds consist of only liquid water? Of only snow and ice? Of both ice and water?   (d) What is supercooled water?   (e) List the four families of clouds.

11. Name and describe the three main cloud types.

12. (a) Why does rising air cool? Why does sinking air warm?   (b) Give the numerical value of the dry-adiabatic lapse rate and the moist-adiabatic lapse rate.   (c) Why is the moist-adiabatic lapse rate smaller?

13. (a) Under what conditions do clouds with vertical development form?   (b) Compare the lapse rate inside and outside the cloud if the air is unstable.   (c) How does unstable air affect the buoyancy of the rising air in the cloud?   (d) What kind of cloud forms when the air is unstable through a deep layer?

14. (a) How is a cumulus cloud formed?   (b) How do meteorologists estimate the height of the cloud base? What is this height called?   (c) Explain how meteorologists estimate the level of the highest possible cloud tops.

15. (a) Under what conditions do layer clouds form?   (b) Compare the lapse rate inside and outside layer clouds.

27.11   These symbols are used on weather maps to show how much of the sky is covered by clouds.

ANSWERS

10. (a) Air above the surface cools below the dew point.   (b) horizontal; vertical   (c) above 0°C; below −18°C; between 0° and −18°C   (d) water cooled below 0°C   (e) high, middle, low, vertical development

11. cirrus—thin, feathery, or tufted high ice-crystal clouds; stratus—low sheets or layers; cumulus—thick fleecy masses formed by rising air currents

12. (a) expansion from lower pressure; compression from higher pressure   (b) 1°C per 100 meters; 0.6°C per 100 meters   (c) Rising cloudy air cools less because condensation releases heat; sinking cloudy air warms less because evaporation absorbs heat.

13. (a) buoyant cloudy air   (b) The cloud has a smaller lapse rate than surrounding air.   (c) The cloud stays buoyant.   (d) cumulonimbus

14. (a) Rising buoyant air from the heated ground cools to the dew point.   (b) The cloud-base height in meters equals 100 times the difference between the surface temperature and dew point, divided by 0.8; condensation level.   (c) Cloud tops are where the cloud temperature from the moist-adiabatic lapse rate equals the environmental temperature.

15. (a) stable conditions; rising air colder than environment   (b) The cloud's moist-adiabatic lapse rate is greater than the lapse rate of the surrounding air.

OBJECTIVES

A Describe the process by which precipitation grows in warm and freezing clouds.

B Identify the various types of precipitation, describe how they form, and explain how they are measured.

C Identify areas where precipitation is scarce and areas where precipitation is abundant, and explain why this difference occurs.

D Discuss some ways in which cloud seeding is used to modify precipitation.

E Define acid rain, explain how it forms, and list some of its effects.

SCIENCE BACKGROUND

Laboratory experiments show that most of the droplets will bounce off each other unless there is a small electric field, which there normally is.

27.12 Compare the relative sizes of cloud droplets, drizzle droplets, and raindrops. A very large raindrop is about 0.25 centimeters in diameter. The diameter of a cloud droplet is only about one hundredth as large.

VIDEODISC SELECTION

Size and formation of cloud droplets
Side 1 movie: 24066 & PLAY

IV Precipitation

Topic 16 How Raindrops Form

Precipitation is the falling of any form of water from the air to Earth's surface. Precipitation occurs when cloud droplets grow into drops heavy enough to fall to Earth.

Raindrops form in two ways: by warm-cloud processes and by ice processes. In the *warm-cloud process,* tiny droplets form by condensation and then grow by bumping into and combining with other droplets. Droplets can collide because they are of different sizes. The bigger drops fall faster than the smaller ones. They catch up with smaller drops, collide with them, and capture them. Some smaller droplets get sucked behind the bigger drop and get captured that way. Still other droplets just bounce off the bigger ones.

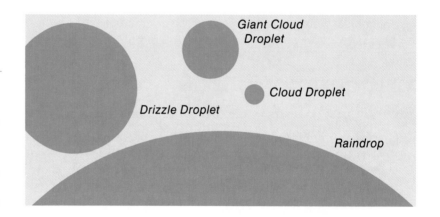

Why do the droplets have different sizes? Droplets that have been in the cloud longer have had more time to "grow." Some cloud droplets start out larger because they formed around a large salt nucleus. Still other cloud droplets get mixed into air that is less than saturated. The droplets shrink from evaporation. Mixing of air from different parts of the cloud or falling of larger drops from higher up in the cloud brings droplets of different sizes together.

Droplets also grow by *ice processes.* Except for the most shallow clouds in the warm tropics, temperatures in the upper layers of clouds are below freezing. Both ice crystals and supercooled droplets are present. Supercooled water evaporates faster than ice, and this water vapor is deposited on the ice crystals. When the larger ice crystals get heavy enough, they start to fall. The falling crystals can then grow by capturing both the smaller ice crystals and water droplets in their paths. If the temperature in the lower part of the cloud is above freezing, the crystal melts and continues to grow by warm-cloud processes.

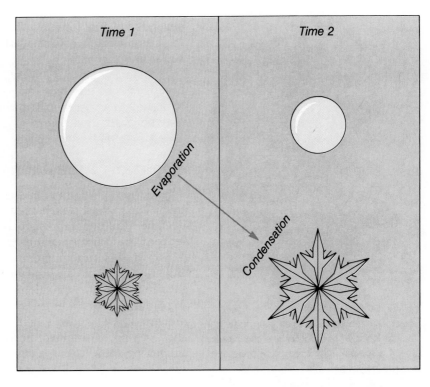

Topic 17   **Forms of Precipitation**

Precipitation comes in many forms. Drizzle consists of very fine drops that are very close together and fall very slowly. Raindrops are larger, farther apart, and fall much faster. A raindrop may have a maximum diameter of 0.25 centimeter. Larger raindrops may form, but they are torn apart as they fall.

Snow usually falls as clumps of six-sided crystals. The clumps grow by collision. When snowflakes fall into warm air, they partially melt into sticky, wet clusters. If the snowflakes melt completely, they fall as rain.

In some wintertime temperature inversions, warm clouds lie above a layer of air with a temperature below freezing. When raindrops fall through the freezing air, they turn into pellets of ice that fall to the ground as **sleet**. An ice storm, on the other hand, occurs when supercooled rain freezes instantly as it hits surfaces that are below freezing. Sheet ice, or glaze, forms on sidewalks, trees, roofs, and power lines. If the ice becomes heavy enough, trees and power lines may break under the weight of the ice.

Hail forms in cumulonimbus clouds. A hailstone begins as a frozen raindrop or small dense clump of ice crystals. A hailstone grows by collecting smaller ice particles, liquid cloud droplets, and supercooled raindrops that freeze onto it. The growing hailstone is kept aloft by a strong updraft until it becomes too heavy and falls out. In the early stages of its life, the hailstone may fall out of one updraft only to be carried aloft again in another. The size of the hailstone

27.13   (a) In the warm-cloud process, large droplets grow by collecting smaller droplets. In this way, they may become heavy enough to fall as rain. (b) In the ice process, supercooled water droplets supply the water vapor that makes ice crystals grow. Thus, from Time 1 to Time 2 the droplet shrinks and the ice crystal grows.

VIDEODISC SELECTION

Snowflake photos
Side 1: 888 to 892, 5-frame sequence

Aftermath of an ice storm
Side 1: 868 to 869, 2-frame sequence

OF INTEREST

The largest documented hailstone fell in Coffeyville, Kansas, on September 3, 1970. Its largest diameter was 15 cm, and it weighed 766 g.

27.14 In this hailstone cross section, each colored area is an individual crystal. The colors are the result of a special light used to photograph the hailstone.

depends on how long it is kept aloft in the cloud and how much moisture it catches. Clearly, the stronger the updraft, the larger the hailstones can be.

Hailstones have a layered structure like an onion. This is because of the different temperatures and different kinds of moisture they meet on their trip through the thundercloud. Hailstones may be as small as 5 mm or as large as 140 mm.

Topic 18 Measuring Precipitation

The National Weather Service reports rainfall in hundredths of an inch. The rainfall is measured by an instrument called a **rain gauge.** The measurement represents the depth of water that the rain would leave if it did not soak into the ground, flow away, or evaporate.

Snowfall is measured in inches and tenths of an inch. A measuring stick is used. The measurement is usually taken in an open location. The rain equivalent of the snowfall is determined by melting a definite depth of the snow. Dry snows are deeper than equal weights of wet snow. On the average, 10 inches of snow equal 1 inch of rain. This ratio, however, may range from as little as 5 inches of snow to as much as 30 inches. Why is the range so great?

Name	Drizzle	Rain	Shower	Snow	Sleet	Fog	Hail	Thunderstorm
USNWS Symbols	◗	●	▽	✳	△	≡	⬨	↱
Newspaper Maps		Ⓡ		Ⓢ		Ⓕ	◗	Hurricane

27.15 These are the symbols used on weather maps to represent different types of precipitation.

SCIENCE BACKGROUND
 Precipitation is also estimated using radars over land and satellites over the ocean.

VIDEODISC SELECTION

Results of a snowstorm
Side 1: 875, single frame

Topic 19 Where Does It Rain?

Precipitation—rain, sleet, hail, or snow—occurs in every part of the world. In some locations it may not rain for years at a time. In other places it may rain almost every day. Parts of Death Valley, California, average only about 1 inch of rain a year. Cherrapunji in India averages 457 inches of rain a year. What accounts for such differences in annual rainfall?

When air rises high enough and in large enough quantities, precipitation often occurs. The warmer the air, the more moisture it may contain. Also, the higher the air rises, the more moisture it can drop.

It follows, therefore, that the rainy areas of Earth will be those where air often rises in large quantities. Such areas are listed below.

1. The windward side of mountain ranges. The normal winds in an area are called prevailing winds. The side of the mountain

range toward which the winds blow is called the windward side. The prevailing winds are forced to climb the windward side of a mountain range to great heights. Because the air cools as it rises, some of its moisture condenses and falls as rain or snow. An example is the rainy western slope of the Cascade Mountains in the northwestern United States.

2. Storm areas of all kinds, including hurricanes, typhoons, low-pressure areas, and fronts. In all of these, air rises and cools to produce precipitation.

3. Areas favored by the global wind belts. As shown in the next chapter, the prevailing winds converge (come together) around the equator. The air can go nowhere but up. The result is almost daily thunderstorms over the land areas. Around the equator lie the dense tropical forests of the Amazon, the Congo, and Indonesia.

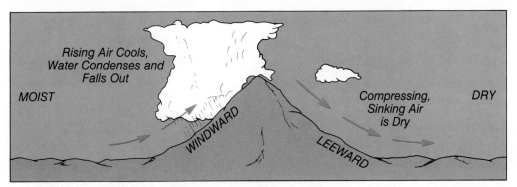

27.16 Rain and snow are usually heavy on the windward side of a tall mountain range and very light on the leeward side.

Topic 20   **Where Does It Not Rain?**

The answer to this question is almost the exact opposite of "Where does it rain?" In areas of sinking air the air is warmed by compression. Thus no precipitation can occur. If sinking air persists, the dry conditions produce deserts. Sinking air occurs on the downwind or leeward side of mountains and in high-pressure areas. It also occurs where the global wind belts diverge, or blow away from a given area, at the surface. The only way air diverging at the surface can be replaced is by air sinking from above. This happens at the North and South Poles, and at the latitudes of the Sahara Desert.

Topic 21   **Weather Modification**

Often it does not rain when or where it is needed most. Ever since people have needed rain, they have tried to make it rain. Attempts to change the weather are called weather modification.

There are two methods of rainmaking. In the first method, very cold solid carbon dioxide, or "dry ice," pellets are dropped into a supercooled cloud. These pellets cool the cloud so much that tiny ice crystals form. The crystals grow by the ice process until they are

OF INTEREST

The first attempt to "seed" a cloud in a laboratory with dry ice pellets was in 1946, by V. J. Schaeffer of the General Electric Research Laboratories in Schenectady, New York.

heavy enough to fall. In the second method, artificial ice nuclei (usually crystals of silver iodide or lead iodide) are put into the cloud. Smoke generators are used to make the tiny crystals, which are very much like ice crystals in shape. Once ice crystals form, precipitation again grows by the ice process.

It is hard to prove that rainmaking works, since the precipitation that falls could have fallen naturally. Also, clouds must be present for rain to occur.

Scientists are not only searching for ways to make it rain. They are also trying to prevent hail and to eliminate fog at airports. Supercooled fogs can be cleared by the same techniques used to make rain. In this case, seeding the clouds makes the droplets grow too large and fall out.

27.17 The effects of acid rain on a sandstone statue in Germany. The left-hand picture was taken in 1913; the right-hand picture is from 1984.

Topic 22 Acid Clouds and Acid Rain

Most acid rain contains nitrate or sulfate particles. Sulfates come from sulfur dioxide, which results from the burning of fuels and from natural sources such as volcanoes. Nitrate-forming gases come from those sources and also from automobiles.

Sulfate and nitrate particles make good condensation nuclei. When water condenses on them, they produce nitric or sulfuric acid droplets. As these droplets grow, they remain acid. The drops that fall to the ground are known as **acid rain**. The dry sulfate and nitrate particles that fall to the ground are called dry acid deposition. They combine with groundwater to make acid.

Cloud droplets that form on these nuclei are very acidic. Mountain forests are heavily damaged by acid clouds as well as acid rain because they are often in clouds. Not only does the soil become too acidic, but the leaves may be damaged by acid falling directly on them.

Acid rain is also destroying life in lakes and streams. Fish can no longer live in many lakes in the Adirondack Mountains of New York State because the water is too acidic. In cities, acid rain weathers rock and concrete and damages metals, paints, plastics, and paper.

SCIENCE BACKGROUND

Some scientists think that evergreen needles grow even in winter when exposed directly to nitrates. The growing needles are easier to freeze. The damage makes the tree more vulnerable to disease.

ANSWERS

16. (a) water falling to Earth's surface (b) They bump into and combine with each other. (c) Ice crystals grow at the expense of fast-evaporating supercooled droplets. (d) Bigger drops form from salt nuclei or have fallen from higher up; also drop sizes mix as air from different parts of the cloud mix.

17. (a) drizzle—small, slowly falling drops; raindrops—larger drops (up to 0.25 cm); snow—clumps of six-sided crystals (b) sleet—rain frozen before it hits the ground; sheet ice—rain frozen after it hits the ground (c) A small frozen particle grows by collecting cloud or raindrops and ice particles.

18. (a) an instrument that measures rain (b) with a measuring stick in an open location

19. (a) where enough air rises high enough (b) windward side of mountains; storm areas such as hurricanes and lows; where the global wind belts produce convergence

20. (a) The air is warmed by compression. (b) leeward side of mountains; high-pressure areas; where global winds diverge

21. (a) rainmaking, preventing hail, stopping fog (b) dropping "dry ice" into supercooled clouds to cool them enough to form ice crystals; putting artificial ice nuclei into clouds

22. (a) acid drops that fall to the ground (b) nitrate and sulfate particles; natural sources, burning fuel, automobiles (nitrates) (c) It makes lakes and streams too acid for life and damages rocks, concrete, metals, paints, plastics, and papers.

TOPIC QUESTIONS

Each topic question refers to the topic of the same number.

16. **(a)** What is precipitation? **(b)** Describe how raindrops grow in warm clouds. **(c)** Describe how precipitation grows by ice processes. **(d)** How are mixtures of drop sizes produced?

17. **(a)** Describe drizzle, raindrops, and snow. **(b)** How does sleet form? Sheet ice? **(c)** How does hail form?

18. **(a)** What is a rain gauge? **(b)** How is snow measured?

19. **(a)** Where does precipitation fall? **(b)** Name three kinds of areas in which rising air causes rain.

20. **(a)** Why are areas of sinking air dry? **(b)** Name three kinds of areas in which sinking air usually keeps precipitation from falling.

21. **(a)** Give some examples of weather modification. **(b)** Describe two methods used in rainmaking.

22. **(a)** What is acid rain? **(b)** What condensation nuclei form acid with water? Where do they come from? **(c)** List some ways in which acid rain harms the environment.

CHAPTER 27

L A B
ACTIVITY

Dew Point and Relative Humidity

27.19 Capacity of Air at 1000mb Pressure

Temp °C	Capacity g/kg	Temp °C	Capacity g/kg
-10	1.8	13	9.5
-9	1.9	14	10.1
-8	2.1	15	10.8
-7	2.3	16	11.6
-6	2.5	17	12.3
-5	2.6	18	13.2
-4	2.9	19	14.0
-3	3.1	20	15.0
-2	3.3	21	15.9
-1	3.6	22	17.0
0	3.8	23	18.1
1	4.1	24	19.2
2	4.4	25	20.4
3	4.8	26	21.7
4	5.1	27	23.1
5	5.5	28	24.6
6	5.9	29	26.1
7	6.3	30	27.7
8	6.8	31	29.4
9	7.3	32	31.2
10	7.8	33	33.1
11	8.3	34	35.1
12	8.9		

For additional activities, see Laboratory Investigations booklet.

Even above the hottest desert areas on Earth, there is water vapor in the air. Water vapor is the source of moisture for clouds and rain. Meteorologists measure both dew point and relative humidity to determine how much water vapor is in the air and to predict chances of precipitation.

Dew point is the temperature at which air is filled or saturated with water vapor. Relative humidity is the extent to which air is saturated with water vapor. When air cools below the dew point, water vapor in the air condenses.

In this lab, you will determine both dew point and relative humidity by using a capacity chart. You will then make and use a psychrometer to find relative humidity.

Lab Skills and Objectives

- To **observe** dew formation, and **compute** relative humidity, using dew point method
- To **compute** relative humidity using psychrometer method
- To **compare** the methods for finding relative humidity

Materials

- shiny metal cans
- stirring rod or coffee stirrer
- ice cubes or crushed ice
- celsius thermometer
- cloth strip, 2.5 cm x 10 cm
- small rubber bands or string
- spoon
- piece of paper
- water at room temperature

27.18
Equipment set up for Part A

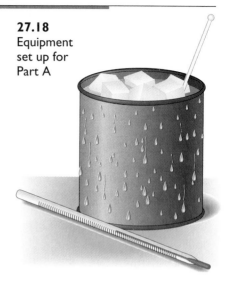

Procedure
Part A—Dew Point Method

1. 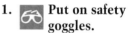 **Put on safety goggles.**

2. Use a thermometer to measure the classroom air temperature in celsius. Record the temperature in Data Table A.

3. Look at Figure 27.19. Find the capacity of air to hold water vapor for the temperature in your classroom. Record the capacity.

4. Fill the metal can halfway with water. Place a thermometer in the water. Add a small amount of ice.

5. Use a stirring rod to stir the water slowly.
   CAUTION: Do not stir with the thermometer; it is fragile and may break.

6. Watch for the first appearance of dew on the outside of the container. At the instant you see dew, record the dew point temperature in Data Table A.

7. To confirm the accuracy of your first dew point reading, repeat steps 3 through 5.

8. Average your two dew point values. Record the average in Data Table A.

9. Use the capacity chart in Figure 27.19 to determine the air capacity to hold water vapor for your average dew point temperature. Your value for capacity at the dew point equals the specific humidity of the air. Record this value in Data Table A.

10. Use your values and the formula in Data Table A to compute the relative humidity of air at room temperature. Record this value in Data Table A.

Part B—Psychrometer Method

11. Read the air temperature in the classroom again. In Data Table B, record this value as your dry-bulb temperature.

12. Construct a paper fan by folding accordian pleats into a piece of paper.

13. Wrap a strip of cloth around the bulb of the thermometer and fasten the cloth with a rubber band or string.

14. Dip the cloth-covered end of the thermometer into room-temperature water. This is now a wet-bulb thermometer.

15. Fan the wet-bulb thermometer briskly with the paper fan. The temperature will drop, then remain constant. Once the temperature becomes constant, read and record the wet-bulb temperature in Data Table B.

16. Subtract the wet-bulb temperature from the dry-bulb temperature and record this value in Data Table B.

17. Turn to the relative humidity table on page 501. Locate the dry-bulb temperature and the difference between the wet-bulb and dry-bulb readings. Determine the relative humidity. Record this value in Data Table B.

18. Answer the questions in *Analysis and Conclusions*.

Analysis and Conclusions

1. Compare the two relative humidity values for the classroom air from Data Tables A and B. Are the two values the same or different? If the values differ, which value do you think will be more accurate? Explain your answer.

2. Suppose you are looking at clouds that have just formed on a summer afternoon. What do you know about the relative humidity of the air at the bottom of the cloud?

3. Imagine that, early one cool morning, you use a psychrometer outdoors and discover that the wet-bulb and dry-bulb values are the same.

   a. What conclusion can you draw about evaporation from the wet-bulb thermometer in this case?

   b. What conclusion can you draw about the relative humidity in this case?

   c. From your knowledge of relative humidity, would this be a good or bad day for hanging the laundry outdoors to dry? Explain your answer.

Data Table A—Dew Point Method	
1. Temperature of classroom air (°C)	_____
2. Capacity of air at classroom air temperature (g/kg)	_____
3. Dew point from trial 1 (°C)	_____
4. Dew point from trial 2 (°C)	_____
5. Average dew point (°C)	_____
6. Specific humidity (capacity at dew point) (g/kg)	_____
7. Relative humidity = $\dfrac{\text{Specific humidity}}{\text{capacity}}$ (%)	_____

Data Table B Psychrometer Method	
1. Temperature of classroom air (dry-bulb temperature) (°C)	_____
2. Wet-bulb temperature (°C)	_____
3. Difference between dry- and wet-bulb temperatures (°C)	_____
4. Relative humidity (%)	_____

CHAPTER

27 REVIEW

Answers to all questions appear in the Teacher's Guide at the back of this book.

■ Summary

I Evaporating water molecules use energy to break away from liquid. This energy is absorbed from the surroundings, which become cooler. When water condenses, this energy is returned to the surroundings.

Warmer air can hold more water vapor. Thus, condensation occurs if air is cooled enough.

When the ground temperature drops below the dew point, dew forms if the surface temperature is above freezing and frost forms if the surface temperature drops below freezing.

II Fog and clouds form when water vapor condenses around tiny particles called condensation nuclei.

The three main types of clouds are cumulus, cirrus, and stratus. Cirrus clouds are high, feathery, ice clouds. Cumulus clouds are fluffy clouds with flat bases. Stratus clouds are layered, low clouds.

Rising air cools at the dry-adiabatic lapse rate with no condensation, and at the moist-adiabatic lapse rate with condensation.

III Cumuliform clouds form when the rising air in the cloud is buoyant; cumulus clouds form from air currents rising from the heated ground.

Stratiform clouds form when the rising air in the cloud is not buoyant. They form when a layer of air is cooled by lifting or other means.

IV Precipitation in warm (above-freezing) clouds grows from drop collisions. In cold (below-freezing) clouds, ice crystals grow from collisions and by using water vapor from evaporating supercooled drops.

Precipitation falls in regions where air tends to rise, producing condensation. Air rises going over mountains and when surface air converges.

Cloud seeding starts the ice process to produce precipitation.

Most acid rain comes from sulfate and nitrate particles, which mix with water to form sulfuric or nitric acid.

■ Vocabulary

acid rain	hygrometer
cirrus	moist-adiabatic lapse
condensation	rate
condensation level	precipitation
condensation nuclei	psychrometer
cumulonimbus	rain gauge
cumulus	relative humidity
dew	sleet
dew point	specific humidity
evaporation	stratus
frost	supercooled water
hail	

■ Review

Number your paper from 1 to 18. Select the best answer to complete each statement.

1. Water is found in the atmosphere as (a) water vapor, (b) solid ice particles, (c) liquid cloud droplets, (d) all of the above.
2. The amount of water vapor present in the air is the (a) saturation specific humidity, (b) specific humidity, (c) capacity, (d) relative humidity.
3. A psychrometer works on the principle that (a) evaporation causes cooling, (b) condensation causes cooling, (c) hair stretches when it is humid, (d) relative humidity is stated as a percent.
4. When air cools below the dew point, (a) it is said to be supercooled, (b) condensation occurs, (c) the air can hold more water vapor, (d) water droplets on plants evaporate.
5. The tiny particles on which water condenses are (a) precipitation, (b) hygrometers, (c) condensation nuclei, (d) hailstones.
6. Air loses heat by (a) expanding when it rises, (b) mixing with warmer air, (c) contacting a warm surface, (d) becoming saturated.
7. Dew forms (a) when the air temperature is above the dew point, (b) when water vapor condenses on ice crystals, (c) when the

For further review, see **Study Guide.**
For assessment, see **Chapter Tests**
and **Computer Test Bank.**

ground temperature cools below the dew
point and the temperature is above 0°C,
(d) when the air temperature is below 0°C.

8. When a whole layer of air is cooled below the
dew point, the result is (a) rain, (b) snow,
(c) fog, (d) supercooled air.

9. Rain falls from (a) cirrostratus clouds,
(b) nimbostratus clouds, (c) stratocumulus
clouds, (d) cirrocumulus clouds.

10. Buoyant air (a) is cooler than the surrounding air, (b) is cooling at a faster rate than the
surrounding air, (c) forms stratus clouds,
(d) is warmer than the surrounding air.

11. Cumulus clouds are formed by (a) horizontally moving air, (b) rising buoyant air,
(c) sinking saturated air, (d) ice crystals high
above the surface.

12. Layer clouds form in (a) stable air, (b) a
deep layer of unstable air, (c) a shallow layer
of unstable air, (d) sinking air.

13. Which of the following is NOT a way in
which raindrops form? (a) Tiny cloud droplets combine. (b) Water vapor is deposited
on ice crystals. (c) Cloud droplets shrink
from evaporation. (d) Falling ice crystals
capture smaller ice crystals and water droplets.

14. Which is NOT a form of precipitation?
(a) sleet (b) fog (c) drizzle (d) hail

15. The rainfall equivalent of 20 inches of snow
(a) is less than 20 inches, (b) is exactly 20
inches, (c) is more than 20 inches, (d) could
be either more or less than 20 inches.

16. Rain occurs (a) in areas where winds diverge
at the surface, (b) on the leeward side of
mountain ranges, (c) in high-pressure areas
where air sinks, (d) in areas where air rises.

17. Attempts to change the weather are known as
(a) condensation nuclei, (b) acid rain, (c) ice
processes, (d) weather modification.

18. Acid rain forms when (a) silver iodide crystals are put into a cloud, (b) rising air begins
to cool, (c) water condenses on nitrate and
sulfate particles, (d) warm, moist air blows
over cool surfaces.

■ Interpret and Apply

On your paper, answer each question in complete
sentences.

1. Jet traffic at altitudes of 10–13 kilometers has
been increasing. (a) What effect would you
expect this increase to have on the cloudiness
at those altitudes? (b) What kinds of clouds
would be produced? (c) What causes them to
form?

2. Nighttime and early morning temperatures
usually are not very useful for predicting the
cloud base. Why not?

3. Why should the average annual precipitation
be greater in Mississippi than in Maine?

■ Critical Thinking

Complete the table by calculating the height at
which clouds will form (the lifting condensation
level) for the temperatures and dew points shown.
Then answer the questions that follow.

Temperature	Dew Point	Condensation Level
16°C	12°C	?
20°C	12°C	1000 m
20°C	16°C	?
28°C	12°C	?
28°C	20°C	?

1. If the dew point stays the same, what effect
does a rise in temperature have on the cloud
base?

2. If the temperature stays the same, what effect
does a rise in the dew point have on the cloud
base?

3. Which contains more water vapor, air at
26.5°C with a relative humidity of 50 percent
or saturated air at 5°C? Why?

4. From your knowledge of how air's capacity
for water vapor increases with temperature,
how would you expect the moist-adiabatic
lapse rate to change with temperature?

521

Atmospheric Pressure and Winds

CHAPTER

28

▲
Sailors enjoying the benefits of local winds.

How Do You Know That . . .

There will be a wind near an ocean or a lake as long as it is a sunny day? Usually there is a wind along the shore even when there is little or no air movement farther inland. At any particular place, the movements of air can be influenced by local conditions. Anything that produces a temperature difference can cause a local wind. The sailors in the picture above are taking advantage of one of the most common local winds called a sea breeze.

This chapter will explore global and local wind patterns. You will also learn how air pressure causes the weather to change and the relationship of air pressure to winds.

I Air Pressure

Topic 1 What Is Air Pressure?

Why is the study of air pressure important? Differences in air pressure cause Earth's winds and weather changes.

Pressure is defined as force per unit area. **Air pressure** is simply the weight of the atmosphere per unit area. At the surface, the atmospheric pressure is about 1 kilogram per square centimeter.

A few examples can illustrate the meaning of pressure. Suppose a girl weighing 45 kilograms is standing on one foot. The pressure underneath her foot is the force (her weight) divided by the area of her foot. If her foot is 20 cm long and 8 cm wide, the pressure underneath is 0.28 kilograms per square centimeter. If she stands on two feet, the pressure under each foot is halved. If she balances on one heel of a pair of thin high-heeled shoes (about a square centimeter), the pressure beneath her foot is 45 kilograms per square centimeter!

Air pressure is directed equally in all directions. To envision this, remember that the gases in air are made up of many tiny molecules. The pressure is the sum total effect of the molecules colliding against any surface. The air molecules move in all directions, so the pressure on any surface is the same. This is true whether the surface is horizontal or vertical.

Topic 2 Measuring Air Pressure

The instrument used to measure air pressure is the **barometer**. There are two main types of barometers—mercury and aneroid barometers—which have very different constructions.

Figure 28.1 shows how a mercury barometer works. The air pressure on the surface of the mercury in the dish supports a column of mercury. At sea level, the column is about 76 centimeters (30 inches) high. The space in the column above the mercury is a vacuum. If air pressure increases, the mercury column rises. If air pressure drops, the mercury column falls.

The aneroid barometer measures pressure with a thin metal can. By pumping most of the air out of the can, the can is made sensitive to air pressure. A spring or similar device keeps the can from collapsing inward. As the shape of the can changes with changes in air pressure, a pointer attached to the can moves over a scale. A *barograph* is a recording aneroid barometer. Its pointer is a pen that writes on a chart.

OBJECTIVES

A Discuss air pressure, describe how it is measured, and compare the different units used to measure air pressure.

B Define *high*, *low*, and *pressure gradient*.

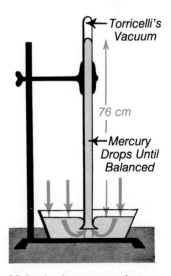

28.1 In the mercury barometer, the atmospheric pressure balances a column of mercury. At sea level, the height of the column is normally 76 centimeters. As air pressure increases and decreases, the column rises and falls.

OF INTEREST
Blood pressure is measured in mm of mercury.

Since air pressure is the weight of the air overhead, the air pressure drops with height. An *altimeter* (height meter used by aircraft) is an aneroid barometer with a scale that reads height above sea level.

The barometer reading drops about 1 centimeter for every 123 meters (or about 1 inch for every 1000 feet) above sea level. This rate applies only to the first few kilometers of air near Earth's surface. Above this level the air thins out rapidly, and pressure changes more slowly. Half the weight of the atmosphere lies within 5.5 kilometers of Earth's surface.

Topic 3   Air Pressure Units

Air pressure is reported in two different ways. The first way gives the height of the mercury column in the barometer. It may be given in centimeters or in inches.

The second way uses a metric unit of pressure called a **millibar**. A millibar equals about one thousandth of standard sea-level air pressure. The following table shows how inch units and millibars are related. Standard sea-level air pressure is 1013.2 millibars (29.92 inches) of mercury. It is the average air pressure at sea level for the whole world.

SCIENCE BACKGROUND
The unit for pressure used by researchers is the Pascal. A hundred Pascals equal one millibar.

Inches of Mercury	Millibars of Pressure
31.00	1050.0
30.00	1015.9
29.92	1013.2
29.53	1000.00
29.00	982.1
1.00*	34.0 (approx.)
0.10	3.4 (approx.)
0.12	4.0** (approx.)
0.03	1.0‡ (approx.)

*   Use this value to convert inches of mercury to millibars.
** Pressure interval used on United States weather maps
‡   Use this value to convert millibars to inches of mercury.

SCIENCE BACKGROUND
The arrival of warm or cold air at any level overhead will change the pressure. Thus a pressure change at the surface can happen without a surface temperature change.

SCIENCE BACKGROUND
Changing humidity has much *less* effect on air pressure than changing temperature does.

SCIENCE BACKGROUND
Large amounts of liquid water overhead, such as in heavy rains, add weight to the air and cause higher pressures.

The average air pressure at an inland weather station is lower than 1013.2 millibars, because the altitude is higher. At Denver, Colorado (altitude 1600 meters), for example, the normal surface pressure is around 835 millibars. The effect of altitude on pressure is eliminated when surface weather maps are made. The corrected air pressure is called the **sea-level pressure**.

The highest sea-level pressures on a typical weather map are from 1030 to 1050 mb, while the lowest values are from 960 to 1000 mb. The more extreme sea-level pressures occur in the winter. Sea-level pressures as low as 870 millibars have been recorded in strong hurricanes.

The National Weather Service prints a daily weather map. On this map barometer readings are shown in two different ways. The first way shows the actual barometer reading in millibars. This number is placed just to the upper right of the station circle. It shows only the last three numbers (1002.2 millibars would appear as 022). The second way of showing barometer readings uses **isobars.** Isobars are lines that join points having the same air pressure at a given time. Isobars make it easy to see how barometer readings compare over large geographic areas.

Topic 4 **Why Air Pressure Changes**

A chart from a barograph shows that the air pressure is always changing. The main reason for daily changes in air pressure is changing temperature. Warm air is lighter than cold air because the molecules of warm air are farther apart. So when warm air replaces an equal volume of cold air, the air pressure at the ground falls. In the same way, the arrival of colder air higher up causes the pressure at the ground to rise.

A second reason for changes in air pressure is changing humidity. The more water vapor the air contains, the lighter it is. This statement sounds wrong, but it is easily explained. When water vapor enters the atmosphere, it pushes out an equal volume of dry air. A cubic meter of dry air is about 99 percent nitrogen and oxygen. A cubic meter of humid air with 2 percent water vapor is only 97 percent nitrogen and oxygen. Water vapor is lighter than the nitrogen and oxygen it pushed out. Therefore, humid air weighs less than dry air and exerts less pressure.

In general, meteorologists have found that a falling barometer means warmer weather and more humid air. It may mean rain or snow. A rising barometer usually means cooler, drier weather. This change in barometer readings gives a simple way of forecasting the weather. Meteorologists do not, however, rely on the barometer alone for their forecasts.

Topic 5 **Highs, Lows, and Pressure Gradients**

The isobars on a weather map look a lot like the contour lines on the topographic maps discussed in Chapter 7. Both isobars and contour lines form sets of closed curves, one inside the other.

If the values of the isobars steadily increase toward a central area, the area of largest pressure is called the *high-pressure center.* The set of closed isobars surrounding the high-pressure center is called a **high-pressure area (high).** The pressure in a high is greater than in the surrounding air. (If isobars were contour lines, the high-pressure area would be a hill and the high-pressure center would be the top of the hill.)

28.2 This diagram shows how temperature and air pressure are indicated on a station model. These numbers represent a temperature of 51°F and air pressure of 1013.3 millibars. Notice that only the last three digits of the pressure are given.

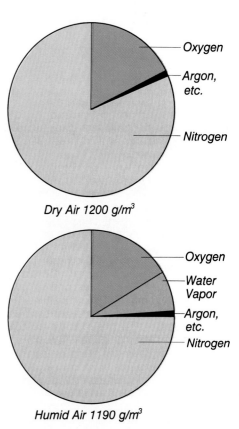

Dry Air 1200 g/m³

Humid Air 1190 g/m³

28.3 A cubic meter of dry air at sea level has a mass of about 1200 grams. The same volume of humid air has less mass because water vapor is lighter than the gases it replaces. (Amount of water vapor in the chart is exaggerated for illustration.)

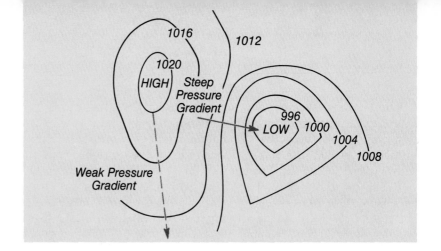

28.4 Isobars on a weather map show areas of high and low pressure, strong pressure gradients, and weak pressure gradients.

ANSWERS

1. (a) the force per unit area (b) the weight of air overhead (c) pressure due to molecules bumping against any surface; this is same in all directions

2. (a) mercury—air pressure on mercury in dish supports mercury in tube; aneroid—air presses on outside of a thin metal can most of whose air has been pumped out (b) drops with height, fastest at sea level; about 1 cm per 123 meters

3. (a) millibars and inches (b) 34 mb; 0.03 in. (c) 1013.2 mb; 29.92 in.; 1030–1050 mb and 960–1000 mb (d) Inland stations are above sea level, where pressure is lower.

4. (a) High temperatures make air lighter; therefore pressure lower; low temperatures opposite. (b) Water vapor is lighter than nitrogen and oxygen, so adding water vapor makes air lighter; pressure underneath is lowered.

5. (a) area with higher pressure than surroundings; area with lower pressure than surroundings; rate of pressure change (b) closed isobars around higher pressure; closed isobars around lower pressure; smaller distance between isobars means larger pressure gradient

Similarly, if the inside isobar has the lowest reading, the set of closed isobars shows a **low-pressure area (low)**. This area has lower pressure than the surrounding air. The low's center is located in the inside isobar, where the pressure is lowest.

High- and low-pressure areas on a weather map are usually more than 1500 kilometers across. Large high-pressure areas can cover most of North America.

When isobars are close together, it means that air pressure changes quickly between two places. When isobars are far apart, air pressure changes slowly. Scientists call this rate of change the **pressure gradient**. Isobars close together are said to have a steep, or strong, pressure gradient. Isobars far apart have a gentle, or weak, pressure gradient. Pressure gradients are measured in millibars per kilometer.

TOPIC QUESTIONS

Each topic question refers to the topic of the same number.

1. **(a)** What is pressure? **(b)** What causes air pressure? **(c)** Explain why air pressure is equal in all directions.

2. **(a)** How do aneroid and mercury barometers work? **(b)** How does air pressure vary with height? How fast does air pressure drop with height near the surface?

3. **(a)** What are the two units of measure commonly used in reporting air pressure? **(b)** How many millibars are in an inch? How many inches are in a millibar? **(c)** What is the sea-level atmospheric pressure in millibars? In inches? List the highest and lowest normal sea-level pressures. **(d)** Why do surface pressures for inland stations need to be corrected before making a weather map?

4. **(a)** How does the temperature of the atmosphere affect the surface air pressure? **(b)** Explain the effect of humidity on air pressure.

5. **(a)** Define high-pressure area, low-pressure area, and pressure gradient. **(b)** How do isobars show a high-pressure center, a low-pressure center, and pressure gradient?

II Winds

Topic 6 What Makes the Wind Blow?

All winds result from uneven heating of the atmosphere. The island in Figure 28.5 is surrounded by cool water. During the day, the island heats faster than the water and so the air above the island becomes warmer. The molecules in the air become farther apart; so the air expands upward and outward. This expansion lowers the air pressure at the island's surface. The cooler ocean air moves in toward the low-pressure area over the island.

There is a pressure gradient between the ocean and the island. The wind moves from high to low pressure. The speed of the wind depends on the pressure gradient. The lower the pressure (the hotter the island), the steeper the pressure gradient and the stronger the wind. The pressure gradient provides the force that makes the wind blow. This force is called the **pressure-gradient force.**

Topic 7 Local Winds

The wind over the island is an example of a *local wind*. A local wind extends over a distance of 100 kilometers or less. A **sea breeze** is a local wind that forms much like the island wind. During the daytime, coastal land is warmer than the nearby water. The air just over the land becomes warmer than the air over the water. The pressure lowers over the land, leading to a pressure gradient between the ocean and the land. The pressure gradient force pushes the cool ocean air inland. This cool wind is the sea breeze.

Over the land, the air rises. It then blows out to sea and sinks to replace the cool air that has flowed inland. As shown in Figure 28.6, the airflow forms a complete circuit—from the sea to the land, up, back to the sea, and down again. Thus the entire wind pattern is sometimes called a *sea-breeze circulation.*

A gentle sea breeze usually begins in the late morning along seacoasts. It increases in speed until midafternoon and dies down toward sunset. The sea breeze is felt inland from 15 to 70 kilometers away from the shoreline. It reaches up to about a kilometer in the atmosphere.

OBJECTIVES

A Show how heating causes low pressure and note that the wind blows from high to low pressure.

B Summarize the causes of land and sea breezes and mountain and valley winds.

C Describe the Coriolis effect.

D Explain why winds are clockwise around highs and counter-clockwise around lows in the Northern Hemisphere and why surface winds blow at an angle to the isobars.

E Describe how winds are named and measured and show how they are depicted on weather maps.

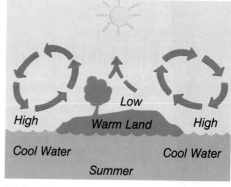

28.5 A heated island surrounded by cooler water becomes a region of low pressure, causing winds to blow toward the land.

SCIENCE BACKGROUND
In the southeastern United States, the sea breezes are strongest in June, when the land is heated strongly but the water is still cold from winter.

28.6 Sea and land breezes develop through unequal heating of land and nearby water. The land breeze blows from land; the sea breeze blows from the water.

Daytime: Warm Air Rises — Cool Air Descends — Sea Breeze

Nighttime: Cool Air Descends — Warm Air Rises — Land Breeze

CHAPTER
29

Air Masses and Fronts

VIDEO
||||||| || |||
Expla
Side 1

▲
A highway near Buffalo,
New York, buried by the
1977 blizzard

SCI
O
vari
to th
at a

542

How Do You Know That . . .

Fronts and air masses affect the local weather? The winter of
1976–1977 was one of the worst winters ever for Buffalo, New
York. The worst storm of the winter started in late January 1977,
when a strong low-pressure area brought with it cold air, snow,
and winds as strong as 70 miles an hour. The storm lasted for 5
days, did 250 million dollars damage, and caused 29 deaths. Nine
people froze to death in their cars. The snow in and around Buffalo
was 4 feet deep, with drifts 30 feet high in some places. This
snowstorm was a spectacular example of what happens when a
strong low-pressure area is followed by a very cold air mass.

II Winds

Topic 6 What Makes the Wind Blow?

All winds result from uneven heating of the atmosphere. The island in Figure 28.5 is surrounded by cool water. During the day, the island heats faster than the water and so the air above the island becomes warmer. The molecules in the air become farther apart; so the air expands upward and outward. This expansion lowers the air pressure at the island's surface. The cooler ocean air moves in toward the low-pressure area over the island.

There is a pressure gradient between the ocean and the island. The wind moves from high to low pressure. The speed of the wind depends on the pressure gradient. The lower the pressure (the hotter the island), the steeper the pressure gradient and the stronger the wind. The pressure gradient provides the force that makes the wind blow. This force is called the **pressure-gradient force.**

Topic 7 Local Winds

The wind over the island is an example of a *local wind*. A local wind extends over a distance of 100 kilometers or less. A **sea breeze** is a local wind that forms much like the island wind. During the daytime, coastal land is warmer than the nearby water. The air just over the land becomes warmer than the air over the water. The pressure lowers over the land, leading to a pressure gradient between the ocean and the land. The pressure gradient force pushes the cool ocean air inland. This cool wind is the sea breeze.

Over the land, the air rises. It then blows out to sea and sinks to replace the cool air that has flowed inland. As shown in Figure 28.6, the airflow forms a complete circuit—from the sea to the land, up, back to the sea, and down again. Thus the entire wind pattern is sometimes called a *sea-breeze circulation*.

A gentle sea breeze usually begins in the late morning along seacoasts. It increases in speed until midafternoon and dies down toward sunset. The sea breeze is felt inland from 15 to 70 kilometers away from the shoreline. It reaches up to about a kilometer in the atmosphere.

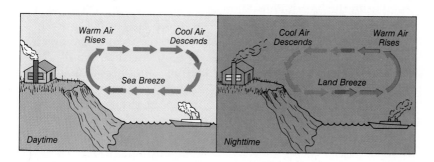

OBJECTIVES

A Show how heating causes low pressure and note that the wind blows from high to low pressure.

B Summarize the causes of land and sea breezes and mountain and valley winds.

C Describe the Coriolis effect.

D Explain why winds are clockwise around highs and counter-clockwise around lows in the Northern Hemisphere and why surface winds blow at an angle to the isobars.

E Describe how winds are named and measured and show how they are depicted on weather maps.

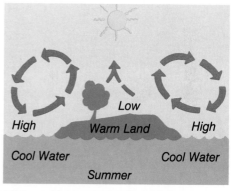

28.5 A heated island surrounded by cooler water becomes a region of low pressure, causing winds to blow toward the land.

SCIENCE BACKGROUND

In the southeastern United States, the sea breezes are strongest in June, when the land is heated strongly but the water is still cold from winter.

28.6 Sea and land breezes develop through unequal heating of land and nearby water. The land breeze blows from land; the sea breeze blows from the water.

At night, the land cools faster than the water, and the air pressure over the land becomes higher. The resulting pressure gradient causes the cool **land breeze** to blow out to sea. Over the sea the air rises and then flows inland at a higher level. The land breeze starts long before midnight and dies down after sunrise.

Mountain-valley winds are local winds that are driven by buoyancy as well as pressure gradients. At night, cold, heavy air sinks from mountaintops into valleys. The narrower the valley, the stronger the breeze. Coming from the mountains, it is called a mountain breeze.

During the daytime, warm air rises from the sunny mountain slopes. This rising air forms a valley breeze that blows up from the valley. Its speed is generally much less than that of the downhill mountain breeze. People who soar in gliders, hang gliders, and balloons ride the rising warm air in mountain regions.

Topic 8 **The Coriolis Effect**

In local winds, such as land and sea breezes, the winds flow from high to low pressure. However, a look at a weather map shows that this is not true for the large highs and lows shown. Instead of blowing from high to low pressure, the winds in the Northern Hemisphere flow clockwise around highs and counterclockwise around lows.

Earth's rotation causes the **Coriolis** (kor-ee-OH-lis) **effect.** The effect is felt by all objects, even air, moving toward or away from the equator. Because of the Coriolis effect, winds are turned to the right relative to Earth's surface in the Northern Hemisphere, and to the left relative to Earth's surface in the Southern Hemisphere.

Suppose a rocket fired from the North Pole is aimed straight south toward a point in central Kansas (39° N, 100° W). Also, suppose it takes an hour for the rocket to get that far south. During that hour, Earth has rotated 15 degrees eastward. So the rocket will land 15 degrees to the west. It will end up in eastern Nevada, 1295 kilometers away from the intended target. This deflection is called the Coriolis effect. It must be taken into account when rocket launches are planned.

The Coriolis effect is larger for higher wind speeds and smaller for lower wind speeds. To understand this, again think of the rocket fired from the North Pole. Suppose its speed is only half of what it was before. In an hour, the rocket will reach only as far as northern Canada. It will still end up 15 degrees to the west of its target, but at these northern latitudes, 15 degrees of longitude is only 718 kilometers. (The distance between longitude lines becomes smaller as they merge at the poles.)

The Coriolis effect is not a force. From space, the rocket appears to travel in a straight line, with Earth moving underneath. It does act like a force to an observer—or an air parcel—on Earth's surface. The Coriolis effect is important for ocean currents, too.

VIDEODISC SELECTION

Explanation of the Coriolis effect
Side 1 movie: 22001 & PLAY

SCIENCE BACKGROUND
On Earth, the Coriolis acceleration varies with latitude. It turns the wind to the right most at the poles and not at all at the equator.

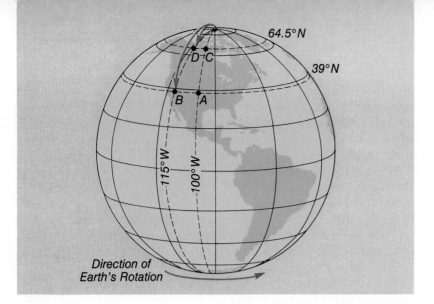

64.5°N

39°N

115°W

100°W

Direction of
Earth's Rotation

28.7 The Coriolis effect on an object fired from the North Pole. It is aimed toward A, but lands at B because Earth rotated 15 degrees during the hour the object was airborne. If a second object is fired toward C at half the speed of the original object, it lands 15 degrees to the west at D. The slower object was only 718 km from its target; the faster object missed by 1295 km.

Topic 9 How the Coriolis Effect Changes the Wind

The Coriolis effect keeps the wind from blowing directly from high to low pressure. Suppose an air parcel begins flowing from high to low pressure. The Coriolis effect turns the wind around to the right. The turning continues until the Coriolis effect exactly balances the pressure gradient force, which occurs when the wind is parallel to the isobars. Thus, in the Northern Hemisphere the air flowing out from a high turns right (clockwise). The air flowing into a low is turned to the right and flows counterclockwise.

At the surface, the wind does not flow exactly parallel to the isobars. This is because friction from the ground slows down the air and lessens the Coriolis effect. Then the air flows at an angle to the isobars, toward lower pressure. If the surface is very smooth, the wind is stronger and more nearly parallel to the isobars. Over the ocean, which is smoother than land, the angle between the surface wind and the isobars is 10 degrees. Over rough land, the surface wind blows at an average angle of about 30 degrees to the isobars. Winds above the surface flow more parallel to the isobars as the effects of surface friction disappear. The wind flows parallel to the isobars above 1 to 2 kilometers above the surface.

Does the Coriolis effect change the local winds? Air parcels have to travel a long time or over a long distance for the effects of Earth's rotation to be felt. Mountain-valley winds cannot be turned to the right because they have to flow up or down valleys. Long-lasting sea breezes, however, do start turning to the right. The Coriolis effect is one of the things that keeps sea breezes from going too far inland.

Topic 10 Measuring Wind

The surface wind direction and speed are usually measured at about 10 meters above the ground.

Wind direction is found by use of the **wind vane**. The wind vane has a broad tail that resists the wind more than its slender arrow-

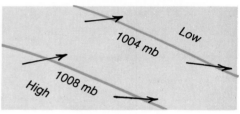

1004 mb   Low

1008 mb

High

At the Surface

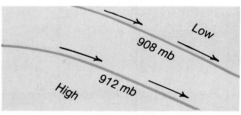

Low

908 mb

912 mb

High

At 1000 m

28.8 Wind changes with altitude. At Earth's surface, winds blow at angles to the isobars. At 1000 meters or higher, they blow along the isobars.

SCIENCE BACKGROUND

Since air moves from high to low pressure near the surface, the air sinks and moves out from the center in highs, and rises and moves in to the center in lows.

SCIENCE BACKGROUND

Sea and land breezes last long enough for the Coriolis effect to turn them to an angle more parallel to the shore.

OF INTEREST

The strongest wind speed ever recorded on Earth's surface was 200 knots (370 km/h) on Mount Washington, New Hampshire.

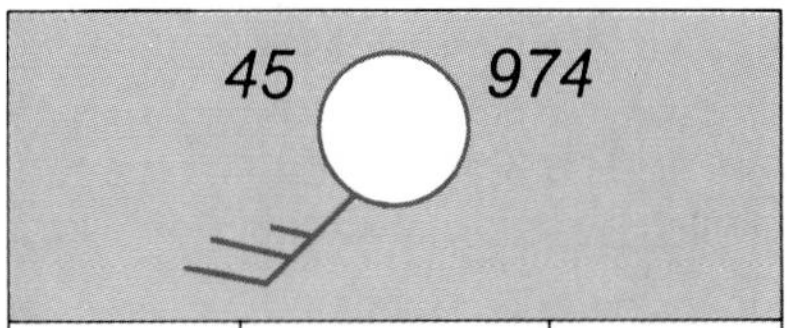

Symbol	Miles/Hour	Knots
	Calm	Calm
	1–2	1–2
	9–14	8–12
	15–20	13–17
	55–60	48–52
	72–77	63–67

28.9 The station model shows a temperature of 45°F, air pressure of 997.4 millibars, and a southwest wind of 25 knots. The symbols show how various wind speeds are represented.

head head. If a south wind is blowing, the wind vane will swing the tail to the north. The arrowhead then points south, into the wind. A wind vane always points to the direction from which the wind comes. Thus winds are named for their place of origin.

Wind speed near the surface is measured by an **anemometer**. A cup anemometer consists of hollow cones or hemispheres, all facing the same way, that catch the wind in their open sides from any direction. The speed of the wind is measured by the rate at which the cups turn. The speed and direction of high-altitude winds are found by tracking special upper-atmosphere weather balloons with radar or telescopes.

Wind and weather are closely related. In North America, winds from a northerly direction (north, northeast, or northwest) come from cooler latitudes. Therefore, they are likely to bring cooler weather. Similarly, winds from a southerly direction bring warmer weather. The opposite is true in the Southern Hemisphere.

Wind direction is shown on weather maps by arrows as shown in Figure 28.9. Wind speed is shown by lines and triangles on the arrow's staff. On weather maps the wind speed is given in knots. Each full line represents a speed of 10 knots. Each half line represents 5 knots. A triangle means a speed of 50 knots. A **knot** is approximately 1.85 kilometers (1.15 miles) per hour. Knots are often used to state the speed of ships, boats and aircraft.

TOPIC QUESTIONS

Each topic question refers to the topic of the same number.

6. **(a)** What is the relationship between air pressure and wind? **(b)** Explain where the pressure-gradient force comes from.
7. **(a)** How do sea and land breezes work? **(b)** Describe mountain and valley winds.
8. **(a)** What is the Coriolis effect? **(b)** What does the Coriolis effect do to a wind in the Northern Hemisphere? How does the Coriolis effect change the path of a southward-moving rocket? **(c)** How does the speed of the wind change the Coriolis effect?
9. **(a)** How does the Coriolis effect change the wind direction relative to the isobars? **(b)** In the Northern Hemisphere, why does the wind flow clockwise around highs and counterclockwise around lows? **(c)** What makes the wind at the surface flow at an angle to the isobars?
10. **(a)** What do an anemometer and wind vane measure? **(b)** How does an anemometer work? **(c)** How does a wind vane work? **(d)** Give some examples of how wind direction is related to weather. **(e)** Explain how wind direction and speed are shown on weather maps.

ANSWERS

6. (a) Air moves horizontally from high to low pressure, creating wind. (b) caused by difference in pressures between two areas.

7. (a) Sea breeze—warming over land lowers pressure, pressure-gradient force causes wind toward land. Land breeze—warmer ocean lowers pressure, pressure-gradient force causes wind toward ocean. (b) Mountain—cooled (dense) air from mountaintops sinks downhill into valleys. Valley—heated (less dense) air on mountain slopes rises, bringing air up valleys.

8. (a) the turning of the wind relative to Earth, caused by Earth's rotation (b) turns it to the right; turns it west (c) Higher speeds have greater effect.

9. (a) turns the wind until it is parallel to the isobars (b) turning right going into low is counterclockwise, going out of high is clockwise (c) Friction slows wind, reducing Coriolis effect, so air flows slightly to low pressure.

10. (a) wind speed and direction (b) cups blown by the wind (c) wind blows tail until opposite end points into wind (d) In the U.S. north winds are cool; south winds are warm. (e) direction—arrow; speed—lines, triangles

III Origin of the World Wind Belts

Topic 11 Winds on a Nonrotating Earth

Suppose Earth did not rotate and were completely covered with oceans. Then the winds would simply flow from high to low pressure. There would be no Coriolis effect. If Earth were heated around its equator, a low-pressure belt would form beneath the warm air at the surface. The relatively cold poles would have higher pressure. Near the surface, the cool air would flow directly from the poles to the equator. The air from both hemispheres would rise at the equator. At higher levels, the air would then flow toward the poles, where it would sink. The complete circulation would be like that of the sea breeze, only bigger. In the Northern Hemisphere the winds would be from the north at the surface and from the south at higher levels.

Earth's winds do not follow this simple pattern for two reasons. One is that Earth rotates on its axis, causing the Coriolis effect. The other reason is the unequal heating of the land and water.

Topic 12 Latitude Wind Cells

What does Earth's rotation do to the simple circulation pattern described in Topic 11? Imagine the warm air rising at the equator. The rising air splits into two currents. One begins moving northward; the other starts to move southward. However, soon they are turned by the Coriolis effect. The northward-moving air in the Northern Hemisphere is turned to the right, or eastward, and the southward-moving air is turned left (again eastward) in the Southern Hemisphere.

In both cases, the air is flowing almost due east by the time it reaches about 30 degrees latitude. Here, the air cooled by its move north, sinks into a zone of relatively high pressure at the surface. The air at the surface flows from the high pressure at 30 degrees latitude to the low pressure at the equator.

A complete circulation such as this is called a *circulation cell.* The equator-to-30 degree cell just described is also called the **Hadley cell.** It was named for George Hadley, who discovered it in the early 1700's. In each hemisphere, there are two more circulation cells between the Hadley cells and the pole.

Surface high-pressure areas lie at both poles. Cold air flows toward the equator at the surface, turned westward by the Coriolis effect. At higher levels above the poles, the air that comes from lower latitudes sinks to replace the outflowing surface air. Rising air at about 60 degrees latitude completes the circulation. This air is forced to rise because the cold air from the poles collides with warmer air coming from lower latitudes.

OBJECTIVES

A Characterize the circulation on a nonrotating Earth heated at the equator and describe the three-celled circulation of a rotating Earth.

B Summarize the main pressure belts and their corresponding winds.

C List some effects of the atmospheric circulation on the weather.

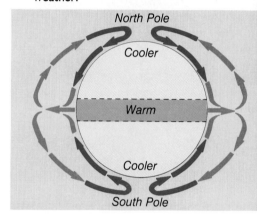

28.10 If Earth's surface were entirely covered by oceans and Earth did not rotate, then heating the equator would produce the simple wind system shown by the arrows.

SCIENCE BACKGROUND

The heat released in condensation in the ITCZ is important in maintaining the Hadley cell circulation.

28.11 Because Earth rotates on its axis, three pairs of circulation cells develop in the atmosphere. The middle cell is weak and does not show up except in long-term averages, so it is dashed.

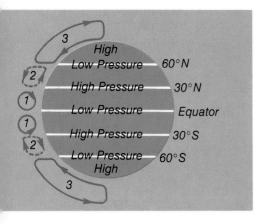

OF INTEREST

It is thought that the horse latitudes get their name from the horses thrown overboard by sailors short of food and water.

SCIENCE BACKGROUND

When the ITCZ shifts to slightly north of the equator as it follows the sun north, the SE trade winds reach into the Northern Hemisphere.

Where the warm and cold air meet, the warm, lighter air flows on top of the cold, heavier air. Meteorologists call the surface between the warm and cold air the **polar front**. Low-pressure areas develop along the polar front. Sixty degrees is only the average latitude of the polar front; it is very irregular.

The circulation cell between 30 and 60 degrees latitude is hard to find. It shows up only in weather data averaged over several years. The air at the bottom of this middle cell flows toward the poles from the high pressure at 30 degrees to the low pressure at 60 degrees. The air at the top of the cell flows toward the equator.

Together, the three circulation cells look like meshing gears. North of 30 degrees, however, the simple pattern is hidden by the passage of highs and lows. Highs and lows will be discussed in the next chapter.

Topic 13 **Pressure Belts and Winds**

The names of some of the pressure belts survive from the days of the great sailing ships. The low-pressure belt at the equator is called the **doldrums**, and the high-pressure belts at 30 degrees are called the **horse latitudes**.

The scientific names for the pressure belts are less colorful but may be easier to remember. The high-pressure belts at 30 degrees are called the *subtropical highs*, the low-pressure belts at 60 degrees are called the *subpolar lows*, and the high-pressure regions at the poles are simply the *polar highs*. The low-pressure zone at the equator is called the **intertropical convergence zone (ITCZ)** because the winds from the two hemispheres converge (come together) there. Notice that the lows and highs alternate: low at the equator, high at 30 degrees, low at 60 degrees, and high at the poles.

The winds between the pressure zones are named for the directions from which they blow. In the Northern Hemisphere, the winds bend to the right. Thus south winds become southwesterlies, and north winds become northeasterlies. In the Northern Hemisphere the prevailing winds are these:

1. *Polar northeasterlies* blow from the polar high to the subpolar low-pressure belt.
2. *Prevailing southwesterlies* blow from the subtropical highs to the subpolar lows.
3. *Northeast trade winds* blow from the subtropical highs toward the ITCZ.

The Southern Hemisphere has a matching set of winds. However, in the Southern Hemisphere, the Coriolis effect bends winds to the left. South winds become southeasterlies, and north winds become northwesterlies. So the prevailing winds in the Southern Hemisphere are the polar southeasterlies, prevailing northwesterlies, and southeast trade winds. Notice again that the winds blow from highs to lows in both hemispheres.

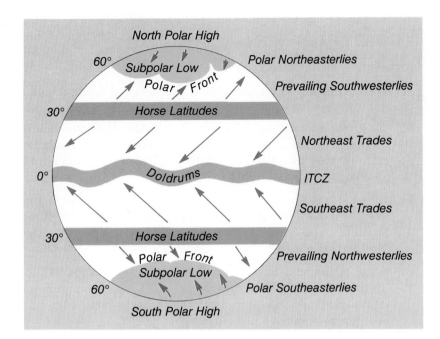

North Polar High

60°

Subpolar Low

Polar Front

Horse Latitudes

30°

0°

Doldrums

Horse Latitudes

30°

Polar Front

Subpolar Low

60°

South Polar High

Polar Northeasterlies

Prevailing Southwesterlies

Northeast Trades

ITCZ

Southeast Trades

Prevailing Northwesterlies

Polar Southeasterlies

28.12 This diagram gives a general picture of the pressure belts and wind directions at Earth's surface.

VIDEODISC SELECTION

Diagram of Earth's prevailing wind belts
Side 1: 803, single frame

Topic 14 **Weather in the Wind and Pressure Belts**

The air in the doldrums is hot and humid, and slowly rising. There is little or no wind. Sailing vessels have been stuck in the doldrums for days at a time. Rainfall is concentrated in the rising air of the ITCZ.

Dry air sinks from above in the horse latitudes. There is little or no wind. Between the doldrums and the horse latitudes the **trade winds** blow. The trade winds are warm and steady in both direction and speed. In the Northern Hemisphere, they blow from the northeast at 10–20 knots. Because the trade winds are so steady, sailing ships used them whenever possible. In fact, the trade winds got their name because they provided regular trade routes for sailing ships.

The prevailing westerlies are southwesterlies at the surface in the Northern Hemisphere and northwesterlies in the Southern Hemisphere. They change direction and speed frequently. The word "prevailing" means that they blow from the same direction on the average. The speed of the westerlies increases with latitude. The Southern Hemisphere's middle latitudes are almost all ocean. So the westerlies there are very strong, with speeds higher than 40 knots.

The polar easterlies, like the trades, are northeasterly in the Northern Hemisphere and southeasterly in the Southern Hemisphere. Their weather is cold and stormy.

The subpolar low-pressure belts are areas of cold, stormy weather. The polar highs are very cold.

OF INTEREST

The westerlies in the Southern Hemisphere are called the roaring 40's, howling 50's, and screeching 60's.

ANSWERS (continued)

12. (a) Air deflection by Coriolis effect causes breakup into three cells. (b) Air flows from 30 degrees to equator at surface, rises at equator, returns to 30 degrees, and sinks. (c) Air sinks at poles, goes to 60 degrees at surface, rises, returns to poles, and sinks. (d) 30-60 degree cell circulation opposite direction and disorganized (e) surface between warm air from tropics and cold air from poles

13. (a) pressure belts and Coriolis effect (b) low-pressure belt at equator; where air from hemispheres comes together; high-pressure belt at 30 degrees (c) NE trades, 0° to 30°N, prevailing southwesterlies, 30° to 60°N; polar northeasterlies, 60°N to poles

14. (a) hot, rising air, little wind (b) rainy (c) dry, little wind (d) cold, stormy (e) warm, steady (f) irregular

TOPIC QUESTIONS

Each topic question refers to the topic of the same number.

11. What kind of circulation would the atmosphere have on a non-rotating Earth with a heated equator and no continents?

12. (**a**) Briefly explain what happens to the circulation as Earth rotates. (**b**) Describe the Hadley cell. (**c**) Describe the polar cell. (**d**) Compare the 30-60 degree cell with the Hadley cell. (**e**) What is the polar front?

13. (**a**) What are the two causes for the wind directions in the main wind belts? (**b**) Define doldrums, ITCZ, and horse latitudes. (**c**) List the three important wind belts in the Northern Hemisphere and give their locations.

14. What is the weather in (**a**) the doldrums, (**b**) the ITCZ, (**c**) the horse latitudes, (**d**) the subpolar low-pressure belt? (**e**) What are the characteristics of the trade winds? (**f**) Of the prevailing westerlies?

CAREERS

Dr. Robert Sheets
Hurricane Meteorologist

As you will learn in Chapter 30, a hurricane is a severe storm associated with marine tropical air masses. Hurricanes are low pressure systems whose high winds and storm surges are capable of great destruction when they strike land.

Dr. Robert Sheets is the director of the National Hurricane Center in Coral Gables, Florida. You have probably seen Dr. Sheets on the news when hurricanes are threatening the Atlantic or Gulf coasts. Part of Dr. Sheets's job is to warn people who are in the path of an approaching hurricane to evacuate or to seek safe shelter. The National Hurricane Center is a part of the National Weather Service. Dr. Sheets and other meteorologists at the Center continually watch for tropical storms, follow their development into hurricanes, and try to predict the paths they will take.

Prior to becoming the director of the National Hurricane Center, Dr. Sheets actively studied hurricanes. For sixteen years, he worked in the National Hurricane Research Laboratory. For a hurricane researcher, gathering data often involves flying directly into the hurricane's powerful winds. Dr. Sheets estimates that he has flown through the eye of a hurricane over 200 times in his career.

Dr. Sheets's greatest concern is for the over 40 million people who now live along the Atlantic and Gulf coasts and are therefore potential hurricane victims. As the 1992 hurricanes Andrew and Iniki reminded us, these dangerous storms are to be respected.

IV   Winds and Wind Shifts

Topic 15   Effects of Continents

Land heats more in summer and cools more in winter. This heating and cooling has two important effects, which are shown in the maps of Figure 28.13(a) and Figure 28.13(b).

The first effect is that the highest temperatures are not usually at the equator. In the Northern Hemisphere summer, the highest temperatures (and therefore the lowest pressures) are as far north as 30° N in southwest Asia and northern Africa. Air flows into the low-pressure belt from the north and south, so the ITCZ moves north with the high temperatures. In the Southern Hemisphere summer, the ITCZ and the hottest temperatures move southward, reaching their southern point over northern Australia (15–20° S). Away from the continents, the ITCZ does not move as far north or south.

The second effect is that the pressure belts are broken up into highs and lows. In the summer, the pressure is low over the continents and high over the oceans. For example, a low-pressure area forms over the hot southwestern United States. Large high-pressure areas form over both the Atlantic and Pacific Oceans. The Atlantic high brings prevailing south winds to the eastern United States.

In the winter, the patterns reverse. Strong lows form over the northern Atlantic and northern Pacific Oceans. The pressure over North America is high. The low in the northern Pacific is associated with the many storms that reach the western coast of the United States.

OBJECTIVES

A Explain the effects of continents and seasons on Earth's pressure and wind circulation.

B Summarize the characteristics of the jet stream and its relationship to the weather.

28.13 The effects of the continents and oceans on average sea-level pressure and winds, for (a) January and (b) July. The thin lines are isobars; the thick solid line is the ITCZ.

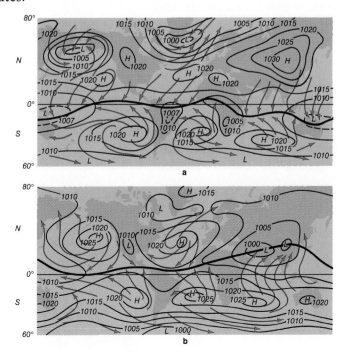

SCIENCE BACKGROUND
Although rainfall is heavy during the monsoon season, there are periods without rain called "monsoon breaks."

28.14 (top) India's dry winter monsoon blows from the land to the sea. (bottom) The wet summer monsoon blows from the sea to the land.

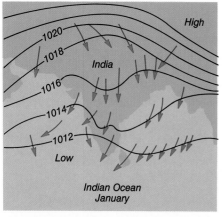

India
1020
1018
1016
1014
1012
High
Low
Indian Ocean
January

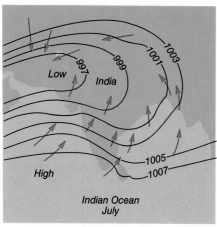

Low
India
997
999
1001
1003
1005
1007
High
Indian Ocean
July

28.15 A typical position of the Northern Hemisphere jet stream over North America

Jet Stream

Topic 16 Monsoons

The most dramatic continental effects on wind and pressure occur on the Indian subcontinent. Here the seasonal pressure changes from the heating and cooling of Asia produce a complete wind reversal. During the winter the sinking, cold air over the continent flows toward the lower pressure over the sea. In summer, the low pressure areas over the Indian subcontinent and Southeast Asia become centers of rising warm, moist air from the surrounding waters.

The changing winds are called **monsoons**. The cold, dry winds that flow from the cold interior are the winter monsoon. The warm, moist winds that flow into Asia from the Indian Ocean are called the summer monsoon. When they rise over the highlands of India and Southeast Asia, heavy rains fall.

Other parts of the world, such as northern Australia, west-central Africa, Spain, and the southeastern and southwestern United States, have seasonal wind changes. In most cases, however, the winds do not turn around as strongly as in India.

Topic 17 Jet Streams

Wind speeds are very high in the upper troposphere. It is here that the spectacular jet stream is found. **Jet streams** are a fairly narrow zone of very strong winds in the upper troposphere. Jet streams are most common in the middle latitudes, so the winds in the jet streams are usually from the west. Sometimes it forms a single meandering band around the entire Earth. More often it is made of two or more separate streams.

The height of jet streams ranges from about 6000 to 12 000 meters. Its strongest winds are about 10 500 meters above Earth. Its separate streams may be from 1600 to 4000 kilometers long, about one tenth as wide, and about 1 kilometer thick. Wind speeds are usually about 150 knots, but they may exceed 300 knots.

Two or more jet streams may be over a continent at once. In the Northern Hemisphere upper-air westerlies, jet streams may reach as far south as 20° N. The jet stream shifts position with the season, moving north in summer and south in winter. Its most common location over North America is around 40° N. A jet stream called the tropical easterly jet forms in the tropics in the Northern Hemisphere summer, but is weaker than the jet stream of the latitudes farther north. Figure 28.15 shows a typical position of the jet stream over North America.

Jet streams help eastward-flying planes to fly faster relative to the ground. Aircraft flying westward are slowed down by the jet streams, so pilots try to avoid them.

Jet streams are closely related to the weather and are strongest during outbreaks of cold polar air. Spring and summer jet streams are related to strong thunderstorms.

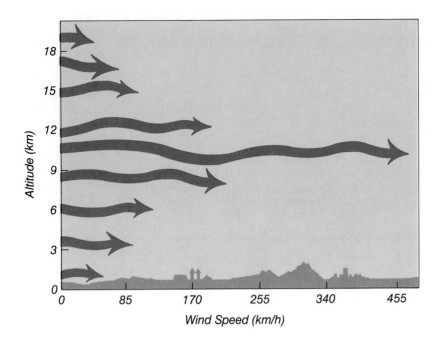

28.16 The arrows show wind speeds above the surface on a winter day in central United States. The very long arrow at about 10.5 kilometers is the jet stream. Its maximum speed is about 400 kilometers per hour.

TOPIC QUESTIONS

Each topic question refers to the topic of the same number.

15. **(a)** How do Earth's continents affect Earth's wind and pressure belts? **(b)** Why does the ITCZ move so far from the equator into the hemisphere where it is summer? **(c)** Describe the pressure pattern around North America for the Northern Hemisphere summer.

16. **(a)** What are monsoons? **(b)** Describe the summer and winter Indian monsoons.

17. **(a)** What are jet streams? **(b)** List the height, location, and wind speeds of the North-American jet stream. **(c)** How is the jet stream related to the weather at the ground?

Map Skills

The following questions refer to the Prevailing World Winds map on page 659 of Appendix B.

1. **(a)** In the Southern Hemisphere, from what direction do the winds near the equator blow? **(b)** From what direction do the winds south of 40°S blow?

2. How are the winds in the Northern Hemisphere different from those in the Southern Hemisphere?

3. What happens to the southeast trade winds to the south of North Africa and Asia?

ANSWERS

15. (a) highest temperatures away from equator; pressure belts broken up into highs and lows (b) highest temperatures mean lowest pressure, air flows into low pressure from both hemispheres (c) low over SW U.S.; highs over Atlantic and Pacific

16. (a) winds that change with seasonal heating and cooling of the continents (b) summer—warm, moist winds blow from oceans toward low pressure over hot continent and bring rain; winter—cold, dry winds flow from high pressure over cold continent toward the oceans

17. (a) narrow, high-speed stream of air in the upper troposphere (b) 6000-12 000 m; mid-latitudes south to 20°N, 150-300 knots (c) stronger during polar-air outbreaks, related to strong thunderstorms

ANSWERS

1. (a) southeast (b) northwest
2. The global wind patterns are broken up; less steady; irregular.
3. They cross the equator and are bent to the right.

CHAPTER 28

L A B ACTIVITY

Recording and Correlating Weather Variables

Wind direction, temperature, clouds, and precipitation in a specific location are all clues to larger weather patterns. With practice, a weather observer can often accurately predict the local weather for the next day.

In this activity, you will make careful observations and records of weather over a period of several days and look for definite relationships among weather variables. You will then try to predict the local weather.

Lab Skills and Objectives
- To **measure** and **record** weather conditions
- To **identify** how weather conditions are related
- To **predict** the local weather for a 24 hours time period

Materials
- chart for recording daily weather data
- outdoor thermometer
- barometer
- wind vane (or flag on a flagpole)
- anemometer, if available
- wet- and dry-bulb thermometers
- rain gauge (or calibrated can)

- relative humidity chart, page 501
- cloud classification photos, page 508, Figure 27.8

Procedure
Part A
1. On the daily weather chart, Figure 28.17, write the date and time. Record data for steps 2 through 10 on this weather chart.
2. Use an outdoor thermometer to read the air temperature outside. Record the temperature in °C.
3. Use a barometer to determine the barometric pressure. Record the pressure in millibars.
4. Use a wind vane to determine the wind direction. Record the direction on the weather chart.
5. Read the wind speed, in knots, with an anemometer and record the data on the weather chart.
6. Use a wet- and dry-bulb thermometer and the chart on page 501 to determine relative humidity. Record that data on the weather chart.
7. Record the total precipitation (in centimeters) for the day.
8. Look at the sky and write in the column labeled *State of Sky* if the sky is clear, partly cloudy, or completely overcast.
9. Use Figure 27.8, page 508, to determine the type of clouds in the sky. Record that information in the column labeled *Cloud Type*.

10. Observe the weather conditions for the day. Is it clear or cloudy, hot or cold, dry or humid, raining, foggy, or snowing? Write the best description for the weather on the weather chart.
11. Repeat steps 1 through 10 every day, including non-school days, for three weeks.

Part B
12. At the end of the three week observation time, locate a period of several days within the data where air pressure rose steadily and remained relatively high. Record the range of temperatures and relative humidities that occurred during that period of time on Data Table A. For the same period, record the most common weather conditions and state of the sky.
13. Locate a second period of time when air pressure dropped steadily and remained low. Repeat procedure step 12 for that time period.
14. Answer the questions in *Analysis and Conclusions*.

Analysis and Conclusions
1. Is there a wind direction that usually brings cooler weather? Explain your answer.
2. Which wind direction usually brings warmer weather? Explain your answer.
3. How is wind speed affected when air pressure changes

rapidly? How is wind speed affected when air pressure holds steady?

4. According to your data, is high pressure associated with clear weather or stormy weather? Is low pressure associated with clear weather or stormy weather?

5. Is the state of the sky a good indicator of the next day's weather? Explain your answer.

6. Which cloud types are associated with precipitation? State your evidence, referring to data on your chart.

7. What is the relationship between relative humidity and weather? Explain your answer.

8. Do changes in relative humidity indicate changes in weather conditions? Explain the relationship, referring to data on your weather chart.

9. On the basis of your data and conclusions, what weather conditions are the most useful for making your own local forecast?

10. Forecast the weather for the next two days and explain your prediction.

Daily Weather Chart

Date/Time		
Temperature (°C)		
Air Pressure (mb)		
Wind Direction		
Wind Speed (km)		
Relative Humidity (%)		
Total Precipitation (cm)		
State of Sky		
Cloud type		
Present Weather Conditions		

Data Table A

Weather Conditions	High Air Pressure	Low Air Pressure
Range of temperatures (°C)		
Relative humidity range		
General weather conditions		
General state of sky		

Answers to all questions appear in the Teacher's Guide at the back of this book.

■ Summary

I Air pressure is caused by the weight of the atmosphere. It is directed equally in all directions. Air pressure is measured with barometers.

Changes in temperature and humidity change the air pressure.

II Winds are caused by differences in air pressure. Air flows from high to low pressure.

Uneven heating of land and water results in the sea breeze. At night, the direction of the breeze is reversed.

In the Northern Hemisphere, the Coriolis effect turns winds to the right. It makes winds blow counterclockwise around lows and clockwise around highs.

In the Southern Hemisphere, the Coriolis effect turns winds to the left. It makes winds blow clockwise around lows and counterclockwise around highs.

A wind is defined by its speed and the direction from which it is blowing.

III Earth's rotation and the uneven heating between its equator and poles result in the global wind and pressure belts.

Belts of low pressure and rising air lie at the equator and at 60 degrees. Belts of surface high pressure and sinking air lie at 30 degrees and at the poles.

In the Northern Hemisphere, surface northeast winds blow from the North Pole to 60°N, and from 30°N to the equator. Southwesterlies blow from 30 to 60 degrees. The flow north of 30 degrees is very irregular.

IV In summer continents have low air pressure and the seas have high air pressure. Winds tend to blow more from the sea to the continents. The pattern reverses in winter. The reversing winds are called monsoons.

Jet streams are localized, very strong winds at heights of 6 to 12 kilometers. They are closely related to the weather.

■ Vocabulary

air pressure	knot
anemometer	land breeze
barometer	low-pressure area
Coriolis effect	(low)
doldrums	millibar
Hadley cell	monsoon
high-pressure area	polar front
(high)	pressure gradient
horse latitudes	pressure-gradient
intertropical	force
convergence zone	sea breeze
(ITCZ)	sea-level pressure
isobar	trade winds
jet stream	wind vane

■ Review

On your paper, write the word or words that best complete each sentence.

1. _____ is the weight of the atmosphere per unit area.
2. Air pressure is measured using an instrument called a _____. An _____ measures height above sea level.
3. The average air pressure at a location with an altitude of 1000 meters would be _____ than average sea-level pressure.
4. Lines on a weather map that connect points with the same air pressure are called _____.
5. Air pressure can be changed by changes in _____ or _____.
6. Dry air weighs _____ than an equal volume of humid air.
7. A set of closed isobars in which the pressures decrease toward the center represents a _____.
8. Isobars that are close together have a _____ pressure gradient, which will result in _____ winds.
9. A _____ is a local wind that blows from the ocean toward the land.
10. Winds in the Northern Hemisphere are turned to the right by the _____.

For further review, see **Study Guide.**
For assessment, see **Chapter Tests**
and **Computer Test Bank.**

11. _____ causes surface winds to blow at an angle to the isobars instead of parallel to them.
12. A wind vane points _____ the direction from which the wind blows.
13. Wind speed is measured in units called _____.
14. The Coriolis effect causes the air flow in each hemisphere to form three _____.
15. The equator-to-30 degree cell is called the _____.
16. The _____ is the surface between warm and cold air at about 60 degrees latitude where low-pressure areas develop.
17. The low-pressure zone at the equator is the _____.
18. Winds blow from areas of _____ pressure to areas of _____ pressure.
19. A wind that reverses direction with the seasons is a _____.
20. The North American jet stream flows from _____ to _____.

■ Interpret and Apply

On your paper, answer each question in complete sentences.

1. The feet of a 4500-kilogram elephant are approximate circles, each about 44 centimeters in diameter. If the elephant is standing on all four feet, what is the pressure under each foot?
2. (a) In what direction do winds circulate around highs in the Southern Hemisphere? (b) In what direction do winds circulate around lows in the Southern Hemisphere?
3. Draw a diagram to show what Earth's major wind belts would look like if Earth rotated from east to west.
4. The Coriolis effect is less at lower latitudes than at high latitudes. How would this reduced Coriolis effect affect a sea breeze at low latitudes?

5. On what time schedule might a fleet of sailboats make the best use of land and sea breezes?
6. Readings of surface air temperature are taken 1-2 meters above ground level, but wind speed and direction are measured about 10 meters above ground level. What is the reason for this difference?
7. Would you or would you not expect the Coriolis effect to affect water going down a drain? Why or why not?
8. How is atmospheric pressure similar to the pressure felt by scuba divers?
9. If you added water vapor to air in a closed container, its pressure would increase. Why then does adding water vapor to air (increasing humidity) lower the air pressure?

■ Critical Thinking

On your paper, answer each question in complete sentences.

1. Suppose Earth did not rotate, but had one side always toward the sun. Describe the winds and pressure field (a) at the surface and (b) at about 10 kilometers above the surface.
2. Speculate on what the atmospheric circulation would be if Earth's speed of rotation were doubled.
3. Explain what might happen to the air pressure at the surface under each of the following circumstances. (a) A deep cumulonimbus cloud is rapidly growing overhead. (b) A deep, cold downdraft from a squall line cools off the summer afternoon. (c) A dying thunderstorm with heavy rains is overhead. (d) A layer of warm, moist air extending from the surface to 1 kilometer above the surface moves northward, warming the temperature a degree an hour. At the same time, a layer of cool, dry air extending from 5 to 6 kilometers above the ground comes from the north, cooling the temperatures at those heights a degree an hour.

541

Air Masses and Fronts

▲
A highway near Buffalo, New York, buried by the 1977 blizzard

How Do You Know That . . .

Fronts and air masses affect the local weather? The winter of 1976–1977 was one of the worst winters ever for Buffalo, New York. The worst storm of the winter started in late January 1977, when a strong low-pressure area brought with it cold air, snow, and winds as strong as 70 miles an hour. The storm lasted for 5 days, did 250 million dollars damage, and caused 29 deaths. Nine people froze to death in their cars. The snow in and around Buffalo was 4 feet deep, with drifts 30 feet high in some places. This snowstorm was a spectacular example of what happens when a strong low-pressure area is followed by a very cold air mass.

I Air Masses

Topic 1 Origin of an Air Mass

Air that stays in one area for a long time takes on the weather of that area. For example, if air stays in the Arctic for a few weeks in January, it becomes quite cold. If the air lies over the ocean, it becomes moist.

An **air mass** is a huge section of the lower troposphere that has the same kind of weather throughout. The temperature and humidity are horizontally uniform within an air mass. Air masses may be several thousand kilometers in diameter and several kilometers deep. Two or three air masses can cover all of the continental United States.

How does a huge section of the troposphere become an air mass? It maintains the same position for days or even weeks over a large uniform surface. An air mass over the Gulf of Mexico, for example, would be warm and humid. An air mass over the Great Plains of Canada in winter would be cold and dry.

Air masses originate in parts of the world where winds are light. These are mainly in the polar and subtropical high-pressure belts.

Topic 2 Kinds, Sources, and Paths of Air Masses

The temperature of an air mass depends on whether it comes from the tropics or the polar regions. The humidity of an air mass depends on whether it comes from land or sea.

Air masses are named for their *source regions*, or places of origin. A **maritime tropical** (abbreviated **mT**) air mass comes from tropical seas. It is warm and humid. Maritime tropical air comes into the United States from the Pacific and Atlantic oceans and the Gulf of Mexico. A **continental tropical (cT)** air mass comes from tropical land areas. In North America, these hot, dry air masses originate in the summer in the desert areas of southwestern United States.

A **maritime polar (mP)** air mass comes from cold ocean waters. It is cold and humid. A **continental polar (cP)** air mass comes from land areas in high latitudes. It is cold and dry. Maritime polar air masses come to the United States from both the Pacific and Atlantic oceans. Continental polar air masses come from Canada and northward.

OBJECTIVES

A Explain how air masses form and list the types of air masses.

B Describe the weather and sky conditions that accompany each type of air mass.

C Describe the techniques used to determine air-mass properties.

29.1 In the summertime, this desert area in southern Utah is part of a source region for hot, dry continental tropical air.

SCIENCE BACKGROUND

Meteorologists indicate whether an air mass, once it has moved away from its source region, is warmer or colder than the surface underneath by adding "w" (warmer) or "k" (colder) to the air-mass symbol. Thus, cPk is a continental polar air mass colder than the surface.

OF INTEREST

Observant students may notice that the air masses named "Arctic" are actually closer to the poles than the air masses named "polar." Meteorologists have in fact named them in reverse!

29.2 Air mass source regions and the paths air masses follow across North America

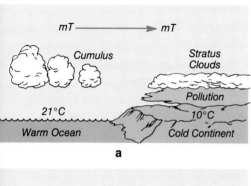

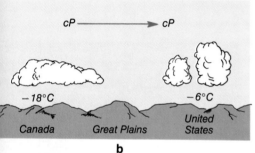

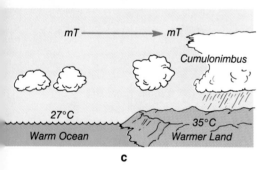

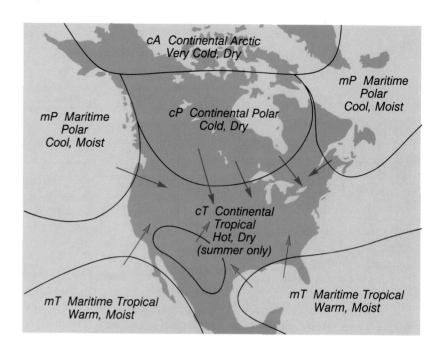

29.3 (a) When a maritime tropical air mass moves from warm sea to cooler land, the air near the surface is stable. Stratus clouds, fog, and drizzle may develop. Pollution may become trapped, forming smog.
(b) When a continental polar air mass moves from Canada across the warmer Great Plains in wintertime, fair-weather cumulus clouds form.
(c) When a maritime tropical air mass moves from sea to warmer land in summer, cumulonimbus clouds and thunderstorms are likely.

Continental Arctic (cA) air masses are very cold and dry. They come from the ice-covered Arctic regions. There is no maritime Arctic air mass because Arctic air is so dry.

Topic 3 Weather in an Air Mass

Air masses are so large that they may take many days to pass a given place. During this time the weather of the place is like the weather of the region where the air mass originated. In winter, cP air usually brings very cold weather. It may reach as far south as Florida. In summer, cP air is felt as a cool spell.

When mP air comes in from the northern oceans, it brings cool, humid weather. The mT air masses bring mild, humid weather in winter. In summer they bring hot, humid spells to central and eastern United States. Maritime tropical air also brings frequent thunderstorms and occasional tornadoes. Continental tropical air masses bring very hot, dry weather.

The weather changes brought by new air masses can be extreme or very slight. Part of the reason for the difference is that air masses change as they move away from their source areas. Polar air masses get warmer as they move southward. Dry air masses become moister over moist ground. Moist air masses become drier over dry ground as water lost due to precipitation is not replaced. Fast-moving air masses spend less time over any one area, so they are usually changed less than slow-moving air masses. Therefore, fast-moving air masses bring more extreme weather changes.

The passage of different air masses is one of the factors that make weather so variable.

Topic 4 **Skies in an Air Mass**

What kinds of clouds do air masses have? Is the weather fair or rainy, windy or calm?

Meteorologists have found that the conditions in an air mass depend mainly on one thing: Is the surface the air mass lies over warmer or colder than the air mass? If the ground surface is colder, it cools the bottom layer of the air mass, with the following results:

1. The bottom layer of the air is stable. Inversions form. Smoke, dust, and other pollutants do not rise. Visibility is poor. *Smog* may develop.
2. Condensation of water vapor occurs at the surface and in the lower air. This condensation may form dew, fog, stratiform clouds, drizzle, or light rain.

If the ground surface is warmer than the air mass, it warms the bottom layer of the air mass, with these results:

1. The bottom layer is unstable. Convection currents form cumulus clouds. The convection mixes lower-layer air with air at higher levels, so air pollution moves out of the area. Visibility is good.
2. If the air mass is a dry one — such as cP — the weather stays fair. If the air mass is humid or the warm surface is water, showers may form.

Topic 5 **Observing an Air Mass**

How do meterologists observe the temperature, humidity, and wind at high levels in an air mass? They use a balloon-carried package of instruments called a **rawinsonde**. Rawinsonde measurements are made twice daily, at noon and midnight, Greenwich, England, time (GMT), at weather stations all over the world.

The rawinsonde contains a radio transmitter that sends out signals about the temperature, air pressure, and relative humidity. An automatic radio receiver at the weather station records the signals. The balloon carries the rawinsonde up to a height of more than 30 kilometers, where the balloon bursts. Radar equipment tracks the rawinsonde and determines the speed and direction of the upper-air winds.

Scientists are developing new ways to measure the temperature, humidity, and wind above the surface. The temperature and humidity are estimated by measuring the air's infrared radiation. (Hotter air and more humid air radiate more infrared rays.) These measurements are made both from satellites and from instruments on the ground. The new *radar wind profiler* is a kind of radar that measures the winds through the troposphere. Unlike rawinsondes, the new instruments can take measurements continuously. However, they cannot provide the detail rawinsondes can.

29.4 This rawinsonde, about to be launched, may float upward to an altitude of about 30 kilometers.

ANSWERS (Continued)

2. (a) for source regions   (b) continental polar; cold and dry; around Canada   (c) maritime polar; cold and moist; north Atlantic and Pacific (d) maritime tropical; warm and moist; Atlantic, Pacific, and Gulf of Mexico   (e) continental tropical; hot and dry; southwestern United States and northwest Mexico

3. (a) cP–very cold in winter, cool in summer; mP–cool and humid; mT–mild and humid in winter, hot and humid with possible thunderstorms in central and eastern United States in summer   (b) Fast-moving air masses are more like their source regions, so they bring more extreme changes.

4. (a) temperature of an air mass relative to the surface   (b) stable air; pollution; poor visibility; dew, fog, stratiform clouds, drizzle possible (c) unstable air, cumulus clouds, good visibility, showers if humid

5. (a) Rawinsonde's radio transmitter sends out signals from temperature, humidity, and pressure instruments; radar tracks rawinsonde to get wind.   (b) They measure the air's infrared radiation, which is related to the air's temperature and humidity.   (c) radar wind profiler (d) continuous but with less detail

ANSWERS

1. (a) huge mass of tropospheric air with the same characteristics throughout   (b) stays over large uniform area for long time, adjusting to environment

TOPIC QUESTIONS

Each topic question refers to the topic of the same number.

1. **(a)** What is an air mass?   **(b)** Explain how an air mass originates.

2. **(a)** How are air masses named? Write the full name, characteristics, and source regions of the North American air masses abbreviated by   **(b)** cP,   **(c)** mP,   **(d)** mT, and   **(e)** cT.

3. **(a)** Briefly describe the weather in each of the following air masses: cP, mP, mT.   **(b)** How does the speed of the air mass affect the expected weather?

4. **(a)** What is the chief factor that determines the type of skies an air mass will have?   **(b)** Describe the sky conditions in an air mass resting on a cooler surface.   **(c)** Describe the sky conditions in an air mass resting on a warmer surface.

5. **(a)** How is a rawinsonde used to obtain temperature, humidity, and wind measurements above the surface?   **(b)** How are satellites and ground instruments used to estimate temperatures and humidities aloft?   **(c)** What is the new instrument for measuring wind at upper levels?   **(d)** How do wind measurements made with this instrument differ from wind measurements made with a rawinsonde?

Current RESEARCH

Chaos: Limits of Predictablity

Sometimes it's amazing what scientists can predict with certainty. For example, eclipses can be predicted down to the minute, decades ahead of time. Chemical reactions can be assumed to work the same way, time and time again, given the same conditions. Even the flipping of a coin takes on a certain predictability when viewed statistically.

Will it ever be possible to accurately predict weather weeks or months ahead of time? Think about the types of data needed to predict the weather. The meteorologist needs to know the humidity of air masses at different elevations, temperatures, air pressures, wind speeds and directions, and other information. To know what the weather will be doing even three days in the future, the meteorologist needs to know how and when any of these conditions may change.

Chaos theory says that, in a system like the weather, predictions have no choice but to get less certain over time. A small change in one part of a complex interacting system— a gust of wind caused by a tree falling in someone's yard— can set off an unpredictable chain of events that can actually change the weather hundreds of miles away a few days later. If this is true, then weather forecasting may never be able to give accurate predictions more than several days ahead of time.

II   Fronts and the Formation of Lows

Topic 6   What Is a Front?

At any given moment several air masses may cover the United States. The boundary between any two air masses is called a **front**. Because the two air masses have different temperatures and humidities, the front is where the temperatures and humidities change. An approaching front means a change in the weather. The greater the differences between the air masses, the greater the change in the weather. On weather maps, fronts are drawn in regions of great change in temperature and wind direction and where isobars tend to bend.

Suppose the front is the boundary between a southward-moving, polar air mass and a slower-moving, tropical air mass. The polar air is colder and more dense than the tropical air. When they meet, the polar air slides under the warmer, lighter tropical air and forces the tropical air to rise. The shape that results is a wedge (Figure 29.5). The temperature and humidity changes across the front are not always sudden. The front can be a mixing zone ranging in thickness from as little as 200 meters to as much as 200 kilometers across.

Observations show that fronts have gentle slopes. The slope may range from 1 in 100 to 1 in 400. A slope of 1 in 100 means that the frontal surface rises 1 kilometer for every 100 kilometers of distance on the ground. Frontal surfaces may reach up to higher than 5 kilometers. As a result, fronts affect the weather in an area several hundred kilometers wide. Fronts may be several thousand kilometers in length.

Fronts almost always bring precipitation. At the frontal surface, warm air is rising high into the troposphere. Rising air means cooling, condensation, and then clouds and precipitation.

OBJECTIVES

A Define *front* and describe the shape of a front.

B Discuss the four kinds of fronts and explain their origin and structure.

C Trace the formation of a typical mid-latitude cyclone.

OF INTEREST

The term "front" was first used to describe the battle lines in World War I.

SCIENCE BACKGROUND

Some fronts divide air masses that differ only in moisture content. If the two air masses have the same temperature, the drier air is denser.

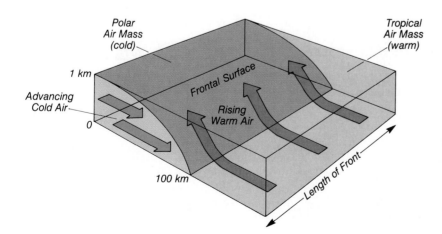

29.5 A front is a boundary between two air masses. At a front, the lighter (less dense) warm air is forced to rise over the heavier cold air. Note that the horizontal and vertical scales are very different. The slope of this front is 1 in 100.

29.6 A cold front passes through Colorado. Dust shows the cold air and the shape of the front. A very steep drop in temperature occurred after this front passed through. The frontal surface in the photo has a very steep slope, about 1 in 2.

SCIENCE BACKGROUND
In both cold and warm fronts, warm air is rising along the front.

29.7 Slopes of fronts near the ground. The cold front (a) has a much steeper frontal surface than the warm front (b). The blue and red arrows indicate the direction of movement of cold and warm air in each front.

Topic 7 **Kinds of Fronts**

There are four kinds of fronts. In a **cold front**, the cold air is advancing and displacing warmer air. The front in Figure 29.6 is a cold front. In a **warm front**, warm air is pushing ahead and displacing colder air. If neither air mass is being displaced, the front does not move. It is called a **stationary front**.

Cold fronts have steeper slopes than warm fronts, particularly in the lowest few kilometers. The slope is steepest near the ground. One of the most important reasons for this difference in slope is that the friction at the ground slows down the cold air, as shown in Figure 29.7. Warm fronts have more gentle slopes. Again, friction is important in keeping the slope shallow near the ground. The surface air, slowed down by friction, is left behind by the retreating cold air at higher levels. A warm frontal surface rises about 1 kilometer for every 400 kilometers.

Figure 29.8 shows the symbols used for fronts on weather maps. When a cold front overtakes a warm front, the result is called an **occluded front**. The solid triangles of the cold front and the solid half-circles of the warm front always point in the direction of the front's movement.

Fronts control the weather only at times when one air mass is displacing another. For a much longer time, the weather is air-mass weather. However, most precipitation comes with fronts.

Direction of Frontal Movement

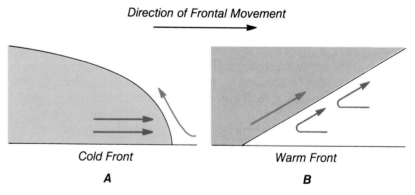

Cold Front
A

Warm Front
B

Topic 8 **How Mid-Latitude Lows Form**

The polar front, described in Chapter 28, is the boundary between cool air masses in the polar easterlies and warm air masses in the prevailing westerlies. Polar air masses lie to the north of the polar front. Tropical air masses lie to the south of it.

According to a theory first put forward in the 1920's, a low starts as a kink or wave in the polar front. Such a wave could be caused by a wave or kink in the jet stream. Also, a kink would develop in the polar front if a cold air mass began moving southward, pushing part of the polar front ahead of it as shown in Figure 29.9(b).

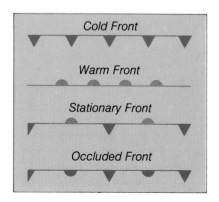

29.8 These are the international standard symbols for fronts.

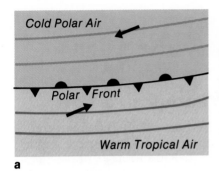

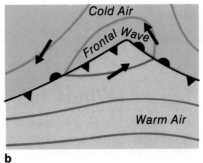

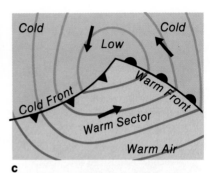

a
b
c

The wave moves from west to east, like a wave passing through a stage curtain shaken at one end. The wave ripples the polar front. The front bulges southward on the west side of the wave, where polar air pushes tropical air southward. This southward-moving portion of the polar front is a southward-moving cold front. On the east side of the wave, the polar front bulges northward as a warm front. Here, tropical air pushes the polar air northward.

Between the cold and warm fronts is a large amount of warm tropical air. The warm air bulges into and over the heavier polar air to form a region of low pressure. The lowest air pressure is at the crest of the wave, where the warm and cold fronts meet. A low, or **cyclone**, has formed. The isobars around a low are roughly oval or circular, with a slight bend at the fronts. Winds whirl about the center of the low in a counterclockwise direction in the Northern Hemisphere.

The whole system moves eastward, but the cold front moves more rapidly than the warm front. The front that forms when the cold front overtakes the warm front, shown in Figure 29.9(d), is called an occluded front. The occluded front lengthens until the low weakens and the two cold air masses mix across the occluded front.

In summary, a low forms from a wave in a polar front. However, lows can also form along other cold or stationary fronts. It takes only 12 to 24 hours to form a fully developed mid-latitude low. Once the occluded front forms, the low can last an additional three days or more.

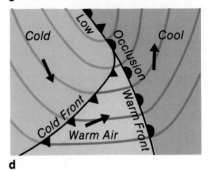

d

29.9   These four diagrams of the atmosphere at Earth's surface trace the origin and growth of a Northern Hemisphere low. The blue lines are isobars. The arrows are pointed the way the wind is blowing.

SCIENCE BACKGROUND

A cyclone is any counterclockwise movement of air, from a slight wind around a weak low to a tornado.

ANSWERS

6. (a) boundary between two unlike air masses   (b) cold air under warm air, frontal slope one in 100 to one in 400   (c) warm air forced to rise; expands, cools, and condenses

7. (a) Cold air displaces warm air in cold front; warm air displaces cold air in warm front; no movement in stationary front; cold front overtakes warm front in an occluded front (b) Cold fronts have steeper slopes. Friction slows down air in a front near the surface.

8. (a) A wave forms; cold air moves south to the west of the wave; warm air moves north to the east of the wave; cold front overtakes warm front, forming occluded front. Pressure falls the whole time, especially at the crest of the wave as warm air bulges into and over colder air. Occluded front lengthens until the low weakens.   (b) north-moving polar front is warm front; south-moving polar front is cold front

TOPIC QUESTIONS

Each topic question refers to the topic of the same number.

6. **(a)** What is a front?   **(b)** Describe the relative positions of the air masses at a front and give the slope of a typical front. **(c)** Why do fronts bring precipitation?

7. **(a)** Describe the four types of fronts.   **(b)** Compare the slopes of warm and cold fronts and explain why their slopes are different near the ground.

8. **(a)** Describe how a mid-latitude low forms on the polar front. **(b)** How is the polar front related to warm and cold fronts?

SCIENCE BACKGROUND
Condensation is not the major source of pressure lowering in mid-latitude lows. Arrival of warm air at upper levels and divergence at upper levels are more important.

OBJECTIVES

A Describe the winds and weather in a low, including the relationship between condensation and the strengthening of the low.

B List the sequence of clouds and weather associated with both warm and cold fronts.

C Summarize the typical winds and weather in a high.

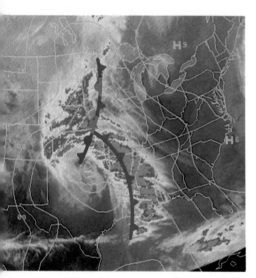

29.10 A strong low-pressure area with cold, stationary, and occluded fronts. Notice that the thick (white) clouds are mostly around the low and fronts. Heavy snows were falling in the Midwest at the time of this picture. The colored areas are probably the tops of precipitating clouds.

OF INTEREST
The prefix *nimbo* means "rain-filled."

III Weather Associated with Lows, Fronts, and Highs

Topic 9 Winds and Weather in a Low

In the Northern Hemisphere, the winds near the surface blow counterclockwise and toward the center of a low. The air converging into the low-pressure area rises, resulting in clouds and precipitation. The air also rises at the cold, warm, and occluded fronts, resulting in more clouds and precipitation. Notice the extensive cloudiness in the low shown in Figure 29.10.

The condensation that produces clouds and precipitation also releases heat energy. The air heated by this energy lowers the pressure at the surface, and the low becomes stronger. This increases the pressure gradient, and the winds also become stronger, particularly near the low center. If other factors do not weaken the low, it will continue to strengthen as long as condensation continues.

Figure 29.11 shows a vertical section through a typical low. The following weather changes occur when a low passes to the north of a locality in the Northern Hemisphere:

1. A long period of steady precipitation in advance of the warm front.
2. Warming and slow clearing after the warm front passes. If the air is humid, showery precipitation may occur, particularly nearer the center of the low.
3. Showery precipitation around the time the cold front passes.
4. Cooling and rapid clearing, with a change toward the weather characteristic of the newly arrived cold air mass.

Topic 10 Warm-Front Weather

A warm front affects the weather long before the arrival of the rains. As shown in Figure 29.11, high cirrus clouds appear first, followed by cirrostratus and lower and thicker stratiform clouds.

These clouds form in the air sliding up the frontal surface. The warm air may travel 1000 kilometers before rising 2 or 3 kilometers. The air is usually stable, so the rising air forms a vast system of stratiform clouds. The clouds may stretch 1500 kilometers ahead of the place where the warm front touches the ground.

Following the cirrus and cirrostratus are altostratus clouds, which almost screen out the sun and moon. Finally, the heavy nimbostratus clouds arrive, and steady rain or snow begins. This area of rain and snow can stretch hundreds of kilometers ahead of where the front touches the ground. Warming follows the passage of the front at the surface. Thunderstorms may form, but they are not typical of warm fronts. Stationary fronts have the same kind of weather as warm fronts.

Topic 11 **Cold-Front Weather**

Cold fronts are steeper and move faster than warm fronts. Thus, the air forced upward by the cold front rises quickly. Also, the air ahead of cold fronts is usually unstable. For these reasons, rapidly growing cumuliform clouds grow around the cold front. Precipitation falls from cumulonimbus clouds. Weather is showery, with heavy precipitation starting and ending quickly, and thunderstorms are common. Because of the cold front's steep slope, its precipitation covers at most 300 to 500 kilometers. The precipitation can occur both before and after a cold front passes at the surface.

When a cold front passes, sharp changes of weather occur. Temperatures fall fast as the cold air arrives. The wind rises in speed and may shift suddenly from a southerly direction to a northerly one. The rain usually ends shortly after the front passes.

Sometimes very humid mT air is being pushed forward ahead of a cold front. In such cases, a whole line of thunderstorms may form ahead of the front, creating a squall line that may be hundreds of kilometers long.

Topic 12 **Weather in a High**

Between the lows and their fronts lie areas of high pressure, or **anticyclones.** Highs usually appear on weather maps as a series of smooth circular isobars. Unlike a low, a high represents a single air mass. Its diameter may be more than 1500 kilometers. Since the air pressure is highest at its center, the winds in a high blow outward. The air moves in a clockwise direction in the Northern Hemisphere and counterclockwise in the Southern Hemisphere. Isobars are generally farther apart than in lows; therefore, the winds are weaker.

Bright, clear weather is usually present throughout a high because of the sinking dry air at its center. Small cumulus clouds may form over the heated ground during the day. At night, heavy dew, frost, and radiation fogs may form in the quiet lower air. Inversions can also form in the mornings, trapping pollution until the sun warms the ground.

TOPIC QUESTIONS

Each topic question refers to the topic of the same number.

9. Give the typical sequence of weather as a low passes to the north.

10. **(a)** List the sequence of clouds and weather that comes before and during the passing of a warm front at the surface.   **(b)** Why are the clouds along a warm front stratiform?

11. **(a)** Describe the clouds, precipitation, and weather changes that occur as a cold front passes.   **(b)** Why are the clouds along a cold front cumuliform?

12. What is the weather like in a high?

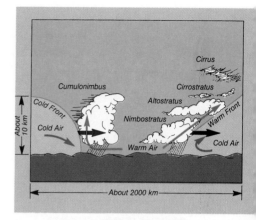

29.11 A cross section through the cold and warm fronts of a fully developed low. The large arrows show the direction of movement of the fronts; the red and blue arrows show the direction of movement of warm and cold air. Notice that the horizontal and vertical scales are very different.

29.12 Squall lines like this one occur ahead of cold fronts in spring and early summer.

ANSWERS

9. steady precipitation from warm front; warming and clearing, with possible showers; increasing precipitation with cold front, cooling after cold front

10. (a) cirrus, cirrostratus, altostratus, nimbostratus with steady precipitation (b) air is stable, goes up gradually

11. (a) cumulonimbus, showers and thunderstorms, stronger winds changing from southerly to northerly, temperatures fall after front passes (b) air unstable, forced upward rapidly

12. bright, clear weather

L A B
ACTIVITY

Evaporation and the Windchill Factor

On a hot summer day, getting wet can be a great way to cool off. But on a cold winter day, becoming wet can be a dangerously chilling experience. Part of the explanation for water's ability to cool is evaporation. When a liquid evaporates, it removes heat from the surrounding material. When the liquid is on your body, the process of evaporation removes your body heat and leaves you feeling cooler. Since the pores in your skin are always producing moisture, your body heat is continually drawn away as your perspiration evaporates.

Figure 29.13

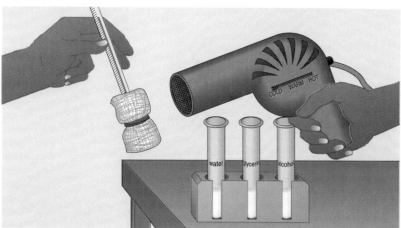

For additional activities, see
Laboratory Investigations booklet.

Moving air, or wind, is one important factor that affects the rate of evaporation. The term *windchill factor* is used to describe the relative discomfort a person feels as a result of the wind and the air temperature. When the wind blows against your skin, evaporation of your body moisture increases, causing rapid cooling of your skin. The result—you feel colder. In this activity, you will investigate the evaporation rates of different liquids and determine how the windchill factor affects the surroundings.

Lab Skills and Objectives
- To **observe** the effect of evaporation on temperature
- To **compare** the rates of evaporation of water, alcohol, and glycerin
- To **identify** the relationship between evaporation and windchill factor

Materials
- safety goggles
- lab apron
- 3 test tubes, 10 mm diameter
- test-tube rack
- wax marking pencil
- alcohol thermometer
- 3 pieces of cheesecloth or muslin, 10 cm × 10 cm
- 3 rubber bands
- water
- glycerin
- rubbing alcohol
- blow dryer with cool setting
- watch or clock with a second hand
- paper towels

Procedure
1. Put on your safety goggles and lab apron.
2. Place three test tubes in a rack. Use a marking pencil to label the test tubes, water, glycerin, and alcohol. Fill the first test tube with water to a depth of about 3 cm. Put 3 cm of glycerin in the second test tube and 3 cm of alcohol in the third test tube.
   CAUTION: Rubbing alcohol is flammable. Make sure there are no flames in the room before pouring alcohol from its container.
3. Allow the three test tubes to sit for about 5 minutes to make sure they reach room temperature. Record the room temperature in Data Table A.
4. Wrap a piece of cheesecloth around the bulb of the thermometer and fasten it with a rubber band. Dip the thermometer into the water and leave it for one minute to saturate the cheesecloth with water. Without removing the thermometer, read

Data Table A	
Initial Room Temperature	
Final Room Temperature	
Water Temperature, Air Drying One Minute	
Water Temperature, Air Drying Two Minutes	

Data Table B			
Liquid	Initial Temperature	Temperature after Blow Drying	
		One Minute	Two Minutes
water			
glycerin			
alcohol			

the initial temperature of the water and record it in Data Table B.

5. Remove the thermometer from the test tube and hold it still. Record the temperature in Data Table A after one minute and after two minutes of air drying.

6. Again dip the thermometer into the water. After a few minutes, remove the thermometer and hold it in front of a blow dryer that is set to the coolest setting. See Figure 29.13. Record the temperature in Data Table B after one minute and again after two minutes of blow drying. **CAUTION: Be sure your hands are dry before touching any part of the blow dryer, including the wire and switch.**

7. Remove the cheesecloth. Clean and dry the thermometer with a paper towel. Attach a new piece of cheesecloth to the thermometer and dip the thermometer into glycerin. After a minute, record the initial temperature of the glycerin in Data Table B.

8. Again hold the thermometer in front of a blow dryer that is set to the coolest setting. Record the temperature in Data Table B after one minute and after two minutes of blow drying.

9. Repeat steps 7 and 8 using alcohol. Record the temperature data.

10. Remove the cheesecloth. Clean and dry the thermometer. Read the final room temperature and record it in Data Table A.

11. Place a drop of water and a drop of rubbing alcohol on the back of your hand. Fan the drops gently and note the effect.

12. Answer the questions in *Analysis and Conclusions.*

Analysis and Conclusions

1. Compare your temperature results from air drying water and blow drying water. In which case was there a greater change in temperature between the first and second minute?

2. What effect did the air from the blow dryer have on the liquids and the thermometer bulb?

3. Why did the change in temperature differ during blow drying for the different liquids?

4. Which liquids had the most rapid and the least rapid evaporation rates?

5. Why was cloth fastened to the bulb of the thermometer?

6. Why was it important to record the room temperature at the beginning and the end of the experiment?

7. If the air in the room was saturated with water vapor, how would the temperatures of the three liquids be affected by blow drying? Explain your answer.

8. When you put a drop of water and a drop of alcohol on the back of your hand, which felt cooler? Why do you think people who have fevers are sponged with rubbing alcohol?

9. How does the wind cool you on a hot summer day?

10. What can a strong wind on a very cold day do to your exposed skin?

11. Explain why windchill is *not* a factor for a car left outside on a cold, windy night.

12. Given that evaporation removes heat from the surroundings, predict the effect that condensation will have on the surroundings. How does condensation affect the weather in a low-pressure system? (See Topic 9, page 550.)

Answers to all questions appear in the Teacher's Guide at the back of this book.

■ Summary

I Air masses are vast areas of air with the same temperature and humidity throughout. They form when air stays for a long time over one place (its source region).

Air masses are named for the climate of their source regions.

The weather in a moving air mass is determined by its humidity and whether its temperature is warmer or colder than the surface beneath.

Rawinsondes are used to measure the temperature, humidity, and wind through the depth of an air mass.

II Fronts are boundaries between unlike air masses. There are four kinds of fronts: cold, warm, stationary, and occluded.

A front is shaped like a wedge, with the less dense air on top of the more dense air.

Mid-latitude lows form along waves in the polar front.

III Rising air in lows brings condensation and precipitation. The condensation releases heat and lowers the pressure even more.

The sequence of clouds and precipitation when a low passes is determined by the location of the low center and the kinds of fronts that pass.

Clouds on a warm-frontal surface are mostly stratiform; clouds on a cold-frontal surface are cumuliform. Precipitation occurs near the surface fronts.

Sinking air in highs bring fair weather.

■ Vocabulary

air mass	cyclone
anticyclone	front
cold front	maritime polar (mP)
continental Arctic (cA)	maritime tropical (mT)
continental polar (cP)	occluded front
continental tropical (cT)	rawinsonde
	stationary front
	warm front

■ Review

Number your paper from 1 to 17. Match the terms in list **A** with the phrases in list **B**.

List A

1. mT
2. front
3. low-pressure area
4. cT
5. air mass
6. polar front
7. anticyclone
8. stable air
9. stationary front
10. cP
11. source region
12. warm front
13. cyclone
14. mP
15. rawinsonde
16. unstable air
17. cold front

List B

a. instrument used to measure weather characteristics high above the surface
b. cold, humid air mass
c. low-pressure area
d. place of origin of an air mass
e. characteristic typical of an air mass resting on a colder ground surface
f. quickly moving front with a steep slope
g. air mass that brings cooler, dry weather
h. characteristic typical of an air mass resting on a warmer ground surface
i. nearly stationary front along which lows form
j. section of the lower troposphere that has the same weather throughout
k. slowly moving front with a gentle slope
l. warm, humid air mass
m. boundary between two air masses
n. high-pressure area

For further review, see **Study Guide.**
For assessment, see **Chapter Tests**
and **Computer Test Bank.**

o. air mass that brings hot, dry weather
p. area where air converges, resulting in clouds
and precipitation
q. a front that does not move

■ Interpret and Apply

On your paper, answer each question in complete
sentences.

1. Why should heavy frosts, dew, and fogs be
associated with highs?
2. In what directions would polar and tropical
air masses move in the Southern Hemisphere?
3. Why does the rawinsonde balloon burst at
very high altitudes? What determines how
high it goes before bursting?
4. In the continental United States, warm and
cold fronts are usually weakest in the summer months. Why is this so?
5. What kind of air-mass weather is likely to follow the passing of a warm front? Of a cold
front?
6. How does the slope of a front affect the type of
clouds associated with it?
7. Maritime polar air masses are moist, but not
as moist as maritime tropical air masses.
What accounts for this difference in moisture?
8. How does an occluded front form?
9. A wintertime continental Arctic air mass
starts out very stable. Explain.
10. Describe the changes in the air mass and its
weather under each of the following circumstances.   (a) In the winter, a continental polar
air mass moves out over the ocean.   (b) In the
winter, a maritime polar air mass crosses the
Rocky Mountains.
11. Describe the front and its associated weather
under each of the following circumstances.
(a) A continental tropical air mass overtakes a
maritime tropical air mass of the same temperature.   (b) A continental polar air mass
overtakes a continental tropical air mass.

■ Critical Thinking

The weather map below shows two lows and two
highs. The arrows indicate wind direction.

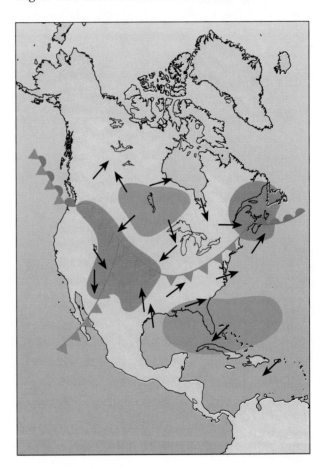

1. How many kinds of fronts are shown on the
map?
2. (a) Which color represents areas of low pressure? (b) Which color represents areas of
high pressure?   (c) What is the evidence for
your answers to   (a) and (b)?
3. Is this most likely a winter or a summer
weather map? How can you tell?
4. What were the probable weather conditions
along the northwestern coast at the time of
this weather map?

555

Storms and Weather Forecasts

▲
A tornado is a small but violent storm with winds up to 500 kilometers per hour.

How Do You Know That . . .

You may be in the path of an approaching tornado? Suppose the weather is hot and humid. However, last night's weather broadcast promised that a fast-moving cold front would bring cooler weather within 48 hours. Off in the distance, in the direction from which the front is moving to your area, you see dark clouds approaching rapidly. The sky looks murky and forbidding. You turn on the radio and hear that a tornado warning has been issued for your area.

Meteorologists use a number of tools to help them forecast and keep track of severe weather. Improved forecasting can help to save lives when a severe storm, such as a tornado, is likely.

I Thunderstorms and Tornadoes

Topic 1 How Thunderstorms Form

Each day about 44 000 thunderstorms occur across Earth's surface. *Thunderstorms* are small-area storms formed by the strong upward movement of warm, unstable, moist air. They are formed of cumulonimbus clouds, are always accompanied by lightning and thunder, and usually produce rain. Strong thunderstorms produce high winds, hail, and even tornadoes. Single thunderstorms are 10–20 kilometers across and commonly are 10–15 kilometers deep.

Thunderstorms fall into two groups: local or **air-mass thunderstorms,** and organized or **frontal thunderstorms.**

Air-mass thunderstorms form within a warm, moist air mass. They start when the surface is strongly heated. Often single storms, they occur mostly in spring or summer and usually last less than an hour. Air-mass thunderstorms are widely scattered and form mostly over land. No one can yet predict exactly where an air-mass thunderstorm will form. Some form over mountains, perhaps started by the rising valley breeze, but others form almost anywhere over flat land or water.

Frontal thunderstorms usually form in warm, moist air on or ahead of cold fronts. Some thunderstorms, however, occur around warm fronts. Frontal thunderstorms often occur in lines along the frontal surface. They also occur in lines ahead of the front, called *squall lines.* The lines of thunderstorms can be hundreds of kilometers long. Slowly moving fronts or squall lines can produce heavy rains and flooding. Frontal thunderstorms occur most often in spring and summer. They are often stronger than air-mass thunderstorms and may last for several hours.

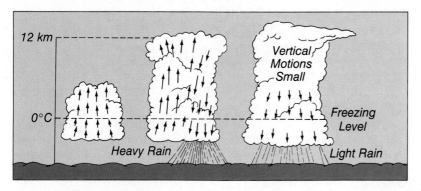

OBJECTIVES

A Compare the types of thunderstorms and show how and where they form.

B Describe and explain lightning and thunder, and list places that are safe during lightning storms.

C Describe tornadoes and severe thunderstorms and list the conditions that produce them.

D Differentiate between watches and warnings issued for severe thunderstorms and tornadoes.

VIDEODISC SELECTION

Development of a thunderstorm
Side 1 movie: 26519 & PLAY

SCIENCE BACKGROUND

Thunderstorms forming over mountains are categorized as air-mass thunderstorms. However, these thunderstorms are not random they have a stationary nature.

VIDEODISC SELECTION

Cumulonimbus thunderstorm cloud
Side 1: 843, single frame

30.1 (left) An air-mass thunderstorm starts when heating of the ground causes vertical motions. (center) The weight of the falling rain and cooling by evaporation cause a downdraft to begin. (right) The downdraft spreads, choking off the vertical motions. The cloud dies.

30.2 Spectacular lightning displays may be seen during a thunderstorm.

SCIENCE BACKGROUND

The reason for the buildup of electrical charge within a cloud is not fully understood. The temperature of lightning is hotter than the temperature of the sun's surface.

SCIENCE BACKGROUND

Lightning is a source of atmospheric nitrous oxide.

VIDEODISC SELECTION

Photo of lightning
Side 1: 876, single frame

Lightning Safety Tips

1. *Go indoors, if possible. If you are traveling, stay in your car.*
2. *Stay off bicycles, motorcycles, scooters, golf carts, or farm equipment.*
3. *If you are swimming, get out of the water. Get off small boats.*
4. *Avoid standing near or being the highest object in an area. Outdoors, the best protection is in a cave, ditch, or canyon. If you are out in the open with only isolated trees nearby, crouch in the open as far away from the trees as possible.*
5. *Indoors, stay away from open doors and windows and metal objects such as pipes, sinks, stoves, and radiators. Do not use the telephone or plug–in appliances.*
6. *If you feel lightning is about to strike — your hair stands on end or your skin tingles — drop to your knees and bend forward with your hands on your knees.*

Topic 2   Electricity in a Thunderstorm

All thunderstorms produce lightning. Lightning is a discharge of electricity from a thundercloud to the ground, to another cloud, or from the ground to a cloud.

The temperature inside a channel of a lightning flash is believed to reach about 28 000°C. At this high temperature, the air expands explosively. This sudden expansion makes the tremendous sound wave called thunder. Light travels at 300 000 kilometers a second, so lightning is seen almost instantly. The sound waves from lightning, however, take 3 seconds to travel a kilometer, so you hear the sound of thunder after seeing a lightning flash.

Lightning strokes are often very long, so that some parts are close and some farther away. In this case, the sound is spread out in time, and the thunder rumbles. Rumbling also happens when thunder echoes from mountainsides. The greatest distance at which it is ordinarily possible for thunder to be heard is about 16 kilometers. Heat lightning is the glow of lightning so far away that its thunder cannot be heard.

Topic 3   Lightning Danger and Protection

Lightning can be very dangerous. Every year in the United States lightning causes thousands of forest fires and electrocutes about 200 people.

When lightning strikes, it is likely to go from the cloud base to the highest point projecting above the ground. It often strikes tall objects, such as trees, church steeples, and the tops of skyscrapers. Lightning rods are based on this fact. They project above the roofs of houses and are connected to the ground by a good conductor, such as a metal wire. When lightning strikes the rod, the electricity is conducted to the ground. Otherwise it might strike some part of the house and set the house on fire.

Where should one take shelter in a lightning storm? The best shelter is inside a building. Stay away from televisions, telephones, sinks, and bathrooms, since the electrical wiring and metal pipes of your house can conduct electricity. Cars are also very safe. Bathers and boaters should seek shelter as soon as a storm develops. A tree or small group of trees in an open field should be avoided. They attract lightning. If you are out in the open during a lightning storm, crouch on the ground.

Topic 4   Tornadoes

Tornadoes are much more frequent in the United States than anywhere else in the world. Most tornadoes in the United States occur in the Mississippi River valley and the Great Plains. The conditions that produce strong thunderstorms often also produce tornadoes. Warm, moist air from the Gulf of Mexico moves northward into the Mississippi River valley and the Great Plains. This air extends from the surface up to 3 kilometers deep. Higher up, cool air moves eastward over the Rocky Mountains. So the air is moist at lower levels. It is also very unstable, with the temperature falling rapidly with height through a deep layer. A cold front approaches. This is ideal for producing thunderstorms. Strong wind increasing with height helps to make the thunderstorms stronger.

A **tornado** is a narrow, funnel-shaped column of spiral winds that extends downward from the cloud base and touches the ground. The strengths of tornadoes vary greatly. The strongest winds in a tornado are between 360 and 500 kilometers an hour. The funnel is usually less than 500 meters across at the ground. A tornado travels with its parent thunderstorm, at speeds ranging from 40 to 65 kilometers an hour. Tornado paths are somewhat irregular and usually less than 25 kilometers long. They pass in a few seconds with a thunderous roar. Tornadoes usually last no more than an hour and are accompanied by heavy rain, lightning, and hail.

The tornado funnel is a mixture of cloud and dust. The pressure gets lower closer to the center of the tornado. As air flows toward the funnel, it expands from the lower pressure and cools. When the air cools to its dew point, tiny water drops form. Clouds form in exactly the same way when rising air reaches the condensation level. The low pressure in a tornado causes the condensation level to dip downward, forming the funnel of clouds. Sometimes the dust picked up by the tornado forms a separate funnel surrounding the condensation funnel.

Tornadoes over water are called **waterspouts.** Waterspouts are usually weaker than tornadoes. They occur with weak thunderstorms and even large cumulus clouds.

30.3   A tornado at the bottom of a thunderstorm cloud

VIDEODISC SELECTION

North American tornadoes
Side 1 movie: 32189 & PLAY

Tornado Safety Tips

1. *If you live in an area frequented by tornadoes, plan safety rules for your family. Choose the best tornado shelter area in your home and make sure everyone knows where it is. Keep a battery–powered radio that you can use in the event of an emergency. Watch any thunderstorm clouds for signs of a funnel, and know how to reach the local authorities if you spot one. Practice tornado drills.*

2. *In the event of a tornado, stay away from outside walls, windows, and doors. At home, go to the basement or an interior room on the lowest level. If possible, get under a heavy table or mattress.*

3. *In a public place, go to the designated shelter area or sit close to an interior wall on the lowest level.*

4. *Get away from mobile homes or vehicles if possible; find more substantial shelter.*

5. *If you are outdoors in an open area, look for a ravine or ditch. Lie flat and protect your head with your arms.*

30.4 Radar view of a severe thunderstorm. The inner colors indicate the largest or heaviest precipitation. The heavy precipitation is drawn into two hook shapes; these "hook echoes" indicate possible tornadoes. The existence of a tornado must be confirmed by spotter reports or winds from the Doppler radar. (The curved lines are 40 km apart.)

ANSWERS

1. (a) small-area storm with lightning, thunder, and usually rain, formed by upward movement of warm, moist air   (b) air-mass: formed by heating of ground, isolated, last less than an hour; frontal; often organized in lines that last several hours, around fronts, stronger

2. (a) electrical discharge from a thundercloud   (b) caused by "slow" speed of sound, different distances of lightning stroke, and (sometimes) echoing from nearby mountains

3. (a) highest place   (b) lightning rod is highest object; connecting wire conducts lightning to ground   (c) inside a building (away from television, sinks, and bathrooms), cars

4. (a) warm, moist Gulf air flows under cool dry air from over Rockies; strong winds increase with height   (b) funnel-shaped, diameter up to 500 meters at bottom, path usually less than 25 kilometers, travel 40–65 km/hour, winds up to 360–500 km/hour   (c) dust and cloud   (d) United States, in Mississippi River valley and Great Plains

5. (a) thunderstorm with wind gusts at least 80 km/h, 2-cm-diameter hail   (b) gives times and area where severe storms are possible; covers 100 to 200 km or greater

Topic 5 Severe Weather Watches and Warnings

When conditions favor the formation of severe thunderstorms or tornadoes, the National Severe Stroms Forecast Center in Kansas City, Missouri, issues watches. A **severe thunderstorm** has wind gusts at least 80 kilometers per hour, hail about 2 centimeters in diameter or greater, or the presence of a funnel cloud or tornado.

Local weather stations issue severe thunderstorm or tornado warnings whenever necessary. Watches and warnings are broadcast over radio and television. Watches and warnings are also given for flash floods.

A *watch* covers an area of 100 kilometers by 200 kilometers or larger. It gives the time during which severe thunderstorms and tornadoes are possible.

A *warning* is issued when a tornado or severe thunderstorm has actually been sighted or detected on radar. It gives the location of the storm when detected, the area into which it is likely to move, and the period of time during which the storm could hit.

Tornadoes and severe thunderstorms are most frequent during spring and summer and are most likely to occur in the late afternoon. The worst tornado ever recorded was the Tri-State tornado which killed 689 people in Missouri, Illinois, and Indiana in 1925. From 1975–1979, tornadoes in the United States killed an average of 54 persons yearly. Fewer people have been killed by tornadoes in recent years because of improved warnings.

TOPIC QUESTIONS

Each topic question refers to the topic of the same number.

1. **(a)** What is a thunderstorm?   **(b)** How are air-mass and frontal thunderstorms different?

2. **(a)** What is lightning?   **(b)** What causes the rolling sound of thunder.

3. **(a)** Where does lightning tend to strike?   **(b)** Explain how a lightning rod works.   **(c)** List the safest places to be during a lightning storm.

4. **(a)** What conditions favor strong thunderstorms and tornadoes?   **(b)** Describe a tornado, giving its shape, diameter, path length, speed of travel, and maximum winds.   **(c)** What is the funnel made of?   **(d)** Where do tornadoes most commonly occur?

5. **(a)** What is a severe thunderstorm?   **(b)** What is a severe thunderstorm watch?   **(c)** When are warnings given?

(c) when a severe thunderstorm or tornado is sighted or detected on radar

II Cyclonic Storms

Topic 6 Hurricanes

People living along the Gulf and Atlantic coasts pay careful attention to weather reports of hurricanes. A **hurricane** is an intense tropical low-pressure area with sustained winds of 120 kilometers per hour or greater. The strong winds and heavy rains produce major damage.

The greatest damage associated with hurricanes is caused by currents called **storm surges.** A storm surge forms when the hurricane piles up water along the shore and then blows it inland. Storm surges are much more damaging during high tide. In May 1991, a tropical cyclone produced a 20-foot storm surge in Bangladesh. It caused 139 000 deaths and left 9 million homeless.

Hurricanes are in some ways like mid-latitude cyclones. They both are low-pressure areas. Winds spiral toward their centers in the same general patterns. As a rule both have areas of heavy precipitation, and both grow larger and more powerful from the vast amounts of energy released in them by condensing water vapor.

In other ways, though, hurricanes are different from mid-latitude lows. A low forms and grows along fronts and gets energy from the air-mass contrast across the fronts. A hurricane has no fronts. Unlike the mid-latitude low, it has a central area of sinking air, known as the **eye** of the storm. The eye is usually 15 to 50 kilometers in diameter. The only clouds in the eye are stratocumulus at low levels and, sometimes, some cirrus at high levels. Because the air in the eye is sinking, there is no rain. There is almost no wind. The eye is surrounded by intense thunderstorms called the *eye wall.* Hurricanes have average diameters of 300 to 600 kilometers, smaller than a mid-latitude low. Finally, hurricanes are by definition intense. Their central pressures are lower and their wind speeds are larger than those of typical mid-latitude lows.

The winds increase toward the center of the hurricane and are most violent just outside the eye. Here, wind speeds may be greater than 240 kilometers an hour. The area of destructive winds may be as large as 800 kilometers across and 1600 kilometers long. Tornadoes and severe thunderstorms often occur as hurricanes come ashore. Like the wind, the rainfall increases toward the center of the storm. It is heaviest just outside the eye.

In 1992, the eye of Hurricane Andrew crossed Florida south of Miami. Sustained winds of over 225 kilometer's cut a 45-kilometer swathe of destruction across South Florida. The storm splintered houses, toppled trees, and flattened cars as shown in Figure 30.7. Andrew's storm surge reached 17 feet near Florida. Andrew then crossed the Gulf of Mexico and hit Louisiana. Over 100 000 people were left homeless. Timely hurricane warnings and the evacuation of residents kept the number of deaths to less than 40.

OBJECTIVES

A Describe hurricanes and their life cycle.

B Explain how hurricanes produce their damage.

C Show how the Weather Service tracks hurricanes and differentiate between hurricane watches and warnings.

D Specify the conditions necessary to produce a heavy snowfall.

OF INTEREST

The world record for a 24-hour rainfall is 46 inches during a tropical cyclone in the Philippines in 1911.

30.5 The 1985 hurricane Elena, photographed from the space shuttle. Notice the cloud spiraling around the eye at the center.

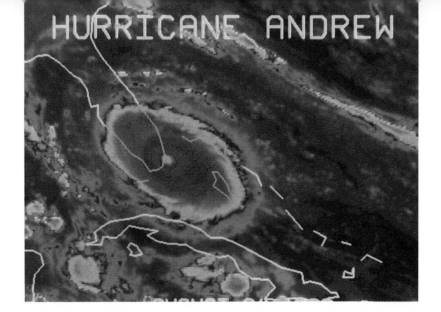

HURRICANE ANDREW

30.6 Radar image of Hurricane Andrew as it approached South Florida.

VIDEODISC SELECTION

Hurricanes
Side 1 movie: 29428 & PLAY

HURRICANE SAFETY TIPS

1. ***When a Hurricane Watch Is Issued.*** *Stay tuned to radio, TV, or NOAA Weather Radio. Secure your home—check mobile home tie-downs; tape, board, or shutter windows; wedge sliding doors shut; bring lawn furniture and other loose items inside; check batteries in radio and flashlights; stock up on canned food and medicines. Moor small boats or put them in a shelter.*

2. ***When a Hurricane Warning Is Issued.*** *Stay tuned to radio, TV, or NOAA Weather Radio.*

   ■ *In case of evacuation or if you live in a mobile home: Leave as early as possible for nearest designated shelter. Shut off water and electricity, leave food and water for pets (shelters will not take them).*

   ■ *If evacuation is not recommended and house is sturdy and on high ground: Board up garage and porch doors; fill containers (bathtubs) with several days supply of drinking water; turn up refrigerator to coldest setting, and don't open it unless necessary. Use phone only for emergencies.*

3. ***When the Hurricane Hits.*** *Stay indoors, away from windows.*

4. ***After the Storm.*** *Watch for downed electrical wires, unsafe roads, flooded areas. Report damaged water, sewer, or electrical lines. Use caution when entering a building. Check for gas leaks.*

Topic 7 **Sources and Tracks of Tropical Storms**

Tropical storms form from tropical lows along the intertropical convergence zone (ITCZ). They get their energy from the heat and water vapor from the sea surface and from the release of heat by condensing water vapor. The strengthening storms usually move westward at about 10 to 20 kilometers an hour. If they move northward through the horse latitudes into the westerlies, they begin to travel eastward. Here, the hurricanes, also known as *Tropical Cyclones* and *Typhoons,* speed up and usually weaken as they encounter colder water. Cooler water supplies the storm with less heat and moisture. Also, cumulonimbus clouds do not grow as deep over cooler surfaces. Hurricanes also weaken when they move over land.

Many of the Atlantic hurricanes that affect the United States start as lows as far away as West Africa. The lows grow into hurricanes when they reach the warm waters of the western Atlantic, the Caribbean, or the Gulf of Mexico.

Before the days of satellites, North America's Pacific hurricanes were thought to be rare. However, eastern Pacific hurricanes are actually more common than the Atlantic ones. Pacific hurricanes form to the west of Mexico and mostly move westward. Occasionally they move as far north as California or as far west as Hawaii, as Hurricane Iniki did in 1992.

Hurricanes are most common in the late summer and early fall in the northern hemisphere because the ITCZ is farther north and the sea surface temperatures are warm. Tropical cyclones are most common in the winter and early spring in the southern hemisphere.

Topic 8 **Naming and Forecasting Hurricanes**

Before 1953, hurricanes were identified only by their dates. From 1953 to 1979, hurricanes were identified by giving them female

30.7 Widespread damage from Hurricane Andrew in South Florida.

names. In 1979, however, the National Weather Service began the present practice of using male names too. Two sets of six lists were prepared—one set for Atlantic hurricanes and the other for eastern Pacific hurricanes. Each set was to be used for six years from 1979–1984 and then repeated in each six-year cycle thereafter. If a particular hurricane is an exceptional one, its name will be retired and a new name substituted. Names are arranged alphabetically, with male and female names alternating. A storm is named once it reaches tropical storm status (sustained winds of 65 kilometers per hour or greater).

Early hurricane forecasts are important in protecting life and property. Several techniques are used to keep close watch on each hurricane and tropical storm as it grows and moves. Weather satellites are used to track hurricanes and estimate their strength and to spot new storms. Weather reconnaissance aircraft fly through hurricanes for direct measurements of storm strength. Also, when the hurricane is within a few hundred kilometers of a radar, the radar can be used to watch the hurricane.

Hurricane watches and warnings are issued by the National Hurricane Center in Miami, Florida. A warning means that hurricane conditions are expected within 24 hours. A 24-hour warning allows communities in the path of the hurricane to take precautions against potential damage from strong winds and floods.

Evacuation of areas threatened by major hurricanes has kept the number of deaths low. However, meteorologists think this is partially luck. The population has increased so much in some beachfront areas that it is nearly impossible to evacuate everyone in time to avoid a major storm.

VIDEODISC SELECTION

Aerial photos of hurricane Allen
Side 1: 935 to 940, 6-frame sequence

Close-up of hurricane Allen crossing the Yucatan peninsula
Side 1: 941 to 947, 7-frame sequence

30.8 A major snowstorm creates work for many people.

ANSWERS

6. (a) intense low with winds at least 120 km/hr; damage caused by storm surge, rain, wind   (b) alike: lows with similar circular wind patterns, heavy precipitation, condensation as source of energy; different: mid-latitude lows have fronts, air-mass contrast a source of energy; hurricane has no fronts, has eye, is smaller and stronger

7. (a) along ITCZ, as lows; get energy from heat and moisture at sea surface and from condensation aloft   (b) forms off Africa, moves west at 10–20 km/hr across Atlantic as a low, strengthens in warm waters near North America, moves northward into horse latitudes, moves eastward, speeds up in westerlies, contacts cooler water and loses energy   (c) late summer to early fall; sea is warm, ITCZ is farther north

8. (a) with satellites, reconnaissance aircraft, radar (near coast)   (b) hurricane watch: hurricane conditions possible; warning: hurricane expected within 24 hours

9. low-pressure area nearby, enough moisture, temperature in the right range

Topic 9   Winter Storms

Strong mid-latitude lows bring the winter's major snowstorms. However, two conditions must be met. First, there must be enough moisture. Second, the temperature must be cold enough for snow.

Mid-latitude lows are strongest in winter along the east coast, and strongest in spring over the continental United States. Lows form and grow along the polar front. Strong lows form when the polar front is strong. The polar front is the strongest when the contrast between air masses is strongest.

Strong mid-latitude lows have minimum pressures around 980 millibars, with some stronger lows having pressures as low as 940 millibars. Since wintertime highs are also stronger, large pressure gradients and strong winds result.

A snowstorm with high winds and low temperatures is called a **blizzard.** The National Weather Service issues winter storm watches and warnings. The definition of winter storm varies with location.

The moisture supply for winter storms differs in different parts of the country. In the midwestern United States, much of the moisture comes from the Gulf of Mexico. To the west, on the Great Plains, water vapor from earlier snowfalls becomes more important. On the East Coast, there is ample moisture over the Atlantic. The West Coast storms are fed by moist air from the Pacific. In the winter, mountains get deep snows as moist air is forced upward on their windward sides.

A temperature difference of a few degrees can be the difference between heavy snow, mixed rain and snow, freezing rain, or rain. For this reason, predicting the amount and type of precipitation expected with a storm is difficult.

TOPIC QUESTIONS

Each topic question refers to the topic of the same number.

6. **(a)** What is a hurricane? How does it cause damage?   **(b)** How are hurricanes and mid-latitude lows alike? How are hurricanes and mid-latitude lows different?

7. **(a)** Where and how do tropical storms form?   **(b)** Describe the path of a hurricane, from its origin as a low-pressure area to its death.   **(c)** When is the best time for Atlantic hurricanes to form? Why?

8. **(a)** How do meteorologists trace the path and strength of a hurricane?   **(b)** What is the difference between a hurricane watch and a hurricane warning?

9. List the conditions necessary to produce a heavy snowfall.

III   Forecasting and Weather Maps

Topic 10   Weather Forecasts in the United States

Daily weather forecasts are based on recent weather maps and the results of computer models of the atmosphere. These computer models use data collected at the surface and data transmitted from the upper atmosphere by rawinsondes. The data are collected around the world at midnight and noon, Universal Time Coordinated (7:00 P.M. and 7:00 A.M. EST). Other data are provided by satellites and commercial aircraft. The models are run at the National Meteorological Center in Camp Springs, Maryland.

Once the data are collected, it takes about an hour to put the data in a form usable by the computer and another hour to run the models. Among the results of these models are maps showing highs, lows, and fronts in 12, 24, 36, and 48 hours. Maps are made for the surface and higher levels. Also produced are maps of model-predicted precipitation probabilities and amounts, high and low temperatures, and other aids to the forecaster. Using these data, forecasts are made at Weather Service Forecast Offices around the country. These forecasts are modified to allow for local conditions.

Major computer model forecasts are produced twice a day, co-inciding with the collection of surface and upper-air data. Weather Service Forecast Offices routinely issue forecasts four times a day at around 10 A.M., 4 P.M., 9 P.M., and 4 A.M., local time. The afternoon and evening forecasts are timed to give television stations the latest information for their evening broadcasts. Forecasts are updated more often during rapid and important weather changes, such as the approach of a snowstorm or other type of severe weather.

Topic 11   Forecasting with Computers

Computer models are very important in making the daily forecasts. Computer models are now better than human forecasters at predicting the movements and strengths of highs and lows. However, human forecasters are still needed to adjust the computer models, and to forecast the weather events that come with the highs and lows.

What is a computer model? A **computer model** is a copy of the atmosphere in the computer. It contains data on the wind, temperature, pressure, humidity, clouds, and precipitation. Like most copies, the model lacks the detail of the original. In global forecast models, data are spaced at height intervals of about 1 kilometer. Horizontal spacing is about 100 kilometers. Thus, each point stands for $100 \times 100 \times 1$-kilometer block of air.

OBJECTIVES

A Explain how computer models, weather maps, satellites, and radars are used in watching and forecasting the weather.

B Describe how weather maps are made.

SCIENCE BACKGROUND

By the mid 1970's, 48-hour computer forecasts of winds and pressures aloft were as good as the 24-hour computer forecasts of the 1950's.

SCIENCE BACKGROUND

Researchers use computer models to study squall lines, thunderstorms, tornadoes, climate, ocean currents, and many other phenomena.

The model predicts future weather patterns. For example, at each point pressure changes from all possible causes are added up to make a total predicted pressure change. This change is added on to the old pressure to make a new, updated pressure. In the same way, other quantities, such as wind, are updated. This updating is done for each 5–10 minutes of "model time" in forecasting models. Standard forecasting models are used to make predictions from 12 hours to 10 days.

The models are not perfect for many reasons. First, the equations that predict the changes in each quantity are not perfect. Second, there are few measurements over the oceans and other areas where people do not live. Finally, the points in the model are too far apart to catch all the weather changes. For example, a thunderstorm affects the atmosphere in a fairly small area, so it can be missed easily with data spaced at points 100 kilometers apart.

Topic 12 Satellites and Radar in Weather Forecasting

Much of the weather missed by computer models and local weather observations is observed by satellites and radar. Satellites are used more and more to fill in data-poor regions in the models. Scientists are learning to obtain temperature and humidity measurements through much of the atmosphere by measuring the air's infrared radiation from satellite and ground stations.

Satellites provide continuous pictures of the clouds. These pictures make it possible to track lows, hurricanes, and even thunderstorms. Satellites are especially valuable over the ocean, where weather observations are difficult to make by other methods.

If a satellite is placed in an orbit 35 850 kilometers above the equator, its revolution will keep time with Earth's rotation. The satellite will be over the same spot at all times. Such a satellite is said to be *geostationary*, meaning "stationary with respect to Earth." Normally the United States has two such satellites in orbit, GOES-East and GOES-West. (GOES stands for "Geostationary Operational Environmental Satellite.") They are positioned to get

VIDEODISC SELECTION

Diagram of GOES satellite
Side 1: 887, single frame

Photos from GOES 4 and 5
Side 1: 924 to 933, 10-frame
sequence

30.9 The widely spaced points or grid used in a forecast model

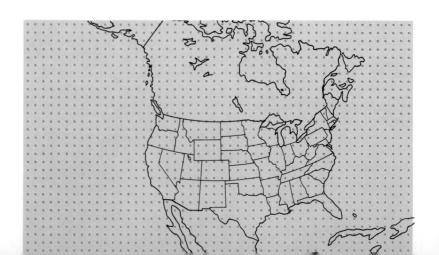

good pictures of all 50 states. Each satellite can see nearly half of Earth's surface. Every 30 minutes, its television cameras take infrared as well as visible pictures. The use of infrared photography allows good pictures to be taken 24 hours a day. Animations from these satellites are used on television weather broadcasts.

How is radar used in observing the weather? Radar waves are reflected from precipitation particles. The radar screen shows the location of the precipitation and therefore the shape of precipitation areas. Heavier precipitation or larger particles show up as more intense radar returns, or "echoes." Thus radar can "see" thunderstorms, hurricanes, and other areas of precipitation. It also gives a rough idea of how heavy the precipitation is. Hurricane-penetrating aircraft use radar to locate the eye.

Currently the Weather Service is installing new Doppler radars around the country. These new radars show echoes with more detail than before. They will also show the wind toward or away from the radar. How is this possible? Radar waves reflected from particles moving *toward* the radar have shorter wavelengths than radar waves reflected from particles moving *away from* the radar. In the same way, the sound of an approaching train whistle has a higher pitch (shorter-wavelength sound waves) than the sound of a train whistle going away. This effect is called the *Doppler effect,* after its discoverer, Johann Doppler.

The radar echoes and winds show up on a color screen. Different echo strengths or wind speeds show up as different colors. The different colors make it easier for the forecaster to spot strong thunderstorms and even tornadoes. Tests of these radars in Oklahoma show that the warning time for tornadoes is increased from around 2 minutes to 20 minutes. They will detect storms as far away as 460 kilometers and winds as far as 230 kilometers.

Topic 13   **Making a Surface Weather Map**

Surface weather maps are essential in following rapidly changing weather or in compensating for poor forecasts from computer models. The data for surface maps are taken hourly at stations all over the world. In the United States alone, surface data are gathered from about 700 National Weather Service Stations.

Official United States weather maps are drawn up every three hours, starting at 1:00 A.M. eastern standard time. After the station reports have been plotted, isobars and fronts are drawn in. Satellite cloud pictures help in finding the fronts and low centers over the ocean. Radar reports are used to add squall lines.

The official maps are made at the National Meteorological Center in Camp Springs, Maryland. They are sent by wire to all forecast centers and by radio or satellite to ships at sea. These maps are available to the public. University meteorology departments and private forecasters often receive the three-hour maps.

Hourly weather information is also transmitted. With this information, local forecast offices, private forecasters, and others watching the weather can prepare more current maps when needed.

SCIENCE BACKGROUND
  Scientists are now working on ways to detect hail on radar.

TEACHING TIP
  Relate Doppler radar to the red shift discussed in Chapter 20.

VIDEODISC SELECTION

Nimbus satellite images
Side 1: 902 to 922, 21-frame sequence

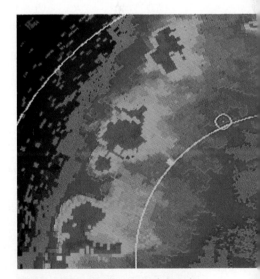

30.10 This is how a line of thunderstorms, or a squall line, appears on radar. From the outside toward the center, the different colors show the strength of the radar echo. Stronger echoes mean higher rainfall or bigger particles, and usually stronger vertical motions.

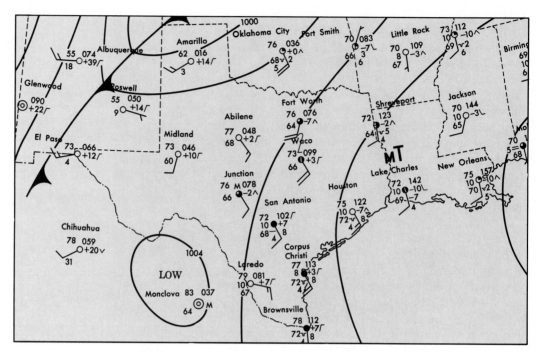

30.11 This is a portion of a printed National Weather Service surface map.

OF INTEREST

Facsimile machines receive weather maps as signals burned on specially treated paper. Weather maps are also available on computer networks.

30.12 A station model. Review symbols for cloud cover, wind direction and speed, and precipitation.

Topic 14 The Station Model

About 20 different weather observations may be plotted next to each station on a weather map. The National Weather Service arranges this information around the station in a form called the **station model.** Where possible, direct readings are given. In all other cases, codes are used. Both station model and codes are based on those of the World Meteorological Organization. They can be read by meteorologists of any country. The coded information can be sent by wire, radio, or over computer networks.

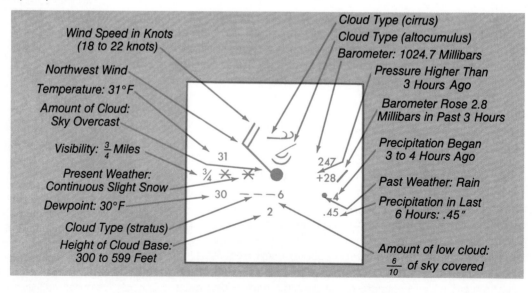

TOPIC QUESTIONS

Each topic question refers to the topic of the same number.

10. Describe how daily weather forecasts are made in the United States.

11. (a) How does a computer model "copy" the atmosphere?   **(b)** List some of the shortcomings of computer models.

12. (a) Why are radar and satellites important in observing the weather?   **(b)** What do satellites observe?   **(c)** What do the new Weather Service Doppler radars observe?

13. Describe how official surface weather maps are prepared in the United States.

14. What is a station model?

Map Skills

The following questions refer to the sequence of weather maps on pages 662–663 of Appendix B.

1. How did the skies over San Antonio change from January 29 to January 30?

2. Where was it snowing on January 31?

3. How many cold fronts are on the map for January 28?

ANSWERS

10. data collected around the world twice a day used in computer models that guide forecasters; forecasts made four times a day

11. (a) contains weather data across Earth at several depths; predicts weather changes   **(b)** equations not perfect, too little data, data points too far apart

12. (a) They observe weather missed by models and by local observations.   **(b)** temperatures, humidities, winds, cloud patterns **(c)** precipitation areas of storms plus associated winds

13. drawn every 3 hours; data plotted from surface observations at 700 stations; isobars drawn; satellite data used in drawing in fronts and locating low centers; squall lines drawn in from radar

14. coded weather information plotted around a circle

ANSWERS

1. changed from overcast to clear
2. eastern U.S. and Canada; Canada north of the Great Lakes
3. two

CAREERS

Dr. Charles E. Anderson
Severe Storm Analyst

Can tornadoes be predicted? Dr. Charles E. Anderson of North Carolina State University is trying to learn enough about these severe storms to be able to predict them. He uses data obtained from past tornadoes. Some of that data comes from photographs taken by satellites. Other information comes from radar on the ground. All of these data, along with the usual weather information on temperature, pressure, and winds, are placed in a MCIDAS (Man/Computer Interactive Data Access System) computer. This special computer allows Dr. Anderson to view images of how air is moving at any elevation within the storm. Other data can be displayed by these computer images. By studying the air movements within the clouds of past storms, Dr. Anderson hopes to learn how to accurately predict the time and location of future tornadoes and other severe storms.

CHAPTER 30

MAP ACTIVITY

Reading Weather Maps

Have you ever thought about how much information it takes to make a weather forecast? In order to make accurate weather forecasts, meteorologists must gather tremendous quantities of data about local weather conditions from across the country. Data are collected from satellites and from over 600 weather stations throughout the country. These data are pooled together to make detailed weather maps. Meteorologists use weather maps to record changing weather patterns and to show the movement of weather systems. In this map exercise, you will study weather maps showing weather conditions across the United States over a four-day period. Based on these maps, you will be able to see for yourself the movement of weather systems and even make rough forecasts about how weather conditions will change over time.

Map Skills and Objectives

- To **recognize** weather map symbols
- To **interpret** weather patterns based on the data on weather maps

Materials

- Weather Maps: Four-Day Series, Appendix B, pages 662–663
- Physical United States map, Appendix B, pages 654–655
- weather map symbols, textbook Chapters 29 to 30

Procedure

1. Look at the weather maps on pages 662–663. Use the Physical United States map on pages 654–655 as a reference and name the cities and states where weather stations, identified as station models, are located.

2. At each station, the station model displays temperature and three other weather variables. What are the three variables?

3. Which city had the highest temperature over the four-day period? Which city had the lowest temperature?

4. Identify the city with the highest wind speed and the city with the lowest wind speed over the four-day period. Give the wind direction and date for each of these cities.

5. Look at the January 28 weather map. List four cities with 100 percent cloud cover and four cities with no cloud cover.

6. On many simplified weather maps, the centers of high-pressure systems are symbolized by an H with a circle around it, and the centers of low-pressure systems are symbolized by an

L with a circle around it. Look at the January 31 weather map. Name two states where high-pressure systems are centered and two states where low-pressure systems are centered.

7. What type of front extends through the western states on January 30? Describe where the front has moved on January 31.

8. What type of precipitation is falling in (a) Ohio on January 28; (b) North Dakota on January 29; and (c) North Carolina on January 30. Refer to page 514, Figure 27.15.

9. Answer the questions in *Analysis and Conclusions.*

Analysis and Conclusions

1. In what general direction do weather systems move across the continental United States? Use evidence from the maps to support your answer.

2. Use the four weather variables on your maps to summarize the weather conditions in Atlanta on January 29, 30, and 31.

3. Explain what factors led to the changes in weather conditions in Atlanta between January 29 and 30 and between January 30 and 31.

4. Predict how weather conditions in Miami will change between January 31 and February 1. Explain the reasons for your prediction.

M A P
ACTIVITY

Forecasting Severe Storms

On April 3 and 4, 1974, a series of severe thunderstorms east of the Mississippi River produced 127 tornadoes over 11 states ranging from Alabama to Michigan. This record number of storms was caused by a set of unusual weather conditions. Forecasters were able to detect conditions that could lead to severe weather the morning before the storms formed. These conditions included a strengthening low pressure system pulling humid air from the south and dry air from the west. In this exercise, you will interpret an early afternoon weather map similar to that for April 3, 1974, just as the severe storms were beginning.

Map Skills and Objectives
■ To **interpret** symbols on a weather map
■ To **understand** conditions that lead to severe thunderstorms

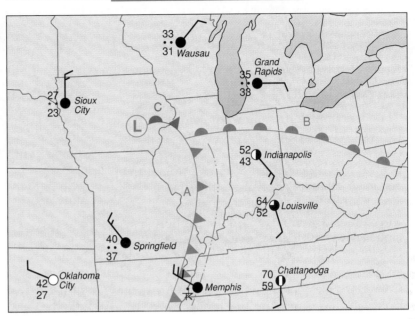

30.13 Early afternoon weather map similar to that for April 3, 1974

Procedure
1. Identify the weather variables shown on the map.
2. What are the dew points in Indianapolis, Louisville, and Chattanooga? What are the temperatures in these three cities?
3. Identify the types of fronts present on the map (Figure 30.13) at locations A, B, and C. Which direction are the fronts moving?
4. Answer the questions in *Analysis and Conclusions.*

Analysis and Conclusions
1. Explain how the low-pressure system centered over southeastern Iowa influences the movement of the fronts.
2. If the wind direction remains the same, predict how the

dew point in Indianapolis will change. Explain your answer.
3. Give two reasons why you would expect the temperature in Indianapolis to rise over the course of the day.
4. The dot-dash line extending from Mississippi up to Illinois represents a line of thunderstorms called a squall line. What are the weather conditions that caused the squall line to form?
5. Explain why the winds in Memphis are stronger than the winds in any other city on the map.
6. Based on your answers for questions 2 and 3, explain why conditions favor the formation of very severe storms.

CHAPTER

30 REVIEW

Answers to all questions appear in the Teacher's Guide at the back of this book.

■ Summary

I Thunderstorms form from warm, moist air rising through unstable air. They can form singly or in groups.

Lightning is an electrical discharge from a thundercloud. Thunder results from the sudden expansion of air in the lightning channel.

Tornadoes are violent, small, funnel-shaped clouds with whirling winds as fast as 500 kilometers/hour. They occur with strong thunderstorms.

Conditions ideal for strong thunderstorms are unstable air that is moist at low levels, strong wind that increases with height, and an approaching cold front. When these conditions occur, the Weather Service issues a severe weather watch. A warning is issued if severe weather is detected.

II Hurricanes start as lows along the ITCZ and grow over warm waters. They move with the prevailing winds and die over land or cold water.

Mid-latitude lows and hurricanes have similar pressure and wind patterns, but hurricanes have a central eye, are smaller and more intense, and do not have fronts.

Hurricanes are tracked with satellites, aircraft, and radars. Warnings are given when the hurricane is less than 24 hours offshore.

Heavy snows occur with strong lows when there is enough moisture and the temperature is below freezing.

III Daily 12- to 48-hour forecasts are made with the help of computer-predicted weather patterns, updated by current surface maps and other observations.

Satellites provide wind, temperature, and humidity data, as well as cloud pictures.

Radars are used to spot and track severe weather and to locate precipitation areas. Newer radars measure wind toward and away from the radar.

The United States surface weather map has isobars and fronts, based mainly on plotted information from about 700 stations.

■ Vocabulary

air-mass thunderstorm
blizzard
computer model
eye
frontal thunderstorm
hurricane

severe thunderstorm
station model
storm surge
tornado
waterspout

■ Review

Number your paper from 1 to 20. On your paper write the word or words that best complete each sentence.

1. Most frontal thunderstorms are associated with _____ fronts.
2. _____ thunderstorms are usually widely scattered single storms.
3. All thunderstorms produce _____, the discharge of _____ from a thundercloud.
4. Lightning generally strikes the _____ point above the ground.
5. The funnel of a tornado is a mixture of _____ and _____.
6. A _____ is the name given to a tornado that forms over water.
7. When a severe thunderstorm or tornado is possible, a _____ is issued; when a severe thunderstorm or tornado has been seen or detected, a _____ is issued.
8. A _____ is an intense storm, about 300–600 kilometers in diameter, with strong winds, heavy rains, and a central area called the _____.
9. _____ create the greatest damage associated with hurricanes.
10. Hurricanes grow _____ as they move over colder water or land.
11. A tropical storm is named once its winds exceed _____ kilometers per hour.
12. A low produces a major snowfall under two conditions: low _____ and sufficient _____.
13. Weather Service Forecast Offices make _____ major forecasts daily. Updated forecasts are made as many times as needed.

For further review, see **Study Guide.**
For assessment, see **Chapter Tests**
and **Computer Test Bank.**

14. A computer _____ contains information about wind, temperature, pressure, humidity, clouds, and precipitation. It is used in making _____.

15. _____ and _____ are used to provide weather data that are missed by computer models and local observations.

16. _____ are especially helpful in collecting data over the oceans.

17. A _____ satellite is always above the same spot on Earth's surface.

18. The new Doppler radar provides information about _____ as well as _____, which is also supplied by earlier weather radars.

19. The data used in drawing surface weather maps are collected from weather stations once each _____.

20. The form in which weather data are arranged around a location on a weather map is called a _____.

■ Interpret and Apply

On your paper, answer each question in complete sentences.

1. How can the fact that hurricanes have no fronts be explained in terms of air masses?

2. What accounts for the heavy precipitation in tropical cyclones?

3. If thunder is heard 15 seconds after lightning is seen, how far away is the storm?

4. How can the time delay between lightning and thunder be used to prevent injury during a thunderstorm?

5. In what kind of air mass are air-mass thunderstorms most likely to develop?

6. In the Northern Hemisphere, the greatest damage caused by a hurricane occurs along the hurricane's right side. Why is this so?

7. Why do air-mass thunderstorms usually last less than an hour?

8. Heavy winter snowstorms occur on the eastern shores of the Great Lakes. What causes these snowstorms to occur there?

■ Critical Thinking

On your paper, answer each question in complete sentences.

1. You are a forecaster in Oklahoma. From 24 hours before a major tornado outbreak to the time it occurs, how will you use each of the following to foresee and then watch the tornado? (a) computer-model maps (b) rawinsonde data (c) the surface weather map (d) hourly weather observations (e) satellite data (f) radar

2. A hurricane approaches Florida from the east. Major thunderstorms and tornadoes break out to the north of the hurricane's eye, but things are relatively quiet to the south. What accounts for this difference?

3. The morning satellite pictures show Nebraska half-covered with low clouds and half clear. The 6:00 A.M. rawinsonde data show that both areas have similar temperatures and moisture and that the entire area is unstable aloft. Where are thunderstorms most likely, and why?

4. (a) Why do most thunderstorms occur in the late afternoon? (b) When and why might thunderstorms continue into the night?

5. Below are shown two station models. Interpret the station models and list the following information for each location: temperature, dew point, wind direction and speed, visibility, air pressure, sky conditions, and precipitation.

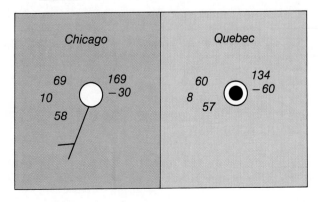

Climate and Climate Change

Home of the Pueblo Indians in a canyon in southwestern Colorado's Mesa Verde plateau

How Do You Know That . . .

The climate has not always been the same as it is today? Around ten centuries ago, the plateaus of Colorado and New Mexico were home to a thriving civilization. Dwellings at Mesa Verde, Chaco Canyon, and faint roads connecting Chaco Canyon to the ruins of outlying villages can still be seen today. The people, however, disappeared around A.D. 1300, victims of a drying climate.

What determines our climate? Will it change in our lifetimes, either naturally or through the effects of people? In order to answer these questions, you need to know about the factors that control the climate of different parts of the world and the factors that cause climate change.

I Climate and Climate Controls

Topic 1 What Is Climate?

A description of the general weather of an area includes many factors. Among these are how hot the summers are, how cold the winters are, and how much precipitation falls at different times of the year. Such a description also includes how the precipitation occurs—in thunderstorms, as gentle rain, or in the form of snow.

The overall weather of an area is its **climate.** The two main factors that determine climate are temperature and rainfall. However, the number of days and hours of sunlight; the direction, speed, and steadiness of the wind; the occurance of severe weather conditions and even the amount of pollution also help define an area's climate.

Numbers, or statistics, are used to compare climates in different parts of the world. To find out how hot or cold a climate is, an average temperature is useful. *Average temperatures* are found by adding two or more readings and dividing by the number of readings. Average temperatures are calculated daily, monthly, and yearly.

The *daily temperature range* is the difference between the highest and lowest temperatures of the day. The *yearly temperature range* is the difference between the average of the warmest month and the coldest month.

Topic 2 Use of Variation in Describing Climate

Averages and ranges alone do not provide a complete picture of a climate. A description of how the weather varies is also important. For example, Beijing (formerly called Peking), China, and Valdivia, Chile, have almost identical yearly average temperatures of 11.7°C. In Beijing, January averages -4°C and July averages 26°C. Compare these with the mild 8°C and 17°C averages for the coldest and warmest months in Valdivia. In Beijing the annual range in temperature is 30°C; in Valdivia it is only 9°C. Certainly their climates are not the same. Similar contrasts exist in the United States between cities on the East Coast and cities on the West Coast, such as New York City and Portland, Oregon.

Bombay, India, has a yearly rainfall of about 188 centimeters. Mobile, Alabama, has almost as much rain, about 173 centimeters.

OBJECTIVES

A Define *climate* and explain how to calculate daily and yearly temperature ranges.

B Show how to describe an area's climate.

C Summarize the factors that control climate and climate change.

OF INTEREST

The types of plants in an area reflect its climate. Vladimir Koppen's famous climate classification system, published in 1918, was based on plant life.

SCIENCE BACKGROUND

By international agreement, climate statistics are averaged over 30 years.

31.1 Although the average yearly temperatures of Beijing, China, and Valdivia, Chile, are the same, their climates are quite different. The cities are about the same distance, though on opposite sides from the equator.

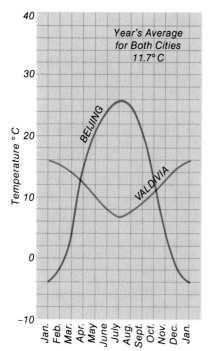

However, almost all of Bombay's rains fall in a monsoon season of four summer months. In Mobile the rains are spread throughout the year. No month averages less than 7.6 centimeters of rain.

It is clear that climate is not necessarily the same as average weather. Climate cannot be described accurately without gathering more information.

Topic 3 **Climate Controls**

The temperature and rainfall patterns of present-day Earth depend upon a set of conditions called climate controls. The six main climate controls are the following:

1. latitude;
2. altitude;
3. prevailing winds;
4. topography;
5. distance from large bodies of water (oceans, lakes);
6. nearby ocean currents.

For a particular area, some factors are more important than others. For example, nearby ocean currents are not important to the climate high in the Rocky Mountains, but altitude and topography are.

Over long periods of time, the climate changes. The global climate is related to the amount of solar energy Earth absorbs and the energy Earth and the atmosphere radiate or reflect into space. The local climate is related to the global climate as well as to the six climate controls. All six can change over geologic time. For example, mountain-building and erosion change the topography and altitude of an area. Plate tectonics changes the latitude of land areas and also changes the ocean currents. The positions of continents, ice, and cloud cover are among the factors that determine the amount of sunlight Earth absorbs.

TOPIC QUESTIONS

Each topic question refers to the topic of the same number.

1. **(a)** What is climate? **(b)** Define *daily temperature range* and *yearly temperature range.*

2. **(a)** Why don't averages give a complete picture of climate? **(b)** How can two cities have the same average temperature but very different climates? **(c)** How can two cities have nearly the same yearly rainfall but very different climates?

3. **(a)** Name six factors that control climate in a region. **(b)** What controls the global climate?

ANSWERS
    1. (a) the overall weather experienced in an area   (b) the difference between the highest and lowest temperatures of the day; the difference between the average of the warmest month and the coldest month.
    2. (a) Temperature ranges can be different; winters and summers are different in different hemispheres; precipitation patterns are different.   (b) They can have different precipitation patterns, different temperature ranges, be in different hemispheres.   (c) They can have different temperature averages, different temperature ranges, different distribution of rainfall through the year.
    3. (a) latitude, altitude, prevailing winds, topography, distance from large bodies of water, nearby ocean currents   (b) changes in the amount of energy Earth absorbs from the sun, and radiate into space

II Factors That Control Temperature

Topic 4 How Latitude Controls Temperature

Latitude is the distance in degrees (north or south) from the equator. The yearly temperature range and average yearly temperature depend mainly on latitude.

At a location within 5 or 10 degrees of the equator, the sun shines for about 12 hours each day and each night is about 12 hours long. At noon the sun is never very far from being directly overhead. The climate is hot throughout the year, and the average temperature is very high, about 27°C. There are no summers and winters, only rainy seasons and dry seasons. The yearly range of temperature is only 3° or 4°C.

At a location 40 or 45 degrees north from the equator, there are 15 or 16 hours of sunshine in July. Nights are only 8 or 9 hours long. Six months later the sun shines only 8 or 9 hours a day and nighttime lasts 15 or 16 hours. On the average the yearly temperature is far lower than it is near the equator. However, the annual range of temperature may be large—as much as 30°C.

In the polar regions most of the sunshine comes in a day that lasts for many months. The winter includes an equally long night. In summer the sun is never high in the sky, so it provides little heating. It goes completely around the sky each day but does not dip below the horizon. Temperatures change very little for days at a time. The summer is comparatively mild. When the long winter night comes, however, the weather becomes very cold. In these latitudes the average annual temperature is very low. The annual temperature range is very large, but the daily temperature range is very small.

Figure 31.2 on page 578 shows the relationship between latitude and yearly temperature range. In general, the higher the latitude, the lower the average yearly temperature and the larger the yearly temperature range.

Topic 5 Altitude and Temperature

Altitude is height above sea level. Its effect on temperature is somewhat like that of latitude. On the average, temperatures drop about 1°C for every 160 meters of altitude. The higher the altitude, the lower the average yearly temperature.

For example, Vera Cruz and Mexico City have the same latitude but very different climates. Vera Cruz, at sea level in the tropics, is hot and humid. Mexico City, 2300 meters above sea level, is pleasantly cool even in summer.

OBJECTIVES

A Show the relationship between latitude and average temperature and between latitude and daily and yearly temperature ranges.

B Differentiate between marine and continental climates.

C Discuss the effects of altitude, prevailing winds, topography, and ocean currents on climate.

OF INTEREST
The lowest surface air temperature ever recorded was −89.2°C at Vostok, Antarctica, which is 3.4 km above sea level.

TEACHING TIP
Figures 26.14 and 26.15 (pages 442 and 443) show average July and January temperatures in °F. Have students compare these maps with Figure 31.2.

SCIENCE BACKGROUND
Higher altitudes also have larger daily temperature ranges.

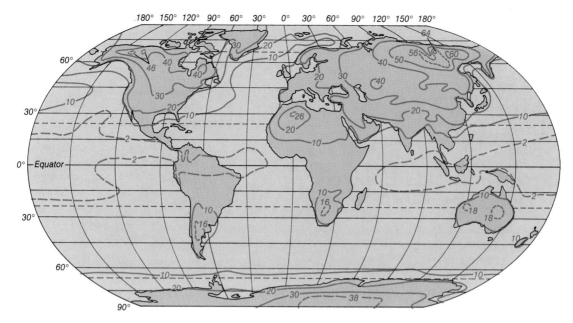

31.2 Average annual range of surface air temperatures (in degrees Celsius)

Topic 6 Land, Sea, and Temperature

Land gains and loses heat much more quickly than water. Land areas in the middle latitudes tend to have hot summers and cold winters. As shown in Figure 31.2, the annual average temperature ranges of land areas are larger than those for the oceans at the same latitudes. These land areas with large yearly temperature ranges have **continental climates.** Areas near the ocean, on the other hand, have small yearly temperature ranges. These areas have **marine climates.**

Reykjavik (RAKE-yuh-vik), Iceland, 64°N, and Verkhoyansk (vyer-koh-YANSK), Siberia, 68°N, are at nearly the same latitude. Reykjavik is on the south coast of Iceland. Its marine climate has an annual temperature range of only 11°C. Verkhoyansk is deep in the interior of the great Asian landmass. It has a continental climate with a yearly temperature range of almost 67°C.

In summary, ocean areas have marine climates with small yearly temperature ranges. Continental interiors have continental climates with large yearly temperature ranges.

Topic 7 Prevailing Winds and Temperature

The west coasts of continents in the middle latitudes have marine climates. The prevailing westerlies blow at these latitudes. When they come from the ocean, they carry maritime air masses onto the west coasts of continents and large islands. Air masses from the Pacific Ocean are carried over the west coasts of North America and South America. Air masses from the Atlantic Ocean are carried over the west coasts of the British Isles and Europe. Portland, Oregon, and London, England, have marine climates.

How far inland does a marine climate reach? The distance depends chiefly on the topography. Usually, a marine climate

SCIENCE BACKGROUND

The air temperature at the surface of the open ocean has a daily temperature range of less than 1°C.

VIDEODISC SELECTION

Satellite images showing global temperatures
Side 1: 894 to 895, 2-frame sequence

reaches no farther than the first high mountain range. Beyond the mountains, the continental interiors have continental climates.

In middle latitudes, east coasts do not have marine climates. Most of the air masses that come to east coasts are brought by the prevailing westerlies from the interiors of the continents. As a result, east coasts have continental climates. Their temperatures are only slightly moderated by the ocean. Boston and New York, for example, are on the Atlantic Coast. Nevertheless, their summers and winters are nearly as extreme as those of the interior of the continent.

In summary, in the latitudes of the prevailing westerlies, west coasts have marine climates with cool summers and mild winters. East coasts have continental climates with hot summers and cold winters.

SCIENCE BACKGROUND
The eastern shores of the Great Lakes have a smaller yearly temperature range than the western shores because of the water and prevailing winds from the west.

Topic 8 **Topography and Temperature**

Mountain ranges may block wind that could affect temperature. For example, the marine climate of the western United States reaches no farther inland than the Coast Ranges. The Sacramento Valley lies just east of the Coast Ranges, not far from the Pacific Ocean. Nevertheless, it has intensely hot summers and cold winters.

Southern Italy has mild winters, mainly because the Alps keep out cold winds from the north. On the Great Plains of Canada and the United States, just the opposite situation occurs. The plains have no mountain range running across them to block winds from the north. Therefore, winter cold waves, with icy winds from the Arctic, may reach all the way to the Gulf of Mexico.

Topic 9 **Ocean Currents and Temperature**

Ocean currents may be considerably warmer or colder than the normal surface air temperatures for their latitudes. Warm currents have an effect on the places they pass. Their effect is greatest when the prevailing winds blow from the water to the land. For example, the warm *Gulf Stream* heats the air above it. The prevailing westerlies blow the warmed air to the shores of Iceland, the British Isles, and Scandinavia. As a result, these regions are as warm as places that are closer to the equator. London, England, is about 1100 kilometers nearer the North Pole than Cleveland, Ohio. Nevertheless, its average annual temperature is higher than Cleveland's.

Cold currents also affect temperature. Northern Labrador is chilled by the *Labrador Current*. Its yearly average temperature is more than 11°C lower than that of Stockholm, Sweden, which is at the same latitude.

31.3 Current meters are used to determine the speed, direction, and properties of both surface and subsurface currents.

ANSWERS (continued)

overhead   (c) daily temperature range larger at low latitudes, since days and nights are of more equal length

5. (a) coldest at higher altitude (b) Mexico City is at higher altitude.

6. continental—large annual temperature range; marine—small annual temperature range

7. (a) marine climates on windward sides of continents; continental climates on lee side   (b) United States East Coast—continental climate; West Coast—marine climate

8. Italy has mild winters since mountains block cold winds from north. Nebraska has cold winters, since nothing blocks cold air from north.

9. (a) They are warmer or colder than the normal temperature of a latitude.   (b) Warm Gulf Stream makes London warmer than Cleveland, even though Cleveland is farther south; cold Labrador Current makes northern Labrador colder than Stockholm, which is at same latitude.

TOPIC QUESTIONS

ANSWERS

4. (a) average yearly temperature warmer at lower latitudes from higher sun angle   (b) average yearly temperature range smaller at lower latitudes, since noontime sun always close to

Each topic question refers to the topic of the same number.

4. Explain the relationship between latitude and each of the following: **(a)** average yearly temperature,   **(b)** average yearly range in temperature,   **(c)** average daily range in temperature.

5. **(a)** How does altitude affect temperature?   **(b)** Why is Vera Cruz warmer than Mexico City?

6. How do the annual temperature ranges of marine climates and continental climates differ?

7. **(a)** How do prevailing winds determine whether a climate is marine or continental?   **(b)** Compare the climates of the eastern and western coasts of the United States.

8. Southern Italy and Nebraska are at the same latitude. How might topography help to explain the difference in their climates?

9. **(a)** How do ocean currents affect temperatures?   **(b)** Give examples to show the temperature effects of the Gulf Stream and the Labrador Current.

Current RESEARCH

Watching for El Niño

The winter weather of 1992 was far from typical. In Los Angeles, three storms in ten days dumped enough rain to cause killer mudslides and floods. In south-central Texas, severe storms brought over 25 inches of rain in only two months, causing severe flooding and loss of property. Much of the United States had milder temperatures than usual, while half a world away, a drought devastated southern Africa. All of these unusual weather patterns appear to have been caused by El Niño (Topic 15), the warming of the Pacific Ocean near the equator that occurs every three to seven years.

Since an El Niño event causes such dangerous weather conditions worldwide, researchers have been working to find ways to predict when El Niños will occur. The El Niño of 1991–1992 was predicted by a computer model in 1990, almost two years before it arrived. This computer model simulates the winds and currents of the tropical Pacific Ocean and uses that data to project future surface water temperatures and sea levels.

Knowing when an El Niño event will occur can in turn make such unusual weather as occurred in 1992 more predictable. Based on historical data, researchers know that the tropical warmth from El Niño waters can displace the jet streams, steering warmer air to the northern United States and rain to the Gulf Coast. Further refinements of the models will make better predictions possible.

III   Factors That Control Rainfall

Topic 10   Latitude, Prevailing Winds, and Rainfall

The prevailing wind belts cause precipitation at some latitudes and dryness at other latitudes. Compare the map of the global winds in Figure 28.12 (page 533) to Figures 31.4 and 31.5.

Yearly rainfall is high in the tropics. The precipitation in the tropics follows the pattern of the prevailing winds. The air in the doldrums rises slowly, forced upward by the coming together (convergence) of the northeast and southeast trade winds. This rising air causes almost-daily thunderstorms over the continents. Over the ocean the precipitation is more concentrated in a roughly 300-kilometer-wide band. This band is the most organized part of the intertropical convergence zone (ITCZ), so called because the winds from the two hemispheres mostly converge there (see Chapter 28).

The position of the ITCZ varies with the seasons. The ITCZ reaches its northernmost point around 10° to 20° N in the Northern Hemisphere summer. It moves down to 10°–20° S during the Southern Hemisphere summer. Therefore, in each hemisphere the summer is the rainy season for the area about 10–20 degrees from the equator.

To the north and south of the ITCZ, the rainfall decreases. The air flows outward (diverges) from the horse latitudes. Some of the diverging air flows toward the poles as westerlies; some flows toward the equator as the trade winds. Air sinks to replace the diverging air at the surface. Since clouds and rain cannot form in sinking air, many of the world's great deserts—the desert of Southwest Africa, the desert of the Australian interior, and the Sahara—lie about 20 to 35 degrees from the equator.

OBJECTIVES

A Correlate the world rainfall patterns with the prevailing wind belts.

B Describe the effects of mountains on rainfall and humidity.

C Explain the effects of nearby oceans on precipitation.

D Discuss the relationship between ocean currents and fogs.

31.4 This satellite image of Earth's clouds shows the change of precipitation patterns with latitude. The belt of clouds around the equator is the ITCZ, where much rain falls. At higher latitudes, precipitation falls around traveling low-pressure systems, which look like commas.

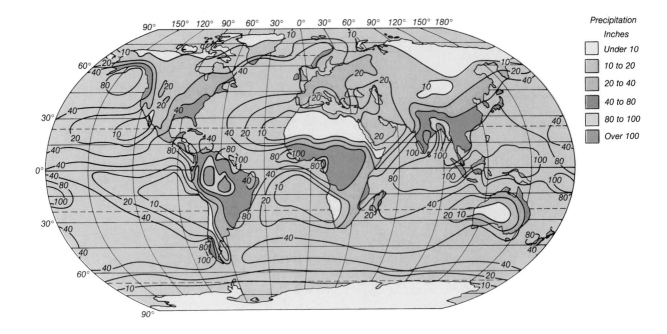

31.5 Earth's pattern of annual precipitation

The pattern of precipitation in the middle latitudes, from about 30 to 65 degrees, is strongly related to the passage of low-pressure areas. A second band of convergence lies between the polar easterlies and the westerlies. The convergence brings together warm and cold air masses, forming a zone of strong temperature gradient. Low pressure areas form here. Precipitation falls mainly around the lows and along the lows' fronts. The position of the fronts has an enormous range of latitude. In the Northern Hemisphere winter, cold fronts can reach as far south as 20°N. In summer, warm fronts can reach 65°N. This zone is far less regular than the ITCZ.

The polar easterlies flow from the poles to about 65 degrees. This diverging air is replaced by sinking air from above. The very cold air at the poles can hold little water vapor. Therefore, precipitation in the high latitudes (near the poles) is light in all seasons. It comes almost entirely in low-pressure areas.

SCIENCE BACKGROUND

The polar front is very irregular. There can be more than one polar front. Polar fronts are usually sequences of warm and cold fronts.

Topic 11 **Mountains and Rainfall**

The prevailing westerlies and trade winds cause consistent patterns of precipitation along mountain chains. Rising air makes the *windward* side of a mountain — its side toward the wind — rainy. Sinking air makes the side of the mountain away from the wind — its *leeward* side — dry.

The trade winds blow from the northeast in the Northern Hemisphere and from the southeast in the Southern Hemisphere. In the trade-wind belts, the rainy windward sides are:

Northern Hemisphere: northern slopes, eastern slopes
Southern Hemisphere: southern slopes, eastern slopes

For this reason, the east coasts of Africa, South America, and Central America have heavy rains.

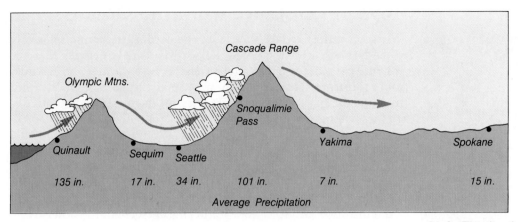

In the prevailing westerlies, relatively strong highs and lows frequently interrupt the prevailing winds. However, on the average, the rainy windward sides of the mountains are these:

Northern Hemisphere: southern slopes, western slopes
Southern Hemisphere: northern slopes, western slopes

The summer *monsoon* dominates the precipitation pattern in the Himalayan Mountains and India. Southwest monsoon winds bring rain to the western slopes of the Western Ghats range. The monsoon winds become southeasterly in the northern Bay of Bengal to the east of India. These winds bring heavy rain to the southern part of the Himalayan Mountains in summer.

Because the water falls out of the air on the windward side of the mountains, the leeward slopes are very dry. They are also warmer than the windward slopes. The leeward slopes are warmer because the raining air traveling up the mountain cools only 0.6°C for each 100 meters it rises. When the dried-out air sinks on the leeward side of the mountains, it warms at a faster rate—1°C for each 100 meters. Warm, dry winds formed in this way often blow down the eastern slopes of the Rocky Mountains and the northern part of the Swiss Alps. These winds are called **chinooks** (shin-OOKS) in the Rockies. In Europe, they are called **foehns** (ferns). The **Santa Anas** are winds that blow shoreward down the Santa Ana Mountains south of Los Angeles. The winds are hot and dry.

When chinooks arrive, they can raise the temperature 20°C in 15 minutes. They melt snow and can cause avalanches. If they blow too long, forests, fields, and buildings dry out. Then a careful watch must be kept against fire. However, chinooks can also make winters milder.

Not all winds blowing down mountains are warm. Some start out so cold that even after heating by compression they remain unpleasantly cold. One such wind is the **mistral** that blows down from the Alps to the Mediterranean Sea. Another is the **bora** that blows down from the mountains of Yugoslavia to the Adriatic Sea. Boras sometimes blow down the eastern slope of the Rockies.

31.6 The distribution of the average annual precipitation in the state of Washington is determined by the mountains and the prevailing west wind.

SCIENCE BACKGROUND
   Chinook winds can exceed 50 meters per second on the lee side of the Rocky Mountains.

SCIENCE BACKGROUND
Precipitation is also greater on the eastern shores of the Great Lakes.

Topic 12 **Distance from the Oceans**

When prevailing winds blow from the oceans, the rainfall is likely to be heaviest near the shore. Rainfall is usually heavier near the warmer parts of the ocean. Here the air is also warmer and can hold more moisture. The air is also more unstable, so rain clouds form more easily. In the eastern United States, the total yearly rainfall is greatest along the coast. There is less rainfall inland and northward.

Locations near oceans do not always have heavy rainfall. Even though the desert of Peru is located beside the Pacific Ocean, it is one of the driest places in the world. There are three reasons for this. First, the southeast trade winds come from the dry interior of the continent, not from the Pacific Ocean. Second, the desert is on the leeward (western) side of the Andes. Third, the prevailing winds off the coast cause a cold upwelling ocean current. The cold water cools the lowest layer of air. The resulting temperature inversion—warm air from the east over cool air from the nearby ocean—traps the ocean's moisture near the ground and prevents rain clouds from forming.

The eastern interior of North America has more precipitation in the summer than in the winter. The main reason is that in the summer, prevailing winds carry moisture northward from the Gulf of Mexico. A second reason is that thundershowers happen more often in summer because the ground is hotter.

31.7 The map shows average annual rainfall in the continental United States. In the far west, rainfall is controlled mainly by mountain ranges. In the interior and eastern parts of the country, rainfall increases closer to the Atlantic Ocean and the Gulf of Mexico.

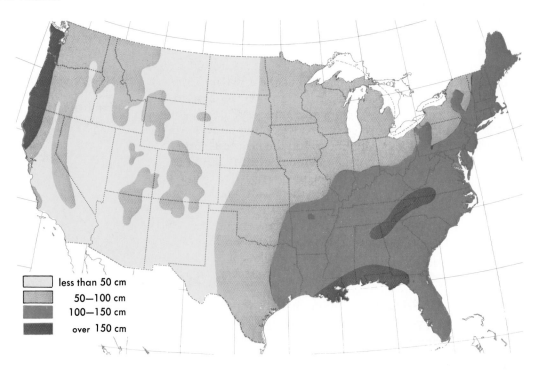

less than 50 cm
50–100 cm
100–150 cm
over 150 cm

Topic 13 **Ocean Currents and Fogs**

Warm air flowing over cold water makes rainfall unlikely in places like Peru. However, warm moist air over a colder surface often produces fogs. Ocean currents often help set up these conditions. The frequent winter fogs of England and Scotland are an example. These fogs form when warm moist air from the Gulf Stream blows over the cold land.

The summer fogs along the New England coast are another example. They form when warm air moving north is cooled over New England's cold coastal waters. The fogs of Newfoundland form when warm air from the Gulf Stream blows over the icy Labrador Current. The summer fogs of the Pacific coasts of the United States, Peru, and northern Chile are also examples. They form when warm ocean winds blow over cold upwelling coastal waters. In general, fogs form where ocean currents are much warmer or much colder than the adjoining land or water.

SCIENCE BACKGROUND
Cold air over warm water produces convection and showery precipitation.

TOPIC QUESTIONS

Each topic question refers to the topic of the same number.

10. **(a)** Why do the latitudes near the equator have dry and wet seasons? **(b)** Why are many locations between 20–30° N or S dry all year? **(c)** What factors affect rainfall in the middle latitudes? **(d)** What factors affect rainfall in the polar latitudes?

11. **(a)** Which are the dry and rainy sides of mountain chains? **(b)** Which is the rainy side of the Western Ghats Mountains of India? Why is the rainy side different from other mountain chains of the trade-wind zone? **(c)** Explain why a chinook is warm and dry.

12. **(a)** Describe the relationship between wind and rainfall in coastal areas. **(b)** Why does the eastern interior of North America have more precipitation in summer than in winter?

13. **(a)** What conditions produce fogs? **(b)** How are the fogs over England and Scotland formed? **(c)** How are the fogs over New England and Newfoundland formed?

ANSWERS
   10. (a) north and south movement of the ITCZ with seasons (b) sinking air (c) passage of low-pressure areas; the polar front (d) sinking air; cold air cannot hold much moisture.
   11. (a) dry—leeward; wet—windward (b) west side because of SW monsoons (c) Rising air on windward side cools less than it warms sinking on the leeward side; air loses moisture by raining on windward side
   12. (a) more rainfall near coasts when winds blow from oceans (b) Prevailing south winds bring moisture; hotter ground helps form thunderstorms.
   13. (a) warm moist air over colder surface (b) warm moist air from Gulf Stream over cold land (c) warm moist air from Gulf Stream over cold Labrador Current

Map Skills

The following questions refer to the map of Earth's Climates on page 664 of Appendix B.

1. At what latitudes are most of the world's major deserts?

2. **(a)** At around 40° N, where are the marine climates? **(b)** Compare the extent of the marine climate in Europe and North America.

3. At what latitudes are the most humid climates?

ANSWERS
   1. 20–30° N and S
   2. (a) Western Europe and western North America (b) Europe much larger because prevailing winds are not blocked by mountains
   3. around the equator

OBJECTIVES

A Relate changes in climate to Earth's energy budget.

B Identify some causes of global cooling and warming.

C Explain the effects of greenhouse gases on global climate.

D Discuss ways scientists are studying global climate changes.

SCIENCE BACKGROUND

Some scientists say that the smoke from the widespread fires that would result from a nuclear war would cause a global cooling. The most extreme forecasts have been referred to as "nuclear winter."

SCIENCE BACKGROUND

Changes in the tilt of Earth's axis, the eccentricity of Earth's orbit, and the orbit at which one pole tilts toward the sun have been linked to the cycle of Ice Ages from 20 000 to 100 000 years.

IV   Climate Change

Topic 14   Sources of Climate Change

The weather varies a lot from day to day and season to season. So it is hard to tell without averaging numbers whether the climate is changing. But what averages are most useful? Is Earth's climate getting warmer? Scientists are using the study of past climate changes to make predictions about future climate changes.

Earth's climate changes with its energy budget. Right now Earth's energy budget is in approximate balance (see Chapter 26, Topic 8). That is, the incoming solar radiation (insolation) is equal to the energy Earth loses to space. To see what can change the balance, one must look at the processes involved. First, solar radiation hits Earth and its atmosphere. Second, Earth loses energy by reflection of sunlight from its surface and from clouds, dust, and air molecules in the atmosphere. Third, Earth's surface, clouds, and atmosphere lose infrared radiation (heat) to space. And fourth, *greenhouse gases,* such as carbon dioxide, let sunlight in but keep infrared radiation from escaping to space. A change in any of these four processes can change the climate.

Do climate changes in Earth's past provide clues about future climate changes? Earth has had at least four ice ages in the last 3 million years. At other times, Earth became so warm that even Greenland and Antarctica had tropical climates. It appears that changes in Earth's heat budget need not be very large to trigger climate changes. For example, temperatures during the last Ice Age were only 5°C cooler than today's temperatures. Scientists from many disciplines—astronomy, geology, chemistry, oceanography, biology, and meteorology—have joined in the study of climate change. These scientists hope that, as they learn more about climate changes in Earth's past, they will be able to predict future changes in Earth's climate.

Topic 15   Causes of Global Cooling

Cooling periods in Earth's history have been linked to variations in the sun's energy output. The less energy put out by the sun, the less energy there is available to reach Earth. There is strong evidence that solar energy output increases with an increase in the number of sunspots (Chapter 22, Topic 4). The opposite is also true. During a cold period on Earth, between the years 1400 and 1800, there were almost no sunspots. Scientists estimate that the amount of solar energy reaching Earth was down by 0.25 percent. Even such a small change in incoming energy has an impact on Earth's climate. Earth cooled so much during this "Little Ice Age" that valley glaciers advanced in Europe and North America.

There may be other ways to decrease the amount of solar energy reaching Earth's surface. Scientists think that changes in

Earth's orbit may cause some of the cooling. The shape of Earth's orbit sometimes puts Earth closer to the sun. This could change the amount of solar energy Earth receives. Climate may also be affected by the wobble of Earth on its axis.

Cooling would also occur if solar energy is prevented from reaching Earth's surface. Dust particles in the upper atmosphere can reflect the sun's energy back into space. These particles can come from volcanoes or rarely from the impact of asteroids. Explosive volcanic eruptions inject dust and sulfur dioxide gas into the stratosphere. The sulfur dioxide reacts with water vapor to form tiny droplets of acid. The dust and the acid droplets are so small that they can stay suspended for one to seven years. During this time, the dust and droplets reflect sunlight back into space. This reduces the amount of sunlight reaching Earth's surface which can cool the temperatures up to a few tenths of a degree Celsius. Once the dust falls into the troposphere, it is washed out by rain. The 1991 eruption of Mount Pinatubo in the Philippines, put 15 to 20 million tons of ash and sulfur dioxide into the stratosphere. A typical explosive eruption can lower mid-latitude temperatures between 0.1°C and 1°C.

Finally Earth's climate can be cooled when heat normally circulated by Earth's atmosphere or ocean currents is changed. Plate tectonics shapes both local and global climate by changing the energy distribution in Earth's heat budget. The continents have not always been located where they are today (Chapters 13 and 34), nor have oceans always been the same shape and size. These changes in sizes and positions of oceans and continents affected wind patterns, ocean currents, and the amount of solar radiation reflected back into space from land and water. For example, today there are large land areas in the cold regions surrounding the North and South poles. In the past, those landmasses were in the middle of oceans where air and ocean currents allowed enough exchange of heat with the atmosphere to distribute temperatures more uniformly. When large landmasses are located near the poles, the heat difference between the poles and the equator increases. During glaciation, when more of the land is covered with snow and ice, a greater amount of sunlight is reflected back into space. This contributes to cooling.

Topic 16   **Causes of Global Warming**

As you learned in Chapter 26, carbon dioxide plays a major role in keeping Earth's temperature constant. However, too much carbon dioxide causes a build-up of heat in Earth's atmosphere. The burning of fossil fuels, such as oil and coal, and the destruction of the world's rain forests are returning carbon dioxide to the atmosphere much faster than carbon dioxide can be removed by plants and by the oceans. Many scientists predict that an increase in carbon dioxide and other greenhouse gases (Chapter 26, Topic 9) can lead to global warming.

31.8 An individual volcanic eruption, such as this eruption, may cool the atmosphere for two to seven years.

SCIENCE BACKGROUND
Variations in volcanic activity could be related to variations in mantle convection.

SCIENCE BACKGROUND
Four hundred and forty million years ago, what is now Antarctica, Australia, South America, Africa, and the Indian Peninsula, formed a supercontinent in the high southern latitudes. The resulting glaciation and cooling climate is thought to have caused the dying off of more than 20 percent of the marine families that left fossil remains.

SCIENCE BACKGROUND
Per molecule, methane is 25 percent more effective than carbon dioxide at trapping heat, nitrous oxide is 250 times as effective, and the 2 most common CFC's are over 17 000 times as effective. Fortunately, these have smaller concentrations in the atmosphere, but they are increasing.

Volcanic eruptions also inject carbon dioxide into the atmosphere. This carbon dioxide stays in the atmosphere long after the volcanic dust and sulfuric acid droplets settle out. If there were many explosive volcanic eruptions over several million years, the increased amount of carbon dioxide could warm the climate. The relative warmth during the Cretaceous Period is thought to be related to volcanic activity.

If global warming did occur, some of today's most productive agricultural areas would become too dry or too hot to support the crops currently grown there. The polar ice caps and alpine glaciers could melt, causing sea level to rise and to flood coastal cities. However, such predictions are controversial and impossible to test.

Not all warming of Earth's climate is long-term. A natural event believed to cause short-term warming is called *El Niño*. Normally the warmest sea-surface temperatures on Earth occur in the western Pacific. Air pressure along the sea surface in that area, is low and the heaviest rains over Earth's oceans occur there. The trade winds blowing towards the west, strengthened by the overlying low pressure, keep warm water piled up in the western Pacific. Occasionally, the winds around the equator blow from the west, opposite the normal direction, as shown in Figure 31.11. During an El Niño event the west winds last long enough to spread the warm water eastward across the Pacific. This happens every two to eight years. El Niño events cause changes in Earth's climate. During a strong El Niño event, global surface temperatures warm by 0.1 to 0.2°C, which affects global weather patterns. Winters over Canada and the northern United States becomes milder, the southeast United States gets more precipitation, and fewer Atlantic hurricanes occur.

31.9 (Top) Carbon dioxide, water vapor and methane absorb radiation leaving Earth. (Bottom) As the concentration of these substances increases, more radiation is absorbed causing a global warming trend.

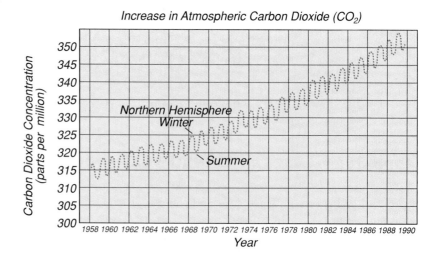

31.10 Concentration of carbon dioxide at Mauna Loa Observatory, Hawaii. Scientists believe that the data represents global trends. The seasonal variations are due to plants uptake of carbon dioxide.

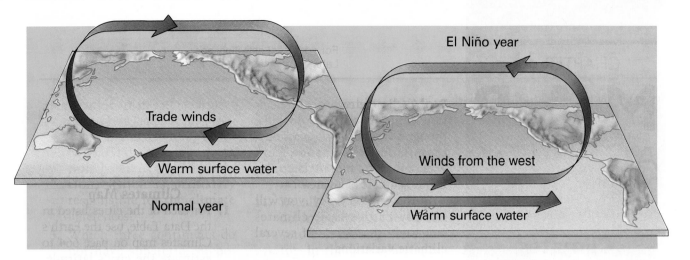

Trade winds

Warm surface water

Normal year

El Niño year

Winds from the west

Warm surface water

Topic 17 Is Climate Getting Warmer?

The severe heat and drought that peaked in the late 1980's have raised questions about Earth's climate and greenhouse gases. Six of the hottest ten years of the last century were in the 1980's. Scientists are sifting through old weather records and building computer models of climate to determine whether that warming is temporary or part of a long-term, global warming trend.

With so many factors influencing Earth's heat budget, it is difficult to make simple models of global climate change. The computer models being used to sort out the many causes of climate change are similar to those used for weather forecasting. The models are used to describe the present climate, its seasonal changes, and to predict the changes that might result from such things as volcanic eruptions or El Niño events. In addition, scientists test the models by trying to reproduce past climates using data pieced together from geologic evidence.

Unfortunately the factors affecting global climate change are numerous and complex. Climate models must take into account such factors as the effects of oceans, changes in greenhouse gases, the effects of different cloud types on sunlight at different altitudes, and so on. This makes predicting climate change difficult.

TOPIC QUESTIONS

Each topic question refers to the topic of the same number.

14. (a) What happens when Earth's energy budget changes? (b) List four ways in which Earth's energy budget can change.

15. (a) List four factors that might cause global cooling. (b) How do volcanic eruptions cause temperatures to lower?

16. (a) Explain how an increase in greenhouse gases produces warming at Earth's surface. (b) Describe what might happen if global warming did occur. (c) What is El Niño? How has El Niño affected weather in North America?

17. (a) Name two ways climate models are tested. (b) List three factors computer models must account for when predicting global climate change.

31.11 El Niño, a warm surface current in the Pacific Ocean can cause short-term climate changes.

SCIENCE BACKGROUND
Low clouds reflect more sunlight and have a cooling effect, while high clouds trap more infrared radiation and have a warming effect.

ANSWERS
14. (a) The climate changes. (b) change in insolation; change in reflection of sunlight by Earth's surface, clouds, dust or air molecules; change in infrared radiation from Earth's surface, clouds, or gases in atmosphere; change in greenhouse gases
15. (a) sunspots; Earth's orbit; dust in atmosphere from volcanoes and asteroids; location of Earth's continents (b) Dust and sulfuric acid droplets in stratosphere screen out sunlight but let Earth's heat escape.
16. (a) Increased greenhouse gases mean that more heat is trapped in the atmosphere. (b) too dry to support crops, polar and alpine glaciers could melt, sea level would rise (c) warm surface current that occurs in the Pacific Ocean; winters milder, southeast gets precipitation, fewer Atlantic hurricanes
17. (a) Models try to predict present climate and its changes; predicting past climates known from geologic evidence (b) clouds, greenhouse gases, oceans

Answers to all questions appear in the Teacher's Guide at the back of this book.

■ Summary

I The climate of a region is the overall description of the weather experienced there.

II Many factors act together to determine Earth's climate. They are latitude, altitude, topography, distance from large bodies of water, ocean currents, prevailing winds, and the amount of heat received from the sun.

Temperatures are cooler with larger yearly ranges at high latitudes, but the daily temperature range is lower.

Ocean currents can affect an area's temperature.

The windward sides of mountains are moister than their leeward sides. Mountains can keep cold air from reaching an area, making the winters milder.

III Precipitation varies with latitude. The rainfall in the tropics is high because of the rising air in the doldrums. Precipitation in the polar latitudes is low because of sinking air and the low temperatures. Mid-latitude precipitation comes with fronts and low-pressure systems.

Coastal fogs form when warm, moist air from the oceans crosses a colder surface.

IV Global climate changes are caused by changes in Earth's energy budget.

Causes for global cooling include variations in dust in sunspots, dust in atmosphere from volcanoes and asteroids, variations in Earth's orbit, and the location of the continents.

Increases in greenhouse gases may account for global warming. El Niño has short term warming effects.

Computer models are being used to try to predict climate trends.

■ Vocabulary

bora	El Niño
chinook	foehn
climate	marine climate
continental climate	mistral
	Santa Ana

■ Review

Number your paper from 1 to 17. Select the best answer for each item. Write the letter of your answer on your paper.

1. A good description of climate includes (a) temperature and temperature range, (b) how the temperature varies through the year, (c) how the precipitation varies through the year, (d) all of the above.

2. Climate is controlled by (a) latitude, (b) altitude, (c) ocean currents, (d) all of the above.

3. Areas near the equator have (a) high average temperatures and large yearly temperature ranges, (b) long days and short nights, (c) high average temperatures and small yearly temperature ranges, (d) very long nights during the winter.

4. Denver and Kansas City are at the same latitude, but Denver's altitude is much higher. Denver would be expected to have (a) higher average temperatures, (b) lower average temperatures, (c) more rain, (d) the same average temperatures.

5. Marine climates (a) are warmer than continental climates, (b) are colder than continental climates, (c) have greater yearly temperature ranges than continental climates, (d) have smaller yearly temperature ranges than continental climates.

6. Prevailing winds (a) have no effect on climate, (b) always come from the ocean, (c) may be blocked by mountains, (d) result in lower average temperatures.

7. Ocean currents (a) do not affect temperature, (b) may be colder or warmer than the places they pass, (c) affect areas that have continental climates, (d) always result in milder temperatures.

8. The intertropical convergence zone is (a) a zone of sinking air, (b) a zone of sharp temperature contrast, (c) located in the middle latitudes, (d) a zone of rainfall.

9. Precipitation in the middle latitudes falls (a) during the summer rainy season, (b) in

For further review, see **Study Guide.**
For assessment, see **Chapter Tests**
and **Computer Test Bank.**

low-pressure areas, (c) where air diverges, (d) when warm air flows over cold water.

10. The windward sides of mountains are usually (a) rainier and warmer than the leeward sides, (b) cooler and rainier than the leeward sides, (c) cooler and drier than the leeward sides, (d) warmer and drier than the leeward sides.

11. Locations near oceans (a) always have heavy rainfall, (b) have heavy rainfall when the prevailing winds blow from the ocean, (c) are always very dry, (d) have heavy rainfall when the prevailing winds blow from the land.

12. Warm air over cold water results in (a) thunderstorms, (b) unstable weather, (c) warming of the air, (d) fogs.

13. Earth's energy budget (a) is not related to climate, (b) is not at all in balance right now, (c) has always been the same as it is today, (d) is in near balance right now.

14. A volcanic eruption may produce (a) cooling for 1-7 years, (b) short-term warming, (c) long-term warming, (d) no effect on climate.

15. El Niño (a) is associated with cold waters across the equatorial Pacific Ocean, (b) is associated with warm waters across the equatorial Pacific Ocean, (c) has happened only once, (d) is caused by greenhouse gases.

16. Sunlight reaching Earth's surface is determined by (a) clouds overhead, (b) the solar output, (c) dust in the air, (d) all of the above.

17. An increase in atmospheric carbon dioxide (a) results in cooling, (b) results in warming, (c) has never occurred, (d) has no effect on climate.

■ Interpret and Apply

On your paper, answer each question in complete sentences.

1. Volcano A has an explosive eruption that causes large amounts of sulfur dioxide and dust to enter the stratosphere. Volcano B's

eruption produces the same amount of material, but it stays mainly in the troposphere. Which volcano will cool the atmosphere for the longer time? Why?

2. Modern civilization is increasing the amounts of carbon dioxide and particulate matter (such as smoke particles) in the atmosphere. Which pollutant might have the greatest effect on the climate? Why?

■ Critical Thinking

The map shows what North America would look like if it were moved so that the United States lay in the trade-wind zones and Canada was in the horse latitudes.

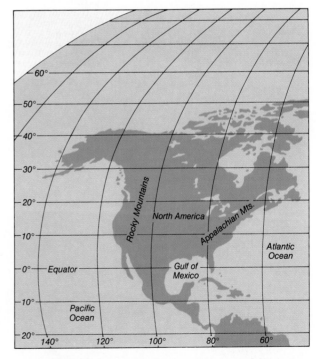

1. Describe the average annual temperature and precipitation (a) on the United States West Coast, (b) just east of the Rocky Mountains in Wyoming, and (c) in Philadelphia, Pennsylvania.

2. What would the climate be like in Canada? Why?

UNIT SEVEN
Earth's History

▲
Geologists have read these rock layers and found that they are ancient sand dunes. Which layers are from older dunes? Which are from younger dunes?

▲
What do these tracks tell about the creature that made them?

What do these fossil ferns reveal about the environment at the time the rock layer was formed? ▶

Where is Earth's history written?

Rock layers on Earth's surface are like pages in a diary; each layer records an event in Earth's history. But the diary isn't written in English. Geologists have had to learn a different language to read the record. This language includes evidence and events seen on Earth today. Look at the photographs. What does each show about reading the diary of Earth's history?

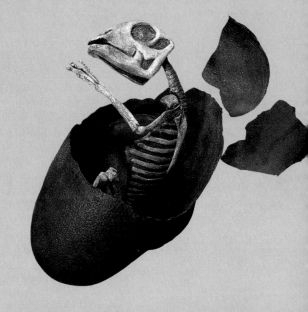

What does this fossil dinosaur show about its life cycle? ▶

How are today's life forms helpful to understanding life forms of the past? ▼

The Rock Record

▲
This fossil plant is more than 200 million years old.

How Do You Know That . . .

Fossil shapes were left in rocks by plants and animals that lived millions of years ago? One way to find out is by learning the age of the sedimentary rock that contains the fossil. The fossil and the rock must have been deposited at the same time in order for the fossil to be a part of the rock layer. Several methods can be used for finding and identifying the age of a rock. First, however, you must learn how to read the rock record and identify the fossils preserved in it.

I Reading the Rock Record

Topic 1 Telling Time

Most of the events earth scientists study took place long before there were people to record them. Without clocks and calendars, it is difficult to determine the order of past events. The ages of past events in Earth's history can be indicated in two different ways. One way records relative time. The other way measures absolute time. Both kinds of time are needed to read the rock record.

Relative time places events in a sequence but does not identify their actual date of occurrence. For example, suppose that several years ago your family took a vacation trip to the Rocky Mountains. Now you cannot remember the exact date of the trip. However, you know that it took place before you entered the fifth grade. In recalling the trip in this way, you are using relative time. Thus relative time does not tell the actual age of an event, but it does indicate the age in comparison with other events.

Absolute time identifies the actual date of an event. The exact date of your visit to the Rocky Mountains would be absolute time. Geologists use absolute time to identify the actual age of rock layers. One rock might be 300 million years old, another rock 200 million years old, and a third rock 50 million years old.

In addition to identifying the actual age of an event, absolute time is important for another reason. If the actual time of two events is known, the length of time between the two events can be calculated. Such values make it possible to determine the rate at which a geologic process such as mountain building occurs.

Absolute time might seem more important than relative time because absolute time gives an actual date. However, absolute dates are difficult and expensive to obtain. Most geologic work is done using relative time.

Topic 2 Finding Age with Relative Time

An important part of reading the rock record is determining the relative ages of events in the record. Several rules for determining relative age by using relative time help to do that.

The *law of superposition* states that in a sequence of undisturbed (that is, not overturned) sedimentary rocks, the oldest rocks will be at the bottom of the sequence and the youngest will be at the top. This is the basis of all relative-age determinations and a fundamental concept in studying Earth's history.

OBJECTIVES

A Explain the difference between relative time and absolute time and list some rules for determining relative time.

B List the eras of the geologic timetable and discuss the basis by which they are defined.

SCIENCE BACKGROUND
Relative time is based primarily upon fossils and the principle of superposition.

SCIENCE BACKGROUND
Absolute time is also called measured time. Radioactive dating made absolute time measurements possible.

OF INTEREST
As a result of extensive analysis, the dates of most time intervals on the geologic timetable are now fairly well established. The original timetable, however, indicated only relative time.

TEACHING TIP
You may wish to review the principle of original horizontality here.

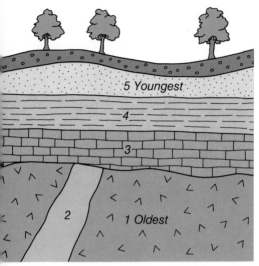

32.1 The relative ages of the rocks are given by numbers. The surface that separates layers 1 and 3 is an unconformity.

SCIENCE BACKGROUND
Unconformities can also occur under water. Turbidity currents (Chapter 18, Topic 6) are a possible cause of underwater unconformities. Nondeposition is another cause.

TEACHING TIP
You may wish to include a discussion of the different kinds of unconformities here. See the Teacher's Guide.

32.2 An unconformity in Paleozoic rock layers

The *law of cross-cutting relationships* states that an igneous rock is younger than the rocks it has intruded, or cut across. This law can also be applied to fault surfaces. The event that caused a fault is younger than any rocks the fault has cut across.

The *law of included fragments* states that pieces of one rock found in another rock must be older than the rock in which they are found. One example would be pebbles in a conglomerate. The pebbles must have existed before the conglomerate formed and, therefore, are older than the conglomerate.

More relative age information comes from the examination of unconformities. An **unconformity** is a place in the rock record where layers of rock are missing. The missing layers may never have been deposited. More often, like pages missing from a book, the rock layers may have been deposited and later removed. For example, an unconformity occurs if a rock surface is raised above sea level, eroded, then resubmerged and buried under new sediment. Such a sequence of events could result in a large age difference between the rocks above and those below the erosional surface. Unconformities are gaps in geologic time.

Topic 3   **The Geologic Timetable**

A geologist studying the rocks in a particular area can use the rules discussed in Topic 2 to determine the relative ages of the rocks in that area. If these rocks can be matched with the rocks in another area, their relative ages can also be determined. By matching rocks over large areas, geologists have determined the relative ages of most of the rocks on Earth's surface. Over many years, geologists have worked out a timetable that subdivides geologic time into units based on the formation of certain rocks.

The **geologic timetable**, shown in Figure 32.3 on pages 600-601, is a summary of the major events of Earth's history preserved in the rock record. Fossils are an important part of that history. In fact, many of the rock layers have been identified and matched based on the fossils in them.

The longest segments of geologic time are called **eras**. The oldest era is the **Archean** Era. The Archean Era began when Earth was formed between 4 and 5 billion years ago. The earliest known rocks formed during the Archean Era.

The **Proterozoic** Era began about 2.5 billion years ago. The difference between Archean and Proterozoic rocks is that Proterozoic rocks contain fossils of simple plants and worms that lived in the oceans. No evidence of life on land has been found in Proterozoic rocks.

The **Paleozoic** Era is marked by a more abundant fossil record. The rocks formed during the Paleozoic Era contain fossils of both land and ocean plants and animals. The Paleozoic Era began about 570 million years ago.

The **Mesozoic** Era began about 250 million years ago. Dinosaurs thrived during most of Mesozoic time.

The youngest of the eras is the **Cenozoic** Era. This era began about 65 million years ago and is still going on today. Recent events of the era are the Ice Age and the appearance of humans.

Eras are also divided into smaller segments. The divisions of eras are called **periods.** Like eras, periods differ from one another in plant and animal life although less so than between eras. Some of the periods are further divided into **epochs**. These divisions are shorter and changes in life are not as large as between periods.

VIDEODISC SELECTION

Geologic time scale
Side 1: 707 to 722, 16-frame sequence

TOPIC QUESTIONS

Each topic question refers to the topic of the same number.

1. **(a)** How is the age of an event defined using relative time? **(b)** What is absolute time? **(c)** Why is it important to know the length of time between two geologic events?

2. **(a)** According to the law of superposition, where are the oldest rocks in an undisturbed sequence of sedimentary rocks? **(b)** How does the age of an igneous intrusion compare to the age of the rocks it has intruded? What law describes this age relationship? **(c)** How is the age of the pebbles within a conglomerate related to the age of the conglomerate? What law describes this relationship? **(d)** What is an unconformity? How does it occur? What does it represent?

3. **(a)** List the eras of geologic time, from oldest to most recent. **(b)** What are periods and epochs?

ANSWERS
  1. (a) by its place in a sequence (b) the actual measured age of an event   (c) to find the rate at which a geologic process occurs
  2. (a) on the bottom   (b) intrusion is younger; law of cross-cutting relationships   (c) pebbles are older; law of included fragments   (d) gap in rock record; erosion or non-deposition of rock; missing part of rock record
  3. (a) Archean, Proterozoic, Paleozoic, Mesozoic, Cenozoic (b) divisions of eras

CAREERS

Dr. Meyer Rubin
Radiocarbon Expert

Radiocarbon dating has undergone a revolution that has greatly increased the number and kinds of carbon specimens whose age can be determined. The major change has been in the size of the specimen needed for analysis. The older method, in which a sample was burned and its gas analyzed with a kind of Geiger counter, required sample sizes of up to ten grams or more of material. The new method utilizes a particle accelerator and requires samples of only a few milligrams in size.

Dr. Meyer Rubin of the U.S. Geological Survey is enthusiastic about the accelerator method because of the greater number of events that can be dated. For example, by examining a piece of charcoal from under a lava flow, it is possible to date the eruption that caused the flow. He adds that dating such events as lava flows or faults may make it possible to establish timetables for them and thus to predict their recurrence in the future.

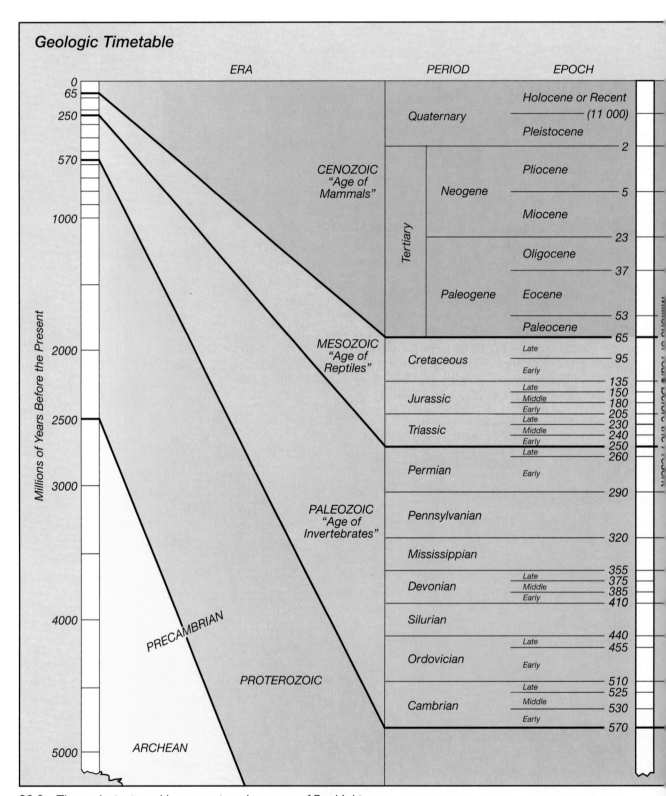

32.3   The geologic timetable summarizes the events of Earth's history.

LIFE	NORTH AMERICAN ROCK RECORD	INFERRED POSITION OF EARTH LANDMASSES*
Humans dominant. "Domestic" animal species develop.	West Coast uplift continues in U.S. Great Lakes form.	
Hominids develop. Elephants flourish in N. America, then die out.	Ice Age. Raising of mountains and plateaus in Western U.S.	Tertiary
Hominids appear. Modern horse, camel, elephant develop. Sequoias decline; tropical trees driven south.	N. America joined to S. America. Sierras and Appalachians re-elevated by isostatic rebound.	
Horse migrates to Asia, elephant to America. Grasses, grazing animals thrive.	N. America joined to Asia. Volcanism in northwest United States, Columbia Plateau.	
Mammal progress. Elephants in Africa. Monkeys die out in N. America.	Alps and Himalayas forming. Volcanism in western United States.	
Pygmy ancestors of modern horse, other mammals. First whales. Diatoms, flowering plants thrive.	Coal forming in western U.S.	
Many new mammals appear.	Uplift in western U.S. continues.	Cretaceous
Dinosaurs, ammonites die out. Mammals, birds advance. Flowering plants, hardwoods rise.	Uplift of Rockies begins. Colorado Plateau raised. Coal swamps in western U.S. Intrusion of Sierra Nevada batholith.	
Giant dinosaurs. First birds, first mammals. Conifers and cycads abundant.	West central N. America under huge sea. Gulf of Mexico, Atlantic Ocean begin to form.	Triassic
Reptiles thrive. Forests of conifers and cycads.	Volcanism and faulting along East Coast. Palisades of Hudson formed.	
Mass extinction of existing species. Trilobites, seed ferns, scale trees die out. Corals abundant.	Final uplift in Appalachians. Ice Age in South America. Salt-forming deserts in western U.S.	
First reptiles. Many giant insects. Spore-bearing plants, amphibians flourish.	Great coal-forming swamps in North America and Europe.	Carboniferous
Amphibians and crinoids flourish. Ferns, conifers abundant.	Extensive submergence of continents.	
First amphibians; fishes abound. First land plants, forests.	Mountain building continues in New England and Canada. White Mountains raised.	Devonian
First land animals (spiders, scorpions). Fish develop; marine invertebrates thrive.	Salt-and-gypsum-forming deserts in eastern U.S.	
Marine invertebrates thrive: mollusks, trilobites, graptolites.	Beginning of Appalachian mountain building. Taconic and Green Mts. form. Half of N. America submerged.	Early Ordovician
Many marine invertebrates (trilobites, brachiopods, snails, sponges). Many seaweeds. First vertebrates (fish).	Extensive deposition of sediments in inland seas.	Cambrian
No life on land. Simple marine plants (algae, fungi) and marine worms. Stromatolites dominant. Others probably existed, but fossil evidence is lacking.	Great volcanic activity, lava flows, metamorphism of rocks. Formation of iron, copper, and nickle ores.	N ▲ * Palaeontological Assoc. Newcastle, England

OBJECTIVES

A Define *fossil*; identify and describe some ways in which fossils are preserved.

B Summarize Darwin's theory of evolution.

C List some ways in which fossils are used to read the rock record.

D Define *correlation* and identify some methods of correlation.

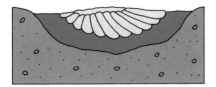

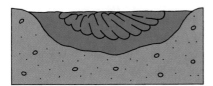

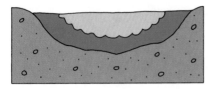

32.4 A mold forms when the original animal or plant dissolves and leaves a hole. New material fills the hole and makes a cast of the original organism.

II The Fossil Record

Topic 4 How Fossils Are Formed

Fossils are both the basis for the geologic timetable and an important part of the rock record. A **fossil** is any evidence of earlier life preserved in a rock. The evidence can be shells, bones, petrified trees, impressions made by plant leaves, footprints, or even burrows made by worms.

Fossils are preserved in the rock record in several ways. In rare cases, the *original remains* — the actual, unchanged remains — of the plant or animal are preserved. One example includes the large elephantlike creatures, called woolly mammoths, that have been found frozen in permafrost in Siberia and Alaska. These fossils are exceptional because the entire animal has been preserved. More often the soft tissues of an animal decay and disappear, leaving only the original hard parts. The bones and teeth of dinosaurs found in the Rocky Mountains are examples.

The remains of some prehistoric insects have been found in hardened resin. Resin is a sticky sap that oozes from pine trees. A hardened resin is called *amber*. Most amber comes from the shores of the Baltic Sea in Europe. It is used as an ornamental material.

A second way in which fossils can be preserved is as *replaced remains*. In these fossils, the soft parts of the original animal have disappeared and the hard parts have been replaced by mineral material. The replacement is usually the work of underground water. Circulating groundwater removes the original organic material, often an atom at a time, and replaces it with a mineral material. The minerals calcite, silica, and pyrite are common replacement materials. The result is an exact copy of the original plant or animal, which is made from minerals. Petrified wood is a good example of replaced remains.

A third method of fossil preservation is through molds and casts of the original animal or plant. Sometimes a fossil shell or bone is dissolved completely out of the rock in which it has been deposited. This leaves a hollow depression in the rock called a *mold*. The mold shows only the original shape of the fossil. When new mineral material fills the mold, this material forms a *cast* of the original fossil. Molds and casts of shellfish are common fossils. The molds of ferns, leaves, and fish are also found in the rock layers of some areas.

Trace fossils are evidence of life other than the remains of a plant or animal. Trace fossils include any impression left in the rock by an animal, such as trails, footprints, tracks, burrows, and borings. Many animals are known only by the impressions they have left behind because their remains have not yet been found. For example, some of the earliest fossils in the rock record are trace fossils in the form of borings. The animals that made the borings are unknown, although they are assumed to have been some kind of worm living on the seafloor.

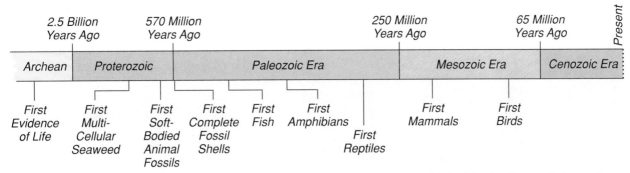

| Archean | Proterozoic | Paleozoic Era | Mesozoic Era | Cenozoic Era |

2.5 Billion Years Ago — 570 Million Years Ago — 250 Million Years Ago — 65 Million Years Ago — Present

First Evidence of Life — First Multi-Cellular Seaweed — First Soft-Bodied Animal Fossils — First Complete Fossil Shells — First Fish — First Amphibians — First Reptiles — First Mammals — First Birds

32.5 The fossil record shows that life forms have changed over time.

Topic 5 Fossils as Evidence for Evolution

The fossil record indicates that the first organisms were simple in structure. As time passed, life forms increased in size and complexity. One place that reveals a great deal about the history of living things is the Grand Canyon in Arizona. The youngest rocks, near the top of the canyon, contain imprints of land reptiles, ferns, and insects. A quarter of the way down the canyon is a layer of sedimentary rock containing marine organisms, including fish. Deeper in the canyon layers there are no fish fossils, only a few shells and traces of worms. The oldest rock layers, at the bottom of the canyon, have no fossils at all.

The rock record shows that through time many kinds of organisms disappear and are replaced by new and different organisms. The evidence indicates a changing or evolving pattern of life forms. This process of change that produces new life forms over geologic time is called **evolution.** The *theory of evolution* provides a scientific explanation for the past and present diversity of life on Earth.

At one time, most people thought that life forms were fixed and unchanging. However, no existing theory accounted for the fossils of enormous dinosaurs that were no longer living. In the 1800's, several new ideas were proposed to explain the changes in life forms preserved in the fossil record. One theory proposed in 1859 by Charles Darwin, a British naturalist, continues to be the best explanation for most of the existing evidence for evolution. Darwin suggested that *natural selection* accounts for the changes that produced new life forms. By that, Darwin meant that organisms who survive to produce offspring are those who inherited the most beneficial traits for surviving in a particular environment.

Darwin observed a wide diversity of life forms that are adapted to their environment. From his observations, Darwin concluded that life forms evolve gradually over many generations. If this were true, the fossil record should show organisms that are gradually different over geologic time. There should be evidence of small changes in organisms leading to modern-day life. But the fossil record is incomplete. Very few organisms have a complete, unbroken fossil record.

Modern scientists offer another explanation for how quickly evolution occurs. Much of the fossil record shows that several types of organisms lived for very long periods without showing much

32.6 The soft parts of dinosaurs decay, but the hard parts have been preserved unchanged in some areas of the Rocky Mountains.

32.7 Petrified wood is an example of replaced remains.

SCIENCE BACKGROUND
Darwin's theory of gradual change is called, not surprisingly, gradualism. The theory for abrupt change followed by long periods of no change is called punctuated equilibrium. Much research on evolution is taking place today.

change. Then "suddenly"—in a million years or less—a whole new set of different, but clearly related, organisms appeared. These organisms also lasted a long time relatively unchanged. (Remember that "sudden" is relative. A million years is a very short time period in all of geologic time.) There is considerable debate about whether evolution follows a steady, gradual path or a path interrupted by short periods of dramatic change.

Topic 6 Index Fossils and Key Beds

Because animals evolve over time, some fossils are typical of a particular time segment of Earth's history. These fossils are very useful to geologists because they identify the relative age of the rock in which they occur. Such fossils are called **index fossils,** or **guide fossils.**

An index fossil has three characteristics. First, a good index fossil must be easily recognizable. Such fossils must be unique in some way so that they can easily be told from other similar but nonindex fossils. Second, an index fossil must be widespread in occurrence. That is, an index fossil must be found over a broad geographical area. This makes it possible to use index fossils to match rock layers of a particular age over wide areas. Some index fossils can be used to match rocks between continents. Third, index fossils are limited in time. The organisms only existed for a short period of time, so their fossils occur in only a few rock layers.

A **key bed** is a single rock layer that has the same characteristics as an index fossil. Key beds are easily recognizable and occur over a wide area. A large volcanic eruption is an excellent source of material for key beds. The layer that results from an eruption represents a single instant in time but is unique and widespread.

32.8 The trilobite *Elrathia* is an index fossil for the middle Cambrian.

VIDEODISC SELECTION

Trilobite fossils
Side 1: 3854 to 3855, 2-frame sequence

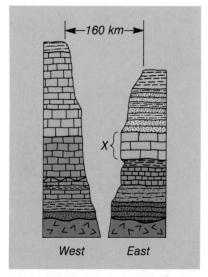

32.9 Which layer on the left correlates with layer *X* on the right?

Topic 7 Rock Correlation

Correlation is the matching of rock layers from one area to another. For example, a geologist might wish to know if a layer of limestone in New York is the same limestone as one in Michigan.

The simplest and most direct method of correlation is "walking the outcrop." An outcrop is the part of a rock layer that can be seen at Earth's surface. Following along an outcrop is an easy way of finding out if two rock layers are the same. However, walking along the outcrop may be difficult in areas where soils are thick, vegetation is heavy, or extensive erosion has occurred. Also, walking an outcrop is not practical when two outcrops are far apart.

Under these conditions, a second method of correlation, matching similar rock characteristics, might be used. In this method, rocks are matched by such characteristics as appearance, color, composition, or some other unique feature. For example, a rock that weathers with a distinctive rust color might be easy to recognize and, therefore, usable for correlation.

The best method of correlation over long distances is index fossils. Good index fossils are often the remains of creatures that floated in the oceans. Waves and currents can carry such organisms throughout the world to be deposited in any kind of sediment.

Key beds, such as volcanic ash, can also be used to correlate rock formations. Volcanic ash becomes a clay material called *bentonite* in sedimentary rock layers. Beds of bentonite have been used to correlate layers in many areas.

Topic 8   **Other Uses of Fossils**

In addition to determining relative time and correlating between rock layers, fossils are important for other reasons as well. One other use of fossils is as indicators of past climate. For example, coral reefs today form only in shallow, warm water between approximately 30° N and 30° S latitudes. When a rock containing fossil coral is found, it can be assumed that the particular area was once an area of shallow warm water.

A second important use of fossils, especially microfossils, occurs in oil exploration. *Microfossils* are fossils so tiny that they have to be studied with a microscope. Foraminifera and diatoms (Chapter 17) are examples of microfossils. In drilling for oil, long cores of sedimentary rock are obtained. The core might contain only bits of large fossils but hundreds of microfossils. The microfossils can then be used to correlate the layers of one core with those of another core taken in a different location.

TOPIC QUESTIONS

Each topic question refers to the topic of the same number.

4. **(a)** What is a fossil?   **(b)** Identify two ways in which original remains are preserved.   **(c)** Describe how fossils are preserved as replaced remains and give an example of replaced remains.   **(d)** How are fossils preserved through molds and casts?   **(e)** Give some examples of fossil impressions.

5. **(a)** What is evolution?   **(b)** How does the fossil record provide evidence for evolution?   **(c)** What did Charles Darwin mean by natural selection?   **(d)** Compare the rate at which Darwin thought evolution occurred with the rate at which some scientists of today think it occurred.

6. **(a)** List the three characteristics of an index fossil.   **(b)** What is a key bed? Identify a material that forms good key beds.

7. **(a)** Define *correlation*.   **(b)** List some methods by which rock layers are correlated.

8. **(a)** How are fossils indicators of past climates?   **(b)** How are fossils used in oil exploration?

32.10   This layer of volcanic ash is a key bed because it represents an instant in geologic time and is widespread in occurrence.

SCIENCE BACKGROUND

An example of a volcanic ash that can be used as a key bed is the Old Crow Tephra. This layer is a very useful Pleistocene time marker across Alaska and the western Yukon. The 1980 eruption of Mount St. Helens is an example of a recent event that formed a key bed.

ANSWERS

4. (a) any evidence of earlier life preserved in a rock   (b) frozen; trapped in amber; some hard parts preserved intact   (c) groundwater removes original materials, puts mineral material in its place; petrified wood   (d) original remains removed leaving mold, which fills with material to become cast   (e) trails, footprints, tracks, burrows, borings

5. (a) the process of change that produces new life forms   (b) shows that many kinds of organisms disappear and are replaced by new, different ones   (c) organisms best suited to surviving in a particular environment survive and produce offspring   (d) steadily and gradually vs. relatively suddenly

6. (a) easily recognizable, widespread, lived only for limited time   (b) single layer with characteristics of an index fossil; volcanic ash

7. (a) matching rock layers from one area to another   (b) "walking the outcrop," similar rock characteristics, index fossils, key beds

8. (a) Some animals live only in particular climates   (b) Microfossils can be used to correlate between drill cores.

OBJECTIVES

A Describe how tree rings and varves are used in determining absolute time.

B Explain how radioactive elements can be used to determine absolute time.

C Identify some radiometric dating methods and discuss the advantages of each.

III Measuring Absolute Time

Topic 9 Tree Rings

Methods of measuring absolute time must provide a specific date for the occurrence of an event. One method for determining absolute dates is by counting tree rings. These are the concentric rings seen in a stump or log. Each ring usually represents a single year. Under magnification, each ring can be seen to consist of two kinds of cells—large, thin-walled cells and smaller, thicker-walled cells. The larger cells form in the spring when the tree is starting its yearly growth. The smaller cells form after the tree has leafed out. The width of a ring depends upon the temperature and rainfall that year. Thus tree rings provide not only dates but a record of the weather as well.

Because each tree ring is different, the pattern of rings in one tree can be correlated, or matched, with those of another tree. By applying this technique to wood in Native American ruins in the southwestern United States, scientists have determined dates back to almost 2000 B.C.

The bristlecone pine is the oldest living tree to be dated by counting tree rings. Bristlecone pines are slow-growing timberline trees found in the Sierra Nevadas of California. One bristlecone pine was found to be more than 4600 years old.

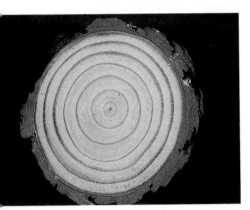

32.11 Tree rings can be counted to determine absolute time.

Topic 10 Varves

A *varve* is any sediment that shows a yearly cycle. Varves can form in any body of water, including the oceans. However, they are clearest in glacial lakes dating from the Ice Age.

Wherever lakes formed at the front of a glacier, streams from the melting ice carried sediments into the lakes. In summer, the ice melted rapidly. Swiftly flowing streams carried a mixture of sands, silts, and clays into the lakes. The sands and silts settled to the bottom of each lake in a thick light-colored layer. Wind blowing across the lakes created currents that kept the fine clays in suspension.

When winter came, the streams slowed or stopped as they froze over. The lakes also froze over. Winds were unable to reach and stir the water. The clays and other fine material that had accumulated in the lake water all summer then settled to the bottom to form a thin layer of fine, dark sediment. Thus each year two distinct layers of sediment were deposited—a thick, light-colored sandy layer in summer and a thin, dark-colored clay layer in winter.

Like tree rings, each annual varve is different. As a result, the varves of one lake can be correlated with the varves of other lakes. By matching deposits, dates back to 15 000 years ago have been determined.

32.12 Varves can be studied to determine how long a glacier was in a particular place before it finally disappeared.

Topic 11 **Radioactive Elements and Absolute Time**

Tree rings and varves are methods of obtaining absolute dates with good accuracy, but neither method can be used to date very far back in time. For older dates, radioactive isotopes (Chapter 3, Topic 6) are used. These are atoms of elements that give off radiation from their nuclei. Three kinds of radiation are involved—alpha, beta, and gamma. *Alpha* ray particles have the same structure as the nucleus of a helium atom (two protons and two neutrons). *Beta* ray particles are high-speed electrons. *Gamma* rays are like X rays.

Each time an alpha ray is released from an atomic nucleus, the atom changes to a new, lighter element. This process is called **radioactive decay**. If the new element is also radioactive, decay takes place again. Radiation continues to be released until an element is formed that is stable, or not radioactive.

Uranium is an element with a radioactive isotope. The most common radioactive isotope of uranium is uranium-238. When U-238 gives off an alpha particle, it becomes an atom of thorium-234, which is also radioactive. The reaction is written as follows:

$$^{238}_{92}\text{U} \rightarrow {}^{4}_{2}\text{He} + {}^{234}_{90}\text{Th}$$

Decay continues with alpha, beta, and gamma rays being given off, until finally an element is formed that is not radioactive. This stable product element for U-238 is an isotope of lead, Pb-206.

Topic 12 **Half-Life**

Radioactive elements decay at characteristic and constant rates. These decay rates are assumed to be unaffected by the passage of time or changes in temperature or pressure. At the moment an igneous rock crystallizes, radioactive elements in the rock begin to decay. The ratio of the amount of radioactive element left in the rock to the amount of stable product element is used to determine the absolute age of the sample.

The rate at which a radioactive element decays is called its **half-life**. The half-life is the time it takes for half of the atoms of the radioactive element to decay to a stable end product. Half-lives range from a fraction of a second to billions of years. For example, the element protactinium has a half-life of about one minute. The half-life of uranium-238 is 4.5 billion years.

An example with thorium-234, shown graphically in Figure 32.15, will show better how half-life can be used to date a material. Thorium-234 has a half-life of about 24 days. In a sample of thorium, half of the atoms will have been converted to a stable product at the end of 24 days and half will remain unchanged. During the next 24 days, half of the remaining unchanged part will decay. During each half-life, half of the radioactive material, no matter how small the amount, will decay to a stable product.

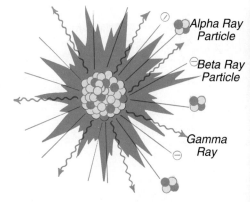

32.13 Radioactive elements produce three different types of radiation. When an alpha ray particle is emitted, the atom changes to a different element.

SCIENCE BACKGROUND

Another product of radioactive decay is heat. This heat may be the source of energy for plate movement.

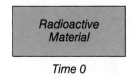

Time 0

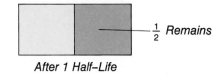

$\frac{1}{2}$ *Remains*

After 1 Half–Life

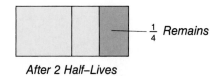

$\frac{1}{4}$ *Remains*

After 2 Half–Lives

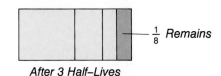

$\frac{1}{8}$ *Remains*

After 3 Half–Lives

32.14 At the end of each half-life, half of the radioactive material remains.

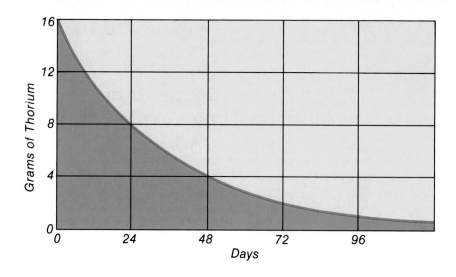

32.15 The radioactive decay of 16 grams of thorium-234. At the end of one half-life (24 days), 8 grams remain. At the end of two half-lives (48 days), 4 grams remain. At the end of three half-lives (72 days), 2 grams remain. At the end of four half-lives (96 days), 1 gram remains.

Topic 13 **Radiocarbon Dating**

Radiocarbon, an isotope of carbon, is used in radioactive dating. Radiocarbon dating was developed by Dr. Willard F. Libby in 1947. The half-life of radiocarbon is about 5700 years. Using radiocarbon, scientists can measure back about 100 000 years.

Radiocarbon dating uses the radioactive isotope carbon-14. All living plant and animal cells contain carbon. Most of that carbon is ordinary carbon-12, but a small percentage is radioactive carbon-14. Libby recognized that the amount of carbon-14 in the cells of a living animal or plant stays constant as long as the animal or plant is alive because the organism continually absorbs carbon-14 from food and water. But, as soon as an organism dies, the percentage of carbon-14 decreases at a rate set by its half-life. Thus, the ratio of the amount of ordinary carbon-12 to the amount of radioactive carbon-14 can be used to tell how long ago a plant or animal died and, in turn, when the organism lived.

Radiocarbon dating has two major problems. First, the method cannot be used on rocks but only on things that once were alive, such as logs and bones. Second, because the half-life of carbon-14 is relatively short, the method cannot date very far back in time. Nevertheless, radiocarbon is invaluable for dating such things as the wooden tools and skeletons of prehistoric people. Radiocarbon can also be used to date plant and animal materials buried in Ice Age deposits.

Topic 14 **Other Radiometric Methods**

The dating of rocks in Earth's crust is done by several radiometric methods. One method is *uranium-lead* in which U-238, the radioactive isotope, decays to lead-206, the stable end product. The half-life of U-238 is 4.5 billion years. This long half-life makes it possible to use this method to date the oldest rocks in the crust. However, the uranium-lead clock cannot be used on every old rock. The reason is that original uranium is rarely found in sedimentary or metamorphic rocks. Neither is it found in all igneous rocks. Thus uranium-lead can be used only on igneous rocks that contain the right kind of uranium isotope. A second difficulty in using uranium-lead is its long half-life. Although the method can be used on very old rocks, it does not give reliable results on rocks less than about 10 million years old because so little of the U-238 will have decayed in that time.

A second method of dating rocks of the crust is the *rubidium-strontium* method. The half-life of rubidium-87 is about 49 billion years, or more than ten times Earth's age! Rubidium-87 decays into the element strontium-87. Rubidium can be used to date almost all igneous rocks because it occurs in common minerals such as the feldspars and micas. If both rubidium-87 and uranium-238 occur in the same rock, one method can be used as a check on the value obtained by the other method.

A third method is the *potassium-argon* method. Potassium-40 decays into the element argon-40. The half-life of potassium-40 is about 1.3 billion years. The potassium-argon method has many advantages. Potassium, unlike uranium and rubidium, is a very common element. It is found in potash feldspar and black mica. Minerals that can be dated by this method are found in metamorphic and sedimentary rocks as well as in igneous rocks. It is possible to date many rocks with potassium-argon that cannot be dated by uranium or rubidium. In some cases, this method can date rocks as young as 50 000 years.

SCIENCE BACKGROUND
Uranium and rubidium are especially good for dating Precambrian rocks.

SCIENCE BACKGROUND
One problem with potassium-argon is that the product of the decay is a gas. Some of the gas may be lost, especially if the minerals are reheated to temperatures over 150°C during metamorphism.

SCIENCE BACKGROUND
Dating sedimentary rocks is difficult. The dates obtained are actually the dates of formation of the mineral crystals, which are earlier than the formation of the sedimentary rock.

TOPIC QUESTIONS

Each topic question refers to the topic of the same number.

9. **(a)** Describe the two parts of a single tree ring and identify what both parts represent.   **(b)** What factors determine the width of a tree ring?   **(c)** What are the oldest living trees?

10. **(a)** What are varves?   **(b)** Describe the two parts of a varve layer and discuss when each forms.   **(c)** How are varves used for determining dates?

11. **(a)** Name and describe three types of radiation given off by radioactive elements.   **(b)** What is the stable end product from the decay of uranium-238?

12. **(a)** Define *half-life*.   **(b)** Describe the radioactive decay of 16 grams of thorium-234.

13. **(a)** What is the half-life of radiocarbon?   **(b)** Which carbon isotope is used for radiocarbon dating and how does it work?   **(c)** On what kinds of materials can radiocarbon dating be used?   **(d)** Identify two problems in using radiocarbon dating.

14. **(a)** What are the disadvantages of the uranium-lead method for measuring geologic time?   **(b)** What is the advantage of the rubidium-strontium method?   **(c)** What is the advantage of the potassium-argon method?

ANSWERS
9. (a) large, thin-walled cells for spring; smaller, thicker-walled cells for summer   (b) temperature and rainfall   (c) bristlecone pines in California

10. (a) sediments that show a yearly cycle   (b) thick, light-colored layer in summer; thin, dark-colored layer in winter   (c) by correlating the varve pattern of one lake with the pattern in another

11. (a) alpha, 2 protons and 2 neutrons; beta, high-speed electrons; gamma, like X rays   (b) Pb-206

12. (a) time for half of radioactive material to decay   (b) 8 g after first half-life, 4 g after second, 2 g after third, 1 g after fourth

13. (a) 5700 years   (b) C-14; ratio of C-14 to "normal" C-12   (c) only things that were once living   (d) cannot use on rocks, cannot date very far back in time

14. (a) works only on igneous rocks with right kind of uranium; half-life too long for more recent dates   (b) can be used on almost all igneous rocks   (c) can be used on almost all rocks

M A P ACTIVITY

Interpreting Geologic History

What do you think about when you hear or see the word *canyon*? Towering cliffs? Whitewater rafting? The breathtaking scenery of the Grand Canyon? What you probably don't think about is the thousands of years it takes to form a canyon— the uplift of rock layers and the slow erosion by running water.

Horseshoe Canyon is one of several spectacular canyons on the Green River in Utah. The area studied in this activity is part of the Flaming Gorge National Recreation Area of Utah and Wyoming and is located on the edge of the Uinta Mountains. Low rainfall and the resulting poor plant cover have made this an area where the layers of bedrock can easily be observed, mapped, and studied. In this activity— since you cannot explore the canyon firsthand— you will learn about the rocks and geologic history by using a geologic map and cross-section.

For additional activities, see Laboratory Investigations booklet.

Map Skills and Objectives
- To **interpret** the geology of an area from geologic map and cross-section data
- To **infer** how the geology and topography relate to the geologic history of the area

Materials
- Physical Map of the United States, pages 654–655
- Geologic Map: Flaming Gorge, Utah, page 653
- Geologic Timetable, pages 600–601

Procedure

1. Using the Physical Map of the United States on pages 654–655, locate Utah, Wyoming, the Rocky Mountains, the Uinta Mountains, and the Green River. In what mountain range does the Green River begin? The Green River is a tributary of what larger river? Record your answers.

2. Now look at the Flaming Gorge geologic map on page 653. Notice the compass direction shown in the lower part of the map. Which edge of the map is the north edge? In which compass direction is the top edge of the map?

3. Use the map scale to calculate the approximate area shown in the map.

4. The relief of an area is the difference between the highest and lowest points of elevation in the area. Using the cross-section, determine the approximate relief of the map area.

5. How does the cement of a calcareous sandstone differ from that of a quartzitic sandstone? Identify rock units from Figure 32.16 that have these two cement types. How could the acid test (page 51) be used to distinguish the two cements?

6. Using the Geologic Timetable on pages 600–601, determine which of the rock units listed in Figure 32.16 were formed during the Paleozoic Era. Which were formed during the Mesozoic Era?

7. Locate the Dinwoody Formation in the cross-section below the map. Name the younger rock unit that is in contact with the Dinwoody. Name the older rock unit that is in contact with the Dinwoody. If you were standing on the Dinwoody Formation on the line of the cross-section, in what direction would you walk along the line of the cross-section to reach the younger formation? In what direction would you walk to find the older rocks?

8. Assuming the rocks have not been turned over, what is the youngest rock shown in the cross-section? How do you know? Which rule for interpreting relative time (Chapter 32, Topic 2) did you use to determine your answer?

9. Locate the fault on both the map and cross-section. This is the Uinta Fault. Identify two rock units in contact with the Uinta Fault. What is the age of the fault rela-

tive to these rock units? How do you know?

10. The Shinarump Formation was deposited on the eroded surface of the Moenkopi Formation. What is such an erosional surface in the rock record called? Describe the steps needed to form this surface. Refer to the names Shinarump and Moenkopi in your description.

11. Which rock unit forms the rim of Horseshoe Canyon? What does that indicate about the resistance to erosion of that unit compared to the rocks above it?

12. Answer the questions in *Analysis and Conclusion*.

Analysis and Conclusions

1. The Shinarump Formation is a coarse-grained sandstone that resembles a conglomerate. How does the age of the sand grains in the sandstone compare with the age of the sandstone itself? Explain your answer using the correct rule for relative time.

2. The geologic map symbol ⊥ indicates the strike of the rock layers (see page 295). The number with the symbol is the measurement of the angle at which the layers dip underground. Locate the Dinwoody and Morgan formations on the map. Note the dip angle of each. Which formation dips more steeply? Does the cross-section verify your answer. Explain.

3. Along the line of the cross-section, how does the dip direction of the Uinta Mountain Group compare with that of the Uinta Fault?

4. Examine the Park City Formation on both the map and the cross-section. In the cross-section, the Park City Formation is one of the thinner units. Why does it cover so much of the map area?

32.16 Rock Units, Flaming Gorge area, Utah

Geologic Period	Rock Unit	Description
Quaternary	alluvium	modern surface deposits of loose sand and gravel
Jurassic	Carmel Formation	limestone at base, with green and red shale at top
	Navajo Sandstone	cross-bedded quartzitic sandstone
Triassic	Chinle and Shinarump formations	Shinarump: coarse-grained sandstone, siltstone grading up into shale Chinle: fine-grained sandstone
	Moenkopi Formation	siltstone with sandstone and shale
	Dinwoody Formation	shale, siltstone, and sandstone
Permian	Park City Formation	limestone with sandstone, shale, mudstone, and dolostone
Pennsylvanian	Weber Sandstone	mostly calcareous sandstone
	Morgan Formation	limestone at base, red shale and siltstone in middle, fine-grained calcareous sandstone at top
Precambrian	Uinta Mountain Group	medium- to coarse-grained, dark red, quartzitic sandstone and quartzite

Answers to all questions appear in the Teacher's Guide at the back of this book.

■ Summary

I Both relative time and absolute time are used to describe geologic time. Several laws are used in the determination of relative time.

The geologic timetable is a summary of the major events of Earth's history.

Unconformities are gaps or breaks in the rock record. They occur when rock layers are eroded or never deposited.

II Fossils are any evidence of earlier life preserved in the rock record.

The order of appearance of fossils in the rock record supports the evolution of life forms.

Index (guide) fossils are easily recognizable and widespread in occurrence but limited in time range. Index fossils are the best method of correlating between outcrops.

Key beds are layers with the same properties as index fossils that can be used for correlation. Walking outcrops and matching rock layers can also be used in correlation.

In addition to evolution and correlation, fossils are also important indicators of past climates. Microfossils are important to oil exploration.

III Tree rings and varves can be used to find absolute ages because each shows an annual cycle.

Radioactive isotopes give off alpha, beta, and gamma radiation at a measurable rate. Radiometric dating methods use the rates of natural decay of radioactive isotopes to determine absolute time.

The half-life is the time needed for half of the atoms of a radioactive element to decay to a stable end product. Each radioactive isotope has a different half-life.

Radiocarbon dating is used on material that was once living, such as prehistoric bones.

Uranium-lead, rubidium-strontium, and potassium-argon are radiometric methods that can be used on the oldest rocks in Earth's crust. Each method has its own particular advantages and disadvantages.

■ Vocabulary

absolute time	index (guide) fossil
Archean	key bed
Cenozoic	Mesozoic
correlation	Paleozoic
era	period
epoch	Proterozoic
evolution	radioactive decay
fossil	radiocarbon
geologic timetable	relative time
half-life	unconformity

■ Review

Number your paper from *1* to *20*. Match the phrases in list **A** with the terms in list **B**.

List A

1. gap in the rock record
2. used to find age of bristlecone pines
3. the method of preservation of woolly mammoths
4. most recent era of geologic time
5. example of a key bed
6. radiometric method with the longest half-life
7. shown by changes in life forms through geologic time
8. divisions within eras
9. the best method for correlating over long distances
10. used to date bones and tools of prehistoric people
11. common method of preservation of shells
12. used to search for oil
13. oldest era on the geologic timetable
14. radiometric dating method that works only on igneous rocks containing the right kind of uranium isotope
15. trails, footprints, tracks, and burrows
16. states that the oldest rocks are on the bottom of an undisturbed sequence
17. time for only half of the atoms of a radioactive element to decay

For further review, see **Study Guide.**
For assessment, see **Chapter Tests**
and **Computer Test Bank.**

18. deposits in glacial lakes that show seasonal changes

19. the dating of an event by its place in a sequence of events

20. process that releases alpha, beta, and gamma radiation

List B

a. absolute time	**m.** periods and epochs
b. Archean	**n.** petrified wood
c. Cenozoic	**o.** potassium-argon
d. evolution	**p.** radioactive decay
e. freezing	**q.** radiocarbon
f. half-life	**r.** relative time
g. index fossils	**s.** rubidium-strontium
h. law of cross-cutting relationships	**t.** trace fossil
	u. tree rings
i. law of superposition	**v.** unconformity
j. microfossils	**w.** uranium-lead
k. molds and casts	**x.** varves
l. Paleozoic	**y.** volcanic ash

■ Interpret and Apply

On your paper, answer each question in complete sentences.

1. Correlation of rocks is difficult within Archean and Proterozoic rocks. What is a probable reason for this difficulty?

2. Fall-winter varves are usually blackish because they contain more organic matter than do spring-summer varves. Why?

3. Dinosaurs lived during the Mesozoic Era. Could radiocarbon be used to date a dinosaur bone? Explain.

4. Arkose is a sandstone made from feldspar. If the feldspar is dated with potassium-argon, will the date be the time of formation of the arkose? Explain.

■ Critical Thinking

The diagram is a model for a radioactive decay. The entire circle represents 100 percent of a radioactive material. The relative amount of material that decays during each half-life is indicated. The unshaded portion of the model represents the amount of undecayed material that remains after five half-lives.

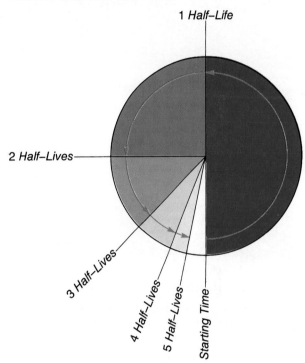

1. What percent of the original material decayed during the first half-life?

2. What percent of the original material remains after the second half-life?

3. If this material has a half-life of 2 billion years, how long will be needed for three half-lives?

4. Will the sixth half-life use all of the unshaded portion that remains? Explain.

5. If the original mass of another radioactive material was 24 grams, how many grams of the radioactive material were left at the end of the third half-life?

6. At the end of the fourth half-life, 10 grams of a third radioactive material remain. What was the total amount of radioactive material at the start?

Precambrian through Paleozoic

▲
Fossil algae near Great
Slave Lake, Canada

How Do You Know That . . .

Plants or animals lived on Earth billions of years ago? These rocks
near Great Slave Lake in Canada are part of a huge fossil reef made
by algae. The algae were living two billion years ago. Similar reefs
were being built by other algae in warm, shallow waters around
the world at that time. Reefs like this are one kind of evidence of
past life.

I Precambrian Time

Topic 1 What is Precambrian Time?

Precambrian time is all geologic time before the start of the Paleozoic Era. It includes the time span between the origin of Earth and 570 million years ago. The Archean and Proterozoic eras discussed in Chapter 32 are part of Precambrian time. Most of geologic time is Precambrian time.

The single most important characteristic of the rocks formed during Precambrian time is their relative lack of fossils. This fossil shortage occurs for two major reasons. First, many Precambrian rocks are igneous or metamorphic in origin. The heat and pressure required to form these rocks usually destroy any plant or animal remains that might have been present. Second, the animals of Precambrian time apparently lacked the hard shells and skeletons needed for preservation. In other eras, fossils with hard parts are preserved in sedimentary rocks. Many examples of Precambrian sedimentary rocks do exist. Nevertheless, few Precambrian animals and plants were preserved in these rocks.

Topic 2 Precambrian Life

Despite intensive searching, few Precambrian fossil's have been found. Most Precambrian organisms were microscopic bacteria and algae. Some of these organisms built algal reefs such as the one shown on the opposite page. These structures are called **stromatolites.** Stromatolites are made of alternating thin layers of silt that settled from the water, and calcium carbonate made by algae. Similar structures are found in Precambrian rocks in many parts of the world. They make up the greatest percentage of Precambrian fossils.

Stromatolites still form today but only in rare locations. Most are found in intertidal or shallow-water areas. Precambrian stromatolites are presumed to have formed in this same kind of environment.

Precambrian fossils are not limited to stromatolites. A variety of other life forms existed during Precambrian time. Fossil remains of jellyfish, simple fungi, marine worms, and what may be ancestors of modern corals and starfish have all been found. At one location, 56 different kinds of algae and other soft-bodied organisms were found dating back to late Proterozoic time.

OBJECTIVES

A Define Precambrian time and identify the two eras that are part of the Precambrian.

B Discuss Precambrian fossils.

C Give some reasons why Precambrian rocks are difficult to interpret and discuss the origin, location, and economic importance of Precambrian rocks.

SCIENCE BACKGROUND

The oldest known fragments of crust are some sedimentary zircon crystals dated at 4.3 billion years. They were found in Australia. The oldest known whole rock is a Canadian gneiss dated at about 3.8 billion years.

SCIENCE BACKGROUND

Stromatolites are not the plants' remains. They are structures that were formed around the plants. Diatoms and bacteria can also make stromatolite structures. Stromatolite-forming algae are thought to have been the source of the oxygen that resulted in the explosion of life in Cambrian time. Stromatolites occur today on the west coast of Australia and in Yellowstone National Park. Often they are preserved in flint or chert nodules of limestone formations.

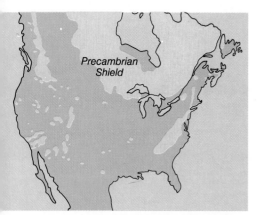

33.1 This map shows the location of surface exposures of Precambrian rocks in North America.

SCIENCE BACKGROUND
Radiometric dating has been the key to understanding the history of the Precambrian shield areas.

33.2 Lead and zinc are mined from Precambrian rocks at this mine in the Yukon.

Topic 3 Precambrian Rock Record

The Precambrian rock record has been very difficult to interpret for three reasons. First, the record covers an incredibly long interval of time. Second, many Precambrian rocks are severely bent and folded. Third and probably most important, the Precambrian is mostly lacking in index fossils, which would have made correlations between rock units possible. Despite these problems, geologists have determined that the same processes that occur on Earth today went on during the Precambrian. Volcanism, plate movements, erosion, and deposition went on as they do today.

Most of the rocks that have survived since Precambrian time are found in the craton, the oldest rocks of the continent. These rocks are the remains of Precambrian mountains and highlands. Such Precambrian rocks can be seen on every continent. In fact, about one fifth of the surface rocks of the continents are Precambrian in age. These exposed areas of the craton are called **shields.** The relationship between the Canadian Shield and the North American craton was discussed in Chapter 13.

The details of plate movements during Precambrian time are not known. However, it is known that the continents were moving about. For example, the North America craton experienced at least four *orogenies*, or mountain-building episodes, as a result of plate movements during Precambrian time. The last Precambrian orogeny occurred about a billion years ago when an unknown landmass collided with eastern Canada. This event is called the Grenville Orogeny. The remnants of the mountains that formed from this collision are seen today on the west side of the St. Lawrence River. The rocks of the Adirondack Mountains in New York State were also formed at this time.

Not all Precambrian rocks are part of the craton. Other areas where Precambrian rocks occur are in the Piedmont between the Appalachian Mountains and the Atlantic Ocean, at the bottom of the Grand Canyon in Arizona, in the core of the Rocky Mountains, and in New York City, as well as many other locations.

Topic 4 Precambrian Mineral Deposits

The economic importance of Precambrian rocks is considerable. About half of the world's metallic mineral deposits occur in Precambrian rocks. Iron, copper, gold, silver, nickel, chromium, and uranium, as well as many other minerals, are all mined from Precambrian rocks.

Several important deposits are found in the Precambrian rocks of North America. These include the nickel deposits of Sudbury, Ontario, the taconite iron deposits of the Lake Superior region, the uranium ores at Great Bear Lake in northwestern Canada, and the magnetite and ilmenite ores from the Adirondack Mountains in New York State. The world-famous gold ores of South Africa also occur in Precambrian rocks.

SCIENCE BACKGROUND
The presence of these great ore deposits was the primary reason for studying the Precambrian.

TOPIC QUESTIONS

Each topic question refers to the topic of the same number.

1. **(a)** Define Precambrian time and identify the two eras that are part of Precambrian time.   **(b)** Give two reasons why Precambrian rocks have few fossils.

2. **(a)** What are stromatolites?   **(b)** How does the abundance of stromatolites compare with that of other Precambrian fossils? **(c)** Where are stromatolites found today?   **(d)** List some examples of Precambrian life other than stromatolites.

3. **(a)** Give three reasons why the Precambrian rock record is difficult to interpret.   **(b)** Where are most Precambrian rocks located on the continents? These rocks are the remains of what feature(s)?   **(c)** What was the Grenville Orogeny? When and why did it occur?   **(d)** Identify some locations in North America where Precambrian rocks can be seen.

4. **(a)** Name some important metals that come from rocks of Precambrian age.   **(b)** Locate some Precambrian mining areas.

ANSWERS
   1. (a) time before Paleozoic or span between origin of Earth and 570 million years ago; Archean, Proterozoic   (b) destroyed, lacked hard parts
   2. (a) finely layered structures of $CaCO_3$ and silt formed by algae (b) stromatolites most abundant (c) intertidal or shallow-water areas (d) jellyfish, fungi, worms, ancestors of corals, starfish
   3. (a) long interval, severely deformed, lacks index fossils (b) craton; Precambrian mountains and highlands   (c) last mountain-building episode for North American craton; 1 billion years ago; collision of unknown landmass with eastern Canada   (d) west side of St. Lawrence River, Adirondack Mountains, Grand Canyon, Rocky Mountains, New York City, others
   4. (a) Fe, Cu, Au, Ag, Ni, Cr, U (b) Sudbury, Ontario; Lake Superior, Great Bear Lake, Adirondack Mts., South Africa

EARTH**MATTERS**

Fossils to Burn

For most of you, the electricity that lights your bedroom comes from a power plant that burns coal or oil. The car or bus you ride in is fueled by gasoline refined from petroleum. Even the rubber and cloth in your sneakers was probably made from petroleum products.

So much of your everyday life is undeniably linked to plants and animals that lived on this planet millions of years before the dinosaurs. Most of the coal burned in the United States was formed about 300 million years ago. Much of the world's oil supply formed from rocks deposited over 100 million years ago.

It has taken less than 100 years to use up an energy supply created over millions of lifetimes. Part of the definition of a *nonrenewable resource is* that it is used up faster than it can be replaced by natural processes. This is the case with fossil fuels. Somewhere on Earth, there are trees falling over into swamps. Those trees may one day become coal. Elsewhere microscopic marine organisms are dying and dropping to the ocean floor. In places where there isn't much oxygen in the water, these organisms form an organic-rich sediment that could one day become the source of oil or natural gas. However, the coal from that tree and the oil from that ocean sediment will not form for millions of years, long after modern humans have used up all of the existing fossil fuels.

Why is it important to pursue the development of alternative energy sources, such as solar or geothermal energy?

OBJECTIVES

A List the periods of the Paleozoic Era, describe the difference between the Precambrian and Paleozoic fossil records, and discuss the location and climate of North America during the Paleozoic Era.

B Identify the major fossils and life changes of each Paleozoic period.

C Discuss the occurrence of mountain-building episodes, the formation of mineral deposits, ice ages, and the formation of Pangaea relative to Paleozoic time.

SCIENCE BACKGROUND

The change in the fossil record between Precambrian and Paleozoic is a fundamental concept of this chapter. The change occurs abruptly in areas where the Cambrian rests unconformably upon the Precambrian but more gradually elsewhere.

VIDEODISC SELECTION

Trilobite fossil
Side 1: 3855, single frame

33.3 Trilobites are the most common Cambrian fossil.

II The Paleozoic Era

Topic 5 Introduction to the Paleozoic Era

The Paleozoic Era marks the beginning of an abundant fossil record. As a result, geologists know a great deal about this era and have been able to divide the era into smaller segments of time called periods. In order from oldest to youngest, these periods are Cambrian, Ordovician, Silurian, Devonian, Mississippian, Pennsylvanian, and Permian. Most of the names of the Paleozoic periods come from Europe. Cambrian, for example, is named for Cambria, the Roman name for Wales. Wales is the part of Great Britain where rocks of this age were first studied. The Permian is named for an area of Russia called Perm. Mississippian and Pennsylvanian are North American names. In Europe, these two periods combined are called the Carboniferous Period.

The most important difference between the rocks of the Paleozoic Era and rocks of Precambrian time is the record of life preserved in the rocks. Precambrian rocks contain few fossils. Starting with the Cambrian, Paleozoic rocks contain an abundance of fossil remains. Fossils formed because many of the Paleozoic animals had hard shells and skeletons that survived burial in the sediment and were preserved in the rocks.

At the beginning of the Paleozoic Era, there were a number of separate continents. They did not look like the continents of today, however. The continent that later became North America was on the equator and was rotated so that what is now the Arctic region faced eastward. As a result, the climate over the entire continent was warm with few seasonal changes. At times, tropical plants and animals lived in what is now Greenland.

Topic 6 The Cambrian Period

The *Cambrian Period* marks the appearance in the fossil record of an abundance of animals with hard preservable parts. The most commonly preserved Cambrian animal is the trilobite. These animals make up more than half of all the Cambrian fossils that have been found. **Trilobites** were crablike animals, some of which were bottom scavengers. Other trilobites were swimmers. They became widespread during the Cambrian Period and are therefore good index fossils for that period. Even though trilobites can be found throughout the remainder of the Paleozoic Era, they are far less common after the Cambrian Period.

The second most common fossil of the Cambrian Period is the **brachiopod.** These are small, shelled animals that are sometimes mistaken for clams. A common brachiopod of the Cambrian Period was the simple smooth-shelled form called *Lingula.*

Although other kinds of brachiopods are now extinct, *Lingula* are still found in some oceans today.

Evidence for Earth's first vertebrates has been found in rocks formed late in Cambrian time. These are pieces of the bony "skin" of *ostracoderms* (OSS-tra-koh-dermz), a primitive fish.

There was little mountain building during the Cambrian Period. Much of what is now North America was covered by warm oceans. These conditions enabled marine life to flourish. In fact, all of the fossils of the Cambrian Period are the remains of life forms that lived in the oceans. No land-living plants or animals of Cambrian age have been found.

Although the Cambrian Period marks the appearance in the fossil record of animals with hard preservable parts, soft-bodied animals were apparently still abundant. The evidence for soft-bodied life forms comes from a famous rock formation in the Rocky Mountains of Canada called the *Burgess Shale*. Here, worms and other soft-bodied animals have been preserved in remarkable detail. Over 120 different kind of animals have been found there. The Burgess Shale is middle Cambrian in age.

Topic 7   The Ordovician Period

The major change from life in the Cambrian Period to life in the *Ordovician Period* is a marked increase in the number of kinds of animals. All major groups of animals with hard parts had appeared by the close of the Ordovician Period. Like the organisms of the Cambrian, all Ordovician life forms lived in the ocean.

The important fossil of the Ordovician is the **graptolite.** Graptolites were tiny animals that lived together in floating groups, or colonies. They spread throughout the world's oceans. Although a few have been found in rocks of other periods, their greatest number and distribution occurred during the Ordovician Period. As a result, graptolites are the index fossils for the Ordovician.

During the Ordovician, brachiopods became more numerous than trilobites. A group of colonial animals called *bryozoans* appeared and became as numerous as the brachiopods. Cephalopods (relatives of the modern *Nautilus*), gastropods (snails), and echinoderms (relatives of the modern starfish) were important. One group of cephalopods, which built shells over six meters long, became the first large animals of the sea. Pelecypods (puh-LESS-uh-pods), the group to which clams belong, and corals appeared for the first time.

The end of the Ordovician Period is marked by the Taconic Orogeny. This mountain-building episode occurred as a small plate broke away from northwestern Africa and collided with eastern North America. Part of the ocean subducted under eastern North America, thrusting offshore island arcs and deep-sea trenches onto the continental margins. The Green Mountains of Vermont and the Taconic Mountains of southeastern New York State are remnants of that collision.

a

b

c

33.4 Cambrian and Ordovician life forms. (a) A Cambrian brachiopod (b) Graptolites were colonial animals. Each sawtooth is the home of one animal. (c) A fossil cephalopod

33.5 A eurypterid (sea scorpion) from the Silurian Period is shown attacking its prey.

VIDEODISC SELECTION

Eurypterid fossil
Side 1: 3853, single frame

SCIENCE BACKGROUND

There is evidence for microbial land ecosystems in the Precambrian and for patches of vascular plants in Ordovician rocks found in Libya.

TEACHING TIP

Point out to students that sponges are animals that live in water. Manufactured sponges are modeled after the properties of those animals.

SCIENCE BACKGROUND

Fish are important in the Devonian. Sharks also appeared at this time and remain essentially unchanged today.

SCIENCE BACKGROUND

A famous fossil forest of Devonian plants exists in the rocks at Gilboa, New York, in the Catskill Mountains. Some of the fossil trees of this forest are still in an upright position.

Topic 8   The Silurian Period

The most interesting group of organisms to appear in the oceans during the *Silurian Period* were the **eurypterids,** sometimes called sea scorpions. These animals seem to be distant cousins of the trilobites. Some grew to three meters in length.

In general, Silurian life was similar to that of the Ordovician. Brachiopods and bryozoans were still important. Corals and echinoderms became more numerous. The oldest known coral reefs are Silurian in age.

One of the most significant events of the Silurian was the appearance of animals on land. The first land animals included distant relatives of today's spiders, millipedes, and scorpions.

The Silurian record of plant life on land is unmistakable. Algal mats may have grown on land during the Cambrian and Ordovician. However, larger plants spread out over the land surface during the Silurian. These plants included club mosses, which are still common today.

Also during the late Silurian, the climate of what is now the northern United States became very dry. Shallow seas in eastern North America evaporated continuously. Thick beds of rock salt and gypsum were left from central New York State to Lake Michigan. The salt deposits near Detroit, Michigan, and Syracuse, New York, are in this belt. The famous Lockport dolomite, the cap rock of Niagara Falls, also formed during this time.

Topic 9   The Devonian Period

Coral reefs reached their greatest development in the *Devonian Period* as North America remained equatorial. At the same time, calcite-forming sponges that lived in warm oceans built reefs.

The major event of the Devonian Period was the appearance of many kinds of fish. Because fish dominated the Devonian oceans, the Devonian Period is called the *Age of Fishes*. The most common Devonian fish were jawless and covered with heavy plates. They are presumed to have been poor swimmers. Some armored fish were giants of the Devonian seas, reaching lengths of nine meters.

The first fossils of lungfish are found in Devonian rocks. When they are out of the water, lungfish can breathe air. Lungfish still exist today. Before the Devonian Period ended, a group of fish similar to lungfish developed very strong fins. With these fins, they could crawl out of the water and live briefly on land. These lobe-finned fish gave rise to the first amphibians.

Land plants multiplied in both number and variety during the Devonian Period. True (spore-bearing) ferns, seed-bearing ferns, and giant rushes (horsetails) developed. Trees appeared with scaly bark resembling snakeskin. Primitive conifers, ancestors of today's cone-bearing pines and fir trees, have also been found. The first forests date from the Devonian Period.

Extensive, thick limestone formations of Devonian age indicate that there was little tectonic activity during most of the Devonian Period. The close of the Devonian, however, is marked by the collision of North America with the northwest coast of Africa. These landmasses had been moving slowly toward each other during the previous periods. The collision raised mountains from Newfoundland to the Appalachian region. Igneous activity that accompanied the collision helped to build the White Mountains of New Hampshire. This episode is known as the Acadian Orogeny.

Topic 10 **The Mississippian Period**

Although advances in the evolution of life were not so striking in the *Mississippian Period* as in earlier periods, two groups from that time did leave an important fossil record. They are the crinoids and the foraminifera.

Crinoids (CRY-noydz) are the most abundant Mississippian fossils. Although crinoids look like plants and are called sea lilies, they are actually invertebrate animals. Crinoids are related to starfish. Unlike starfish, however, crinoids spend most of their lives attached to the seafloor. Crinoids are found today in all of the world's oceans but not nearly in the numbers that lived during the Mississippian.

Foraminifera are one-celled animals related to the amoeba. Foraminifera build tiny calcite shells that are usually less than one millimeter in diameter. Foraminifera first appear in the fossil record during the Cambrian Period, but they became common during the Mississippian Period. They are still found in the oceans.

There was little mountain-building during much of the Mississippian Period. It was not until late in the period that the Allegheny Orogeny began. During this episode, uplift occurred in the middle and southern Appalachians, stretching from southern New York to central Alabama.

Topic 11 **The Pennsylvanian Period**

During the *Pennsylvanian Period*, the interior basins of what is now the eastern United States were almost always underwater. At that time, North America still straddled the equator. As a result, the climate was warm and rainy. The flooded basins became the sites of huge freshwater swamps, filled with trees, ferns, and rushes. Dead trees and ferns that fell into the swamp slowly changed to peat, which in time changed to coal. Today these deposits form the rich coalfields of Pennsylvania, West Virginia, Ohio, Kentucky, Indiana, and Illinois.

Whenever sea level rose slightly, the interior basins became huge inland seas. Without the swamps, no coal formed. Instead, sand, mud, and calcite were deposited and eventually became the layers of sandstone, shale, and limestone that now separate the coalbeds.

VIDEODISC SELECTION

Crinoid calyx and stem
Side 1: 3852, single frame

a

b

33.6 Mississippian life forms. (a) Although they look like plants, crinoids are actually animals. They are relatives of modern starfish. (b) The eye of the needle shows how tiny the foraminifera are.

622

33.7 The swampy forests of the Pennsylvanian Period became a major source of coal in the United States.

In the animal world, the first reptiles appeared. These reptiles resembled today's lizards. The reptiles were the first true land vertebrates. They spread into those areas—farther from water—where amphibians could not live.

Insects increased in number and variety during the Pennsylvanian Period. The largest insects were giant dragonflies with a wingspan of almost a meter. Cockroaches reached lengths of ten centimeters. Their number and variety is the reason that the Pennsylvanian Period is known as the *Age of Cockroaches.*

The Allegheny Orogeny reached its peak during the Pennsylvanian Period. As the continents collided, causing this mountain building episode, one great super-continent was taking shape.

SCIENCE BACKGROUND
The Pennsylvanian is also known as the *Age of Coal Swamps.*

Topic 12 **The Permian Period**

The *Permian Period* is noted for its dry climate. Repeated evaporation of shallow inland seas left great deposits of salt and gypsum in many parts of the world. In the United States, Permian beds of rock salt and gypsum are widespread. These deposits occur in Nebraska, Kansas, Oklahoma, and Texas.

Corals, algae, and sponges thrived in the warm waters of the oceans and in the deeper inland seas. Large reefs of Permian age are found in the Guadalupe Mountains of West Texas.

During the Permian Period, a great ice age took place, mostly in the Southern Hemisphere. The ice covered parts of South America, Australia, South Africa, and India.

SCIENCE BACKGROUND
The first mammal-like animals appeared in the Permian.

Topic 13 **The Close of the Paleozoic Era**

The close of the Permian is marked by a time of unusually widespread mountain building as the result of continental collisions. The Appalachians were probably fully elevated and appeared all along the eastern border of North America. Siberia and Europe collided to form the Ural Mountains. Other collisions involved southeast Asia, South America, Australia, and Antarctica. Before the end of the Permian, most of the continental crust in the world had welded together into one supercontinent. Alfred Wegener, in his theory of continental drift, named this continent Pangaea.

SCIENCE BACKGROUND
Pangaea is thought to have existed from about 300 to about 200 million years ago. Therefore, the formation of the Appalachian Mountains and the other mountains occurred before the start of Permian time. The large joined land area made it easy for land life to disperse throughout the world.

At the close of the Paleozoic Era, nearly half of all known animal groups became extinct. By some estimates, 96% of all species died out at that time. The worst losses were among the marine invertebrates. Trilobites and eurypterids, two groups that had been abundant in earlier periods of the Paleozoic Era, were extinct by the end of the Paleozoic. Other groups, including corals, brachiopods, and crinoids, were greatly reduced in number and variety. On land, amphibians and some plants suffered setbacks.

Among the land plants, the seed ferns, scale trees, and primitive conifers that had been so important to the formation of the coal beds of Mississippian and Pennsylvanian times were almost all extinct by the end of the Permian.

Among the survivors of the Paleozoic extinctions were two groups that became important in the Mesozoic Era. These groups are the cephalopods in the oceans and the reptiles on the land.

TOPIC QUESTIONS

Each topic question refers to the topic of the same number.

5. **(a)** What is the most important difference between Precambrian rocks and Paleozoic rocks? **(b)** Describe the climate of North America during the Paleozoic Era.

6. **(a)** Why are trilobites important to Cambrian time? **(b)** What is the evidence that Cambrian life forms all lived in the oceans?

7. **(a)** What is the basic difference between Cambrian and Ordovician life? **(b)** Why are graptolites important in Ordovician rocks? **(c)** What caused the Taconic Orogeny and what mountains were formed by it?

8. **(a)** Compare Silurian life to that of the Ordovician. **(b)** Describe the cause and location of the late Silurian salt and gypsum deposits.

9. **(a)** Why is the Devonian called the Age of Fishes? **(b)** Why were the lobe-finned fish important? **(c)** What caused the Acadian Orogeny and what mountains resulted?

10. Identify and describe the two groups of organisms that were important during Mississippian time.

11. What conditions of sea level and climate resulted in the formation of the Pennsylvanian coal fields?

12. **(a)** In which states did rock salt and gypsum deposits form in Permian time? **(b)** Which modern land areas were affected by the Permian ice age?

13. **(a)** What was Pangaea and when did it form? **(b)** List some groups that died out at the close of the Paleozoic. **(c)** List some life forms that were reduced in number.

VIDEODISC SELECTION

Assorted Paleozoic fossils (described in disc directory)
Side 1: 3822 to 3828, 7-frame sequence

ANSWERS
  5. (a) abundance of fossils in Paleozoic rocks   (b) warm, few seasonal changes
  6. (a) index fossils   (b) no land-living fossils found
  7. (a) many more kinds of animals in Ordovician   (b) index fossils   (c) subduction of ocean under eastern North America; Green and Taconic
  8. (a) similar, but more corals and echinoderms; first coral reefs   (b) very dry climate; central New York State to Lake Michigan
  9. (a) fish dominated the seas   (b) ancestors of first amphibians   (c) collision of North America and Africa; Appalachian, White
  10. crinoids, related to starfish; foraminifera, one-celled animals that build shells
  11. eastern United States almost always underwater; warm and rainy
  12. (a) Nebraska, Kansas, Oklahoma, Texas   (b) South America, Australia, Africa, India
  13. (a) large continent made from almost all other continents; close of Permian   (b) trilobites, eurypterids   (c) corals, brachiopods, crinoids, also land plants such as seed ferns, scale trees, and primitive conifers

CHAPTER 33

L A B
ACTIVITY

Analysis of Brachiopod Fossils

33.8 Paleozoic brachiopod from the order *Spirifera*.

When they study fossils, paleontologists not only try to determine what the living organism looked like, but also they try to figure out where and how the organism lived. For example, how numerous was the organism at that point in time? Did the organism change? What was the environment in which it lived?

One way to find out information about how an organism lived is to study records of a population. In this exercise, you will be analyzing data from a group of brachiopod fossils. Brachiopods were a common shelled animal that lived on the ocean floor during the Paleozoic.

Look at Figure 33.8. This is a picture of the brachiopod *Spirifera*. Notice how the *Spirifera* shell is divided in two by a central ridge. You will be provided data taken from 100 Spirifera fossils collected from two different areas. The data tells you the number of ridges on one side of the *Spirifera's* central ridge. You will use these data to determine whether the two brachiopods' populations differ.

In order to do your analysis, you will need to be familiar with several terms. The *frequency* will be the number of brachiopods with a given number of ridges. The *median* will be the middle value of all the data. Half the brachiopods will have more ridges than the median; half the brachiopods will have fewer ridges. The *mode* will be the number of ridges that occurs most frequently in the sample population.

Lab Skills and Objectives

- To **graph** and **interpret** fossil data
- To **predict** characteristics of another fossil population based on these data

Materials

- graph paper
- colored pencils

Data Table A									
Population 1					Population 2				
12	10	11	9	11	21	19	18	14	18
12	11	13	11	14	18	17	19	22	18
10	12	11	14	10	20	16	17	19	18
11	11	9	10	15	17	18	18	15	19
10	11	11	12	11	19	17	18	16	19
12	12	10	10	11	18	17	16	20	20
11	10	9	11	13	20	18	20	19	17
11	11	11	12	8	16	15	21	16	19
10	11	10	11	11	17	18	19	19	17
12	11	12	10	12	17	18	16	17	20

Procedure

1. Data Table A contains data for the number of ridges on each brachiopod collected from two different populations. Look at the data for Population 1. The first value is 12. Count the number of times that 12 appears in Population 1. This is the frequency of that value. Record your frequency for 12 in your copy of Data Table B.

2. Determine and record the frequency of each of the other values in Population 1. Do the same for each value in Population 2.

3. Find the sum of the values in your frequency columns. The total for each population should be 50, which is the number of fossils counted at that location. If your frequencies do not add up to 50, recheck your counts.

4. Draw a pair of axes on a sheet of graph paper. Label the x-axis *Number of Ridges*. Number this axis from 5 to 25.

5. Use a colored pencil to graph the Population 1 frequencies from Data Table B. On the same graph, use a different colored pencil to graph the Population 2 frequencies.

6. Use Data Table B to determine the medians for Populations 1 2. Mark the medians on your graphs.

Analysis and Conclusions

1. What are the modes for each population? Are the modes for each population the same as the medians?

Data Table B		
Number of Ridges (Frequency)	Population 1	Population 2
7	0	0
8	1	0
9	3	0
10	11	0
11	20	0
12	10	0
13	2	0
14	2	1
15	1	2
16	0	6
17	0	10
18	0	12
19	0	10
20	0	6
21	0	2
22	0	1
23	0	0
Total	50	50

2. Based on your graph, do you conclude that there are distinct differences between the two populations? Explain your answer.

3. Counting the number of ridges on the brachiopod shells is just one way to analyze the brachiopod population. What are some other ways?

4. You are given three brachiopod fossils that were collected at the same location as Population 1 or 2. You do not know where these samples were collected. Two shells have 9 ridges, and one shell has 11 ridges. Based on your data, can you determine to which population they belong? Explain your answer.

5. You are brought three more brachiopod fossils. Two have 14 ridges and one has 15 ridges. Can you determine to which population these brachiopod fossils belong? Explain your answer.

6. You return to the site where the Population 2 fossils were collected. You find 50 more brachiopod fossils in a layer of younger rocks. You count the number of ridges on each shell and determine that the mode is 23 ridges and the median is 21 fossils. How would the shape of the graph for these fossils differ from the shape of the graph for the older fossils?

7. Based on these new Population 2 fossils, what would you conclude about the evolution of brachiopods at that location?

Answers to all questions appear in the Teacher's Guide at the back of this book.

■ Summary

I All geologic time before the Paleozoic Era is called Precambrian. Large fossils are rare in Precambrian rocks. Stromatolites are the most abundant Precambrian fossils.

The Precambrian rock record is difficult to interpret due to a relative lack of fossils.

Shield areas contain exposures of Precambrian rocks from a continent's craton.

Precambrian rocks are the source of about half of the world's metallic mineral deposits.

II The Paleozoic Era is divided into seven periods.

During the Paleozoic Era, North America was located over the equator.

The Cambrian Period marks the start of an abundant fossil record. Trilobites and brachiopods were most important. The Burgess Shale is Cambrian in age.

Animal life increased in variety during Ordovician time. Graptolites are the index fossil for the period. Other groups, including primitive fish, also appeared for the first time. The Taconic Orogeny closed the period.

Eurypterids were important during the Silurian, along with the first land plants and animals. The dry climate allowed salt and gypsum to form in the northeastern United States.

Corals reached their peak in Devonian time. Several kinds of fish developed, one of which gave rise to the first amphibians. Land plants thrived. The Acadian Orogeny closed the period.

Crinoids and foraminifera were important during the Mississippian Period. The Allegheny Orogeny began late in the period.

Swamps of the Pennsylvanian Period became the rich coalfields of today. The first reptiles also appeared during the Pennsylvanian. Insects thrived.

Rock salt and gypsum formed in some western states during the Permian, and an ice age occurred in the Southern Hemisphere.

Many animals and plant groups became extinct or nearly extinct at the close of the Paleozoic Era. Cephalopods and reptiles survived.

Pangaea formed before the close of Paleozoic time.

■ Vocabulary

brachiopod	foraminifera	shield
crinoid	graptolite	stromatolites
eurypterid	Precambrian	trilobite

■ Review

On your paper, write the word or words that best complete each sentence.

1. The single most important characteristic of Precambrian rocks is that they contain few _____ remains.
2. Stromatolites, the most common fossil of the Precambrian, form today in areas where the water depth is _____.
3. The major reason that the Precambrian rock record is difficult to interpret is that these rocks lack _____ fossils.
4. The Canadian _____ is the exposed part of the North American craton.
5. The nickel deposits at Sudbury, Ontario, and the gold ores of South Africa both formed during _____ time.
6. The Carboniferous Period of Europe is the same as the Mississippian and Pennsylvanian periods of North _____.
7. The two most important fossils of the Cambrian Period were crablike animals called _____ and shelled animals called brachiopods.
8. No land-living animals are known for either the _____ or Ordovician periods.
9. The first vertebrate, a primitive _____ called ostracoderm, is known from pieces found in Cambrian rocks.
10. Tiny floating animals called graptolites are the index _____ for the Ordovician Period.

For further review, see **Study Guide**.
For assessment, see **Chapter Tests**
and **Computer Test Bank**.

11. The first fossil record of animals and large land plants comes from the _____ Period.
12. The _____ Period is known as the Age of Fishes because of the number and variety of fish in the fossil record.
13. The collision of North America with Africa at the close of the Devonian raised mountains all along the _____ coast of North America.
14. Crinoids, the most abundant fossil of the Mississippian Period, are also called _____ lilies.
15. Foraminifera, one-celled animals of the Mississippian Period, build tiny _____ made of calcite.
16. The great swamps of the Pennsylvanian Period became the rich _____ beds of today.
17. Insects thrived in the Pennsylvanian, including a giant _____ with a wingspan of almost one meter.
18. The _____ climate of the Permian resulted in deposits of rock salt and gypsum in Nebraska, Kansas, Oklahoma, and Texas.
19. The Southern Hemisphere had an _____ age in the Permian Period.
20. Trilobites and eurypterids had become _____ by the end of the Permian Period.

■ Interpret and Apply

On your paper, answer each question in complete sentences.

1. Why are there no Precambrian coal beds?
2. The oldest known rock is a metamorphosed sedimentary rock. How do you know that even older rocks must have existed at one time?
3. Why are graptolites likely to be better index fossils than crinoids?
4. Imagine yourself standing in the Pennsylvanian swampy forest shown in Figure 33.7. If you had stood in that exact same spot during the Cambrian Period, how would the view have been different?
5. What effect would a supercontinent like Pangaea be expected to have on the distribution of land plants and animals?

■ Critical Thinking

The chart shows the occurrence in the rock record of 10 different Paleozoic fossils. The periods of the Paleozoic are indicated across the top of the chart—*C* stands for Cambrian, *O* for Ordovician, *S* for Silurian, *D* for Devonian, *M* for Mississippian, *P* for Pennsylvanian, and *PR* for Permian. The fossils are indicated along the left side of the chart. The name of each fossil genus is shown in parenthesis after the name of the group to which it belongs.

Fossil	C	O	S	D	M	P	PR
Porifera (**Actinostroma**)							
Coral (**Halysites**)							
Bryozoa (**Hallopora**)							
Brachiopod (**Neospirifer**)							
Brachiopod (**Atrypa**)							
Pelecypod (**Myalina**)							
Eurypterida (**Eurypterus**)							
Trilobite (**Phacops**)							
Trilobite (**Isoteles**)							
Crinoid (**Pentremites**)							

1. During which geologic period(s) did the trilobite *Isoteles* live?
2. What is the range of geologic periods for the porifera *Actinostroma?*
3. Two brachiopods appear in the list. Neither brachiopod can be used to identify a Mississippian age rock. Why?
4. What is the probable age of a rock layer that contains the porifera *Actinostroma* and the crinoid *Pentremites?*
5. What is the possible age of a rock layer that contains *Halysites* and *Atrypa?*
6. List the fossils that might be expected to occur in a rock of Devonian age.
7. Two trilobites are shown on the list. How do you know that at least one other kind of trilobite must exist?

627

The Mesozoic and Cenozoic Eras

▲

Based on fossil evidence, scientists have been able to construct full-scale models of dinosaurs like this *Tyrannosaurus*.

How Do You Know That . . .

Dinosaurs were not warm-blooded? One way to find out the temperature of an animal that has been extinct for 65 million years is by the structure of its bones. The bones of active, warm-blooded animals are full of tiny channels where blood vessels were located. Less active cold-blooded animals have few blood vessel channels in their bones. Surprisingly, the bones of many dinosaurs are full of the tiny channels common to warm-blooded animals. Although some scientists vigorously disagree, others now think that at least some dinosaurs were warm-blooded like modern mammals and birds rather than cold-blooded like modern reptiles.

I The Mesozoic Era

Topic 1 Highlights of the Mesozoic Era

Dinosaur bones are probably the most famous fossil remains. However, the rise and fall of the dinosaurs was just one event of the Mesozoic Era. Other groups of animals and plants also appeared for the first time in the Mesozoic. Some, like dinosaurs, were extinct by the close of the era. Others went on to become important in the Cenozoic Era.

The Mesozoic Era began 250 million years ago and ended 65 million years ago. This span of 185 million years is the second shortest of the five geologic eras. Mesozoic time is divided into three periods—Triassic, Jurassic, and Cretaceous.

Throughout most of Mesozoic time, the Appalachian Mountains and eastern North America were being worn down. However, new mountains were raised in western North America. Pangaea, the supercontinent that had formed at the end of the Paleozoic Era, broke into the familiar continents of today.

The Mesozoic climate was mild. Coral grew in what is now Europe. The poles were free of glacial ice. Some evidence indicates that ocean surface temperatures, even in the Arctic, were 10°C to 20°C warmer than today.

Several areas of geologic interest were formed in the western and southwestern United States during the Mesozoic Era. The Navajo Sandstone, a widespread deposit of fossil sand dunes, was formed during the Triassic Period. The Morrison Formation, a rock unit famous for dinosaur bones, was formed during the Jurassic Period. The famous aquifer of the Great Plains, the Dakota Sandstone, is Cretaceous in age.

OBJECTIVES

A Name the periods of the Mesozoic Era and a famous rock unit that formed during each, discuss the changes in Pangaea during the Mesozoic, and summarize the Mesozoic climate.

B Explain why dinosaurs are important to the Mesozoic Era, name the different kinds of dinosaurs and give examples of each, and identify some locations where dinosaur bones are found.

C Discuss other Mesozoic animal and plant life; explain the importance of ammonites.

D Identify some animal groups that died out at the close of the Mesozoic Era and list some possible causes of their extinction.

SCIENCE BACKGROUND
The Mesozoic Era is known as the Age of Reptiles.

TEACHING TIP
Aquifers and the Dakota sandstone were discussed in Chapter 9.

34.1 This mesa in Utah was carved from Mesozoic rocks.

SCIENCE BACKGROUND
The floors of the Mediterranean, Black, and Caspian seas are remnants of the Tethys Sea.

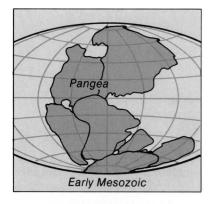

Early Mesozoic

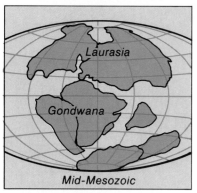

Mid-Mesozoic

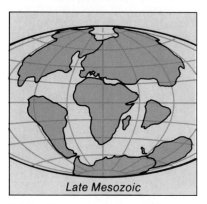

Late Mesozoic

34.2 During the Mesozoic Era, Pangaea split apart forming smaller continents that more resembled the continents of today.

Topic 2   Continent Formation

At the close of the Paleozoic Era and continuing into the Mesozoic Era, almost all of Earth's land areas were joined together into a single large continent, Pangaea. The total land area of that continent was about the same as the total land area of all of the continents today. A large bay called the *Tethys Sea* separated what are now the continents of Africa and Eurasia.

Starting in the late Triassic, faulting and igneous activity in Europe, North America, South America, and Africa began the process that would eventually split Pangaea into two parts. The northern part, containing the future continents of North America and Eurasia, is called *Laurasia.* The southern part, with the remainder of the continents, is called *Gondwana.* The basaltic lavas of the Palisades Sill in New Jersey as well as the igneous rocks of several other east coast locations formed at this time.

By the close of Jurassic time 135 million years ago, the North Atlantic and Indian oceans had both formed. The South Atlantic Ocean between South America and Africa was just starting to open. India had separated from Antarctica and Australia and had begun to move toward Asia.

During most of the Cretaceous Period, much of central and southeastern North America was underwater. The close of the period, however, saw the birth of the Rocky Mountain chain and the re-elevation of the Appalachians.

When the Mesozoic Era ended 65 million years ago, the South Atlantic had become a major ocean, and all of the continents had taken on their present appearance. However, North America and Eurasia were still joined together. Australia and Antarctica also remained connected.

Topic 3   The Rise of the Dinosaurs

The best-known land vertebrates of the Mesozoic Era were the **dinosaurs,** a group of large terrestrial reptiles. Dinosaurs lived on all of the continents. The western United States and Canada seem to have been a particularly good environment for dinosaurs and, as a result, most dinosaur fossils come from there. Montana, Utah, Wyoming, Colorado, Kansas, Texas, Oklahoma, and New Mexico all have yielded important dinosaur fossils. The richest dinosaur graveyard known is at Como Bluff, Wyoming. The major digging there occurred between 1877 and 1889. Universities and museums throughout North America are still sorting and studying bones removed from the Como Bluff quarry at that time.

The oldest known dinosaur fossil is 225 million years old. The youngest dinosaur fossil is 65 million years old. Thus dinosaurs dominated Earth for 160 million years. By comparison, humans developed only during the last 2 to 3 million years.

The first dinosaurs were small, some no larger than rabbits. Although some dinosaurs were 1.5 to 2 meters long by the end of

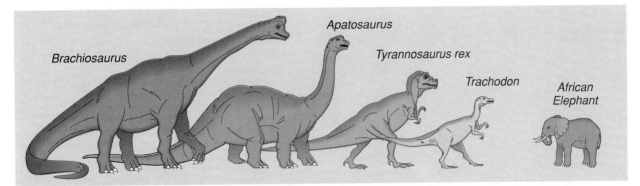

the Triassic, the largest dinosaurs lived during the Cretaceous. These dinosaurs averaged 25 to 30 meters in length. The largest dinosaur known came from the Dry Mesa quarry near Delta, Colorado. This dinosaur could have seen *over* a five-story building.

Dinosaurs were either meat eaters (carnivores) or plant eaters (herbivores). The largest of the meat eaters was *Tyrannosaurs rex*. This dinosaur walked on its rear feet, stood about 6 meters high, and had a huge head with razor-sharp, banana-size teeth. Although carnivorous dinosaurs lived throughout the Mesozoic Era, *Tyrannosaurs rex* did not appear until the Cretaceous Period. *Allosaurus*, another carnivore, lived in the Jurassic Period.

The plant-eating dinosaurs are often divided into four groups: armored dinosaurs, horned dinosaurs, duck-billed dinosaurs, and sauropods. *Stegosaurus*, with a long row of bony plates down its back, was an armored dinosaur. Three-horned *Triceratops* was a horned dinosaur, and *Trachodon* was a duck-billed dinosaur. The sauropods were the largest of the dinosaurs and the largest land animals that ever lived. *Apatosaurus* (formerly called *Brontosaurus*) is the most familiar example. Other sauropods included *Diplodocus* and *Brachiosaurus*. The five-story monster from Dry Mesa quarry was a kind of *Brachiosaurus*.

Topic 4 **Other Land Animals**

Although the dinosaurs were significant land animals of the Mesozoic, other groups also lived on land. Among them were the mammals. Mammals first appeared as tiny, primitive, rodentlike creatures in the Jurassic Period. Mammals developed throughout the Mesozoic and became the dominant Cenozoic land animal.

The Jurassic Period also marks the appearance of the first birds. For many years, the oldest known bird has been *Archeopteryx*. The fossil record clearly shows that the immediate ancestor of this bird was a dinosaur. Although *Archeopteryx* had wings and feathers, it probably could not fly. It also had teeth and is assumed to have laid eggs. In 1984, fossils of what would be an even older bird, called *Protoavis*, were found in Texas. The pelvis, tail, hindlegs, and claws of *Protoavis* resemble those of dinosaurs, but other features are more birdlike than similar features on *Archeopteryx*. Two *Protoavis* skeletons were found, both about the size of a modern crow.

34.3 Compared to elephants, some dinosaurs were enormous in size.

34.4 *Stegosaurus* was an armored dinosaur.

OF INTEREST
Archeopteryx means "ancient wing."

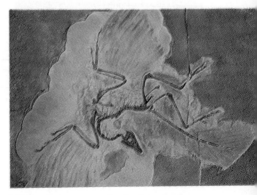

34.5 *Archeopteryx* had wings and feathers but probably could not fly for any distance.

VIDEODISC SELECTION

Assorted ammonites (described in
disc directory)
Side 1: 3869 to 3878, 10-frame
sequence

SCIENCE BACKGROUND
Only one ammonite family survived
the Triassic. This family gave rise to
1200 genera in the Jurassic and
Cretaceous. All became extinct at the
end of the Cretaceous.

SCIENCE BACKGROUND
The deciduous trees are the
largest, most successful group of
plants. Their rapid development parallels that of the mammals.

34.6 The giant redwoods are a
remnant of the warmer climates of
the early Cenozoic Era.

Other land creatures that appear for the first time in the Mesozoic fossil record are still around today. Insects that could change
form (like a caterpillar becoming a moth), flies, termites, and grasshoppers first appeared in the Jurassic Period. Ants and anteaters
first appeared in the Cretaceous Period.

Topic 5   Marine Life

An important index fossil of the Mesozoic Era was the **ammonite,**
a kind of cephalopod. Many kinds of ammonites occurred worldwide during the Triassic Period, but almost all became extinct at
the close of that period. A single group that survived gave rise to
even more new varieties in the Jurassic and Cretaceous periods.

Some of the Mesozoic reptiles invaded the seas. *Ichthyosaurs*
were reptiles that looked like swordfish. Some grew to lengths of 8
meters. Snakelike *plesiosaurs* were even longer, up to 15 meters.

Some Paleozoic invertebrates become more numerous during
the Mesozoic Era. Corals almost became extinct at the end of the
Paleozoic Era. The survivors gave rise to a new group of corals in the
Triassic Period that developed a modern appearance by the Cretaceous Period. Bryozoans, along with certain varieties of clams,
became important again during the Cretaceous. Many groups of
plankton, including diatoms, evolved during the Mesozoic.

Topic 6   Land Plants

Early Mesozoic plant life was based upon the survivors of the Paleozoic Era. These plants included tree ferns, spore-bearing ferns,
rushes, and conifers. New plants of the early Mesozoic Era were
pines, yews, and cypresses.

Plant life made its greatest change during the Cretaceous Period,
when flowering plants appeared. Chief among these were the deciduous trees. These trees developed rapidly until they crowded the
forests. First came magnolia, sassafras, fig, willow, laurel, and the
tulip tree. Later came oak, maple, beech, birch, walnut, chestnut,
and other modern trees. Evergreen conifers continued. The sequoia,
ancestor of California's giant redwoods, first appeared.

Topic 7   The Mesozoic Era Closes

One of the great puzzles of the rock record is the cause of the dis-
appearance of many kinds of plants and animals at the close of the
Mesozoic Era. All of the dinosaurs vanished along with the flying
and swimming reptiles, most marine turtles, crocodiles, lizards,
and many others. Scientists believe that over 50 percent of the plant
and animal groups on Earth were wiped out at that time.

Many reasons have been suggested for this mass extinction.
These reasons include a change in climate, the rise of mammals,

a drop in global sea level, the uplift of mountains from plate motions, massive volcanic eruptions, and worldwide disease. The theory now receiving the widest acceptance is that a large asteroid struck Earth 65 million years ago. Dust from the impact blocked sunlight for several years. Land plants and marine plankton that needed sunlight to live and grow died, starving the animals that used the plants for food. Strong support for the asteroid-impact theory came with the discovery of a large, buried crater in the Yucatan Peninsula of Mexico. Rock samples that were obtained by drilling down to the crater are the same age as the time of extinction. Bits of rock called *tektites* have been found that also match the extinction in age. Tektites form in an impact n rock material melts and sprays into the air.

TOPIC QUESTIONS

Each topic question refers to the topic of the same number.

1. **(a)** How long was the Mesozoic Era?   **(b)** List the three periods of the Mesozoic.   **(c)** Describe what was happening to the land in North America during Mesozoic time.   **(d)** List some evidence for a mild Mesozoic climate.

2. **(a)** How did the total land area of Pangaea compare to the total land area on Earth today?   **(b)** Which continents made up Laurasia? Which made up Gondwana?   **(c)** What was the Tethys Seaway?   **(d)** Which two oceans had formed by the close of Jurassic time?   **(e)** Identify two pairs of modern continents that were still joined at the end of the Mesozoic Era.

3. **(a)** Compare the duration of dinosaur history with human history.   **(b)** How did the size of typical dinosaurs change during the Mesozoic?   **(c)** What name is applied to meat-eating dinosaurs? List two examples.   **(d)** What are plant-eating dinosaurs called?   **(e)** Name the four groups of plant-eating dinosaurs and give an example of each.

4. **(a)** When did the first mammals appear? What were they like?   **(b)** Which fossil bird was found first? Which possible bird lived earlier?   **(c)** When did the first anteater appear?

5. **(a)** What is the most important index fossil of the Mesozoic Era?   **(b)** List two Mesozoic marine reptiles.   **(c)** Name two Paleozoic invertebrates that thrived in the Mesozoic Era.

6. Describe the changes that took place in plant life during the Mesozoic Era.

7. **(a)** Name animal groups that became extinct at the close of the Mesozoic Era.   **(b)** What reasons have been suggested for these extinctions?   **(c)** Which extinction theory is now most widely accepted?   **(d)** How does extinction occur according to this theory?   **(e)** Give two pieces of evidence for this theory.

SCIENCE BACKGROUND

This is the most recent of five mass extinctions that have been identified.

SCIENCE BACKGROUND

The asteroid is theorized to have been 10 kilometers in diameter.

VIDEODISC SELECTION

Various Mesozoic fossils (described in disc directory)
Side 1: 3830 to 3839, 10-frame sequence

ANSWERS

  1. (a) 185 million years
(b) Triassic, Jurassic, Cretaceous
(c) eastern being worn down; western being raised up   (d) corals in Europe, ice-free poles, possible warmer ocean than today

  2. (a) about the same
(b) North America and Eurasia; South America, Africa, Australia, Antarctica   (c) sea between Laurasia and Gondwana   (d) North Atlantic and Indian   (e) North America and Eurasia; Australia and Antarctica

  3. (a) 165 million years vs. about 2-3 million years   (b) increased
(c) carnivores; *Tyrannosaurus rex, Allosaurus*   (d) herbivores
(e) armored, *Stegosaurus;* horned, *Triceratops;* duck-billed, *Trachodon;* sauropods, *Apatosaurus, Diplodocus, Brachiosaurus*

  4. (a) Jurassic; tiny, primitive, rodentlike creatures   (b) *Archeopteryx* was known first; *Protoavis* is older.   (c) Cretaceous

  5. (a) ammonite   (b) *Ichthyosaurs, plesiosaurs*   (c) corals, bryozoans

  6. ferns, conifers continued; flowering plants first appeared and crowded the forests

  7. (a) dinosaurs, flying and swimming reptiles, most marine turtles, crocodiles, lizards   (b) change of climate, drop in global sea level, rise of mammals, uplift of mountains, worldwide disease   (c) asteroid-impact
(d) dust from impact blocks sunlight, plants die, animals starve   (e) crater and tektites

SCIENCE BACKGROUND

The continents are, of course, continuing to move about. Positions of the continents have been projected 50 million years into the future.

SCIENCE BACKGROUND

Two other terms are now being applied to Cenozoic epochs. The Paleocene, Eocene, and Oligocene are collectively called the *Paleogene* while Miocene, Pliocene, and Quaternary are called the *Neogene*. Paleogene and Neogene are more nearly equal in length to the periods of pre-Cenozoic time. Epochs are relatively much shorter intervals.

OF INTEREST

Most of the spectacular canyons and mountains of the western and southwestern United States were formed during the Cenozoic Era.

SCIENCE BACKGROUND

Volcanic ash is abundant throughout Paleocene, Eocene, and Oligocene rocks.

OF INTEREST

Eocene limestones were used to construct the pyramids of Giza.

II   The Cenozoic Era

Topic 8   Highlights of the Cenozoic Era

The Cenozoic Era is called the Age of Mammals. The tiny mammals that survived extinction at the close of the Mesozoic evolved into the familiar animals of today. Modern plants also evolved. At the same time, the plate movements that began with the breakup of Pangaea in the Mesozoic continued into the Cenozoic, moving the continents into their present locations. And finally, ice moved from the polar regions to cover large parts of several continents, including North America.

The Cenozoic Era began 65 million years ago. Early geologists divided the era into two periods. The first, covering the time before the Ice Age, was called the *Tertiary*. The second, from the Ice Age to the present, was named the *Quaternary* (qua-TUR-na-ry). Because the Cenozoic is the most recent of the eras, more is known about events of that era than about events of any other. As a result, Cenozoic time is divided into smaller segments. Geologists divide the Tertiary Period into five epochs—*Paleocene, Eocene, Oligocene, Miocene,* and *Pliocene*. The Quaternary contains two epochs, the *Pleistocene,* or Ice Age, and the *Recent*.

Early Cenozoic climates were warm and humid, much like the climate throughout the Mesozoic. Although warmer weather occurred in the Eocene and Miocene, Cenozoic temperatures generally and steadily decreased. By the Pleistocene Epoch, the temperature had become very cold almost everywhere. Great sheets of ice covered large areas of North America, Europe, Asia, and all of Greenland and Antarctica. Altogether, about one fourth of all the land was covered by glaciers at that time. About one tenth of that area remains covered by ice today.

Topic 9   Crustal Activity in the Cenozoic Era

When the Cenozoic Era began, North America looked much as it does today. Only the Atlantic and Gulf coastal plains and parts of California were submerged. These areas were covered and uncovered by seawater several times during the Cenozoic Era.

Both the Appalachian and Rocky mountains were worn down and raised again in this era. The Colorado Plateau was raised a number of times. During its last uplift, the Colorado River carved out the Grand Canyon. Faulting created the fault-block mountains of the Basin and Range of Nevada and the Sierra Nevadas of California and Nevada.

Volcanism was also active during the Cenozoic. Lava flows built up the Columbia Plateau in what is now Washington, Oregon, Idaho, and California. Erupting volcanoes were common features of the landscape from the Cascade Mountains to the Southwest. In the Yellowstone National Park area, lava and ash buried whole forests of trees several times. Later these trees were petrified by minerals in groundwater.

Mountain building also took place on other continents besides North America. The highest mountains of today, the Himalayas, were uplifted as India crashed into Asia. The Alps were formed as the African Plate pushed into Europe. The Andes Mountains in South America already existed but were raised higher in late Cenozoic time, as the Nazca Plate subducted under the South American Plate.

Topic 10 **Rise of the Mammals**

Mammals have left the most extensive fossil record of any plant or animal group. Although the first mammal fossils were found in rocks of early Jurassic age, these animals were often very difficult to tell from reptiles. They were also very tiny—the largest were only the size of mice or squirrels. With the extinction of the dinosaurs at the end of the Mesozoic, mammals began to increase in number, variety, and size.

Among the first mammals of the Cenozoic were the *creodonts.* These primitive carnivores flourished in the early Tertiary. Some resembled modern cats or dogs, but all died out by the Oligocene, the fourth epoch of the Tertiary. Other mammals that appeared in the Cretaceous and are now extinct are the *oreodon,* an early grazing animal that resembled modern deer; the mastodon, a kind of elephant; *brontotherium,* a giant animal with a head like a rhinoceros and a body like an elephant; *baluchitherium,* a giant rhinoceros and the largest land mammal of all time; the giant armadillo; and the giant ground sloth.

Some animals that first appeared in the Cenozoic continue today. In almost every case, the first animal of each group to appear was very much smaller than the modern animal. Horses, for example, first appeared in the Eocene and were about the size of a large cat. Other examples of animals that appeared and remain today are camels, rhinoceroses, pigs, dogs, whales, bats, and rabbits.

34.7 Liberty Bell Mountain and the rest of the Cascades were formed during the Cenozoic Era.

34.8 This oreodon fossil was found in Wyoming, near the White River.

SCIENCE BACKGROUND

The fossil record of the horse is both continuous and fairly abundant. The record shows that earlier horses had feet with two, three, or four toes. Modern horses have only one toe.

VIDEODISC SELECTION

Skeletons of Cenozoic mammals (described in disc directory)
Side 1: 3863 to 3867, 5-frame sequence

34.9 *Brontotherium* stood nearly 3 meters high at the shoulder.

34.10 Invertebrates like these starfish were common during the Cenozoic Era.

SCIENCE BACKGROUND
The insects diversified with the expansion of the flowering plants.

Topic 11 Other Cenozoic Animals

Throughout the Cenozoic Era, the oceans were home to nearly the same invertebrate animals as today. Foraminifera were very abundant in the early half of the era and are still common today. Sponges, corals, starfish, sea urchins, and sand dollars were common as well. Brachiopods and cephalopods were rare. Mollusks—clams, oysters, mussels, and snails—thrived throughout the era. Crabs and barnacles were common as well.

On land, the spiders, centipedes, scorpions, and insects continued to thrive. Insects included butterflies, moths, bees, wasps, ants, beetles, and many others.

Most Cenozoic fish were like those of Late Mesozoic time. Sharks and rays were abundant and gigantic. Some sharks were 20 meters long with jaws nearly 2 meters wide.

Amphibians, such as frogs, toads, and salamanders, were about as common as they are now. The reptiles—turtles, lizards, snakes, and crocodiles—resembled those of today.

Birds developed that were similar to those of today. At times, there were many large, flightless, ostrichlike types. Some were three meters tall.

Topic 12 Plant Life

Many modern trees first appeared in the Cretaceous Period. Most of them still exist today. At the beginning of the Cenozoic Era, the warm and humid climate favored the growth of tropical plants even in the northern United States. These included palm, fern, fig, and camphor trees. Cypress, laurel, and sequoia grew as far north as Greenland and northern Canada.

As temperatures cooled late in the era, tropical plants died off except in equatorial areas. By the end of the era, these plants had disappeared from western North America. Sequoia trees remained although they were reduced to only two kinds. The Giant Sequoias of the California Sierras and the redwoods of coastal California and Oregon are examples.

Replacing the forests in colder, drier areas were grasses. Grasses began to appear in about the middle of the Cenozoic Era. Animals that grazed on the grasses thrived. These grasses are thought to be the cause of the almost explosive evolution of grazing animals such as horses. Some of the grasses developed into the familiar grains of today, such as wheat, corn, barley, rye, oats, and rice.

SCIENCE BACKGROUND
The grasses are the most important Cenozoic plant development.

Topic 13 The Rise of Humans

The fossil record contains extensive traces of early human life. Over 3000 early human fossils, consisting of jaws, teeth, skulls, and other bones, have been found with ages placed between 2.5 and 7 million years old.

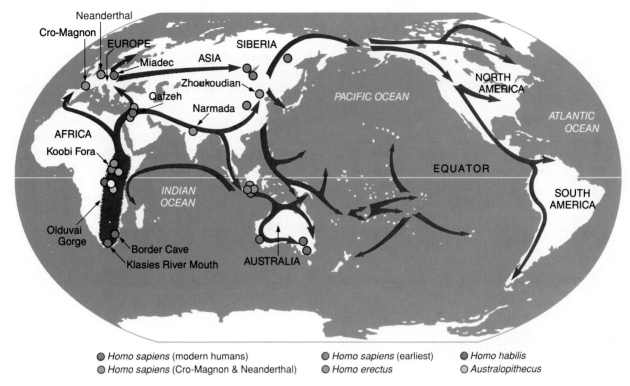

Homo sapiens (modern humans)
Homo sapiens (Cro-Magnon & Neanderthal)
Homo sapiens (earliest)
Homo erectus
Homo habilis
Australopithecus

34.11 This map shows the movement of hominids from Africa and locations of major fossil finds.

Two chief characteristics distinguish humanlike fossils from apelike fossils. One is brain size. Modern humans have brains that occupy a volume of about 1300 cubic centimeters, larger than the brains of apes. The other distinguishing characteristic is that humans are bipedal. That is, they walk on two legs rather than four. The term **hominids** is used to refer to humanlike, bipedal primates.

The oldest generally accepted hominid is known as *Australopithecus*. *Australopithecus* skeletons show that they had apelike brains, humanlike jaws, and were bipedal. *Australopithecus* is thought to have lived from 3.8 to 2.8 million years ago. The skeleton of a 20-year-old female *Australopithecus* found in Africa in the early 1970's has become famous as *Lucy*.

In the 1960's and 1970's, hominid fossils were found with a brain size of about 700 cubic centimeters—much larger than that of *Australopithecus*. This fossil was given the name *Homo habilis*. *Homo habilis* was able to make and use simple tools. They lived from about 2 to 1.75 million years ago.

Homo erectus is another species of hominid. This hominid had a brain volume of about 1000 cubic centimeters. *Homo erectus* lived from 1.5 million years to 300 000 years ago and is thought to be the first hominid to control fire. *Homo erectus* is thought to have first appeared in Africa and then migrated to Asia and Europe.

Hominid fossils from the last 300 000 years have been placed in the species *Homo sapiens*. Modern humans are *Homo sapiens*. But early *Homo sapiens* were somewhat different from those of today. One group of *Homo sapiens* is referred to as *Neanderthal*. Neanderthals were somewhat shorter and more robust than modern

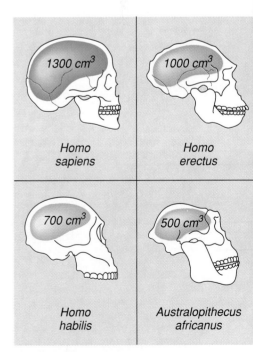

1300 cm³ — *Homo sapiens*

1000 cm³ — *Homo erectus*

700 cm³ — *Homo habilis*

500 cm³ — *Australopithecus africanus*

34.12 The brain size of hominids has increased over time.

humans. The other group of early *Homo sapiens,* known as *Cro-Magnons,* had skeletons almost identical to modern humans. These *Homo sapiens* may have migrated out of Africa about 100 000 years ago.

Tracing human evolution from the fossil record is difficult. In one hypothesis, *Australopithecus* is considered to be an ancestor of modern humans. In another hypothesis, *Australopithecus* is considered to be an offshoot, not in the direct line that led to humans. More research is necessary.

34.13 The dodo became extinct during the 1600's.

ANSWERS

8. (a) dominant Cenozoic life form   (b) Paleocene, Eocene, Oligocene, Miocene, Pliocene epochs are Tertiary; Pleistocene, Recent epochs are Quaternary   (c) cooled to Pleistocene Ice Age

9. (a) Atlantic, Gulf coastal plains and parts of California under water, other parts of continent similar   (b) worn down and raised again   (c) uplift; lava flows   (d) Himalayas, Alps, Andes raised

10. (a) creodont—dog- or cat-sized carnivore; oreodon—early grazing animal that resembled modern deer; mastodon—kind of elephant; brontotherium-rhinoceros head, elephant body; baluchitherium-giant rhinoceros; giant armadillo; giant ground sloth   (b) horses, camels, rhinoceroses, pigs, dogs, whales, bats, rabbits   (c) smaller brain size: 500, 700, and 1000cm^3 compared with 1300cm^3

Topic 14 **The Past 11 000 Years**

The Pleistocene Epoch came to an end when the last ice sheets disappeared from North America, Europe, and Siberia about 11 000 years ago. That time marks the beginning of the Holocene Epoch.

In the Holocene, humans have been the main cause for the extinction of animal and plant species. Within the past 400 years, the Great Auk, passenger pigeon, Dodo, and Moa have become extinct. The America bison was nearly wiped out. The great whales and many more species such as the golden eagle, whooping crane, American alligator, and rhinoceros have become endangered species.

Hunting is not the only reason that some animal groups have become extinct or nearly extinct. Civilization itself is also a cause. As swamps are filled and forests are cut down, the breeding grounds of many animals are destroyed.

How can endangered species be saved? Conservation groups and many governments have adopted protective programs for both animals and plants. Wildlife sanctuaries have been created. Attempts are being made to establish international agreements to regulate commercial hunting, fishing, and whaling.

TOPIC QUESTIONS

Each topic question refers to the topic of the same number.

8. (a) Why is the Cenozoic called the Age of Mammals? **(b)** How is the Cenozoic Era divided? **(c)** What changes in climate occurred during the Cenozoic?

9. (a) At the start of the Cenozoic, how did North America look different from the way it looks today? **(b)** What happened to the Appalachian and Rocky mountains during the Cenozoic? **(c)** How was the Colorado Plateau formed? The Columbia Plateau? **(d)** List some mountain ranges that were formed or raised higher during the Cenozoic Era.

10. (a) List and describe some examples of mammals that appeared in the Cenozoic but are now extinct. **(b)** List some animals that first appeared in the Cenozoic and have not become extinct. **(c)** Identify and explain one way in which *Australopithecus, Homo habilis,* and *Homo erectus* differed from *Homo sapiens.*

11. (a) foraminifera, sponges, corals, starfish, sea urchins, sand

11. (a) What invertebrates of the Cenozoic Era lived in the seas? On land?   **(b)** List examples of Cenozoic fish, amphibians, and reptiles.   **(c)** How did Cenozoic birds differ from modem birds?

12. (a) Describe the change in plant life at northern latitudes during the Cenozoic.   **(b)** What effect did this change have on animal life?

13. (a) What does *hominid* mean?   **(b)** What two characteristics distinguish hominids?

14. (a) Name some animals that people have caused to become extinct or endangered.   **(b)** In what ways do people cause animals to become extinct?   **(c)** List some ways in which endangered species can be saved.

dollars, clams, oysters, mussels, snails, crabs, barnacles; spiders, centipedes, scorpions, many kinds of insects   (b) sharks, rays; frogs, toads, salamanders; turtles, lizards, snakes, crocodiles   (c) could not fly

12. (a) tropical plants at start, grasses later   (b) Grasses favored evolution of grazing animals like the horse.

13. (a) humanlike, bipedal primates   (b) brain size, bipedal

14. (a) Great Auk, passenger pigeon, Dodo, Moa, bison, whales, golden eagle, whooping crane, alligator, rhinoceros   (b) hunting, reduction of places for animal to live and breed   (c) conservation; government protection; wildlife sanctuaries; regulation of hunting, fishing, whaling

Current RESEARCH

Mass Extinctions

A new, highly-sensitive form of radioactive age dating has provided what may be the final evidence needed to tie a buried crater on Mexico's Yucatan Peninsula with the massive extinction of life that occurred 65 million years ago at the end of the Cretaceous.

In 1992, scientists using the argon-argon method determined that the age of tektites found near the Yucatan crater and the age of the crater itself were each almost exactly 65 million years old. This date coincides with a layer of the element iridium found in rocks from Canada to Italy. Normally iridium is not very abundant in the rocks of Earth's crust. However, iridium is abundant in meteorites. These various pieces of evidence point to an asteroid impact on Earth.

Scientists have proposed other theories to explain the causes of mass extinctions. One such theory involves the possible existence of a tenth planet in our solar system. Theorists have named this Planet X. According to this theory, Planet X has a very large, elliptical orbit that takes it out of what is normally thought of as the solar system and into the Oort cloud. Every 26 million years, when Planet X passes through the Oort cloud, it pulls comets out of the cloud, sending them speeding toward Earth. The impact of comets on Earth would heat Earth's atmosphere to levels that would be intolerable for some life forms. This theory is useful in that it explains why the geologic record shows that Earth has undergone extinctions about every 26 million years for hundreds of millions of years.

Some theories of mass extinctions are tied to plate tectonics. The mass extinction that took place at the end of the Paleozoic may have been caused by the formation of Pangaea. The new supercontinent may have changed ocean circulation patterns enough to alter Earth's climate. Similarly, patterns of sea level rise and fall seem to match the cycle of extinctions.

So perhaps the buried impact crater in the Yucatan is not the smoking gun in the mystery of what caused the death of the dinosaurs. It is possible that the asteroid impact only hastened an extinction process already underway.

L A B
ACTIVITY

How Big Was That Dinosaur?

Terrible lizards! For over 150 million years, dinosaurs were the dominant land animal on planet Earth. Before they became extinct 65 million years ago, some dinosaurs evolved to truly enormous size. How big were the dinosaurs compared to modern humans?

In this activity, you will use the models of dinosaurs and your knowledge of scale to calculate the approximate mass of a dinosaur.

Lab Skills and Objectives
- To **measure** and record data from a model dinosaur
- To **infer** information about real dinosaurs from model data
- To **compare** dinosaur size with human size

For additional activities, see Laboratory Investigations booklet.

Materials
- dinosaur model
- lab balance
- ruled paper
- metric ruler
- bathroom scale
- Figure 34.14, Dinosaur Size Data
- copy of Data Table
- calculator

Procedure

1. Select a dinosaur model. Use this textbook or another appropriate reference to determine the kind of dinosaur your model represents. Write the dinosaur's name in the Data Table.

2. Use the lab balance to determine, to the nearest tenth of a gram, the mass of the model. Record the measurement in the Data Table.

3. Determine the length of the model. (For some models, the height may be easier to obtain. See Figure 34.14 for available dimensions). Lay one end of the model on a line drawn on the ruled paper. Mark off the distance to the other

end of the model. If the model has a curved neck or tail, turn the model along the line to obtain its total length. Do not attempt to bend the model. Use the metric ruler to determine, to the nearest tenth of a centimeter, the distance between the starting line and your mark. Record the length or height in the Data Table.

4. Find the length or height of your dinosaur in Figure 34.14. Record the dimension in the Data Table.

5. Using 1 meter = 100 centimeters, convert the dinosaur's length or height in step 4 from meters to centimeters.

6. Determine how many times greater the dimension of the real dinosaur was than the model is. For example, if the length of the model is 10 centimeters and the length of the actual dinosaur was 500 centimeters, the actual animal was 50 times larger than the model. Record the result for your model beside *Scale* in the Data Table.

7. Assume that if the actual dinosaur was 50 times larger in one dimension, it was also 50 times larger in all dimensions— length, width, and height. To find how many times larger the dinosaur's volume was than the model, cube your scale value. For example, a dinosaur that is 50 times longer than the model would be 50 x 50 x 50

| Dinosaur Size Data ||
Name	Dimensions
Tyrannosaurus	6 meters high, 15 meters long
Stegosaurus	8 meters long
Triceratops	9 meters long
Trachodon	5 meters high, 9 meters long
Apatosaurus	70 meters long

34.14

or 125 000 larger in volume. Record your results in the Data Table.

8. If the volume of the actual dinosaur is 125 000 times that of the model, its mass is also 125 000 times that of the model (assuming both have the same density). To find the mass of the actual dinosaur, multiply the mass of the model by the cubed scale. Record your value for actual mass in grams in the Data Table.

9. Using 1 kilogram (kg) = 1000 grams, convert the actual dinosaur's mass in grams to mass in kilograms of mass.

10. Use a bathroom scale to determine your weight in pounds. Record it in the Data Table.

11. Obtain weights for four other students from the class. Record the weights as students 2 through 5 in the Data Table. Try to select students of several sizes for your sample.

12. Find and record the average weight of the five students.

13. Using 1 kilogram = 2.2 pounds, convert the average student weight in pounds to the average mass in kilograms.

14. Imagine a huge pan balance with the actual dinosaur on one of the pans. Use the average student mass value to determine, to the nearest whole student, the number of students that would be needed on the other pan to balance the dinosaur.

15. Answer the questions in *Analysis and Conclusions*.

Data Table	
Kind of dinosaur	
Model mass	g
Model length or height	cm
Actual dimension of real dinosaur	m
Actual dimension of real dinosaur	cm
Scale	
Scale cubed	
Mass of actual dinosaur	g
Mass of actual dinosaur	kg
Your weight from bathroom scale	lbs
Weight of student 2	lbs
Weight of student 3	lbs
Weight of student 4	lbs
Weight of student 5	lbs
Weight of an average student	lbs
Mass of average student	kg
Number of students equal in mass to one dinosaur	students

Analysis and Conclusions

1. Consider your value for the number of students equal in mass to one dinosaur. Do you think that the value is reasonable and logical? Explain.

2. Is the volume of your classroom more or less than the volume of your dinosaur? List the specific steps to take to find out. (Note: Only list the steps. Do not perform the calculation unless you wish.)

3. *Tyrannosaurus rex* had a huge head with teeth that could measure up to 18 centimeters long. If *Tyrannosaurus* were around today, could it swallow a human whole? Based upon the scaling methods used in this lab, propose a method of finding out. (Note: Again, only explain how you would determine the answer. Do not do the calculation unless you wish.)

Answers to all questions appear in the Teacher's Guide at the back of this book.

■ Summary

I The Mesozoic Era consists of three periods. During the Mesozoic, Pangaea broke up into Laurasia in the north and Gondwana in the south, with the Tethys Sea between them. The climate was mild throughout the Mesozoic.

Dinosaurs were the largest land vertebrates of the Mesozoic. *Tyrannosaurs rex, Allosaurus, Triceratops, Apatosaurus, Diplodocus,* and *Brachiosaurus* are examples of dinosaurs.

The first birds appeared during the Mesozoic. Other land creatures that appeared were flies, termites, grasshoppers, ants, and anteaters.

Ammonites are index fossils for the Mesozoic Era. Corals, bryozoans, and clams also thrived in the Mesozoic oceans.

The evolution of flowering plants in the Cretaceous led to the development of deciduous trees.

Dinosaurs as well as many other groups died out at the end of the Mesozoic Era. Asteroid impact may have been the cause.

II The Cenozoic Era is divided into two periods and seven epochs.

During the Cenozoic, the continents moved to their present locations as the Himalayas, Rockies, and other mountains were formed or raised.

The climate of the Cenozoic was mild at first but gradually cooled to an Ice Age during the Pleistocene Epoch.

Mammals thrived during the Cenozoic Era and left an extensive fossil record. Plant and animal groups took on modern characteristics during the Cenozoic.

The development of grasses during the Cenozoic Era led to the rapid evolution of many different kinds of grazing animals.

Hominids evolved in late Cenozoic time.

Humans have caused the extinction or near extinction of many animal and plant groups. Efforts are now being made to save endangered groups.

■ Vocabulary

ammonite   dinosaur   hominid

■ Review

Number your paper from *1* to *16*. Select the best answer to complete each statement.

1. Which is evidence for a mild Mesozoic climate? (a) glaciers in Africa (b) iridium in sediments (c) palm trees in Florida (d) corals in Europe
2. Laurasia consisted of (a) North America and Eurasia, (b) Eurasia and Africa, (c) Africa and South America, (d) South America and North America.
3. Como Bluff and Dry Mesa are famous quarries for (a) flightless birds, (b) flowering plants (c) iron ore, (d) dinosaur bones.
4. The largest dinosaurs were the (a) sauropod dinosaurs, (b) armored dinosaurs, (c) duck-billed dinosaurs, (d) carnivorous dinosaurs.
5. *Archeopteryx* is an early (a) mammal, (b) dinosaur, (c) bird, (d) tree.
6. Ammonites are (a) flying reptiles of the Cenozoic, (b) grazing mammals of the Cenozoic, (c) carnivorous dinosaurs of the Mesozoic, (d) index fossils of the Mesozoic.
7. Flowering plants appeared during the (a) Paleocene Epoch, (b) Cretaceous Period, (c) Triassic Period, (d) Quaternary Period.
8. Tektites and a buried crater in the Yucatan are thought to be evidence of (a) asteroid impact, (b) cooler climates, (c) volcanic activity, (d) flowering plants.
9. The Cenozoic is the Age of (a) Reptiles, (b) Ammonites, (c) Mammals, (d) Cockroaches.
10. The two periods of the Cenozoic are (a) Tertiary and Quaternary, (b) Archeozoic and Proterozoic, (c) Mississippian and Pennsylvanian, (d) Triassic and Jurassic.
11. Two mountain ranges that formed during the Cenozoic are (a) Adirondacks and Appalachians, (b) Appalachians and Urals, (c) Urals and Alps, (d) Alps and Himalayas.

For further review, see **Study Guide.**
For assessment, see **Chapter Tests**
and **Computer Test Bank.**

12. Creodonts and oreodons are examples of (a) Precambrian stromatolites, (b) Cambrian trilobites, (c) Mesozoic dinosaurs, (d) Cenozoic mammals.
13. Cenozoic invertebrates that lived in the ocean (a) were nearly the same as marine invertebrates of today, (b) were much smaller than marine invertebrates of today, (c) were rare, (d) were nearly the same as Triassic marine invertebrates.
14. Which animal groups benefited most during the change from trees to grasses in the Cenozoic? (a) grazing mammals (b) herbivorous dinosaurs (c) egg-laying amphibians (d) nest-building birds
15. The two main factors that distinguish hominids from other primates are (a) tooth size and erect posture, (b) robust skeletons and use of fire, (c) prominent eyebrows and large arm muscles, (d) bipedal movement and a large brain.
16. What do the Great Auk, passenger pigeon, and Dodo have in common? (a) All thrived during the late Mesozoic. (b) All are marine invertebrates. (c) All died out within the past 400 years. (d) All were saved from extinction by conservation groups.

Interpret and Apply

On your paper, answer each question in complete sentences.

1. What might the plant and animal life of the world be like today if Pangaea had not rifted apart?
2. Aside from radioactivity, in what ways might a nuclear war today be similar to the asteroid impact that is theorized to have occurred at the close of the Mesozoic Era?
3. During the Miocene Epoch, horses migrated from Alaska to Siberia while mastodons moved from Asia to North America. Today the Bering Strait separates Alaska and Siberia. How did the animals get from one continent to the other?

Critical Thinking

The chart shows the geologic time ranges for ten groups of Mesozoic and Cenozoic plants and animals. The width of each column on the chart represents the relative abundance of each group.

1. Which groups have steadily increased in abundance since the early Triassic Period?
2. According to the chart, which group(s) died out at the end of the Mesozoic?
3. Which group expanded rapidly in the Cretaceous and remained abundant during the Tertiary and Quaternary periods?
4. Which group existed only during the Mesozoic Era?
5. Which group still found today was more abundant in the Jurassic?
6. What is the most likely age of a rock layer that contains the fossil remains of sauropods, conifers, and flowering plants?
7. According to the chart, which group would be the best index fossil?
8. Compared to the abundance of insects today, how abundant were insects during the Jurassic Period?
9. Could a rock that contains sauropods also contain impressions of ammonites? Why or why not?

643

Appendix A Properties of Some Common Minerals

The minerals are arranged alphabetically, and the most useful properties in identification are printed in italic type. Most minerals can be identified by means of two or three of the properties listed below. In some minerals, color is important; in others, cleavage is characteristic; and in others, the crystal shape identifies the mineral.

Name and Chemical Composition	Hard-ness	Color	Streak	Type of Cleavage	Remarks
Amphibole (complex ferromagnesian silicate)	5–6	*Dark green to black*	Greenish black	Two directions at angles of 56° and 124°	Vitreous luster. Hornblende is the common variety. Long, slender, six-sided crystals. *Black with shiny cleavage surfaces at 56° and 124°.*
Apatite (calcium fluorophosphate)	5	Green, brown, red, variegated	White	Indistinct	Crystals are common as are granular masses; vitreous luster.
Beryl (beryllium silicate)	8	*Greenish*	Colorless	None	*Hardness, greenish color, six-sided crystals.* Aquamarine and emerald are gem varieties. Nonmetallic luster.
Biotite mica (complex silicate)	2.5–3	Black, brown, dark green	Colorless	*Excellent in one direction*	*Thin elastic films peel off easily.* Nonmetallic luster.
Calcite (CaCO₃)	3	Varies	Colorless	*Excellent, three directions, not at 90° angles*	*Fizzes in dilute hydrochloric acid. Hardness.* Nonmetallic luster.
Chalcopyrite (CuFeS₂)	3.5–4	*Golden yellow*	Greenish black	None	*Hardness and color distinguish from pyrite.* Metallic luster.
Copper (Cu)	2.5–3	*Copper red*	Red	None	*Metallic luster on fresh surface. Ductile and malleable. Sp. gr. 8.5 to 9.*
Corundum (Al₂O₃)	9	Dark grays or browns common	Colorless	None, parting resembles cleavage	*Barrel-shaped, six-sided crystals with flat ends.*
Diamond (C)	10	Colorless to black	Colorless	Excellent, four directions	Hardest of all minerals.
Chlorite (complex silicate)	1–2.5	*Greenish*	Colorless	Excellent, one direction	*Nonelastic flakes, scaly, micaceous.*
Dolomite (CaMg(CO₃)₂)	3.5–4	Varies	Colorless	*Good, three directions, not at 90°*	*Scratched surface fizzes in dilute hydrochloric acid. Cleavage surfaces curved.*
Feldspar (Potassium variety)(silicate)	6	*Salmon pink, and red are diagnostic; may be white and light gray*	Colorless	*Good, two directions, 90° intersection*	*Hardness, color, and cleavage taken together are diagnostic.*
Feldspar (sodium plagioclase variety) (silicate)	6	*White to light gray*	Colorless	*Good, two directions, about 90°*	*If striations are visible, they are diagnostic.* Nonmetallic luster.
Feldspar (calcium plagioclase variety) (silicate)	6	*Gray to dark gray*	Colorless	*Good, two directions, about 90°*	*Striations commonly visible;* may show iridescence. Associated with augite, whereas other feldspars are associated with hornblende. Nonmetallic luster.
Fluorite (CaF₂)	4	Varies	Colorless	*Excellent, four directions*	Nonmetallic luster. In cubes or octahedrons as crystals and in cleavable masses.
Galena (PbS)	2.5	*Bluish lead gray*	Lead gray	*Excellent, three directions, intersect 90°*	*Metallic luster.* Occurs as crystals and cleavable masses. *Very dense.*
Gold (Au)	2.53–3	*Gold*	Gold	None	Malleable, ductile, *dense.* Metallic luster.
Graphite (C)	1–2	*Silver gray to black*	Grayish black	Good, one direction	Metallic or earthy luster. *Foliated, scaly masses common. Greasy feel, marks paper.* This is the "lead" in a pencil (mixed with clay).

Properties of Some Common Minerals (cont.)

Name and Chemical Composition	Hardness	Color	Streak	Type of Cleavage	Remarks
Gypsum (hydrous calcium sulfate)	2	White, yellowish, reddish	Colorless	*Very good in one direction*	Vitreous luster. *Can be scratched easily by fingernail.*
Halite (NaCl)	2–2.5	Colorless and various colors	Colorless	*Excellent, three directions, intersect at 90°*	*Taste, cleavage, hardness.*
Hematite (Fe_2O_3)	5–6 (may appear softer)	*Reddish or silvery*	*Reddish*	None	Sp. gr. 4.9 to 5.3. Metallic *or earthy luster*
Kaolinite (hydrous aluminum silicate)	2–2.5	White	Colorless	None (without a microscope)	Dull, earthy luster. Claylike masses.
Limonite (group of hydrous iron oxides)	4–5.5	*Yellowish brown*	*Yellowish brown*	None	Earthy, granular. Rust stains.
Magnetite (Fe_3O_4)	5.5–6.5	*Black*	Black	None	Metallic luster. Occurs in eight-sided crystals and granular masses. *Magnetic. Sp. gr. 5.2.*
Muscovite mica (complex silicate)	2–2.5	Colorless in thin films; yellow, red, green, and brown in thicker pieces	Colorless	*Excellent, one direction*	*Thin elastic films peel off readily.* Nonmetallic luster.
Olivine (iron magnesium silicate)	6.5–7	*Yellowish and greenish*	*White to light green*	None	*Green, glassy, granular.*
Opal (hydrous silica)	5–6.5	Varies	Colorless	None	*Glassy and pearly lusters, conchoidal fracture.*
Pyrite (FeS_2)	6–6.5	*Brass yellow*	Greenish black	None	*Cubic crystals and granular masses. Metallic luster. Crystals may be striated. Hardness important.*
Pyroxene (complex silicate)	5–6	Greenish black	Greenish gray	*Two, nearly at 90°*	*Stubby four or eight-sided crystals. Augite* is a common variety. Nonmetallic.
Quartz (SiO_2)	7	Varies from white to black and colors	Colorless	None	Vitreous luster. *Conchoidal fracture. Six-sided crystals common.* Many varieties. Very common mineral. *Hardness.*
Serpentine (hydrous magnesium silicate)	2.5–4	*Greenish (variegated)*	Colorless	Indistinct	*Luster resinous to greasy. Conchoidal fracture.* The most common kind of asbestos is a variety of serpentine.
Sphalerite (ZnS)	3.5–4	Yellowish brown to black	White to yellow	*Good, six directions*	*Color, hardness, cleavage, and resinous luster.*
Sulfur (S)	1.5–2.5	*Yellow*	White to yellow	Indistinct	Granular, earthy.
Talc (hydrous magnesium silicate)	1	White, green, gray	Colorless	Good, one direction	*Nonelastic flakes, greasy feel. Soft.* Nonmetallic luster.
Topaz (complex silicate)	8	Varies	Colorless	*One distinct (basal)*	Vitreous. *Crystals commonly striated lengthwise.*
Tourmaline (complex silicate)	7–7.5	Varies; *black* is common	Colorless	Indistinct	*Elongated, striated crystals with triangular-shaped cross sections are common.*

Periodic Table of the Elements

(based on $^{12}_{6}C = 12.0000$)

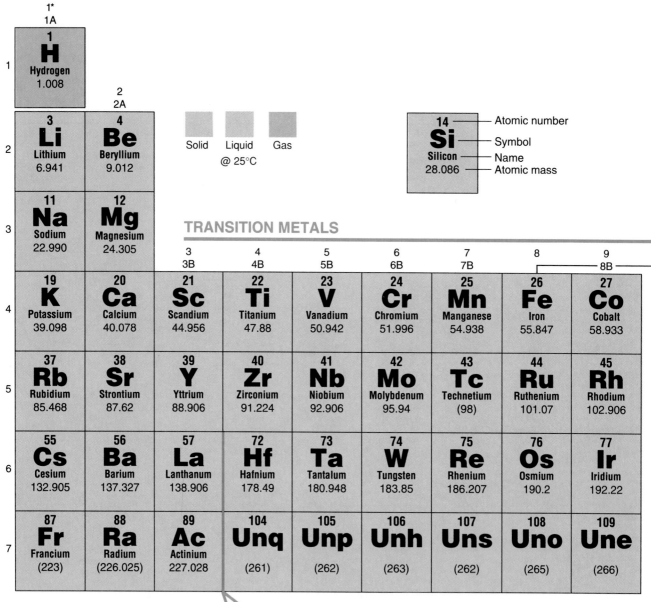

An atomic mass given in parentheses is the mass number of the isotope of longest half-life for that element.

*The 1–18 group designation has been recommended by the International Union of Pure and Applied Chemistry (IUPAC) but is not widely used. In this book, we refer to the standard U.S. notation for group numbers (1A–8A and 1B–8B).

					2 **He** Helium 4.003

13 3A	14 4A	15 5A	16 6A	17 7A	
5 **B** Boron 10.811	6 **C** Carbon 12.011	7 **N** Nitrogen 14.007	8 **O** Oxygen 15.999	9 **F** Fluorine 18.998	10 **Ne** Neon 20.180
13 **Al** Aluminum 26.982	14 **Si** Silicon 28.086	15 **P** Phosphorus 30.974	16 **S** Sulfur 32.066	17 **Cl** Chlorine 35.453	18 **Ar** Argon 39.948

10	11 1B	12 2B					
28 **Ni** Nickel 58.693	29 **Cu** Copper 63.546	30 **Zn** Zinc 65.39	31 **Ga** Gallium 69.723	32 **Ge** Germanium 72.61	33 **As** Arsenic 74.922	34 **Se** Selenium 78.96	35 **Br** Bromine 79.904	36 **Kr** Krypton 83.80
46 **Pd** Palladium 106.42	47 **Ag** Silver 107.868	48 **Cd** Cadmium 112.411	49 **In** Indium 114.82	50 **Sn** Tin 118.710	51 **Sb** Antimony 121.757	52 **Te** Tellurium 127.60	53 **I** Iodine 126.904	54 **Xe** Xenon 131.29
78 **Pt** Platinum 195.08	79 **Au** Gold 196.967	80 **Hg** Mercury 200.59	81 **Tl** Thallium 204.383	82 **Pb** Lead 207.2	83 **Bi** Bismuth 208.980	84 **Po** Polonium (209)	85 **At** Astatine (210)	86 **Rn** Radon (222)

63 **Eu** Europium 151.965	64 **Gd** Gadolinium 157.25	65 **Tb** Terbium 158.925	66 **Dy** Dysprosium 162.50	67 **Ho** Holmium 164.930	68 **Er** Erbium 167.26	69 **Tm** Thulium 168.934	70 **Yb** Ytterbium 173.04	71 **Lu** Lutetium 174.967
95 **Am** Americium (243)	96 **Cm** Curium (247)	97 **Bk** Berkelium (247)	98 **Cf** Californium (251)	99 **Es** Einsteinium (252)	100 **Fm** Fermium (257)	101 **Md** Mendelevium (258)	102 **No** Nobelium (259)	103 **Lr** Lawrencium (260)

The Metric System and SI Units

Some Base Units of Measurement in the SI (International System of Units)

Quantity	Name	Symbol
length	meter	m
mass	kilogram	kg
time	second	s
temperature	kelvin	K*

Metric System Prefixes

Prefix	Symbol	Multiples
kilo	k	1000
hecto	h	100
deka	da	10
		Divisions
deci	d	0.1 (1/10)
centi	c	0.01 (1/100)
milli	m	0.001 (1/1000)

Examples Using the Meter

Name	Symbol	Equivalent
kilometer	km	1000 m
meter	m	1 m
centimeter	cm	0.01 m
millimeter	mm	0.001 m

Metric and American Equivalents in the SI (International System)

Length

1 meter = 39.37 in
    = 3.280 ft
    = 1.093 yd
    = 0.00062 mi

1 cm = 0.393 in
1 km = 0.62 mi

1 inch = 0.0254 m or 2.54 cm
1 foot = 0.3048 m or 30.48 cm
1 yard = 0.9144 m or 91.44 cm
1 mile = 1609 mi or 1.609 km

Area

1 square meter = 1550.0 in^2
    = 10.76 ft^2
    = 1.19 yd^2

1 sq in = 0.000645 m^2 or 6.45 cm^2
1 sq ft = 0.09290 m^2
1 sq yd = 0.8361 m^2
1 sq mi = 2589900 m^2 or 2.589 km^2

Volume

1 liter = 1.06 qt
    = 33.9 oz

1 quart = 0.95 L

1 cu in = 0.000016 m^3
    or 16.38 cm^3

Mass

1 kilogram = 2.204 lb
    = 35.374 oz

1 pound = 0.4536 kg
    = 453.6 g

Temperature*

*Even though kelvin is the SI base unit for temperature, the unit "degree Celsius" is most often used in your study of earth science. The relationship between the two scales is 0° C = 273 K.

°C or Celsius = 5/9 × (°F or Fahrenheit − 32)

0° C or 32° F = freezing point of water
100° C or 212° F = boiling point of water
37° C or 98.6° F = normal human body temperature
20° C or 68° F = room temperature

Graphing Skills

You use a line graph when you are comparing two continuously changing values. For example, the table below shows data for two changing quantities: the mass of a sample of the mineral galena, and the volume of that same sample. Both values are changing, so a line graph is appropriate for graphing these data.

Mass and Volume of Galena	
Mass (g)	Volume (mL)
15.0	2.0
22.7	2.8
29.6	4.2

When making a line graph from a table of data, follow these general rules:

1. *Put a title on your graph.* The title tells your reader what the graph is about. Print the title at the top of your graph paper.

2. *Leave a space for axis labels.* Leave some space between the edge of your paper and the horizontal and vertical axes.

3. *Decide which quantity to plot on the horizontal axis and which quantity to plot on the vertical axis.* Sometimes, one of the two quantities is being changed by you in a regular way. This would be called your controlled quantity and you would plot it along the horizontal axis. Label the vertical axis with the other quantity.

4. *Choose a scale for each axis.* The scales on the two axes do not have to be the same. Your scale should

do two things. First, it must allow you to plot all the data. Therefore, the scale must have a range wide enough to include the highest and lowest data. Second, the scale should be easy to use. Make each square of your graph paper stand for a multiple of 1, 2, 5 or 10. Once you have chosen your scales, clearly mark them along the axes of your graph.

5. *Plot your data.* On a line graph, each data point is a combination of two values—one for each axis. To plot a data point, first find its horizontal axis value on the scale. For the mass given, the first horizontal axis value is 15.0 g. Follow that value up from the horizontal axis until you are across from the vertical axis value for that data point. In this case, the vertical axis value for 15.0 g is 2.0 mL. Where the horizontal and vertical axes meet, make a small dot or x. Plot all of the available data points in the same manner.

6. *Look at the data points to determine the pattern.* Often data points will appear to fall along a straight line. Other times the points will follow a smooth curve.

7. *Draw a line or curve to show the general trend of the data points.* Science data points are usually measured data. All measurements have some error. Therefore, measured data seldom fall exactly on a straight line, even if the points at first appear to fall on a straight line. Rather than connecting each data point, draw a straight line or curve that best fits the data points. A good best-fit line often passes through some points, but also has some points above it and some below it.

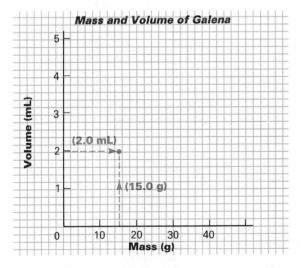

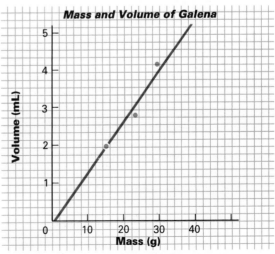

Appendix B   Map Atlas
Topographic Map: Monadnock, NH *(Partial)*

SCALE 1:62 500

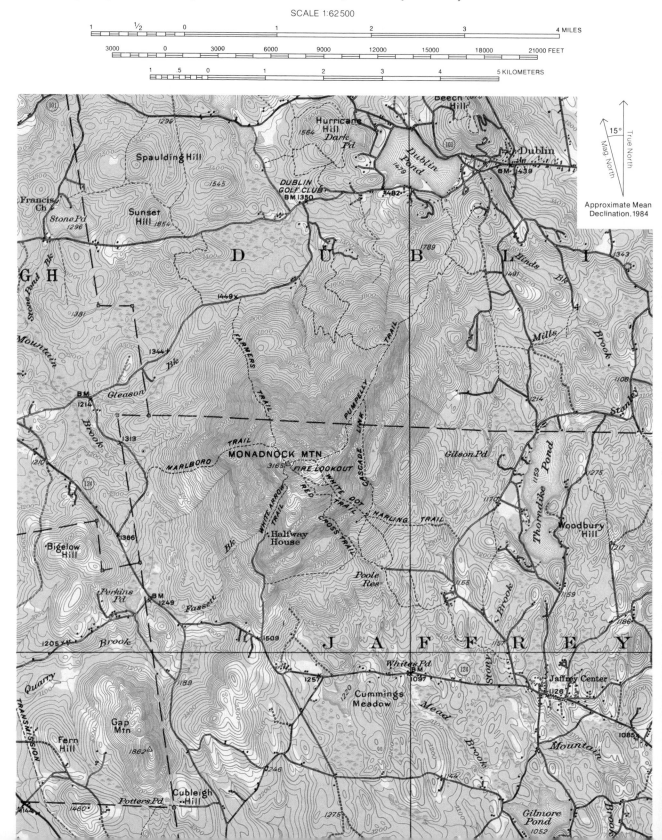

Stereophotos: Monadnock, NH

Two aerial photographs of the same location, each taken from a slightly different angle, can be viewed as a stereoimage. The photos shown were taken, one right after the other, from an airplane as it flew over Monadnock Mountain. To view the stereoimage, you will need a stereoscope like the one shown in the sketch at right. Turn the book sideways. Place the stereoscope over the two images of the mountain. The center of the stereoscope should be over the white space between the photos. Look through the stereoscope and adjust the distance between the two lenses until the mountain appears in 3-D.

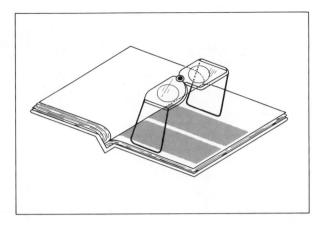

Topographic Map: Harrisburg, PA
(15-minute series, *partial*)

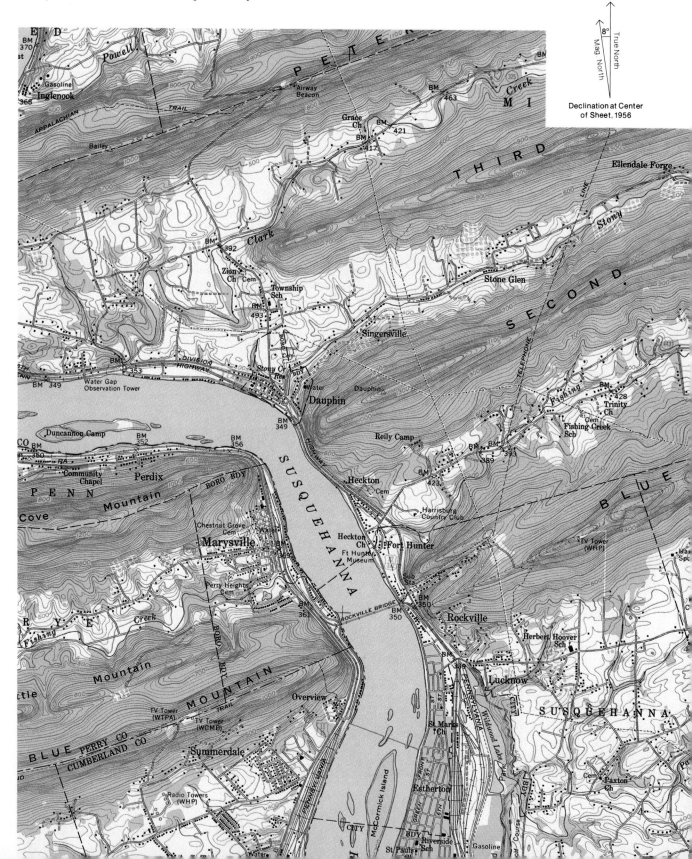

Declination at Center
of Sheet, 1956

True North

8°

Mag North

Geologic Map: Flaming Gorge, UT
(Simplified, partial)

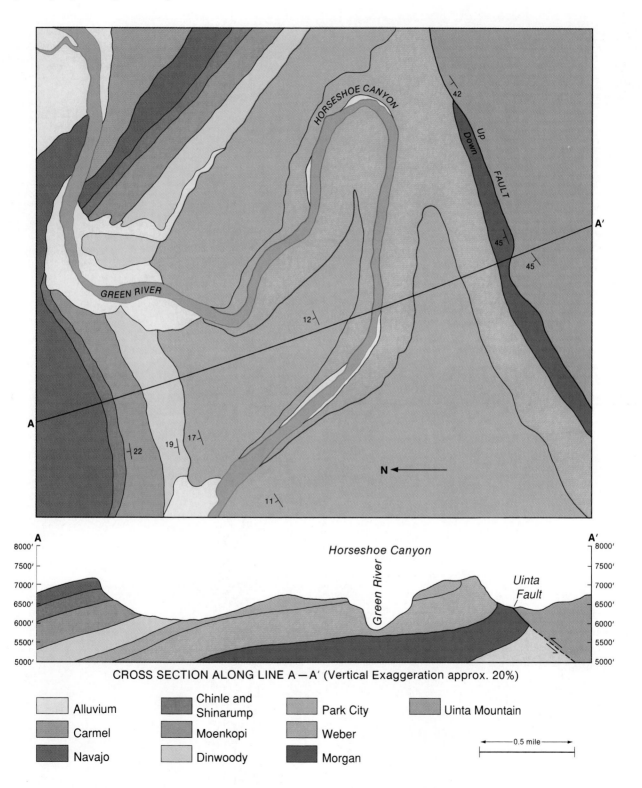

CROSS SECTION ALONG LINE A — A' (Vertical Exaggeration approx. 20%)

Alluvium

Carmel

Navajo

Chinle and Shinarump

Moenkopi

Dinwoody

Park City

Weber

Morgan

Uinta Mountain

0.5 mile

Physical United States

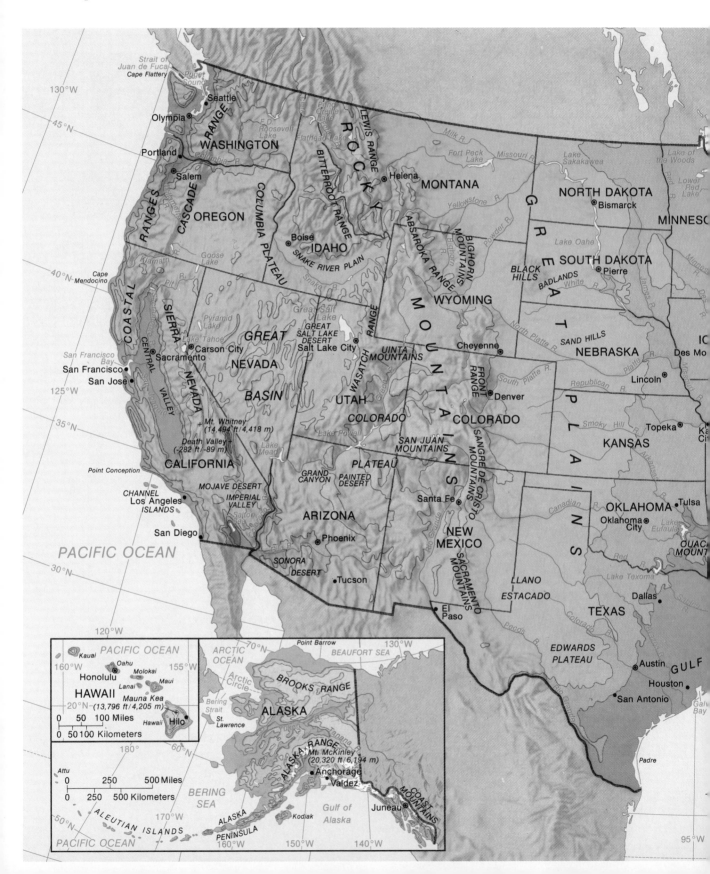

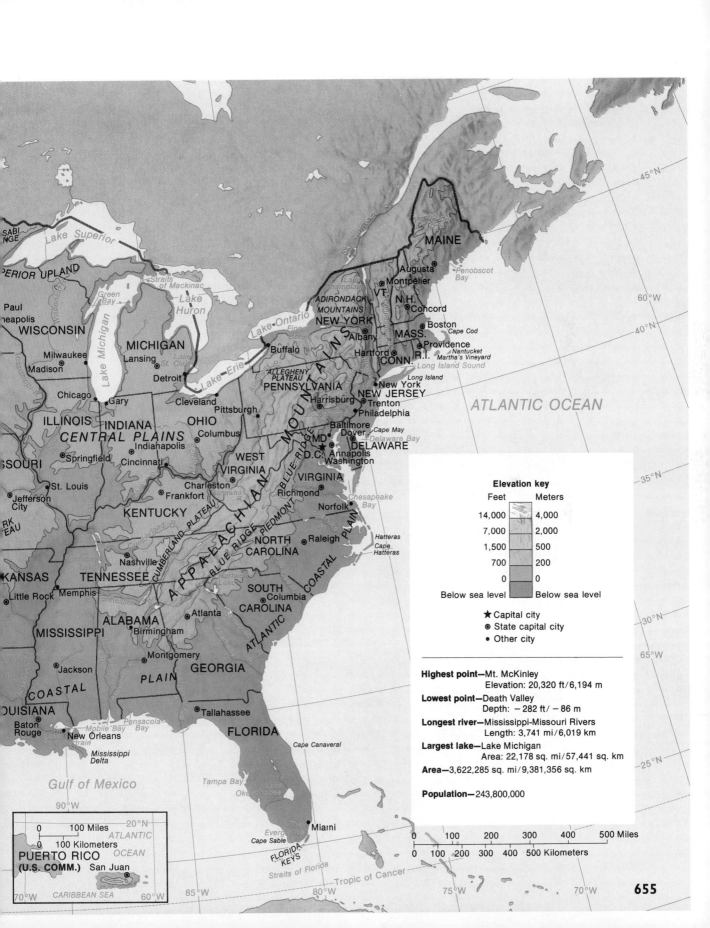

Lake Superior

PERIOR UPLAND

SABI
NGE

Paul
neapolis

WISCONSIN

Milwaukee

Madison

Green
Bay

Straits
of Mackinac

Lake
Huron

Lake Michigan

MICHIGAN

Lansing

Detroit

Lake Erie

Buffalo

Lake Ontario

Finger
Lakes

Albany

NEW YORK

ADIRONDACK
MOUNTAINS

VT.

Montpelier

Augusta

MAINE

Penobscot
Bay

N.H.

Concord

Boston

MASS.

Cape Cod

Hartford

CONN.

Providence

R.I.

Nantucket
Martha's Vineyard

Long Island Sound

45°N

60°W

40°N

Chicago

Gary

Cleveland

Pittsburgh

ALLEGHENY
PLATEAU

PENNSYLVANIA

Harrisburg

NEW JERSEY

Trenton

New York

Long Island

ATLANTIC OCEAN

ILLINOIS

INDIANA

OHIO

Columbus

Indianapolis

Cincinnati

CENTRAL PLAINS

SSOURI

Springfield

St. Louis

Jefferson
City

RK
EAU

**WEST
VIRGINIA**

Charleston

Frankfort

KENTUCKY

CUMBERLAND PLATEAU

Nashville

KANSAS

TENNESSEE

Little Rock

Memphis

Columbus

Philadelphia

Baltimore

Dover

MD

D.C.

Annapolis

Washington

DELAWARE

Cape May

Delaware Bay

VIRGINIA

Richmond

Norfolk

Chesapeake
Bay

PIEDMONT

Raleigh

**NORTH
CAROLINA**

COASTAL

Hatteras

Cape
Hatteras

BLUE RIDGE

APPALACHIAN MOUNTAINS

BLUE RIDGE

**SOUTH
CAROLINA**

Columbia

Atlanta

ATLANTIC

35°N

MISSISSIPPI

ALABAMA

Birmingham

Montgomery

Jackson

GEORGIA

PLAIN

COASTAL

UISIANA

Baton
Rouge

New Orleans

Mobile Bay

Pensacola
Bay

Tallahassee

FLORIDA

Cape Canaveral

30°N

65°W

Mississippi
Delta

Gulf of Mexico

90°W

Tampa Bay

Okeechobee

Evergiades

Miami

Cape Sable

25°N

20°N

ATLANTIC

OCEAN

**PUERTO RICO
(U.S. COMM.)**

San Juan

70°W

60°W

CARIBBEAN SEA

FLORIDA
KEYS

Straits of Florida

Tropic of Cancer

85°W

80°W

75°W

70°W

655

0   100 Miles

0   100 Kilometers

Elevation key

Feet		Meters
14,000		4,000
7,000		2,000
1,500		500
700		200
0		0
Below sea level		Below sea level

★ Capital city
◎ State capital city
● Other city

Highest point—Mt. McKinley
       Elevation: 20,320 ft/6,194 m
Lowest point—Death Valley
       Depth: −282 ft/−86 m
Longest river—Mississippi-Missouri Rivers
       Length: 3,741 mi/6,019 km
Largest lake—Lake Michigan
       Area: 22,178 sq. mi/57,441 sq. km
Area—3,622,285 sq. mi/9,381,356 sq. km

Population—243,800,000

0   100   200   300   400   500 Miles

0   100 200 300 400 500 Kilometers

Physical World: Continents and Ocean Floor

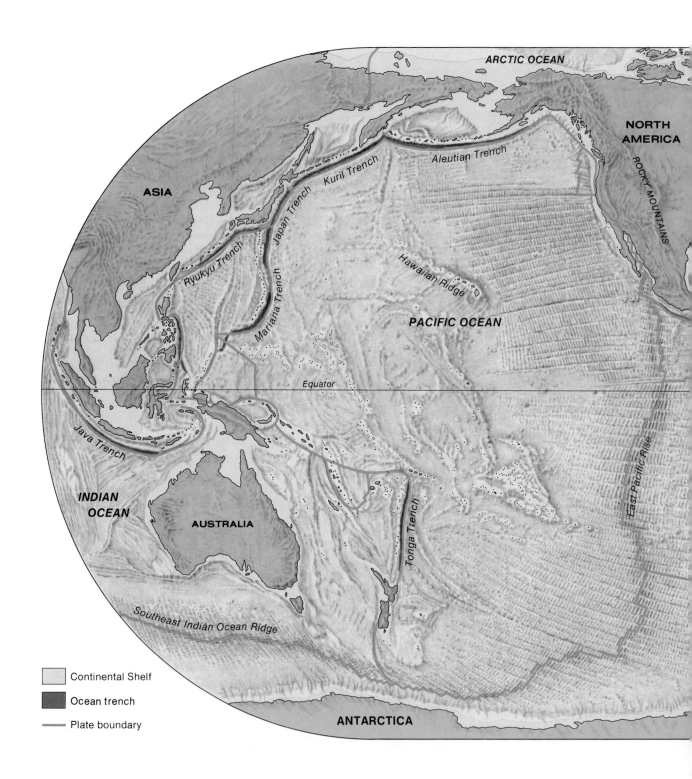

Continental Shelf

Ocean trench

Plate boundary

ARCTIC OCEAN

NORTH AMERICA

ROCKY MOUNTAINS

ASIA

Aleutian Trench

Kuril Trench

Japan Trench

Ryukyu Trench

Mariana Trench

Hawaiian Ridge

PACIFIC OCEAN

Equator

East Pacific Rise

Java Trench

INDIAN OCEAN

AUSTRALIA

Tonga Trench

Southeast Indian Ocean Ridge

ANTARCTICA

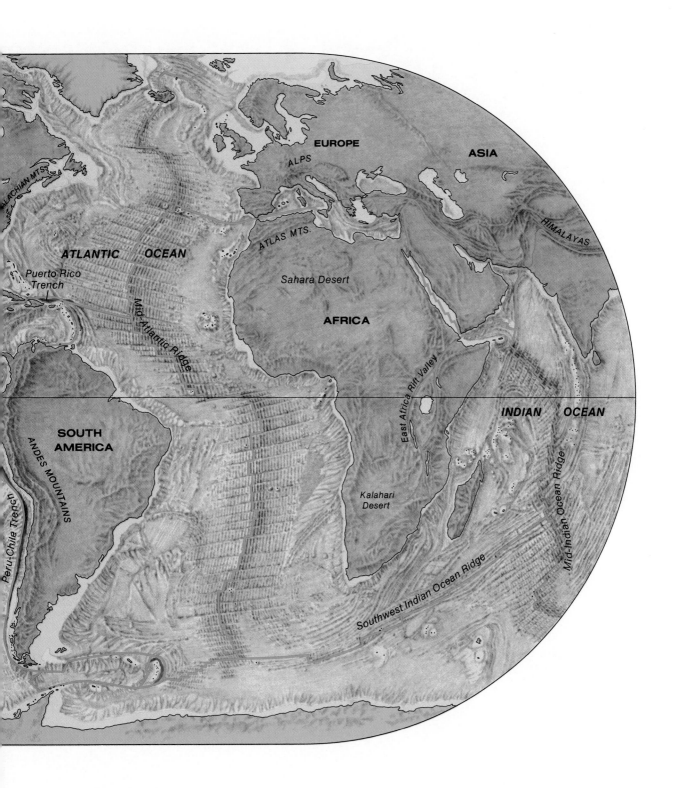

EUROPE

ASIA

ALPS

APPALACHIAN MTS.

ATLANTIC   OCEAN

Puerto Rico
Trench

ATLAS MTS.

HIMALAYAS

Sahara Desert

AFRICA

Mid-Atlantic Ridge

East Africa Rift Valley

INDIAN   OCEAN

SOUTH
AMERICA

ANDES MOUNTAINS

Peru-Chile Trench

Kalahari
Desert

Mid-Indian Ocean Ridge

Southwest Indian Ocean Ridge

Surface Ocean Currents

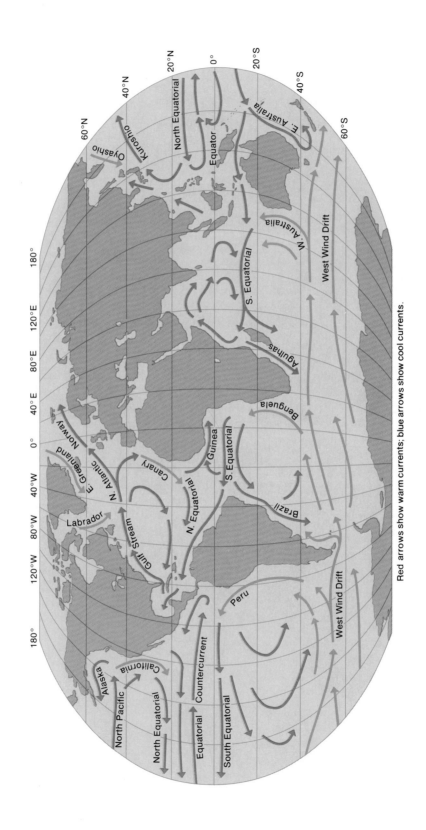

Red arrows show warm currents; blue arrows show cool currents.

Prevailing World Winds
(July average)

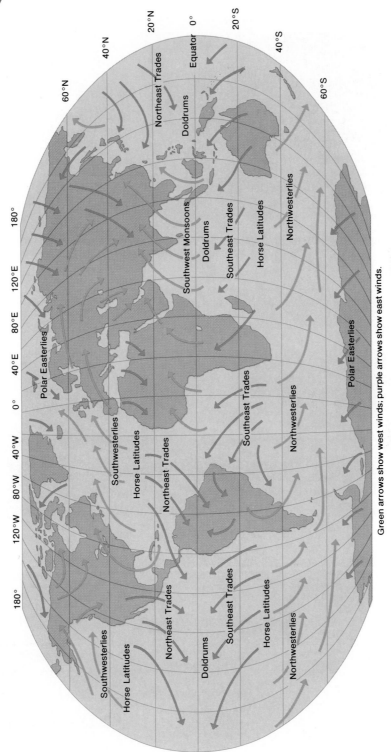

Green arrows show west winds; purple arrows show east winds.

Seasonal Star Maps

Viewed in evening skies from mid-latitude North America

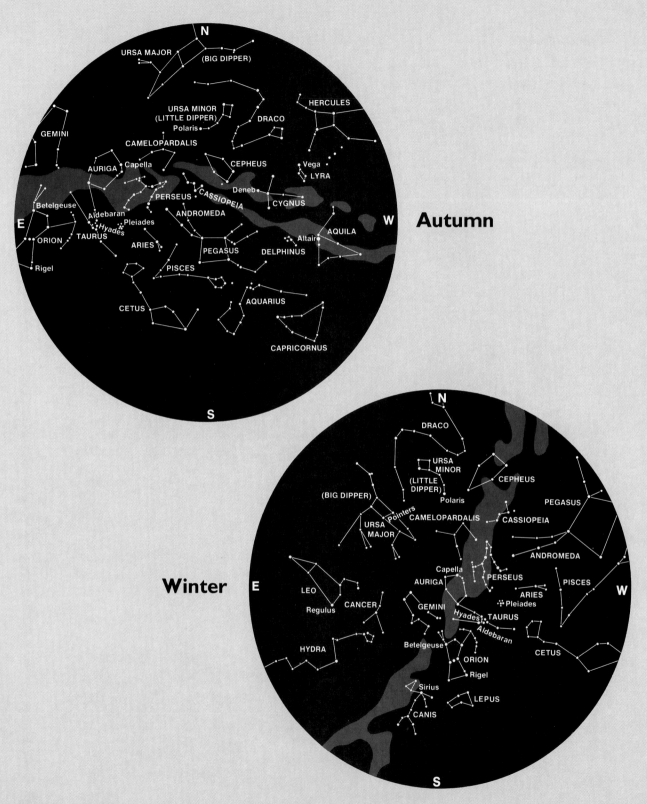

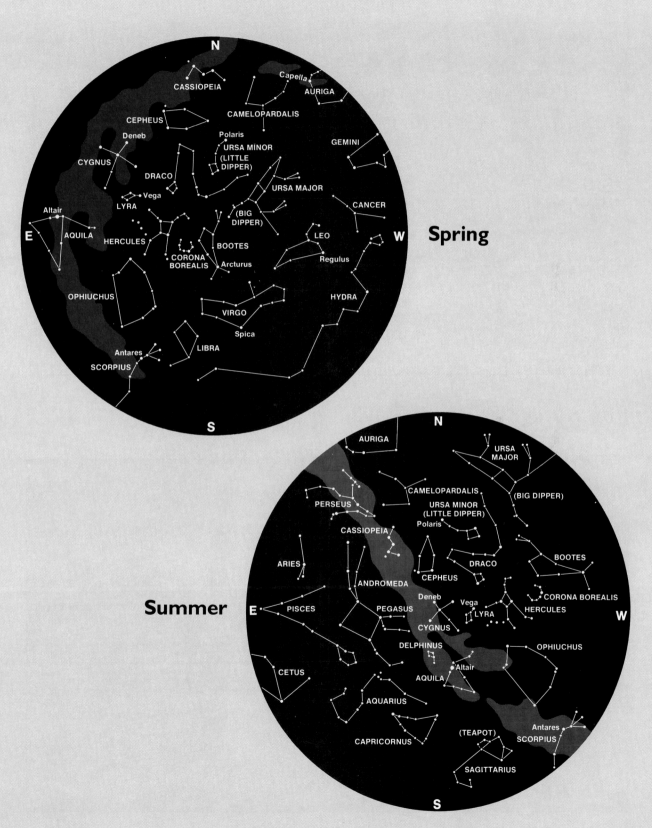

Spring

Summer

Weather Maps: Four-Day Series

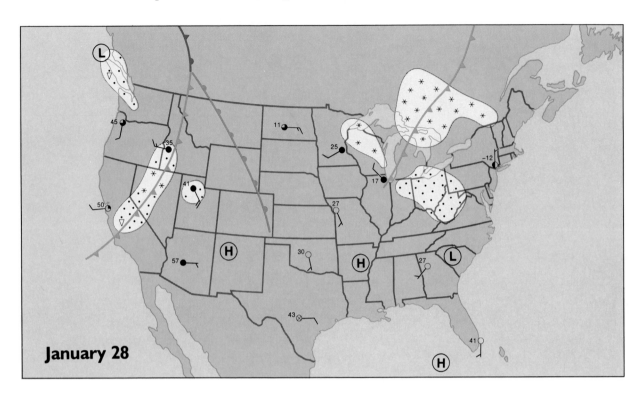

January 28

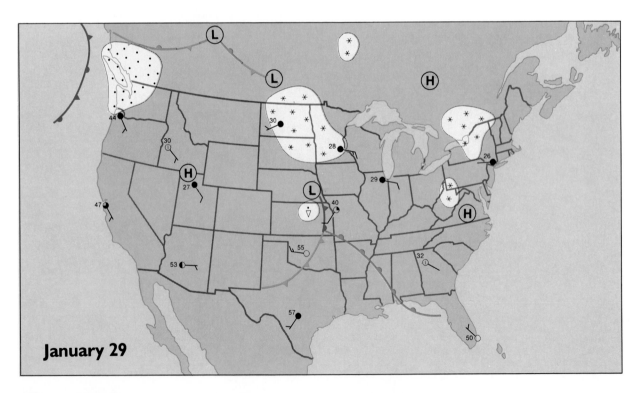

January 29

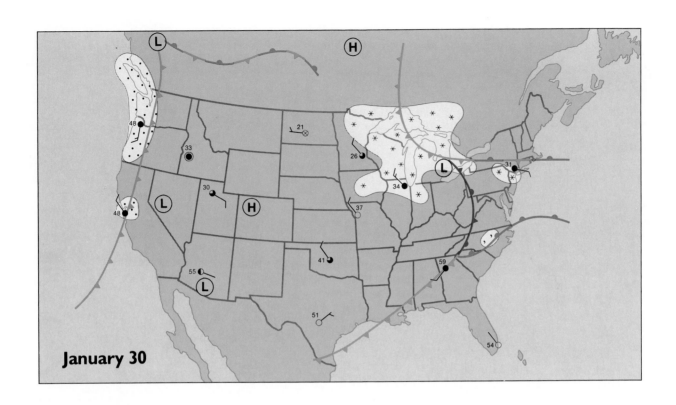

January 30

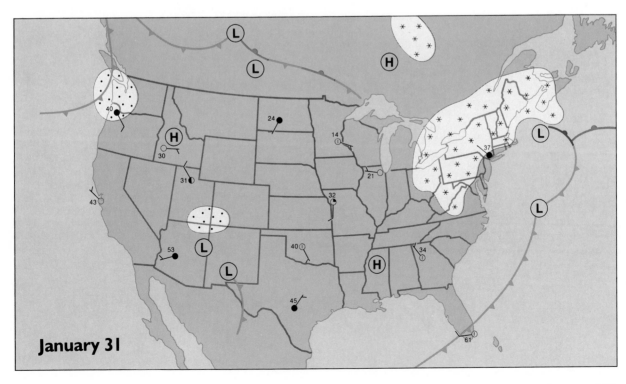

January 31

Earth's Climates

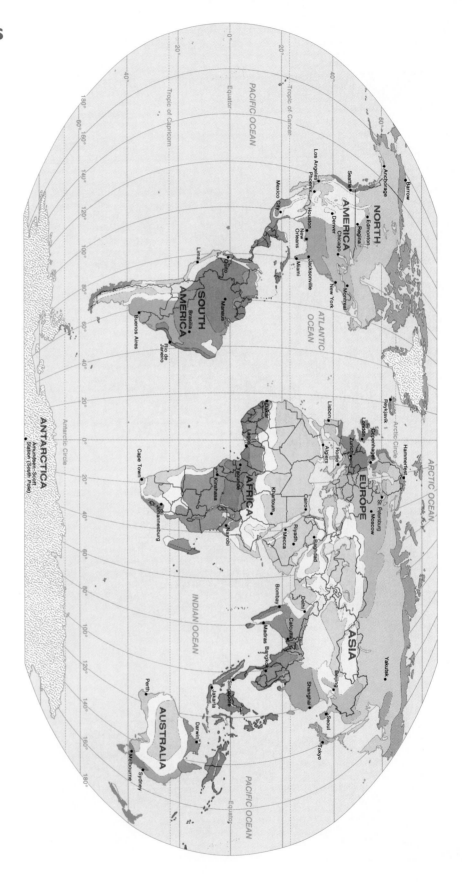

Humid Tropical Climates

Wet Tropical
(Hot and very rainy all year)

Wet-and-Dry Tropical (Hot all year
with wet and dry seasons)

Subtropical Climates

Humid Subtropical (Hot, humid
summers and mild winters)

Mediterranean Subtropical (Hot, dry
summers and mild, rainy winters)

Dry Climates

Arid
(Desert climate with very little rain)

Semiarid
(Semi-desert climate with some rain)

Midlatitude Climates

Temperate Marine
(Mild and rainy all year)

Humid Continental (Warm summers
and cold, snowy winters)

Subarctic (Short summers and long,
cold, snowy winters)

Cold Polar Climates

Subpolar (Always cold and dry with
short, cool summers)

Polar (Ice cap, with freezing
temperatures all year)

Highland Climates

(Temperature and precipitation vary
greatly with latitude and elevation)

Glossary

A

abrasion: wearing away of rock by grinding action (p. 169)

absolute magnitude: the apparent magnitude of a star if placed 32.6 light-years from the sun (p. 381)

absolute time: method of recording events that identifies actual date of an event such as when a rock formed (p. 597)

abyssal hill: small rolling hills on the ocean floor that occur next to continental margins and oceanic ridges (p. 330)

abyssal plain: large flat area on the deep ocean floor (p. 330)

acid rain: rain that contains dissolved sulfur or nitrogen gases; a dangerous pollutant (p. 101)

active continental margin: continental margin that occurs along a plate boundary, marked by earthquakes, volcanoes, and mountain building (p. 291)

air mass: a large section of the lower troposphere that has the same weather throughout (p. 543)

air-mass thunderstorms: widely scattered thunderstorms that form within a warm, moist air mass, usually lasting less than an hour (p. 557)

air pressure: weight of the atmosphere per unit area (p. 523)

alluvial fans: sloping triangular deposits of sediment located where a mountain stream reaches level land (p. 181)

altitude: height of an object in the sky above the horizon (p. 468)

amphiboles: a family of complex silicate minerals that tend to form long, needlelike crystals (p. 54)

anemometer: an instrument that measures wind speed (p. 530)

annular eclipse: an eclipse that occurs when the moon's shadow fails to reach Earth, causing the sun to be seen as a thin, bright ring around the moon; also called a ring eclipse (p. 448)

anticline: an upfold in rock layers (p. 294)

anticyclone: an area of high pressure (p. 551)

aphelion: the point in a planet's orbit when it is farthest from the sun (p. 405)

apogee: the point farthest from Earth in the orbit of an Earth satellite (p. 444)

apparent magnitude: how bright a star appears to an observer on Earth (p. 380)

aquifer: permeable earth material that contains and carries groundwater (p. 156)

arête: sharp divide that separates two adjoining cirques (p. 198)

artesian formation: the arrangement of a permeable layer of rock (aquifer) sandwiched between two layers of impermeable rock (p. 156)

asteroids: many small planetlike bodies revolving around the sun between the orbits of Mars and Jupiter (p. 425)

asthenosphere: the partially melted layer of the mantle that underlies the lithosphere (p. 234)

astronomical unit (AU): the average distance between Earth and the sun, about 150 million kilometers (p. 379)

astronomy: the study of the universe (p. 3)

atoll: a ring-shaped island or chain of islands, usually made of corals, and which nearly encircle a lagoon (p. 225)

atom: the smallest part of an element that has all of the properties of that element (p. 29)

atomic number: number of protons in nucleus of atom (p. 31)

aurora: a glow in the nighttime sky produced in the upper atmosphere by solar radiation hitting Earth's magnetic field (p. 400)

autumn equinox: the first day of fall, about September 23, in the Northern Hemisphere; daylight and nighttime are equal in length (p. 468)

average slope: the slope, or gradient, between any two points on a hill; easily determined from a contour map (p. 119)

axis of rotation: an imaginary straight line through Earth between the North Pole and the South Pole on which Earth rotates; it is tilted 23 1/2° from the plane of Earth's orbit (p. 457)

B

backwash: a gentle current of water that runs down a beach slope under an oncoming wave (p. 218)

barometer: an instrument that measures atmospheric pressure (p. 523)

barrier islands: islands formed by waves and currents located parallel to a straight shoreline (p. 221)

barrier reef: a reef separated from the mainland by a wide lagoon (p. 225)

base level: the level of the body of water into which a stream flows (p. 172)

baseline: the distance between two radio telescopes that are used for interferometry (p. 366)

batholith: name for the largest of all igneous intrusions; form the cores of many mountain ranges (p. 265)

beach: the area of the shoreline located between the high tide and low tide levels (p. 222)

Beaufort scale: a scale that relates the wind speed to its effects both on land and at sea (p. 478)

bed load: sand, pebbles, and boulders that are moved along the bed of a stream and that are too heavy to be carried in suspension (p. 170)

bench mark: a marker in the ground indicating the exact elevation above sea level (p. 116)

big bang hypothesis: theory that the universe was originally a single dense sphere of hydrogen that exploded into a gigantic expanding cloud that eventually condensed into separate galaxies (p. 390)

black holes: massive objects in space whose gravitational forces are so strong that light rays cannot escape (p. 387)

black smokers: hot springs where hot water is spewed up through chimneylike vents and metallic sulfides precipitate when the 350°C water comes in contact with 2°C water (p. 317)

blizzard: a snowstorm with high winds and low temperatures (p. 564)

blowout: small, shallow depressions formed by deflation (p. 212)

C

calving: process by which a block of a glacier breaks off and falls into the sea to form an iceberg (p. 196)

carbonate: ion group of one carbon atom combined with three oxygen atoms and having a negative charge of two (p. 55)

carbonic acid: a weak acid formed when carbon dioxide dissolves in water (p. 134)

carrying power: a measure of the total amount of sediment in a stream and the size of the particles being moved by the stream (p. 171)

Cenozoic: the current and most recent era of geologic time, starting 65 million years ago (p. 598)

cepheid variable: a pulsating star whose distance can be determined from its period of pulsation (p. 383)

charge-coupled device (CCD): photocells more sensitive to light than a photographic plate, used with an optical telescope, and thereby improving the image (p. 364)

chemical rocks: sedimentary rocks formed from mineral's precipitate by evaporation or by chemical action (p. 69)

chemical weathering: breakdown or decomposition of rock that takes place when minerals are changed into different substances (p. 131)

chlorofluorocarbons (CFCs): gases containing chlorine, fluorine, and carbon atoms that break down the ozone layer and weaken protection from ultraviolet waves (p. 480)

chromosphere: the layer of the sun's atmosphere just above the photosphere (p. 399)

cirque: a semicircular basin formed at the head of a glacial valley (p. 198)

cirrus clouds: thin, feathery, or tufted clouds of ice crystals at high altitudes (p. 506)

clastic rocks: sedimentary rocks formed from fragments of other rocks (p. 69)

cleavage: the tendency of a mineral to split easily along planes parallel to the crystal faces, leaving smooth, flat surfaces in one or more directions (p. 49)

climate: typical weather patterns over a period of years in a given location (p. 575)

cold front: leading edge of a mass of cold air (p. 548)

collision boundary: a converging boundary that is formed when two continents collide and are welded into a single, larger continent (p. 242)

comet: a mass of rock, ice, dust, and gas revolving around the sun, usually in a highly eccentric orbit (p. 424)

compound: a substance consisting of two or more elements chemically combined (p. 32)

condensation: change from water vapor to liquid water (p. 499)

condensation level: altitude at which water vapor begins to condense; where dew point reaches air temperature (p. 509)

condensation nuclei: microscopic particles on which water vapor condenses, forming cloud droplets (p. 504)

conduction: the movement of heat to an object by its contact with a hotter object (p. 484)

constellation: a group of stars that appears to form a pattern in the sky (p. 377)

contact metamorphism: the process of rock-forming that results when hot magma forces its way into overlying rock and changes that rock (p. 78)

continental climate: a climate with large yearly temperature ranges (p. 578)

continental glaciers: large sheets of ice covering a large part of a continent (p. 192)

continental rise: gently rolling slope between continental slope and abyssal plain (p. 329)

continental shelf: gently sloping submerged part of the continent (p. 292)

continental slope: steep sloping boundary between the continental shelf and the continental rise (p. 293)

contour interval: the difference in elevation between two consecutive contour lines (p. 115)

contour line: line on topographic map that connects points on land having the same elevation (p. 115)

convection: the movement of heat by currents within a heated material (p. 484)

converging boundary: a boundary that forms when two lithospheric plates come together, or converge (p. 242)

coral: tiny, colonial sea animals that form a large part of Earth's reefs (p. 224)

core (inner): spherical center of Earth, about 2800 kilometers in diameter and made of solid iron and nickel (p. 10)

core (outer): the zone of Earth's interior, extending about 2100 kilometers between Earth's inner core and mantle and made of liquid iron and nickel (p. 10)

Coriolis effect: the effect of Earth's rotation that causes the deflection of moving objects toward or away from the equator (p. 458)

corona: sun's outer atmospheres located above the chromosphere (p. 399)

correlation: the process of matching rock layers from different locations (p. 604)

countercurrent: a current flowing in a direction opposite to that of the wind-related current (p. 346)

covalent bond: the bond formed from the sharing of electrons by atoms (p. 36)

craters: depressions on the surface of a moon or a planet, usually caused by the impact of huge rocks (p. 442)

craton: the ancient core of a continent, usually the oldest and most altered rocks of the continent (p. 245)

creep: slow, often invisible, movement of soil down a slope (p. 141)

crevasse: a great fissure or crack in a glacier (p. 196)

crust: outer layer of earth that covers Earth's mantle (p. 11)

crystal: solid substance in which the atoms or ions are arranged in an orderly pattern that repeats over and over again (p. 38)

crystal shape: the pattern a mineral's ions or atoms form if there is enough time and room to grow (p. 48)

cumulonimbus: a cloud formed from a deep layer of unstable air that brings lightning, thunder, and heavy showers; also called a thundercloud (p. 509)

cumulus clouds: thick, puffy masses of clouds formed by vertically rising air currents (p. 507)

cyclone: any counterclockwise movement of air (p. 549)

D

daylight saving time: standard time advanced one hour for six or more months each year, adding an hour of daylight to the part of the day when people are awake (p. 463)

deferent: an orbit along which the center of a planet's epicycle moved around Earth in Ptolemy's geocentric model of the solar system (p. 404)

deficit: a condition in which stored soil water is gone and the need for moisture is greater than the rainfall (p. 151)

deflation: removal of loose rock particles by the wind (p. 212)

degree: (a) unit used in measuring temperature; a definite fraction of the difference between two fixed temperatures; (b) a position of space on Earth or in space as measured by degree of latitude (p. 491)

delta: a fan-shaped deposit of sediment formed at the mouth of a stream or river (p. 181)

density: ratio between mass and volume of substance (p. 21)

density current: a subsurface current that is heavier, or more dense, than the surrounding water (p. 348)

depression contour: a contour line joining points of equal elevation within a depression (p. 116)

desertification: the removal of soil by wind or rain in areas left exposed by the removal of plant covers (p. 87)

desert pavement: pebbles and boulders left in a desert when the sand and silt are blown away (p. 212)

dew: water vapor that condenses on a surface as a liquid when the air is saturated (p. 503)

dew point: the temperature at which air becomes saturated with water vapor (p. 503)

dike: an igneous intrusion that cuts across rock layers, and is formed when magma intrudes into vertical or nearly vertical fissures in bedrock (p. 264)

dinosaur: group of large Mesozoic (p. 630)

discharge: the volume of water flowing past a given point in a stream at a given time (p. 171)

diverging boundary: the spreading center where two lithospheric plates are moving apart and new lithosphere is formed (p. 240)

divide: the higher land separating two adjacent drainage basins (p. 174)

doldrums: a rainy equatorial belt of low air pressure and slowly rising air (p. 532)

dome mountain: a nearly circular folded mountain (p. 300)

Doppler effect: an apparent change in the wavelength of radiation, in which there is relative motion between the source of radiation and the receiver (p. 371)

drainage basin: area of land surface drained by a river system (p. 174)

drumlin: a long, canoe-shaped hill made of till and shaped by an advancing glacier (p. 200)

dust storm: a storm with strong, steady winds that lift great amounts of silt and clay from topsoil (p. 211)

dwarf stars: stars of an absolute magnitude of +1 or less (p. 382)

E

earthquake: the shaking of Earth's crust caused by a sudden release of energy (p. 271)

eclipsing binary: two stars of unequal brightness that revolve around and pass in front of each other at regular intervals (p. 383)

elastic-rebound theory: the theory that earthquakes occur when the stress building up between two lithospheric plates overcomes the force of friction, causing the plates to suddenly move, release energy, and then snap back to their former shapes (p. 271)

electron: a negatively charged particle that spins around the nucleus of an atom (p. 30)

electromagnetic energy: forms of energy that travel at a speed of 300 000 kilometers per second, each form having a different frequency and wavelength (p. 365)

electromagnetic spectrum: total range of electromagnetic waves, from radio waves to gamma rays (p. 365)

element: a substance that cannot be broken down into simpler substances by ordinary chemical or physical means (p. 29)

elliptical orbits: ellipse-shaped orbits with two foci (p. 405)

El Niño: warm surface current in Pacific ocean that contributes to a short-term warming trend (p. 587)

environment: all of the resources, influences, and conditions by which one is surrounded (p. 85)

epicenter: point on Earth's surface directly above the focus of an earthquake (p. 272)

epicycle: a small orbit along which a planet traveled in Ptolemy's model of the solar system (p. 404)

epoch: a subdivision of a geological period on the geologic timetable (p. 599)

equal area law: law that states that as a planet moves around the sun, an imaginary line joining the two will sweep over equal areas of space in equal periods of time (p. 405)

era: a major division of geologic time (p. 598)

erosion: process by which earth materials are moved by natural agents like moving water, wind, and ice (p. 131)

escape velocity: the minimum velocity needed for an object to escape from another object to which it is held by the force of gravitation (p. 407)

esker: a long, winding ridge formed when sand and gravel fill meltwater tunnels beneath a glacier (p. 201)

eutrophication: the destruction of a lake as it is gradually filled in by sediments and plants (p. 88)

evaporation: change of liquid water to water vapor (p. 499)

evapotranspiration: addition of water vapor to the atmosphere by evaporation from Earth's surface or from plant leaves (p. 149)

evolution: the process of gradual change that produces new life forms over geologic time (p. 603)

exfoliation: peeling of surface layers from exposed bedrock (p. 133)

eye (of a storm): calm, clear center of a tropical low (p. 561)

F

false-color image: a computer image that assigns different colors for each wavelength of light, each of which depicts a certain surface feature (p. 122)

fault: a break or crack in Earth's crust along which movement has occurred (p. 241)

fault-block mountains: mountains formed from blocks of crust that have been faulted and tilted at the same time (p. 298)

feldspar: a family of the most common and abundant of all minerals; formed by silica tetrahedrons that are joined by ions of aluminum and other metals (p. 53)

felsic rocks: light-colored, high-silica rocks (p. 65)

ferromagnesian silicate: a silicate mineral containing atoms of iron and magnesium and dark in color (p. 54)

fertility: the ability of the soil to support plant life (p. 86)

fetch: the length of open water over which a wind blows steadily (p. 215)

fiord: long, deep, steep-sided bay formed when the sea floods a glacial trough (p. 224)

firn: partially compacted and refrozen snow which has yet to become a glacier (p. 193)

flash flood: a sudden rush of water, usually caused by a single cloudburst over the narrow valley of a young mountain stream (p. 184)

flood plain: wide, level area that borders a stream and is covered by its water in time of flood (p. 179)

focus: a point within Earth at which an earthquake originates (p. 272)

fossils: the remains, impressions, or other evidence of the former existence of life preserved in rock (p. 602)

fossil fuels: nonrenewable fuels formed from the remains of plants and animals that lived long ago (p. 93)

fracture: appearance of a mineral surface where it breaks along other than cleavage planes (p. 49); (2) a crack in bedrock along which no movement has occurred (p. 300)

fringing reef: a reef found close to the shore (p. 225)

front: the boundary between two unlike air masses (p. 547)

frontal thunderstorms: thunderstorms that usually form in warm, moist air on or ahead of a cold front and last for several hours (p. 557)

frost: water vapor that has condensed on a surface as a solid when the temperature is at or below 0°C (p. 504)

G

galaxy: a group of millions, or even billions, of stars held together by gravity (p. 389)

gangue: nonvaluable rock or vein matter in which valuable metals or minerals occur (p. 90)

geocentric: model that has Earth at its center, as in a geocentric universe (p. 404)

geologic timetable: a system by which the major events of Earth's history are arranged in the order in which they occurred (p. 598)

geology: the study of Earth's surface and interior (p. 3)

geyser: a boiling hot spring that erupts periodically (p. 159)

glacial trough: a U-shaped valley formed by glacial erosion (p. 199)

granules: individual cells about 1500 kilometers across that are the tops of gas columns that form below the sun's photosphere (p. 398)

great circle: a circle whose plane passes through the center of a sphere (p. 112)

greenhouse effect: the ability of Earth's atmosphere to absorb long heat waves from Earth after allowing the sun's short waves to pass through it (p. 415)

gully: a miniature valley formed by erosion from heavy rains (p. 173)

guyot: flat-topped seamount (p. 331)

H

Hadley cell: the circulation cell in which air flows between the equator and 30 degrees latitude (p. 531)

hail: precipitation in the form of irregular balls or lumps made of concentric layers of ice (p. 513)

half-life: time required for half of the atoms in a radioactive substance to decay to a stable end product (p. 607)

hardness: the resistance of a mineral to scratching (p. 49)

harmonic law: law that states: the period of a planet squared is equal to the cube of its distance from the sun (p. 406)

headward erosion: the wearing away of land at the head of a gully or a stream valley (p. 173)

heliocentric: model that has the sun at its center, as in heliocentric solar system (p. 404)

high-pressure area (high): an area where the pressure is greater than the surrounding air (p. 525)

hominids: the general name for modern humans and their recent humanlike, bipedal primates (p. 637)

horn: pyramid-shaped peak formed where three or more cirques meet (p. 198)

horse latitudes: belts of high air pressure and very dry descending air, located at about 30 degrees latitude north and south of the equator (p. 532)

hot spots: areas of volcanic activity near the center of lithospheric plates (p. 257)

hurricane: a tropical cyclone with sustained winds of 120 kilometers per hour or greater (p. 561)

hydrolysis: any chemical reaction of water with other substances (p. 134)

hydrosphere: all the waters of Earth, including both surface and subsurface water (p. 149)

hygrometer: an instrument that measures relative humidity (p. 500)

hypothesis: possible explanation for an event or solution to a problem, which is based on information (p. 7)

I

ice cap: small ice sheet, such as that found in Iceland (p. 195)

ice front: the end of a glacier (p. 196)

ice sheet: another name for a continental glacier (p. 195)

ice wedging: mechanical weathering process in which water freezing in cracks of rocks wedges rocks apart (p. 132)

igneous rocks: rocks formed by the solidification of hot molten rock material called magma (p. 254)

imaging radar: the radar system in which a signal is sent out and then "heard" echoing off Earth's surface, a method of remote sensing (p. 121)

impermeable: describes a rock material through which water does not pass easily (p. 153)

index (guide) fossils: fossils that help identify the age of the rock in which they occur; found over a wide geographic area but which lived for a narrow range of time (p. 604)

inner planets: the four planets nearest the sun, separated from the outer planets by the asteroid belt (p. 413)

insolation: the solar energy that reaches Earth (p. 484)

interferometry: the use of two radio telescopes to detect a radio signal from the same point in space and to determine the signal's location (p. 366)

international date line: imaginary line through the Pacific Ocean, roughly following 180th meridian where date changes; travelers moving westward advance the date, travelers moving eastward set back the date (p. 463)

intertropical convergence zone (ITCZ): the low-pressure zone at the equator, where the winds from the two hemispheres converge (p. 532)

ion: electrically charged atom or group of atoms (p. 27)

ionic bond: the force of attraction between oppositely charged ions that holds them together (p. 27)

ionosphere: the part of Earth's atmosphere from about 65 kilometers to 500 kilometers above the surface, in which layers rich in electrified particles exist (p. 482)

isobar: a line on a weather map connecting places of the same atmospheric pressure at a given time (p. 525)

isotherm: a line drawn on a weather map through places having the same atmospheric temperature at a given time (p. 492)

isotopes: atoms of the same chemical element with different atomic masses (p. 32)

J

jet stream: a narrow band of very strong westerly winds at high levels in the middle latitudes, usually at heights of 6000 to 12 000 meters (p. 536)

joint: a crack or break in bedrock along which no movement has occurred (p. 300)

Jovian planets: gaseous planets that are much larger and less dense than terrestrial planets; all outer planets except Pluto are terrestrial planets (p. 413)

K

kames: small, cone-shaped hills formed at the glacial front by meltwater pouring sediment off the glacier's surface (p. 201)

kettle: circular hollow left in an outwash plain when a buried ice block melts (p. 201)

key bed: a single, widespread rock layer that is easily recognizable; has same characteristics as an index fossil (p. 604)

knot: a speed of approximately 1.85 kilometers (1.15 miles) per hour (p. 530)

L

laccolith: a dome-shaped mass of intruded igneous rock (p. 265)

lagoon: a shallow, protected area of water located landward from a sandbar (p. 221)

land breeze: a cool, local wind blowing out to sea that occurs when the air pressure over land becomes higher than the air pressure over the water (p. 528)

landslide: a sudden movement of a mass of bedrock or loose rock down the slope of a hill, a mountain, or a cliff (p. 141)

latitude: distance in degrees north or south of the equator (p. 111)

lava: molten rock that reaches Earth's surface (p. 254)

laws of planetary motion: three laws conceived by Johannes Kepler to describe the shape of planetary orbits and the speed at which they travel (p. 405)

levee: a natural or artificial bank confining a stream or a river channel (p. 183)

light-year (LY): the distance a ray of light travels in one year, about 9.5 trillion kilometers (p. 379)

lithosphere: the outer solid shell of Earth that extends to a depth of about 100 kilometers (p. 234)

loess: fine sediment deposited by wind erosion (p. 212)

longitude: the distance in degrees east and west of the prime meridian (p. 111)

longshore current: a current that flows parallel to the shoreline (p. 218)

low-pressure area (low): an area that has lower pressure than the surrounding air (p. 526)

luminosity: the actual, or true, brightness of a star (p. 380)

lunar eclipse: an eclipse that occurs when the moon passes into Earth's total shadow, or umbra (p. 446)

lunar month: the time from one new moon to the next new moon, about 29.5 days (p. 446)

luster: the way a mineral reflects light (p. 47)

L wave: an earthquake wave that travels along Earth's surface (p. 273)

M

mafic rocks: dark-colored, low-silica rocks (p. 65)

magma: the hot liquid rock beneath Earth's surface (p. 63)

magnetic variation or declination: the angle by which the compass needle varies from true north (p. 118)

manganese nodules: potato-shaped masses 1 to 10 centimeters in diameter of manganese rich material that occurs on the ocean floor (p. 337)

mantle: the layer of rock in Earth extending from the crust downward 2850 kilometers (p. 10)

map scale: the ratio of distance on the map to distance on Earth (p. 112)

maria: the Latin word for seas; extensive dark areas that represent great basins on the moon (p. 437)

marine climate: the climate of areas near oceans, with a small yearly temperature range (p. 578)

mascon: an area of higher gravity, existing over the moon's more circular maria (p. 440)

mass movement: the downslope movement of large masses of earth materials due to the pull of gravity (p. 141)

mass number: the number of protons and neutrons in an atom (p. 31)

matter: anything that has mass and volume (p. 29)

meander: one of a series of broad, looping bends in a stream (p. 179)

mechanical weathering: disintegration that takes place when rock is broken into smaller pieces without changing its chemical composition (p. 131)

meridian: an imaginary half circle that runs in a north-south direction from the North Pole to the South Pole (p. 111)

mesosphere: the layer of Earth's atmosphere between the stratosphere and thermosphere (p. 482)

Mesozoic: an era of geologic time lasting from 250 to 65 million years ago (p. 598)

metamorphic rocks: rocks formed by the effect of heat, pressure, and chemical action on other rocks (p. 64)

meteor: a light produced when a meteorite streaks through Earth's atmosphere (p. 425)

meteorite: the part of a meteoroid that reaches Earth's surface (p. 426)

meteoroid: a rock fragment traveling in space (p. 425)

meteorology: the study of Earth's atmosphere (p. 3)

meteor shower: a time when many meteoroids enter Earth's atmosphere (p. 426)

mica: soft silicate minerals with flat, shiny flakes that are found in many rocks such as granite and gneiss (p. 54)

millibar: a unit used by meteorologists to measure air pressure; 34 millibars equal 1 inch of mercury (p. 524)

mineralogy: study of minerals and their properties (p. 47)

mineral: naturally occurring inorganic solid substance with a definite chemical composition and structure (p. 34)

mixed layer: the surface layer of ocean water (p. 314)

Mohorovicic discontinuity (Moho): the boundary between Earth's crust and mantle (p. 281)

moist-adiabatic lapse rate: the rate at which the temperature of saturated air changes when it rises or sinks (usually 0.6°C per 100 meters) (p. 509)

molecule: the smallest part of a compound that has all the properties of the compound (p. 32)

monsoon: a periodic wind especially in Indian ocean (p. 536)

moon: any natural satellite of a planet (p. 421)

moraines: accumulations of glacial till (p. 197)

mudflow: the rapid downhill movement of a water-saturated mass of clay and silt (p. 142)

multiple-mirror telescope (MMT): a reflector that forms an image by combining the light from each of several mirrors and focusing it on a single point (p. 362)

N

native minerals: minerals composed of single elements; also called native elements (p. 35)

neap tide: a tide of small range occurring at the quarter phase of the moon (p. 450)

nebula: a large cloud of gas and dust in space (p. 385)

neutron: one of three basic atomic particles; has a mass slightly greater than a proton, but no electric charge (p. 30)

neutron star: the dense core that remains after a large star explodes (p. 387)

nonrenewable resource: a resource that is used up faster than it can be replaced in nature (p. 85)

normal fault: a fault where the rocks above the fault plane move down with respect to the rocks on the other side; caused by stresses pulling rocks apart (p. 294)

normal lapse rate: the rate at which atmospheric temperature changes with altitude; about 1°C for every 160 meters (p. 487)

nova: a star that has flared into intense brightness (p. 386)

nunataks: mountains that project through ice sheets (p. 195)

O

oblate spheroid: a sphere that flattens at its poles and bulges at its equator (p. 18)

occluded front: a front formed when a cold front overtakes a warm front (p. 548)

ocean current: any continuous flow of water along a definite path in the oceans (p. 343)

oceanography: the study of the world's oceans (p. 3)

oozes: fine lime or silica muds found on ocean floor (p. 336)

optical telescope: a tool that uses a large lens or mirror to gather rays of light and focus them on one spot, and smaller lenses to magnify the image (p. 359)

orbit: the path of a revolving body, such as that followed by Earth revolving around the sun (p. 403)

ore: a valuable mineral or metal that is mixed and worked (p. 80)

organic rocks: sedimentary rocks formed from the remains of plants and animals (p. 69)

outer planets: the five planets farthest from the sun, separated from the inner planets of the solar system by the asteroid belt (p. 413)

outwash: sediment deposited in front of a glacier by streams of meltwater (p. 200)

outwash plain: a broad, stratified, gently-sloping deposit of sediment formed beyond the terminal moraine by streams from a melting glacier (p. 201)

oxbow lake: the crescent-shaped lake formed when a river meander gets cut off from the river and the ends of the original bend have silted up (p. 180)

oxidation: the chemical reaction of oxygen with other substances (p. 134)

P

Paleozoic: an era of geologic time lasting from 570 to 250 million years ago (p. 598)

parallax: apparent shift in an object's position caused by the motion of the observer (p. 465)

parallelism of the axis: the behavior of Earth's axis during its revolution (p. 457)

parallels: east-west circles around Earth, parallel to the equator (p. 111)

parent material: rock material from which a soil is formed (p. 138)

passive continental margins: stable continental margin where major activity is buildup of sediments (p. 291)

penumbra: the part of a shadow that is only partly illuminated; partial shadow (p. 446)

perigee: point nearest Earth in orbit of Earth satellite (p. 444)

perihelion: point in planet's orbit when nearest sun (p. 405)

period: (1) a subdivision of a geologic era (p. 599); (2) the time needed for one full wavelength to pass a given point (p. 216)

permeability: a measure of a rock's ability to transmit water or other liquids (p. 153)

phases: daily changes in the moon's appearance (p. 445)

photogrammetry: a way to determine the position and elevation of surface features from aerial photographs (p.109)

photosphere: visible bright yellow surface of sun (p. 398)

photosynthesis: the process by which green plants manufacture sugars and starches from carbon dioxide and water in the presence of sunlight (p. 10)

phytoplankton: floating plants such as diatoms and sargassum weed (p. 284)

plate tectonics: theory of the formation and movement of the rigid pieces, or plates, that cover Earth's surface (p. 233)

plutonic: rocks, usually igneous, formed at great depth (p. 64)

polar front: a front between the prevailing westerlies and polar easterlies (p. 532)

pollution: a condition in which some part of the environment is changed so that it is unfit for human, plant, or animal use (p. 86)

porosity: percentage of a material's volume that is pore space (p. 153)

porphyry: rocks containing conspicuous phenocrysts (crystals) surrounded by a fine grained mass (p. 58)

pothole: deep oval or circular hole cut into a stream bed by abrasion from swirling sand and pebbles (p. 177)

Precambrian: large division of geologic time occurring before 570 million years ago (p. 615)

precipitation: the falling of any form of water from the air to Earth's surface, occurring when cloud droplets become heavy enough to fall to Earth (p. 512)

pressure-gradient force: the force that causes the wind to blow, which is produced by a pressure gradient (p. 527)

prime meridian: zero meridian; the meridian that passes through Greenwich, England, Spain, Algeria, Ghana, Burkina, and Mali and from which longitude is measured (p. 462)

profile: a line that shows the changes in elevation across a section of a topographic map (p. 120)

proton: a positively charged particle in the nucleus of an atom (p. 30)

protoplanets: hypothetical whirling gaseous masses within a giant cloud of gas and dust rotating around a sun; protoplanets are thought to have given rise to planets and moons (p. 8)

protostar: a large glowing dust cloud that eventually becomes a star (p. 385)

psychrometer: an instrument that measures relative humidity by using wet-bulb and dry-bulb thermometers (p. 501)

pulsar: a distant heavenly object that emits rapid pulses of light and radio waves (p. 383)

***P* waves:** primary (compressional) earthquake waves, that can travel through any material (p. 272)

pyroxenes: silicate minerals that have cleavage surfaces that meet nearly at right angles (p. 54)

Q

quasars: very distant radio sources that resemble stars but are far larger, more luminous, and more massive; also called quasi-stellar radio sources (p. 390)

R

radiation: transfer of heat in the form of short waves (p. 484)

radioactive decay: process by which alpha rays (protons) are released from an atomic nucleus, thus changing the atom to a new, lighter element (p. 607)

radio astronomy: the study of radio waves from space (p. 366)

radiocarbon: the radioactive isotope of carbon with atomic mass 14, which is used in radioactive dating of plant and animal materials (p. 608)

radio telescope array: a group of radio telescopes, instruments that pick up radio waves emitted by bodies in space (p. 367)

rain gauge: an instrument for measuring the amount of precipitation (p. 514)

rawinsonde: a small balloon-carried observatory, which carries a radio transmitter that sends out signals about temperature, air pressure, and relative humidity (p. 545)

rays: bright streaks of shattered rock and dust that radiate from a number of the moon's craters (p. 442)

recharge: the refilling of soil water supply at times when plants need little moisture (p. 151)

red giants: large, red stars that are cooler and more luminous than blue-white stars (p. 382)

reflecting telescope: a telescope that uses one concave mirror as its objective; also called a single-mirror reflector (p. 61)

refracting telescope: a telescope that uses a convex lens as its objective; also called a refractor (p. 360)

refraction: the bending of light waves as they pass from one kind of substance to another of different density, or when water waves reach shallow water (p. 216)

regional metamorphism: process of rock-forming that results from large areas of rocks being under intense heat and pressure of mountain-building movements (p. 76)

regolith: lunar soil, a grayish-brown mixture of small pieces and fine particles (p. 442)

relative humidity: the extent to which air is saturated with water vapor; it is expressed in percent (p. 500)

relative time: the method of recording events that places events in a time sequence by comparing the events with other events, but does not identify their actual date of occurrence (p. 597)

remote sensing: mapmaking done by gathering data about the land from above Earth's surface (p. 121)

renewable resource: a resource that can be replaced in nature at a rate close to its rate of use (p. 85)

reserves: the amount of known deposits of a mineral in ores that are worth mining at the present time (p. 90)

residual soil: soil that has the local bedrock as its parent material (p. 138)

respiration: the process by which food is changed to energy (p. 85)

retrograde motion: a periodic backward, or westward, loop made by a planet in front of the background of constellations (p. 404)

reverse fault: a fault where the rocks above the fault plane are driven up over the other side; caused by stresses pushing rocks toward each other (p. 294)

revolution: the movement of Earth in its orbit around the sun (p. 465)

Richter scale: a numerical description of an earthquake's magnitude (p. 277)

rift eruptions: volcanic eruptions that occur at long, narrow fractures in Earth's crust (p. 256)

rilles: long deep clefts, or cracks, running through the moon's maria bedrock (p. 440)

rip current: a strong surface current that flows away from the beach (p. 218)

roches moutonées: mass of glacially-eroded bedrock (p. 198)

rock: a group of minerals bound together (p. 63)

rock flour: fine sand and silt formed by the crushing of rock beneath a glacier (p. 197)

rotation: the turning of an object on its axis (p. 457)

S

salinity: a measure of the dissolved solids in seawater (p. 312)

salinization: a soil condition caused by the evaporation of irrigation water, which leaves too much mineral matter on the soil's surface for crops to grow (p. 87)

sandbar: a bar of sand formed by ocean currents depositing sand near the shore (p. 221)

satellite: a smaller body revolving around a larger body; a natural satellite is also called a moon (p. 421)

Schmidt telescope: an optical telescope that uses both a reflecting mirror and a refracting lens for an unusually wide field of view (p. 363)

sea breeze: a local wind carrying cool ocean air inland, occurs when the air pressure over land decreases (p. 527)

sea cliff: cliff formed at a shoreline by wave erosion undercutting rock followed by collapse (p. 220)

sea-level pressure: corrected air pressure calculated by removal of the effect that altitude has on pressure (p. 524)

seamount: a submerged, steep-sloped peak rising from the ocean floor; flat-topped peaks are called *guyots* (p. 330)

sedimentary rocks: rocks formed from sediments bound together in some way (p. 64)

seismic moment: a more accurate measurement of earthquake magnitude than the Richter scale (p. 277)

seismogram: the recording of an earthquake made by a seismograph; it records the time the earthquake takes place and the type and strength of earthquake waves (p. 274)

seismograph: an instrument that detects and records earthquake (seismic) waves (p. 274)

severe thunderstorm: a storm that has wind gusts of at least 80 kilometers per hour and hail 2 or more centimeters in diameter (p. 560)

shadow zone: a wide area around Earth on the side opposite the focus of an earthquake where neither *P* nor *S* waves are received (p. 281)

shield: the exposed area of the oldest rocks, or craton, of a continent (p. 616)

silicates: compounds of the elements silica and oxygen; they include more than 90 percent of the minerals in Earth's crust (p. 39)

silica tetrahedron: a grouping of one silicon ion and four oxygen ions that forms the building blocks of silicate minerals (p. 39)

sill: a sheet of intrusive igneous rock forced between rock layers parallel to the rock layers it intrudes (p. 264)

sleet: frozen raindrops (p. 513)

snow line: the lowest level that permanent snow reaches in summer (p. 193)

soil: loose, weathered rock and organic material in which plants with roots can grow (p. 138)

soil depletion: a condition in which soil no longer can grow usable crops, brought on by the removal of nutrients during harvesting (p. 87)

soil erosion: removal of valuable topsoil by wind or moving water (p. 142)

soil profile: cross section of soil layers above the parent material, usually consisting of the A-, B-, and C-horizons (p. 138)

solar eclipse: an eclipse that occurs when the moon's total shadow, or umbra, falls on Earth (p. 447)

solar flare: a sudden outburst of energy that rises up in areas of sunspot activity (p. 400)

solar prominences: huge, red, flamelike arches of material that occur in the corona of the sun (p. 399)

solar system: the sun and its family of orbiting planets, asteroids, meteoroids, and comets (p. 403)

solar telescope: an instrument used to observe changes on the sun's surface; it projects a large image of the sun into a dark underground room (p. 397)

solar time: time kept by the sun's location in the sky (p. 461)

solar wind: a stream of electrically-charged particles that are blown out from the sun in all directions (p. 400)

solution: the state in which mineral matter dissolved from bedrock is carried in a river (p. 170)

specific gravity: the ratio of the weight of a substance to the weight of an equal volume of water (p. 50)

specific humidity: the number of grams of water vapor in one kilogram of air (p. 500)

spectroscope: an instrument that can disperse a beam of light into a spectrum of its component wavelengths (p. 369)

spreading center: the area where lithospheric plates are moving apart (p. 238)

spring equinox: the first day of spring; about March 21, the Northern Hemisphere; when daylight and nighttime are equal in length (p. 468)

spring tide: a tide of large range occurring at new-moon and full-moon phases (p. 450)

standard time zone: an area in which time is based on average solar time at one particular meridian but used over a belt of about 15 degrees of longitude (p. 461)

stationary front: the boundary between two air masses that are not moving (p. 548)

station model: a listing of about 20 different weather observations around the location of a National Weather Service station on a weather map (p. 568)

stock: a large igneous intrusion, similar to a batholith, but with an exposed surface area of less than 100 square kilometers (p. 265)

storm surges: currents formed when a hurricane piles up water along the shore and blows it inland (p. 561)

stratification: the arrangement of rock beds in visible layers (p. 72)

stratosphere: the layer of Earth's atmosphere that extends from the troposphere to the mesosphere (p. 482)

stratus clouds: clouds that are arranged in unbroken, low, horizontal layers, or sheets (p. 507)

streak: the color of a mineral when powdered or rubbed on a streak plate (p. 48)

stream piracy: the diversion of the upper part of one stream by the headward growth of another stream (p. 175)

striations: scratches left on rocks and bedrock by glacier movement (p. 198)

strike-slip fault: fault where the rocks on opposite sides of the fault plane move horizontally with respect to each other (p. 294)

subduction boundary: converging boundary where one plate is plunging beneath another, overriding plate (p. 243)

submarine canyons: gigantic gullies that cut into continental slopes (p. 327)

subsoil: the B-horizon of soil that contains clay and iron oxides washed from the topsoil (p. 138)

summer solstice: the first day of summer in the Northern Hemisphere, about June 21; it has the longest period of daylight (p. 467)

sunspot: a dark area on the sun's photosphere (p. 399)

supercooled water: water that has cooled below 0°C without freezing (p. 506)

supergiants: a large, low-density star that is hundreds of times more luminous than a red giant (p. 382)

supernova: an intensely bright object caused by the explosion of a massive red giant star (p. 387)

surplus: condition of having rainfall greater than the need for moisture when the soil is already saturated (p. 151)

suspension: the state in which rock materials carried by a river are stirred up and kept from sinking by the turbulence of stream flow (p. 170)

swash: the motion of water pushed up a beach by breaking waves (p. 218)

S waves: secondary, or shear, earthquake waves, which can travel through solids, but not liquids or gases (p. 273)

syncline: a downfold of rock layers (p. 294)

T

temperature inversion: the increase in temperature with an increase in altitude; occurs when a layer of cold air is trapped beneath a layer of warm air (p. 487)

tephra: pieces of cooled lava that are sprayed in the air and fall back to the ground (p. 255)

terrane: a large block of lithosphere that has been moved, often thousands of kilometers, and attached to the edge of a continent (p. 246)

terrestrial planets: another name for inner planets; they have a rocky crust, a dense mantle layer, and a very dense core (p. 413)

texture: characteristic structure of a rock given by its size, shape, and arrangement of its mineral crystals (p. 65)

thermocline: the transitional layer between warm surface waters and cold bottom waters in oceans or lakes (p. 315)

thermosphere: the layer of Earth's atmosphere above the mesosphere (p. 482)

thin-skinned thrusting: the pushing of thin, horizontal sheets of rock from continental margins over great distances along nearly level fault surfaces (p. 246)

tidal range: the distance in level between low and high tide in a given area (p. 450)

tides: the daily rise and fall of ocean waters (p. 449)

till: unsorted and unstratified rock materials carried in the bottom of a glacier (p. 200)

time-travel graph: a graph that shows the relationship between *P* and *S* wave travel times and epicenter distance (p. 275)

topsoil: the A-horizon of soil; contains organic material, or humus, that forms from decayed plant and animal materials (p. 138)

tornado: a narrow, violent, funnel-shaped column of spiral winds that extends downward from the cloud base to Earth (p. 559)

toxic waste: a poisonous chemical waste that must be disposed of extremely carefully (p. 102)

trade winds: winds that originate in the horse latitudes and blow toward the doldrums (p. 533)

transported soil: soil that formed from parent material left by winds, rivers, or glaciers or soil that itself was moved from its original location (p. 138)

troposphere: the convective region of the atmosphere that extends from Earth's surface to the stratosphere; its height ranges from 8 kilometers at the poles to 18 kilometers at the equator (p. 481)

tsunami: a gigantic wave that results from an underwater earthquake, or a landslide, or volcanic eruption (p. 216)

turbidity currents: undersea landslides of mud and sand that form currents carving canyons into continental slopes (p. 329)

U

umbra: darkest part of shadow of moon or Earth (p. 446)

unconformity: a surface between two rock layers that represents a gap in the rock record (p. 598)

uniformitarianism: the concept that the present is the key to the past (p. 63)

universal law of gravitation: Newton's law that states that the gravitational force is greater between objects of greater mass and less between objects of lesser mass (p. 406)

upwelling: the vertical movement of cold ocean water toward the surface (p. 350)

usage: the condition where plants draw water from the soil at times when the need for moisture is greater than the rainfall (p. 151)

V

valley glacier: a long, slow-moving, wedge-shaped stream of ice (p. 192)

variable stars: stars that change in brightness at regular periods, or cycles (p. 383)

ventifacts: wedge-shaped rocks formed by wind erosion in deserts (p. 211)

visible spectrum: band of visible colors; they are the colors of the rainbow and have different wavelengths (p. 369)

volcanic (extrusive) rock: igneous rock that forms from cooled lava, or from volcanic dust and ash (p. 64)

volcanic neck: the solidified lava filling the central vent of an extinct volcano (p. 265)

volcano: an opening in Earth's crust through which an eruption takes place (p. 268)

W

waning: the decreasing of the moon's visible illuminated surface, from full moon to new moon (p. 445)

warm front: the leading edge of a mass of relatively warm air (p. 548)

water budget: describes the income and the spending of water in a region (p. 150)

water cycle: the hydrologic cycle; the never-ending movement of water from one part of the hydrosphere to another (p. 149)

water gap: a pass in a mountain ridge through which a stream flows (p. 176)

watershed: the entire area drained by a stream and its tributaries (p. 174)

waterspout: a funnel-shaped rotating cloud, or tornado, extending from the base of a cumulonimbus or cumulus cloud down to the surface of an ocean or lake (p. 559)

water table: the surface below which the ground is saturated with water (p. 154)

wave height: vertical distance between the bottom of a trough and the top of a crest (p. 215)

wavelength: the distance between two successive wave crests (p. 215)

waxing: the increasing of the moon's visible illuminated surface, from new moon to full moon (p. 445)

weather: the state of the atmosphere at a given time and place (p. 478)

weathering: the process in which rocks are broken up by the action of water, the atmosphere, and organisms (p. 131)

winter solstice: the first day of winter in the Northern Hemisphere, about December 21; it has the shortest daylight period (p. 467)

Z

zenith: point in the sky directly above the observer (p. 468)

Index

615; mineral deposits from, 616; rock record of, 616; *illus.*, 616
Precipitation, 512–517. *See also* Rainfall; forms of, 513–514; measurement of, 514; *illus.*, 582, 583; *table,* 514
Pressure, air, 523–525
Pressure belt, 532–533; *illus.*, 533
Pressure gradient, 526; *illus.*, 526
Pressure–gradient force, 527
Prevailing wind, 515, 533, 576; rainfall and, 581–582; temperature and, 578–579; *illus.*, 583
Prime meridian, 111, 462; *illus.*, 111
Profile, from contour map, 120; *illus.*, 120
Prominence, solar, 399
Proterozoic Era, 598
Protoavis, 631
Proton, 30–31; *illus.*, 30, 31
Protoplanet hypothesis, 8; *illus.*, 8
Protostar, 385
Psychrometer, 501; *illus.*, 501
Ptolemy, 404
Pulsar, 383; *illus.*, 384
Pulsating star, 383
Pumice, 67, 153–154; *illus.*, 67; *table,* 68
P **wave,** 272–275, 279–280; *illus.*, 273, 280, 281
Pyrite, 38, 47–48, 57, 134; *illus.*, 57
Pyroxene, 54–55; *illus.*, 40

Quadrangle, 116–117; *illus.*, 117
Quartz, 28, 34–36, 38, 41, 47, 50, 53, 70, 135; *illus.*, 28, 39, 48, 49, 53, 90; *table,* 50
Quartzite, 53, 76–77, 136; *illus.*, 76; *table,* 78
Quasar, 390
Quaternary Period, 635

Radar, Doppler, 567; imaging, 121; side–looking, 121; weather forecasting with, 566–567; *illus.*, 121, 567
Radar wind profiler, 545
Radiation, 484
Radioactive decay, 607
Radioactive element, absolute time and, 607; half–life of, 607; heat from, 22; *illus.*, 607, 608
Radioactive mineral, 9, 51
Radio astronomy, 365–366
Radiocarbon dating, 608
Radiometric dating, 608–609
Radio wave, 365, 482; *illus.*, 482
Radon, 279
Rain, 150–151, 480, 503, 513, 550–551; acid, 101, 135, 517; formation of raindrop, 512; location of, 514–515; *illus.*, 101, 135, 513, 515, 516
Rainfall, annual, 514–515; latitude and, 581–582; mountains and, 582–583; oceans and, 584–585; prevailing winds and, 581–582; *illus.*, 581, 584
Rain gauge, 514
Rainmaking, 515–516
Raised beach, 297; *illus.*, 297
Ranger **lunar probe,** 434–435

Rawinsonde, 545; *illus.*, 545
Recent Epoch, 635, 638
Recycling, 102; *illus.*, 102
Red giant, supergiant, 382, 386; *illus.*, 386
Red shift, 371; *illus.*, 371
Redwood, 632, 636; *illus.*, 632
Reef, barrier, 225; coral, 224–225; fossil, 614–615; fringing, 225; *illus.*, 225, 614
Refractor, *See* Telescope
Regolith, 442; *illus.*, 442
Relative humidity, 500–501; *illus.*, 500; *table,* 501
Relative time, 597–598
Relief, 115
Remains, original, 602; replaced, 602; *illus.*, 603
Remote sensing, in mapmaking, 121–122; *illus.*, 121
Renewable resource, 85–89; energy, 98
Reserve, mineral, 90
Resource, conservation of, 102–103; energy, 93–96; mineral, 90; nonrenewable, 90–92; renewable, 85–89
Respiration, 85
Retrograde motion, 404; *illus.*, 404
Revolution of Earth, 465–466; effects of, 466; evidence for, 465; path of, 465–466; rate of, 465–466; *illus.*, 465
Richter scale, 277
Ridge, mid–ocean, 240, 317, 332–333; *illus.*, 240, 333
Rift eruption, 256, 259; *illus.*, 256
Ring system, of Jovian planet, 417
Rip current, 218
Ripple mark, 73, 298; *illus.*, 73
River, flooding of, 184–185; sediment deposition by, 180–181; *illus.*, 184, 185
River valley, 172–176; lengthening of, 173; V–shaped, 172; widening of, 172; *illus.*, 172, 173
Roches moutonnees, 198
Rock, 62–79; cap, 156; carried by wind, 211; definition of, 63; erosion by water waves, 220; felsic, 65; igneous, 63–68, 78; impermeable, 70, 94; lunar, 438–439; mafic, 65; metamorphic, 63, 76–83; permeability of, 153–154; permeable, 70; porosity of, 153; porous, 70; sedimentary, 63, 69–74, 78; toadstool, 210; transport by glacier, 197; volcanic, 246; *illus.*, 246, 439
Rock correlation, 604–605; *illus.*, 604
Rock cycle, 78; *illus.*, 78
Rock–forming mineral, 47, 53–57
Rock record, 596–597, 616
Rotation, axis of, 457
Rotation of Earth, 456–464; effects of, 458–459; evidence for, 458; rate of, 459; time measurement and, 461–464; winds and, 528–529; *illus.*, 459
Rubidium–strontium dating, 609
Running water, 168–189; effect on bedrock, 169; energy of, 169; removal of weathered rock, 170; *illus.*, 168, 170

Salinity, definition of, 312; measurement of, 312–313; of ocean water, 312–313
Salinization, of soil, 87
Salt, 92, 313; *illus.*, 92
Sample, core, 324; grab, 323–324
San Andreas Fault, 241, 272, 284; *illus.*, 242, 284
Sand, 53, 70, 92, 136, 153, 170; beach, 222; tar, 97; windblown, 211; *illus.*, 70, 153; *table,* 78
Sandbar, 218; attached, 221–222; unattached, 221–222; *illus.*, 221–223
Sand dune, 298; composition of, 213–214; leeward side of, 213; migration of, 214; types of, 213–214; windward side of, 213; *illus.*, 213, 214
Sandstone, 53, 69–70, 73, 77, 136; *illus.*, 70, 71, 76, 153, 516; *table,* 74, 78
Sargasso Sea, 345; *illus.*, 345
Satellite, *See also* Moon; Galilean, 421; geostationary, 566; solar, 397–398; study of ocean floor, 323; weather forecasting with, 566–567; *illus.*, 421
Saturation, zone of, 154
Saturn, 417–418; moons of, 422; *illus.*, 7, 418; *table,* 406
Sea, *See* Ocean
Sea floor, *See* Ocean floor
Sea–level pressure, 524
Seamount, 330–331, 333; *illus.*, 330
Season, 467–469, 488–489; changes in constellations, 377–378
Sediment, 69, 131, 246, 291; authigenic, 337; carried by wind, 211; deposition by river, 180–181; on flood plain, 183; glacial–marine, 336; kinds of, 69; ocean, 245–246, 322–341; sorting of, 70; *illus.*, 69, 70, 72, 337
Sedimentary rock, 63, 69–74, 78; chemical, 69, 71; clastic, 69–70; fossils in, 73; organic, 69, 71–72; stratification of, 72; weathering of, 136; *table,* 74, 78
Seismic moment, 277
Seismograph, 274; *illus.*, 274
Shadow zone, 281–282; *illus.*, 281
Shale, 55, 69–70, 73, 136, 153–154; metamorphism of, 77; *illus.*, 70, 71, 77; *table,* 74, 78
Shear wave, 273
Sheet jointing, 133; *illus.*, 133
Shoreline, 216–217, 220–225, 450–451; irregular, 223; regular, 224; types of, 223–224; *illus.*, 3, 223
Shoreline current, 218; *illus.*, 218
Silica, 69, 136, 163, 253
Silicate, 39–40, 53–55; ferromagnesian, 54–55; *illus.*, 53, 54
Silica tetrahedron, 39–40; *illus.*, 39, 40
Silicon, 34; *illus.*, 34; *table,* 35
Sill, 264–265; *illus.*, 264, 265
Silt, 70, 170; *illus.*, 70, 153; *table,* 78
Silurian Period, 620; *illus.*, 620
Silver, 35; *illus.*, 91
Single–mirror reflecting telescope, 361–362; *illus.*, 361
Sinkhole, 162; *illus.*, 160, 162

Acknowledgments

ABBREVIATION KEY

MWLCO — Mt. Wilson and Las Campanas Observatories, Carnegie Institute of Washington
NASA — National Aeronautics and Space Administration
NCAR — National Center for Atmospheric Research
NOAA/AOML — National Oceanic and Atmospheric Administration / Atlantic Oceanographic and Meteorological Laboratory
NOAA/NESDIS/SDSD — National Oceanic and Atmospheric Administration/National Environmental Satellite Data, and Information Service/Satellite Data Services Division
NOAA/PROFS — National Oceanic and Atmospheric Administration / Program for Regional Forecasting and Observing Services
NOAO — National Optical Astronomy Observatories
USGS — United States Geological Services
WHOI — Woods Hole Oceanographic Institution

Photo Research: Sue McDermott
Cartography in Appendices:: 653, 656-663, 666, Sanderson Associates
Technical Illustration — vii, 12, 13, 24, 25, 39, 42, 43, 80, 81, 178, 183, 187, 207, 226, 227, 240, 248, 249, 273, 274, 287, 292, 303, 315, 319, 338, 392, 409, 419, 453, 471, 495, 513, 518, 552, 555, 571, 587, 600, 601, 603, 624, 631, 637, 664: Morgan Cain & Associates

Photo Credits:

i, iii: Telegraph Colour Library(FPG International). iv: *t* Burr(Gamma-Liason); *b* H. Stein(Photo Researchers, Inc.). v: *t* Tom Bean; *mr* Courtesy of L.R. Kittleman; *ml* Breck Kent; *br* Breck Kent. vi: *t* Grant Heilman(Grant Heilman Photography); *m* Nancy Sheehan/©D.C. Heath; *b* Stephen J. Krasemann(DRK Photo). vii: *t* Phil Degginger; *b* Michael Dwyer(Stock Boston). vii: *t* Ben Barnhart; *b* David Weintraub(Photo Researchers, Inc.). viii: *t* Peter Menzel; *m* Lanny Johnson(Mountain Stock); *b* Jeff Rotman. x: *t* Jeff Rotman; *b* Roger Ressmeyer(Starlight). xi: *t* AAT No. 48A Photographed with the 3.9m Anglo-AustralianTelescope by D.F. Malin/Anglo-Australian Telescope Board; *m* NASA/Mark Marten(Photo Researchers, Inc.); *b* NASA. xii: *t* NASA; *b* Peter Menzel. xiii: *t* Howard Bluestein; *b* Siskind(Gamma-Liason). xiv: *t* NASA; *m* Phil Degginger; *b* David Muench Photography. xv: *l* Earth Satellite Corporation/Science Photo Library(Photo Researchers, Inc.); *r* Tyrrell Museum of Palaeontology/Alberta Culture and Multiculturism. xvi: Telegraph Colour Library(FPG International). xvii: *t* Ralph Perry (Black Star); *b* Lester Lefkowitz(Tony Stone Worldwide).

UNIT ONE: xviii: *l* Burr(Gamma-Liason); *tr* Breck Kent; *br* Breck Kent. 1: *l* Jack Fields(Photo Researchers, Inc.); *r* Elliott Varner Smith. 2: Wide World Photo. 3: Chuck Place(The Image Bank). 4: *t* Kraft-Explorer(Photo Researchers, Inc.). *b* NASA. 5: *t* Howard Bluestein; *b* Bob Evans(Peter Arnold, Inc.). 6: Courtesy of Peggy LeMone. 16: Gray Baskerville(*Hot Rod* Magazine). 18: NASA. 21: Ken O'Donoghue/©D.C. Heath. 22: Marc Muench. 23: John Earle(The Stock Market). 28: H. Stein(Photo Researchers, Inc.). 30: Russ Kinne(Photo Researchers, Inc.). 32: *t* E.R. Degginger; *b* Ken O'Donoghue/©D.C. Heath. 33: Breck Kent. 35: Tom McHugh(Photo Researchers, Inc.) 37: Breck Kent. 46: Mary Root(Root Resources). 47: *t* E.R. Degginger(Earth Scenes); *b* Breck Kent. 48: *t* Breck Kent; *b* *Encyclopedia of Minerals* by Roberts. 49: *l, br* Breck Kent; *tr* Hubbard Scientific Company. 51: Photo Courtesy of Ward's Natural Science. 52: Courtesy of Laurence Kittleman. 53: Breck Kent. 54: *t* E.R. Degginger; *m* *Encyclopedia of Minerals* by Roberts; *bl* Lee Boltin Picture Library; *br* Jerome Wycoff. 55: *tl* Hubbard Scientific Company; *tr, m* Jerome Wycoff, *b* Breck Kent. 56: Hubbard Scientific Company. 57: Breck Kent. 62: Breck Kent. 63: The Granger Collection. 64: Kraft-Explorer(Photo Researchers, Inc.). 65: Breck Kent. 66: *t* & *b* Jerome Wycoff; *m* Breck Kent. 67: *t, tm* & *b* Breck Kent; bm Jerome Wycoff. 69: Dave Davidson(Tom Stack & Associates). 70: Hubbard Scientific Company. 71: *tl, tr* Breck Kent; *m* E.R. Degginger; *b* Jerome Wycoff. 72: *t* Breck Kent; *m* Randall Chew(Photo Researchers, Inc.); *b* Samuel Namowitz. 73: *t* Jerome Wycoff; *m, br* Breck Kent; *bl* Michael Collier. 75: Lester Lefkowitz(Tony Stone Worldwide). 76: *t* Michael Collier; *bl, br* Hubbard Scientific Company. 77: *t* Hubbard Scientific Company; *m, b* Jerome Wycoff. 84: T.J. Florian(Rainbow). 86: William E. Ferguson. 87 & 88: Harold Hungerford. 89: Larry Ulrich(DRK Photo). 90: Breck Kent. 91: Grant Heilman(Grant Heilman Photography). 92: M.P. Kahl(Photo Researchers, Inc.). 93: Breck Kent. 94: *l* Craig Aurness(West Light); *r* Chris Sorenson(The Stock Market). 98: Rochester Gas & Electric Company. 99: *t* Peter Menzel; *b* Anne Heimann(The Stock Market). 100: Tom McHugh(Photo Researchers, Inc.). 101: Bill Weedmark (Panographics). 102: *t* Gary Milburn(Tom Stack & Associates); *b* Steve Elmore(The Stock Market). 103: Peter Beck(The Stock Market). 108: Nancy Sheehan/©D.C. Heath. 114: Courtesy of Kathryn Neff. 116: Jerome Wycoff. 122: *t* NASA; *b* Science Magazine/Jet Propulsion Laboratory. 123: Photri.

UNIT TWO: 128: *l* Wide World Photo; *tr* Breck Kent; *b* Mark Wexler(Woodfin Camp). 129: *t* Stephen J. Krasemann(DRK Photo); *b* B. Bartholomew(Black Star). 130: R.B. Sanchez(The Stock Market); *inset* The Bettmann Archive. 132: Tod Gerstein(Photo Researchers, Inc.). 133: *t, br* Samuel Namowitz; *bl* Jerome Wycoff. 134: Courtesy of Luray Caverns. 136: Jerome Wycoff. 137: John Cunningham(Visuals Unlimited). 139: Kevin Schafer(Tom Stack & Associates). 141: Breck Kent. 142: Lawrence Burr. 143: George Gerster(Photo Researchers, Inc.). 148: Breck Kent. 158: Anne Sager(Photo Researchers, Inc.). 159: Breck Kent. 162: St. Petersburg Times. 163: Breck Kent. 168: Harold Hungerford. 173: *l* Grant Heilman Photography; *r* Phil Degginger. 174: *l* Grant Heilman(Grant Heilman Photography) *r* Breck Kent. 176: Breck Kent. 177: William E. Ferguson. 178: Benjamin Rondel(First Light). 179: Jerome Wycoff. 180-181: E.R. Degginger. 182: Courtesy of Sandra Duncan. 183: E.R. Degginger. 184: U.S. Air Force. 185: Don Getsus(Photo Researchers, Inc.). 190: Tom Bean. 192: Gary Milburn(Tom Stack & Associates). 193: E.R. Degginger. 194: Samuel Namowitz. 195: Jerome Wycoff. 196: Tom Bean. 197: *t* Maurice Rosalsky; *b* Stephen J. Krasemann(Peter Arnold, Inc.). 198: B.F. Molnia(Terraphotographics/BPS). 199: Tom Stack(Tom Stack & Associates). 200: *t* Steve McCutcheon(Visuals Unlimited); *b* E.R. Degginger. 202: E.R. Degginger. 204: Tom McHugh(Photo Researchers, Inc.). 205: Michael Dwyer(Stock Boston). 210: Tom Bean. 211: M. Brandenburg(Bruce Coleman, Inc.). 212: Jerome Wycoff. 213: E.R. Degginger. 215: Randy Hufford(Tom Stack & Associates). 216: NOAA. 218: Alex McLean(Landslides). 219: Ben Barnhart. 220: Breck Kent. 221: John S. Shelton. 224: Stephen J. Krasemann(Peter Arnold, Inc.). 225: *l*, Al Grotell; *r* G.R. Roberts.

UNIT THREE: 230: *l* David Weintraub(Photo Researchers, Inc.); *tr* Tom Bean(DRK Photo); *br* Breck Kent. 231: *t* Stephen J. Krasemann(DRK Photo); *b* Owen Franken(Picture Group). 232: Museum of Comparative Zoology, Harvard University, Photograph by Ron Eng. ©Presidents and Fellows of Harvard University. 239: NASA. 241: *l* Randall Hyman; *tr* Fred Grassle(WHOI); *br* D. Foster(Visuals Unlimited). 242: John S. Shelton. 243: USGS/EROS Data Center. 246: Randall Hyman. 247: D.L. Jones(USGS). 252: S. Jonasson & Frank Lane(Bruce Coleman, Inc.). 254: Keith Gunnar(Bruce Coleman, Inc.). 255: Harold Hungerford. 256: E.R. Degginger. 258: Ralph Perry(Black Star). 259: West-Manner-Inseln(Peter Arnold, Inc.). 260: William E. Ferguson. 261: Don King(The Image Bank). 262: *t* F. Grohier(Photo Researchers, Inc.); *b* AP/Wide World Photo. 263: NASA. 264: G.R. Roberts. 265: *l* Tom Bean; *r* Breck Kent. 270: Peter Menzel. 282: Courtesy of Dr. Waverly Person. 283: Wide World Photo. 284: *t* Peter Menzel(Stock Boston); *b* Chuck O'Rear(West Light). 290: Keith Gunnar(Bruce Coleman, Inc.). 295: *l* Jerome Wycoff; *r* Peter Dunwiddle(Visuals Unlimited). 297: John S. Shelton. 298: *l* Steinberg(Photo Researchers, Inc.); *r* Jerome Wycoff. 299: Lanny Johnson(Mountain Stock).

UNIT FOUR: 306: *t* Alfred Pasieka(Taurus); *l* & *b* WHOI. 307: *t* NOAA/NESDIS/SDSD; *b* M.P. Kahl(DRK Photo). 308: Jeff Rotman. 310: *t* The Granger Collection; *b* Bob Catanach(WHOI). 311: Courtesy of Dr. Taro Takahashi. 314: Lewis Trusty(Animals Animals). 316: *t* Richard Hoover; *b* Editorial Photo Color Archives(Art Resource). 317: Dudley Foster(WHOI). 322: Jeff Rotman. 324: Peter Wiebe(WHOI). 325: D. Foster(Visuals Unlimited). 331: Douglas Faulkner(Photo Researchers, Inc.). 332-333: Dr. William Haxby(Lamont-Doherty Geological Observatory). 336: Tom Bean(Tom Stack & Associates). 337: Robert Hessler(WHOI). 342: Frederik D. Bodin(Stock Boston). 345: O. Brown, R. Evans and M. Carle, University of Miami Rosensteil School of Marine and Atmospheric Science. 346: George Hunter(Tony Stone Worldwide). 351: T.E. Andrews(Visuals Unlimited).

UNIT FIVE: 356: *l* NASA; *t* Hale Observatories; *b* Kazmori(Taurus). 357: *tl* ©1984 Regents; University of Hawaii; *tr* NASA; *bl* Roger Ressmeyer(Starlight); *br* Smithsonian Institution. 358: AAT No. 48A Photographed with the 3.9m Anglo-Australian Telescope by D.F. Malin/Anglo-Australian Telescope Board. 359: Jay Pasachoff(©Pasachoff Educational Trust). 360: Lick Observatory Photograph. 361: California Institute of Technology & Carnegie Institute of Washington. 362: Roger Ressmeyer/Starlight. 363: NASA. 364: Dennis di Cicco. 366: *t* Commonwealth of Puerto Rico; *b* National Radio Astronomy Observatory. 367: NASA. 368: Courtesy of Dr. Sidney Wolff. 376: Dennis di Cicco. 377: Royce Bair(The Stock Solution). 380: Mt. Wilson & Las Campanas Observatories, Carnegie Institute of Washington. 384: *t* California Institute of Technology and Carnegie Institute of Washington; *b* Jim Pickerell(West Light). 385: *t* Lick Observatory Photography; *b* Hansen Planetarium. 387: AAT No. 48 Photographed with 3.9m Anglo-Australian Telescope by D.F. Malin & R, Sharpies/Anglo-Australian Telescope Board. 390: *t* Jet Propulsion Laboratory(California Institute of Technology); *m* Lick Observatory Photograph; *b* © 1984 Regents, Universityof Hawaii. 396: NASA. 397: National Optical Astronomy Observatories. 398: NASA. 399: *t* NASA; *b* ISIS(Visuals Unlimited). 400: SAO/IBM. 402: NASA. 412: NASA. 413: Lunar and Planetary Institute. 414: *l* NASA; *r* NASA/Mark Marten(Photo Researchers, Inc.).415: *t* Dennis di Cicco; *b* NASA. 416: NASA. 418: *l* NASA; *r* NASA. 419: Jet Propulsion Lab(NASA). 420: NASA(Photri). 421: Jet Propulsion Lab(NASA). 422: NASA. 423: *t* Jet Propulsion Lab(NASA); *b* NASA. 424: *t* The Planetarium, Armagh-Northern Ireland; *b* NASA. 426: *t* Neg. No. 1449 Department of library Service; American Museum of Natural History; *b* Grant Heilman(Grant Heilman Photography). 427: NASA. 432: NASA. 434: Wide World Photo. 436-440: NASA. 441: Lunar and Planetary Institute. 442: *t* Lunar and Planetary Institute; *m* Mt. Wilson and Palomar Observatories *b* Lunar and Planetary Institute. 443: Courtesy of Andrea Mosie. 448: Tom Pantages. 451: Greg Scott(Masterfile). 456: Dennis di Cicco. 458: Courtesy of Smith College. 460: Photri. 461: Dennis di Cicco. 467: SSC-Photo Centre-ASC/Photo by Chris Brunn.

UNIT SIX: 474: *tr* Roger J. Cheng, Atmospheric Research Center at SUNY Albany; *l* NASA; *br* Siskind(Gamma-Liason). 475: *l* NASA-Goddard Institute for Space Studies, NY; *r* Michael Giannechini(Photo Researchers, Inc.); *b* Steve McCurry(Magnum Photos). 476: George Hall/Imagery Unlimited. 477: Breck Kent. 482: F.J. Baker(Dembinsky Photo Associates). 483: Peter Menzel. 490: NOAA/NESDIS/SDSD. 491: Roger J. Cheng, Atmospheric Sciences Research Center, at SUNY Albany. 498: Tom Bean(DRK Photo). 501: Taylor/Thermometer Corporation of America. 502: Gregory G. Dimijian(Photo Researchers, Inc.). 508: *tl* Tom Bean(DRK Photo); *bl* Breck Kent; *tm, tr, br* E.R. Degginger. 509: Jim Brandenburg(DRK Photo). 514: NCAR. 516: Deutsches Nationalkomitee fur Denkmalschutz(Geschaftselle beim Bundesminister des Innern, Bonn). 522: Hank Andrews(Visuals Unlimited). 534: Courtesy of Dr. Robert Sheets. 542. Ira Block. 543: B. Wilcox, Stanford Univ./BPS. 545: O. Brown, R. Evans and M. Carle, University of Miami Rosenteil School of Marine and Atomospheric Science. 546: Stephen Johnson(Tony Stone Worldwide). 548: Edward J. Szoke. 550: NOAA/PROFS. 551: John D. Cunningham(Visuals Unlimited). 556: Edi Ann Otto. 558: Ralph Wetmore(Photo Researchers, Inc.). 559: Allan Moller(National Weather Service). 560: NCAR. 561: NASA. 562: NOAA. 563: Steve Starr(SABA). 564: Ira Block. 569: Courtesy of Charles E. Anderson. 574: David Hiser(Photographers Aspen). 579: WHOI. 580: Phil Degginger. 581: NOAA/NESDIS/SDSD. 587: Roger Werths/Longview Daily News(West Light).

UNIT SEVEN: 594: *l* Tom Bean; *tr* Henry D. Meyers(Berg & Associates); *br* T.A. Wiewandt(DRK Photo). 595: *t* E.R. Degginger; *bl* Carl Roessler(Bruce Coleman, Inc.); *br* Breck Kent. 596: William B. Ferguson. 598: Jerome Wycoff. 599: Courtesy of Dr. Meyer Rubin. 603: t Breck Kent; b National Park Service Photo. 604: A.J. Copley(Visuals Unlimited). 605: G.R. Roberts. 606: *t* H.A. Miller(Visuals Unlimited); *b* Samuel Namowitz. 614: Paul Hoffman(Geological Survey of Canada). 616: John Fowler(Valan Photos). 617: Chris Sorrenson(Stock Market). 618: Photo Courtesy of Ward's Scientific. 619: *t* William E. Ferguson; *m* Photo Courtesy of Ward's Scientific; *b* D. Schwimmer(Bruce Coleman, Inc.). 620: Neg. #K10250 Dept. of Library Services, American Museum of Natural History. 621: *t* Breck Kent; *b* Bruce Iverson. 622: American Museum of Natural History, Neg. #K10250, Department of Natural History. 628: Steve Elmore(Tony Stone Worldwide). 629: David Muench Photography. 631: *t* Model by Stephan Czerkas; *b* William E. Ferguson. 632: Jerome Wycoff. 635: *l* Field Museum of Natural History; *tr* E.R. Degginger; *br* T.A. Wiewandt(DRK Photo). 636: William E. Ferguson. 639: Tyrrell Museum of Palaeontology/Alberta Culture & Multiculturalism. 665: Earth Satellite Corporation/Science Photo Library(Photo Researchers, Inc.).

Teacher's Edition:

T685: *t* Telegraph Colour Library(FPG International); *b* David Muench Photography. T700: Morgan Cain & Associates; T702: Gary Milburn(Tom Stack & Associates).

To The Teacher

The following material has been developed to help you more easily and efficiently prepare to teach Heath Earth Science. Articles, such as *Concept Mapping* and *Developing Writing Skills,* provide suggestions for skill development that will help your students be more successful in the learning environment.

For your convenience, scientific background information, teaching strategies, and answers to questions for each chapter can be found beginning on page T708. Useful periodicals and book references, as well as audiovisual and educational technology suggestions, are provided by chapter beginning on page T692.

Table of Contents: Teacher Reference Material

Safety during Activities

The activities in *Heath Earth Science* are designed to give students an active involvement in the processes of science. Each activity has been developed with safety as a major concern. The activities use readily accessible materials and can easily be performed by high-school earth science students.

Laboratory safety can only be achieved by constant vigilance on the part of both teachers and students. Be alert to potential danger. Chemicals, sharp instruments, glassware, electric circuits, and fire are often used. By your continuous insistence on the use of precautions, you can prevent mishaps.

General Safety Procedures

Safety Rules General safety rules are summarized for you and your students on pages xviii–xix. Additional safety information can be found in the Teacher's Edition of the Laboratory Investigations booklet for *Heath Earth Science*.

Each activity should begin with a review of appropriate safety procedures. Pay special attention to the safety symbols used to flag specific caution statements necessary for each activity. Each caution statement provides a brief explanation of the specific danger present and signals you and your students to take appropriate safety precautions. These safety symbols are listed on page xix. Also, be sure to read the safety information provided in the margins of the teacher's edition. Here you will find additional precautions and a list of potential hazards for the activity.

Facilities It is your responsibility to provide a safe environment for laboratory work. Check your work area on a regular basis to ensure that all possible safety precautions are being taken. Equipment and materials should be properly stored. Hazardous materials should never be left exposed. Never keep food or drink in the classroom or laboratory, or in a refrigerator that is used for chemicals or biological samples. Your laboratory, classroom, and storage facilities should be locked at all times when not under your direct supervision.

Safety Equipment Check smoke detectors, safety showers, and eyewash facilities before each activity. Know the location of and how to operate all master shutoffs for any utilities used.

Activity Preparation Before handling equipment and materials, thoroughly familiarize yourself with the necessary precautions. Read and follow the instructions in equipment manuals and material safety data sheets, and on labels for chemicals. You should always perform each activity before assigning it to your students. Always wear required safety equipment when performing demonstrations for your students and when showing them the proper use of equipment and materials.

Time Allotment The size of the group working on an activity should be limited to a number that you can safely supervise without causing confusion and accidents. Be sure to allow sufficient time for students to perform each activity and to clean up afterward. Students hurrying to finish their work often become careless and inattentive to safety procedures.

Waste Disposal Dispose of dangerous waste chemicals and materials as prescribed by appropriate standards and the laws of your community. Provide separate labeled waste receptacles for certain chemicals as called out in the margins of this Teacher's Edition; also provide labeled receptacles for broken glass, waste paper, and used matches.

Accident Policies In case of accidents, know your school's policy and procedures. Make accident reports promptly, accurately, and completely.

■ Using Chemicals Safely

Review the safety rules listed on page xix regarding chemical use. Both you and your students should wear plastic gloves when working with poisonous, corrosive, or irritating chemicals. Instruct students never to smell a chemical directly. Vapor should be wafted toward the nose by fanning with the hand. When diluting acid with water, always add acid TO water. Once a chemical has been removed from its stock bottle, discard the chemicals properly. Do not return any unused chemical to its stock bottle for future use. Equip chemical storage shelves with ledges to prevent slipping or sliding of stock bottles.

Using Glassware Safely

Broken Glass Examine all glassware for chips or cracks before dispensing to your students. Avoid glass breakage by directing your students to keep flasks, bottles, beakers, and other equipment away from the edges of tables or lab benches. If glass breakage does occur, use a dustpan and brush, not your fingers, to pick up broken glass.

Inserting Glass Tubing The ends of glass tubing are very sharp and should always be polished before use. Warn students to allow glass tubing that has just been bent or polished to cool before handling. Protect hands with leather gloves or several layers of cloth toweling when inserting glass tubing into stopper holes. Lubricate the glass and the stopper with water or with glycerine. Do not force the glass into the stopper. Use these same precautions when removing glass tubing from stoppers.

Storage Make sure all glassware is clean before returning it to its storage location. Shelves in your classroom used for glassware storage should also be equipped with ledges.

Using Heat and Fire Safely

Be especially cautious when dealing with fire hazards. Review the cautions listed on page xix regarding heat and fire safety. Familiarize your students with the school's fire regulations, drills, and evacuation procedures. You should know the location and use of first-aid supplies and of fire-fighting equipment such as fire extinguishers and fire blankets.

Demonstrate the correct procedure for lighting a Bunsen burner; instructions can be found in the Laboratory Investigations booklet for *Heath Earth Science*. When lighting a Bunsen burner, students should wear safety goggles and a lab apron; long hair should be confined; and long, floppy sleeves should be rolled up. Instruct students to immediately turn off the gas if the burner does not light or if the flame goes out. Instruct your students never to reach over an open flame or other heat source. Remind students to keep books and papers as far away from a flame as possible.

Give your students only Pyrex glassware to use when heating substances. When students are heating test tubes, always supervise closely to ensure that students point the test tube opening away from themselves and their classmates.

Before using any flammable chemical, be sure there are no ignition sources in the room.

Using Electrical Equipment Safely

All devices using 110-115 volt AC power should be equipped with three-wire cords and three-prong plugs. Each socket should be three-hole, be protected with a ground fault interrupter (GFI), and be checked for correct polarity (polarity testing devices display a coded sequence of red and green lights). Instruct students to switch off equipment before plugging it into the socket and to turn equipment off and unplug it after an activity is completed. Use 1.5 volt or 9 volt "dry-cell" batteries as direct current sources; do not use 6 or 12 volt automobile storage batteries. Wiring hookups should not be made, or altered, except when both the power switch is off and the apparatus has been disconnected from its AC or DC power supply. Cover battery terminals with insulating tape when storing the batteries.

Student Safety Contract

The following student safety contract was adapted from one that was developed by the National Science Teachers' Association. Before being allowed to work on activities, students should sign the safety contract. However, students must be thoroughly familiar with the rules for proper laboratory behavior and safety precautions before signing.

I will
- follow all instructions given by the teacher
- protect eyes, face, hands, and body while conducting class and laboratory activities
- carry out good housekeeping practices
- know the location of first-aid and fire-fighting equipment
- conduct myself in a responsible manner at all times.

I, _____ have read and agree to abide by the safety regulations set forth above and also any additional printed instructions provided by the teacher and/or the district. I further agree to follow all other written and oral instructions given to me by the teacher in charge.

SIGNATURE:

DATE:

Concept Mapping

An Effective Learning Technique in Earth Science*

* Adapted from work by
Dr. 'Laine Gurley-Dilger, Rolling Meadows
High School, Rolling Meadows, IL

Rationale: Your students want to do well in earth science. "Doing well" in their minds frequently means getting a good grade, because most teenagers do not see beyond the immediate. Many students regard earth science as a tremendous body of facts to be memorized and then carefully repeated back on a test. Their approach to studying often reflects this perspective. As their teacher, you want them to do well too. But *your* definition of the goal is probably different. Most teachers would like to see their students finish a year's course in earth science with an understanding of the subject that can become part of each individual's knowledge base— a foundation the student can use in the future, rather than some jumble of facts to be forgotten by next September.

Educators realize that information stored in one's long-term memory becomes more valuable than what is quickly committed to short-term memory and then forgotten. The problem is how to point out that fact to your students and encourage them to embrace study techniques that will serve them well. If you teach your students a learning strategy that improves their grades, they will be more inclined to use it. If that same learning strategy also improves their understanding, then one of your goals is reached as well.

Concept mapping is a technique that can improve your students' understanding of earth science, strengthen their study skills, and ultimately help them do better in school. In learning to do concept maps, your students also learn to organize information and establish relationships between ideas. The student begins a map with concepts that are most familiar. As new concepts are linked to established ones, the connections help the student remember what is new. Building a concept map also encourages students to detect errors in content or logic— a step that clarifies what students are learning and further reinforces knowledge. If you want further information about concept mapping, consult the book *Learning How to Learn*, by Joseph D. Novak and D. Bob Gowin, Cambridge University Press, 1984.

Characteristics of Good Concept Maps: Although there is no such thing as the right concept map for a given topic, there are several characteristics that well-constructed maps have in common:

1. A concept map usually stems from one main idea.
2. The main idea branches into related general concepts.
3. General concepts can be subdivided into more specific concepts (frequently in several tiers).
4. Specific concepts are elaborated by example.
5. Concepts are usually nouns, representing objects or events. Each concept should be a single idea and appear only once in the map.
6. Relationships between concepts are shown by linking words (usually verbs, verb phrases, adverbs, or prepositions). All concepts should be linked.
7. Crosslinkages are used to connect concepts in two different paths of the map. The more crosslinkages the better, since they demonstrate an increased depth of understanding. Lines for linkages should not cross.
8. Any two concepts taken in isolation with their linking word should form a complete thought.

To illustrate the structure of a concept map, the following map has been constructed from some of the guidelines just described. Note that the concepts are enclosed in ovals (or circles). This emphasis helps students distinguish the concepts from the linking words. However, any method that accomplishes the same objective is equally useful. The map is constructed in a vertical hierarchy. Another alternative is to place the main concept at the center and extend the map around that point.

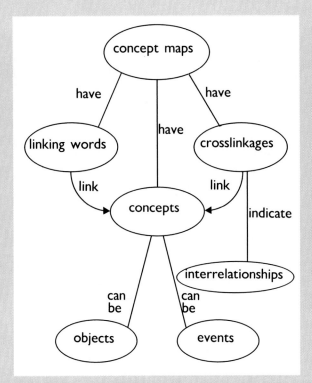

Strategies for Teaching Concept-Mapping Skills: Give students a scrambled list of concepts and linking words and ask them to separate the words into two lists. Once students have distinguished the concepts from the linking words, they should then attempt to rank the concepts from general to specific. Using the main idea as a starting point, they can then begin to construct a map.

Emphasize that no single map is the correct one. Rather, maps should have organizational elements that are logical and useful. One student's map is sure to differ from another student's, so having students compare their maps may increase understanding of the technique.

Uses of Concept Maps: The flexibility of this study tool is one of its strongest assets. The following list describes some of the ways you can assign concept map work. You may discover additional uses as you work with your students.

1. Have students construct concept maps to improve notes previously taken in class.
2. Have students construct concept maps in class as part of note-taking activities.
3. Have students construct maps as a reading assignment prior to class discussion to improve reading comprehension and class participation.
4. Assign a concept map as a homework review exercise.
5. Construct a map in class at the start of a discussion to see what students know and to spark interest. Add more concepts as knowledge grows.
6. Have students use concept maps to summarize movies or videos viewed in class.
7. Have students use concept maps to study for tests.
8. Use a partial map as a short quiz in which students fill in missing concepts and/or linkages.
9. Use concept maps to replace essay questions on an exam.

Evaluating Student Concept Maps: Since student maps will vary, rather than looking for conformity, look for the characteristics of good concept maps described earlier. You may want to assign a breakdown of points that accounts for the following items:

Organization
1. general to specific
2. number of levels in the hierarchy
3. degree of branching
4. clear distinction between concepts and linkages
5. no repetition of concepts
6. linking words included for all linkages
7. degree of crosslinking

Content
1. logical relationships cited between concepts
2. appropriate linking words used
3. logical crosslinkages present

Encourage your students to construct concept maps for other classes too. As students increase their use of the technique, they will become more comfortable with it. Most students will find that their study skills improve. Many will benefit by doing better in their coursework. Concept mapping can ultimately become a permanent study tool your students will use and value.

Developing Writing Skills in the Earth Science Classroom

The ability to communicate effectively on paper is a critical skill in science. The implications of any scientific research are undermined if the results are not stated clearly, accurately, and concisely. With every unit in Earth Science, your teacher's edition offers students opportunities to sharpen their writing skills. To aid students in this endeavor, this section gives you some basic background on the writing process, and how to apply these steps to writing assignments in science.

The Writing Process: Good writing, like good research, results from following an organized method. The four main steps in the writing process are:

- **Prewriting**, which is the planning stage.
- **Writing**, which is putting the first draft down on paper.
- **Revising**, which consists of rereading the first draft from the point of view of the reader rather than the author, and making appropriate changes.
- **Editing**, which is checking for errors in grammar, usage, spelling, and punctuation.

The writing activities in Earth Science can be classified as one of three composition types.

1. *Expository essays* explain a factual main idea or a personal insight.
2. *Research papers* are lengthy exposition based on research drawn from books, periodicals, and interviews with experts.
3. *Laboratory reports* describe the procedure used to test a hypothesis, the data gathered, and the conclusions drawn from the data to support, reject, or revise the hypothesis.

Techniques for Fostering Good Writing Skills for Essays and Research Papers: The prewriting or planning stage is critical in the writing process. When given a writing assignment, students often begin long before they have thought through the assignment. Selecting and narrowing the subject keeps the writing tight and on-track from the beginning. One method of helping students limit a topic is to ask them a series of "what about" questions related to their topic.

Writing: Once a topic is selected (which is oftentimes done for the student), the next step is to organize ideas related to the topic (supporting details) in an outline or concept map. Students then write a first draft. A common error made at this stage is overlooking a thesis statement which sets the tone and focuses the writing. The thesis statement should appear in the introductory paragraph.

In writing the body of an essay or paper, focus students' attention on the need for transitional statements that add coherence to their writing. Good transitions can be achieved by:

1. repeating a key word from an earlier sentence
2. repeating an idea from an earlier sentence using different words
3. using a pronoun in place of a word used earlier.

All good writing closes with concluding paragraph(s). Some techniques to give students in developing good concluding paragraph(s) are:

1. summarize or review the thesis statement
2. refer to questions or ideas posed in the introduction
3. draw a conclusion based on the supporting detail in the body of the essay or paper.

Revising and Editing: Before submitting a final draft, encourage students to:

1. check for unity, coherence, and emphasis of the writing piece as a whole
2. check for errors in spelling, grammar, and usage.

Analyzing Student Compositions: The following evaluation form may be used as a model in evaluating student writing.

Evaluation Form

Structure	Point Value	Score
1. Title	5	_____
2. Introduction	10	_____
3. Thesis Statement	10	_____
4. Body	15	_____
5. Conclusion	10	_____
Sources (research papers)		
6. Sufficient number	5	_____
7. Used appropriately	10	_____
8. Correct footnote form	5	_____
9. Correct bibliography form	5	_____
Revising and Editing		
10. Report revised	10	_____
11. Report edited	10	_____
12. Correct manuscript form	5	_____
TOTAL	100	

Laboratory Reports: In the Earth Science program, if your teaching preference is to have students do formal lab reports, the reports should include the following:

- **Title** of the experiment.

- **Introduction** that covers the objectives of the experiment and a hypothesis statement.

- **Procedure** that describes all materials and methods used in running the experiment.

- **Observations** section that includes qualitative observations, data tables, graphs, and diagrams when necessary to organize and display results.

- **Conclusions** are based on the recorded data and should relate to the purpose statements/hypothesis in the beginning of the lab report.

Evaluating Laboratory Reports: To keep the evaluation of laboratory reports a manageable task, the following strategies may help:

1. Evaluate the clarity and comprehensiveness of a formal lab report by having other students use the report to repeat the experiment.

2. Consider grading group reports, oral reports, or some combination thereof.

Writing Assignments in the Earth Science program: The correlation table shows the options available for student writing skills.

Student Text	Writing Activity
Unit One	Expository essay on Earth's surface and internal structures
Unit Two	Compare/Contrast Expository Essays
	■ Positive vs. negative effects of weathering on people
	■ Agents of erosion versus agents of deposition
	■ Chemical agents versus physical agents
Unit Three	Expository essay on relationships between the plate tectonics theory and the occurrence of volcanoes, earthquakes, and mountains on Earth
Unit Four	Research paper in oceanography
	■ Using marine fossils to date the ocean floor
	■ Food sources from the ocean
	■ Types of research vessels and their applications
	■ Using satellites for ocean research
	■ Physical and chemical properties of ocean water
Unit Five	Research paper in astronomy
	■ Research three different events during the past 12 months
	■ Write a paper based on three different reports of an event that occurred during the past 12 months
Unit Six	Expository essay on global warming
Unit Seven	Expository essay on local and global conditions at the time of fossil formation
Earth Science Laboratory Investigations	Laboratory Report/Experiment Design all 40 labs in the lab manual

Teacher Resources

CHAPTER 1

Reference Books

Abell, George O., David Morrison, and Sidney C. Wolff. *Realm of the Universe.* Saunders, 1988.

Bates, Robert L., and Julia A. Jackson, editors. *Dictionary of Geological Terms.* Doubleday, 1987.

Montgomery, Carla W. *Physical Geology, 3rd ed.* Wm. C. Brown, 1993.

Press, Frank, and Raymond Siever. *Earth.* Freeman, 1986.

Tarbuck, Edward J., and Frederick K. Lutgens. *Earth Science.* Macmillan, 1991.

Weiner, Jonathan. *Planet Earth.* Bantam, 1986.

Periodicals

Knox, Pamela Naber. "El Niño: A Current Catastrophe." *Earth*, September 1992.

Swindle, Timothy D., John S., Lewis, and Lucy-Ann A. McFadden. "Near-Earth Asteroids and the History of Planet Formation." *Earth in Space*, February 1992.

Audio-Visual & Technology

Earth Science: Exploring Planet Earth. 20-minute film or video. Encyclopaedia Britannica Educational Corporation.

How Solid Is Rock? 22-minute film or video. Encyclopaedia Britannica Educational Corporation.

Message in the Rocks. 57-minute film. Time-Life Video.

The Rich, High Desert. 57-minute film. Films Incorporated, 1986.

CHAPTER 2

Reference Books

Thompson, Graham R. and Jonathan Turk. *Modern Physical Geology.* Saunders, 1993.

Audio-Visual & Technology

How We Know the Earth's Shape. 11-minute film. Phoenix-BFA Films and Video.

Measuring in Astronomy. 13-minute film. Phoenix-BFA Films and Video.

CHAPTER 3

Reference Books

Herron, J. Dudley, et al., *Heath Chemistry.* D.C. Heath, 1993.

Holden, Alan, and Phyllis Morrison. *Crystals and Crystal Growing.* MIT Press, 1982.

Klein, Cornelius, and Cornelius S. Hurlbut, Jr. *Manual of Mineralogy.* Wiley, 1985.

Audio-Visual & Technology

Introduction to Crystal Systems. Set of twenty 35-mm slides. JLM Visuals.

Simple Methods of Mineral Identification. Set of twenty 35-mm slides. JLM Visuals.

Survey of Minerals. Set of twenty 35-mm slides. JLM Visuals.

CHAPTER 4

Reference Books

The Audubon Society Field Guide to North American Rocks and Minerals. Alfred A. Knopf, Inc., 1985.

Headstrom, Richard. *Suburban Geology: An Introduction to the Common Rocks and Minerals of Your Back Yard and Local Park.* Prentice, 1985.

Hurlbut, Cornelius S., Jr., and Robert C. Kammerling. *Gemology.* Wiley, 1991.

Periodicals

Baily, James. "Uncommon Light from Common Rocks." *Earth*, March 1992.

Audio-Visual & Technology

Common Rock-Forming Minerals. Set of twenty 35-mm slides. JLM Visuals.

Gems and Minerals. Interactive videodisc (Mac and Hypercard). Videodiscovery.

Materials of the Earth's Crust. Set of six filmstrips. Ward's.

Minerals and Rocks. 15-minute film or video. Encyclopaedia Britannica Educational Corporation.

CHAPTER 5

Reference Books

Deer, W. A., R. A. Howie, and J. Zussman. *An Introduction to Rock-Forming Minerals.* Wiley, 1992.

Mitchell, Richard S. *Dictionary of Rocks.* Van Nostrand Reinhold Company, 1985.

Periodicals

Roberts, David. "Magical Marble, That Gleaming Rock for the Ages." *Smithsonian,* May 1992.

Audio-Visual & Technology

The Rock Cycle. 22-minute film or video. Encyclopaedia Britannica Educational Corporation.

Rocks That Form on the Earth's Surface. 17-minute film or video. Encyclopaedia Britannica Educational Corporation.

Rocks That Originate Underground. 23-minute film or video. Encyclopaedia Britannica Educational Corporation.

CHAPTER 6

Reference Books

Evans, Anthony M. *An Introduction to Ore Geology.* Blackwell Scientific, 1987.

Miller, G. Tyler, Jr. *Living in the Environment.* Wadsworth, 1990.

Skinner, Brian J. *Earth Resources.* Prentice, 1986.

Periodicals

Barreto, Laura. "Sphalerite—The Sulfide Chameleon." *Earth,* September 1992.

Harben, Peter. "Strategic Minerals." *Earth,* July 1992.

Warner, Barry G. "Peat: Nature's Compost." *Earth,* March 1992.

Audio-Visual & Technology

Decisions, Decisions: The Environment. Software (Apple II, Mac, MS/DOS). Tom Snyder Productions.

Energy: The Problems and the Future. 23-minute film or video. National Geographic Society.

Gifts From the Earth. 58-minute film from the *Planet Earth* series. Films Incorporated.

Hold the Land. 22-minute film. Environmental Protection Agency.

Interactive NOVA: Race to Save the Planet. Interactive videodisc. Scholastic Inc.

Planet Earth. Interactive CD-ROM (Mac and Hypercard). Intellimation.

Recycling: The Endless Circle. 25-minute film or video. National Geographic Society.

CHAPTER 7

Reference Books

Garrett, Wilbur E., editor. *Atlas of North America: Space Age Portrait of a Continent.* National Geographic Society, 1985.

Lillesand, Thomas M., and Ralph W. Kiefer. *Remote Sensing and Image Interpretation.* Wiley, 1987.

Periodicals

Graf, Gary. "Putting Mars on the Map." *Air and Space,* October/November 1987.

Morong, Dana M. "Using the Latitude and Longitude Coordinate System to Pinpoint Localities." *Rocks and Minerals,* January/February 1992.

Morrison, Philip. "One Topography, Two Ways." *Scientific American,* June 1992.

Pike, Richard J., and Gail P. Thelin. "Building a Better Map." *Earth,* January 1992.

Audio-Visual & Technology

Introduction to Topographic Maps. Set of twenty 35-mm slides. JLM Visuals.

CHAPTER 8

Reference Books

Andrews, William A. *Investigating Terrestrial Ecosystems.* Prentice, 1986.

Hausenbuiler, R.L. *Soil Sciences: Principles and Practices.* Wm. C. Brown Company Publishers, 1985.

Sparks, B.W. *Geomorphology.* Longman, 1986.

Periodicals

Dungca, Daniel V. "Lahars from Mt. Pinatubo." *Earth,* September 1992.

Audio-Visual & Technology

Chemical and Organic Weathering. Set of twenty-seven 35-mm slides. Ward's.

Erosion and Weathering. 17-minute film or video. Encyclopaedia Britannica Educational Corporation.

Erosion—Leveling of the Land. 14-minute film or video. Encyclopaedia Britannica Educational Corporation.

Weathering. Set of twenty 35-mm slides. JLM Visuals.

Why Do We Still Have Mountains? 20-minute film or video. Encyclopaedia Britannica Educational Corporation.

CHAPTER 9

Reference Books
Price, Michael. *Introducing Groundwater.* Allen & Unwin, 1985.

Periodicals
Bryan, T. Scott. "The Valley of the Geysers." *Earth,* July 1992.

Audio-Visual & Technology
Caves and Other Groundwater Features. Set of twenty 35-mm slides. JLM Visuals.

Groundwater. 18-minute film or video. Encyclopaedia Britannica Educational Corporation.

The Water Cycle. 14-minute film or video. Encyclopaedia Britannica Educational Corporation.

CHAPTER 10

Reference Books
Bangs, Richard, and Christian Kallen. *Rivergods.* Random House, 1985.

Periodicals
Titamgim, R. Dirk. "How Are Natural Bridges Formed?" *Rocks and Minerals,* November/December 1992.

Audio-Visual & Technology
Features of Rivers. Set of twenty 35-mm slides. JLM Visuals.

Flood Forecasting. 20-minute film or video. Encyclopaedia Britannica Educational Corporation, 1986.

The Great River. 57-minute film. Films Incorporated, 1986.

Rivers and Streams. Set of thirty-nine 35-mm slides. Ward's.

Work of Streams: The Erosion Cycle. Set of fifteen transparencies. Ward's.

CHAPTER 11

Reference Books
Bramwell, Martyn. *Glaciers and Ice Caps.* Watts, 1986.

Radlauer, Ruth, and Lisa Sue Gitkin. *The Power of Ice.* Childrens, 1985.

Periodicals
Carroll, Michael. "Probing an Iceberg Barrier." *Earth,* May 1992.

Hushagen, Susanne. "Greenland's Glaciers." *World Press Review,* July 1992.

Parfit, Michael. "Antarctic Meltdown." *Discover,* September 1990.

Ruddiman, William F., and John E. Kutzback. "Plateau Uplift and Climatic Change." *Scientific American,* March 1991.

Thomson, David. "Big Ice." *Sierra,* May/June 1989.

Audio-Visual & Technology
Active Glaciers. Set of twenty 35-mm slides. JLM Visuals.

Evidence for the Ice Ages. 14-minute film or video. Encyclopaedia Britannica Educational Corporation.

CHAPTER 12

Reference Books
Kopper, Philip. *The Wild Edge: Life and Lore of the Great Atlantic Beaches.* Globe Pequot Press, 1991.

Periodicals
Kemper, Steve. "This Beach Boy Sings a Song Developers Don't Want to Hear." *Smithsonian,* October 1992.

Audio-Visual & Technology
The Beach, a River of Sand. 21-minute film or video. Encyclopaedia Britannica Educational Corporation.

Coastal Dunes. 20-minute film. Films for the Humanities and Sciences, 1985.

Oceans and Shorelines. Set of forty 35-mm slides. Ward's.

Portrait of a Coast. 29-minute film. Circle Oak Productions.

Primary Coastlines. Set of forty 35-mm slides. JLM Visuals.

Waves and Beaches. 20-minute film. Films for the Humanities and Sciences, 1985.

Waves on Water. 16-minute film or video. Encyclopaedia Britannica Educational Corporation.

CHAPTER 13

Reference Books
Cox, Allan, and Robert Brian Hart. *Plate Tectonics: How It Works.* Blackwell Scientific, 1986.

Menard, H.W. *Islands.* Scientific American, 1986.

Menard, H.W. *The Ocean of Truth.* Princeton University Press, 1986.

Periodicals
Flam, Faye. "Earliest Evidence for Plate Tectonics." *Science News,* 11 March 1989.

Fryer, Patricia. "Mud Volcanoes of the Marianas." *Scientific American,* February 1992.

Kerr, Richard A. "Puzzling Out the Tectonic Plates." *Science,* 16 February 1990.

Audio-Visual & Technology

Collision Course. 55-minute film. Films Incorporated, 1986.

Continental Drift: The Theory of Plate Tectonics. 22-minute film or video. Encyclopaedia Britannica Educational Corporation.

Continents Adrift. 16-minute film. American Educational Films.

Earthquakes and Volcanoes. 12-minute film. Phoenix-BFA Films and Video.

The Living Machine. 58-minute film from the *Planet Earth* series. Films Incorporated, 1985.

The Moving Crust. Software (Apple II). Focus Media, Inc.

CHAPTER 14

Reference Books

Lauber, Patricia. *Volcano: The Eruption and Healing of Mount St. Helens.* Bradbury, 1986.

Wood, Robert Muir. *Earthquakes and Volcanoes.* Weidenfeld & Nicholson, 1987.

Periodicals

Beard, Jonathan D. "Ash in the Air." *Popular Science,* April 1992.

Carey, Steven, Haraldur Sigurdsson, and Charles Mandeville. "Fire and Water and Krakatau." *Earth,* March 1992.

Dvorak, John J., Carl Johnson, and Robert I. Tilling. "Dynamics of Kilauea Volcano." *Scientific American,* August 1992.

Heliker, Christina, and Thomas L. Wright. "The Pu'u'O'o-Kupaianaha Eruption of Hawaii's Kilauea Volcano." *Earth in Space,* April 1992.

Hersch, Sandy. "Volcanoes Disrupted Earth." *Sea Frontiers,* December 1991.

Monastersky, Richard. "Volcanic Suspect in Global Murder Mystery." *Science News,* 13 July 1991.

Nash, J. Madeleine. "What Makes Them Blow." *Time,* 24 June 1991.

White, Robert S. "Ancient Floods of Fire." *Natural History,* April 1991.

Audio-Visual & Technology

Anatomy of a Volcano. 57-minute film. Time-Life Video.

Features of Igneous Activity. Set of twenty 35-mm slides. JLM Visuals.

Heartbeat of a Volcano. 22-minute film or video. Encyclopaedia Britannica Educational Films.

Laccoliths, Volcanic Plugs, and Dikes. Set of twenty-seven 35-mm slides. Ward's.

Restless Earth. Interactive videodisc (Mac and Hypercard). National Geographic Society.

CHAPTER 15

Reference Books

Bolt, Bruce A. *Earthquakes.* Freeman, 1988.

Howell, Benjamin F., Jr. *An Introduction to Seismological Research.* Cambridge University Press, 1990.

Mogi, Kiyoo. *Earthquake Prediction.* Academic Press, 1985.

Periodicals

Colt, George Howe. "How Earthquakes Happen." *Life,* February 1989.

Finkbeiner, Ann. "Terra Infirma." *Discover,* November 1991.

Johnston, Arch C. "The Rift, the River and the Earthquake: The Story of the New Madrid Fault Zone." *Earth,* January 1992.

Monastersky, Richard. "Did Earth Give Clues Prior to Bay Quake?" *Science News,* 15 December 1990.

Nash, J. Madeleine. "News from the Underground." *Time,* 24 August 1992.

Audio-Visual & Technology

ABC News Interactive: The Great Quake of '89. Interactive videodisc (Mac and Hypercard). Videodiscovery.

Earthquake! 14.5-minute film. Phoenix-BFA Films and Video.

Earthquakes: Exploring Earth's Restless Crust. 21-minute film or video. Encyclopaedia Britannica Educational Corporation.

A Predictable Disaster. 32-minute film. Time-Life Video.

The San Andreas Fault. 21-minute film or video. Encyclopaedia Britannica Educational Corporation.

Science Toolkit: Earthquake Lab. Software and probes (Apple II, MS/DOS). Brøderbund Software.

CHAPTER 16

Reference Books

Powell, Derek. *Interpretation of Geological Structures Through Maps.* Wiley, 1992.

Ragan, Donal M. *Structural Geology: An Introduction to Geometrical Techniques.* Wiley, 1985.

Periodicals

Bykek-Kauffman, Ann. "How Faults Shape the Earth." *Earth,* November 1992.

Chew, Berkeley. "Anatomy of a Mountain Range." *Earth,* January 1993.

Murphy, J. Brendan, and R. Damian Nance. "Mountain Belts and the Supercontinent Cycle." *Scientific American*, April 1992.

Audio-Visual & Technology

Anticlines and Synclines. Set of thirty-two 35-mm slides. Ward's.

Diagrams—Crustal Movement. Set of twenty 35-mm slides. JLM Visuals.

The Birth and Death of Mountains. 12.5-minute film. Phoenix-BFA Films and Video.

CHAPTER 17

Reference Books

Thurman, Harold V. *Introductory Oceanography.* Macmillan, 1991.

Periodicals

Kunzig, Robert. "Invisible Garden." *Discover*, April 1990.

Audio-Visual & Technology

Challenge of the Oceans. 27-minute film. McGraw-Hill Films.

Oceanography II. Set of twelve transparencies with two overlays. Ward's.

Sea Water and the Floor. 17-minute film. Wiley.

The Earth Beneath the Sea. 27-minute film. McGraw-Hill Films.

CHAPTER 18

Reference Books

Emery, K. D., and Alazar Uchupi. *The Geology of the Atlantic Ocean.* Springer-Verlag, 1984.

Periodicals

Rona, Peter A. "Mineral Deposits from Sea-Floor Hot Springs." *Scientific American*, January 1986.

Stakes, Debra, Willard S. Moore, and Tom Tengdin. "Alvin Brings New Tools to Deep-Sea Research." *Earth in Space*, October 1992.

Walsh, Don. "A Scientist Looks at the Sea." *The Unesco Courier*, August/September 1991.

Audio-Visual & Technology

Dive to the Edge of Creation. 59-minute film. Karol Media.

History: Layer by Layer. 23-minute film. McGraw-Hill Films.

The Living Reef. Videodisc. AIMS Media, Inc.

CHAPTER 19

Periodicals

Huyghe, Patrick. "The Storm Down Below." *Discover*, November 1990.

Lowenstein, Frank. "Seasons, Seas, and Satellites." *Air and Space*, February/March 1988.

Audio-Visual & Technology

The Blue Planet. 58-minute film from the *Planet Earth* series. Films Incorporated.

Currents. 30-minute film. Time-Life Video.

Gulf Stream. 28-minute film. Bullfrog Films.

Ocean Currents. 16-minute film. McGraw-Hill Films.

Oceanography I. Set of six transparencies with six overlays. Ward's.

CHAPTER 20

Reference Books

Abell, George O., David Morrison, and Sidney C. Wolff. *Exploration of the Universe.* Saunders, 1987.

Lightman, Alan. *Time for the Stars: Astronomy in the 1990's.* Viking, 1992.

Walker, Gordon. *Astronomical Observations: An Optical Perspective.* Cambridge University Press, 1987.

Periodicals

Cole, Stephen. "Astronomy on the Edge: Using the Hubble Space Telescope." *Sky and Telescope*, October 1992.

Maran, Stephen P. "Hubble Illuminates the Universe." *Sky and Telescope*, July 1992.

Robinson, Leif J. "Spinning a Giant Success." *Sky and Telescope*, July 1992.

Audio-Visual & Technology

Beyond the Milky Way. 57-minute film. Time-Life Video.

Optical Telescopes. Set of twenty 35-mm slides. JLM Visuals.

Radio Astronomy. Set of twenty 35-mm slides. JLM Visuals.

The Radio View of the Universe. 29-minute film. Ward's.

A Whisper from Space. 57-minute film. Time-Life Video.

CHAPTER 21

Reference Books

Dickinson, Terrance, and Alan Dyer. *The Backyard Astronomer's Guide*, Camden House Publishing, 1991.

Kaler, James B. *Stars.* Freeman, 1992.

Periodicals

Freedamn, Wendy L. "The Expansion Rate and Size of the Universe." *Scientific American,* November 1992.

Goldsmith, Donald. "The Fingerprint of Creation." *Discover,* October 1992.

Nather, R. Edward, and Donald E. Winget. "Taking the Pulse of White Dwarfs." *Sky and Telescope,* April 1992.

Soker, Noam. "Planetary Nebulae." *Scientific American,* May 1992.

Van der Bergh, Sidney. "Star Clusters: Enigmas in Our Backyard." *Sky and Telescope,* May 1992.

Audio-Visual & Technology

Deep Space and the Mysteries of the Cosmos. Three 17–18-minute sound filmstrips from *The Universe: Frontiers of Discovery* series. National Geographic Society.

The Sky for Windows. Software (MS/DOS and Windows 3.x). Software Bisque, 912 Twelfth Street, Golden, CO 80401.

CHAPTER 22

Reference Books

Taylor, Peter O. *Observing the Sun.* Cambridge University Press, 1991.

Thoren, Victor E. *The Lord of Uraniborg: A Biography of Tycho Brahe.* Cambridge University Press, 1990.

Periodicals

Akasofu, Syun-Ichi. "What Causes the Aurora?" *Earth in Space,* September 1992.

Folger, Tim. "Fire in the Sky." *Discover,* August 1992.

Audio-Visual & Technology

The Solar Sea. 58-minute film from the *Planet Earth* series. Films Incorporated.

The Solar System. Five 17–20-minute sound filmstrips from *The Universe: Frontiers of Discovery* series. National Geographic Society.

CHAPTER 23

Reference Books

Schaaf, Fred. *Seeing the Solar System.* Wiley, 1991.

Periodicals

Ainsworth, Diane. "Mars Observer: Return to the Red Planet." *Astronomy,* September 1992.

Chaikin, Andrew. "Four Faces of Mars." *Sky and Telescope,* July 1992.

Goldman, Staurt J. "Venus Unveiled." *Sky and Telescope,* March 1992.

Audio-Visual & Technology

Exploring Our Solar System. Interactive videodisc (Mac). AIMS Media, Inc.

Mission to Mars! Interactive CD-ROM (Mac and Hypercard). Intellimation.

The Planet That Got Knocked on Its Side. 60-minute film. Coronet/MTI Films & Video, 1987.

The Search for Planet X. 26-minute film. Films for the Humanities and Sciences, 1986.

Space Science: Comets, Meteors and Asteroids. 12-minute film. Coronet/MTI Films & Video, 1987.

Tales From Other Worlds. 58-minute film from the *Planet Earth* series. Films Incorporated.

Voyager at Uranus. Set of fifteen 35-mm slides. Astronomical Society of the Pacific, 1986.

The Voyager Missions to Jupiter and Saturn. 30-minute video. Finley-Holiday Films.

CHAPTER 24

Reference Books

Hockey, Thomas A. *The Book of the Moon: A Lunar Introduction to Astronomy, Geology, Space Physics, and Space Travel.* Prentice, 1986.

Rükl, Antonin. *Atlas of the Moon.* Paul Hamlyn Publishing, 1990.

Periodicals

Pasachoff, Jay M. "The Great Eclipse." *National Geographic,* May 1992.

Audio-Visual & Technology

Eclipses of the Sun and Moon. 10-minute film or video. Encyclopaedia Britannica Educational Corporation.

One Small Step. 57-minute film. Time-Life Video.

The Moon—A Giant Step in Geology. 24-minute film or video. Encyclopaedia Britannica Educational Corporation.

The Moon and Its Lunar Features. Set of twenty 35-mm slides. JLM Visuals.

CHAPTER 25

Reference Books

Branley, Franklyn M. *Sunshine Makes the Seasons.* Harper, 1985.

Turner, A.J. *Time Measuring Instruments, Vol. 1, Part 1: Astrolabes and Related Instruments.* The Time Museum, 1985.

Audio-Visual & Technology

Bradford Sky Travel. Software (Mac). William K. Bradford Publishing Co.

How We Know the Earth Moves. 10-minute film. Phoenix-BFA Films and Video.

Latitude, Longitude, and Time Zones. 13-minute film. Coronet/MTI Films & Video.

CHAPTER 26

Reference Books

Bohren, Craig F. *Clouds in a Glass of Beer: Simple Experiments in Atmospheric Physics.* Wiley, 1987.

Lydolph, Paul E. *Weather and Climate.* Rowman and Allanheld, 1985.

Periodicals

Horgan, J. "Volcanic Eruption: A Giant Eruption Frays the Tattered Ozone Layer." *Scientific American,* March 1992.

Lemonick, M.D. "The Ozone Vanishes." *Time,* 17 February 1992.

Mitchell, J. Murray. "Carbon Dioxide and Future Climate." *Weatherwise,* August/September 1991.

Zaburnov, Steven A. "As the World Breathes: The Carbon Dioxide Cycle." *Earth,* January 1992.

Audio-Visual & Technology

Above the Horizon. 21-minute film. American Meteorological Society.

Assault on the Ozone Layer. 18-minute video. Films for the Humanities and Sciences.

The Hole in the Sky. 60-minute film. Coronet/MTI Films & Video, 1987.

The Infinite Voyage: Crisis in the Atmosphere. 60-minute video. Intellimation.

What Makes Weather. 14-minute film or video. Encyclopaedia Britannica Educational Corporation.

CHAPTER 27

Reference Books

Firor, John. *The Changing Atmosphere: A Global Challenge.* USA Today, 1992.

Scorer, R. *Clouds of the World: A Complete Color Encyclopedia.* Yale University Press, 1990.

Periodicals

Carey, John. "Scientific Sleuths Solve the Mystery of Arctic Haze." *Weatherwise,* April 1988.

Gedzelman, S.D. "In Praise of Altocumulus." *Weatherwise,* June 1988.

Schlatter, T. "Dew vs. Fog." *Weatherwise,* October 1989.

Audio-Visual & Technology

Clouds: A Guide to the Sky. Cloud Chart. Sky Guide.

The Formation of Raindrops. 26-minute film. American Meteorological Society.

What Makes Clouds? 15-minute film or video. Encyclopaedia Britannica Educational Corporation.

CHAPTER 28

Reference Books

Watson, Lyall. *Heaven's Breath: A Natural History of the Winds.* Morrow, 1985.

Williams, Jack. *The Weather Book: An Easy-to-Understand Guide to the USA's Weather.* USA Today, 1992.

Periodicals

Schatler, T. "Low Level Winds." *Weatherwise,* April 1991.

Audio-Visual & Technology

What Makes the Wind Blow? 12-minute film or video. Encyclopaedia Britannica Educational Corporation.

CHAPTER 29

Periodicals

Dorr, B. "Bombs and Ultrabombs: Exploring Explosive Ocean Storms." *Weatherwise,* April 1990.

Rummel, Lynette. "A 'Visible' Cold Front." *Weatherwise,* August 1987. (See the December 1987 issue of *Weatherwise* for more information on this cold front.)

Audio-Visual & Technology

Weather Features Using Weather Maps. Set of twenty 35-mm slides. JLM Visuals.

CHAPTER 30

Reference Books

Branley, Franklyn M. *Hurricane Watch.* Thomas Cromwell, 1985.

Periodicals

Case, Bob. "Hurricanes: Strong Storms out of Africa." *Weatherwise,* February 1990.

Clary, Mike. "The Human Dimension in Hurricane Forecasting." *Weatherwise,* August 1987.

Corcoran, E. "Calculating Reality." *Scientific American,* January 1991.

Leftwich, P. W., L. F. Wilson, and H.G. Crowther. "Tornadoes: Record Pace Continues." *Weatherwise,* February/March 1992.

Masters, Jeffrey M. "Flying into the Eye of a Hurricane." *Weatherwise,* June 1987.

Wood, Richard A. "When Lightning Strikes." *Weatherwise,* August 1988.

Audio-Visual & Technology

Hurricane. 60-minute video from the *NOVA* series. Coronet/MTI Films & Video, 1989.

A Look at the Tornado and Other Local Storms. Set of 35-mm slides. National Audio-Visual Center.

Storms and Other Atmospheric Disturbances. Set of twenty 35-mm slides. JLM Visuals.

Storms: The Restless Atmosphere. 22-minute film or video. Encyclopaedia Britannica Educational Corporation.

Weather: Come Rain, Come Shine. 22-minute film or video. National Geographic Society.

Weather Satellites. 15-minute film or video. Encyclopaedia Britannica Educational Corporation.

CHAPTER 31

Reference Books

Firor, John. *The Changing Atmosphere: A Global Challenge.* Yale University Press, 1990.

Lydolph, Paul E. *The Climate of the Earth.* Rowman and Allanheld, 1985.

Periodicals

Jones, P.D., and T.M.L. Wigley. "Global Warming Trends." *Scientific American*, August 1990.

Knox, Pamela Nabor. "El Niño." *Earth*, September 1992.

Simarski, Lynn Teo. "Volcanism and Climate Change." *Earth in Space*, May 1992.

Waters, Tom. "Global Cooling." *Earth*, November 1992.

White, R.M. "The Great Climate Debate." *Scientific American*, July 1990.

Audio-Visual & Technology

Climate, Weather and People. Two sound filmstrips in color, one video. Hawkhill Associates.

The Climate Puzzle. 58-minute film from the *Planet Earth* series. Films Incorporated, 1985.

The Greenhouse Effect. 17-minute video. Scott Resources, Inc., 1990.

CHAPTER 32

Reference Books

Rudwick, Martin J.S. *The Meaning of Fossils: Episodes in the History of Paleontology.* University of Chicago Press, 1985.

Wicander, Reed, and James S. Monroe. *Historical Geology.* West, 1989.

Periodicals

Matthews, William Henry. "American Fossil Hunters." *Earth Science*, Spring 1990.

Shreeve, James. "The Dating Game." *Discover*, September 1992.

Willis, Delta. "A Brief History of Human Time." *Omni*, October 1991.

Audio-Visual & Technology

Fossils and Fossilization. Set of twenty 35-mm slides. JLM Visuals.

Fossils: Clues to the Past. 23-minute film or video. National Geographic Society.

Geologic Time. 24-minute film or video. Encyclopaedia Britannica Educational Corporation, 1986.

CHAPTER 33

Reference Books

Arduini, Paolo, and Giorgio Teruzzi. *Guide to Fossils.* Simon and Schuster, 1986.

Lambert, David. *The Field Guide to Prehistoric Life.* Facts on File, 1985.

Levin, Harold. *The Earth Through Time.* Saunders, 1991.

Periodicals

Briggs, Derek E. G., and Gregory D. Edgecomb. "The Gold Bugs." *Natural History*, November 1992.

Davidow, Beth. "Forests of Stone." *Earth*, November 1992.

Feldman, Howard R. "Against All Odds, a Brachiopod Survives." *Earth*, July 1992.

Levinton, Jeffrey S. "The Big Bang of Animal Evolution." *Scientific American*, November 1992.

Audio-Visual & Technology

Evolution: Inquiries into Earth Science. Videodisc with barcodes. Videodiscovery.

Fossils of the Precambrian and Lower Paleozoic. Set of twenty 35-mm slides. JLM Visuals.

CHAPTER 34

Reference Books

Stanley, Steven M. *Extinctions.* Freeman, 1986.

Sutcliffe, Antony J. *On the Track of Ice Age Mammals.* Harvard University Press, 1986.

Zallinger, Peter. *Dinosaurs and Other Archosaurs.* Random House, 1986.

Periodicals

Zimmer, Carl. "Ruffled Feathers." *Discover*, May 1992.

Audio-Visual & Technology

Dinosaurs. Interactive videodisc (Mac and Hypercard). Videodiscovery.

Fossils of the Cenozoic. Set of twenty 35-mm slides. JLM Visuals.

Fossils of the Mesozoic. Set of twenty 35-mm slides. JLM Visuals.

Hot-Blooded Dinosaurs. 49-minute film. Time-Life Video.

The Infinite Voyage: The Great Dinosaur Hunt. 60-minute video. Intellimation.

Sources of Audiovisuals and Software Materials

AIMS Media, Inc.
9710 DeSoto Avenue
Chatsworth, CA 91311

Ambrose Video
1290 Sixth Avenue
Suite 2245
New York, NY 10104

American Geophysical Union
2000 Florida Avenue, NW
Washington, DC 20009

American Meteorological
Society
45 Beacon Street
Boston, MA 02108

Audiovisual Center
University of Indiana
Bloomington, IN 47405

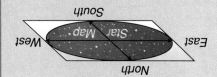

William K. Bradford
Publishing Co.
310 School Street
Acton, MA 01729

Brøderbund Software
P.O. Box 6125
Novato, CA 94948

Celestron International
2835 Columbia Street
Torrance, CA 90503

Coronet / MTI Film & Video
108 Wilmot Road
Deerfield, IL 60015

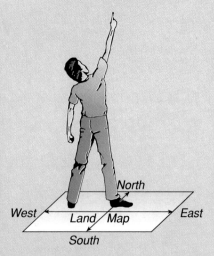

Dino Productions
P.O. Box 3004
Englewood, CO 80155

Educational Materials and
Equipment Co.
P.O. Box 2805
Danbury, CT 06813

Encyclopaedia Britannica
Educational Corporation
310 South Michigan Avenue
Chicago, IL 60604

Films for the Humanities and
Sciences
P.O. Box 2053
Princeton, NJ 08543

Films Incorporated
5547 North Ravenswood
Chicago, IL 60640

Focus Media, Inc.
P.O. Box 865
Garden City, NY 11530

Hubbard Scientific Company
3101 Iris Avenue
Boulder, CO 80301

Intellimation
P.O. 1530
Santa Barbara, CA 93116

International Film & Video
Bureau
332 South Michigan Avenue
Chicago, IL 60604

JLM Visuals
1208 Bridge Street
Grafton, WI 53024

Journal Films, Inc.
A Division of Altschul Group
Corp.
1569 Sherman Avenue
Evanston, IL 60201

Kalmbach Publishing
   Company
21027 Crossroads Circle
Waukesha, WI 53187

Macmillan/McGraw-Hill
4635 Hilton Corporate Drive
Columbus, OH 43232

The Media Guild
11722 Sorrento Valley Road
Suite E
San Diego, CA 92121

Modern Talking Picture
   Service
5000 Park Street North
St. Petersburg, FL 33709

NASA CORE
Lorain County JVS
15181 Route 58 South
Oberlin, OH 44074

National Audiovisual Center
8700 Edgeworth Drive
Capitol Heights, MD 20743

National Geographic Society
   Educational Services
P.O. Box 98019
Washington, DC 20090

NOAA Office of Public Affairs
Room 6013
Department of Commerce
   Building
Washington, DC 20230

Optical Data Corp.
30 Technology Drive
Warren, NJ 07060

Phoenix-BFA Films & Video
468 Park Avenue South
New York, NY 10016

Scholastic, Inc.
P.O. Box 7502
Jefferson City, MO 65102

The Science Man Company
A Division of TSM Marketing,
   Inc.
4738 North Harlem Avenue
Harwood Heights, IL 60656

Time-Life Video
1271 Avenue of the Americas
New York, NY 10020

Tom Snyder Productions
90 Sherman Street
Cambridge, MA 02140

TVOntario
143 West Franklin Street
Suite 206
Chapel Hill, NC 27516

U.S. Department of the
   Interior
Bureau of Mines
Audiovisual Library
2401 E Street, NW
Washington, DC 20277

U.S. Forest Service
Office of Public Affairs
Audiovisual Services
Auditor's Building
Box 96090
Washington, DC 20090-6090

U.S. Geological Survey
Geologic Inquiries Group
907 National Center
Reston, VA 22092

Videodiscovery
1700 Westlake Avenue
Suite 600
Seattle, WA 98109-3012

The Voyager Company
1351 Pacific Coast Highway
Santa Monica, CA 90401

Ward's Natural Science
   Establishment, Inc.
P.O. Box 1712
Rochester, NY 14692

John Wiley and Sons, Inc.
605 Third Avenue
New York, NY 10158

Master Materials List

The materials list includes equipment and supplies needed for one class of 24 students to complete all activities in Earth Science.

EQUIPMENT	Quantity	Chapter
anemometer (optional)	1	28
balances, laboratory	12	3, 34
bar magnets	12	4
barometer	1	28
bathroom scales	6	34
beakers, 1-L	2	13
beakers, 250-mL	30	3, 8, 20
beakers, 500-mL	12	1, 12
blow dryers with cool settings	12	29
Bunsen burners	12	20
calculators	24	34
clamps, test tube	12	1
compass, drawing (safety)	24	2, 23

EQUIPMENT (continued)	Quantity	Chapter
compound microscopes	12	6
diffraction gratings	12	20
droppers, medicine	12	1, 4, 13
funnels, 75-mm diameter	12	3
funnels, 150-mm diameter	12	1
graduated cylinders, 50-mL or 100-mL	12	1
graduated cylinders, 250-mL	12	3
hobby knives, or other sharp knives	12	20
hot plates	12	3, 13
incandescent lamps	12	20
lab aprons	24	3, 4, 29
metersticks	24	23
metric rulers	24	1, 5, 2, 12, 18, 20, 23, 26, 34
petri dishes	12	6
protractors	24	2, 15
racks, test tube	12	29
rain gauge	1	28
ring stands	12	1
safety goggles	24	3, 4, 20, 29
slides, microscope	84	4, 6
stirring rods	12	3, 27
stoppers, to fit funnel	12	1
stopwatches	6	8
streak plates	12	4
test tubes, 10-mm diameter	36	29
thermometer, outdoor	1	28
thermometers, Celsius, (alcohol only)	30	8, 27, 28, 29
wall clock with second hand, or stopwatches	12	12, 29
wind vane	1	28

SUPPLIES	Quantity	Chapter
adding machine tape	40 meters	23
aluminum foil	1 roll	20
ammonium alum	500 g	3
antacid tablets	308	
blocks, wooden (5 cm x 10 cm)	121	2
cans, shiny metal	1227	
cardboard	15 sheets	13, 31
cheesecloth or muslin	2 square meters	27, 28, 29
corks, small	1220	
dinosaur models, to scale		
Tyrannosaurus	2	34
Stegosaurus	2	34
Triceratops	2	34
Trachodon	2	34
Apatosaurus	2	34
filter paper, for 75-mm funnel	12	3
foam cups, 6-oz	72	13
food coloring, blue, red, or green	1 bottle	13
glycerin	150 mL	29
gravel	2400 cc	12
hydrochloric acid, dilute	25 mL	4
index cards	12	20
mineral samples, numbered		
biotite	12	4
calcite	12	4
chalcopyrite	12	4
feldspar	12	4
galena	12	4
gypsum	12	4
halite	12	4
hematite	12	4
Iceland spar	12	4
magnetite	12	4
olivine	12	4
pyrite	12	4

SUPPLIES (continued)	Quantity	Chapter
quartz	12	4
sphalerite	12	4
sulfur	12	4
talc	12	4
nails, steel	12	4
paper, graph, 5 lines/cm	24 sheets	1, 3, 8, 11, 14, 15, 17, 18, 22, 24, 25, 26, 33
paper, tracing	84 sheets	10, 11, 16, 19, 21
paper clips	1 box	10
pencils, colored	12 sets	10, 11, 17, 19 20, 22, 33
pencils, marking	12	1, 3, 6, 12, 29
pennies	12	4
rubber bands, small	50	27, 29
rubbing alcohol	150 mL	29
sand	2400 cc	12
scissors	12	20
shoeboxes, cardboard, with covers	12	20
shoeboxes, clear plastic	12	12, 13
sodium chloride (table salt)	1 container	20
spoons	12	27
string	40 meters	23
tape, cellophane	2 rolls	6, 20
tape, masking	2 rolls	3
thread	150 cm	3
water, distilled	2 L	3
wire, nichrome	1 roll	20
wood splints	12	3

Sources of Earth Science Supplies and Equipment

General Science Materials

American Geological Institute
4220 King Street
Alexandria, VA 22302

Carolina Biological Supply
Company
2700 York Road
Burlington, NC 27215

Central Scientific Company
[CENCO]
11222 Melrose Avenue
Franklin Park, IL 60131

Delta Education, Inc.
P.O. Box 915
Hudson, NH 03051

Edmund Scientific Company
101 East Gloucester Pike
Barrington, NJ 08007

Fisher Scientific Company
Educational Materials
Division
4901 West LeMoyne Street
Chicago, IL 60651

Flinn Scientific, Inc,
131 Flinn Street
P.O. Box 219
Batavia, IL 60510

Frey Scientific Company
905 Hickory Lane
Mansfield, OH 44901

LaPine Scientific Company
13636 South Western Avenue
Blue Island, IL 60406

McKilligan Supply
Corporation
435 Main Street
Johnson City, NY 13790

Nasco
901 Janesville Avenue
Fort Atkinson, WI 53538
or
Nasco West Inc.
1524 Princeton Avenue
Modesto, CA 95352

Sargent-Welch Scientific
Company
911 Commerce Court
Buffalo Grove, IL 60089

Science Kit and Boreal Labs
777 East Park Drive
Tonawanda, NY 14150

Astronomy Slides, Photos, Charts

Division of Photography
American Museum of Natural
History
Central Park West & 79th
Street
New York, NY 10024

Lick Observatory
P.O. Box 85
Mount Hamilton, CA 95140

Lunar and Planetary Institute
3600 Bay Area Boulevard
Houston, TX 77058

MMI Space Science
Corporation
2950 Wyman Parkway
P.O. Box 19907
Baltimore, MD 21211

Sky Publishing Corporation
Sky and Telescope Magazine
P.O. Box 9111
Belmont, MA 02178

Yerkes Observatory
Photographic Service
Department
373 West Geneva Street
Williams Bay, WI 53191

Geology Slides

Crystal Productions
P.O. Box 2159
Glenvue, IL 60025

Hubbard Scientific Company
3101 Iris Avenue
Suite #215
Boulder, CO 80301

Ward's Natural Science
Establishment, Inc.
5100 West Henrietta Road
P.O. Box 92912
Rochester, NY 14692-9012

Rocks and Minerals

Connecticut Valley Biological
Supply Company, Inc.
82 Valley Road
P.O. Box 326
Southampton, MA 01073

Crystal Productions
(See Geology Slides)

Fisher Scientific Company
(See General Science
Materials)

Ideal School Supply Company
11000 South Lavergne Avenue
Oak Lawn, IL 60453

Lab-Aids,Inc.
17 Colt Court
Ronkonkoma, NY 11779

Omni Resources, Inc.
P.O. Box 2096
Burlington, NC 27216-2096

Ward's Natural Science
Establishment, Inc.
(See Geology Slides)

Wall Maps, Charts, Globes, Models

Crystal Productions
(See Geology Slides)

Hammond, Inc.
515 Valley Street
Maplewood, NJ 07040

Hubbard Scientific Company
(See Geology Slides)

Learning Things, Inc.
68A Broadway
P.O. Box 436
Arlington, MA 02174

Nystrom
3333 Elston Avenue
Chicago, IL 60618

Omni Resources, Inc.
(See Rocks and Minerals)

Rand McNally Company
School Order Department
P.O. Box 1906
Skokie, IL 60076-8906

Schoolmasters Science
745 State Circle
P.O. Box 1941
Ann Arbor, MI 48106

Trippensee Planetarium
Company
301 Cass Street
Saginaw, MI 48602

U.S. Geological Survey
Map Distribution
Federal Center, Building 41
Box 25286
Denver, CO 80225

U.S. Geological Survey
Books and Open-File Reports
Federal Center, Building 41
Box 25425
Denver, CO 80225

Ward's Natural Science
Establishment, Inc.
(See Geology Slides)

Meteorological, Astronomical, and Oceanographic Supplies Information

American Meteorological
Society
45 Beacon Street
Boston, MA 02108

Edmund Scientific Company
(See General Science
Materials)

Hubbard Scientific Company
(See Geology Slides)

MMI Space Science
Corporation
(See Astronomy Slides, etc.)

NOAA
Office of Public Affairs
Room 6013 Commerce
Department Building
14th Street and Constitution
Avenue, NW
Washington, D.C. 20230

Sky Publishing Corporation
Sky and Telescope Magazine
(See Astronomy Slides, etc.)

Taylor Instrument Companies
95 Ames Street
Rochester, NY 14601

Ward's Natural Science
Establishment, Inc.
(See Geology Slides)

Pacing Chart / Student Ability Tracks

Earth Science by Spaulding/Namowitz will be used by a variety of students in different settings. You—the teacher—are in the best position to judge how much time to allocate each of the many topics your students need to cover in a one-year course. In addition, you may need to modify the content in the text to suit the needs of students with different abilities. The following pacing chart will help you with both of these tasks.

This pacing chart suggests how many class sessions may be devoted to each Earth Science chapter with a mixed-ability class, assuming a school year of 180 days. All topics for each chapter should be taught except those listed as *Optional* or *Omit*. As you teach the first few chapters, you will learn which pace works best for you and your students. By comparing your natural pace with that shown in the pacing chart, you should be able to then use the chart to make more refined time estimates for the rest of the year.

As you get acquainted with this annotated teacher's edition, you will notice topic-referenced Planning Charts for every chapter. These Planning Charts correlate text topics to the supplementary materials in the Earth Science program. Select the text topics you want to teach and the Planning Charts will aid you in easily choosing the corresponding supplementary materials.

	Chapter	Class Sessions
UNIT ONE	1	4
	2	4
	3	6
	4	6
	5	7
	6	6
	7	7
UNIT TWO	8	4
	9	5
	10	6
	11	5
	12	5
UNIT THREE	13	7
	14	6
	15	7
	16	6
UNIT FOUR	17	6
	18	6
	19	4
UNIT FIVE	20	4
	21	5
	22	4
	23	6
	24	6
	25	5
UNIT SIX	26	6
	27	7
	28	5
	29	4
	30	5
	31	5
UNIT SEVEN	32	3
	33	4
	34	4

Typical Track	Survey Track	Honors Track
All	Omit Lesson II	All
All	All	All
All	Omit Topics 5, 6, 12	All
All	All	All
Optional Topic 6	Omit Topics 1, 6	All
All	All	All
All	Optional Lesson IV	All
All	Optional Topic 9	All
Optional Topics, 3, 4	Omit Topics 3, 4, 18	All
All	Omit Topics 10, 11	All
Optional Lesson IV	Omit Topics 1, 7, 8, and Lesson IV	All
Optional Topics 14, 15	Optional Topics 4, 5, 6 Omit Topics 12, 14, 15	All
Optional Lesson IV	Omit Lesson IV	All
All	All	All
Optional Topics 6, 7	Omit Topics 6, 7 Omit Lesson IV	All
Optional Lesson III	Omit Lessons III & IV	All
All	All	All
All	Omit Topic 13	All
All	Omit Topic 4	All
Optional Lesson III	Omit Topics 2, 11, and Lesson III	All
All	Optional Lesson III	All
Optional Lesson III	Omit Topic 6 and Lesson III	All
All	All	All
Optional Lesson I	Optional Lesson I Omit Topics 12, 20, 22	All
All	Omit Topics 2, 9, 15	All
All	Optional Topics 8, 11, 16, 18, 19	All
Optional Topics 12, 13, 14	Omit Topics 12, 13, 14 Optional Topics 3, 6, 7, 19, 20, 21, 22	All
All	Optional Topics 2, 7, 13, 14	All
All	Optional Topic 8	All
All	Optional Lesson III	All
All	Omit Lesson IV	All
All	Omit Lesson III	All
All	Omit Topics 3, 4	All
All	Omit Topics 1, 2, 8, 9	All

CHAPTER I
Introduction to Earth Science

PLANNING CHART

Topic	Support Material
Lesson I **What is Earth Science?**	**Laboratory Investigation:** Laboratory Safety **Laboratory Investigation:** Working in the Earth Science Laboratory **In-Text Lab Activity:** Collecting and Analyzing Data
1 Branches of Earth Science	**Content Evaluation:** p. 6 *Topic Review:* 1; p. 14-15 *Chapter Review:* 1, 4, 5; Interpret and Apply: 1, 2
2 Activities of Today's Geologists	**Content Evaluation:** p. 6 *Topic Review:* 2; p. 14-15 *Chapter Review:* 6; Interpret and Apply: 2
3 What Astronomers Do	**Content Evaluation:** p. 6 *Topic Review:* 3; p. 14-15 *Chapter Review:* 11; Interpret and Apply: 2
4 What Meteorologists Do	**Content Evaluation:** p. 6 *Topic Review:* 4; p. 14-15 *Chapter Review:* 13; Interpret and Apply: 2
5 What Oceanographers Do	**Content Evaluation:** p. 6 *Topic Review:* 5; p. 14-15 *Chapter Review:* 12; Interpret and Apply: 2
Lesson II **The Origin of Earth**	**Laboratory Investigation:** Observations of a Sample of Earth Material
6 Where Earth Science Begins: The Solar System	**Content Evaluation:** p. 11 *Topic Review:* 6; p. 14-15 *Chapter Review:* 8, 16; Interpret and Apply: 3, 4
7 The Protoplanet Hypothesis	**Content Evaluation:** p. 11 *Topic Review:* 7; p. 14-15 *Chapter Review:* 16; Interpret and Apply: 3, 4, 5
8 Origin of the Oceans	**Content Evaluation:** p. 11 *Topic Review:* 8; p. 14-15 *Chapter Review:* 2, 7; Interpret and Apply: 5
9 Origin of the Atmosphere	**Content Evaluation:** p. 11 *Topic Review:* 9; p. 14-15 *Chapter Review:* 7, 15; Interpret and Apply: 5
10 Structure of the Solid Earth	**Content Evaluation:** p. 11 *Topic Review:* 10; p. 14-15 *Chapter Review:* 3, 9, 10, 14; Interpret and Apply: 5
11 How the Continents Formed	**Content Evaluation:** p. 11 *Topic Review:* 11; p. 14-15 *Chapter Review:* 3; Interpret and Apply: 5
Lab Activity p. 12-13	Collecting and Analyzing Data

Topic	Support Material
Chapter Review p. 14-15	Critical Thinking 1-11 **Study Guide:** Vocabulary; Interpreting and Applying
Chapter I Assessment Program	**Chapter Tests; Computer Test Bank**

Introducing UNIT **ONE**

Student Writing

Begin Unit One with a brief discussion of how each photo on pages xii-1 portrays an aspect of Earth's structure. Throughout the unit, students will learn about topics related to the photos and captions.

At the conclusion of Unit One, refer students to the Unit One introduction on pages xii-1. Have students write an expository essay describing how the photos in the introduction relate to the unit theme, Earth's structure. They should use examples of concepts from Unit One to support their statements. Before writing, students need to focus their thoughts and to provide direction and organization for their essays Drawing a concept map is suggested. See page T689 for information on concept mapping.

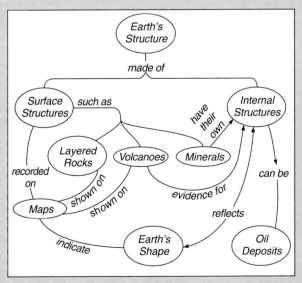

CHAPTER I

Motivator

This chapter is the introduction to the text and to the course. One method of introducing both is with clippings of newspaper and magazine articles about earth science events of the past summer (unusual weather, volcanic eruptions, earthquakes, meteor showers, and the like). In preparation, try to have clippings that relate to each of the four areas of earth science— geology, astronomy, meteorology, and oceanography. Use the clippings to identify and discuss each of the areas of earth science as well as to discuss the impact of earth science on people.

Lesson I: What is Earth Science?

(Topics 1-5)

Teaching Suggestions

There are two points to be made with this lesson. First, earth science events occur everywhere, and they occur constantly. Second, many earth science events involve more than one branch of earth science or even involve areas outside earth science. The first point, earth science events occur constantly, can be made with the articles. The articles, however, will probably reflect unusual or even catastrophic events. Point out that many everyday events such as moon phases, tides, and day-to-day weather, are also earth science changes. A long-term assignment that would help emphasize both the nature of earth science and the number of earth science events that occur is to require students to collect newspaper or magazine items about earth science events over the year. An assignment of an item a month is not unreasonable. A written summary of each article could also be part of the assignment.

The second point about the interrelationship of the sciences may not be apparent from news items. The following example could be used: Some scientists suspect that warmer climates of the past (paleoclimatology) corresponded to periods of increased tectonic activity (geology) because the volcanic activity that accompanies tectonic activity increases carbon dioxide in the atmosphere, which in turn traps more heat near Earth's surface (meteorology). This has implications today because the burning of fossil fuels and the destruction of forests are causing an increase in atmospheric carbon dioxide. (Coal and oil are fossil fuels. Green plants use carbon dioxide during photosynthesis; if carbon dioxide is not used, it stays in the atmosphere.) Increased carbon dioxide may in turn cause worldwide warming. Scientists fear that such warming may melt some of the polar ice caps (glaciology), which in turn would cause a rise in sea level and submergence of coastal cities. Another effect of warming could be an increase in the size of the world's deserts (climatology), already a problem in Africa.

Lesson II: The Origin of Earth

(Topics 6-11)

Teaching Suggestions
Start this lesson by listing the facts that must be explained by any hypothesis about the origin of the solar system. This subject is difficult to understand. The drawings in the text should help.

Although Earth's internal structure will be discussed again in Chapter 15, it should be introduced at this time.

Science Background
Computer simulations indicate that collisions may have been important to the early evolution of the solar system, at least for the inner

planets (Mercury, Venus, Earth, and Mars). The simulation started with 500 newly-condensed bodies, each one-third the size of the moon. During the simulation, collisions and near misses were very common, and continued until only one object remained in each of the planetary orbits. The four inner planets of today are the survivors of those chaotic times. In the computer simulation, the inner solar system is swept clear of gases by solar wind. The outer solar system—where Jupiter, Saturn, Uranus, and Neptune are forming—is not. As a result, the outer planets are enclosed in large gas envelopes, while the inner planets all have rocky surfaces.

CHAPTER I LAB ACTIVITY
Collecting and Interpreting Data

■ A student report sheet for this activity can be found in the *Laboratory Investigations* booklet.

Time estimate
40-50 minutes

Materials
The funnel needs to have a diameter of about 15 centimeters. Smaller funnels can be used but the amount of water added each time will need to be decreased. As funnel size decreases, the levels are more difficult to mark and measure.

Process Skills
■ Measuring: Procedure 4, 5, 7
■ Constructing Tables and Graphs: Procedure 8
■ Comparing/Contrasting: Analysis and Conclusions 4
■ Describing: Analysis and Conclusions 1
■ Analyzing Data: Analysis and Conclusions 6

Procedural Hints
Locate each of the graphs in the textbook with students before starting the lab.

Students who have trouble with *Analysis and Conclusions* question 6 should be encouraged to actually subtract each pair of readings and plot the graph. Students who have trouble with *Analysis and Conclusions* question 7 could measure and plot the distance between 50-mL levels on a calibrated 500 mL beaker.

Sample student data can be found in the annotated table and graph on page 13 of this Teachers Annotated Edition.

Answers—Analysis and Conclusions

1. The spaces between the lines decreased because the funnel became wider.
2. The spaces between the lines would increase.
3. Flooding would be a greater concern if the lake were wide side down.
4. The graph on page 189. The graph on page 15 goes up sharply to the right. The graph on page 269 is a straight line. The graph on page 608 goes down to the right.
5. The greatest distance between the lines occurred at the start and then decreased. This resembles the graph on page 608.
6. If a beaker had been used, the spaces between marks would have been uniform. This resembles the graph on page 269.

ANSWERS TO

CHAPTER 1 REVIEW

Review

1–k, 2–j, 3–i, 4–n, 5–f, 6–h, 7–p, 8–c, 9–g, 10–d, 11–m, 12–a, 13–o, 14–l, 15–b, 16–e

Interpret and Apply

1. Your discussion of Lesson 1 should bring up some responses. Other relationships include the following:

   ■ the effect of volcanic dust on climate. Students may be familiar with the eruption of Krakatau and the "year without a summer" that followed (1816).

   ■ the effect of ocean currents on atmospheric circulation. For example, the much-publicized El Niño current off the coast of Ecuador and Peru in 1991-1992 may have been the cause of such events as recent winters over Canada and the United States becoming milder, southeast United States getting more precipitation, and excessive heat and drought in the mid-continent.

   ■ the effect of asteroid impact on climate. Dinosaur extinction may have been caused by this event.

2. Direct evidence—geology, meteorology, oceanography; the subjects of study are generally reachable from Earth. Indirect evidence—astronomy; the subjects are distant and difficult to observe directly. There are many exceptions. For example, paleogeologists studying Earth's early atmosphere rely on indirect evidence. Geologists studying Earth's inner structure use indirect evidence. Astronomers studying moon rocks are using direct evidence.

3. The original cloud of gas and dust is thought to have been slowly rotating. This rotation continued as the cloud shrank and the sun and planets formed. These objects should have the same direction of rotation as the original cloud. Therefore, statements about the direction of rotation (numbers 1, 4, 5, and the second part of 6) fit the hypothesis. Statement 3 is also satisfactory because the original cloud is hypothesized to have been disk-shaped.

4. Statement 2 is not easy to explain. The formation of material into protoplanets should have involved collisions of particles. Collisions tend to push objects out of orbit; thus, the orbits would become less circular. Statement 6 is also difficult. The pileup of single eddies would be easier to understand if it formed a single planet each time instead of separate planets and moons.

5. Other planets should have some kind of atmospheres, oceans, layers, and continents. (In fact, all planets except Mercury and Pluto do have atmospheres, and evidence suggests some sort of layered structure for all planets. Oceans and continents are not apparent, but there is evidence of past water on Mars and of past crustal movement on Venus.)

Critical Thinking

1. y-axis
2. about 2.5 billion
3. answers will vary between 5.8 and 7.2
4. 1800
5. about 3 billion
6. about 1930
7. about 130 years
8. about 1975
9. about 45 years
10. The second doubling took less time.
11. Another doubling will take even less time.

CHAPTER 2
Earth's Shape, Dimensions, and Internal Heat

PLANNING CHART

Topic	Support Material
Lesson I **Earth's Shape and Size**	**In-Text Lab Activity:** Eratosthenes and Earth's Circumference
1 Earth Is Spherical	**Content Evaluation:** p. 20 *Topic Review:* 1; p. 26-27; *Chapter Review:* 1, 2, 3, 4, 5; Interpret and Apply: 1
2 The Sphere Is Not Perfect	**Content Evaluation:** p. 20 *Topic Review:* 2; p. 26-27; *Chapter Review:* 6, 7, 9; Interpret and Apply: 2, 4, 5
3 Measuring Earth's Circumference	**Content Evaluation:** p. 20 *Topic Review:* 3; p. 26-27; *Chapter Review:* 8; Interpret and Apply: 3
4 Earth's Dimensions	**Content Evaluation:** p. 20 *Topic Review:* 4; p. 26-27; *Chapter Review:* 9, 10, 11; Interpret and Apply: 5
Lesson II **Earth's Density and Temperature**	**Laboratory Investigation:** The Density of Earth Materials
5 Earth's Density	**Content Evaluation:** p. 23 *Topic Review:* 5; p. 26-27; *Chapter Review:* 12, 13, 14; Interpret and Apply: 6, 7, 8
6 Temperatures Below the Surface	**Content Evaluation:** p. 23 *Topic Review:* 6; p. 26-27; *Chapter Review:* 15, 16
7 What Makes the Crust Hot?	**Content Evaluation:** p. 23 *Topic Review:* 7; p. 26-27; *Chapter Review:* 17, 18
Lab Activity p. 24-25	Eratosthenes and Earth's Circumference
Chapter Review p. 26-27	Critical Thinking **Study Guide:** Vocabulary; Interpreting and Applying
Chapter 2 Assessment Program	**Chapter Tests; Computer Test Bank**

CHAPTER 2

Motivator

DEMONSTRATION: This activity demonstrates why the mast of a ship is the first part to appear over the horizon. Have a student position herself or himself so that her/his eye is even with the top of a globe or another spherical object. The level of the eye is the horizon line. Use a small object to represent a ship. Move the "ship" up the side of the globe away from the student until the student sees it. Ask the student to tell which part of the "ship" appeared first and to explain why.

Lesson I: Earth's Shape and Size

(Topics 1-4)

Teaching Suggestions

The changing position of the North Star with latitude as a proof of sphericity is a fundamental concept. Be prepared to draw a sketch on the chalkboard, similar to Figure 2.1, to explain this. Northern Hemisphere latitudes have been accurately determined since ancient times because of the relationship between latitude and the angular distance of Polaris above the horizon.

With slight modification, Eratosthenes' method can be used to find the circumference of Earth using any two locations. You need only know the angular separation of two locations and the great-circle distance (shortest distance) between them. The necessary data can be obtained from an atlas. Use your location and any other location directly north or south of it. The difference in the latitudes of the two locations is their angular separation. Use the map scale to find the distance between the points. The angular separation is the same proportion of 360° (a whole circle) as the distance is to the circumference of Earth, or

$$\frac{angle}{360°} = \frac{distance}{circumference}$$

Solve the equation for circumference and compare to the actual value. You can have your students do the calculation by doing the lab activity found at the end of this chapter.

Science Background

Although he was Greek, Eratosthenes (276?-195 B.C.?) lived in Alexandria, Egypt. At that time, the greatest library of the ancient world was in Alexandria. Eratosthenes was second librarian there.

Eratosthenes is thought to have learned about the well at Syene from travelers. He used the shadow of an obelisk at Alexandria to determine the angle of the sun there. Eratosthenes assumed that Syene was due south of Alexandria. He learned that a camel needed 50 days to walk from Syene to Alexandria and that a camel could walk 100 stadia a day. From this, he calculated that the distance from Syene to Alexandria was 5000 stadia. Although scholars are not sure of the length of a stadia, it is thought to be equal to 607 English feet. If so, Eratosthenes' calculation was equal to 28 700 miles, an error of about 15 percent.

It is worth noting that Eratosthenes could have performed exactly the same calculation by using the altitude of Polaris at the two locations.

Lesson II: Earth's Density and Temperature

(Topics 5-7)

Teaching Suggestions

Density is a fundamental concept in the earth sciences. Many earth processes (wind, plate movements, energy transfer, ocean circulation, and so on) are the result of differences in density. You may wish to make the following additional points about density (these points could also be covered later in the course):

1. As long as the conditions of temperature and pressure remain unchanged, objects made of the same material will have the same density no matter what their size or shape.

2. Heating most materials causes them to have slightly lower density.

3. Cooling most materials causes them to have slightly higher density.

4. Most materials have their greatest density in the solid state.

5. Water is an important exception to rule 4; it is most dense as a liquid (at 4°C).

DEMONSTRATION: To emphasize both the method for finding density and the value for the density of Earth's crust, have several students each bring in a rock of their choosing. Balances will be needed to find the mass of each rock. Since few rocks have a convenient shape, water displacement will be needed to find their volumes. If the rock is small enough, it can be submerged in water in a graduated cylinder. The change in the water level is the volume of the rock. If the rock is too large for a cylinder, an overflow can may be used. Such cans have spouts on their sides and are available from science supply houses. The can is filled with water to the level of the spout. The water that flows from the spout when the rock is placed in the can is equal to the volume of the rock.

Once the mass and volume of each rock are known, the density can be calculated. If the values for density are averaged, the result is usually close to the average density of Earth's crust, which is 2.8 grams per cubic centimeter.

Science Background

Temperature estimates of Earth at various depths are based on a number of data. The behavior of earthquake waves (*P*-waves and *S*-waves) indicates the solid or molten state of each of Earth's inner layers. *P*-waves (compression waves) can pass through liquids or solids, but travel faster through solids. *S*-waves (shear waves) cannot pass through a liquid; they do not travel beyond a depth of about 2900 kilometers. *P*-waves travel through Earth's core, but slow down at 2900 kilometers and speed up again at about 5200 kilometers. These data suggest that below about 2900 kilometers (the outer core), Earth is liquid. Below 5200 kilometers (the boundary between the inner and outer cores), Earth is solid.

The temperatures and pressures at which rock, iron, and other Earth materials are solid or liquid can be measured under laboratory conditions, or this information can be extrapolated from such measurements. Estimates of Earth's inner temperature are continually being revised as further data become available.

CHAPTER 2 **LAB** ACTIVITY
Eratosthenes and Earth's Circumference

■ A student report sheet for this activity can be found in the *Laboratory Investigations* booklet.

Time estimate
90 minutes

Process Skills
■ Measuring: Procedure 9, 11
■ Interpreting Diagrams: Analysis and Conclusions 1
■ Calculating: Procedure 10, 12; Analysis and Conclusions 2, 3, 5, 6
■ Analyzing Data: Analysis and Conclusions 4
■ Applying a Strategy: Analysis and Conclusions 7

Procedural Hints
Although the use of fractions is usually discouraged in calculations for this course, students seem to be able to grasp what to do in *Analysis and Conclusions* questions 1 and 7 by using them.

You may need to remind students that one tenth of a centimeter equals a millimeter.

Answers—Analysis and Conclusions
1. Answer will vary depending upon student drawings. If, for example the angle is 36°, 36° is 1/10th of a circle.
2. Student answers will depend upon student data. If 1/10th of the circle is 6.2 cm, then the whole circle must be 10 x 6.2 or 62.0 cm.
3. If, for example, the length of AC is 9.8 cm then, 2 π r = 2 x 3.14 x 9.8 = 61.5 cm (to the nearest tenth).
4. $62.0 - 61.5 = 0.5; \frac{0.5}{61.5} \times 100 = 0.8\%$ With any care at all, students values can come within 1 or 2 percent of each other.
5. 20° is 1/18th of the circle.
6. 2200 x 18 = 39 600 km
7. $\left(\frac{40\,000 - 39\,600}{40\,000}\right) \times 100 = 1\%$

ANSWERS TO
CHAPTER 2 REVIEW

Review
1–spherical, 2–North Pole, 3–circle, 4–sphere, 5–weight, 6–less, 7–more, 8–circumference, 9–oblate spheroid, 10–greater, 11–oceans, 12–Density, 13–crust, 14–core, 15–increases, 16–molten, 17–radioactive, 18–friction

Interpret and Apply
1. The moon is spherical. (In fact, the moon is not a perfect sphere. The shape of the moon is discussed in Chapter 24, Topic 6.)

2. Decrease; as distance from Earth's center increases, the weight of an object should decrease. (The change in this case, however, will be too small to detect except with very sensitive, specialized equipment.)

3. (a) Ten degrees is 1/36 of 360°. Therefore, the distance between the two points should be multiplied by 36.

$$1500 \text{ km} \times 36 = 54\ 000 \text{ km}$$

   The circumference of Planet X is 54 000 km.
   (b) Earth's circumference is about 40 000 km. Planet X is larger than Earth.

4. Since the apparent force is greatest at the equator, the tendency to move away from the center of rotation (the axis) will be greatest there. The result is an equatorial bulge and an oblate shape. (Planets that spin more rapidly than Earth, such as Jupiter and Saturn, are even more oblate.)

5. More, for at least two reasons. First, if Earth did not rotate, it would lack an equatorial bulge. Objects at the equator would be closer to Earth's center and would weigh more. Another reason is centripetal force. Since centripetal force pushes away from Earth, it causes objects on Earth's surface to weigh slightly less. If Earth did not rotate, this force would cease and objects would weigh more.

6. Density is calculated as follows.

$$D = \frac{m}{V}; \quad D = \frac{10 \text{ g}}{5 \text{ cm}^3}; \quad D = 2 \text{ g/cm}^3$$

   The density is 2 grams per cubic centimeter.

7. First, calculate the density of the wood. Then compare it with the density of water.

$$D = \frac{m}{V}; \quad D = \frac{3.21 \text{ g}}{3 \text{ cm}^3}; \quad D = 1.07 \text{ g/cm}^3$$

   The wood will not float in water. (The wood of some trees is denser than water. Such wood is collectively called ironwood.)

8. (a) Density is calculated as follows.

$$D = \frac{m}{V}; \quad D = \frac{6 \text{ g}}{2 \text{ cm}^3}; \quad D = 3 \text{ g/cm}^3$$

   The density is 3 grams per cubic centimeter.
   (b) The same, 3 grams per cubic centimeter. All objects of the same material have the same density. Cutting an object in half will not change the density of the material, only its size and shape.

Critical Thinking
Probably the first error that students will see is that Syene (Aswan) and Alexandria are not directly north and south of each other. This, however, is not a real error because any two points on a sphere determine a great circle and therefore could be used to find the circumference. The fact that Syene is slightly north of the Tropic of Cancer introduces a real error. An even larger error may have resulted from the determination of the distance between Alexandria and Syene. The distance a camel can walk in a day is not a constant measurement. Also, since camel caravans had to travel near sources of water, the road used between the cities probably followed the Nile River, which is not a straight-line distance. An additional error could result from the fact that the two locations are not very far apart when compared to the size of Earth. A larger separation would yield more accurate results.

CHAPTER 3
Atoms to Minerals

PLANNING CHART

Topic	Support Material
Lesson I Atomic Structure of Matter	**Laboratory Investigation**
1 Earth's Matter	**Content Evaluation:** p. 33 *Topic Review:* 1; p. 44-45 *Chapter Review:* 1; Interpret and Apply: 1
2 Elements and Atoms	**Content Evaluation:** p. 33 *Topic Review:* 2; p. 44-45 *Chapter Review:* 2, 3; Interpret and Apply: 1
3 Model of an Atom	**Content Evaluation:** p. 33 *Topic Review:* 3; p. 44-45 *Chapter Review:* 4; Interpret and Apply: 1
4 Examples of Atomic Structure	**Content Evaluation:** p. 33 *Topic Review:* 4; p. 44-45 *Chapter Review:* 4
5 Atomic Number and Mass Number	**Content Evaluation:** p. 33 *Topic Review:* 5; p. 44-45 *Chapter Review:* 5; Interpret and Apply: 2
6 Isotopes	**Content Evaluation:** p. 33 *Topic Review:* 6; p. 44-45 *Chapter Review:* 6
7 Compounds	**Content Evaluation:** p. 33 *Topic Review:* 7; p. 44-45 *Chapter Review:* 7; Interpret and Apply: 3, 5
Lesson II Chemical Composition of Minerals	
8 What Is a Mineral?	**Content Evaluation:** p. 37 *Topic Review:* 8; p. 44-45 *Chapter Review:* 8, 9; Interpret and Apply: 4
9 Minerals May Be Elements or Compounds	**Content Evaluation:** p. 37 *Topic Review:* 9; p. 44-45 *Chapter Review:* 10, 12;
10 Ionic Bonds in Minerals	**Content Evaluation:** p. 37 *Topic Review:* 10; p. 44-45 *Chapter Review:* 11; Interpret and Apply: 5
11 Covalent Bonds in Minerals	**Content Evaluation:** p. 37 *Topic Review:* 11; p. 44-45 *Chapter Review:* 13
12 How Minerals Form	**Content Evaluation:** p. 37 *Topic Review:* 12; p. 44-45 *Chapter Review:* 14

PLANNING CHART (continued)

Topic	Support Material
Lesson III **Structure of Minerals**	**In-Text Lab Activity:** Growing Crystals
13 Minerals Have Crystalline Structure	**Content Evaluation:** p. 41 *Topic Review:* 13; p. 44-45 *Chapter Review:* 15 **Transparency 17:** Crystals
14 The Silica Tetrahedron	**Content Evaluation:** p. 41 *Topic Review:* 14; p. 44-45 *Chapter Review:* 16 **Transparency 18:** Some Bonding Arrangements for Silica Tetrahedrons
15 Crystals and Physical Properties	**Content Evaluation:** p. 41 *Topic Review:* 15; p. 44-45 *Chapter Review:* 17
Lab Activity p. 42-43	Growing Crystals
Chapter Review p. 44-45	Critical Thinking 1-7 **Study Guide:** Vocabulary; Interpreting and Applying
Chapter 3 Assessment Program	**Chapter Tests; Computer Test Bank**

CHAPTER 3

Motivator

Students are usually fascinated with the mica minerals muscovite (white mica) and biotite (black mica). The most obvious property of these minerals is that they can be peeled into very fine sheets. If possible, obtain a sample of mica and hand it around so students can look at it. Ask them to describe the sample and invite discussion and speculation on the reasons for its unusual properties. Students are often curious about how thin a mica sheet can be peeled. Point out that the sheeting is a result of the underlying atomic arrangement, and that by the end of the chapter students will have learned enough about the composition and structure of minerals to be able to answer this question themselves. (Theoretically, mica can be peeled to a single molecular layer.)

Lesson I:
Atomic Structure of Matter

(Topics 1-7)

Teaching Suggestions

This may be a difficult lesson to present, in part because many students feel that they already understand matter, elements, and atoms when in fact their knowledge is limited, and in part because the abstract nature of the subject makes it difficult to visualize. Models of atoms and molecules drawn on the board or constructed with Styrofoam balls and pipe cleaners, tinker toys, or other materials may help with the latter.

Keep in mind that you are presenting only a simple outline of atomic structure and that this is not a chemistry course. You need not become more involved than one or at most one and a half class periods allow.

Lesson II:
Chemical Composition of Minerals

(Topics 8-12)

Teaching Suggestions

DEMONSTRATION: Use samples of common substances and mineral specimens to emphasize that *compounds* are two or more chemically combined elements. Examples of two separate elements along with the compound they form when combined are especially helpful in emphasizing the difference in properties between elements and compounds. One possible example is hydrogen and oxygen gases obtained by electrolysis plus a sample of water.

Lesson III:
Structure of Minerals

(Topics 13-15)

DEMONSTRATION: To emphasize the importance of the silica tetrahedron, construct a model of quartz. (The structure of quartz is shown in the diagram that follows.) This could be a ball-and-stick model made from the standard kit or, if unavailable, a model made from other materials similar to those used for models of atomic structure in Lesson I. If enough equipment is available, consider having each student make a single tetrahedron and then join all together into a single structure.

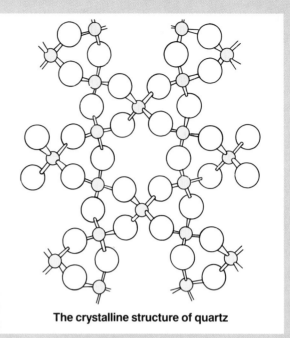

The crystalline structure of quartz

If ball-and-stick models are built, the tetrahedra will be expanded so that each of the parts can be seen. Be sure to indicate that this type of model is not to scale. Very likely the relative sizes of the two atoms will not be to the correct scale either.

Teaching Suggestions

Differentiate between "crystal" and "crystalline." Almost all minerals are crystalline—that is, the atoms within the mineral are arranged in an orderly manner. Crystals occur only when the mineral has room enough to form smooth crystal faces that reflect its orderly internal atomic arrangement.

Students often assume that the faces of a crystal are artificially cut. The Lab Activity at the end of this chapter, *Crystal Growing*, will help students observe that smooth faces are a natural property of well-developed crystals. (Crystals used in jewelry, such as diamonds, have been artificially cut. An uncut diamond has an octahedral shape.)

The point to emphasize in Topic 15 is the relationship of cleavage, hardness, density, and other mineral properties to atomic structure. *Do not* concentrate on the definitions of these properties, as they will be covered in detail in Chapter 4. Refer to the model of quartz made during the demonstration at the beginning of the lesson. One of the reasons that quartz has no cleavage is that every oxygen is shared by two silicons. There are no natural planes of weakness within the mineral, which students should be able to see from the model. This network structure is the reason that quartz is so hard.

Science Background

Examples of minerals that occur in various shapes include:

- *cubes:* galena, halite, and pyrite
- *octahedrons:* magnetite, rough diamonds, and cleavage fragments of fluorite
- *hexagonal prisms:* quartz, beryl, and corundum

The silica tetrahedron is a fundamental concept of mineralogy. It is a basic building block of Earth's crust. The structure of individual silicate minerals is determined by the way in which the silica tetrahedrons within the minerals combine with themselves and with other elements. There are four major groups of silicate minerals:

1. *Orthosilicates.* In the orthosilicates, none of the tetrahedrons share oxygen atoms with other tetrahedrons. The ratio of silicon to oxygen in these minerals is 1:4. Olivine is an example of an orthosilicate.

2. *Chain silicates.* There are two types of chain silicates—single chain and double chain. The single-chain silicates share two oxygen atoms between tetrahedrons. The ratio of silicon to oxygen is 1:3. Minerals of the pyroxene group, such as augite, are examples.

   The double-chain silicates have a somewhat more complex structure because they alternately share two and then three oxygens between tetrahedrons. This produces a silicon-oxygen ratio of 4:11. All chain silicates have cleavage parallel to the chain length and thus break apart into slivers. Minerals of the amphibole group, such as hornblende, are examples.

3. *Sheet silicates.* The silicon-oxygen tetrahedrons in the sheet silicates share three oxygen atoms with other tetrahedrons. The ratio of silicon to oxygen is 4:10.

   The three shared oxygens in the sheet silicates are located in the same plane. As a result, a sheet silicate has one direction of cleavage parallel to the plane. Two examples of sheet silicates are mica and talc.

4. *Framework silicates.* The silicon-oxygen tetrahedrons in the three-dimensional silicates are joined in such a way that every oxygen is shared by two tetrahedrons. The ratio of silicon to oxygen in each tetrahedron is 1:2. Quartz and orthoclase feldspar are two examples of framework silicates.

   For some members of the three-dimensional silicates, other elements, such as aluminum, sodium, potassium, or calcium, will take the place of one or more of the oxygens in the tetrahedron. The tetrahedrons are still linked in a continuous network, but the chemical formula is more complicated.

CHAPTER 3 LAB ACTIVITY
Crystal Growing

■ A student report sheet for this activity can be found in the *Laboratory Investigations* booklet.

Time estimate

A minimum of 40 minutes to prepare the crystal growing solution. A few minutes of each class period for the next several days.

Process Skills

- Measuring: Procedure 3, 4, 5
- Observing: Procedure B 2; Analysis and Conclusions 4, 5
- Forming Hypothesis: Analysis and Conclusions 1, 6
- Predicting: Analysis and Conclusions 2

Preparation

The seed crystals can be prepared using the same concentrations as the student solutions. The crystals will form in the bottom of a beaker. Ideally each seed is a single crystal. Like the student solutions, the best seeds will grow slowly. Therefore, several days of preparation are needed before doing this lab.

Procedural Hints

Watch for students trying to accelerate the dissolving process by turning up the heat on the hot plates. Solutions heated in this way also cool rapidly and yield masses of cloudy crystals.

Be sure to select a location for the beakers that is easily observable but out of the way.

Answers—Analysis and Conclusions

1. The paper towel slowed the rate of evaporation and prevented dust from contaminating the solution.
2. The seed crystal would have dissolved.
3. The source of crystal material is the solution which contained dissolved ammonium alum.
4. Depending upon the shape of the seed crystal, some may have seen cubes as the crystal formed.
5. Over time, the crystal should become more octahedral. Preliminary phases might resemble cubes with flat corners where the octahedron surfaces are starting to form.
6. Each crystal is free to grow only upward and sideways, since they can not grow downward only half of each crystal could form.

ANSWERS TO
CHAPTER 3 REVIEW

Review

1–c, 2–d, 3–b, 4–d, 5–b, 6–d, 7–d, 8–b, 9–c, 10–c, 11–a, 12–c, 13–a, 14–d, 15–b, 16–d, 17–c

Interpret and Apply

1. Yes to both. Even though an atom is very tiny, it has mass and volume. An electron is far smaller and less massive than an entire atom, but it does have measurable mass and volume.

2. (a) nitrogen (b) iron (c) potassium
3. (a) Since the substance is a mixture and not a compound, the ingredients can be separated by physical means. A magnet will remove the iron filings. Water will dissolve the salt. If the solution is passed through filter paper, the salt will remain in solution while the sand is left on the filter. Evaporating the water will reclaim the salt. (b) No; the sand is a compound, which can only be separated by chemical means.
4. Glacier ice is a mineral because it is a naturally occurring solid with definite physical and chemical properties and thus meets the requirements of the definition. Mercury is not a mineral because it is a liquid. However, the ore of mercury, cinnabar, is a mineral.
5. Most minerals are compounds. In a compound, the elements lose their individual properties. The properties of a metal element are not necessarily the same as the properties of compounds that contain metal elements.

Critical Thinking

1. 4
2. 1
3. 1:4
4. 4
5. 2
6. 1:3
7. A – ionic; B – single chain

CHAPTER 4
How to Know the Minerals

PLANNING CHART

Topic	Support Material
Lesson I **Identifying Minerals**	**Laboratory Investigation** **In-Text Lab Activity:** Identification of Minerals
1 Rock-Forming Minerals	**Content Evaluation:** p. 52 *Topic Review:* 1; p. 60-61 *Chapter Review:* 1, 2
2 Identification by Inspection	**Content Evaluation:** p. 52 *Topic Review:* 2; p. 60-61 *Chapter Review:* 3, 4; Interpret and Apply: 1, 5
3 Identification by Simple Tests	**Content Evaluation:** p. 52 *Topic Review:* 3; p. 60-61 *Chapter Review:* 5, 6, 7; Interpret and Apply: 2, 3, 5 **Software:** Dating and Geologic Time
4 Specific Gravity	**Content Evaluation:** p. 52 *Topic Review:* 4; p. 60-61 *Chapter Review:* 8; Interpret and Apply: 4
5 The Acid Test	**Content Evaluation:** p. 52 *Topic Review:* 5; p. 60-61 *Chapter Review:* 9; Interpret and Apply: 5
6 Special Properties of Minerals	**Content Evaluation:** p. 52 *Topic Review:* 6; p. 60-61 *Chapter Review:* 10; Interpret and Apply: 5
Lesson II Descriptions of Rock-Forming Minerals	
7 Silicates: From Silica Tetrahedrons	**Content Evaluation:** p. 57 *Topic Review:* 7; p. 60-61 *Chapter Review:* 11, 12, 13, 14, 15; Interpret and Apply: 1, 5
8 Carbonate Minerals: Calcite and Dolomite	**Content Evaluation:** p. 57 *Topic Review:* 8; p. 60-61 *Chapter Review:* 16; Interpret and Apply: 3, 5
9 Iron Oxides and Sulfides	**Content Evaluation:** p. 57 *Topic Review:* 9; p. 60-61 *Chapter Review:* 17; Interpret and Apply: 5
Lab Activity p. 58-59	Identification of Minerals
Chapter Review p. 60-61	Critical Thinking 1-5 **Study Guide:** Vocabulary; Interpreting and Applying
Chapter 4 Assessment Program	**Chapter Tests; Computer Test Bank**

CHAPTER 4

Motivator

Display on your desk the following white minerals; milky quartz, calcite, dolomite, feldspar, and talc. Also display a glass plate and a dropper bottle of dilute hydrochloric acid.

CAUTION: Hydrochloric acid is corrosive to skin and eyes. Be sure students do not handle the acid. This is a thinking and discussion exercise. Write the names of the minerals on the board. Ask students to explain how to tell each mineral apart, using the materials at hand. Since all the minerals are white, students may at first view this as an impossible task. In fact, distinguishing them is simple. Quartz is the only one of the five that easily scratches the glass plate; talc is the only one that can be scratched with a fingernail; calcite is the only one that bubbles vigorously in acid. That leaves just dolomite and feldspar. Dolomite reacts slowly to acid. Feldspar scratches glass, but much more pressure is needed than for quartz.

Lesson I: Identifying Minerals

(Topics 1-6)

Teaching Suggestions

Ask students why color is not usually a good property to use for mineral identification. If you did the motivator, students should recognize that many minerals can have the same color. Use classroom samples of rose quartz, amethyst, smoky quartz, and milky quartz to show that the same mineral can occur in different colors. A piece of chalcopyrite can be used to show mineral tarnish.

Try to avoid getting into a lengthy discussion and demonstration of each of the properties used to identify minerals because students quickly and justifiably lose interest. However, they usually remain attentive if they have a sample in hand to look at and test. If possible, put together student mineral sets. (See Lesson II *Teaching Suggestions*.) Use of student mineral sets will tie together the two lessons in the

chapter and will also make the presentation of mineral properties more interesting.

You may prefer to demonstrate the acid test rather than allow student experimentation.

DEMONSTRATIONS: The specific gravity determination in Topic 4 is a good demonstration or laboratory exercise for your class. It is best to use spring scales graduated in newtons, but in many cases the available spring scales are marked in grams. If this is the case, determine the weights in grams but be prepared to explain that grams are a unit of mass and not of weight. Results are the same using newtons or grams, since specific gravity is a ratio in which the units cancel.

If the equipment and mineral specimens are available, a demonstration of magnetism, fluorescence, phosphorescence, and even radioactivity will interest students. When demonstrating magnetism, suspend a bar magnet with a string so that the magnet is free to swing. Bring the mineral to be tested toward the lower end of the magnet. If the mineral is attracted to the magnet, you can feel the pull even if very little movement occurs.

Science Background

Rock-Forming Minerals: Rocks made entirely of one mineral are called *monomineralic* rocks. The rock quartzite may be a monomineralic rock if it is made entirely of quartz. Marble is primarily made of calcite. Most rocks are made of more than one rock-forming mineral and are called *polymineralic* rocks. An example is granite. Granite is composed primarily of the minerals quartz, feldspar, and mica.

Gemstones: Some precious and semiprecious gems are varieties of common minerals. Amethyst, for example, is a purple variety of quartz. Sapphire and ruby are varieties of corundum, while emerald and aquamarine are varieties of beryl. Peridot is a kind of olivine. The property common to all gemstones is hardness, so that they resist scratching when worn as jewelry. Some students might enjoy investigating further a particular gemstone, such as a birthstone. An encyclopedia is a good place to start. Most mineralogy textbooks and even some chemistry textbooks include sections on gemstones.

Lesson II: Descriptions of Rock-Forming Minerals

(Topics 7-9)

Teaching Suggestions

Students will best understand mineral properties by doing the lab activity at the end of this chapter, *Identification of Minerals*. Expect attrition and breakage of items in the mineral identification sets, especially streak plates, glass plates, and fragile minerals. Mica, for example, seldom survives beyond one year. Talc is rubbed into a powder. Galena breaks easily into little cubes, which often disappear. Minerals like quartz and feldspar are relatively indestructible but become grimy from handling. One way to cut down on student "borrowing" of minerals from the sets is to save the little pieces that are broken off in normal usage. Place them in a special set. Allow students to take any minerals from that set that they wish. You might want to add the restriction that they first identify the mineral.

Science Background

Feldspars: Albite and oligoclase are just two of the plagioclase feldspars. These feldspars are actually a series of six minerals that change gradually in chemical composition from pure albite, $NaAlSi_3O_8$, to anorthite, $CaAl_2Si_2O_8$. In between albite and anorthite, decreasing in sodium and increasing in calcium, are oligoclase, andesine (named for the Andes Mountains), labradorite (named for the Canadian region of Labrador), and bytownite. The distinction between them cannot be made in a hand specimen. Do not confuse the feldspar, anorthite, with the monomineralic rock, anorthosite.

CHAPTER 4 **LAB** ACTIVITY

Identification of Minerals

■ A student report sheet for this activity can be found in the *Laboratory Investigations* booklet.

Time estimate

50 minutes

Process Skills

■ Observing: Procedure 2, 4, 5, 7; Analysis and Conclusions 2
■ Comparing and Contrasting: Procedure 6; Analysis and Conclusions 3, 4, 5, 6
■ Classifying: Procedure 8, 10
■ Verifying Results: Procedure 11
■ Analyzing Data: Analysis and Conclusions 1, 7

Materials

Prepare numbered sets of minerals for the students. Each set should contain the following minerals: biotite, calcite, chalcopyrite, feldspar, galena, gypsum, halite, hematite, magnetite, olivine, pyrite, quartz, sulfur, talc.

Safety

CAUTION: If you dilute 12M hydrochloric acid to make the 0.5M acid, use the hood and wear safety goggles, a lab apron, face shield, and gloves.

Procedural Hint

Remind students to keep glass plates and streak plates flat on the table.

Answers—Analysis and Conclusions

1. The most useful property for the identification of sulfur is its bright yellow color.
2. Black, brown, or dark green; Biotite has excellent cleavage in one direction and the pieces that cleave (peel off) are thin, elastic films.
3. The mineral is muscovite and it is a mica. Muscovite is lighter in color than biotite.
4. Talc has a greasy feel; gypsum does not.
5. Feldspar has good, two-directional cleavage and quartz has conchoidal fracture.
6. Although both have excellent, three directional cleavage, their cleavage planes meet at different angles. The cleavage planes in halite meet at right angles and those in calcite do not meet at right angles.
7. Taste, cleavage and hardness; Olivine has a yellowish and greenish color, a white to light green streak, and a glassy and granular appearance.

ANSWERS TO

CHAPTER 4 REVIEW

Review
1–m, 2–p, 3–e, 4–k, 5–d, 6–i, 7–q, 8–r, 9–b, 10–h, 11–o, 12–f, 13–l, 14–g, 15–a, 16–c, 17–j

Interpret and Apply
1. The green color of malachite is inherent to the mineral. Quartz can be almost any color.
2. The hardness of corundum is greater than that of the streak plate. It would scratch the plate.
3. The cleavage planes of calcite meet at an oblique angle, so that each cleavage fragment is a rhomb. The cleavage planes of galena meet at right angles. Each cleavage fragment of galena is a cube.
4. Specific gravity is the ratio of the weight of the specimen in air to its loss of weight in water.

$$\text{specific gravity} = \frac{13.25\text{N}}{13.25\text{ N} - 8.25\text{ N}}$$

$$= \frac{13.25\text{N}}{5\text{ N}}$$

$$= 2.65$$

The specific gravity of the sample is 2.65.

5. (a) hardness, cleavage (b) magnetism (c) hardness (d) acid test, cleavage, hardness (e) color (f) luster (g) acid test, cleavage (h) streak

Critical Thinking
1. approximately 25%
2. approximately 65%
3. granite
4. gabbro
5. 40%–45% plagioclase, 20%–25% amphibole, 15%–20% quartz, about 15% biotite, 5% orthoclase

CHAPTER 5
How Earth's Rocks Were Formed

PLANNING CHART

Topic	Support Material
Lesson I **Igneous Rocks**	**Laboratory Investigation:** A Study of Igneous Rocks
1 **Uniformity of Process**	**Content Evaluation:** p. 68 *Topic Review:* 1; p. 82-83 *Chapter Review:* 1
2 **Three Groups of Rocks**	**Content Evaluation:** p. 68 *Topic Review:* 2; p. 82-83 *Chapter Review:* 2
3 **Recognizing Igneous Rocks**	**Content Evaluation:** p. 68 *Topic Review:* 3; p. 82-83 *Chapter Review:* 3; Interpret and Apply: 1
4 **Kinds of Magma**	**Content Evaluation:** p. 68 *Topic Review:* 4; p. 82-83 *Chapter Review:* 4; Interpret and Apply: 1
5 **Textures of an Igneous Rock**	**Content Evaluation:** p. 68 *Topic Review:* 5; p. 82-83 *Chapter Review:* 5
6 **Porphyritic Texture**	**Content Evaluation:** p. 68 *Topic Review:* 6; p. 82-83 *Chapter Review:* 6
7 **Families of Igneous Rocks**	**Content Evaluation:** p. 68 *Topic Review:* 7; p. 82-83 *Chapter Review:* 7; Interpret and Apply: 1
8 **Description of Common Igneous Rocks**	**Content Evaluation:** p. 68 *Topic Review:* 8; p. 82-83 *Chapter Review:* 8; Interpret and Apply: 1
Lesson II **Sedimentary Rocks**	**Laboratory Investigation:** A Study of Sedimentary Rocks
9 **Kinds of Sediments**	**Content Evaluation:** p. 74 *Topic Review:* 9; p. 82-83 *Chapter Review:* 9
10 **How Clastic Rocks Form**	**Content Evaluation:** p. 74 *Topic Review:* 10; p. 82-83 *Chapter Review:* 10
11 **Sorting of Sediments**	**Content Evaluation:** p. 74 *Topic Review:* 11; p. 82-83 *Chapter Review:* 11
12 **Conglomerate, Sandstone, and Shale**	**Content Evaluation:** p. 74 *Topic Review:* 12; p. 82-83 *Chapter Review:* 12; Interpret and Apply: 2
13 **Sedimentary Rocks of Chemical Origin**	**Content Evaluation:** p. 74 *Topic Review:* 13; p. 82-83 *Chapter Review:* 13; Interpret and Apply: 3

PLANNING CHART (continued)

Topic	Support Material
Lesson II (continued) **14 Sedimentary Rocks of Organic Origin**	**Content Evaluation:** p. 74 *Topic Review:* 14; p. 82-83 *Chapter Review:* 13
15 Sedimentary Features: Stratification	**Content Evaluation:** p. 74 *Topic Review:* 15; p. 82-83 *Chapter Review:* 14, 16
16 Fossils in Sedimentary Rocks	**Content Evaluation:** p. 74 *Topic Review:* 16; p. 82-83 *Chapter Review:* 15; Interpret and Apply: 2
17 Ripple Marks and Mud Cracks	**Content Evaluation:** p. 74 *Topic Review:* 17; p. 82-83 *Chapter Review:* 16
18 Nodules, Concretions, Geodes	**Content Evaluation:** p. 74 *Topic Review:* 18; p. 82-83 *Chapter Review:* 17
Lesson III **Metamorphic Rocks**	**Laboratory Investigation:** A Study of Metamorphic Rocks **In-Text Lab Activity:** Studying Rocks in Thin Sections
19 What Metamorphic Rocks Are	**Content Evaluation:** p. 79 *Topic Review:* 19; p. 82-83 *Chapter Review:* 18
20 Regional Metamorphism	**Content Evaluation:** p. 79 *Topic Review:* 20; p. 82-83 *Chapter Review:* 19, 20; Interpret and Apply: 3, 4
21 The Metamorphism of Shale	**Content Evaluation:** p. 79 *Topic Review:* 21; p. 82-83 *Chapter Review:* 21
22 Contact Metamorphism	**Content Evaluation:** p. 79 *Topic Review:* 22; p. 82-83 *Chapter Review:* 19
23 The Rock Cycle	**Content Evaluation:** p. 79 *Topic Review:* 23; p. 82-83 *Chapter Review:* 22; Interpret and Apply: 4 **Transparency 19:** The Rock Cycle
Lab Activity p. 80-81	Studying Rocks in Thin Sections
Chapter Review p.82-83	Critical Thinking 1-4 **Study Guide:** Vocabulary; Interpreting and Applying
Chapter 5 Assessment Program	**Chapter Tests; Computer Test Bank**

CHAPTER 5

Motivator

To introduce the chapter and present an important concept of Lesson I, start with a piece of granite and a hand lens. If possible, have enough pieces of granite and enough lenses so that each student has a chance to examine the rock. As a class, have students list all the minerals they can see in the granite. They should be able to recognize quartz by its glassy appearance, and feldspar by its flat cleavage surfaces. Biotite, hornblende, pyroxene, and pyrite may also be present. Ask which minerals are most abundant in the rock (quartz and feldspar are probably about 75 percent) and which mineral has the same color as the overall color of the rock (probably the feldspar). From this activity, students will learn something about a common igneous rock, granite, and will also observe that rocks are made of minerals.

Lesson I:
Igneous Rocks

(Topics 1-8)

Teaching Suggestions

This chapter is more interesting and meaningful to the students if hand specimens of rocks are available for them to study. Rocks are generally more difficult to identify than minerals because several different rocks may be similar in appearance. For example, a dark gray limestone can resemble basalt. Shale and slate can also be difficult to tell apart. Select samples for student use carefully The properties of each rock must be clear. For example, a fossiliferous limestone can be readily distinguished from a basalt. A dull, earthy shale and a hard, semi-shiny slate are also easy to tell apart.

The most difficult part of the lesson is likely to be the table summarizing the common igneous rocks. You may want to develop the chart on the chalkboard to be sure that all parts are clear to your students.

Science Background

Syenite: A quartz-poor granite is called a syenite. The rock resembles granite but contains less than 5 percent quartz. Syenites are made of orthoclase and oligoclase feldspar with smaller amounts of hornblende, biotite, and pyroxene. Trachyte is a fine-grained syenite.

Pegmatite: Pegmatite is an especially coarse-grained granite. Dissolved gases in the magma mobilize the ions. This allows for rapid crystal growth. Individual mineral crystals in a pegmatite can be enormous, sometimes having a mass of thousands of kilograms. A 12-meter long crystal of the mineral spodumene was found in a pegmatite in the Black Hills of South Dakota. A single beryl crystal over 8 meters long and nearly 2 meters across was found in a pegmatite in Maine.

Lesson II:
Sedimentary Rocks

(Topics 9-18)

Teaching Suggestions

The classification of sedimentary rocks as clastic, chemical, and organic is fundamental. The origin of each should be discussed.

DEMONSTRATION: The idea of a chemical precipitate is unfamiliar to many students. One simple way to demonstrate this is to allow salt water to evaporate. The salt forms a white precipitate. Another demonstration can be done by mixing solutions of sodium chloride and silver nitrate that were prepared beforehand.

☠ ✋ **CAUTION: Silver nitrate is poisonous and it is corrosive to skin and eyes. Wear safety goggles while handling silver nitrate. Wash hands afterwards. Do not allow students to handle silver nitrate.** When one solution is poured into the other, a precipitate of insoluble silver chloride forms.

Science Background

Limestones can form by all three sedimentary methods. Chemical and organic limestones are discussed in the text. If shells are broken up and redeposited, the result may be considered a clastic limestone. Most coquina limestones are clastic. Another clastic limestone is the Indiana Limestone, a rock widely used in buildings. Indiana Limestone was used in the interior walls of the Lincoln Memorial in Washington, D.C.

Modern ripple marks are common features of beaches and streams. Fossil mud cracks may also have fossil raindrop impressions on the same bedding plane. These features can be used to tell if a sedimentary layer is right side up.

Lesson III: Metamorphic Rocks

(Topics 19-23)

Teaching Suggestions

In addition to metamorphic processes, an important point to make is the origin of each of the metamorphic rocks. The metamorphic series from shale to slate to phyllite to schist can also be mentioned. Student rock sets should help with this presentation.

The chart of the rock cycle should be discussed to tie together the different rock types. Draw the chart on the chalkboard and develop the steps.

Science Background

Even though granite is usually considered an igneous rock, you might consider discussing the two theories of granite formation (crystal settling and granitization) with Lesson III, because one theory involves a metamorphic process.

The theory of crystal settling tries to explain how several kinds of igneous rock come from one magma. In this theory, ferromagnesian minerals (olivine, augite, and hornblende, for example) and plagioclase feldspars are the first to form. These minerals are common in mafic igneous rocks. They are denser than the remaining magma, thus they settle to the bottom of the magma. Slow cooling of this material yields a dark-colored plutonic rock such as gabbro. If this denser material is pushed near the surface and cools rapidly, a dark-colored, volcanic rock such as basalt forms. The removal of ferromagnesian minerals leaves a fluid rich in aluminum, sodium, potassium, and silica—elements that make up minerals such as orthoclase and quartz. Such a magma has a felsic composition. Slow cooling of this magma yields a light-colored, plutonic rock such as granite. If this material is pushed near the surface and cools quickly, a light-colored volcanic rock, felsite, forms. In summary, minerals that make up dark-colored igneous rocks form first and settle to the bottom, leaving behind minerals that make up light-colored igneous rocks. In this way, one magma could yield all kinds of igneous rock.

In the theory of granitization, granite results from intense metamorphism or melting of a sandy shale. In that case, slate, phyllite, schist, and gneiss are steps in the formation of granite, and granite could be considered a metamorphic rock.

CHAPTER 5   LAB ACTIVITY
Studying Rocks in Thin Section

■ A student report sheet for this activity can be found in the *Laboratory Investigations* booklet.

Time estimate
40-50 minutes

Process Skills
■ Interpreting Diagrams: Procedure 2
■ Measuring: Procedure 3, 4
■ Classifying: Analysis and Conclusions 1, 3

Procedural Hints
Look at the graph on page 53 before doing this lab. The *Critical Thinking* exercise need not have been done but the graph will need to be discussed.

If possible, an actual thin section or a photomicrograph of a thin section for students to examine would help to make the activity more meaningful.

Tell students to avoid choosing grains at the edge of the drawing when doing *Procedure* step 5.

Answers—Analysis and Conclusions

1. Rock C is sedimentary; Rock D is metamorphic; Rock A and Rock B are Igneous.

2. The average grain diameter is approximately 0.5 cm. Therefore the actual diameter of the rock sample is

$$\frac{0.5 \text{ cm}}{4.0 \text{ cm}} = \frac{X \text{ cm}}{0.5 \text{ cm}}$$

$$X = 0.06 \text{ cm}$$

3. The grain size is 0.06 cm which makes the sedimentary rock sandstone.

4. Quartz and orthoclase feldspar; amphibole, biotite mica, and plagioclase feldspar

5. Plagioclase feldspar and amphibole; pyroxene, biotite mica and olivine and quartz

6. Granite because quartz and feldspar are over 50% of a granite while other minerals make up much less. Gabbro because plagioclase

and amphibole are most abundant in that rock.

7. Rock B or the gabbro is mafic, it contains dark minerals such as amphibole, olivine, biotite. Rock A or the granite is felsic, it contains the lighter colored minerals such as orthoclase feldspar and quartz.

8. Rock C has rounded grains of quartz, with calcite between the minerals. Rock D has interlocking grains of quartz, elongated in a planar pattern.

9. Rock E is metamorphic evidenced from the foliation and linear patterns of the grains.

ANSWERS TO

CHAPTER 5 REVIEW

Review

1–key, 2–magma, 3–plutonic, 4–mafic, 5–coarse-grained, 6–porphyry, 7–orthoclase, 8–basalt, 9–sedimentary, 10–cements, 11–sand, 12–conglomerate, 13–limestone, 14–stratification, 15–fossil, 16–mud, 17–nodule, 18–metamorphic, 19–contact, 20–marble, 21–slate, 22–sediment

Interpret and Apply

1. (a) Both plutonic; granite–felsic, gabbro–mafic (b) Both felsic; granite–plutonic, rhyolite–volcanic (c) Both mafic; gabbro–plutonic, basalt–volcanic (d) Both volcanic; rhyolite–felsic, basalt–mafic.

2. Pebbles of a conglomerate are deposited in rough water; fewer organisms live there and the remains of those that do would be ground to bits. More organisms live in deeper, quieter waters where sandstones and shales form. Their remains are preserved by gentle burial in soft sands and clays.

3. Any fossils were likely destroyed by the heat, pressure, and chemicals of metamorphism.

4. Marble can be scratched by steel or glass; quartzite cannot. Marble will bubble in cold dilute hydrochloric acid; quartzite will not.

5. No. The rock is igneous because it formed from melted rock or magma.

Critical Thinking

1. 60% kaolin, 30% feldspar, 10% quartz; graywacke

2. 80% kaolin, 10% feldspar, 10% quartz; gritty mudstone

3. graywacke

4. pure quartz sandstone

CHAPTER 6
Resources and Our Environment

PLANNING CHART

Topic	Support Material
Lesson I Renewable Environmental Resources	**Laboratory Investigation** **In-Text Lab Activity:** Measuring Particulate Air Pollution
1 Renewable versus Non-renewable Resources	**Content Evaluation:** p. 89 *Topic Review:* 1; p. 106-107 *Chapter Review:* 1; Interpret and Apply: 1, 2
2 Air	**Content Evaluation:** p. 89 *Topic Review:* 2; p. 106-107 *Chapter Review:* 2
3 Air Pollution	**Content Evaluation:** p. 89 *Topic Review:* 3; p. 106-107 *Chapter Review:* 3; Interpret and Apply: 2, 3
4 Land and Soil	**Content Evaluation:** p. 89 *Topic Review:* 4; p. 106-107 *Chapter Review:* 4
5 Problems in Land and Soil Use	**Content Evaluation:** p. 89 *Topic Review:* 5; p. 106-107 *Chapter Review:* 5
6 Water	**Content Evaluation:** p. 89 *Topic Review:* 6; p. 106-107 *Chapter Review:* 6
7 Water Pollution	**Content Evaluation:** p. 89 *Topic Review:* 7; p. 106-107 *Chapter Review:* 7
Lesson II Nonrenewable Resources: Metals and Nonmetals	
8 Minerals and Ores	**Content Evaluation:** p. 92 *Topic Review:* 8; p. 106-107 *Chapter Review:* 8; Interpret and Apply: 4
9 Mineral Availability	**Content Evaluation:** p. 92 *Topic Review:* 9; p. 106-107 *Chapter Review:* 9
10 Important Nonmetals	**Content Evaluation:** p. 92 *Topic Review:* 10; p. 106-107 *Chapter Review:* 10
Lesson III Nonrenewable Energy Resources	
11 Energy Use	**Content Evaluation:** p. 97 *Topic Review:* 11; p. 106-107 *Chapter Review:* 11
12 Fossil Fuels: Coal	**Content Evaluation:** p. 97 *Topic Review:* 12; p. 106-107 *Chapter Review:* 12; Interpret and Apply: 5

PLANNING CHART (continued)

Topic	Support Material
Lesson III (continued) **13 Fossil Fuels: Petroleum and Natural Gas**	**Content Evaluation:** p. 97 *Topic Review:* 13; p. 106-107 *Chapter Review:* 13
14 Other Fossil Fuels and Gasohol	**Content Evaluation:** p. 97 *Topic Review:* 14; p. 106-107 *Chapter Review:* 15
15 Uranium	**Content Evaluation:** p. 97 *Topic Review:* 15; p. 106-107 *Chapter Review:* 14
16 Energy Conservation	**Content Evaluation:** p. 100 *Topic Review:* 16; Interpret and Apply: 6
Lesson IV Alternative Energy Sources	
17 Renewable Energy Sources	**Content Evaluation:** p. 100 *Topic Review:* 17; p. 106-107 *Chapter Review:* 16
18 Water Power	**Content Evaluation:** p. 100 *Topic Review:* 18; p. 106-107 *Chapter Review:* 17
19 Wind Power	**Content Evaluation:** p. 100 *Topic Review:* 19; p. 106-107 *Chapter Review:* 18
20 Solar Energy	**Content Evaluation:** p. 100 *Topic Review:* 20; p. 106-107 Chapter Review: 19
21 Geothermal Energy	**Content Evaluation:** p. 103 *Topic Review:* 21; p. 106-107 *Chapter Review:* 20
Lesson V Environmental Problems and Solutions	
22 Acid Rain	**Content Evaluation:** p. 103 *Topic Review:* 22; p. 106-107 *Chapter Review:* 21
23 Toxic Wastes	**Content Evaluation:** p. 103 *Topic Review:* 23; p. 106-107 *Chapter Review:* 22
24 Nuclear Waste Disposal	**Content Evaluation:** p. 103 *Topic Review:* 24; p. 106-107 *Chapter Review:* 23
25 Conserving the Nonrenewables	**Content Evaluation:** p. 103 *Topic Review:* 25; p. 106-107 *Chapter Review:* 24
Lab Activity p. 104-105	Measuring Particulate Air Pollution
Chapter Review p. 106-107	Critical Thinking 1-5 **Study Guide:** Vocabulary; Interpreting and Applying
Chapter 6 Assessment Program	**Chapter Tests; Computer Test Bank**

CHAPTER 6

Motivator

DEMONSTRATION: Although students have probably heard of *acid rain*, they may not be familiar with what the term means or with the way acid rain affects the environment. One way to introduce the chapter is with a demonstration of the meaning of the terms *acid* and *acid rain*. Obtain pH indicator paper for a pH range of about 0 to 7, and a variety of substances such as lemon juice (pH 2), grapefruit juice (pH 3), tomato juice (pH 4), black coffee (pH 5), cow's milk (pH 6), and distilled water (pH 7). (pH values listed represent average points in the pH ranges for these substances.) Briefly explain that the pH scale indicates how acidic or basic a substance is, that the most acidic substances have a pH value of 0, neutral substances have pH values near 7, and substances with pH values over 8 are basic, or alkaline. Have student volunteers test the pH values of the substances using the test paper. Ask them which substance is the most acidic (probably the lemon juice). Explain that pure rainwater is slightly acidic, having a pH of about 5.6. Acid rain has a pH of about 3, about as acidic as grapefruit. Point out that most plants and animals cannot tolerate a pH this strong.

Lesson I: Renewable Environmental Resources

(Topics 1-7)

Teaching Suggestions

A fundamental point of this lesson and of the entire chapter is the difference between *renewable* and *nonrenewable* resources. One method of presentation is to have students list resources and determine whether they are renewable or nonrenewable. Put the lists on the board. Discuss why each resource is in its category. You should ask whether it is possible for a renewable resource to become non-renewable. For example, if trees are used at a rate greater than their rate of growth, then they might not be considered entirely renewable. This can lead to a discussion of renewability, mismanagement, overuse and recycling.

Science Background

Seasonal air pollution has been occurring at some Rocky Mountain ski resorts in recent winters. A fireplace fire is an expected part of a skiing vacation, but so many people were making fires that severe air pollution resulted. Laws have been enacted to limit the number of hours that a fireplace can be used each day during ski season, in an effort to reduce the air pollution.

Lesson II: Nonrenewable Resources: Metals and Nonmetals

(Topics 8-10)

Teaching Suggestions

You may wish to introduce the lesson by displaying a set of economic minerals such as hematite, bauxite, sphalerite, galena, sulfur, halite, and the like. Students will be familiar with many economic minerals, but others will be new to them. Identify each mineral, discuss its economic use. Point out that, unlike air and water, once a mineral resource has been mined it is not replaced by natural processes.

Science Background

In many cases, new materials are developed to replace dwindling mineral resources. There has been one case in which the reverse was true. Sodium carbonate is used in making glass, paper, water softeners, detergents, and baking soda. The original method for making sodium carbonate was the Solvay process, which involves a long series of reactions. The mineral trona is a natural source of sodium carbonate. Trona occurred in small amounts around dried-up salt lakes, but there was not enough to mine. In 1938, a thick layer of trona was discovered in Wyoming. That discovery eliminated one entire chemical industry. In 1938, there were 17 Solvay process plants in the United States. By 1969, there were only 10 and today there are none. Trona is the unusual case of a natural mineral making a manufactured product obsolete. Of course, when the trona deposit is used up, there may again be Solvay process plants.

Lesson III: Nonrenewable Energy Resources

(Topics 11-16)

Teaching Suggestions

This lesson emphasizes the use of four nonrenewable energy sources: coal, petroleum, natural gas, and uranium. Specimens of peat, lignite, soft coal, and hard coal will help students understand the differences between them. You might wish to discuss these mineral fuels as an example of a metamorphic series (clay to shale to slate to phyllite to schist to gneiss, presented in Chapter 5, is another). Chalkboard drawings may help with the concept of an oil trap and as an introduction to the petroleum discussion.

Oil shales and tar sands may receive serious consideration again and should be mentioned as possible oil sources. The availability of gasohol tends to increase with the price of oil.

Plan to spend some time with the concept of how a nuclear reactor works. The drawings in the text should help. Students may be surprised that electricity in a nuclear power plant is produced in the same way as in a coal-burning power plant— that is, through the conversion of water to steam, which turns turbines. A point worth making is that the main pollutant from a properly functioning nuclear reactor is not radiation, but the hot water left over from cooling the reactor. Of course, the disposal of nuclear wastes presents problems of its own.

Science Background

The process by which petroleum is separated into different substances is called *fractional distillation*. No chemical change is involved. The separation is accomplished using differences in boiling points. As petroleum is heated, liquids with progressively higher boiling points evaporate, rise to a certain level in a distillation tower, and are then condensed. For example, the boiling point of gasoline ranges from 100°C to 200°C, while that of kerosene is between 200°C and 300°C. Gasoline condenses at a lower point than kerosene. In this way kerosene, gasoline, naphtha, benzine, fuel oils, lubricating oils, paraffin waxes, and asphalt can all be obtained from the same substance, petroleum.

Lesson IV: Alternative Energy Sources

(Topics 17-21)

Teaching Suggestions

List the four renewable energy sources discussed in this lesson: water power, wind power, solar energy, and geothermal energy. Ask students to explain why each is considered renewable and why the use of each is limited. Of the four, water power is probably already at its maximum possible use. The other sources are still largely experimental. Try to list the advantages and disadvantages of each.

Reykjavik, Iceland, is one place where geothermal energy is used extensively. In addition to using it to heat homes, the city has a year-round outdoor swimming pool heated by geothermal energy. Many of the island's vegetables are grown in huge geothermal greenhouses.

The geothermal site at Fenton Hill is worth watching the news for because the technique used there could theoretically be used anywhere.

Lesson V: Environmental Problems and Solutions

(Topics 22-25)

Teaching Suggestions

If you did the pH demonstration in the *Motivator*, you might want to refer to it here. Toxic wastes and acid rain are often in the news. You or your students may find some current newspaper clippings on the topic that are helpful.

Methods of conserving nonrenewable resources should be stressed, for example eliminating waste, recycling, and finding substitutes. If returnable containers are used in your area, part of your discussion could include what happens to those containers once they have been returned to collection points. In some places, some containers are reused as is; in others, the materials are recycled into new containers.

CHAPTER 6 **LAB** ACTIVITY
Measuring Particulate Air Pollution

■ A student report sheet for this activity can be found in the *Laboratory Investigations* booklet

Time Estimate:
25-35 minutes first day, a few minutes of each class for next 7 days, 40-50 minutes final day

Process Skills
■ Observing: Procedure 5, 6
■ Describing: Procedure 3
■ Predicting: Procedure 3
■ Calculating: Procedure 11, 12
■ Determining Cause and Effect: Analysis and Conclusions 3, 4, 5
■ Analyzing Data: Analysis and Conclusions 1, 2

Materials
Students can use petroleum jelly on the slides to collect the particulates instead of cellophane tape.

Safety
Caution students to be careful when carrying glass slides.

Answers—Analysis and Conclusions
1. Answers will vary.
2. Answers will vary based on the locations of the slides.
3. Indoor sources include dirt and dust that has been brought in from outside, insulation, and furnaces. Outdoors sources include pollen from plants, dust from soil, particulates from factories and power plant emissions
4. Answers may include older buildings that lack filtering systems, open windows, poorly maintained furnaces, and whether the building is cleaned regularly.
5. Dry weather increases dust and other particulates in air. Wind can either disperse particulates from an area or bring in particulates from other areas.

CHAPTER 6 REVIEW

Review
1–b, 2–d, 3–a, 4–d, 5–c, 6–a, 7–b, 8–d, 9–c, 10–b, 11–d, 12–d, 13–a, 14–d, 15–b, 16–b, 17–b, 18–c, 19–c, 20–a, 21–c, 22–b, 23–d, 24–a

Interpret and Apply
1. As long as the replanting and growth of trees keeps pace with the use of wood, wood can be considered a renewable resource.
2. If everyone burned wood, the level of pollutants would increase. Also, trees would be used faster than they could be replaced.
3. Noise is expected at the pep assembly, but an equal level of noise outside a classroom would make the environment unfit for learning.
4. The reserves of a mineral are its known deposits that are economically workable. Reserve estimates may change when new deposits are discovered, or when poorer deposits become usable because of higher prices for the mineral. Resources are estimates of the total amount of a mineral in the rocks. This should not change if the estimates are correct.
5. Anthracite coal. The amount of energy in a fossil fuel is directly related to the percentage of carbon in the fuel. Peat is barely decomposed plant material containing little carbon. Anthracite is almost pure carbon.
6. Conservation methods include lowering the thermostat, walking instead of driving, and turning off unneeded lights. Some conservation techniques may require changes in student routines.

Critical Thinking
1. The concentration is slightly higher on Wednesday.
2. Approximately 8 A.M. and 5 P.M.
3. The probable cause is automobile traffic going to work at 8 A.M. and returning home at 5 P.M.
4. The pollutant level is higher on Wednesday than on Tuesday, indicating a buildup of pollutants. Lower levels would be expected following a cleansing rain.
5. 5 P.M., the same time as the highest peaks on the two previous days

CHAPTER **7**
Using Maps

PLANNING CHART

Topic	Support Material
Lesson I Map Projections, Location, Scales	**Laboratory Investigation:** Mapping a Mountain **In-Text Map Activity:** Latitude and Longitude
1 Making Accurate Map Projections	**Content Evaluation:** p. 114 *Topic Review:* 1; p. 126-127 *Chapter Review:* 1, 2; Interpret and Apply: 1, 2, 3; **Transparency 21:** Map Projections
2 Latitude: Distance North and South	**Content Evaluation:** p. 114 *Topic Review:* 2; p. 126-127 *Chapter Review:* 3, 4 **Transparency 6:** Physical United States; **Transparency 16:** World Climates
3 Longitude: Distance East and West	**Content Evaluation:** p. 114 *Topic Review:* 3; p. 126-127 *Chapter Review:* 5; Interpret and Apply: 3, 5
4 Great Circles	**Content Evaluation:** p. 114 *Topic Review:* 4; p. 126-127 *Chapter Review:* 6
5 Map Scales	**Content Evaluation:** p. 114 *Topic Review:* 5; p. 126-127 *Chapter Review:* 7; Interpret and Apply: 4; **Transparency 1:** Topographic Map Symbols
Lesson II Parts of a Topographic Map	
6 Showing Elevation— Contours	**Content Evaluation:** p. 117 *Topic Review:* 6; p. 126-127 *Chapter Review:* 8
7 Depression Contours	**Content Evaluation:** p. 117 *Topic Review:* 7; p. 126-127 *Chapter Review:* 9
8 Bench Marks, Spot Elevations	**Content Evaluation:** p. 117 *Topic Review:* 8; p. 126-127 *Chapter Review:* 10
9 U.S. Geological Survey Maps	**Content Evaluation:** p. 117 *Topic Review:* 9; p. 126-127 *Chapter Review:* 11; Interpret and Apply: 5
Lesson III Reading a Topographic Map	**In-Text Map Activity:** Reading a Topographic Map
10 Reading the Contour Map	**Content Evaluation:** p. 120 *Topic Review:* 10; p. 126-127 *Chapter Review:* 12; Interpret and Apply: 7 **Transparency 4:** Topographic Map: Harrisburg, PA
11 Landforms on Contour Maps	**Content Evaluation:** p. 120 *Topic Review:* 11; p. 126-127 *Chapter Review:* 13, 14; Interpret and Apply: 7

PLANNING CHART (continued)

Topic	Support Material
Lesson III (continued) **12 The Average Slope**	**Content Evaluation:** p. 120 *Topic Review:* 12; p. 126-127 *Chapter Review:* 15; Interpret and Apply: 6, 7
13 Profiles from Contour Maps	**Content Evaluation:** p. 120 *Topic Review:* 13; p. 126-127 *Chapter Review:* 16; **Transparency 2:** Topographic Map: Monadnock, NH
Lesson IV Modern Methods of Mapmaking	
14 Remote Sensing	**Content Evaluation:** p. 123 *Topic Review:* 14; p. 126-127 *Chapter Review:* 17; **Transparency 2:** Topographic Map: Monadnock, NH; **Transparency 3:** Stereophotos: Monadnock, NH
15 Computer Imaging	**Content Evaluation:** p. 123 *Topic Review:* 15; p. 126-127 *Chapter Review:* 18
16 Uses of Computer-Drawn Maps and Images	**Content Evaluation:** p. 123 *Topic Review:* 16; p. 126-127 *Chapter Review:* 18
Map Activities p. 124-125	Latitude and Longitude Reading a Topographic Map
Chapter Review p. 126-127	Critical Thinking 1-6 **Study Guide:** Vocabulary; Interpreting and Applying
Chapter 7 Assessment Program	**Chapter Tests; Computer Test Bank**

CHAPTER 7

Motivator

DEMONSTRATION: Give each student or small group of students one piece of standard-size blank paper. Have them draw a map that shows how to get from school to some other location. Select a location that is near enough to be familiar to everyone but far enough to involve some thinking on the part of the students. Once the student maps are drawn, discuss and compare the results. Although all of the maps are intended to show the same area and features, it is unlikely that the maps will be very much alike in appearance. This exercise demonstrates first hand the need for map scale, compass direction, and accurate representation of shape.

Lesson I: Map Projections, Location, Scale

(Topics 1-5)

Teaching Suggestions

Discuss with students the various map projections in Figure 7.2. Wall maps using various projections, if available, will aid the discussion. Using either Figure 7.2 (a) or another Mercator projection, point out the location of Greenland and compare its size to that of North America. The surface area of Greenland is about 2 million square kilometers, while that of North America is about 24 million square kilometers.

Latitude and longitude are sometimes difficult concepts for students to understand

and to keep straight. The major stumbling block seems to be that distances north and south (latitude) are measured by lines that run east and west (parallels), while distances east and west (longitude) are measured by lines that run north and south (meridians). Be prepared to spend some time reviewing and practicing these terms and concepts with your students.

Science Background
Map Projections: The Mercator projection is one of a group called *cylindrical projections.* These maps are drawn as if a cylinder were rolled around a globe along the equator. The gnomonic projection is the best known of a group called *azimuthal projections.* They are made by projecting the surface of a globe on a flat surface that touches the globe at only one point. The polyconic projection is one of the *conic group.* These are made as if a cone were laid over the globe so that the cone and globe are in contact only along one of the circular parallels. There are many other types of projections.

Great-Circle Routes: On a flat map, such as a Mercator projection, a great-circle route appears to be a longer distance than a straight line between two points. This is a result of the distortion involved in projecting a sphere onto a plane.

The first known navigation of a great-circle route was in 1524 when Giovanni da Verrazano, an Italian navigator, sailed to America. Today, great-circle routes are used to determine major air routes.

Lesson II: Parts of a Topographic Map

(Topics 6-9)

Teaching Suggestions
Students are usually interested in seeing the topographic map of the area in which they live. If possible, obtain a number of copies of the quadrangle sheet that includes your area. (USGS quadrangle maps may be obtained from the Distribution Branch, USGS, Box 25286, Federal Center, Building 41, Denver, Colorado, 80225. Write for an index and ordering information.) As a starting exercise, have students locate your town, school, and selected landmarks such as a river, hill, or highway. Then ask them to locate examples of topographic map symbols and colors, such as those shown on pages 666–667 of Appendix B (Map Atlas).

Another appropriate activity is a visit to a local bench mark. Students often do not realize how common bench marks are. Use your local topographic map to find locations of bench marks. Assign a student to find the mark and to bring to class a copy, photograph, or rubbing of the plate.

Lesson III: Reading a Topographic Map

(Topics 10-13)

Teaching Suggestions
DEMONSTRATION: A simple demonstration of contour lines involves placing an irregularly shaped object in a deep pan and filling the pan to a depth of one inch. The line where the water surrounds the object is the one-inch contour line. Adding water to the depth of two inches will reveal the two-inch contour line, and so forth. Contour map kits, which include model mountains in deep containers, can be purchased from science supply houses.

Once students are familiar with contour maps, they should be able to construct a map from the following directions. Using a scale of 0.5 inch to 1 mile and a contour interval of 20 feet, draw a contour map of an ocean island 6 miles long from due north to due south, 5 miles wide from due east to due west, steepest on the north side, and rising to a single peak 167 feet above sea level. Include a stream that starts at an altitude of 143 feet and flows southwest to the sea. A sample sketch from these instructions is shown on the next page.

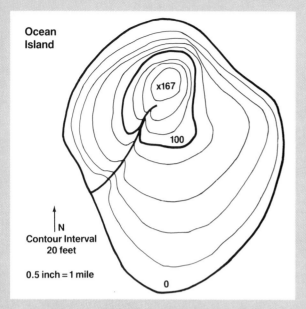

Ocean Island

x167

100

↑ N

Contour Interval 20 feet

0.5 inch = 1 mile

0

The best map to use for a profiling exercise is the map of your own area. If possible, select a familiar route that involves two different slopes so that the students can both visualize and calculate the difference. Additional questions about elevations of specific points (your school, student homes, and so on) can easily be part of the exercise.

Lesson IV:
Modern Methods of Mapmaking

(Topics 14-16)

Teaching Suggestions

The purpose of this lesson is to make students aware of the technologies used to produce maps. Start the lesson by discussing the difference between a ground survey and remote sensing. Stress that the methods of remote sensing are faster, cheaper, and far more accurate. For example, in the 1970's the government of Egypt commissioned a geologic map of that country. Using remote sensing, the map was made in about 5 years and cost about $15 million. If the map had been made by ground survey, it would have taken twice as long, cost twice as much, and the maps would have contained only half as much detail.

Science Background

Landsat Scanners: Landsat satellites have two sensors: the Multispectral Scanner (MSS) and the Thematic Scanner (TM). *Landsat* sensors are designed to detect wavelengths of green, blue, and red visible light and several wavelengths in the infrared spectrum. The wave bands used are those that best show contrast in surface features. The green bands, for example, are used to tell the difference between a coniferous forest and a deciduous forest. These bands also show coastal features such as reefs and sediment load. The red bands are used to identify different crops. The middle infrared bands can be used to tell white clouds from white snow. The TM can "see" more surface detail than the MSS.

Computer Imaging: The data used to make a false color image can be processed in different ways for different purposes. Tiny variations in color tone can be made to stand out by a process called density slicing. In the process, a specific range of color tones is imaged in another color. The technique is used to show such features as water depth.

Another computer technique uses wavelengths called a target signature. These are the wavelengths that identify a specific surface feature. Once the exact colors used to identify that feature are known, the computer can be directed to show these areas of the image in some other, more obvious, color. In this way, the feature is made to stand out on the map. For example, a ground feature that reflects two shades of green might be imaged as bright yellow to make it stand out from all other green features. Discuss the images shown in the text and the advantages of using false-color images.

The largest computers available are needed to process the huge amount of data obtained by imaging radar. At first, even with the fastest computer available, 500 seconds of computer time were needed to process the data collected by the imaging radar every second. Of course, newer computers are faster.

CHAPTER 7 MAP ACTIVITY
Latitude and Longitude

■ A student report sheet for this activity can be found in the *Laboratory Investigations* booklet.

Time estimate
40–50 minutes

Process Skills
■ Interpreting Diagrams: Procedure 1, 2, 3; Analysis and Conclusions 3, 5, 6
■ Calculating: Analysis and Conclusions 1, 3
■ Analyzing Data: Analysis and Conclusions 2, 4, 6
■ Applying a Strategy: Analysis and Conclusions 2, 4, 6

Procedural Hints
Help students locate the maps in the textbook before starting the activity. Obtain a topographic map for your area so that students can determine the latitude and longitude of your school. Have a globe available in the classroom to help students answer *Analysis and Conclusions* question 6.

Answers—Procedure
1. (a) New York (b) Moscow (c) Lima (d) Sydney (e) Rome (f) Johannesburg (g) Hammerfest (h) Jakarta (i) Beijing (j) Nairobi (k) Buenos Aires (l) Anchorage
2. (Student's answers may vary by 2° or 3°) (a) 2°S, 60°W (b) 36°N, 140°E (c) 71°N, 155°W (d) 39°S, 146°E (e) 1°N, 104°E
3. (a) San Jose, CA (b) Boston, MA (c) Houston, TX (d) Tallahassee, FL (e) Augusta, ME (f) San Diego, CA (g) Portland, OR (h) Pittsburgh, PA (i) Denver, CO

Answers—Analysis and Conclusions
1. From Topic 2, 1° of latitude = 112 km. Therefore, 13° of latitude = 13 x 112 or 1456 km.
2. No. Latitude cannot be greater than 90°.
3. 10° or 600'
4. Austin. Spacing increases toward the equator.
5. Answers will depend upon the location.
6. Indian Ocean, for most of the United States

CHAPTER 7 MAP ACTIVITY
Reading a Topographic Map

■ A student report sheet for this activity can be found in the *Laboratory Investigations* booklet.

Time estimate
40–50 minutes

Process Skills
■ Interpreting Diagrams: Procedure 1, 2, 3, 4, 5; Analysis and Conclusions 1, 2, 3
■ Stating a Conclusion: Procedure 2, 4; Analysis and Conclusions 1
■ Calculating: Procedure 5; Analysis and Conclusions 3
■ Determining Cause and Effect: Analysis and Conclusions 2, 3

Procedural Hints
Help students locate the map in the textbook before starting. Expect students to need help in using the edge of the paper to measure the distances in *Procedure* question 5 and *Analysis and Conclusions* question 3.

Answers—Procedure
1. Cove, Second, and Blue
2. Contour lines are closer together on the ridges, farther apart in the valleys. Ridges are steeper.
3. Cove: 1300 feet; Second: 1380 feet; Third: 1320 feet
4. Contours increase away from the river. Contours crossing the creek point away from the river.
5. between 0.6 and 0.7 miles

Answers—Analysis and Conclusions
1. The ridges are green while the valleys are white indicating that the ridges are wooded. People have probably cleared more trees from the valley areas. (Accept any reasonable explanation.)
2. No, the Rockville Bridge is not visible because the tip of Cove Mountain blocks the view. Yes, Heckton could be seen because no mountains block the view.
3. (a) The mountain is too steep. By jogging the highway toward the beacon, the elevation changes more gradually. (b) between 1.7 and 1.8 miles (c) between 2.2 and 2.3 miles

ANSWERS TO

CHAPTER 7 REVIEW

Review

1–e, 2–p, 3–j, 4–o, 5–n, 6–h, 7–t, 8–c and d, 9–d, 10–b, 11–u, 12–m, 13–k, 14–s, 15–a, 16–q, 17–r, 18–f

Interpret and Apply

1. too awkward to use; impossible to produce using a large enough scale

2. North is away from the center. South is toward the center. East is clockwise and west is counterclockwise on the parallel circles.

3. On Earth, the meridians come together at high latitudes and meet at the poles. On a Mercator projection, the meridians are drawn with a constant distance from the top to the bottom of the map. This causes the polar regions to take up more space proportionally on a Mercator projection than they actually do.

4. 100 meters contains 100 x 100 or 10 000 centimeters. The numerical scale is 1: 10 000. This is a large scale map.

5. Because meridians converge at the North Pole, they are farther apart at the southern edge of the map than they are at the northern edge.

6. Find average slope as follows.

$$\text{average slope} = \frac{200 \text{ m}}{5 \text{ km}} = 40 \text{ m/km}$$

Average slope equals 40 meters per kilometer.

7. (a) *J*–1099′, *L*–1159′, *M*–1139′, *N*–1119′ (b) *S*–about 1085′, *Y*–1040′, *Z*– 1020′, *A*–1000′, *B*–1060′ (c) top elevation (1100′) minus base elevation (1060′) equals 40′ (d) *J*–southwest (SW), N–NE, Q–W, Y–SE (e) from northwest to southeast (f) just above 1080′ (g) Distance from where Moose River crosses 1080′ contour to where it crosses 960′ contour is about 2.2 miles. Change in elevation is 1080′ – 960′ = 120′. 120 ft/2.2 mi = 54.5 ft/mi (h) 2.6 to 2.7 miles (i) depression, 961 feet

Critical Thinking

1. B is at 1600 feet; A is at 1400 feet; 1600 – 1400 = 200 feet

2. about 0.38 miles, or about 2000 feet (along horizontal line between them)

3. Average slope calculated as follows:

$$\text{average slope} = \frac{200 \text{ feet}}{0.38 \text{ miles}} = 526.3 \text{ ft/mi}$$

Average slope is 526 feet per mile.

4. Point C is at 1660 feet; Point D is at 1560 feet. 1660 – 1560 = 100 feet. The distance between the two points is 0.55 miles.

$$\text{average slope} = \frac{100 \text{ feet}}{0.55 \text{ miles}} = 181.8 \text{ ft/mi}$$

Average slope equals about 182 feet per mile.

5. The lowest point on the profile is 1300 feet. The highest point is above 1690 feet but below 1700 feet. Therefore, any answer between 391 and 399 feet is correct.

6. Every 100 feet on the profile is about 900 feet on the true scale. Therefore, the vertical scale is exaggerated by 9 times the true scale.

CHAPTER 8
Weathering, Soils, and Mass Movement

PLANNING CHART

Topic	Support Material
Lesson I **Weathering**	**Laboratory Investigation:** Weathering of Rock Materials **In-Text Lab Activity:** Temperature and Chemical Weathering
1 Weathering and Erosion	**Content Evaluation:** p. 137 *Topic Review:* 1; p. 146-147 *Chapter Review:* 1, 2
2 Types of Weathering	**Content Evaluation:** p. 137 *Topic Review:* 2; p. 146-147 *Chapter Review:* 3, 4;
3 Types of Mechanical Weathering	**Content Evaluation:** p. 137 *Topic Review:* 3; p. 146-147 *Chapter Review:* 5; *Interpret and Apply:* 1, 2
4 Chemical Weathering	**Content Evaluation:** p. 137 *Topic Review:* 4; p. 146-147 *Chapter Review:* 6
5 Which Minerals and Rocks Resist Most?	**Content Evaluation:** p. 137 *Topic Review:* 5; p. 146-147 *Chapter Review:* 7; *Interpret and Apply:* 3, 4
6 The Rate of Weathering	**Content Evaluation:** p. 137 *Topic Review:* 6; p. 146-147 *Chapter Review:* 8, 9; *Interpret and Apply:* 2, 3
Lesson II **Soils, Mass Movements, and Soil Conservation**	
7 Soils: Result of Weathering	**Content Evaluation:** p. 143 *Topic Review:* 7; p. 146-147 *Chapter Review:* 10, 11; *Interpret and Apply:* 4, 5
8 A Mature Soil Profile	**Content Evaluation:** p. 143 *Topic Review:* 8; p. 146-147 *Chapter Review:* 12, 13;
9 Soil Types and Climates	**Content Evaluation:** p. 143 *Topic Review:* 9; p. 146-147 *Chapter Review:* 14, 15; *Interpret and Apply:* 6
10 Mass Movements	**Content Evaluation:** p. 143 *Topic Review:* 10; p. 146-147 *Chapter Review:* 16; *Interpret and Apply:* 7
11 Soil Conservation	**Content Evaluation:** p. 143 *Topic Review:* 11; p. 146-147 *Chapter Review:* 17; *Interpret and Apply:* 8

PLANNING CHART (continued)

Topic	Support Material
Lab Activity p. 144-145	Temperature and Chemical Weathering
Chapter Review p. 146-147	Critical Thinking 1-5 **Study Guide:** Vocabulary; Interpreting and Applying
Chapter 8 Assessment Program	**Chapter Tests; Computer Test Bank**

Introducing UNIT **TWO**

Student Writing

Begin Unit Two with a brief discussion of how each photo on pages 128-129 illustrates forces that attack Earth's surface.

   At the conclusion of Unit Two, have students write an essay to compare and contrast aspects of weathering and erosion. Possible essay subjects include: 1) positive versus negative effects of weathering and erosion on people; 2) discuss water, gravity, groundwater, running water, ice, wind, ocean waves each as an agent of erosion and as an agent of deposition; and 3) chemical agents versus physical agents. Before writing, students need to focus their thoughts in order to provide direction and organization for their essays. Drawing a concept map is suggested. See page T688 for information on concept mapping. The concept map shown here illustrates one way to tie together some major ideas from Unit Two.

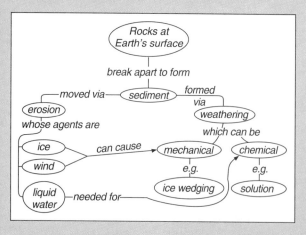

CHAPTER **8**

Motivator

DEMONSTRATION: An easy demonstration of chemical weathering can be done with two pads of dry (and preferably soapless) steel wool. The day prior to starting the chapter, show students both dry pads. Thoroughly wet one pad with water. Leave the other pad dry. Let both pads "weather" overnight in an open dish. The next day, introduce the concept of weathering by asking students to compare the appearance of the two pads. The rust on the wet pad is a good example of the chemical weathering process called *oxidation*.

Lesson I: Weathering

(Topics 1-6)

Teaching Suggestions

A point to emphasize in Lesson I is the endless conflict between the forces that raise Earth's surface and the forces of weathering and erosion that wear down Earth's surface. This is a fundamental concept of geology and is worth stressing.

   Try to make the difference between mechanical and chemical weathering processes clear. The steel wool pad you used in the *Motivator* can be used to show this difference. Tearing the pad apart is a physical change; rusting is a chemical change. Or break a match in half to show a physical change; burn the match to show a chemical change. You may be able to find some evidences of weathering around your school, such as potholes or crumbling concrete, to aid your discussion.

Part of the *Science Background* is a comparison of the crystallization order of minerals in a magma with the susceptibility of minerals to weathering. This material might help students remember that quartz is not greatly affected by weathering processes while ferromagnesian minerals are.

DEMONSTRATION: The relationship between particle size, surface area, and weathering rate can be shown by comparing the rate at which a whole sugar cube and a crushed sugar cube of equal mass dissolve. Use the same amount of water at the same temperature to dissolve the whole cube and the crushed cube. If stirring is necessary, be sure to stir (or have students stir) each solution the same amount. Students will see that the broken-up sugar cube, which has more surface area, dissolves much faster than the whole sugar cube.

Science Background

Climate and Weathering: Warm, wet climates favor chemical weathering for two reasons. First, all chemical weathering processes involve water. Second, the rate of most chemical reactions is increased by heat. Dry climates are deficient in water and cold climates lack liquid water. Thus, in dry or cold climates mechanical weathering is dominant. This does not mean that chemical weathering never occurs in dry, cold climates or that mechanical weathering never occurs in warm, moist climates. It simply means that each climate tends to favor one type of weathering over the other.

Resistance of Minerals: An interesting relationship exists between the order that minerals crystallize in a cooling body of magma (*Science Background*, Chapter 5, Lesson III) and the resistance of a mineral to weathering. The first minerals to form as magma cools are the ferromagnesian minerals (olivine, augite, hornblende) and the calcium-rich plagioclase feldspars. These minerals are most susceptible to weathering because they formed under conditions most unlike those at Earth's surface. The last minerals to form are orthoclase, muscovite, and quartz. These minerals are least susceptible to weathering because they formed under conditions most like those at Earth's surface.

Lesson II: Soils, Mass Movements, and Soil Conservation

(Topics 7-11)

Teaching Suggestions

Use the soil in your own area to differentiate between residual and transported soils. What is your soil's parent material? If a field trip is not feasible, samples and photos of topsoil, subsoil, and parent material from your area should help with your presentation.

Look for evidences of mass movement in your own area to help with your presentation of Topic 10. The work of gravity applies to more than mass movements of rock and soil. For example, old window glass sometimes shows flow marks.

The problems of soil conservation are discussed in Topic 11. List and describe the methods that can be used to conserve topsoil. Look for evidences of soil conservation in your own area to use as examples. For example, steep-sided highway road-cuts are usually landscaped to prevent soil erosion.

In many parts of the country, scientists from the Soil Conservation Service are willing to come to schools and speak to students about soil use and soil conservation. Contact your local Soil Conservation Service.

Science Background

While many farmers understand the long-term advantages of soil conservation, they do not always practice it because of short-term economic considerations. For example, suppose the market price of corn promises a good return while the market price of alfalfa is so low that the farmer would lose money by planting it. In such a situation, it is difficult for the farmer to justify strip cropping corn with alfalfa. A farm, like any business, has to pay its bills. Some county soil conservation programs encourage the practice of soil conservation by arranging for farmers to share costs and equipment.

CHAPTER 8 **LAB** ACTIVITY
Temperature and Chemical Weathering

■ A student report sheet for this activity can be found in the *Laboratory Investigations* booklet.

Time estimate
30-40 minutes

Materials

The effervescent antacid tablets can be Alka-Seltzer or a similar brand.

Process Skills

- Constructing Tables and Graphs: Procedure 6, 10
- Calculating: Procedure 8, 9
- Determining Cause and Effect: Analysis and Conclusions 1, 2, 5
- Comparing/Contrasting: Analysis and Conclusions 4
- Interpreting Diagrams: Analysis and Conclusions 7

Safety

Students should be discouraged from tasting either the tablets or the post-reaction solution.

Preparation

Containers of ice water and hot water will need to be ready for student use. The hot water should not be warmer than 50°C. A hot plate might be needed to maintain the hot water temperature throughout a lab period or throughout a day.

Procedural Hints

If time and tablet supplies permit, encourage students to take the average of several readings at the same temperature and/or to take additional readings at other temperatures.

Answers—Analysis and Conclusions

1. (a) Beaker 1 (b) Beaker 5 (c) As temperature increases, the rate of the reaction increases.
2. As temperature increases, the rate of chemical weathering increases.
3. Students should realize that their highest temperature is unlikely to occur in nature.
4. (a) A limestone should weather faster in Rio de Janeiro because the climate there is hotter. (b) The soil would be expected to be thicker in Rio as well.
5. The climate at Barrow is cold and dry, which would slow down chemical reactions.
6. The rate of the reaction would have increased. Grinding the tablet into pieces increases the surface area, making more surfaces available to chemically react. The curve would be below the actual data curve because the reaction would occur in less time.
7. (a) below (b) The observed reaction was slower. (c) Grinding the sample would have speeded up the reaction and might have made it more like the theoretical curve.

CHAPTER 8 REVIEW

Review

1–surface, 2–agents of erosion, 3–mechanical, 4–chemical, 5–ice wedging, 6–clays, 7–cement, 8–surface area, 9–chemical, mechanical, 10–parent, 11–Transported, 12–topsoil, 13–subsoil, 14–Tropical, 15–grassland, 16–landslide, 17–soil erosion

Interpret and Apply

1. Exposed bedrock weathers largely by mechanical processes. The soil-covered bedrock weathers largely by chemical processes.
2. Weathering in winter is greater because of (a) ice wedging in cracks in the pavement, (b) chemical action of salt and other chlorides used to melt snow, and (c) mechanical action of snowplows on pavement. In summer, these conditions do not exist.
3. The calcite cement is more soluble and therefore more easily removed by chemical weathering.
4. Chemical weathering of feldspar leaves a residue of fine clay. Black mica leaves hematite, limonite, and clay. Quartz is left as pebbles and sands. There may be chips of granite, feldspar, and muscovite mica in the residual soil.
5. The A-horizon is the layer directly exposed to the atmosphere and is farthest removed from the parent material; it has been weathered longest.
6. Answers will depend upon your location.
7. A drought should reduce the frequency of both landslides and mudslides.
8. Soils depleted of nutrients are artificially fertilized.

Critical Thinking

1. moderate chemical weathering
2. moderate mechanical weathering
3. The AYP would have to increase to at least 65 cm.
4. 13°C is well above freezing.
5. A climate with strong chemical weathering is hotter and wetter than a climate with strong mechanical weathering.

CHAPTER 9
Water Moving Underground

PLANNING CHART

Topic	Support Material
Lesson I Fresh Water and Water Budgets	**In-Text Lab Activity:** Interpreting Water Budgets
1 All the World's Water	**Content Evaluation:** p. 152 *Topic Review:* 1; p. 166-167 *Chapter Review:* 1
2 The Water Cycle	**Content Evaluation:** p. 152 *Topic Review:* 2; p. 166-167 *Chapter Review:* 2 **Transparency 23:** The Water Cycle
3 The Water Budget	**Content Evaluation:** p. 152 *Topic Review:* 3; p. 166-167 *Chapter Review:* 3; Interpret and Apply: 1
4 Water Budget Graphs	**Content Evaluation:** p. 152 *Topic Review:* 4; p. 166-167 *Chapter Review:* 3 **Transparency 24:** Water Budget Graphs
Lesson II Water in the Ground	**Laboratory Investigation:** Porosity, Permeability, and Capillarity
5 Can Rocks Hold Water?	**Content Evaluation:** p. 158 *Topic Review:* 5; p. 166-167 *Chapter Review:* 4; Interpret and Apply: 2
6 Can Rocks Transmit Water?	**Content Evaluation:** p. 158 *Topic Review:* 6; p. 166-167 *Chapter Review:* 5; Interpret and Apply: 2
7 Forming the Water Table	**Content Evaluation:** p. 158 *Topic Review:* 7; p. 166-167 *Chapter Review:* 6; Interpret and Apply: 3
8 Water Table Depth and Use	**Content Evaluation:** p. 158 *Topic Review:* 8; p. 166-167 *Chapter Review:* 7; Interpret and Apply: 3
9 Ordinary Wells and Springs	**Content Evaluation:** p. 158 *Topic Review:* 9; p. 166-167 *Chapter Review:* 7; Interpret and Apply: 4
10 Artesian Formations	**Content Evaluation:** p. 158 *Topic Review:* 10; p. 166-167 *Chapter Review:* 8
11 Artesian Wells	**Content Evaluation:** p. 158 *Topic Review:* 11; p. 166-167 *Chapter Review:* 8; Interpret and Apply: 4
12 Conserving Groundwater	**Content Evaluation:** p. 158 *Topic Review:* 12; p. 166-167 *Chapter Review:* 9

PLANNING CHART (continued)

Topic	Support Material
Lesson III Groundwater Characteristics	
13 Groundwater is Usually Cool	**Content Evaluation:** p. 161 *Topic Review:* 13; p. 166-167 *Chapter Review:* 10; Interpret and Apply: 1, 5
14 Hot Springs, Geysers, and Fumaroles	**Content Evaluation:** p. 161 *Topic Review:* 14; p. 166-167 *Chapter Review:* 11; Interpret and Apply: 5
15 The Minerals in Groundwater	**Content Evaluation:** p. 161 *Topic Review:* 15; p. 166-167 *Chapter Review:* 12; Interpret and Apply: 5
16 Mineral Springs	**Content Evaluation:** p. 161 *Topic Review:* 16; p. 166-167 *Chapter Review:* 13
Lesson IV Caverns and Mineral Deposits	
17 How Caverns Form	**Content Evaluation:** p. 163 *Topic Review:* 17; p. 166-167 *Chapter Review:* 14
18 Karst Topography	**Content Evaluation:** p. 163 *Topic Review:* 18; p. 166-167 *Chapter Review:* 14
19 Mineral Deposits by Groundwater	**Content Evaluation:** p. 163 *Topic Review:* 19; p. 166-167 *Chapter Review:* 15; Interpret and Apply: 6, 7
Lab Activity p. 164-165	Interpreting Water Budgets
Chapter Review p. 166-167	Critical Thinking 1-6 **Study Guide:** Vocabulary; Interpreting and Applying
Chapter 9 Assessment Program	**Chapter Tests; Computer Test Bank**

CHAPTER 9

Motivator

A good motivator is the "How Do You Know That…" described in the chapter opener. A more ambitious motivator is described below:

DEMONSTRATION: Quicksand is a groundwater phenomena you can demonstrate in the following way: Obtain the largest glass container possible, such as a bell jar or aquarium. Also obtain plastic or rubber tubing and a means of attaching the tubing to your faucet. The tubing must be long enough to reach from the faucet to the bottom center of the tank, following a path down the side of the tank. Tape the tubing to the side and bottom of the tank. Fill the tank almost to the top with clean, sifted sand—no clay, lumps, or pebbles. Each sand grain must be free to slide past every other sand grain. (Note: Remember that wet sand is heavy. If the equipment must be moved after the demonstration, such as for storage while drying out, set it up on a movable cart.) Next place some kind of weight on the surface of the sand to represent a building. An iron cube from a density kit works well, though any fairly heavy object will do. Start the demonstration by showing students that the building does not sink into the sand when the sand is dry. Then connect the tube to the faucet and start filling the tank with water. As the tank fills, the building sinks into the sand and will, in time, completely disappear. Relate the rising water level in the container to the groundwater level.

The major drawback to this demonstration is that it takes a long time for the sand to dry out. Separate setups are needed for each class. However, even though the demonstration is somewhat awkward, students do not forget it. Also, once the equipment is set up, it can be left assembled for another year. (Look at it this way: The sand should be dry by then.) However, if you have a plastic model of a lift pump, you can use the tank for another demonstration in Lesson III.

Lesson I: Fresh Water and Water Budgets

(Topics 1-4)

Teaching Suggestions
Consider starting this lesson by asking students if they know the sources of drinking water in your community. Using your water source as a starting point, discuss the steps in the water cycle. The water cycle is a fundamental concept in earth science and worthy of the time needed to make a sketch on the board. Be sure to include the relative amounts of fresh water and salt water on Earth in your presentation.

Water budgets are useful tools for quickly comparing the water conditions and climate of one area with those of another area. You may wish to supplement the text in this lesson with a longer discussion of the topic, including closer examination of Figure 9.3 and of the water budget graphs in Figures 9.4 and 9.5, or by doing the Chapter 9 activity on pages 164 and 165.

When discussing Figure 9.3, point out that periods of recharge, usage, deficit, and surplus occur in an annual cycle and that not all locations have all four periods. Identify the water budget graph in Figures 9.4 or 9.5 that best corresponds to conditions in your area.

Lesson II: Water in the Ground

(Topics 5-12)

Teaching Suggestions
Porosity and *permeability* are two terms that students may have a difficult time mastering. Porosity is the space between the particles. For all spherical particles of uniform size, porosity has a constant value. Permeability is the rate at which a fluid moves through a material. Larger particles have better permeability; that is, the fluid flow increases as particle size increases. Part of the reason for increased permeability of larger particles is that larger pore space makes it easier for water to pass through. In addition, larger particles have less surface area than an equal volume of small particles. There is less friction between the particles and the water. These two facts may help students to remember the relationship — bigger is better for permeability.

DEMONSTRATIONS: To compare the permeability of rocks, allow water to drip onto gently-inclined slabs of slate (impermeable) and sandstone (permeable) standing side by side.

If you did the quicksand demonstration in the *Motivator*, the same tank and a model lift pump can be used to model an ordinary well. The demonstration can also be used to show and discuss the need for a return well to recharge groundwater.

Lesson III: Groundwater Characteristics

(Topics 13-16)

Teaching Suggestions
DEMONSTRATION: To show the effect of water hardness, obtain several water samples: distilled water, tap water, limewater, river water, spring water, salt water, and so on.

(Limewater can be made by dissolving 3 grams of $Ca(OH)_2$ in 1 liter of water.) You will also need soap solution in a dropper bottle, test tubes labeled for each water type, stoppers for the test tubes, and a marking pen. Mark a line on each test tube at the same level — about 2 centimeters from the bottom. Place equal amounts of the water samples in the appropriate tubes. Add soap solution, a drop at a time, to each tube. Stopper the tube and shake vigorously after each drop is added. Count the number of drops of soap solution needed to make lasting suds in each test tube. Compare the number of drops needed to make suds in each sample with the amount needed for the distilled water. The more soap needed to make lasting suds, the harder the water.

Lesson IV: Caverns and Mineral Deposits

(Topics 17-19)

Teaching Suggestions

DEMONSTRATION: The formation of stalactites can be demonstrated in the following manner: Obtain a piece of thick cotton cord, two containers, and some Epsom salts (magnesium sulfate heptahydrate). Make enough saturated solution of Epsom salts to fill each container about two thirds full. Unravel the ends of the cord and set an end well down into each container. Let the center section of cord hang down between the containers, forming a V. Leave the solutions and cord undisturbed for 24 hours. A "stalactite" will form at the point of the V.

Science Background

The first step in the solution of limestone is carbon dioxide in the atmosphere dissolving in rainwater to form carbonic acid:

$$CO_2 + H_2O \rightarrow H_2CO_3$$
carbon dioxide in air   rain   carbonic acid

Carbonic acid dissolves rocks made of calcium carbonate (calcite), such as limestone.

$$CaCO_3 + 2H_2CO_3 \rightarrow Ca^{+2} + 2HCO_3^- + CO_2 + H_2O$$
limestone   carbonic   ions in   gas
acid   solution   bubbles

The CA^{+2} and HCO_3^- ions in the solution can precipitate to form stalactites and stalagmites under the right conditions.

$$H_2CO_3 + Ca^{2+} + 2HCO_3^- \rightarrow 2CO_2 + 2H_2O + CaCO_3$$
calcium bicarbonate   gas   calcite
in solution   released   precipitated

CHAPTER 9 LAB ACTIVITY
Interpreting Water Budgets

■ A student report sheet for this activity can be found in the *Laboratory Investigations* booklet.

Time estimate
30-45 minutes

Process Skills
- Calculating: Procedure 10
- Interpreting Diagrams: Procedure 11; Analysis and Conclusions 2, 3, 4
- Comparing/Contrasting: Analysis and Conclusions 1, 5

Procedural Hints
You may find it a good idea to go through *Procedure* steps 1-8 with your students so that you can be certain they understand how to label the water budget sections with the proper letters.

Answers—Procedure
Answers to *Procedure* questions 2-8 can be found in the annotated table, page 165, of this Teachers Annotated Edition. Answers to questions 9-11 are provided below:

Cumberland: J+62,S; F+63,S; M+62,S; A+24,S; M-9,U; J-26,U; J-63,U; A-38,U/D; S-20,D; O+13,R; N+39,R; D+62,R

Duluth: J+27,R/S; F+25,S; M+39,S; A+30,S; M+13,S; J+5,S; J-32,U; A-29,U; S+5,R; O+16,R; N+41,R; D+27,R

Fresno: J+31,R; F+20,R; M+4,R; A-39,U; M-89, U/D; J-136,D; J-180,D; A-165,D; S-110,D; O-57, D; N-9,D; D+28,R

Answers—Analysis and Conclusions
1. Both have all four water budget sections.
2. Surplus occurs in Albany but not in Fresno. Deficit occurs in Albany but not in Duluth.
3. Fresno; no surplus and over 6 months of deficit

4. Duluth; has no deficit but has 5 months of surplus

5. Fresno is most like Phoenix because neither has a surplus period and both have long deficit periods. Albany and Cumberland are most like Little Rock because each has all four water budget sections. Duluth is most like Hartford because neither has a deficit period and both have long surplus periods.

CHAPTER 9 REVIEW

Review
1–d, 2–a, 3–c, 4–a, 5–b, 6–c, 7–c, 8–d, 9–c, 10–d, 11–a, 12–a, 13–d, 14–c, 15–b

Interpret and Apply
1. Largely because (a) precipitation is frozen (snow and ice), and (b) frost in upper soil layers makes the ground impermeable.

2. The sand has greater porosity. Silt fills the pore spaces between sand grains, reducing porosity. The permeability of the sand is also greater, for the same reason.

3. The distance should decrease because the water table would probably rise.

4. Hillside springs occur where the water table crosses a hillslope. Fissure springs rise through a crack in the cap rock of an artesian formation. The hillside spring contains ordinary groundwater. The fissure spring contains artesian water.

5. The shallower well should have cooler water with lower mineral content. Reasons: Deeper water would be warmer due to temperature rise at depth. Warmer water can dissolve more minerals. Also, deep groundwater has probably been underground longer and has had more time to dissolve minerals. Because it is far from surface contaminants, it may be less polluted.

6. In order for dripstone to be deposited from groundwater, the water must be able to evaporate. If the cavern is below the water table, no water can evaporate.

7. The mineral that replaces wood to form petrified wood will be whichever mineral is carried in solution in the groundwater. This, in turn, depends on the materials that the groundwater passed through.

Critical Thinking
1. July
2. Zero. The ground is frozen and plants need no moisture at that time.
3. May and June
4. December
5. All have their peak moisture need in July.
6. Moisture need is higher in Little Rock in both summer and winter. Therefore, temperatures in Little Rock must be higher in both summer and winter.

Lesson I: Stream Erosion and Transportation

(Topics 1-4)

Teaching Suggestions

Students often have a natural interest in stream dynamics, especially if there are a number of streams in their local area. Students may have explored these local streams on their own. They may have also tried damming up small rivulets of runoff after a storm and watched the effect of their dams. Good techniques for enhancing the lesson include the use of slides, photos, topographic maps, field trips (if possible), and stream table equipment (if available). You may be able to take students to observe a local river at its different stages during different seasons of the year, or to show them slides of the same river during its normal and flood stages. Because the action of streams changes the land, any method you can use to show the motion and action of streams will enhance student understanding.

Science Background

The carrying power of a stream is further defined by the terms *competence* and *capacity*. The competence of a stream is a measure of the size of particles it can carry. Capacity is a measure of the total stream load. A small mountain stream might be competent to move large boulders, but it would have little capacity for carrying a large quantity of sediment. The lower Mississippi River, however, lacks competence to move large boulders but has the capacity to carry enormous amounts of fine sediment.

Lesson II: The River Valley

(Topics 5-10)

Teaching Suggestions

Students probably have little idea of the watersheds within their own area. One way to start this topic might be with a map of the streams within your area—either a topographic map or a small photocopied map of the area's streams. Have students use the maps to locate each local stream and to identify the direction of stream flow. On the photocopied maps, they could highlight different watersheds in different colors. Using the maps, the concepts of stream divides and drainage basins can be made clear. You may also be able to use a stream from the map to discuss youthful V-shaped valleys, gullies, and headward erosion.

Students sometimes do not realize that the Mississippi River drainage system includes more than just the Mississippi River itself. Point out that the Ohio, Cumberland, Tennessee, Missouri, Platte, and Arkansas rivers, along with hundreds of other smaller rivers and streams, are all part of the Mississippi River system.

Science Background

Stream Patterns: The pattern that streams form on Earth's surface is determined in part by the bedrock structure over which the stream passes. There are three basic stream patterns:

- *Dendritic* is the most common drainage pattern. This pattern looks like the branches of a deciduous tree. It is common in areas in which the bedrock does not have any large-scale structure. The Mississippi River system has a dendritic stream pattern.

- A *rectangular* stream pattern occurs in areas where fractures in the bedrock affect the direction of stream flow. In areas where bedrock is fractured, streams typically make right-angle bends to follow the fractures. Rectangular patterns are much less common than dendritic patterns.

- A *radial* stream pattern occurs when a number of streams flow away from a single point, such as a mountain peak.

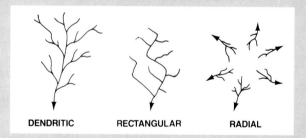

DENDRITIC   RECTANGULAR   RADIAL

Stream Piracy: A classic example of stream piracy occurs in the Catskill Mountains of New York, where the eastward-flowing Kaaterskill Creek has captured the headward drainage of the westward-flowing Gooseberry Creek.

Another example occurs in the Appalachian Mountains, where the Shenandoah River has successively captured the streams that flow through the Snicker, Ashby, and Manassas gaps.

The Mississippi River is at risk of a major stream capture event. The course of the lower Mississippi has been artificially maintained since the mid-1950's, when the U.S. Army Corps of Engineers built a river control station near Simmesport, Louisiana. Prior to this time, water that would have flowed through the Mississippi was starting to flow through the Atchafalaya River instead. The Atchafalaya runs through a back swamp of the Mississippi, and headward erosion has worn away the land between these two rivers. Almost 40 years later, the river control structures are weakened. If the structure were breached during a heavy flood, it would result in the capture of the Mississippi by the Atchafalaya. Such a flood would cause many millions of dollars worth of damage and would divert the Mississippi away from Baton Rouge, New Orleans, and other delta cities.

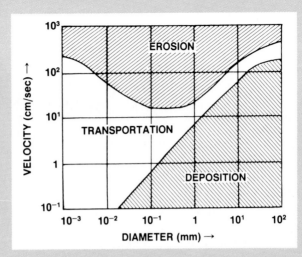

Lesson III:
Waterfalls and River Deposits

(Topics 11-15)

Science Background
Hjulstrom's diagram (shown at the top of the next column) relates stream erosion, transportation, and deposition of various particle sizes to the velocity of water flow. The graph shows the following:

■ Very fine particles are transported by very slow moving currents. However, once fine particles have been deposited, very large currents are required to erode them. This is because fine particles, especially clays, tend to be flakes rather than spheres. Flakes are difficult for the stream to pick up from its bed.

■ For large particles, a small increase in velocity causes a change from deposition to erosion.

■ The velocity required to erode a particle from the stream bed is largest for fine and large sizes; it is least for medium sizes.

Lesson IV:
The Flood Plain and Floods

(Topics 16-19)

Teaching Suggestions
For students who live in areas where flooding occurs, this lesson should be especially meaningful. The cause and effect of local flooding could be discussed. Slides of familiar local areas under water are useful.

You might want to discuss with students whether floods are examples of *cyclic* (repeating) or *noncyclic* (once-in-a-lifetime) phenomena. It is easy to assume that serious floods will not happen again, when in fact they do recur over and over. While floods do not follow highly predictable cycles, they are nonetheless cyclic. Preventive steps should be taken to reduce damage and loss of life due to floods.

CHAPTER **10** **MAP** ACTIVITY
Stream Divides and River Systems

■ A student report sheet for this activity can be found in the *Laboratory Investigations* booklet.

Time estimate
30-40 minutes

Process Skills
■ Observing: Analysis and Conclusions 1-7
■ Interpreting Diagrams: Analysis and Conclusions 8, 9

Procedural Hints

Teachers either can duplicate the blackline version of the river map in the lab manual, or have the students trace the map from the textbook. If reproductions of the blackline map are used, have students color the ocean areas blue. This step will prevent students from drawing rivers down coastlines. This happens frequently with the Colorado River and the Gulf of California.

Some students may be aware that the Colorado River no longer flows into the Gulf of California. Because of heavy water use in that area, the river now ends in a desert in Mexico, several miles short of the Gulf. The Colorado River on the map is shown as it originally flowed.

Students may need help understanding that the major sources of water for the St. Lawrence River are the Great Lakes and that these lakes are therefore also part of the St. Lawrence River system.

Answers—Procedure

Answers to *Procedure* questions 4-7 can be found on the annotated map, page 187 of this Teachers Annotated Edition.

Answers—Analysis and Conclusions

1. Rain falling west flows into the Pacific Ocean, rain falling east flows into the Atlantic Ocean
2. Colorado, Rio Grande, Mississippi
3. (a) Columbia, (b) Mississippi, (c) Colorado, (d) Mississippi, (e) Mississippi (f) Colorado
4. The Great Lakes; flows northeast
5. Any river that flows into the Mississippi such as the Ohio, Missouri, Arkansas, Illinois, Wisconsin, and Red
6. (a) San Francisco Bay, (b) Mobile Bay, (c) Long Island Sound
7. Appalachian Mountains
8. Answers will vary.
9. These rivers do not drain into an ocean.

CHAPTER 10 REVIEW

Review

1–n, 2–a, 3–u, 4–h, 5–m, 6–o, 7–x, 8–f, 9–b, 10–i, 11–p, 12–s, 13–d, 14–j, 15–q, 16–v, 17–k, 18–c, 19–w, 20–e, 21–y

Interpret and Apply

1. Due to its greater speed, the Rocky Mountain stream could move larger particles than the Mississippi River, but the total amount of material being carried by the much larger volume of the Mississippi River would be far greater than that of the Rocky Mountain stream.

2. (a) According to Topic 12, Niagara Falls has retreated 11 kilometers in 11 000 years. 11 km/11 000 years x 1000 m/1 km = 1 m/years Niagara Falls retreats about 1 meter every year. (b) As the falls recede, the elevation above sea level of the dolostone layer decreases and the height of the falls decreases.

3. It shifts its course frequently by further meandering and occasionally by cutoffs.

4. Yes, if it deposits sediment at its mouth faster than the main stream can remove it. There are many examples of this in the Colorado River.

5. The first rain that fell soaked into the pore spaces in the ground and did not immediately become part of the stream flow. Once the ground was saturated, the surplus water ran over the ground and collected in the stream channels. This process took time—in this case, 36 to 48 hours.

Critical Thinking

1. sand.
2. clay
3. 300 cm/s
4. clay, silt, sand, and small pebbles

CHAPTER **11**
Glaciers

PLANNING CHART

Topic	Support Material
Lesson I **Types of Glaciers**	
1 The Problem of the Strange Boulders	**Content Evaluation:** p. 195 *Topic Review:* 1; p. 208-209 *Chapter Review:* 1
2 What Is A Glacier?	**Content Evaluation:** p. 195 *Topic Review:* 2; p. 208-209 *Chapter Review:* 4
3 The Snow Line	**Content Evaluation:** p. 195 *Topic Review:* 3; p. 208-209 *Chapter Review:* 2; *Interpret and Apply:* 1
4 Birth of a Glacier	**Content Evaluation:** p. 195 *Topic Review:* 4; p. 208-209 *Chapter Review:* 3
5 Where Valley Glaciers Occur	**Content Evaluation:** p. 195 *Topic Review:* 5; p. 208-209 *Chapter Review:* 4; *Interpret and Apply:* 4
6 Where Continental Glaciers Occur	**Content Evaluation:** p. 195 *Topic Review:* 6; p. 208-209 *Chapter Review:* 5
Lesson II **Glacier Movement**	
7 How Glaciers Move	**Content Evaluation:** p. 199 *Topic Review:* 7; p. 208-209 *Chapter Review:* 6; *Interpret and Apply:* 2, 3
8 How Far Glaciers Move	**Content Evaluation:** p. 199 *Topic Review:* 8; p. 208-209 *Chapter Review:* 7, 8; *Interpret and Apply:* 2
9 Glaciers Transport Loose Rock	**Content Evaluation:** p. 199 *Topic Review:* 9; p. 208-209 *Chapter Review:* 9 **Software:** Mountains and Crustal Movement
10 Glaciers Leave Their Mark	**Content Evaluation:** p. 199 *Topic Review:* 10; p. 208-209 *Chapter Review:* 10, 11; *Interpret and Apply:* 4
11 Recognizing Glacial Valleys	**Content Evaluation:** p. 199 *Topic Review:* 11; p. 208-209 *Chapter Review:* 12; *Interpret and Apply:* 4
12 What Continental Glaciers Do	**Content Evaluation:** p. 199 *Topic Review:* 12; p. 208-209 *Chapter Review:* 13

PLANNING CHART (continued)

Topic	Support Material
Lesson III **Deposits by Glaciers**	**Laboratory Investigation:** Analysis of Glacial Till
13 Deposition Occurs	**Content Evaluation:** p. 202 *Topic Review:* 13; p. 208-209 *Chapter Review:* 14; Interpret and Apply: 5
14 Glaciers Leave Moraines	**Content Evaluation:** p. 202 *Topic Review:* 14; p. 208-209 *Chapter Review:* 15
15 Drumlins	**Content Evaluation:** p. 202 *Topic Review:* 15; p. 208-209 *Chapter Review:* 16
16 Outwash Plains and Eskers	**Content Evaluation:** p. 202 *Topic Review:* 16; p. 208-209 *Chapter Review:* 17; Interpret and Apply: 6
17 Kames, Kettles, and Deltas	**Content Evaluation:** p. 202 *Topic Review:* 17; p. 208-209 *Chapter Review:* 18
18 Lakes Made by Glaciers	**Content Evaluation:** p. 202 *Topic Review:* 18; p. 208-209 *Chapter Review:* 19; Interpret and Apply: 7
Lesson IV **The Ice Age**	**In-Text Map Activity:** Glacial Rebound
19 How It Happened	**Content Evaluation:** p. 205 *Topic Review:* 19; p. 208-209 *Chapter Review:* 20
20 Ice Age Evidence	**Content Evaluation:** p. 205 *Topic Review:* 20; p. 208-209 *Chapter Review:* 21; Interpret and Apply: 8
21 Causes of Glacial Climates	**Content Evaluation:** p. 205 *Topic Review:* 21; p. 208-209 *Chapter Review:* 22; Interpret and Apply: 8
Map Activity p. 206-207	Glacial Rebound
Chapter Review p. 208-209	Critical Thinking 1-5 **Study Guide:** Vocabulary; Interpreting and Applying
Chapter II Assessment Program	**Chapter Tests; Computer Test Bank**

CHAPTER II

Motivator

One way to introduce the topic is with a discussion of Figure 11.3, which shows the relationship between latitude and elevation of the snow line. Using the following list of mountain elevations and latitudes and Figure 11.3, have students determine which of these peaks are above the snow line:

Mountain	Elevation (meters)	Latitude (degrees)
Kilimanjaro, Tanzania	5895	3°S
Popocatepetl, Mexico	5452	19°N
Mt. Mitchell, NC	2037	36°N
Mt. Whitney, CA	4418	37°N
Pikes Peak, CO	4301	39°N
Mt. Marcy, NY	1629	44°N
Mt. Katahdin, ME	1606	46°N
Mt. McKinley, AK	6194	63°N

All of the above mountains are above the snow line except Mt. Mitchell, Mt. Marcy, and Mt. Katahdin. At what latitude would each of these three mountains have permanent snow on their peaks?

Lesson I: Types of Glaciers

(Topics 1-6)

Teaching Suggestions

Refer to the *Motivator* to introduce this lesson. Then move to the story in Topic 1 about the discovery of glacial deposits in Europe. The following are additional points to emphasize:

■ Glaciers form above the snow line where more snow falls in winter than is melted in summer. The snow is compressed and recrystallized into granular snow, or firn, which becomes solid but flows from the pressure of the overlying ice.

■ Valley glaciers occur in mountain areas.

■ Continental glaciers or ice sheets form in polar latitudes. Ice sheets occur in Greenland and Antarctica. Nunataks are mountain peaks that project through ice sheets. Ice caps are the small ice sheets found on Iceland, Baffin Islands, Spitsbergen, and other large islands of the Arctic Ocean.

Lesson II: Glacier Movement

(Topics 7-12)

Teaching Suggestions

This lesson contains many terms that will need to be defined, discussed, and illustrated. If you live in an area that has been glaciated, there are probably examples of some of these features nearby. Slides, photos, and even short field trips, would greatly enhance student mastery of the material. Discussing the photographs and illustrations in the text will also help.

Science Background

The Finger Lakes area of New York has many glacial features. In addition to glacial troughs and hanging trough waterfalls, several of the lakes also have hanging deltas. These formed when streams draining the lakes eroded through dams at their northern ends, dropping the lake level. At each successive lake level, streams deposited new deltas, only to have the new delta left hanging above the lake the next time the lake level dropped. One of the best examples is on the west side of Cayuga Lake between the upper and lower falls at Taughannock State Park.

Lesson III: Deposits by Glaciers

(Topics 13-18)

Teaching Suggestions

Like Lesson II, this lesson contains many terms for the students to master. Try to make the distinction between *till* and *outwash* clear. You may need to review the terms *stratified* (Chapter 5) and *sorted* (Chapter 9).

Science Background

The term *moraine* refers both to material carried in the ice and to till deposited by the ice. *Ground moraine* refers to both material carried in the bottom of the ice and material left on the ground after the ice has retreated. *Lateral moraine* is both carried and deposited on the sides of the ice, while *medial moraine* is both carried and deposited down the middle of the ice.

Lesson IV:
The Ice Age

(Topics 19-21)

Teaching Suggestions

Topic 21 provides an opportunity to review the characteristics of a good hypothesis. A good hypothesis explains known facts, is supported by those facts, and correctly predicts new facts. Ask students to consider what kind of information scientists should be gathering to test each of the hypotheses listed in the text. For example, if ice ages are caused by changes in the sun's energy, then scientists should make regular measurements of the sun's energy and look for changes. To explore the idea that volcanic dust is involved, scientists might look for evidence of excessive volcanic dust output just prior to the Ice Age.

Science Background

The hypothesis for the origin of glacial climates that involves Earth's axis and orbit is called the Milankovitch Theory, after Milutin Milankovitch, a Yugoslav scientist who proposed it in the early twentieth century. Although the theory was largely untestable at the time, new techniques for the study of deep-sea sediments have provided evidence supporting glacial/interglacial cycles. When water evaporates from the oceans as part of the water cycle, oxygen-18, a heavy isotope of oxygen, tends to stay behind while oxygen-16 enters the atmosphere as water vapor. When water evaporated from the oceans builds up as snow and ice on land, the amount of oxygen-18 in ocean water tends to become concentrated. Animals that build calcium carbonate shells use whatever oxygen that is currently available in the ocean water.

The ratio of oxygen-18 to oxygen-16 in the shells of such animals is an indication of the amount of oxygen-18 in seawater at the time the shell was formed. This ratio, in turn, indicates the amount of ice on land. The graph used in the *Critical Thinking* exercise is taken from a graph of oxygen-18 concentration in shells from deep sea cores.

CHAPTER II MAP ACTIVITY
Glacial Rebound

■ A student report sheet for this activity can be found in the *Laboratory Investigations* booklet.

Time estimate
30-40 minutes

Process Skills
■ Interpreting Diagrams: Procedure 1, 2; Analysis and Conclusions 4
■ Constructing Tables and Graphs: Procedure 3
■ Determining Cause and Effect: Analysis and Conclusions 2, 3, 5

Preparation
Tracing paper will need to be cut to an appropriate size ahead of time.

Procedural Hints
If enough different colored pencils are available, students could color the area between each rebound contour.

Answers—Procedure
1. (a) The highest rebound contour shown on the map is 100 meters. (b) One area is just west of Hudson Bay and the other is on the eastern shore of the bay.
2. see annotated data table, page 206 of this Teachers Annotated Edition

Answers—Analysis and Conclusions
1. Keewatin Center and Labrador Center
2. The centers of rebound are probably places where the ice was thickest.
3. The centers of rebound are probably the places where the ice first accumulated.
4. (a) This value will depend on student graphs, but will probably be about 50 meters. (b) probably less than 5 meters (c) The rate of

uplift has not been constant. It was faster 5000 to 6000 years ago— just after the ice left the area—than it is today.

5. (a) subside, (b) rebound, (c) subside, (d) subside, (e) subside

ANSWERS TO

CHAPTER II REVIEW

Review

1–flood, 2–decreases, 3–firn or neve, 4–valley, 5–continental, 6–surface; center, 7–front, 8–icebergs, 9–moraine, 10–scratches, 11–cirques, 12–glacial trough, 13–rounded, 14–till; outwash, 15–terminal; recessional, 16–drumlins, 17–plain, 18–kames, 19–kettle lakes, 20–North America, 21–an ice age, 22–axis; orbit

Interpret and Apply

1. The greater the yearly snowfall, the lower the snow line should be. If both sides have equal snow coverage at the end of the winter, the shady side will generally have the lower snow line. In the Northern Hemisphere, north is the shady side.

2. because of more frequent melting and refreezing or because of easier grain-over-grain movement

3. Crevasses form where the slope of the glacial valley is too steep for smooth flow. Watching the surroundings to detect steeper areas might help to detect crevasses.

4. Glacial troughs, hanging troughs, and other signs of valley glaciers are superimposed on features caused by the continental glacier.

5. The deposits left by ice took some time to develop into soils and be covered by vegetation that would reduce erosion. During that time, the sediment load in North American rivers must have been higher than it is today. Also, the volume of water in the river would have been greater.

6. Eskers were formed in glacial tunnels high above the ground on which the glacier rested. When the glacier melted, the deposits in the tunnels were laid down over uneven surface features.

7. These irregular inlets and bays are the drowned lower valleys of tributary streams.

8. The period must have been long enough for soil to develop and for a forest to grow.

Critical Thinking

1. It is much warmer today. There was a glacial period 150 000 years ago.

2. Temperatures 120 000 years ago were warmer.

3. two, the older between 160 000 and 140 000 years ago and the more recent between 30 000 and 20 000 years ago

4. The change from interglacial to glacial is more gradual than the change from glacial to interglacial. According to the graph, ice ages end more rapidly than they start.

5. About 100 000 years from now. The two ice ages shown are separated by about 120 000 years. The last one occurred about 20 000 years ago. Therefore the next should occur in 100 000 years.

CHAPTER 12
Effects of Winds, Waves and Currents

PLANNING CHART

Topic	Support Material
Lesson I Wind as an Agent of Change	**Laboratory Investigation:** Effects of Blowing Wind
1 Rock Materials Carried by Winds	**Content Evaluation:** p. 214 *Topic Review:* 1; p. 228-229 *Chapter Review:* 1; Interpret and Apply: 1, 4
2 Abrasion by Windblown Sediments	**Content Evaluation:** p. 214 *Topic Review:* 2; p. 228-229 *Chapter Review:* 2; Interpret and Apply: 2, 4
3 Deflation: An Erosional Effect	**Content Evaluation:** p. 214 *Topic Review:* 3; p. 228-229 *Chapter Review:* 3
4 Loess	**Content Evaluation:** p. 214 *Topic Review:* 4; p. 228-229 *Chapter Review:* 4; Interpret and Apply: 4
5 Composition and Types of Sand Dunes	**Content Evaluation:** p. 214 *Topic Review:* 5; p. 228-229 *Chapter Review:* 5; Interpret and Apply: 3, 4
6 Migration of Dunes	**Content Evaluation:** p. 214 *Topic Review:* 6; p. 228-229 *Chapter Review:* 6
Lesson II Waves in the Sea	
7 Winds and Waves	**Content Evaluation:** p. 219 *Topic Review:* 7; p. 228-229 *Chapter Review:* 7
8 Features of Water Waves	**Content Evaluation:** p. 219 *Topic Review:* 8; p. 228-229 *Chapter Review:* 8, 9, 10; *Interpret and Apply:* 5, 6 **Transparency 24:** Waves
9 Origin of Breakers	**Content Evaluation:** p. 219 *Topic Review:* 9; p. 228-229 *Chapter Review:* 9; Interpret and Apply: 6
10 Shoreline Currents	**Content Evaluation:** p. 219 *Topic Review:* 10; p. 228-229 *Chapter Review:* 11; Interpret and Apply: 7
Lesson III Shoreline Features	**In-Text Lab Activity:** Beach Erosion and Deposition
11 How Waves Erode Rock Materials	**Content Evaluation:** p. 225 *Topic Review:* 11; p. 228-229 *Chapter Review:* 12
12 Attached and Unattached Sandbars	**Content Evaluation:** p. 225 *Topic Review:* 12; p. 228-229 *Chapter Review:* 12

PLANNING CHART (continued)

Topic	Support Material
Lesson III (continued) 13 Beach Materials	Content Evaluation: p. 225 *Topic Review:* 13; p. 228-229 *Chapter Review:* 13, 14
14 Types of Shorelines	Content Evaluation: p. 225 *Topic Review:* 14; p. 228-229 *Chapter Review:* 15
15 Corals, Coral Reefs, and Coral Atolls	Content Evaluation: p. 225 *Topic Review:* 15; p. 228-229 *Chapter Review:* 14, 16
Lab Activity p. 226-227	Beach Erosion and Deposition
Chapter Review p. 228-229	Critical Thinking 1-5 **Study Guide:** Vocabulary; Interpreting and Applying
Chapter 12 Assessment Program	**Chapter Tests; Computer Test Bank**

CHAPTER 12

Motivator

DEMONSTRATION: Obtain a sample of quartz sand, preferably from a sand dune or beach, and a sample of silt or loess. Introduce the chapter by allowing students to examine the composition and texture of each sample. Ask for comparisons between the two. Which sediment is coarser? (sand) Which feels harsher when rubbed between the fingers? (sand) Once students have made their observations, ask them to imagine each material being carried in a strong wind. Which material would probably have a greater effect on the objects it hits and why? (sand, because it is sharper and harder) Which material would be carried more readily? (silt) Finish your discussion by having students use their observations to make predictions about the toadstool rock formation shown in the chapter opener, page 210.

Lesson I: Wind as an Agent of Change

(Topics 1-6)

Teaching Suggestions

If you live in an area that normally receives heavy snowfall, take the opportunity to point out similarities between snow drifts and sand dunes. Snow drifts often exhibit many of the same features as sand dunes, such as a gentle windward side, a steep leeward side, ripples, movement down the slipface, and migration.

Emphasize that sedimentary terms like *sand* and *silt* refer only to particle size and not to composition. Sand, for example, may be composed of quartz, gypsum, calcite, feldspar, or other minerals. However, sand grains will generally be made of minerals that resist weathering. Softer materials, such as calcite, are more easily broken into smaller particles.

Science Background

Dust Bowl: The Dust Bowl of the late 1930's affected land in New Mexico, Texas, Oklahoma, Kansas, Colorado, Nebraska, North Dakota, and South Dakota. Two factors were involved in its origin. First, there was a large increase in wheat cultivation. Large areas of land were plowed for the first time, destroying the natural grassland vegetation. Second, the early 1930's was a period of severe drought in these areas. The bare, dry soil that resulted from plowing and drought was easily picked up by wind. Exceptionally intense dust storms were formed. Many millimeters of humus-rich topsoil were blown away, leaving behind sand, which accumulated in drifts around buildings. The plight of the farmers and their migration to other parts of the country has been well documented in several novels and films, including *Grapes of Wrath*.

Lesson II: Waves in the Sea

(Topics 7-10)

Teaching Suggestions

DEMONSTRATION: Water waves are an example of a transverse wave—a wave in which the particles move at right angles to the direction of wave motion. A length of rope can be used to show how the wave motion moves forward while the actual medium (the rope) does not. Fasten one end of a rope to a doorknob or other anchor, or have two energetic students hold the rope between them. Shake the rope either vertically or horizontally to produce transverse waves. A drawing of the rope on the chalkboard will help identify these wave features: crest, trough, wavelength, and period.

Sample calculations of wave speed, such as the ones that follow, will be helpful to students.

- wavelength = 2 meters, period = 1 second; wave speed= 2 m / 1 s or 2 m/s
- wavelength = 16 meters, period = 4 seconds; wave speed = 16 m / 4 s or 4 m/s

Science Background

The arrival of a tsunami on a beach is often preceded by an unusually large and fairly rapid withdrawal of water, which corresponds to the trough of the tsunami wave. People who stand looking at the newly exposed seafloor are swept up by the wave, then thrown far inland. Few survive the trip.

Lesson III: Shoreline Features

(Topics 11-15)

Teaching Suggestions

The presentation of Topic 14 may be centered around three types of shorelines— drowned, glaciated, and rising. The coast of Maine is a drowned shoreline, with drowned valleys and many small islands and inlets. The coasts of Norway and Alaska are glaciated and have fiords. The Pacific coast is a young, rising shoreline caused by plate motions. There is more about the nature of the Atlantic and Pacific coasts in both Chapter 13, *Plate Tectonics*, and Chapter 18, *The Ocean Floor and Its Sediments*.

A sample of coral would be helpful for the presentation of Topic 15. Few students realize that coral is actually an animal, and that the hard material they call coral is made of the shells of many such animals. The fact that most corals live in warm, shallow water is important to understanding the formation of barrier reefs and atolls. The environments in which most corals grow today can also be used to interpret former environmental conditions for areas in which fossil coral reefs are found.

Science Background

The same beach has a different shape, or profile, in winter than it does in summer. This is due to differences in the size of the waves striking the beach during these two seasons. Summer waves are gentle. In the summer, sand from offshore is pushed up onto the beach, leaving a wide beach that slopes toward the sea. Winter waves are much larger and break farther out at sea. These waves scour the beachfront and move the sand out to sea, leaving a narrow profile. Thus the familiar beach of summer is moved out to sea in the winter but is returned again the next summer. A beach profile is changed more permanently by erosion. Erosional effects may not be as apparent in summer as in winter. Anyone who is considering the purchase of beachfront property should view the property in winter, when the beach is narrowest.

CHAPTER 12 **LAB** ACTIVITY
Beach Erosion and Deposition

■ A student report sheet for this activity can be found in the *Laboratory Investigations* booklet.

Time estimate
40-50 minutes

Process Skills
■ Comparing/Contrasting: Analysis and Conclusions 1, 3, 5
■ Determining Cause and Effect Analysis and Conclusions 4, 7
■ Predicting: Analysis and Conclusions 6

Materials
Approximately 4 kg of each dry sand/gravel mixture will be needed for the lab. Also supply 2 buckets for collecting the sand/gravel mixture at the end of class.

Preparation
Make the two sand/gravel mixtures prior to class rather than having the students make the mixtures. Once the mixtures have dried, they can be stored and reused next year.

Procedural Hints
Remind students to pour water containing the sand/gravel mixture into the bucket, not the sink. When all the sand/gravel mixture has been collected in the buckets, allow it to settle overnight. Then decant the water off onto the ground outdoors and allow the sand/gravel mixture to dry.

Answers—Analysis and Conclusions
1. The rate of beach erosion increases as the rate of wave action increases. Erosion may also occur higher up on the shore as the rate increases.
2. Steep-sloping beach erodes more rapidly.
3. The smallest particles are eroded from the beach and transported just offshore, where they are deposited. Because gravel is heavier, it is not moved as far by the waves. Instead, the gravel is left exposed on the shore.
4. The more gravel in the beach, the less erosion will occur.
5. The only apparent depositional feature is the low mound of sand just offshore. The deposited sand may be more noticeable with the steeply sloped beach.
6. A storm produces larger waves at a greater frequency. The waves reach high up on the beach, causing rapid erosion.
7. Answers may include building sea walls that prevent large waves from reaching the shore.

ANSWERS TO
CHAPTER 12 R E V I E W

Review
1–c, 2–a, 3–c, 4–b, 5–c, 6–a, 7–d, 8–a, 9–a, 10–c, 11–c, 12–b, 13–d, 14–b, 15–d, 16–a

Interpret and Apply
1. In a sandstorm, most particles are carried within a meter of the ground surface. Above this elevation, visibility should be satisfactory. In a dust storm, the particles may be lifted high into the air and visibility could be zero.
2. quartz is a harder mineral than either gypsum or calcite
3. The sketches may show dunes of any shape except perhaps longitudinal. In each case, the gentle slope of the dune should be the side from which the wind blows.
4. Wind-deposited sand grains in a dune should be more scoured, pitted, and angular than the water-deposited sand grains in a delta.
5. speed = wavelength/period
   speed = 300 meters/25 seconds = 12 m/s
   The speed of the wave is 12 meters per second.
6. The wave touches bottom at about half the wavelength. 300 meters / 2 = 150 meters and 10 meters / 2 = 5 meters.
7. No. The lagoon is protected from longshore currents by the sandbar.

Critical Thinking
1. 250-500 μm
2. dune: fine sand, 125-250 μm, about 55%; loess: medium silt, 15.6-31.3 μm, 36%
3. 1% more coarse silt in the dune, about equal
4. Loess—7 sizes; sand dune—4 sizes
5. sand dune is better sorted

Chapter 12 Effects of Winds, Waves and Currents **T763**

CHAPTER 13
Plate Tectonics

PLANNING CHART

Topic	Support Material
Lesson I **What is Plate Tectonics?**	**In-Text Lab Activity:** Convection Currents
1 Moving Plates Cover the Globe	**Content Evaluation:** p. 235 *Topic Review:* 1; p. 250-251 *Chapter Review:* 1; Interpret and Apply: 2 **Transparency 7:** Physical World: Continents and Ocean Floor
2 How Thick Are the Plates?	**Content Evaluation:** p. 235 *Topic Review:* 2; p. 250-251 *Chapter Review:* 2
3 Why Do the Plates Move?	**Content Evaluation:** p. 235 *Topic Review:* 3; p. 250-251 *Chapter Review:* 3 **Transparency 26:** Convection and Asthenosphere
Lesson II Evidence for Plate Tectonics	**Laboratory Investigation:** Magnetism and Mid-Ocean Ridges
4 Africa and South America	**Content Evaluation:** p. 239 *Topic Review:* 4; p. 250-251 *Chapter Review:* 4; Interpret and Apply: 1, 2
5 Earthquakes and Volcanoes	**Content Evaluation:** p. 239 *Topic Review:* 5; p. 250-251 *Chapter Review:* 5 **Transparency 8:** World Volcano Belts **Transparency 9:** World Earthquake Belts
6 Magnetism	**Content Evaluation:** p. 239 *Topic Review:* 6; p. 250-251 *Chapter Review:* 6; Interpret and Apply: 3
7 Heat Flow and Seafloor Elevation	**Content Evaluation:** p. 239 *Topic Review:* 7; p. 250-251 *Chapter Review:* 7; Interpret and Apply: 3
Lesson III Kinds of Plate Boundaries	**Laboratory Investigation (map):** Plate Boundaries
8 Diverging Boundaries	**Content Evaluation:** p. 244 *Topic Review:* 8; p. 250-251 *Chapter Review:* 8
9 Sliding Boundaries	**Content Evaluation:** p. 244 *Topic Review:* 9; p. 250-251 *Chapter Review:* 9
10 Converging Boundaries: Collision	**Content Evaluation:** p. 244 *Topic Review:* 10; p. 250-251 *Chapter Review:* 10
11 Converging Boundaries: Subduction	**Content Evaluation:** p. 244 *Topic Review:* 11; p. 250-251 *Chapter Review:* 11, 12; Interpret and Apply: 4 **Transparency 27:** Plate Boundaries

Topic	Support Material
Lesson IV Continental Growth and Plate Tectonics	
12 The Craton	**Content Evaluation:** p. 247 *Topic Review:* 12; p. 250-251 *Chapter Review:* 13
13 Sources of Growth Material	**Content Evaluation:** p. 247 *Topic Review:* 13; p. 250-251 *Chapter Review:* 14
14 Growth by Thin-Skinned Thrusting—The Southern Appalachians	**Content Evaluation:** p. 247 *Topic Review:* 14; p. 250-251 *Chapter Review:* 15
15 Growth by Terranes— Western North America	**Content Evaluation:** p. 247 *Topic Review:* 15; p. 250-251 *Chapter Review:* 16
Lab Activity p. 248-249	Convection Currents
Chapter Review p. 250-251	Critical Thinking 1-5 **Study Guide:** Vocabulary; Interpreting and Applying
Chapter 13 Assessment Program	**Chapter Tests; Computer Test Bank**

Introducing UNIT **THREE**

Student Writing

Begin Unit Three by asking students to consider how each photo on pages 230-231 illustrates forces that form and uplift Earth's surface. Upon completing Unit Three, a good summary activity is to have students write compositions on the relationships between the plate tectonics theory and the occurrence of volcanoes, earthquakes, and mountains on Earth. In their compositions, students should explain the theory, discuss the evidence for it, and give examples of events that occur at each kind of plate boundary.

Another option is to have students draw a concept map. See page T688 for information on concept mapping. The concept map shown here illustrates one way to tie together some major ideas from Unit 3.

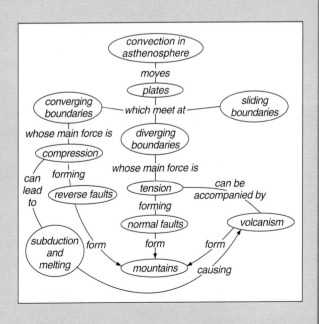

CHAPTER 13

Motivator

One way of introducing this chapter is to show how some of the continents fit together. Photocopy a page-size map of the world for each student. Have the students cut out Africa, South America, and North America and then fit them together into a single continent. The fit between South America and Africa is shown in Figure 13.3. North America fits nicely along the part of the west African coast that remains. The resulting map can then be used to discuss the Chapter Opener about *Paradoxides*. This fossil is thought to have been deposited 500-570 million years ago in a shallow sea off the coast of Africa.

Lesson I:
What is Plate Tectonics?

(Topics 1-3)

Teaching Suggestions

Once you have completed the *Motivator*, the relative movements of some of the plates can be discussed. The examples from the text can be used. A wall map will help students locate these plates more easily. If possible, a wall map of plate boundaries could also be used.

Drawing a convection current on the chalkboard will help students see how these currents drive the plates apart or together. Mid-ocean ridges and deep sea trenches need not be discussed at this point.

Lesson II:
Evidence for Plate Tectonics

(Topics 4-7)

Teaching Suggestions

DEMONSTRATION: If students are not familiar with magnetic fields, a bar magnet can be used to demonstrate this concept. This can be done easily with an overhead projector and a clear transparency. Place the magnet on the overhead projector and lay the transparency over the magnet. Sprinkle iron filings over the transparency until the pattern of the magnetic field is clear on the screen. Relate this field pattern to Earth's magnetic field.

Science Background

Alfred Wegener was both an explorer and a scientist. His interest in meteorology led him to spend several winters in Greenland making weather observations. In 1913, he and a companion crossed the Greenland ice cap. Although Wegener was not the first person to speculate that South America and Africa had once formed a single continent, he was the first to seriously investigate the idea. Despite Wegener's rock and fossil evidence, his 1915 book *The Origin of the Continents and Oceans* was regarded by many as the work of a crank who should stick to weather observations. Wegener lost his life in Greenland in 1930 at the age of 50.

The next part of the plate tectonics story came about as a result of submarine warfare in World War II. Researchers found that the sonar developed at that time to locate enemy submarines could also be used to map the seafloor. In fact, the United States Navy mapped the area around Iwo Jima by this method before the famous amphibious assault there. One of the naval officers involved in that mapping was Harry Hess. After the war, Hess returned to Princeton and set out to map the strange seamounts of the Atlantic Ocean. These seamounts turned out to be an enormous and continuous undersea mountain range, now called the Mid-Atlantic Ridge. Two features of the ridge became significant—first, the huge rift down the middle of the ridge was unlike anything in a mountain range on land; and second, the rocks of the ridge, instead of being ancient as expected from an ancient ocean basin, were young. Hess suggested, with tongue in cheek, that perhaps the rifts were places where hot rocks rose from Earth's interior and pushed older crust aside. In 1961, the process was dubbed "seafloor spreading" by Robert Dietz, a marine geologist.

The confirmation of seafloor spreading came from two sources. Allan Cox and Brent Dalrymple of Berkeley were investigating magnetic polarity and ages of rocks on the land at the same time that Fred Vine and Drummond Matthews of Cambridge in England were studying the magnetic polarity patterns on the seafloor. Once these scientists realized that both sets of magnetic patterns matched, the ideas of both Wegener and Hess were confirmed.

The pattern of magnetic anomalies shown in Figure 13.5 is a generalization. As shown in the diagram below, four epochs of normal and reversed magnetism have occurred within the past four million years. Brunhes and Gauss were normal intervals, while Matuyuma and Gilbert had reversed magnetism. We are still in Brunhes. Within each epoch, short reversals called *events* also occurred. Thus, the polarity has reversed many more times than the four epochs shown in the text.

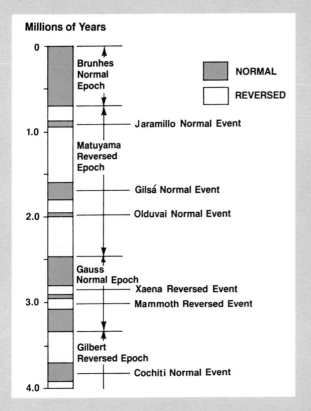

Lesson III: Kinds of Plate Boundaries

(Topics 8-11)

Teaching Suggestions

Chalkboard drawings should help students to visualize the different kinds of plate boundaries. The following outline may help with your presentation:

I. Converging boundaries (coming together)
    A. Collision—two continental plates colliding
        1. Himalayas being formed as India careens into Eurasia
        2. Ural Mountains formed 300 million years ago by collision between Europe and Asia
        3. Southern Appalachians formed by collision between North America and Africa
    B. Subduction— oceanic plate being pushed beneath another oceanic plate or a continental plate
        1. oceanic–oceanic collision: results in trench and island arc
            a. Pacific Plate under Philippine Plate: forms Mariana Trench and Mariana Islands
            b. Pacific Plate under Eurasian Plate: forms Aleutian Trench and Aleutian Islands
        2. oceanic–continental collision: results in trench and coastal mountains
            a. Nazca Plate under South American Plate: forms Peru–Chile Trench and Andes Mountains

II. Diverging boundaries (moving apart)
    A. Mid-Atlantic Ridge
        1. North American and Eurasian plates
        2. South American and African plates
    B. East Pacific Rise
        1. Pacific and Nazca plates

III. Sliding boundaries (moving sideways)
    A. North American and Pacific plates: San Andreas fault, California

Lesson IV: Continental Growth and Plate Tectonics

(Topics 12-15)

Teaching Suggestions

The point of this lesson is that continents change over time. Continents grow as pieces of crust are added to the craton by tectonic processes. Thin-skinned thrusting is one of these processes. Accretion of terranes is another. You will probably need to illustrate a thrust fault for your students in order for them to visualize thin-skinned thrusting. In a thrust fault, the overlying block moves up the slope of the fault plane. In thin-skinned thrusting, the overlying block is very thin relative to the length of the fault plane. The Appalachians are the classic example of thin-skinned thrusting.

CHAPTER 13 **LAB** ACTIVITY
Convection Currents

■ A student report sheet for this activity can be found in the *Laboratory Investigations* booklet.

Time estimate
40-50 minutes

Process Skills

■ Observing: Procedure 5, 8, 13

■ Describing: Analysis and Conclusions 4

■ Comparing/Contrasting: Analysis and Conclusions 6

■ Forming Models: Analysis and Conclusions 1, 2, 5

■ Determining Cause and Effect: Analysis and Conclusions 3

■ Stating a Conclusion: Analysis and Conclusions 8

Materials

Use red, green, or blue food coloring. Yellow does not provide enough contrast.

Safety

CAUTION: Unless necessary, avoid using an open source of flame to heat the water. The area under and around the hot plates should be dry. Cords should not lie in puddles of spilled liquid.

You may wish to place a card labeled "HOT!" adjacent to the hot plates. For safety reasons, you, not the students, should fill the cups with hot water. It is not necessary to fill the foam cups to the rim. Spilling hot water on skin may cause burns.

Procedural Hints

Heat the water in the beaker to near boiling; then remove from the heat source. Boiling water is not necessary to illustrate this concept.

Answers—Analysis and Conclusions

1. The shoebox represents Earth's asthenosphere, the water represents the molten material within the asthenosphere, and the cup of hot water represents the heat source from Earth's core.

2. Any flat object that floats in water could be used to represent the lithospheric plates floating on the asthenosphere.

3. In the first part of the experiment, the food coloring moved about in a random manner. When heat was added, the particles within the food coloring gained energy and their speed increased. The particles then collided more frequently and violently, and as a result, moved farther apart. The food coloring became less dense and rose toward the surface of the water. At the surface, the substance cooled, its particles lost energy, and moved closer together again. The substance then became more dense and sank back toward the bottom of the box.

4. Between the two cups, the food coloring from each cup moved toward the center, cooled, and sank back toward the bottom of the box.

5. The region over the hot water represents a diverging boundary. The region between the two cups represents a converging boundary.

6. Students' answers will vary, but may include heated air that rises, cools, and forms clouds or heated water currents that cool at the surface and sink. Differences between students' answers and the asthenosphere should include composition of material, speed of the convection, and source of heat.

7. diverging boundary; converging boundary

8. No; While new material emerges from diverging boundaries, old material can be subducted at converging boundaries.

ANSWERS TO
CHAPTER 13 REVIEW

Review
1–tectonics, 2–crust, 3–sinking, 4–continental drift, 5–volcanoes, 6–spreading, 7–more (greater, higher, highest, etc.), 8–apart (away), 9–American, 10–continental, 11–ocean (oceanic), 12–subduction, 13–Shield; craton, 14–continents, 15–Appalachian, 16–magnetic polarity

Interpret and Apply

1. Coal is the remains of trees, ferns, and other plants. Such plants do not grow in Antarctica today because the climate there is too cold. Therefore Antarctica must have had a warmer climate at the time these coal beds were formed. Presumably Antarctica was closer to the equator at that time.

2. An error on the part of the ancient surveyors is unlikely. The more likely explanation is that the continent of Africa has shifted enough in 4000 years to rotate the pyramid slightly out of its original alignment.

3. As distance from a spreading center increases, the age of the seafloor increases, while heat flow and seafloor elevation decrease. If spreading centers are places where hot convection currents are rising, bringing new material to the surface and driving the plates apart, the rocks should be younger and heat flow greatest there. Elevation should be highest at spreading centers because heated materials are expanded. As the material moves away from the center, it cools and contracts, causing a decrease in elevation.

4. Because continents do not subduct, they remain at Earth's surface to become older and larger. Oceanic crust, however, does subduct. Before oceanic crust can become very old, it will be returned to the mantle at a subduction zone.

Critical Thinking

1. The point is on an isotherm— a line of equal temperature. The value of that isotherm is halfway between 1000°C and 1500°C, or 1250°C.

2. about 250 kilometers

3. As distance increases, depth increases.

4. At both depths, the plate is much cooler. This would be expected because the plunging plate came from the surface and is cold. The plate warms as it penetrates more deeply into the mantle.

5. 600 km in this diagram

CHAPTER **14**
Volcanism and Plate Tectonics

PLANNING CHART

Topic	Support Material
Lesson I Volcanism Releases Magma	Laboratory Investigation
1 Magma	**Content Evaluation:** p. 255 *Topic Review:* 1; p. 268-269 *Chapter Review:* 1, 3; *Interpret and Apply:* 1, 3
2 Gases in Magma	**Content Evaluation:** p. 255 *Topic Review:* 2; p. 268-269 *Chapter Review:* 3, 4
3 Lava	**Content Evaluation:** p. 255 *Topic Review:* 3; p. 268-269 *Chapter Review:* 2
4 Lava Fragments	**Content Evaluation:** p. 255 *Topic Review:* 4; p. 268-269 *Chapter Review:* 5; *Interpret and Apply:* 2, 5
Lesson II Kinds of Eruptions	**In-Text Lab Activity:** Patterns of Volcanism
5 Rift Eruptions	**Content Evaluation:** p. 258 *Topic Review:* 5; p. 268-269 *Chapter Review:* 6, 7, 8 **Transparency 7:** Physical World: Continents and Ocean Floor **Transparency 8:** World Volcano Belts
6 Subduction Boundary Eruptions	**Content Evaluation:** p. 258 *Topic Review:* 6; p. 268-269 *Chapter Review:* 9; *Interpret and Apply:* 3
7 Hot Spots	**Content Evaluation:** p. 258 *Topic Review:* 7; p. 268-269 *Chapter Review:* 10; *Interpret and Apply:* 4
Lesson III Examples of Volcanic Eruptions	
8 Eldfell	**Content Evaluation:** p. 263 *Topic Review:* 8; p. 268-269 *Chapter Review:* 11
9 Mount St. Helens	**Content Evaluation:** p. 263 *Topic Review:* 9; p. 268-269 *Chapter Review:* 12
10 Kilauea	**Content Evaluation:** p. 263 *Topic Review:* 10; p. 268-269 *Chapter Review:* 10
11 Some Famous Eruptions	**Content Evaluation:** p. 263 *Topic Review:* 11; p. 268-269 *Chapter Review:* 13, 14

PLANNING CHART (continued)

Topic	Support Material
Lesson III (continued) **12 Extraterrestrial Volcanism**	**Content Evaluation:** p. 263 *Topic Review:* 12; p. 268-269 *Chapter Review:* 15, 16
Lesson IV **Plutonic Activity**	
13 Plutons and Volcanism	**Content Evaluation:** p. 265 *Topic Review:* 13; p. 268-269 *Chapter Review:* 17, 18, 19, 20
14 Dikes, Sills, Laccoliths, Necks	**Content Evaluation:** p. 265 *Topic Review:* 14; p. 268-269 *Chapter Review:* 17, 18, 19; Interpret and Apply: 5 **Software:** Mountains and Crustal Movement
15 Batholiths and Stocks	**Content Evaluation:** p. 263 *Topic Review:* 15; p. 268-269 *Chapter Review:* 20
Lab Activity p. 266-267	Patterns of Volcanism
Chapter Review p. 268-269	Critical Thinking 1-7 **Study Guide:** Vocabulary; Interpreting and Applying
Chapter 14 Assessment Program	**Chapter Tests; Computer Test Bank**

CHAPTER 14

Motivator

DEMONSTRATION: You might want to introduce this chapter with a model of a mild volcanic eruption. You will need plaster of Paris, water, a small candle, a container about 8 cm high and 12 cm in largest diameter, and an implement to mix the plaster of Paris.

Mix up enough plaster of Paris in the container to nearly fill it. Press the candle into the plaster of Paris. Except for the wick at the top, the candle must be completely within the plaster of Paris. Avoid pressing the candle against the bottom of the container. Allow the plaster to harden overnight. Then cut or tear the container away from the hardened plaster of Paris.

In this model, the candle is the magma reservoir for the volcano and the wick is the volcanic vent through which the volcano will erupt. The model needs only to be heated to melt the "magma" and cause the "volcano" to erupt.

⚠ **CAUTION: Be careful of handling hot materials, no matter which heat source you choose to use.** Heating can be done by placing the model in a pan of water on a hot plate. The water level must be as high as the top of the candle. A speedier eruption can be achieved by heating the model in a microwave oven. After about three minutes in the microwave, water will begin to seep from the plaster of Paris and the wax will begin to ooze up around the wick. Remove the model from the oven at that time. The wax will continue to ooze up around the wick ("erupt") with small sputtering noises.

Once the reaction stops and the wax cools, a chisel and hammer can be used to break apart the model and see the "magma reservoir." Some of the unmelted candle will remain, but the shape of the original reservoir will be easy to recognize. Follow this demonstration with your Lesson I discussion of felsic versus mafic magma and lava.

Lesson I:
Volcanism Releases Magma

(Topics 1-4)

Magma Compositions and Lava Eruptions		
Type	felsic	mafic
Silica	higher	lower
Fluidity	thick	thin
Color	light	dark
Movement	slow	more rapid
Dissolved Gases	cannot easily escape	escape easily
Nature of Eruption	explosive	smoothly flowing
Cone Shape	steep-sided	broad-based

Teaching Suggestions

The major point of this lesson is the relationship between the chemical composition of magma and the nature of the lava eruption that results. Constructing a chart like the one shown above may help to summarize these relationships. The shape of the volcanic cone that forms from each kind of eruption could be emphasized.

This lesson also includes the types of tephra. *Tephra* is the name for any lava particle. The size of specific tephra is as follows:

- ■ < 2 mm = ash
- ■ 2–64 mm = lapilli
- ■ > 64 mm = bombs and blocks

Science Background

The lava in flows can assume a variety of interesting shapes. *Pahoehoe* (pa-HOY-hoy) forms from highly fluid basaltic lavas that spread in sheets. The lava surface develops a ropy appearance as flow continues beneath a cooling surface. *Aa* (AH-ah) lava is a slower-moving lava that is broken into jagged pieces by the moving lava beneath it. A single lava flow may grade from pahoehoe near its start to aa near its end. Other volcanic rocks of interest are:

- ■ Pillow lavas are characteristic of basalts that erupt underwater. They look like stacks of rounded pillows.
- ■ Volcanic tuffs are rocks formed from solidified deposits of volcanic ash.
- ■ Volcanic breccias are rocks composed of coarser volcanic particles.

Lesson II:
Kinds of Eruptions

(Topics 5–7)

Teaching Suggestions

Lessons I, II, and III are all short and may be combined into a single lesson. The important concept in Lesson II is that three kinds of plate boundaries produce volcanism. A wall map is helpful with Lessons II and III. The following outline could be used for your presentation:

I. Rift Eruptions
  A. smooth, quiet eruptions that occur along a line rather than at a point
  B. occur in two places:
    1. undersea at mid-ocean ridges, such as Mid-Atlantic Ridge, East Pacific Rise
    2. on land
      a. today—East African Rift
      b. past—basalt plateaus (Columbia, Karroo, Parana, Deccan); these may show columnar jointing

II. Subduction Boundary Eruptions
  A. explosive eruptions that form steep-sided cones
  B. this type forms majority of world's volcanoes
  C. lead to two landforms:
    1. island chains—islands of Indonesia, Philippine Islands, islands of Japan, Aleutian Islands
    2. young mountain ranges—Cascades, Andes

III. Hot Spot Eruptions
  A. mid-plate volcanism with smooth flow
  B. show movement of plates; Hawaiian Islands

Lesson III: Examples of Volcanic Eruptions

(Topics 8–12)

Teaching Suggestions

This lesson contains specific examples of volcanoes that have erupted at each of the plate boundaries presented in Lesson II. Remind your students that violent volcanoes are not just things of the past. There are more than 485 active volcanoes in the world today. With growing world populations, the chance of people being harmed by future eruptions increases every year.

Topic 12 makes the following points about extraterrestrial volcanism:

- Other objects in the solar system besides Earth have evidence of volcanic activity.

- None of this volcanism seems to be related to plate movements as on Earth.

- Io is the only object in the solar system besides Earth that is known to have active volcanism.

Science Background

In terms of human life, Krakatau was the most devastating volcanic eruption known. The second most devastating was the eruption of Mount Pelee on the island of Martinique in 1902 (Topic 4). The third most severe was the eruption of Nevada del Ruiz in Colombia in November of 1985. About 25 000 people lost their lives in the mudflows that resulted when the eruption melted about 10 percent of the snow on the peak. The eruption of Vesuvius in A.D. 79 killed 20 000 people.

Lesson IV: Plutonic Activity

(Topics 13–15)

Teaching Suggestions

With the drawing in the text or with your own drawing on the chalkboard, review the kinds of plutons described in these three topics.

If time permits, you might consider doing this activity with Lesson IV. The following diagram is a cross-section of an area that has experienced periods of igneous activity at different times. Help students determine the correct sequence in which the rocks formed.

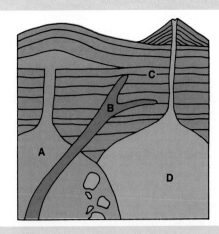

The correct order, from oldest to youngest, is C, D, A, B. B is youngest because it cuts both A and C. A is younger than D because pieces of D are included in A. D cuts across C and therefore must be younger.

CHAPTER **14** **LAB** ACTIVITY
Patterns of Volcanism

- A student report sheet for this activity can be found in the *Laboratory Investigations* booklet.

Time estimate
40-50 minutes

Process Skills

- Calculate: Procedure 2, 3, 4; Analysis and Conclusions 2

- Constructing Tables and Graphs: Procedure 6

- Analyzing Data: Analysis and Conclusions 1, 3, 4, 5

- Interpreting Diagrams: Analysis and Conclusions 6, 7

Procedural Hints

Help students recognize that the data table and graph contain only three kinds of information— the number of volcanoes within a belt, the number of years those volcanoes were active, and the number of eruptions that were violent.

Answers—Procedure

Answers to *Procedure* questions 2-5 can be found in the annotated table, Figure 14.17, on page 267 of this Teachers Annotated Edition.

Answers—Analysis and Conclusions

1. The Aleutian belt is the longest at 1457 km. The Central America belt has the greatest number of volcanoes (79).

2. If all 7 volcanoes had been active every year of the past 100, the value would be 7 x 100 = 700.

3. The volcanoes in the central America belt have been active the greatest number of years; those of the Taiwan belt, the least.

4. The central America belt has had the greatest number of explosive eruptions (30).

5. Belts with greater total numbers of volcanoes have greater numbers of years of volcanic activity and a greater number of explosive eruptions per 100 km.

6. The Halmahera belt would be expected to have a high number of explosive eruptions, but it does not. Apparently most eruptions along this belt are smooth.

7. The point for the Italy belt is farthest to the right; therefore, the Italy belt should have the highest rate of convergence. It is the result of the subduction of the African Plate beneath the Eurasian Plate.

ANSWERS TO

CHAPTER 14 REVIEW

Review

1–n, 2–1, 3–f, 4–g, 5–v, 6–q, 7–a, 8–c, 9–u, 10–h, 11–e, 12–o, 13–w, 14–j, 15–p, 16–i, 17–s, 18–k, 19–x, 20–b

Interpret and Apply

1. The earthquake activity is presumed to result as magma rises toward the volcanic vent. Once the volcano's magma reservoir is filled, earthquake activity should stop. Volcanoes that erupt long after earthquake events are assumed to be erupting magma that moved at the time of the earthquakes.

2. When particles settle in water, the larger particles are deposited first. Volcanic deposits behave in the same way. The larger particles (bombs) are deposited nearer the volcano and the ash is carried farther away, in some cases completely around the world.

3. A more rapidly moving plate may tend to create more friction and therefore more melting. A rapidly moving plate would also have more volume subducted each year; this represents a greater volume of rock available for melting. The plate under Indonesia must be moving more rapidly than the plate under the Cascades. (In fact, the rate under the Indonesian arc is 6–7 cm/yr while the rate under the Cascades is only 2–3 cm/yr.)

4. The African Plate must be moving very slowly. (In fact, there is some evidence that the African Plate is not moving at all. Africa has more hot spots for its area than any other location. There seems to be a relationship between the number of hot spots and the rate of plate movement. As plate motion decreases, the number of hot spots increases.)

5. No, because sills are plutons; that is, sills form from magma that cooled underground. The ash must come from a volcano and was deposited with the limestone after settling through the air and water. It was not intruded.

Critical Thinking

1. approximately 6.6 million years

2. about 460 kilometers

3. The rock age for Hawaii is zero; therefore, the island must now be forming. In fact, Mauna Loa and Kilauea are both active volcanoes on the island.

4. Kauai, because the age of the rocks there is about 5.0 billion years

5. Necker. Several other islands not shown on the graph are older.

6. Rocks on Oahu are about 1.4 million years older.

7. According to the graph, Nihea is about 800 kilometers from the hot spot.

$$\frac{800 \text{ km}}{8 \text{ million yr}} = \frac{80\ 000\ 000 \text{ m}}{8\ 000\ 000 \text{ yr}} = 10 \text{ cm/yr}$$

PLANNING CHART

Topic	Support Material
Lesson I Earthquakes Result From Stress	**In-Text Lab Activity:** Earthquakes and Subduction Boundaries
1 What Is an Earthquake?	**Content Evaluation:** p. 273 *Topic Review:* 1; p. 288-289 *Chapter Review:* 1 **Transparency 7:** Physical World: Continents and Ocean Floor **Transparency 9:** World Earthquake Belts
2 Causes of Earthquakes	**Content Evaluation:** p. 273 *Topic Review:* 2; p. 288-289 *Chapter Review:* 2
3 Depth of Earthquakes	**Content Evaluation:** p. 273 *Topic Review:* 3; p. 288-289 *Chapter Review:* 3, 4; Interpret and Apply: 1
4 Earthquake Waves	**Content Evaluation:** p. 273 *Topic Review:* 4; p. 288-289 *Chapter Review:* 5, 6, 7; Interpret and Apply: 2; **Transparency 28:** Earthquake Waves
Lesson II Locating an Earthquake	**Laboratory Investigation:** Locating and Earthquake Epicenter
5 Seismographs	**Content Evaluation:** p. 276 *Topic Review:* 5; p. 288-289 *Chapter Review:* 8
6 Determining the Distance to the Earthquake Epicenter	**Content Evaluation:** p. 276 *Topic Review:* 6; p. 288-289 *Chapter Review:* 9; Interpret and Apply: 3
7 Locating the Epicenter	**Content Evaluation:** p. 276 *Topic Review:* 7; p. 288-289 *Chapter Review:* 10
Lesson III Measuring an Earthquake	
8 Earthquake Magnitude	**Content Evaluation:** p. 279 *Topic Review:* 8; p. 288-289 *Chapter Review:* 11
9 Earthquake Damage	**Content Evaluation:** p. 279 *Topic Review:* 9; p. 288-289 *Chapter Review:* 12
10 Earthquake Risk and Prediction	**Content Evaluation:** p. 279 *Topic Review:* 10; p. 288-289 *Chapter Review:* 13

PLANNING CHART (continued)

Topic	Support Material
Lesson IV Earthquake Waves Inside Earth	
11 *P* and *S* Wave Velocities	**Content Evaluation:** p. 282 *Topic Review:* 11; p. 288-289 *Chapter Review:* 14
12 The Moho	**Content Evaluation:** p. 282 *Topic Review:* 12; p. 288-289 *Chapter Review:* 15, 16; Interpret and Apply: 4
13 The Shadow Zone	**Content Evaluation:** p. 282 *Topic Review:* 13; p. 288-289 *Chapter Review:* 17; **Transparency 29:** The Shadow Zone
Lesson V Examples of Earthquakes	
14 Alaska—1964	**Content Evaluation:** p. 285 *Topic Review:* 14; p. 288-289 *Chapter Review:* 18
15 Earthquakes along the San Andreas Fault	**Content Evaluation:** p. 285 *Topic Review:* 15; p. 288-289 *Chapter Review:* 19; Interpret and Apply: 4
16 New Madrid— 1811 and 1812	**Content Evaluation:** p. 285 *Topic Review:* 16; p. 288-289 *Chapter Review;* 20
Lab Activity p. 286-287	
Chapter Review p. 288-289	Critical Thinking 1-6 **Study Guide:** Vocabulary; Interpreting and Applying
Chapter 15 Assessment Program	**Chapter Tests; Computer Test Bank**

CHAPTER 15

Motivator
A good introduction to this chapter would be a class discussion or debate on whether construction should be allowed in earthquake-prone areas or along major fault zones. Students could argue the different points of view—developer, scientist, city official, and so on. Students who feel that building should be allowed could be asked what type of "earthquake proof" building codes a developer should have to meet. Who will be responsible for the additional costs? Also, should all existing structures be modified to make them safer for earthquakes?

Lesson I: Earthquakes Result from Stress

(Topics 1-4)

Teaching Suggestions
The purpose of this lesson is to present some basic facts and terminology about earthquakes. You might consider starting with the chart in the *Science Background* to determine where the major earthquakes that have occurred within students' lifetimes were located.

DEMONSTRATIONS: Silly Putty® can be used to help demonstrate the behavior of rocks under stress. Mold the Silly Putty into any convenient shape and place it on a surface. As the stress of gravity causes the Silly Putty to change shape, point out that rocks gradually change shape under stress too. Then pick up the Silly Putty and snap it into two pieces. Point out that if the stresses are applied too quickly to a rock, the rock will break like the Silly Putty.

A Slinky® can be used to demonstrate compressional, or *P*, waves. Place the Slinky on its side on a smooth surface. Hold each end and stretch it out to a convenient length. Hold one end steady and create an abrupt horizontal pulse at the other end. The compressions can be seen traveling along the Slinky.

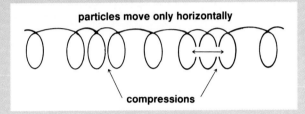

particles move only horizontally

compressions

Discuss the fact that the waveform moves, but the particles within the Slinky move only back and forth in the same place. Relate this behavior to *P* waves and sound waves.

A length of rope can be used to demonstrate an *S* wave. A piece equal to the width of your classroom can be very effective. Have a student hold tightly to one end while you create a vertical pulse at the other. The waveform can be seen traveling the length of the rope and — if

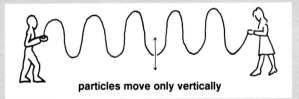

particles move only vertically

you snap the rope hard enough and the student holds on tightly enough — traveling back. Discuss the motion of the particles in the rope relative to the waveform and relate it to *S* waves.

Science Background

Recent Large Earthquakes		
Year	Location	Deaths
1970	Guatemala	22 778
1976	Tangshan, China	800 000
1978	Northeastern Iran	25 000
1985	Mexico City, Mexico	30 000
1988	Afghanistan	25 000
1989	Loma Prieta	68
1990	Iran	40 000

Lesson II: Locating an Earthquake

(Topics 5-7)

Teaching Suggestions
The major point of this lesson is how seismographs are used to locate the epicenters of earthquakes. The lesson could be developed by making the following points:

- *S* waves always lag behind *P* waves.
- The amount of the lag can be used to determine the distance to the epicenter.
- A minimum of three seismograph tracings are needed to locate the epicenter. (Ideally, two circles can meet in a single point. However, this is not likely to happen using real seismic data from actual recording sites.)

Interpret and Apply question 3 could be done so that students can practice using the time-travel graph.

Lesson III: Measuring an Earthquake

(Topics 8-10)

Science Background
Many of the changes that are being studied as earthquake predictors seem to be interrelated; they are the result of the process of dilatancy. The rock dilates, or swells up, causing tiny cracks to form. The increased spaces in the rock make it more difficult for *P* waves to

travel through the rock, and therefore their velocity is slowed. Just before the rock breaks, water enters the cracks and *P* wave velocities can return to normal. Water makes it easier for an electrical current to travel through the rock, so resistance drops. The fissures increase the amount of rock surface in contact with water, and more minerals dissolve from the rock into the water, increasing the radon concentration.

Lesson IV:
Earthquake Waves inside Earth

(Topics 11-13)

Teaching Suggestions
An important point to make with this lesson is that earthquake waves are the major method of learning about the composition, state, and structure of Earth's interior. An analogy to X rays for humans could be made because seismograph tracings provide a kind of X ray picture of the interior. You may want to review the Current Research feature on seismic tomography on page 235.

A second point to make is that two discontinuities occur inside Earth. One occurs at the boundary between the core and mantle and shows clearly on the graph of *P* and *S* wave velocities in Figure 15.9. The other discontinuity is the Moho.

The third important concept in this lesson is the shadow zone. Although the drawing in the text is clear, you may need to develop the drawing on the chalkboard with students before they fully understand the concept. Emphasize that both *P* and *S* waves are received between the earthquake and the shadow zone, while neither is received in the shadow. Only *P* waves are received beyond the shadow zone because *S* waves do not pass through the liquid outer core. You may also want to warn students not to interpret Figure 15.11 to mean that all earthquakes occur at the North Pole. The epicenter is at the top just for convenience in making the drawing. The shadow zone can be located anywhere, depending upon the location of the epicenter. To help stress this point, have students rotate their textbooks to change the orientation of the diagram. They should see that the area of the shadow zone depends on the location of the epicenter.

Science Background
Using a computer to combine the results of many seismic waves has given scientists a new look at Earth's interior. One result has been the confirmation that the mantle is closest to the surface under mid-ocean ridges and hot spots and farthest from the surface at deep-sea trenches. A second result was the discovery that the interface between the core and mantle is not smooth but instead has features that mimic the topography of Earth's surface.

Lesson V:
Examples of Earthquakes

(Topics 14-16)

Teaching Suggestions
One way to introduce this lesson might be to ask students for areas in the United States where a nuclear reactor should not be built and why. They should realize that tectonically active places might be poor locations for reactors. If possible, use a wall map to locate each of the areas discussed in the text. Then summarize each of the areas, possibly in a chart.

CHAPTER 15   LAB ACTIVITY
Earthquakes and Subduction Boundaries

■ A student report sheet for this activity can be found in the *Laboratory Investigations* booklet.

Time estimate
30-35 minutes

Process Skills
■ Constructing Table and Graphs: Procedure 4, 5
■ Interpreting Diagrams: Analysis and Conclusions 1-4
■ Calculating: Analysis and Conclusions 5
■ Comparing/ Contrasting: Analysis and Conclusions 6, 7

Materials

Have protractors available for students who wish to measure the angle of the subducting plates in their graph.

Procedural Hints

Be sure students understand that their graph are profiles, not maps. Depending upon their prior graphing experience, your students may need help drawing a best-fit line. Although it is unlikely in this case, a best-fit line need not go exactly through a single plotted point on their profile.

Answers—Procedure

Answers to *Procedure* questions 1-3 can be found in the annotated Data Table B on page 287 of this Teachers Annotated Edition.

Answers—Analysis and Conclusions

1. For the Tonga area, the Pacific Plate is subducting and the Indian Plate is overriding. For Chile, the Nazca Plate is subducting and the South American Plate is overriding.

2. (a) The Tonga area is farther from the East Pacific Rise than the Chile area. (b) The subducting plate at Tonga must be older than the subducting plate at Chile.

3. At Tonga, most earthquakes foci are deep (>300 km) while at Chile most earthquake foci are intermediate (70-300 km) in depth.

4. (a) Tonga, (b) Chile, (c) Plate at Chile is subducting beneath a continent; plate at Tonga is subducting beneath an oceanic plate.

5. $\dfrac{1000\ km}{1} \times \dfrac{1000\ m}{km} \times \dfrac{100\ cm}{m} \times \dfrac{1}{10\ 000\ 000\ yr} = 10\ cm/yr$

6. The rate at Tonga would be more because the subducting plate at Tonga is older and therefore denser.

7. (a) The Tonga is farther from the source. The subducting plate at Tonga is: (b) older, (c) steeper, (d) faster, and (e) has more deep focus earthquakes than the subducting plate at Chile.

ANSWERS TO

CHAPTER 15 REVIEW

Review

1–earthquake, 2–friction, 3–subduction, 4–focus, 5–*P*, 6–liquids, 7–surface, 8–earthquake (or seismic), 9–increases, 10–3, 11–magnitude, 12–collapse, 13–decrease, 14–liquid, 15–crust, 16–continents, 17–shadow, 18–Pacific, 19–Pacific, 20–zones of weakness.

Interpret and Apply

1. The basic reason is the type and temperature of the rocks in the two different locations. The cooler rocks in the east transmit seismic waves more efficiently than the warmer rocks near the western plate boundary.

2. The time interval between both increases as the distance to the observer increases.

3. (a) 2900 km (b) 4300 km (c) 5600 km

4. In the ocean, because the crust is thinner and the Moho is not as deep there. In fact, there was once a program to drill to the Moho to get a piece of mantle. The program was called *Project Mohole*. It was proved to be unnecessary when scientists realized that mantle material was coming to the surface at mid-ocean ridges.

Critical Thinking

1. *P*, because *P* waves travel nearly twice as fast as *S* waves

2. 10 h 9 min

3. 10 h 7 min 20 sec

4. 5 min 30 sec

5. (1) The *P* wave arrived at station *B* first and station *A* last. (2) The difference in arrival times of the *P* and *S* waves is least for station *B*, greatest for station *A*. (3) The amount of displacement of the tracing line is greatest for station *B*, least for station *A*.

6. The tracing for any station can be used and the result should be the same. For example, the difference in the arrival times of the *P* and *S* waves at station *C* is 5 minutes 30 seconds. From the time-travel graph, the epicenter is 4000 kilometers away. A *P* wave takes 7 minutes to travel 4000 kilometers. Therefore the earthquake must have occurred 7 minutes before 10 h 7 min or at 10 hr exactly.

CHAPTER 16
Mountains and Plate Tectonics

PLANNING CHART

Topic	Support Material
Lesson I Mountains Result from Collisions	**In-Text Map Activity:** Mountains and Plate Tectonics
1 Active and Passive Continental Margins	**Content Evaluation:** p. 293 *Topic Review:* 1; p. 304-305 *Chapter Review:* 1, 2; Interpret and Apply: 1
2 Collisions between Oceans and Continents	**Content Evaluation:** p. 293 *Topic Review:* 2; p. 304-305 *Chapter Review:* 3 **Transparency 7:** Physical World: Continents and Ocean Floor
3 Collisions between Two Continents	**Content Evaluation:** p. 293 *Topic Review:* 3; p. 304-305 *Chapter Review:* 4
Lesson II Features of Collision Mountains	**Laboratory Investigation:** Faulting and Folding **In-Text Map Activity:** Folded Mountains
4 Faults	**Content Evaluation:** p. 296 *Topic Review:* 4; p. 304-305 *Chapter Review:* 5
5 Folds	**Content Evaluation:** p. 296 *Topic Review:* 5; p. 304-305 *Chapter Review:* 6, 7 **Transparency 5:** Geological Map: Flaming Gorge, UT; **Transparency 30:** Faults and Folds; **Software:** Mountains and Crustal Movement
6 Volcanoes	**Content Evaluation:** p. 296 *Topic Review:* 6; p. 304-305 *Chapter Review:* 8
Lesson III Other Evidence of Mountain Building	
7 Uplifting	**Content Evaluation:** p. 299 *Topic Review:* 7; p. 304-305 *Chapter Review:* 9
8 Tilting	**Content Evaluation:** p. 299 *Topic Review:* 8; p. 304-305 *Chapter Review:* 10 **Transparency 4:** Topographic Map: Harrisburg, PA
9 Overturning	**Content Evaluation:** p. 299 *Topic Review:* 9; p. 304-305 *Chapter Review:* 11

PLANNING CHART (continued)

Topic	Support Material
Lesson IV **Other Tectonic Features**	
10 Joints	**Content Evaluation:** p. 301 *Topic Review:* 10; p. 304-305 *Chapter Review:* 12
11 Dome Mountains	**Content Evaluation:** p. 301 *Topic Review:* 11; p. 304-305 *Chapter Review:* 13; Interpret and Apply: 2
Map Activities p. 302-303	Mountains and Plate Tectonics Folded Mountains
Chapter Review p. 304-305	Critical Thinking 1-5 **Study Guide:** Vocabulary; Interpreting and Applying
Chapter 16 Assessment Program	**Chapter Tests; Computer Test Bank**

CHAPTER 16

Motivator
The locations of several mountain ranges around the world are an important part of this chapter. This is a good opportunity to review a little geography. One way to start the chapter is by giving students an outline map of the world with these mountain chains indicated but not named. Ask students to write the names of the indicated mountains on the map. Mountain ranges that should be shown on the map are the Andes, the Coast Ranges, Cascades, Himalayas, Alps, Rockies, Sierra Nevadas, Wasatch Range, Tetons, Adirondacks, Henry Mountains, and the Black Hills. Other mountain ranges that could be included are the Atlas Mountains of North Africa, the Caucasus Mountains of Turkey, and the Appalachian Mountains. You may wish to include others.

Lesson I: Mountains Result from Collisions

(Topics 1-3)

Teaching Suggestions
The following are the basic ideas in this lesson:

■ Active continental margins are plate boundaries that involve two different lithospheric plates.

■ Passive continental margins involve only one plate. These margins are important because these are the only places where sediments can accumulate in large quantities.

■ In the collision of an oceanic plate with a continental plate, the oceanic plate subducts beneath the continent. Earthquakes and volcanoes are common, and a mountain range forms on the land.

- In some ocean-continent collisions, pieces of the oceanic plate have been scraped off and attached to the continent. These are the terranes that were discussed in Chapter 13.
- The collision between two continents starts as an ocean-continent collision with subduction until the two continents are in contact. Then subduction ceases and the rocks of the continents crumple into mountains. The Himalayas and the Alps are examples.

Lesson II: Features of Collision Mountains

(Topics 4-6)

Teaching Suggestions

Chalkboard drawings will be essential to your presentation of this lesson. Models made of wood, modeling clay, or even books might also be helpful.

The important thing to emphasize about fault types is the relationship of each to collision mountains. Normal faults are not common but do occur at these plate boundaries. Reverse faults are very important because they shorten the crust. Strike-slip faults are important where the collision is pushing material to one side.

You might consider the opener activity as an introduction to folds and a method of teaching students the terminology. Be sure that the students understand that strike and dip describes any rock layer, not just folded layers.

The important point with volcanoes is their relationship to subduction. Subduction zones are places where rocks are melted, and the associated volcanism occurs as long as subduction continues.

Lesson III: Other Evidences of Mountain Building

(Topics 7-9)

Teaching Suggestions

DEMONSTRATIONS: A simple demonstration can be done to show that most sedimentary rocks start out in level layers. The following materials will be needed: a transparent beaker large enough for your hand to fit inside; enough modeling clay or Plasticene to cover the bottom of the beaker with "hills and valleys"; slurry material, which can be kaolin (available at drugstores) or a mixture of silt and clay-sized particles; and a large test tube for mixing the slurry material with water.

Press the clay or Plasticene into the bottom of the beaker. Mold it into an uneven surface with high peaks and deep depressions. Fill the beaker one half to three quarters full of water. Place a quantity of the slurry material in the test tube, add water, and shake well. The amount of slurry material to be used will depend upon the size of the beaker and the thickness of the sediment layer to be made. After shaking, quickly pour the contents of the test tube into the beaker and allow it to settle. The material will settle into the depressions and leave the peaks bare, forming a horizontal layer over the bottom. The demonstration can be repeated daily until the clay is completely covered. A little food coloring added to the slurry material makes each layer of sediment easier to identify.

Another simple demonstration can be used to show how a surveyor measures the difference in elevation between two points. The following materials are needed: a pointer flashlight or any other light that can be brought to a slit or to a point; two metersticks; a ring stand; and a clamp large enough to hold the light to the ring stand.

Use the clamp and the ring stand to set up the light as level as possible. Set up the metersticks vertically in two different places in the room and at slightly different elevations. Shine the light on one of the metersticks and have a student take a reading on the illuminated part of the meterstick. Turn the ring stand to point the light at the other meterstick and take a second reading. The difference in the two readings is the difference in elevation between the two locations. This is essentially the method used by surveyors to detect changes in elevation.

Science Background

Surveyors using bench marks to determine changes in elevation use a small telescope called a *level* and two rods marked at equal intervals. The rods are placed about 60 meters apart on the route to be measured. The level is then set up halfway between the two rods. Looking through the level, the scale is read on one rod and then the other rod. The first rod is then moved ahead of the second by 60 meters, and the procedure is repeated. As many as 1000 readings may be taken to determine the elevations over a 50-kilometer route.

Lesson IV: Other Tectonic Features

(Topics 10-11)

Teaching Suggestions

Differentiate between *faults* and *joints* or *fractures*. All are cracks, but only faults have movement along the cracks. You might point out that the occurrence of joints is not limited to mountains—they can occur anywhere the crust has been stressed, including plateaus. Both the Colorado and Appalachian plateaus show extensive fracturing.

The distinction between plutonic and tectonic dome mountains may need some clarification. Plutonic domes have been pushed upward by an igneous intrusion. The intrusion came about after the sedimentary rocks were deposited. This means that the rock in the intrusion is younger than the sedimentary rocks it pushed up. Tectonic domes have been pushed up by vertical forces. For both the Adirondacks and the Black Hills, the core is Precambrian in age. The Precambrian rocks were beneath the sedimentary layers when a younger intrusion below all of the rocks caused the doming.

CHAPTER 16 MAP ACTIVITY
Mountains and Plate Boundaries

Time estimate
30-40 minutes

Process Skills
- Interpreting Diagrams: Procedure 2; Analysis and Conclusions 1
- Summarizing: Procedure 3, 4

- Determining Main Ideas: Procedure 6; Analysis and Conclusions 2, 3, 4

Procedural Hints
Before allowing students to start work on this activity, turn with them to each of the textbook pages used for the activity.

Answers—Procedure
2. Rockies and Appalachians on North American Plate, Andes on South American Plate, Atlas on African Plate, Alps and Himalayas on Eurasian Plate
3. Andes at the Nazca/South American plate boundary; Atlas and Alps at the African/Eurasian plate boundary; Himalayas at the Indian/Eurasian plate boundary
4. All are at active continental margins.
6. Active continental margins are converging boundaries. Mid-ocean ridges occur at diverging boundaries. The mountain chains on continents are the result of plates coming together; mountains form from the folding and faulting of the rocks due to compression. The mountains of the seafloor are the result of plates pulling apart and associated volcanism.

Answers—Analysis and Conclusions
1. The Andes are on an active continental margin and are therefore still forming. The Appalachians are on a passive continental margin. They were formed long ago when the eastern coast of North America was also an active continental margin. The Appalachians are smaller because of weathering and erosion over millions of years.
2. No. Australia is in the center of a plate and is surrounded by passive continental margins.
3. The Andes. The Andes are presently on an active continental margin; volcanoes are often associated with such margins. The Rockies are not near a plate margin.
4. Students know that *seismic* means that the boundary must be associated with earthquakes. Therefore, an aseismic boundary must lack earthquakes. *Seismic* is appropriate for active plate boundaries because they have earthquakes. *Aseismic* is appropriate for passive plate boundaries as they would not be expected to have earthquakes.

CHAPTER 16 MAP ACTIVITY
Folded Mountains

Time estimate
30-40 minutes

Process Skills
- Interpreting Diagrams: Procedure 1-6
- Summarizing: Analysis and Conclusions 1, 2

Materials
You can substitute any thin paper for the tracing paper.

Procedural Hints
Locate each of the maps your students will be using before setting your students to work. Familiarize yourself with the maps. Also have your students trace the outline of the cross-section before starting. They should set this paper aside until it is needed for *Procedure* question 6.

Answers—Procedure
1. Harrisburg is located in the Appalachian Mountains.
2. Peters, Third, Second, and Blue Mountains appear on both the map and cross-section. The cross-section was drawn in a mostly N-S direction.
3. Peters and Second Mountains are both formed from the Pocono Sandstone.
4. The overall structure is a syncline.
5. The ridges are made of sandstone and conglomerate while the valleys are made of limestone and shale.
6. Locknow is located on the oldest rock. Third Mountain is made of the youngest rock.

Answers—Analysis and Conclusions
1. The rock layers must be examined for such sedimentary features as ripple marks, cross-bedding, and mud cracks. Such features are not shown on topographic maps.
2. Any state that contains the Appalachian Mountains would be expected to have folded layers. Virginia, West Virginia, Tennessee, and North Carolina are four examples. Folded layers would not be expected to occur on the Atlantic Coastal Plain because it is a passive continental margin.

ANSWERS TO
CHAPTER 16 REVIEW

Review
1–d, 2–b, 3–d, 4–b, 5–a, 6–a, 7–d, 8–b, 9–c, 10–d, 11–b, 12–c, 13–a

Interpret and Apply
1. Passive, because the western edge of the continent is not on the edge of the plate. The African Plate extends to the mid-Atlantic Ridge.
2. The low hill must be a dome because the ridges of rock surround it. The fact that the oldest rocks are at the center of the dome indicates that it is a tectonic dome.
3. The sedimentary layers of a tectonic dome were deposited on the igneous rock and therefore will not have been metamorphosed by it. The sedimentary layers of a plutonic dome, however, were pushed upward by the intrusion and would be expected to show thermal metamorphism.

Critical Thinking
1. east; west
2. The rocks at *B* are more resistant to weathering than the rocks at *C*; the elevation of *B* is higher than *C*.
3. Since the rock layers have not been overturned, the oldest layers must be at the bottom of the profile and the youngest at the top. Therefore, the rocks become older from *B* to *D* and younger from *E* to *D*.
4. The oldest rocks are at the center of an anticline, the youngest at the center of a syncline.
5. A normal fault will lengthen the distance because the east side would drop down the fault plane. A reverse fault will shorten the distance because the east side would be pushed up the fault plane.

CHAPTER **17**
Properties of Ocean Water

PLANNING CHART

Topic	Support Material
Lesson I Earth — The Water Planet	
1 The World Ocean	**Content Evaluation:** p. 311 *Topic Review:* 1; p. 320-321 *Chapter Review:* 2, 3; **Transparency 31:** Ocean Floor Profiles
2 Beginnings of Oceanography	**Content Evaluation:** p. 311 *Topic Review:* 2; p. 320-321 *Chapter Review:* 10
3 Seagoing Oceano-graphic Research	**Content Evaluation:** p. 311 *Topic Review:* 3; p. 320-321 *Chapter Review:* 1, 11
Lesson II The Salinity of Sea Water	**Laboratory Investigation:** Sea Water and Fresh Water **In-Text Lab Activity:** Interpreting a Salinity Profile
4 Salinity	**Content Evaluation:** p. 313 *Topic Review:* 4; p. 320-321 *Chapter Review:* 6, 7, 13, 17
5 Measuring Salinity	**Content Evaluation:** p. 313 *Topic Review:* 5; p. 320-321 *Chapter Review:* 9, 19
6 The Composition of Sea Water	**Content Evaluation:** p. 313 *Topic Review:* 6; p. 320-321 *Chapter Review:* 8; Interpret and Apply: 3
7 Mining Sea Water	**Content Evaluation:** p. 313 *Topic Review:* 7; p. 320-321 *Chapter Review:* 12
Lesson III The Temper-ature of Ocean Water	
8 Heating the Oceans	**Content Evaluation:** p. 315 *Topic Review:* 8; p. 320-321 *Chapter Review:* 14
9 The Mixed Layer	**Content Evaluation:** p. 315 *Topic Review:* 9; p. 320-321 *Chapter Review:* 14
10 Temperatures under the Mixed Layer	**Content Evaluation:** p. 315 *Topic Review:* 10; p. 320-321 *Chapter Review:* 16, 18; Interpret and Apply: 1, 4

PLANNING CHART (continued)

Topic	Support Material
Lesson IV **Life in the Sea**	
11 Sunlight and Marine Life	**Content Evaluation:** p. 317 *Topic Review:* 11; p. 320-321 *Chapter Review:* 15, 20; Interpret and Apply: 2
12 Oxygen and Marine Life	**Content Evaluation:** p. 317 *Topic Review:* 12; p. 320-321 *Chapter Review:* 16; Interpret and Apply: 1, 4
13 Ocean-Floor Vents	**Content Evaluation:** p. 317 *Topic Review:* 13; p. 320-321 *Chapter Review:* 4, 5
Lab Activity p. 318-319	Interpreting a Salinity Profile
Chapter Review p. 320-321	Critical Thinking 1-3 **Study Guide:** Vocabulary; Interpreting and Applying
Chapter 17 Assessment Program	**Chapter Tests; Computer Test Bank**

Introducing UNIT **FOUR**

Student Writing

New discoveries about the oceans are often reported in popular science magazines and in newspapers. A unit on oceanography provides a good opportunity for students to practice the skills required for a research paper. Students should select a general research topic early in their study of Unit Four to allow time for research, the narrowing of the topic, making a concept map, and the actual writing before they have finished the unit. Several topics are suggested by the photos and captions in the Unit Four introduction on pages 306–307. Some topics are listed below. There are many more that could be pursued.

- Use of radar in ocean research, or in the fishing industry
- Role of estuaries in marine life cycles
- Life at ocean-floor vents
- Mining and using ocean resources
- Discovery of the mid-Atlantic Ridge
- International laws governing ocean use and resources

- Preventing pollution of the ocean
- Effects of ocean current changes on climate
- Importance of marine plankton to climate
- Farming the ocean
- Oceans as buffers for the greenhouse effect

CHAPTER 17

Motivator

DEMONSTRATION: Obtain or prepare a sample of ocean water. If you prepare it, use accurate proportions—965 grams of water to 35 grams of common salt. For this demonstration you will also need four 400-mL beakers, an hydrometer, and a hot plate. Determine the mass of one of the empty beakers. Record the value for use with Lesson II. Then pour a quantity of the ocean water sample (3/4 beaker or more) into the pre-massed beaker and find the new mass. Save this value for Lesson II also. Now pour an equal quantity of tap water (or local lake or river water) into another 400-mL beaker. Then place both beakers on a hot plate and evaporate to dryness.

For class, prepare two other beakers—one of

ocean water, one of the other water. Ask students how to determine which beaker contains ocean water. Taste may be suggested, but remind students that taste tests are not allowed in science class. Other possibilities include the following. *Density:* Use the hydrometer to show that one solution has a higher density than the other solution. *Evaporation:* Show the two evaporated beakers and ask which was ocean water and how that answer was determined. Students should be able to see that the ocean water beaker has more material left in it than the fresh water beaker.

Lesson I: Earth—The Water Planet

(Topics 1-3)

Teaching Suggestions
Use the graph below to introduce this lesson. Either prepare the graph for projection or have students draw the graph themselves. With the graph, ask these questions:

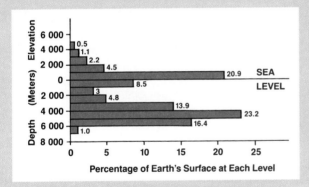

1. Between what elevations above sea level does the greatest percentage of the land surface occur? (sea level to 1000 meters)
2. What is the total percentage of landmass above sea level? (0.5 + 1.1 + 2.2 + 4.5 + 20.9 = 29.2%)
3. If sea level rose 1000 meters, how would the percentage of land above sea level be affected? How would this affect people? (The land area would be reduced by 20.9 percent. In the United States, all of our coastal cities and the large population areas around them would be underwater, along with a great deal of important agricultural land. A map would help to show this. In addition, have students speculate on what could cause sea level to rise. Work toward the idea of the melting of the polar ice caps as a result of increased atmospheric temperature from increased CO_2 absorption in the greenhouse effect.)
4. At what depth below sea level does the greatest percentage of land surface occur? (4000 to 5000 meters)
5. The depth of the Marianas Trench is 11 040 meters. Why doesn't it show on a chart? (So little of Earth's surface is at depths below 7000 meters.)

Be sure to relate this graph to Figure 17.1 in the text and establish the fact that most of Earth's surface is below sea level.

Science Background
The expedition of *H.M.S. Challenger* was not the only early scientific cruise. The voyages of Christopher Columbus in 1492, Magellan from 1519 to 1522 (he is supposed to have tried a depth sounding in the Pacific Ocean), James Cook in 1772 (he sailed around Antarctica), the voyage of the *Beagle* carrying Charles Darwin, and the voyages of *Discovery I, Discovery II, Carnegie,* and *Meteor* can also be counted as scientific expeditions. There were many others. If students have an interest in history of oceanography, it makes an excellent research topic.

Glomar Challenger was an important oceanographic research ship. It was commissioned in 1967 by the Scripps Institution of Oceanography in La Jolla, California. The *Challenger* was the research vessel for the Deep Sea Drilling Project (DSDP). The *Glomar Challenger* carried equipment that was able to drill into rock located as deep as 4 km beneath the ocean surface. The ship was retired in November of 1983 after more than 96 voyages. The JOIDES *Resolution* is the research ship for the Ocean Drilling Program (ODP), an international program that is funded by many nations. The National Science Foundation is the U.S. sponsor of ODP. As with the DSDP, regular summaries of the cruises of the *Resolution* appear in *Geotimes Magazine.*

The deepest piloted submarine is the U.S. Navy's *Sea Cliff,* which can carry a crew of three to a depth of about 6000 meters. *Alvin* was also built by the Navy; however it is operated by the Woods Hole Oceanographic Institution on Cape Cod in Massachusetts.

J.J. (Jason Jr.) is one of a group of remotely operated vehicles (ROV) now being used extensively for seafloor exploration. An advanced ROV, the *Gemini*, played an important part in the recovery of the wreckage of the space shuttle *Challenger*.

The location of the *Titanic* was discovered in November of 1984. In 1986, the *Titanic* was visited by *Alvin* and *J.J.* Neither craft is expected to return to the wreck. According to legend, the *Titanic* sank because an iceberg tore a hole in its hull. Yet, no gash was found. Scientists now think that the iceberg buckled the plates of the hull, allowing water to pour in.

Lesson II: The Salinity of Sea Water

(Topics 4-7)

Teaching Suggestions

DEMONSTRATION: Use the data set aside from the *Motivator* to determine the salinity of your sample of ocean water. Write the mass of the empty beaker on the board along with the mass of the beaker with the sample. Then determine the mass of the beaker once again, this time with the water evaporated and the salts remaining. From these data, have students determine the following:

1. the mass of the sea water placed in the beaker,
2. the mass of the residue that remained in the beaker, and
3. the salinity of the sample. To do this, divide the mass of the residue by the original mass of the sea water and then multiply by 1000. Your value for salinity should be close to 35‰.

Stress with this lesson the difference between salinity and composition. *Salinity* is the amount of dissolved material; *composition* is the ions that make up the dissolved material. No matter what the salinity, the relative percentage of the different ions remains constant, that is, the "recipe" for salts is the same—55.04% chloride ion, 7.68% sulfate ion, and so on—no matter what the total amount of salts.

Lesson III: The Temperature of Ocean Water

(Topics 8-10)

Teaching Suggestions

Ask students for the relationship between water temperature and depth in the ocean. Use their answers to develop the three temperature layers of the ocean—surface mixed layer, thermocline, and cold bottom layer. A chalkboard drawing should help.

The temperature reading of –2°C in Topic 9 may need some explanation. Point out that, unlike fresh water, sea water does not freeze at 0°C. At a salinity of 35‰; sea water freezes at –1.9°C. When water freezes in the polar regions, the salt is left behind, making the salinity of the water there higher. As salinity increases, the freezing point decreases. Therefore a –2°C temperature could still not be cold enough to freeze sea water with a high salinity.

Specific heat could be added to this discussion. The specific heat of water is 1.0 cal/g/°C. This is the highest specific heat of any natural substance and is another reason why water is difficult to heat. It is also the reason why oceans and lakes retain heat in the fall and make nearby locations warmer in the winter.

Lesson IV: Life in the Sea

(Topics 11 - 13)

Teaching Suggestions

Samples of diatoms are interesting to look at and easy to obtain. Diatoms are present in freshwater lakes and rivers as well as in the ocean. You may need to boil a sample in order to concentrate the diatoms. Place a drop on a glass slide and examine with a microscope.

Diatoms serve as water pollution indicators. In addition to a change in species with pollution, population diversity decreases. A crude estimate of pollution in your water sample would be a count of the number of different kinds of diatoms in the sample.

CHAPTER 17 LAB ACTIVITY
Interpreting a Salinity Profile

■ A student report sheet for this activity can be found in the *Laboratory Investigations* booklet.

Time estimate
40-50 minutes

Process Skills
■ Constructing Tables and Graphs: Procedure 4
■ Interpreting Diagrams: Analysis and Conclusions 1, 3, 4, 7, 8
■ Determining Cause and Effect: Analysis and Conclusions 4, 5, 6

Procedural Hints
It may help if the students color code the data points before drawing the lines. Make sure that students understand that the lines they draw should not intersect and that all lines should begin and end at the graph's margins.

Answers—Procedure
Answers to *Procedure* questions 4–5 can be found on the annotated graph, page 319, of this Teachers Annotated Edition.

Answers—Analysis and Conclusions
1. Average salinity is 35‰. The average is found at 2200 and 2400 meters on the profile.
2. The highest values are located at station 79 at depths of 0 and 1000 meters. The lowest values are located at stations 74 and 75 at a depth of 2200 meters and at stations 74–78 at a depth of 2400 feet.
3. Hot, dry summers, and mild, rainy winters
4. A hot, dry climate would cause evaporation, increasing salinity at the surface but not affecting the salinity at deeper levels. High salinity at the surface of the profile and low salinity at the deepest levels supports this.
5. Salinity increases from west to east with very high salinity at station 79. Such a profile would not directly be caused by climate.
6. The Mediterranean Sea has very high salinity. Water from the Mediterranean Sea is responsible for higher salinity in deeper levels.
7. A current flows west from the Mediterranean Sea at a depth of 800–1200 meters.

8. No. Except for depths of 800–1200 meters, the highest salinity is at the surface and lowest salinity at deepest levels.

CHAPTER 17 REVIEW

Review
1–d, 2–i, 3–o, 4–n, 5–a, 6–h, 7–q, 8–k, 9–c, 10–l, 11–p, 12–s, 13–t, 14–b, 15–j, 16–r, 17–f, 18–g, 19–e, 20–m

Interpret and Apply
1. There are two factors. One is that the bottom of the Mediterranean Sea never gets the benefit of oxygen brought in by deep water flow. The other factor is that the temperature of the bottom of the Mediterranean Sea is relatively warm and cannot hold as much dissolved oxygen as colder water.
2. Diatom shells are made of silica. The removal of silica for the building of these shells is thought to be the major cause of the smaller oceanic concentration.
3. These are the two major ions in sea water. They accumulate and build up in the ocean because (a) no organisms remove them and (b) they are too soluble to precipitate out.
4. Deep water masses formed in the polar regions. Once the water mass sank, no oxygen could be added, but oxygen could be lost. Thus the amount of dissolved oxygen would be expected to decrease the longer ago the water mass left the surface.

Critical Thinking
1. Sink. Using the graph, the average Atlantic water has a density slightly less than 1.028 g/cm³, while Mediterranean water is slightly above the same value. Therefore, Mediterranean water is more dense and should sink.
2. By extrapolating below the graph, the density is about 1.028 g/cm³.
3. The density of the new water mass will be more. The density lines are curved. The new point will be on the concave side of the line and therefore on the denser side of the line.

CHAPTER 18
The Ocean Floor and Its Sediments

PLANNING CHART

Topic	Support Material
Lesson I Studying the Ocean Floor	
1 Echo Sounding and Satellites	**Content Evaluation:** p. 325 *Topic Review: 1;* p. 340-341 *Chapter Review: 1;* Interpret and Apply: 5
2 Sampling the Sediments	**Content Evaluation:** p. 325 *Topic Review: 2;* p. 340-341 *Chapter Review: 2*
3 Direct Observations	**Content Evaluation:** p. 325 *Topic Review: 3;* p. 340-341 *Chapter Review: 3*
Lesson II The Continental Margins	**Laboratory Investigation:** Seafloor Analysis **In-Text Map Activity:** The Ocean Floor **In-Text Lab Activity:** Contour of the Ocean Floor
4 Continental Shelves	**Content Evaluation:** p. 329 *Topic Review: 4;* p. 340-341 *Chapter Review: 4, 5,* **Transparency 31:** Ocean Floor Profiles
5 Continental Slopes	**Content Evaluation:** p. 329 *Topic Review: 5;* p. 340-341 *Chapter Review: 6, 7*
6 The Origin of Submarine Canyons	**Content Evaluation:** p. 329 *Topic Review: 6;* p. 340-341 *Chapter Review: 7, 8;* Interpret and Apply: 1, 3, 4
7 Continental Rises	**Content Evaluation:** p. 329 *Topic Review: 7;* p. 340-341 *Chapter Review: 6*
Lesson III The Temperature of Ocean Water	
8 Abyssal Plains	**Content Evaluation:** p. 335 *Topic Review: 8;* p. 340-341 *Chapter Review: 9;* Interpret and Apply: 2, 3
9 Abyssal Hills	**Content Evaluation:** p. 335 *Topic Review: 9;* p. 340-341 *Chapter Review: 10;* Interpret and Apply: 2
10 Seamounts, Guyots, and Coral Atolls	**Content Evaluation:** p. 335 *Topic Review: 10;* p. 340-341 *Chapter Review: 11, 12*
11 Trenches	**Content Evaluation:** p. 335 *Topic Review: 11;* p. 340-341 *Chapter Review: 13*

PLANNING CHART (continued)

Topic	Support Material
Lesson III (continued) **12 Mid-Ocean Ridges**	**Content Evaluation:** p. 335 *Topic Review:* 12; p. 340-341 *Chapter Review:* 14, 15; Interpret and Apply: 2
13 Fracture Zones	**Content Evaluation:** p. 335 *Topic Review:* 13; p. 340-341 *Chapter Review:* 16
Lesson IV **Life in the Sea**	
14 Oozes	**Content Evaluation:** p. 337 *Topic Review:* 14; p. 340-341 *Chapter Review:* 17
15 Muds and Clays	**Content Evaluation:** p. 337 *Topic Review:* 15; p. 340-341 *Chapter Review:* 18
16 Turbidites	**Content Evaluation:** p. 337 *Topic Review:* 16; p. 340-341 *Chapter Review:* 19; Interpret and Apply: 4
17 Authigenic Sediments	**Content Evaluation:** p. 337 *Topic Review:* 17; 340-341 *Chapter Review:* 20
Map and Lab Activities p. 338-339	The Ocean Floor Contour of the Ocean Floor
Chapter Review p. 340-341	Critical Thinking 1-5 **Study Guide:** Vocabulary; Interpreting and Applying
Chapter 18 Assessment Program	**Chapter Tests; Computer Test Bank**

CHAPTER 18

Motivator

It is important to emphasize how difficult it is to learn about the seafloor because it cannot be seen from the ocean surface. Ask students how many of them can swim underwater. For those who can, ask them how far down they can swim. Use their answers to point out that even with scuba equipment, they could not explore very far down into the ocean, much less explore most of the ocean floor.

  DEMONSTRATION: If time allows, a more involved motivator demonstrates how difficult it is to learn about a surface (the seafloor) that cannot be seen directly. First, obtain a large cardboard box and a wood dowel. The dowel must be long enough to reach from the top to the bottom of the box with enough left over at the top to grasp. Calibrate the dowel so that it can be used to make measurements. Turn the box so that a smooth side, which will represent the ocean surface, is at the top. Draw a grid on the top of the box. (Five-centimeter squares work well; smaller boxes require smaller grid scales.) Drill or punch holes at the intersections of the grid. The holes must be large enough for the dowel rod to slide into. Next, place an object on the bottom of the box. A plastic hemisphere works well, but any other object with simple dimensions could be used. The object should not be visible to the students. Now use the calibrated dowel to determine the depth to the "seafloor" at each location on the grid. Students should soon see the difficulty of

Chapter 18 The Ocean Floor and Its Sediments **T791**

obtaining data about a surface that cannot be seen.

Have students use the data to draw seafloor profiles across the box. Relate their profiles to those drawn by a precision depth recorder. A contour map of the "seafloor" could also be drawn from the data.

Although this demonstration requires some preparation time, the preparation time is needed only once. The same box with the same "seafloor" can be used for several years.

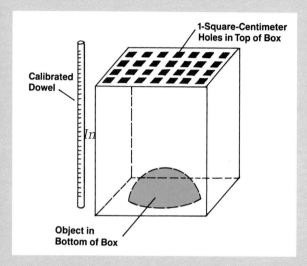

1-Square-Centimeter Holes in Top of Box

Calibrated Dowel

In

Object in Bottom of Box

Lesson I: Studying the Ocean Floor

(Topics 1-3)

Teaching Suggestions
The following problem could be done to show how an echo can be used to determine depth: If sound waves travel 1500 meters per second in sea water, what is the water depth if the echo of a sound pulse takes 6 seconds to return? *Answer:* 4500 meters. If sound travels at 1500 meters per second for 6 seconds, the total distance is 9000 meters. However, this is the total distance to the seafloor and back. The water depth is only half that number, or 4500 meters.

Lesson II: The Continental Margins

(Topics 4-7)

Teaching Suggestions
DEMONSTRATION: Demonstrate a turbidity current using the following equipment: a large graduated cylinder (1000 mL), a small amount of kaolin or clay, a small test tube, and water. Mix the kaolin with water in the test tube. This mixture will represent the turbidity current. Fill the graduated cylinder with water, but not all the way to the top. The cylinder will represent the ocean at a continental slope. Tilt the cylinder at about a 30° angle. Pour the kaolin mixture into the top of the cylinder and watch the resulting cloud flow down the tube. The flowing cloud is a model of a turbidity current.

Science Background
The final confirmation of the existence of turbidity currents was made possible by a magnitude 7.2 earthquake that occurred on the continental slope off the Grand Banks of Newfoundland in 1929. Several transatlantic telephone and telegraph cables crossed the area. After the earthquake, the cables were snapped in sequence down the slope and away from the epicenter of the earthquake. Some of the breaks occurred as much as 13 hours later, much too long after the earthquake to have been directly caused by the earthquake. The only plausible explanation was a turbidity current activated by the earthquake. By knowing the exact time when each cable snapped, it was determined that the turbidity current had reached speeds of 40 to 55 kilometers per hour. Similar patterns were then found for cable breaks on continental slopes in other parts of the world.

The Grand Banks turbidity currents deposited a graded bed of sediment (turbidite) as far as 700 kilometers away from its source. A survey of the area in the late 1980's using sidescan sonar and a minisubmarine led to the discovery of "gravel dunes." These are 2- to 3-meter-high ridges located 50 to 100 meters apart. Scientists feel that such large ridges could only result from the rapid flow associated with a turbidity current. A search for similar dunes along other coastlines has begun.

Lesson III:
The Ocean Basins

(Topics 8-13)

Teaching Suggestions

Points to be made with this lesson include the following:

1. The abyssal plains are flat surfaces that cover extensive portions of the ocean basin, with slopes of less than 1:1000.

2. The abyssal hills may be the original seafloor that forms at the ridges and is buried by turbidity currents to form abyssal plains. (If the demonstration in Chapter 16 of the kaolin layers on the hilly surface of clay in the bottom of the beaker was performed, remind students that they have already seen that sediment is deposited in horizontal layers that hide irregular topography.)

3. Seamounts are volcanic peaks. Guyots are flat-topped seamounts. Most occur in the Pacific Ocean.

4. The trenches are locations where one lithospheric plate is moving down beneath another lithospheric plate. The major trenches occur around the margin of the Pacific Ocean. The Peru-Chile Trench is the longest, and the Marianas Trench is the deepest.

5. The mid-ocean ridges form a mountain chain that circles the world. These ridges are places where new material is being added to the plates as they move apart. The characteristics of the ridge are determined by the rate of spreading. In general, movement of less than 2.5 centimeters a year results in ridges with central rift valleys and rugged profiles, such as the mid-Atlantic Ridge, while faster-forming ridges, such as the East Pacific Rise, lack rift valleys and are less rugged.

6. Mid-ocean ridges are interrupted at fracture zones. Earthquakes occur along transform faults where opposite sides of the fault move in opposite directions.

Science Background

Deep-Sea Trenches: The dimensions of the ten deepest trenches are listed here for your convenience.

Trench	Depth (km)	Length (km)	Average Width (km)
Marianas	11.0	2550	70
Philippine	10.5	1400	60
Tonga	10.8	1400	55
Kermadec	10.0	1500	40
Aleutian	7.7	3700	50
Middle American	6.7	2800	40
Peru-Chile	8.1	5900	100
Puerto Rico	8.4	1500	120
South Sandwich	8.4	1450	90
Java	7.5	4500	80

Fracture Zones: The first fracture zones to receive careful study were off the Pacific coast of N. America. Geologists speculated that the San Andreas Fault system was a family of faults connecting the East Pacific Rise with the Juan de Fuca Ridge. The East Pacific Rise ends in the Gulf of California and the Juan de Fuca Ridge is off the Washington coast.

Lesson IV:
Sediments of the Ocean Floor

(Topics 14-17)

Teaching Suggestions

DEMONSTRATION: Start the lesson with a demonstration of a graded bed. The materials needed are a large graduated cylinder (500 to 1000 mL); a mixture of sand, silt, and clay-size particles (dry); and water. Fill the graduated cylinder nearly to the top with water. Then drop a handful of the particle mixture into the tube. The larger particles will settle faster than the smaller particles, and a graded bed with coarse particles on the bottom and fine particles on the top will form. If you repeat the demonstration over a period of several days, the relationship to the thick sequence of graded beds on the abyssal plains will be seen even better.

CHAPTER 18 **MAP** ACTIVITY
The Ocean Floor

■ A student report sheet for this activity can be found in the *Laboratory Investigations* booklet.

Time estimate
25–30 minutes

Process Skills
■ Interpreting Diagrams: Procedure 1, 2, 3, 4, 5, 6
■ Determining Cause and Effect: Analysis and Conclusions: 1, 2, 3
■ Summarizing: Analysis and Conclusions 4

Answers—Procedure
1. Most trenches occur near the edges of continents or other landmasses.
2. The longest trench is the Peru-Chile Trench, which extends along the west coast of South America.
3. Most mid-ocean ridges occur at a distance from landmasses.
4. The long parallel lines represent transform faults.
5. The line along the mid-ocean ridge can be described as a jagged line with steplike features; the ridges are offset at the transform fault.
6. The features are trenches and seamounts. Trenches form when one plate subducts beneath another plate. Seamounts are submerged underwater volcanoes.

Answers—Analysis and Conclusions
1. Trenches occur where one plate subducts below another plate. According to the plate tectonic theory, this occurs where two plates converge.
2. The shelf along the east coast is wider than the shelf along the west coast. The east coast is a passive margin; the west coast is an active margin.
3. Ocean trenches are smooth curves; mid-ocean ridges are jagged. The transform faults along the mid-ocean ridge are responsible for the differences.
4. Japan lies along a plate boundary where the movement causes earthquakes. Australia lies in the middle of a plate.

CHAPTER 18 **LAB** ACTIVITY
Contour of the Ocean Floor

■ A student report sheet for this activity can be found in the *Laboratory Investigations* booklet.

Time estimate
40–50 minutes

Process Skills
■ Constructing Tables and Graphs: Procedure 1, 2, 3, 4, 5, 6; Analysis and Conclusions 3
■ Interpreting Diagrams: Analysis and Conclusions 1
■ Determining Cause and Effect: Analysis and Conclusions 2
■ Calculate: Analysis and Conclusions 4

Answers—Analysis and Conclusions
1. The shelf is about 160 km wide at Cape May and 40 km wide at Cape Roca.
2. The continental shelf on the east coast of North America is approximately four times as wide as that of the west coast of Europe.
3. See student graphs.
4. Slope at Cape May is 1000 – 100 fathoms/ 200 – 160 kilometers = 900/40 = 22.5 fathoms per kilometer and at Cape Roca, 1000 – 100 fathoms/ 5560 – 5440 kilometers = 900/120 = 7.5 fathoms per kilometer.

ANSWERS TO
CHAPTER 18 R E V I E W

Review
1–weight, 2–history, 3–deep-towed, 4–shelf, 5–active, 6–rise, 7–canyons, 8–currents, 9–plains, 10–ridges, 11–seamounts, 12–tops, 13–Pacific, 14–mountain, 15–rift, 16–faults, 17–shells, 18–suspended clay, volcanoes, icebergs, 19–graded, 20–nodules

Interpret and Apply
1. Turbidity currents are undersea landslides. The continental shelf edge near rivers is the place sediments build up in enough quantity to form these landslides.
2. The highest elevations are the mid-ocean ridges, where the rough topography beneath

abyssal hills forms. Because heated material expands, mid-ocean ridges are higher than the rest of the seafloor. As the lithosphere moves away from the mid-ocean ridges, the rock cools and contracts, lowering the ocean floor.

3. The basic reason goes back to active versus passive continental margins. The Atlantic Ocean is primarily an ocean of passive margins. As a result, there is an unlimited supply of accumulating sediment available for movement to the deep seafloor and for the formation of abyssal plains. The Pacific Ocean, on the other hand, is surrounded by active continental margins. Active margins have deep-sea trenches that trap sediment before it reaches the deep seafloor.

4. (1) Glaciers left large quantities of loose debris, which was easily picked up and moved to stream mouths by rivers. (2) River flow increased as the ice melted and therefore rivers could carry more material. (3) Sea level was lower, exposing large areas of continental shelf sediments to erosion.

5. (a) Setting up a proportion:

$$\frac{1500 \text{ m}}{1 \text{ s}} = \frac{x}{12 \text{ s}}$$

$$x = \frac{1500 \text{ m} \times 12 \text{ s}}{1 \text{ s}}$$

$$x = 18\ 000 \text{ m}$$

This is the distance to the seafloor and back. Depth is equal to half that distance, or 9000 meters. (b) A deep sea trench.

Critical Thinking

1. deposition
2. glacial marine
3. glacial, cosmic, and volcanic
4. Globigerina are calcareous oozes. Calcite dissolves below about 4500 meters. Many abyssal plains are deeper than that.
5. Authigenic materials form in place on the seafloor. They are not deposited from the surface.

CHAPTER 19
Ocean Currents

PLANNING CHART

Topic	Support Material
Lesson I **Surface Currents**	**In-Text Map Activity:** World Ocean Currents
1 Ocean Currents	**Content Evaluation:** p. 347 *Topic Review:* 1; p. 354-355 *Chapter Review:* 1, 2; Interpret and Apply: 1, 3, 4; **Transparency 10:** Surface Ocean Currents
2 Currents and Winds	**Content Evaluation:** p. 347 *Topic Review:* 2; p. 354-355 *Chapter Review:* 3; Interpret and Apply: 2
3 Warm Currents	**Content Evaluation:** p. 347 *Topic Review:* 3; p. 354-355 *Chapter Review:* 4, 5; Interpret and Apply: 3, 4, 5
4 Gulf Stream Rings	**Content Evaluation:** p. 347 *Topic Review:* 4; p. 354-355 *Chapter Review:* 6
5 Cold Currents	**Content Evaluation:** p. 347 *Topic Review:* 5; p. 354-355 *Chapter Review:* 2; Interpret and Apply: 1, 3, 4
6 Countercurrents	**Content Evaluation:** p. 347 *Topic Review:* 6; p. 354-355 *Chapter Review:* 7; Interpret and Apply: 5
Lesson I Currents **Under the Surface**	**Laboratory Investigation:** Density Currents
7 Density Currents	**Content Evaluation:** p. 351 *Topic Review:* 7; p. 354-355 *Chapter Review:* 8; Interpret and Apply: 6
8 Density Currents by Evaporation	**Content Evaluation:** p. 351 *Topic Review:* 8; p. 354-355 *Chapter Review:* 9; Interpret and Apply: 6, 7
9 Density Currents from Polar Water	**Content Evaluation:** p. 351 *Topic Review:* 9; p. 354-355 *Chapter Review:* 10, 11; Interpret and Apply: 6
10 Upwelling	**Content Evaluation:** p. 351 *Topic Review:* 10; p. 354-355 *Chapter Review:* 12
Map Activity p. 352-353	World Ocean Currents
Chapter Review p. 354-355	Critical Thinking 1-5 **Study Guide:** Vocabulary; Interpreting and Applying
Chapter 19 Assessment Program	**Chapter Tests; Computer Test Bank**

CHAPTER 19

Motivator

DEMONSTRATION: While students may be aware of the existence of surface ocean currents, they may not be aware that there are also vertical currents in the ocean. Try the following demonstration. Obtain a soup plate with a wide, flat rim. Fill it with water until half the rim is covered. Tell the students that the soup plate represents an ocean, and the rim is the continental shelf. Gently squirt a few drops of ink into the water at the very edge of the plate. The ink will form a current that slowly moves over the edge of the rim and down the side to the bottom. Ask students whether this kind of movement would be considered a current and why. Then lead into a discussion of the definition of *ocean current* as given in Topic 1.

Lesson I: Surface Currents

(Topics 1-6)

Teaching Suggestions

Draw a generalized ocean basin between two continents. Then divide the basin into northern and southern halves and draw the current pattern that flows in each.

Students need to know that winds and ocean currents turn to their right in the Northern Hemisphere and to their left in the Southern Hemisphere. The Coriolis effect is discussed in a later chapter.

DEMONSTRATION: A drift bottle floats just below the surface of the water, where it is moved by currents but not by wind. Although the use of drift bottles to trace currents in oceanography is largely obsolete, such a demonstration has merit because it illustrates density adjustment. To make a drift bottle, fill a small test tube with water and seal it with a stopper. Fill a large container with water. Place the test tube in the large container of water and

point out that it sinks. Then, pour off water from the test tube a little at a time, until it floats just below the surface of the water. Ask students why the tube needs to float below the surface. (If the bottle were partly above the water, it might be moved by winds and would not accurately show the path of the current.)

Teaching Suggestions

Two math problems help compare the relative sizes of the currents and rivers discussed in Topic 3.

1. Based upon the data in Topic 3, how much more water moves in the Gulf Stream than in the Mississippi River? (Answer: 5000 times more. The Gulf Stream moves 100 000 000 cubic meters each second, or 1×10^8 m³/s. The Mississippi River discharges 20 000 cubic meters each second, or 2×10^4 m³/s. 1×10^8 divided by 2×10^4 is 5×10^3, or 5000.)

2. The largest transport system in the world is the West-Wind Drift that circles Antarctica. The current there can move 200 000 000 cubic meters of water each second. How does this compare with the Gulf Stream and the Mississippi River? (Answer: The West-Wind Drift carries twice the water of the Gulf Stream and 10 000 times the water of the Mississippi River.)

Science Background

In addition to wind, geostrophic flow helps drive ocean currents. This flow occurs because the ocean surface is uneven; it bulges upward inside the current circles. One reason for an upward bulge is the lower density of water in areas such as the Sargasso Sea. The less dense water floats as a lens on top of the rest of the ocean. The density differences between the Sargasso and the rest of the ocean result in unequal water pressure. The force of gravity pulls the water particles in the bulge down toward the level of the rest of the ocean. While the particles are being pulled down, they are turned clockwise in the Northern Hemisphere and counterclockwise in the Southern Hemisphere. Geostrophic flow may be an important factor in the flow of the Gulf Stream.

Lesson II:
Currents under the Surface

(Topics 7-10)

Teaching Suggestions

DEMONSTRATION: A salt fountain demonstrates how currents form as a result of density differences. To make a model of a salt fountain, you will need a small container (a cardboard frozen juice container works well), something to punch a hole in the small container, another container large enough to submerge the small container, several paper clips, food coloring, cold water, warm water, and warm salt water. Begin by punching a hole in the bottom of the small container. Place several paper clips around the open end of the small container so that it will set up slightly off the bottom of the large container. Place the small container open side down in the large container. Pour cold water into the large container to a level about halfway up the small container. Then pour hot water on top of the cold water, taking care to avoid mixing the two temperatures. Continue pouring until the warm water has forced cold water into the fountain container to the level of the hole. Then carefully pour warm salt water over the top of the small container. Finally place a drop of food coloring or other dye over the hole in the small container. The dye makes it possible to follow the water rising through the hole forming the salt fountain. The fountain starts to flow immediately and continues to flow for some time.

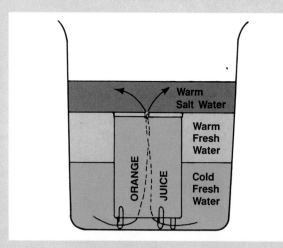

The salt fountain works because the warm and cold fresh water at the bottom of the fountain are less dense than the salt water on top. Once the fresh water begins to come out through the hole, water from the bottom rises through the container. The water warms and becomes less dense as it rises. The fountain flows until temperature and salt content are more uniform. In tropical oceans, surface water tends to be warmer and saltier than bottom water. Theoretically, water should flow indefinitely through a pipe from the surface to the bottom once a pump sets the process in motion.

CHAPTER 19 MAP ACTIVITY
World Ocean Currents

■ A student report sheet for this activity can be found in the *Laboratory Investigations* booklet.

Time estimate
35–45 minutes

Process Skills

■ Comparing/Contrasting: Analysis and Conclusions 1

■ Interpreting Diagrams: Procedure 1; Analysis and Conclusions 3, 4

■ Determining Cause and Effect: Procedure 7, 11

■ Stating a Conclusion: Analysis and Conclusions 2

■ Analyzing Data: Procedure 1, 2

Procedural Hints
The different directions of wind and ocean current can be attributed to the Coriolis effect. If students raise the question, the Coriolis effect could be discussed at this time. Otherwise it is covered in both Chapters 25 and 28, at which time reference could be made to this activity.

Answers—Procedure

1. Answers to *Procedure* question 1 can be found on the annotated table, page 353 of this Teachers Annotated Edition.

2. Warm currents flow away from the equator; cold currents flow toward the equator. The equator is warm, and therefore currents flowing from equatorial regions are warm.

Currents flowing toward the equator originate in colder areas and are therefore cold.

3. Warm ocean currents are found on the west sides of ocean basins, while cold ocean currents occur on the east sides.

4. west

5. southwest

6. right

7. Ocean currents in the Northern Hemisphere flow to the right of the winds that cause them.

8. west

9. northwest

10. left

11. Ocean currents in the Southern Hemisphere flow to the left of the winds that cause them.

Answers—Analysis and Conclusions

1. clockwise in Northern Hemisphere; counterclockwise in Southern Hemisphere

2. East coasts have warm currents flowing away from the equator (poleward) while west coasts have cold currents flowing toward the equator.

3. Fog is more likely to occur on the west coast where warm, moist air from the South Equatorial current meets the cold waters of the West Australia current.

4. The West Wind Drift flows around Antarctica.

ANSWERS TO

CHAPTER 19 REVIEW

Review

1–a, 2–c, 3–c, 4–d, 5–a, 6–a, 7–d, 8–a, 9–d, 10–b, 11–b, 12–c

Interpret and Apply

1. The west coasts of continents have cold ocean currents, which flow from the polar regions. This is in the Southern Hemisphere; therefore this current is flowing north from the South Pole.

2. Continents prevent the continuous flow of the West Wind Drift in the Northern Hemisphere. The Southern Hemisphere is mostly water.

3. A south-flowing current in the Northern Hemisphere is flowing from polar regions and thus is a cold current. A south-flowing current in the Southern Hemisphere is flowing from the equator and thus is a warm current.

4. California has a cold ocean current offshore. Cooler water temperatures would be expected. The warm Gulf Stream flows past Myrtle Beach; thus water temperatures there should be warmer.

5. In Topic 3, the flow in the Gulf Stream is given as 100 million cubic meters per second.

$$\frac{\text{Gulf Stream}}{\text{Cromwell}} = \frac{100\ 000\ 000\ \text{m}^3}{40\ 000\ \text{m}^3} = 2.5\ \text{times}$$

Gulf Stream flow is 2.5 times greater than Cromwell flow.

6. Both processes leave the salt behind in the water, increasing salinity and thus water density.

7. Mediterranean water only sinks until its density is the same as that of the Atlantic Ocean. That level is 1000 meters.

Critical Thinking

1. (a) Mixing layer: 7.00 m – 0.01 m = 6.99 m; Layer of smooth flow: 0.01000 – 0.00001 = 0.00999 m (b) about 700 times

2. (a) 4.5 m/s (b) 1.9 m/s

3. outer flow layer

4. The bottom of the graph is the floor of the ocean. Current speed there is nearly zero because of friction.

5. The mixing layer would extend into the layer of smooth flow, making the mixing layer larger.

CHAPTER 20
Studying the Universe

PLANNING CHART

Topic	Support Material
Lesson I Studying the Universe	**Laboratory Investigation:** The Refracting Telescope
1 The Functions of a Telescope	**Content Evaluation:** p. 364 *Topic Review:* 1; p. 374-375 *Chapter Review:* 1; Interpret and Apply: 1
2 Telescopes and Domes	**Content Evaluation:** p. 364 *Topic Review:* 2; p. 374-375 *Chapter Review:* 2, 3; Interpret and Apply: 2
3 The Refracting Telescope	**Content Evaluation:** p. 364 *Topic Review:* 3; p. 374-375 *Chapter Review:* 4; **Transparency 32:** Optical Telescope
4 The Reflecting Telescope	**Content Evaluation:** p. 364 *Topic Review:* 4; p. 374-375 *Chapter Review:* 5
5 Multiple-Mirror Reflectors	**Content Evaluation:** p. 364 *Topic Review:* 5; p. 374-375 *Chapter Review:* 6
6 Other Optical Telescopes	**Content Evaluation:** p. 364 *Topic Review:* 6; p. 374-375 *Chapter Review:* 7; Interpret and Apply: 3
7 Devices for Improving Images	**Content Evaluation:** p. 364 *Topic Review:* 7; p. 374-375 *Chapter Review:* 8; Interpret and Apply: 4
Lesson II Studying Energy Beyond Visible Light	
8 The Electromagnetic Spectrum	**Content Evaluation:** p. 368 *Topic Review:* 8; p. 374-375 *Chapter Review:* 9, 10; **Transparency 33:** The Electromagnetic Spectrum
9 Radio Astronomy	**Content Evaluation:** p. 368 *Topic Review:* 9; p. 374-375 *Chapter Review:* 11
10 The Radio Telescope	**Content Evaluation:** p. 368 *Topic Review:* 10; p. 374-375 *Chapter Review:* 12; Interpret and Apply: 5
11 Radio Telescope Arrays	**Content Evaluation:** p. 368 *Topic Review:* 11; p. 374-375 *Chapter Review:* 13; Interpret and Apply: 5
12 Telescopes for Other Wavelengths	**Content Evaluation:** p. 368 *Topic Review:* 12; p. 374-375 *Chapter Review:* 14

PLANNING CHART (continued)

Topic	Support Material
Lesson III A Closer Look at Visible Light	**In-Text Lab Activity:** The Simple Spectroscope
13 The Spectroscope	**Content Evaluation:** p. 371 *Topic Review:* 13; p. 374-375 *Chapter Review:* 15
14 Kinds of Visible Spectra	**Content Evaluation:** p. 371 *Topic Review:* 14; p. 374-375 *Chapter Review:* 16; Interpret and Apply: 7
15 Dark-Line Spectra and the Solar System	**Content Evaluation:** p. 371 *Topic Review:* 15; p. 374-375 *Chapter Review:* 16; Interpret and Apply: 6
16 The Doppler Effect	**Content Evaluation:** p. 371 *Topic Review:* 16; p. 374-375 *Chapter Review:* 17; Interpret and Apply: 8
Lab Activity p. 372-373	The Simple Spectroscope
Chapter Review p. 374-375	Critical Thinking 1-2 **Study Guide:** Vocabulary; Interpreting and Applying
Chapter 20 Assessment Program	**Chapter Tests; Computer Test Bank**

Introducing UNIT **FIVE**

Student Writing Skills

Students can become familiar with outside sources of astronomy information through an astronomy current events report. There are two suggested approaches to this exercise: (1) Have students research three different events in astronomy that took place during the past 12 months. When they have gathered sources on at least three events, have them write an article describing and summarizing the events. These student reports should focus on the sequence of developments. (2) Have students find three different news reports of a single event that occurred during the past 12 months. The three news reports may be sequential, describing updates on the event throughout the year, or they may be from three different sources published at about the same time. Students should discuss the similarities and differences of the three reports.

Listed below are several periodicals that frequently cover topics in astronomy. Many libraries store back issues of these periodicals. General-interest publications, such as *Time and Newsweek* also cover astronomy news.

- *Air and Space*
- *Astronomy*
- *Aviation Week and Space Technology*
- *Discover*
- *National Geographic*
- *Planetary Report*
- *Popular Science*
- *Science News*
- *Scientific American*
- *Sky and Telescope*

CHAPTER **20**

Motivator

Most students are aware that rockets and space probes have only been developed over the last few decades. Students may be interested to learn that over the same period of time, the technology of telescopes has greatly improved

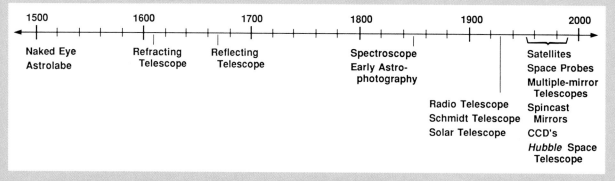

and expanded. Display a time line similar to the one above or sketch it on the chalkboard. As an example of the power of very early telescopes, cover one lens of a standard field binocular (7 x 35) with paper. Pass the binocular around and explain to the students that one side of the binocular is about as powerful as a good telescope 300 years ago. Point out how many important technological breakthroughs occur in the last few years of the time line. Explain that this boost in technology has contributed immensely to what amounts to an explosion in knowledge about the universe during the last few decades.

Lesson I: Optical Telescopes

(Topics 1-7)

Teaching Suggestions
If your school or one of your students has a telescope, it could be used to introduce this topic and to start a discussion of the two major types of optical telescopes. Most telescopes for advanced amateurs and astrophotographers have clock-drive mechanisms to keep the telescope pointed at the same object as Earth rotates. Such a telescope could be displayed or discussed to emphasize the need for a telescope to turn with Earth.

A visit to a planetarium or an observatory sometime during your study of Unit Five would be an excellent experience for your students. Or you may want to schedule an evening star-watching session. There are amateur star clubs located in many areas throughout the country. You may wish to contact a club in your area for information or assistance.

Science Background
There are two broadcasts that you and your students may find interesting. The first, "Star Hustler" with Jack Horkheimer, is a public television program originating in Miami but available in many regions of the country. The 15-minute program describes celestial objects and events during the week of broadcast. The second broadcast of interest is "Star Date", a 2-minute radio program originating from the McDonald Observatory, Austin, Texas. "Star Date" explains what is happening in the sky each evening, and mentions important astronomical and historical notes about particular dates. A new broadcast is aired each day.

Lesson II: Studying Energy Beyond Visible Light

(Topics 8-12)

Teaching Suggestions
A chart showing the kinds of electromagnetic energy will be very helpful in this lesson. Emphasize the differences in the wavelengths of different forms of electromagnetic energy. If the wavelengths are indicated in nanometers, you may need to explain how tiny this unit is.

1 meter   = 1000 millimeters
1 millimeter = 1000 micrometers
1 micrometer = 1000 nanometers

(An older unit that may be present on some charts is the angstrom, abbreviated A. An angstrom is equal to 10^{-10} meters. The nanometer is equal to 10^{-9} meters.)

Point out that radio telescopes must be larger than optical telescopes because radio waves are much longer than visible light waves. In order for a radio telescope operating at 1 meter (300 MHz) to equal the resolution of the *Hubble Space Telescope*, it must be 2000 times in size. Use the drawing in the text to explain interferometry. Show the location on the electromagnetic spectrum of the infrared rays studied by *IRAS* and the X rays studied by *Exosat*.

Science Background

Interferometry is possible with optical telescopes, but it is much more difficult because the wavelength of visible light is much shorter than that of radio waves.

Very Long Baseline Interferometry (VLBI) has become increasingly important to astronomy in recent years. The addition of an orbiting antenna, successfully tested in 1986, allows very accurate measurements of the location in the sky of distant objects such as quasars. The VLBI method is useful to the geological sciences as well. Because quasars are so distant, they have never been observed to change position relative to other quasars. Thus, quasars can be used as "fixed-point" references. The angular position of two telescopes relative to the quasar will change only when the positions of the telescopes change. Measuring the position of the quasar with two telescopes over a period of time allows measurements of very small changes in the position of Earth's crust due to continental drift.

Lesson III: A Closer Look at Visible Light

(Topics 13-16)

Teaching Suggestions

DEMONSTRATIONS: Several demonstrations can be done to enhance this lesson. A possible starting point is the use of a simple prism to demonstrate the spectrum of sunlight or of an incandescent bulb filament. Point out that the refraction of white light into its wavelengths is the basic principle behind the methods of analyzing distant stars and our own sun.

The spectra of elements can be observed by using spectra tubes and accompanying apparatus. Check with a chemistry or physics teacher to find out if your school has such equipment.

The Doppler effect can be demonstrated in the following way: Attach a string very securely to a loud tuning fork. Strike the fork on the heel of your hand and slowly swing it around your head. **CAUTION: Be sure the tuning fork does not strike any object or person, and that the string is securely attached to the fork.** The Doppler effect could also be discussed with a drawing or a film, such as *Sound Waves and Stars: The Doppler Effect* (12 minutes), available from B.F.A. Educational Media, 468 Park Avenue South, New York, NY 10016.

CHAPTER 20 **LAB** ACTIVITY
The Simple Spectroscope

■ A student report sheet for this activity can be found in the *Laboratory Investigations* booklet.

Process Skills

■ Observing: Procedure 9–13
■ Describing: Analysis and Conclusions 1, 3
■ Comparing/Contrasting: Analysis and Conclusions 2, 3
■ Determining Cause and Effect: Analysis and Conclusions 4

Preparation

Before class, cut the nichrome wire into 3 inch lengths and put a small loop in one end.

Procedural Hints

If a Geissler tube is available, set it up in the front of the class. Have students observe the tube through their spectroscopes and draw the spectra.

Answers—Analysis and Conclusions

1. White light is composed of many individual colors.
2. All three show a continuous spectrum composed of all colors from red through violet. The spectrum of the fluorescent light is continuous but shows distinct bright lines in the green and violet.
3. It is a bright-line spectrum with two very bright yellow lines.
4. The colors were absorbed by gases in the sun's atmosphere. Earth's atmosphere is also an absorber.

CHAPTER 20 REVIEW

Review

1–a, 2–a, 3–d, 4–d, 5–b, 6–b, 7–a, 8–c, 9–b, 10–b, 11–a, 12–b, 13–d, 14–b, 15–b, 16–b, 17–b

Interpret and Apply

1. The diameter of the telescope's lens or mirror is much greater than the iris of an eye.

2. The light-gathering power is proportional to the square of the mirror's diameter. The Hale Telescope collects about $5^2/3^2 = {}^{25}/_9 = 2{}^7/_9$ times as much as a 3-meter reflector; the Cerro Tololo Telescope collects about $4^2/3^2 = {}^{16}/_9 = 1{}^7/_9$ times as much as a 3-meter reflector.

3. The *Hubble* is outside Earth's atmosphere. The atmosphere causes a star's image to blur. Without the atmosphere's interference, the *Hubble* focuses starlight into a smaller area on the detector, allowing fainter stars to be separated better.

4. With a time exposure, a photographic plate can store up light energy. This is like a CCD, but not like the eye.

5. Radio waves have very long wavelengths compared to visible light. The dish need only be made of a mesh that appears solid at radio wavelengths.

6. Helium is the second most abundant element in the sun and was discovered from the sun's absorption spectrum.

7. These stars may be within a larger emission nebula—for example, the Orion Nebula.

8. There is no shift because the star is neither approaching nor receding from Earth.

Critical Thinking

1. Some factors that might be listed are: (a) elevation—higher elevation means less air and lower humidity to interfere with the view; it also allows for the use of infrared telescopes (b) clouds—look for sites that are cloud-free most of the year (c) winds—look for places without strong winds (d) latitude—a location nearer the equator will have day and night periods more consistent in length, and will have better visibility of stars in both hemispheres (e) accessibility—personnel and equipment should be able to get to the site easily (f) light pollution—site should be well away from major sources of artificial light. (Students could research the situations at Palomar and Lick.)

2. With the help of a drawing of two radio telescopes pointing to the same point in space, students should be able to see that the length of the baseline could be determined. Changes in the length of the baseline could result from movements of the lithospheric plates. VLBA can also be used to study such things as the wobble of Earth on its axis.

CHAPTER **21**
Stars and Galaxies

PLANNING CHART

Topic	Support Material
Lesson I Stars and Their Characteristics	**Laboratory Activity:** Properties of Stars **In-Text Map Activity:** Constellations and the Seasons
1 Constellations	**Content Evaluation:** p. 381 *Topic Review:* 1; p. 394-395 *Chapter Review:* 1, 2; Interpret and Apply: 1
2 Seasonal Changes in Constellations	**Content Evaluation:** p. 381 *Topic Review:* 2; p. 394-395 *Chapter Review:* 2; **Transparency 12:** Star Maps (Autumn and Winter); **Transparency 13:** Star Maps (Spring and Summer)
3 Distances to Stars	**Content Evaluation:** p. 381 *Topic Review:* 3; p. 394-395 *Chapter Review:* 3; Interpret and Apply: 2, 3, 6
4 Physical Properties of Stars	**Content Evaluation:** p. 381 *Topic Review:* 4; p. 394-395 *Chapter Review:* 7
5 Elements in Stars	**Content Evaluation:** p. 381 *Topic Review:* 5; p. 394-395 *Chapter Review:* 4
6 Star Brightness	**Content Evaluation:** p. 381 *Topic Review:* 6; p. 394-395 *Chapter Review:* 5, 6; Interpret and Apply: 4, 5, 6
Lesson II Kinds of Stars	
7 Giants, Supergiants, and Dwarfs	**Content Evaluation:** p. 384 *Topic Review:* 7; p. 394-395 *Chapter Review:* 7; **Transparency 35:** Star Classification
8 Variable Stars	**Content Evaluation:** p. 384 *Topic Review:* 8; p. 394-395 *Chapter Review:* 8
9 Pulsars	**Content Evaluation:** p. 384 *Topic Review:* 9; p. 394-395 *Chapter Review:* 9
Lesson III Formation of Stars	
10 Origin of a Star	**Content Evaluation:** p. 388 *Topic Review:* 10; p. 394-395 *Chapter Review:* 10
11 Formation of Red Giants	**Content Evaluation:** p. 388 *Topic Review:* 11; p. 394-395 *Chapter Review:* 11

PLANNING CHART (continued)

Topic	Support Material
Lesson III (continued) **12 Formation of White Dwarfs**	**Content Evaluation:** p. 388 *Topic Review:* 12; p. 394-395 *Chapter Review:* 12
13 Supernovas	**Content Evaluation:** p. 388 *Topic Review:* 13; p. 394-395 *Chapter Review:* 13
14 Neutron Stars and Black Holes	**Content Evaluation:** p. 388 *Topic Review:* 14; p. 394-395 *Chapter Review:* 14
Lesson IV Galaxies and the Universe	
15 What Are Galaxies?	**Content Evaluation:** p. 391 *Topic Review:* 15; p. 394-395 *Chapter Review:* 16
16 Types of Galaxies	**Content Evaluation:** p. 391 *Topic Review:* 16; p. 394-395 *Chapter Review:* 17
17 Quasars	**Content Evaluation:** p. 391 *Topic Review:* 17; p. 394-395 *Chapter Review:* 15
18 Origin of the Universe	**Content Evaluation:** p. 391 *Topic Review:* 18; p. 394-395 *Chapter Review:* 18
Map Activity p. 392-393	Constellations and the Seasons
Chapter Review p. 394-395	Critical Thinking 1-5 **Study Guide:** Vocabulary; Interpreting and Applying
Chapter 21 Assessment Program	**Chapter Tests; Computer Test Bank**

CHAPTER 21

Motivator

DEMONSTRATION: Many students are not aware that stars are in the sky all day but are invisible due to sunlight. Try the following demonstration. Obtain a box with a lid, or a box that is open only at one end. Prepare a planetarium by punching holes in the lid or in the end opposite the opening. Place a light source such as a flashlight or desk lamp in the box and direct the end of the box with the holes at the ceiling. When the room is dark, the "stars" will be visible as spots of light. When the classroom lights are turned on, the stars will no longer be visible, even though the light source is still on. Likewise, stars in our sky are invisible when Earth is facing the sun.

Lesson I: Stars and Their Characteristics

(Topics 1-6)

Teaching Suggestions

Teaching students the configurations and locations of a few constellations could be the start of a lifetime of stargazing for some of them. Use the text discussion and the star charts in the Appendix (pages 660–661) as your introductions. Slides of individual constellations are available from science supply houses and can be shown to help students recognize major constellations. Point out how to use the Big Dipper and Orion to locate other constellations, as shown in the diagrams.

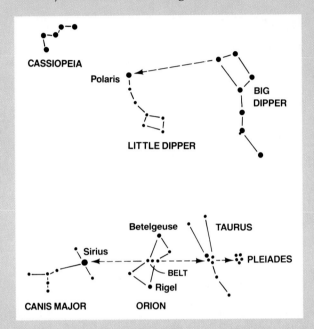

Some students may wish to make star-trail photographs. They will need a clear, unobstructed view of the northern sky, a tripod to keep the camera stable, and a method of holding the camera shutter open. Earth's rotation will do the rest.

DEMONSTRATION: In addition to astronomical units and light-years, you may wish to introduce the *parsec*. A parsec is the distance to an object in space that has a parallax of one second of arc. You will need to explain parallax because it is not presented to students until Chapter 25. Have the students hold a pencil vertically at arm's length and sight against a "distant" vertical line, such as a windowpane frame. As students alternately close each eye, the pencil will appear to shift back and forth against the background. The greater the distance between a student's eyes (the baseline), the greater the "parallax shift" of the pencil will be. For astronomers measuring distances in parsecs, the baseline is the diameter of Earth's orbit. For your reference, 1 parsec is equal to 206 265 astronomical units or 3.26 light-years.

Science Background
Constellations: Although most constellations began as recognized patterns of stars, astronomers define and refer to constellations as areas of the sky, not just the bright stars within those areas. Every part of the sky is included in a constellation.

Lesson II: Kinds of Stars

(Topics 7-9)

Teaching Suggestions
The stars discussed in Topic 7 should be correlated with the groups of stars in the diagram shown in Figure 21.6. The graph is a simplified form of the Hertzsprung-Russell, or H-R, diagram, a fundamental concept in astronomy. The diagram compares star temperatures with their absolute visual magnitudes. Discuss the meaning of both graph axes so that the students do not interpret the graph to be a kind of star map.

Science Background
H-R Diagram: Main-sequence stars occur in the band that extends from the upper left of the H-R diagram, where stars are hot and bright, to the lower right, where stars are cool and dim. Ninety percent of all known stars, including our sun, are on the main sequence. Giants and supergiants occur to the upper right of the main sequence. Dwarfs appear at the lower left of the main sequence.

Cepheids: The importance of the cepheid variable stars in determining distances in space could be emphasized here. The basic formula is:

$$m - M = 5 \log \frac{r}{10}$$

where m is the apparent magnitude, *M* is absolute magnitude, and *r* is distance from Earth in parsecs. The formula contains three variables—knowing any two allows determination of the third. Apparent magnitude is easy to determine because it depends only upon the way the star appears to us. However, absolute magnitude is not easy to find unless the distance to the star is known. Conversely, the distance to the star can be calculated if the absolute magnitude is known. That is why the relationship between pulsations and absolute magnitudes is so significant. The period of pulsation can be used to find the absolute magnitude, which then enables the calculation of distance to the star and its galaxy. This relationship was first discovered from the Hyades star cluster. The Hyades cluster is near the red star Aldebaran in the constellation Taurus and, like the more famous Pleiades star cluster, is an impressive sight with binoculars.

Pulsars: The first pulsar was discovered by Jocelyn Bell-Burnell when she was a graduate student at Cambridge University. She was using a radio telescope that consisted of an array of wires stretched a few feet above the ground. The pulses she detected arrived every 1.33728 seconds. There was speculation at first that the pulses were coming from an intelligent civilization in space; thus the source was labeled "LGM" for "little green men." However, other pulsing radio sources were soon discovered in widely-separated regions of the sky, which eliminated little green men as the source. Hundreds of such radio sources are now known. The name *pulsar* comes from *pulsating radio source.*

Lesson III:
Formation of Stars

(Topics 10-14)

Teaching Suggestions
The Hertzsprung-Russell diagram used with Topic 7 can be used again with this lesson to enhance the discussion of a star's life. Stars which are forming begin as large, cool (red giant) stars. As they mature, they become hotter, moving to the left on the diagram. They also become brighter but smaller. This means that their absolute magnitude decreases and they move down on the diagram. They then enter the main sequence band. Average stars like our sun will spend about ten billion years in the main sequence. Very massive stars may stay in the main sequence for only a few million years. The more massive a star is, the stronger its gravity and hotter its core. Stars with a very hot core use up their fuel faster. As stars die, they first

move to the red giant stages and finally to the white and red dwarf areas of the diagram. Eventually, they cool into a dark cinder.

Lesson IV:
Galaxies and the Universe

(Topics 15-18)

Teaching Suggestions
Some students have trouble understanding that our sun is one of many in the Milky Way galaxy and that there are many other galaxies, each containing billions of stars. Photos and slides of other galaxies may help. Point out that the stars in the photo are in our galaxy and that we are looking out through our galaxy to see other galaxies. It is worth stressing that the Andromeda galaxy can be seen with the unaided eye. Sketch the Great Square of Pegasus and Andromeda on the chalkboard to locate the Andromeda galaxy. The Great Square is at its zenith for the northern United States in the evening in October and November.

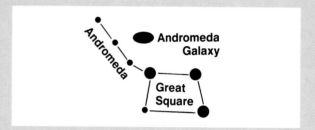

Science Background
The Big Bang: Fifteen billion years is an estimate of the time elapsed since the big bang. The estimate is based on the locations of the most distant galaxies. These galaxies have the greatest red shift in their spectra and therefore the greatest velocities. If distance and velocity are known, time can be calculated with the formula v = d/t (velocity equals distance divided by time). Distance can also be calculated by this formula if velocity and time are known. Therefore, the use of the formula requires an estimate of either time or distance, which makes the period of 15 billion years very much an estimate.

COBE and the Origin of the Universe: In April 1992, astronomers announced that the

Cosmic Background Explorer satellite *(COBE)* had measured minute variations in the temperature of the universe's background microwave radiation. The variations— which appear as ripples (see photo, page 367)— could represent the earliest structures in the universe as matter began to coalesce. While the *COBE* results are still being debated, they may provide support for the big bang theory and the long-debated presence of so-called "dark matter" in the universe.

CHAPTER 21 **MAP** ACTIVITY
Constellations and the Seasons

■ A student report sheet for this activity can be found in the *Laboratory Investigations* booklet.

Time estimate
40–50 minutes

Process Skills
■ Determining Cause and Effect: Analysis and Conclusions 1

■ Interpreting Diagrams: Analysis and Conclusions 2, 4, 5

■ Analyzing Data: Analysis and Conclusions 3

■ Calculating: Analysis and Conclusions 6

Materials
For a class of 24 students, prepare 72 sheets of 13 cm x 13 cm tracing paper before class begins. Have a supply of pencils and a pencil sharpener on hand in the classroom.

Procedural Hints
Some students may notice that Polaris is not in exactly the same location on each map. This is an artifact of the printing process. Sorry!

Remind students that the star maps they are using are for mid-latitudes in the *Northern Hemisphere*. The seasonal star maps for the Southern Hemisphere show different stars.

Students may be interested in finding the constellation that matches their zodiac sign. If so, you will need to emphasize the *important differences* between astronomy and astrology. Some may notice that constellations corresponding to their zodiac signs are visible in the night sky in the season *opposite* their birthdays. Explain that astrological signs refer to the constellation in which the sun appears to be. In January, for example, the sun appears to be in the constellation Capricorn. Thus, Capricorn is not visible in the night sky in January, but instead is visible in July.

Answers—Procedure
1. The position of Polaris does not change.
2. Polaris; The Big Dipper points toward Polaris, which is north.
3. Canis
4. (a) Ursa Minor, (b) Scorpius, (c) Lyra, (d) Virgo, (e) Orion, (f) Orion, (g) Bootes
5. See the annotated data table on page 393 of this Teachers Annotated Edition.
7. Gemini moves east to west (or northeast to northwest).
8. The Summer Triangle rises in the spring, moves westward across the sky, and sets in the autumn.
9. Cassiopeia moved counterclockwise relative to Polaris. Other constellations must move counterclockwise. Make sure students understand that the counterclockwise motion of constellations around Polaris is consistent with the east to west motion of constellations that students discovered by drawing Maps A and B.

Answers—Analysis and Conclusions
1. Polaris is over Earth's northern axis of rotation. Polaris is always north.
2. Certain stars within constellations, such as the Pointer stars in the Big Dipper and the three stars in Orion's belt, can be used to locate other stars and constellations. Another example to share with students is that the handle in the Big Dipper arcs toward Arcturus, then continues toward Spica. (See the Spring map on page 661.)
3. The best viewing occurs when the constellations are directly overhead. In this way, haze on the horizon cannot obscure the view. This occurs for Bootes in spring, Lyra in summer, Orion in winter, and Pegasus in autumn.
4. In summer, Gemini is over the northern horizon and cannot be seen.
5. east; clockwise; since the observer is facing in the opposite direction, toward the South Pole instead of the North Pole, the motion of the stars rising in the east and setting in

the west will be clockwise around the point in the sky directly over the South Pole.

6. Six hours; since there are four maps for one year, the maps must be one fourth of a year apart in time. For one day, the maps must be one fourth of a day apart. One fourth of a 24 hour day is 6 hours.

ANSWERS TO

CHAPTER 21 REVIEW

Review

1–a, 2–b, 3–c, 4–d, 5–d, 6–b, 7–a, 8–d, 9–c, 10–b, 11–a, 12–b, 13–c, 14–a, 15–d, 16–b, 17–b, 18–b

Interpret and Apply

1. Star trails can be complete circles if night-time lasts 24 hours. This can occur only in the polar regions.

2. From Topic 3:

$$1 \text{ AU} = 150 \text{ million km} = 1.5 \times 10^8 \text{ km}$$
$$1 \text{ LY} = 9.5 \text{ trillion km} = 9.5 \times 10^{12} \text{ km}$$

Distance to Sirius in km:

$$4.3 \text{ LY} \times \frac{9.5 \times 10^{12} \text{ km}}{1 \text{ LY}} = 40.85 \times 10^{12} \text{ km}$$

Distance equals about 4.1×10^{13} km

Distance to Sirius in AU:

$$4.1 \times 10^{13} \text{ km} \times \frac{1 \text{ AU}}{1.5 \times 10^8 \text{ km}} = 2.7 \times 10^5 \text{ km}$$

3. The speed of light is about 300 000 (3×10^5) kilometers per second (Topic 2). 380 000 km = 3.8×10^5 km

$$\frac{3.8 \times 10^5 \text{ km}}{3 \times 10^5 \text{ km/s}} = 1.3 \text{ s}$$

Moonlight takes 1.3 seconds to reach Earth.

4. Planets shine by reflected sunlight. If a planet is close enough to the sun and Earth, it may appear brighter than the stars. It is not uncommon for Venus, Mars, and/or Jupiter to be the brightest object in the sky.

5. Topic 6 gives the magnitude of the moon and Mars as –12.6 and –2.5 respectively, or about 10 magnitudes apart. This means a ratio of approximately 2.5 to the 10th power or $2.5^5 \times 2.5^5$ which is 100 x 100 or 10 000. Therefore, the full moon is about 10 000 times as bright as Mars can ever be.

6. Yes. See Topic 6. The distance 32.6 LY is the basis of the absolute magnitude scale. At 32.6 light-years the sun would have a magnitude of 4.8 and would be faint but visible.

Critical Thinking

1. Distance equals 10^3 (1000) parsecs (Graph A).

2. Distance modulus equals 25 (Graph A).

3. Dis. mod. = m – M = 10 – (–10) = 20
   Distance equals 10^5 (100 000) parsecs (Graph A).

4. Absolute magnitude equals –3 (Graph B).

5. A cepheid with a period of 50 days has an absolute magnitude (M) of –5 (Graph B).
   Distance modulus = m – M = 0 – (–5) = 5
   Distance equals 10^2 parsecs (100 parsecs) (Graph A).

CHAPTER 22
The Sun and Its Solar System

PLANNING CHART

Topic	Support Material
Lesson I **The Sun**	
1 Studying the Sun	**Content Evaluation:** p. 402 *Topic Review:* 1; p. 410-411 *Chapter Review:* 1, 2; *Interpret and Apply:* 3
2 Properties of the Sun	**Content Evaluation:** p. 402 *Topic Review:* 2; p. 410-411 *Chapter Review:* 3; *Interpret and Apply:* 1
3 The Sun's Atmosphere	**Content Evaluation:** p. 402 *Topic Review:* 3; p. 410-411 *Chapter Review:* 4, 5
4 Sunspots	**Content Evaluation:** p. 402 *Topic Review:* 4; p. 410-411 *Chapter Review:* 6, 7
5 The Solar Wind and Magnetic Storms	**Content Evaluation:** p. 402 *Topic Review:* 5; p. 410-411 *Chapter Review:* 8; *Interpret and Apply:* 2
6 Source of the Sun's Energy	**Content Evaluation:** p. 402 *Topic Review:* 6; p. 410-411 *Chapter Review:* 9
Lesson II Observing the Solar System	**Laboratory Investigation:** Retrograde Motion of Mars
7 The Solar System	**Content Evaluation:** p. 404 *Topic Review:* 7; p. 410-411 *Chapter Review:* 10
8 Planets and Stars	**Content Evaluation:** p. 404 *Topic Review:* 8; p. 410-411 *Chapter Review:* 11
9 Solar System Models	**Content Evaluation:** p. 404 *Topic Review:* 9; p. 410-411 *Chapter Review:* 12, 13
Lesson III Motion in the Solar System	**In-Text Lab Activity:** Ellipses and Eccentricity
10 The Contribution of Tycho	**Content Evaluation:** p. 407 *Topic Review:* 10; p. 410-411 *Chapter Review:* 14
11 Johannes Kepler and the Laws of Planetary Motion	**Content Evaluation:** p. 407 *Topic Review:* 11; p. 410-411 *Chapter Review:* 14, 15, 16; *Interpret and Apply:* 3, 4, 5

PLANNING CHART (continued)

Topic	Support Material
Lesson III (continued) **12 Galileo and the Telescope**	**Content Evaluation:** p. 407 *Topic Review:* 12; p. 410-411 *Chapter Review:* 17
13 Isaac Newton and the Universal Law of Gravitation	**Content Evaluation:** p. 407 *Topic Review:* 13; p. 410-411 *Chapter Review:* 18; Interpret and Apply: 3, 6
Lab Activity p. 408-409	Ellipses and Eccentricity
Chapter Review p. 410-411	Critical Thinking 1-4 **Study Guide:** Vocabulary; Interpreting and Applying
Chapter 22 Assessment Program	**Chapter Tests; Computer Test Bank**

CHAPTER 22

Motivator

▲ **DEMONSTRATION:** If the sun cooperates, sunspots are relatively easy to show your students. Since the sun must **never** be viewed directly with the unaided eye or through a lens, the image must be projected. Use a large magnifying glass to direct an image of the sun onto a white paper or cardboard screen. **CAUTION: Be sure the screen does not catch fire.** The screen should be in the shade for best viewing. Experiment with the distance between the magnifying glass and the screen to find the best image.

If your school has a telescope, it can be used to form a larger and clearer image. **CAUTION: DO NOT LOOK THROUGH THE TELESCOPE TO LOCATE THE SUN.** You will be able to tell by the telescope's shadow when it is pointed directly at the sun. The screen can then be moved back and forth to obtain the best image. Some telescopes have solar filters. While some solar filters are very satisfactory, solar filters attached to eyepiece lenses have been known to explode. A projected image is far better for a demonstration. It is safer, can be made larger, and is viewable by more than one student at a time.

Lesson I: The Sun

(Topics 1-6)

Teaching Suggestions

👓 🔥 **DEMONSTRATION:** This demonstration will help you warn students about the danger of looking directly at the sun. Use a magnifying glass or other convex lens to focus the sun's rays on a piece of paper so that the paper just begins to burn. **CAUTION: Wear safety goggles. Handle the burning paper carefully. Have a bucket of water nearby and use it to extinguish the paper as soon as it begins to burn.** Point out that the human eye contains a lens that would focus sunlight onto the retina in a similar destructive manner.

Science Background
Corona: The corona is made almost entirely of arched loops between the magnetic fields of sunspots. It is larger during sunspot maxima because there are more loops at that time. Prominences connect the magnetic fields of sunspots. Coronal holes were one of the great discoveries of *Skylab*. Solar scientists had known for years that some regions of the sun were periodically spewing solar wind into

space. They called these areas *M-regions* (for mystery regions). X ray photographs made by *Skylab* revealed holes in the corona.

Fusion: The conversion of mass to energy in the fusion process is described by Einstein's famous equation, $E=mc^2$, in which E is the amount of energy, m is the mass, and c is the speed of light. Thus a tiny amount of mass multiplied by the speed of light squared yields a huge amount of energy.

Maunder Minimum: An interesting aspect of sunspots is the *Maunder Minimum*. This was a period of time, from 1645 to 1715, during which there was little or no sunspot activity. No auroras were observed and no corona could be seen during solar eclipses. During this same time, the sun's equatorial rotation rate increased, so that one rotation required 24 days rather than the present 25 days.

Sunspots: Early observers proposed interesting theories for sunspots. One hypothesis was that sunspots were holes in Earth's atmosphere that were revealed by the bright light of the sun. In 1801, Sir William Hershel, who discovered the planet Uranus, proposed that sunspots were holes in bright solar clouds. He thought that the sun's surface was probably inhabited by living beings adapted to the conditions there. The most recent sunspot peak occurred in late 1991. A sunspot minimum can be expected in 1994 or 1995.

Lesson II:
Observing The Solar System

(Topics 7-9)

Teaching Suggestions

Topic 9 introduces the ideas of *geocentric* and *heliocentric* solar systems. It may be worth pointing out how difficult it is, standing on Earth and looking out into space, to tell what kind of system we are in. The fact that Ptolemy's system was accepted for so many centuries is a reflection of this difficulty. To emphasize this, ask students to think of evidence that proves Earth turns on its axis and revolves around the sun. This is much more difficult than it sounds. (The evidence for Earth's motions is discussed in Chapter 25.)

Science Background

The heliocentric model of the solar system is actually a very recent idea. If your students had been sitting in your classroom 350 years ago, you would have been teaching them the Ptolemaic system. In fact, the geocentric model was taught at Harvard University for the first 20 years of that school's existence. (Galileo was still alive when Harvard was founded in 1636.)

A point to make with Topic 9 is the difficulty of explaining retrograde motion in a geocentric system compared to a heliocentric system. This is thought to be one factor that led Copernicus to propose the heliocentric system. Although Copernicus offered no mathematical proofs for his system, its simplicity made it immediately appealing to most advanced thinkers of the time.

Lesson III:
Motion in the Solar System

(Topics 10-13)

Teaching Suggestions

DEMONSTRATION: To begin your discussion of Kepler's Laws in Topic 11, draw an ellipse on the chalkboard. Get two suction cup darts and a loop of string. Wet the darts so they will stay attached to the chalkboard. Place them 10 to 20 centimeters apart. The two darts represent the foci of the ellipse. The string loop should be longer than the distance between the darts. Loop the string around the darts. Then, using a piece of chalk to keep the string tight, move the chalk around the darts until an ellipse is drawn. Vary the distance between the darts to show the effect on the shape of the ellipse. Ask the students what shape will result if two foci are in the same place. Point out that the result, a circle, is just a special kind of ellipse.

The shape of an ellipse is described by the term *eccentricity*. The equation for eccentricity is:

$$e = \frac{d}{L}$$

where e is the eccentricity, d the distance between foci, and L the length of the major axis. For a circle, $e = 0$. Values for eccentricity increase as the orbit becomes less and less like a circle.

Chapter 22   The Sun and Its Solar System   **T813**

Once the elliptical shape of orbits is established, Kepler's second law can be explained. Select one of the foci of the ellipse on the board to be the sun. By eye, draw two equal areas on the ellipse as shown in Figure 22.10 in the text. An imaginary line from the planet to the sun sweeps out equal areas in equal times. The planet moves more rapidly when it covers the larger area, which is when it is closest to the sun (perihelion). This is also the time when the planet's kinetic energy (energy of motion) is greatest, but its potential energy (energy of position) is least. At the point where the sun and planet are farthest apart (aphelion), the planet moves more slowly. Its kinetic energy is least at this time, but its potential energy is at a maximum because it has the greatest distance to "fall" to the sun.

An example of Kepler's third law that students can calculate for themselves will help students comprehend its use. Data from the chart in the *Science Background* of Chapter 23, Lesson I can be used to show the calculations for an actual planet, but the arithmetic involved will not be simple. The example given in the text is simplified; the actual value for Jupiter's period is 11.86 years (to the nearest hundredth). The problem given in the *Interpret and Apply* section of the Chapter 22 Review is imaginary data, but it comes out evenly.

The formula for Newton's law of gravitation is:

$$F = G \frac{m_1 m_2}{d^2}$$

where F is the gravitational force of attraction between any two objects in the universe, m_1 and m_2 are the masses of the two objects, d is the distance between the centers of the two objects, and G is a constant equal to 6.672×10^{-11} Newton m^2/kg^2. Students need only understand the implications of the full equation. They need not be expected to solve an actual problem.

Science Background

Tycho: Tycho Brahe was certainly the most colorful of the early astronomers. He was the "lord" of his island and apparently not especially beloved by his serfs. And with good reason! He had a dungeon in his castle. According to legend, Tycho lost part of his nose in a duel. The duel was fought, it is said, over which combatant was the better mathematician. Despite Tycho's shortcomings, his

observatory was the best in Europe at that time. The data he collected were very important to the development of ideas on the structure of the solar system.

Gravitation: The law of gravitation is an example of an inverse square law. Such laws also apply to the relationship between distance and such quantities as the effects of magnetism, electrical charges, light, and heat.

CHAPTER **22** **LAB** ACTIVITY
Ellipses and Eccentricity

■ A student report sheet for this activity can be found in the *Laboratory Investigations* booklet.

Time estimate
40–50 minutes

Process Skills
- Constructing Tables and Graphs: Procedure 2, 3
- Comparing/Contrasting: Analysis and Conclusions 1, 3, 6
- Interpreting Diagrams: Analysis and Conclusions 2, 4
- Calculating: Procedure 7; Analysis and Conclusions 9, 10

Procedural Hints
Some students tire of plotting points and try to draw freehand ellipses. Point out to students that such drawings will not be acceptable. Have students use a different color for each ellipse in case the ellipses overlap.

Answers—Procedure
Answers to *Procedure* questions 6 and 7 can be found in the annotated Data Table B on page 409 of this Teachers Annotated Edition.

Answers—Analysis and Conclusions
1. Ellipse 3 appears most circular and has an eccentricity of 0.3. Ellipse 1 appears least circular and has an eccentricity of 0.9.
2. As ellipses become more circular, the eccentricity decreases.
3. Ellipse 4 has the same eccentricity and shape as Ellipse 1. Ellipse 6 has the same eccentricity and shape as Ellipse 3.

4. The eccentricity (*e*) must be the same if the ellipses are to have the same shape. Ellipses with the same focal length but different eccentricities, such as Ellipse 2 and 4, have different shapes. Ellipses with the same major axis length but different eccentricities such as Ellipses 1, 2, and 3 have different shapes.

5. The shape would be a circle (*e* = 0).

6. The eccentricities of Ellipses 3 and 6 (0.3) are closest to those of the planet orbits.

7. Venus' orbit has the lowest eccentricity and therefore has the most circular orbit. Pluto's orbit has the highest eccentricity and therefore has the least circular orbit.

8. The comet's orbit would be very elliptical. It would be most similar to Ellipses 1 and 4.

9. Deimos' orbit has a lower eccentricity (.0005) than Phobos (.015) and is therefore more circular.

10.

$$\frac{d}{e} = L; \quad \frac{0.283}{0.093 \text{ AU}} = 3.04 \text{ AU}$$

$$3.04 \text{ AU} - 1.38 \text{ AU} = 1.66 \text{ AU}$$

ANSWERS TO

CHAPTER 22 REVIEW

Review

1–spectroscope, 2–telescope, 3–photosphere, 4–cooler, 5–rotates, 6–auroras, 7–flares, 8–magnetic, 9–hydrogen, 10–moons; asteroids; meteoroids; comets, 11–retrograde, 12–geocentric, 13–sun, 14–ellipses, 15–increases, 16–distance, 17–telescope, 18–decrease

Interpret and Apply

1. A proportion is one way to solve the problem. The SST *Concorde* would take 10 years to travel from Earth to the sun (Topic 2). The time needed for the SST *Concorde* to travel from the sun to Jupiter is found by:

$$\frac{150\,000\,000 \text{ km}}{778\,000\,000 \text{ km}} = \frac{10 \text{ years}}{x \text{ years}}; x = \frac{778 \times 10 \text{ years}}{150} = 51.9 \text{ yrs.}$$

Subtract the 10 years needed to go from the sun to Earth to get 41.9 years.

2. The following equation can be used to find the length of time it takes a particle in a solar wind to reach Earth.

$$\text{time} = \frac{150\,000\,000 \text{ km}}{400 \text{ km}} \times \frac{\text{s}}{1} \times \frac{1 \text{ day}}{86\,400 \text{ s}}$$

Kilometers, seconds, and four zeros will cancel.

$$\text{time} = \frac{15\,000 \text{ yrs}}{4 \times 864} = \frac{15\,000 \text{ yrs.}}{3456} = 4.34, \text{ or about 4 days}$$

3. Combining the effects predicted by Kepler's harmonic law with those of Newton's law of gravitation, the orbital speed increases if the gravitational force increases. A mass coming closer to Earth's surface speeds up due to greater gravitational force. In the case of *Skylab*, the increased speed increased friction with the atmosphere and thus increased the rate at which it burned.

4. A line between the object and the sun sweeps out equal areas in equal times. In an ellipse, equal areas have different arc lengths; thus the object is moving faster when the arc length is longer. In a circle, equal areas have equal arc lengths; thus the speed of the object does not change.

5. The distance from Earth to the sun equals 1 AU. The unnamed planet is at 4 AU from the sun. Using the equation:

$P^2 = D^3; P^2 = 4^3; P^2 = 64; P = 8$

The planet's period is 8 times that of Earth.

6. Gravity will be (a) 1/9, (b) 1/100, (c) 4 times, (d) 100 times as great.

Critical Thinking

1. Figure B, phases 8, 7, and 6 match Figure A, phases 1, 2, and 3, respectively.

2. Figure B, phases 1, 2, 4, and 5. He could not see phase 3 because it was blocked by the sun at that time; however, if students list phase 3, it should not be counted against them. The point is to identify which phases are not possible in a geocentric system.

3. In a geocentric system, Venus would be a crescent or a totally dark disk. Galileo saw Venus as an almost full disk.

4. Yes; Mercury, the other planet with an orbit inside the orbit of Earth

CHAPTER 23
The Planets and the Solar System

PLANNING CHART

Topic	Support Material
Lesson I **The Inner Planets**	**In-Text Lab Activity:** Dimensions of the Solar System **Laboratory Investigation**
1 Two Groups of Planets	**Content Evaluation:** p. 416 *Topic Review:* 1; p. 430-431 *Chapter Review:* 1
2 Planet Mercury	**Content Evaluation:** p. 416 *Topic Review:* 2; p. 430-431 *Chapter Review:* 2
3 Planet Venus	**Content Evaluation:** p. 416 *Topic Review:* 3; p. 430-431 *Chapter Review:* 3; Interpret and Apply: 1
4 Evening and Morning Stars	**Content Evaluation:** p. 416 *Topic Review:* 4; p. 430-431 *Chapter Review:* 3; Interpret and Apply: 2
5 Planet Mars	**Content Evaluation:** p. 416 *Topic Review:* 5; p. 430-431 *Chapter Review:* 4; Interpret and Apply: 1, 3
Lesson II **The Outer Planets**	
6 The Jovian Planets	**Content Evaluation:** p. 420 *Topic Review:* 6; p. 430-431 *Chapter Review:* 5
7 Planet Jupiter	**Content Evaluation:** p. 420 *Topic Review:* 7; p. 430-431 *Chapter Review:* 6
8 Planet Saturn	**Content Evaluation:** p. 420 *Topic Review:* 8; p. 430-431 *Chapter Review:* 6
9 Planet Uranus	**Content Evaluation:** p. 420 *Topic Review:* 9; p. 430-431 *Chapter Review:* 7
10 Neptune and Pluto	**Content Evaluation:** p. 420 *Topic Review:* 10; p. 430-431 *Chapter Review:* 8; Interpret and Apply: 4
Lesson III **Planetary Satellites**	
11 Satellites of Earth and Mars	**Content Evaluation:** p. 423 *Topic Review:* 11; p. 430-431 *Chapter Review:* 9; Interpret and Apply: 5
12 Jupiter's Moons	**Content Evaluation:** p. 423 *Topic Review:* 12; p. 430-431 *Chapter Review:* 10

Topic	Support Material
Lesson III (continued) **13 Saturn's Moons**	**Content Evaluation:** p. 423 *Topic Review:* 13; p. 430-431 *Chapter Review:* 11
14 The Moons of Uranus	**Content Evaluation:** p. 423 *Topic Review:* 14; p. 430-431 *Chapter Review:* 12
15 The Moons of Neptune and Pluto	**Content Evaluation:** p. 423 *Topic Review:* 15; p. 430-431 *Chapter Review:* 13
Lesson IV Comets, Asteroids, and Meteoroids	
16 Comets	**Content Evaluation:** p. 427 *Topic Review:* 16; p. 430-431 *Chapter Review:* 15
17 Asteroids	**Content Evaluation:** p. 427 *Topic Review:* 17; p. 430-431 *Chapter Review:* 14
18 Meteors and Meteoroids	**Content Evaluation:** p. 427 *Topic Review:* 18; p. 430-431 *Chapter Review:* 16
19 Meteorites	**Content Evaluation:** p. 427 *Topic Review:* 19; p. 430-431 *Chapter Review:* 16
20 Meteorite Craters	**Content Evaluation:** p. 427 *Topic Review:* 20; p. 430-431 *Chapter Review:* 17
Lab Activity p. 428-429	Dimensions of the Solar System
Chapter Review p. 430-431	Critical Thinking 1-7 **Study Guide:** Vocabulary; Interpreting and Applying
Chapter 23 Assessment Program	**Chapter Tests; Computer Test Bank**

CHAPTER **23**

Motivator

DEMONSTRATION: A scale drawing of the relative distances between planet orbits can be created with the following demonstration. In addition to a chalkboard and chalk, you will need metersticks and at least one piece of string the length of the chalkboard.

The second column of the table at the top of the next page shows the average distance in kilometers between each planet and the sun. The third column gives the distance in centimeters between each planet and the sun for a scale model drawn on a 6-meter chalkboard. If the chalkboard in your room is only 3 meters long, the values in column 3 will need to be halved.

Chapter 23 The Planets and the Solar System **T817**

Planet	Distance from sun (millions of km)	Distance on model (cm)
Mercury	58	5.8
Venus	108	10.8
Earth	150	15.0
Mars	228	22.8
Jupiter	778	77.8
Saturn	1425	142.5
Uranus	2872	287.2
Neptune	4499	449.9
Pluto	5942	594.2

- The inner planets are terrestrial— that is, these are the planets most like Earth.
- The terrestrial planets are similar in density, which indicates that they are also similar in composition, internal structure, and origin.
- Mercury has a cratered surface and very little—if any—atmosphere.
- Venus is similar to Earth in size and density, but rotates backwards and has a dense, corrosive atmosphere.
- Venus and Mercury can be seen only at sunrise or sunset because both orbit between Earth and the sun. Other planets can be seen during the nighttime.
- Mars has dust storms, huge extinct volcanoes, and evidence of past running water.

Science Background
The table at the bottom of this page can provide you with extra information on the planets.

Lesson I:
The Inner Planets

(Topics 1-5)

Teaching Suggestions
Lesson I contains a great deal of information. Bear in mind that the intent of the lesson is not to have students memorize every fact about each planet, but to have them acquire some overall concepts. One method of managing the lesson is to have students construct tables to summarize the information. While going over the lesson, the following points may help students organize some of the information:

Lesson II:
The Outer Planets

(Topics 6-10)

Teaching Suggestions
In most years, at least one of the planets will be in a position where it can be easily viewed in the evening. Several monthly publications

	Avg. Distance from Sun (Millions of Kilometers)	Average Distance from Sun (AU)	Equatorial Diameter (Kilometers)	Period of Revolution	Period of Rotation	Number of Satellites	Density (gm/cm³)	Axial Tilt	Escape Velocity (km/s)
Mercury	58	0.4	4878	88 days	59 days	0	5.4	0	4.3
Venus	108	0.7	12 104	225 days	–243 days*	0	5.2	177°	10.4
Earth	150	1.0	12 756	365¼ days	23 h 56 min	1	5.5	23½°	11.2
Mars	228	1.5	6787	687 days	24 h 37 min	2	3.9	25°	5.0
Jupiter	778	5.2	142 980	12 years	9 h 50 min	16**	1.3	3°	59.6
Saturn	1425	9.5	120 540	29½ years	10 h 39 min	18**	0.7	27°	35.6
Uranus	2872	19.2	51 120	84 years	–17 h 14 min*	15	1.3	98°	21.3
Neptune	4499	30.1	49 530	165 years	16 h 6 min	8	1.6	29°	23.8
Pluto	5942	39.7	2300	248 years	6.4 days	1	2.0	94°	1.2

*negative rotation period indicates reverse rotation

**at least

regularly provide the information needed to locate the planets in the sky.

Science Background

Galileo saw the rings of Saturn in July of 1610, but he was unable to discern that they were rings and called them moons. Shortly after that, other observers were unable to see the rings because the ring system was no longer inclined toward Earth and was difficult to see edge-on. The rings were recognized as rings by the astronomer Huygens around the year 1650.

Lesson III: Planetary Satellites

(Topics 11-15)

Teaching Suggestions

Your presentation of this lesson could—dare we say it?—revolve around the fact that the planetary moons have interesting characteristics. A possible starting point is the Galilean satellites. If Jupiter is in a good viewing position, urge students to look for these satellites. They are easily seen with binoculars.

Science Background

Moons of Saturn

Titan: Titan apparently has an ocean. Titan's ocean, however, is not water. Temperatures are much too cold that far from the sun for liquid water. Titan's ocean consists of materials that are gases on Earth: ethane (70 percent), methane (25 percent), and nitrogen (5 percent).

Iapetus: Like Earth's moon, this moon rotates synchronously with its planet, so the same side of the moon always faces the planet. As Iapetus orbits Saturn, its leading hemisphere is dark, while its trailing hemisphere is bright. The cause is not yet confirmed, but some planetologists suspect that Iapetus is sweeping up the dust from impacts on its neighboring moon, Phoebe.

Janus and Epimetheus: The orbits and orbital velocities of these moons are nearly— but not quite— identical (with average radii of 151.47 x 10^3 kilometers and 151.42 x 10^3 kilometers). Thus the inner moon slowly overtakes the outer moon. As they come closer, gravitational attraction between them causes the inner moon to gain momentum and move into a slightly larger orbit. At the same time, the outer moon loses momentum and moves into a smaller orbit. The result is that about every four years the two moons switch orbits— the inner moon becomes the outer moon and starts to fall behind.

Lesson IV: Comets, Asteroids, and Meteoroids

(Topics 16-20)

Teaching Suggestions

Use a photograph of Comet Halley to identify and discuss the parts of a comet and to summarize the features of Halley. The fact that several spacecraft were used to study comets for the first time in 1985-1986 is worth emphasizing, both for Halley and for Comet Giacobini–Zinner. The international cooperation involved in these comet investigations is also important.

You might mention that many new comets are discovered every year and are named after their discoverer, who is often an amateur astronomer. This is one area of astronomy where an amateur with a simple telescope or large binoculars can make a contribution.

The terminology in Topics 18 and 19 is often a stumbling block to students. You may need to take some time to explain that meteoroids are rock fragments in space, meteors are meteoroids that are burning as they enter the atmosphere, and meteorites are pieces of meteoroid that have survived the trip through the atmosphere. Most students consider meteors to be rare events, so it is worth stressing that meteor showers occur each year and that meteors are very easy to see. The Perseids shower and the Geminids shower average 50 meteors per hour, while the Orionids shower averages about 20 per hour. The Taurids shower averages about 5 per hour.

You may wish to use the data in the table at the top of the next page to discuss the size of some meteor craters.

Science Background

Comets: Most scientists think comets formed at the same time as the rest of the solar system. There may be a huge cloud of comets, the Oort cloud, surrounding the solar system. Only a small number of comets are pulled out of the Oort Cloud and into orbits that bring them near the sun.

Examples of Meteor Craters

Name	Location	Est. Original Diameter (km)
Manicouagan Lake	Canada	65
Vredefort Ring	South Africa	40
Clearwater Lakes	Canada	32 (2 craters)
Rieskessel	Germany	24
Deep Bay	Canada	12
Ashanti	Ghana	11
Wells Creek	Tennessee	10 (4 craters)
Crooked Creek	Missouri	6.5
Sierra Madera	Texas	4.9
Brent	Canada	3.5
Chubb	Canada	3.4
Holleford	Canada	2.3
Meteor	Arizona	1.2

Fireballs: One of the most puzzling fireball events occurred in 1908 over an uninhabited forest area, the Tunguska River region of central Siberia. An explosion was heard a thousand kilometers away. Seismographs and barographs recorded the event. Vast areas of trees were scorched and blown down. However, no crater was found. Over the years, several theories have been proposed to explain the event. Collisions with a neutron star or a black hole were given consideration. The explosion of a comet or a meteorite in the atmosphere above the area has been proposed and seems to be the most likely explanation. In 1983, tiny pieces of stony meteorite traceable to the Tunguska fireball were found, giving support to the comet/meteorite theories. Despite much research and thought, the Tunguska event remains an intriguing mystery.

CHAPTER 23 LAB ACTIVITY
Dimensions of the Solar System

■ A student report sheet for this activity can be found in the *Laboratory Investigations* booklet.

Time estimate
50–60 minutes

Process Skills
■ Calculating: Procedure 2,7,8; Analysis and Conclusions 4, 5, 6
■ Comparing/Contrasting: Analysis and Conclusions 1 , 2

Materials
The paper tape used should be about 7 cm wide. The larger planets will not fit on a narrower tape. Have students use safety compasses if they are available. Safety compasses do not have the sharp point.

Preparation Hints
Have the strings and tape cut to the proper length before class.

Answers—Procedure
Answers to *Procedure* questions 2, 6, and 7 can be found in the annotated Data Table A on page 429 of this Teachers Annotated Edition.

Answers—Analysis and Conclusions
1. The inner planets are much smaller than the outer planets. Pluto, which is the smallest planet in the solar system, is the exception.
2. The distances between the orbits of the inner planets are much smaller than distances between the orbits of the outer planets.
3. Currently, Pluto is closer to the sun than Neptune.
4. Pluto is at an average distance of 5900 million km from the sun. Earth is at an average distance of 150 million km.

$$\frac{5900 \text{ million km}}{150 \text{ million km}} = 39.3 \text{ times farther}$$

5. The diameter of Uranus is 51.8 thousand km. The diameter of Earth is 12.8 thousand km.

$$\frac{51.8 \text{ thousand km}}{12.8 \text{ thousand km}} = 4.0 \text{ times larger}$$

6. $\dfrac{5900 \text{ million km}}{1} \times \dfrac{1 \text{ cm}}{2.2 \times 10^4 \text{ km}} = 268\,181.8 \text{ cm}$

ANSWERS TO

CHAPTER 23 REVIEW

Review

1–c, 2–d, 3–c, 4–b, 5–a, 6–b, 7–d, 8–a, 9–b, 10–c, 11–b, 12–c, 13–a, 14–c, 15–a, 16–d, 17–d

Interpret and Apply

1. The astronomer on Mars would have an easier time. Even though Venus comes closer to Earth than Mars, Venus' dense atmosphere would make surface astronomy there a frustrating occupation. Except when dust storms rage, Mars has clear skies.

2. Mercury and Venus; in order to pass between Earth and the sun, the planet must be inside Earth's orbit.

3. Earth makes one complete orbit for every year of your age. For Mars, multiply your age by 365 days and then divide by 687 to get Mars years, which is the same as the number of complete orbits around Mars.

4. Neptune requires 165 years to complete one orbit of the sun. Since the planet was discovered in 1846, an observed orbit will not be completed until 2011.

5. Phobos rises in the west and sets in the east.

Critical Thinking

1. Jupiter. Yes, Jupiter is the most massive planet.

2. Pluto. Yes.

3. Earth and Venus, Uranus and Neptune

4. Mercury and Pluto. All gas lines are located above their points on the graph. All gases would escape.

5. The Jovian planets. All are above the lines for hydrogen and helium.

6. Earth retains some helium; Mars does not.

7. The point for Titan will fall between the lines for water vapor and for methane and helium. Titan would retain carbon dioxide, nitrogen, oxygen, water vapor, and methane.

CHAPTER **24**
Earth's Moon

PLANNING CHART

Topic	Support Material
Lesson I Lunar Exploration	
1 Getting to the Moon	**Content Evaluation:** p. 436 *Topic Review:* 1; p. 454-455; **Transparency 36:** Lunar Exploration
2 First Spacecraft to the Moon	**Content Evaluation:** p. 436 *Topic Review:* 2; p. 454-455 *Chapter Review:* 2
3 Mercury and Gemini	**Content Evaluation:** p. 436 *Topic Review:* 3; p. 454-455 *Chapter Review:* 3
4 Apollo	**Content Evaluation:** p. 436 *Topic Review:* 4; p. 454-455 *Chapter Review:* 4, 5
5 The Space Shuttle	**Content Evaluation:** p. 436 *Topic Review:* 5; p. 454-455 *Chapter Review:* 1
Lesson II Properties and History of the Moon	
6 Properties of the Moon	**Content Evaluation:** p. 439 *Topic Review:* 6; p. 454-455 *Chapter Review:* 5; *Interpret and Apply:* 1, 2
7 The Moon's Front and Back	**Content Evaluation: p.** 439 *Topic Review:* 7; p. 454-455 *Chapter Review:* 7
8 Origin and History of the Moon	**Content Evaluation:** p. 439 *Topic Review:* 8; p. 454-455 *Chapter Review:* 8
9 Lunar Rocks: Evidence of the Moon's History	**Content Evaluation: p.** 439 *Topic Review:* 9; p. 454-455 *Chapter Review:* 9; *Interpret and Apply:* 2
Lesson III The Moon's Surface Features	
10 The Lunar Maria	**Content Evaluation:** p. 443 *Topic Review:* 10; p. 454-455 *Chapter Review:* 10
11 The Lunar Highlands	**Content Evaluation:** p. 443 *Topic Review:* 11; p. 454-455 *Chapter Review:* 11

PLANNING CHART (continued)

Topic	Support Material
Lesson III (continued) **12 Lunar Craters and Rays**	**Content Evaluation:** p. 443 *Topic Review:* 12; p. 454-455 *Chapter Review:* 13
13 Lunar Soil	**Content Evaluation:** p. 443 *Topic Review:* 13; p. 454-455 *Chapter Review:* 12
Lesson IV The Moon's Motions and Phases	**Laboratory Investigation:** Diameter of the Moon and the Ecliptic Limit **In-Text Laboratory Activity:** Moon, Sun, and Seasons
14 The Moon's Orbit	**Content Evaluation:** p. 448 *Topic Review:* 14; p. 454-455 *Chapter Review:* 14; Interpret and Apply: 6
15 Moonrise and Moonset	**Content Evaluation:** p. 448 *Topic Review:* 15; p. 454-455 *Chapter Review:* 15; Interpret and Apply: 3
16 The Moon's Phases	**Content Evaluation:** p. 448 *Topic Review:* 16; p. 454-455 *Chapter Review:* 16; Interpret and Apply: 4, **Transparency 37:** Lunar Phases
17 Lunar Months	**Content Evaluation:** p. 448 *Topic Review:* 17; p. 454-455 *Chapter Review:* 17; Interpret and Apply: 5
18 Lunar Eclipses	**Content Evaluation:** p. 448 *Topic Review:* 18; p. 454-455 *Chapter Review:* 18
19 Solar Eclipses	**Content Evaluation:** p. 448 *Topic Review:* 19; p. 454-455 *Chapter Review:* 19, 20; Interpret and Apply: 6; **Transparency 38:** Eclipses
Lesson V Sun, Moon, Tides	
20 The Moon and Tides	**Content Evaluation:** p. 451 *Topic Review:* 20; p. 454-455 *Chapter Review:* 21; **Transparency 39:** Tides and the Moon
21 Rise and Fall of Tides	**Content Evaluation:** p. 451 *Topic Review:* 21; p. 454-455 *Chapter Review:* 22; Interpret and Apply: 7
22 Spring and Neap Tides	**Content Evaluation:** p. 451 *Topic Review:* 22; p. 454-455 *Chapter Review:* 23
23 Ocean Basins, Shorelines, and Tidal Range	**Content Evaluation:** p. 451 *Topic Review:* 23; p. 454-455 *Chapter Review:* 24
Lab Activity p. 452-453	Moon, Sun, and Seasons
Chapter Review p. 454-455	Critical Thinking 1-6 **Study Guide:** Vocabulary; Interpreting and Applying
Chapter 24 Assessment Program	**Chapter Tests; Computer Test Bank**

CHAPTER 24

Motivator

Introduce the chapter by asking students to consider ways in which a volleyball game on the moon would be different from a volleyball game on Earth. Most students know enough about the moon, and about volleyball, to think of at least one way. If they have trouble getting started, suggest that they comment on such factors as the players' uniforms (these would need to be pressurized and include air), the distance the ball would travel when hit (much farther than on Earth), the chance of the game being called because of rain (no atmosphere, no rain), and how the fans could boo the umpire (no air, no way for the sound to carry).

Lesson I: Lunar Exploration

(Topics 1–4)

Teaching Suggestions

The purpose of this lesson is to provide students with a background on the space program. A copy of the chart in the *Science Background* could be used to introduce the lesson. Of the 77 probes represented by this list, about 50 percent failed in one way or another. Some blew up or had to be destroyed close to launch. Some fell back to Earth. Some headed toward the moon but were too far off course to orbit or land. It is worth stressing that soft-landing *any* spacecraft on the moon is an incredible achievement.

You might discuss further reasons for humans to return to the moon:

1. *Apollo* astronauts explored only six small areas. The rest has yet to be investigated.

2. Some samples brought back have good percentages of iron, titanium, and aluminum. A mining base could well be one of the first lunar establishments.

3. An astronomical observatory on the back side of the moon would not be affected by either atmospheric disturbances or by radio interference from Earth.

4. Because much less energy is needed to launch from the moon, it is a logical base for further space exploration.

Science Background

Lunar Probes: In the chart below, note that the Soviet Union was still sending probes to the moon long after the *Apollo* astronauts were there. These were robot probes designed to go to the moon, take a sample, and return to Earth. *Luna 24* returned with a rock sample 160 cm long.

Lunar Probes 1958-1976 (American and Soviet)			
Series Name	Dates	Total Launched	Total Successes
Pioneer	1958–1960	7	1
Luna (Soviet)	1959–1976	30	15
Ranger	1961–1965	9	3
Cosmos (Soviet)	1965–1969	6	0
Zond (Soviet)	1965–1970	9	6
Centaur	1965–1966	2	2
Surveyor	1966–1968	7	5
Explorer	1966–1967	2	1
Lunar Orbiter	1966–1967	5	5
	totals	77	38

Teaching Suggestions

You may want to talk about the future of space explorations. Discuss how space exploration has changed now that space shuttles are used. In addition, the space shuttle has paved the way for future construction projects in space. Plans include space stations in Earth's orbit as a base for travel to other planets, as well as plans to construct spacecraft in orbit. Spacecraft constructed in orbit could be large because they would not have to support their own weight or survive a launch from Earth.

Lesson II: Properties and History of the Moon

(Topics 5–8)

Teaching Suggestions

DEMONSTRATION: An important point about the moon is that the same side always faces Earth. One method of demonstrating this point is to pin a sign to the back of a student. Have the student walk around the classroom in such a way that no one can see the sign. Students will soon realize that this works only if the "moon" always faces the class. Then point out that one trip around the classroom is both one rotation and one revolution.

Science Background

Structure of the Moon: The seismographs left on the moon by the *Apollo* astronauts detected only about 3000 moon tremors each year. Similar instruments on Earth would detect hundreds of thousands of tremors and quakes each year. All moonquakes are very weak. Each releases about the same amount of energy as a firecracker. Moonquakes occur at depths of about 600–800 kilometers, much deeper than any earthquakes. Some kinds of moonquakes occur at the same time each month. This indicates that they may be related to strains resulting from the moon orbiting Earth.

The thickness and other characteristics of the moon's crust and mantle eliminate any possibility of lunar plate tectonics. The lunar crust and mantle are simply too massive to be subjected to any tectonic processes, such as those that occur on Earth.

Origin of the Moon: A collision between Earth and a Mars-sized object occurred at the same time the terrestrial planets were forming. Unraveling the origin of the moon was one objective of *Apollo.* While this was not completely fulfilled, three earlier theories on the moon's origin (fission, capture, and accretion) were proved either impossible or extremely improbable by data collected during the missions.

Lesson III: The Moon's Surface Features

(Topics 9–12)

Teaching Suggestions

This lesson describes the moon's surface features—maria, rilles, highlands, craters, rays, and the lunar regolith. Drawings, photographs, and models of the moon, used to locate the features as they are being discussed, are very helpful.

Lesson IV: The Moon's Motions and Phases

(Topics 13–18)

Teaching Suggestions

Following the phases of the moon can provide lifelong pleasure to the interested student. Many students may already be familiar with the topic of moon phases, but few fully understand the cause. Even though Topic 15 explains the origin of phases, you should still draw and develop Figure 24.12 with your students. You may need to point out that the moon's terminator (the line between light and dark) is always perpendicular to the sun. Students tend to draw it at the orbit line for all phases.

DEMONSTRATION: Moon phases can be demonstrated using a slated globe, basketball, or other sphere. Cover half the sphere with chalk or washable paint. Have a student "revolve" the sphere around the perimeter of the room with the "illuminated" half (chalked or painted half) constantly facing the assumed direction of the sun. As the full orbit is made, students will see all phases.

The reason for the difference between the moon's period of revolution and the period from one new moon to the next will undoubtedly need classroom discussion. If Earth did not move around the sun, the two periods would be identical in length. Because Earth does continue around the sun as the moon orbits Earth, the moon must travel slightly more than one orbit to get back to the new moon position.

DEMONSTRATION: The parts of a shadow, the umbra and penumbra, can be observed using a sphere (such as a Ping-Pong ball), a light bulb, a white screen, and a strip of transparent tape. Attach the tape to the sphere so that you can dangle the sphere in front of the light, about 10 centimeters from the screen. The shadow becomes clearer as the sphere is brought closer to the screen. At 10 centimeters, both umbra and penumbra are optimum for a Ping-Pong ball.

The most recent total solar eclipse seen in the United States was visible in Hawaii on July 11, 1991. The next total solar eclipse visible in the continental United States will occur in 2017. This explains why many people travel great distances to see a solar eclipse. Although a solar eclipse is rarely visible, lunar eclipses occur at least once each year. Lunar eclipses are often publicized in advance, so try to alert your students. Unfortunately, the best viewing time for a lunar eclipse is often 3 A.M.

Lesson V: Sun, Moon, and Tides

(Topics 19–22)

Teaching Suggestions

While students who live near the ocean are very aware of tides, tides have little meaning to students who have never seen the ocean. Use the chalkboard to show Earth, the moon, and the direct and indirect high tides. Emphasize that the bulges of water toward and away from the moon do not move; the change from high tide to low tide and back to high tide is due to Earth rotating beneath the bulges.

Add the effect of the sun to your drawing to explain spring tides and neap tides and to discuss tidal range. The Bay of Fundy is the classic example of a large tidal range.

Science Background

Most students accept the explanation for the cause of direct and indirect high tides given in Topic 19, but some may question how the moon's force on Earth can cause indirect high tides. For this reason, you may prefer to discuss the indirect high tide as the result of another force—the spinning of Earth around the barycenter. *Barycenter* is the center of mass of the Earth-moon system (barycenters occur between planets and moons, between the sun and planets, and so on). The idea that the moon revolves around Earth is oversimplified—Earth and its moon are both turning around the barycenter, a point 1700 kilometers below Earth's surface on the side toward the moon. As a result of this rotation, the water on the side of Earth away from the barycenter is being thrown away from Earth—that is the indirect high tide. At the center of Earth, the pull of the moon and the force of rotation are the same. On the side toward the moon, the moon's gravitational force is greater and causes most of the bulge of the direct high tide.

CHAPTER 24 LAB ACTIVITY
Moon, Sun, and Seasons

■ A student report sheet for this activity can be found in the *Laboratory Investigations* booklet.

Time estimate
50–60 minutes

Process Skills
■ Comparing/Contrasting: Analysis and Conclusions 2
■ Constructing Tables and Graphs: Procedure 4, 5
■ Determining Cause and Effect: Analysis and Conclusions 4
■ Predicting: Analysis and Conclusions 5
■ Analyzing Data: Analysis and Conclusions 1, 3, 5

Materials
With English graph paper, the vertical axis should be scaled so that each square is equivalent to five degrees. Along the horizontal axis, dates should be marked from one grid line to the next so that one square separates each date.

For metric graph paper (10 squares per cm), each square on the vertical axis should be equivalent to one degree. Along the vertical axis, dates should be marked every five grid lines. (Generally every fifth line is darker on metric paper.)

Preparation
Students can review graphing skills in Appendix A, page 649.

The data shown is for 40°N latitude but can be transposed to your latitude. For latitudes south of 40°N, add the difference in latitudes to the altitudes. For latitudes north, subtract the difference.

Answers—Procedure
An annotated graph for *Procedure* steps 4–5 can be found on page 453 of this Teachers Annotated Edition.

Answers—Analysis and Conclusions
1. The first full moon would be January 8. With the exception of February, each full moon occurred one calendar day earlier than on the previous month.

2. The new moon is always on the same side of Earth as the sun. Therefore, the new moon's apparent location in the sky must always be near that of the sun. The variations in the altitudes of the sun and new moon over the course of the year will be the same.

3. (a) The sun is highest in June, lowest in December (b) The moon is highest in December, lowest in June (c) When the sun is at its highest altitude, the full moon is at its lowest altitude. When the sun is at its lowest altitude, the moon is at its highest altitude.

4. In June, the sun will be high in the sky, and the full moon will be low. On the graph, the sun is at its highest altitude in June when the moon is at its lowest altitude. Summer begins in the Northern Hemisphere in June.

5. In December, the sun is low in the sky and the full moon is high. The Northern Hemisphere is tipped away from the sun and toward the full moon. Winter begins in the Northern Hemisphere in December.

ANSWERS TO
CHAPTER 24 REVIEW

Review

1–t, 2–q, 3–m, 4–d, 5–b, 6–f, 7–k, 8–n, 9–h, 10–l, 11–c, 12–s, 13–r, 14–a, 15–g, 16–y, 17–j, 18–x, 19–o, 20–e, 21–i, 22–w, 23–u, 24–v

Interpret and Apply

1. A meteor is the light produced when a meteoroid streaks through Earth's atmosphere. The moon has no atmosphere and therefore could not have a meteor.

2. Tectonic and erosional processes have long ago removed and reworked Earth's original surface.

3. The moon turns on its axis once every 27.3 days. The sun would rise once every 27.3 days.

4.

Moon Phase	Earth Phase
New Moon	Full Earth
Waxing Crescent	Waning Gibbous
Waxing Quarter	Waning Quarter
Waxing Gibbous	Waning Crescent
Full Moon	New Earth
Waning Gibbous	Waxing Crescent
Waning Quarter	Waxing Quarter
Waning Crescent	Waxing Gibbous

5. If the moon revolved east to west, it would return to the new moon position before it had completed one revolution. The lunar month would be 24.8 days, which is 2.5 days *less* than one revolution instead of 2.5 days *more*.

6. Umbra size and eclipse frequency would not change. The moon would appear much larger in the sky than the sun, thus, a total solar eclipse would last longer. An annular eclipse could not occur.

7. The sketch below shows how unequal tides can occur. The direct high tide is north of the equator, while the indirect high tide is south. When the location where the tide is measured is at point A, it experiences the maximum direct high tide. When the location has moved to point A′ (12 h 25 m later), it experiences a much smaller indirect high tide.

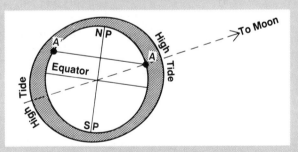

Critical Thinking

1. 6 P.M., 12 noon, 12 midnight

2. Rises at 9 P.M., sets at 9 A.M.

3. 9 A.M.

4. Full moon, waning gibbous, and waning quarter phases; they are on the opposite side of Earth from 3 P.M. Waxing gibbous would just be setting, and waning crescent would just be rising.

5. 3 A.M.

6. waxing crescent

suitable device. (Take care that the mount does not determine the direction of pendulum swing.) Once in motion, the pendulum will continue to swing in the same plane. The turntable, like Earth, turns beneath the swinging pendulum.

The same turntable can be used to demonstrate the Coriolis effect. Roll a steel sphere slowly across the gently-turning platform. The sphere appears to travel straight relative to the rim of the platform, but its actual path relative to the turntable changes. The sphere rolls to the right if the platform is turned counterclockwise and to the left if it is turned clockwise. Relate this motion to the counterclockwise rotation of Earth if viewed from above the North Pole and the clockwise motion if viewed from above the South Pole.

Science Background
Precession: The orientation of Earth's axis gradually changes in a motion called *precession*. Due to precession, Earth's axis describes a complete circle in space approximately once every 26 000 years, during which time other stars or no visible stars are at or near the Celestial North Pole. For example, the star Alpha Draconis (also called Thuban) in the constellation Draco was the northern pole star at the time of the ancient Egyptian civilizations, around 3000 B.C. The bright summer star Vega in the constellation Lyra will be the northern pole star in about 12 000 years. Vega, however, will not be as close to the Celestial North Pole as Polaris is now.

Coriolis effect: If a student notices that the explanation of the Coriolis effect given in the text only applies to objects moving toward the equator, you may wish to expand on the explanation. The Coriolis effect is actually the result of differing speeds of rotation with latitude. The most rapid speed of rotation in kilometers per hour on Earth occurs at the equator. As discussed in Topic 4, the speed of rotation decreases away from the equator. A missile fired from the equator toward the North Pole has, in addition to its northward speed, an eastward speed of about 1700 kilometers per hour resulting from Earth's rotation. The missile retains that eastward speed of 1700 kilometers per hour as it moves north, even as the speed of rotation of Earth beneath it decreases. The result is that relative to the ground the missile veers eastward, or to its right.

Lesson II: Time Measurement and Earth's Rotation

(Topics 5–8)

Teaching Suggestions
You may wish to begin this lesson with a review of the latitude-longitude coordinate system. Even though students may feel that they are familiar with it, often they are easily confused. For example, students who live in the eastern United States are sometimes under the false impression that they live in the Eastern Hemisphere. Such misconceptions need to be cleared up before moving on to a discussion of time and time zones.

The following story could be presented as an example of the importance of understanding changes that occur at time zone boundaries. Miguel, a student from San Francisco, is going to Tokyo, Japan, to visit his friend, Cliff. Miguel's flight leaves San Francisco at 9 A.M. Saturday. The flight will take 12 hours. He tells Cliff that he will arrive at 9 P.M. Saturday. In Tokyo, Cliff phones the airport at 8 P.M. Saturday to verify the flight arrival time. The airline informs Cliff that the flight is not scheduled to leave San Francisco for another six hours. It will arrive in Tokyo at 2 P.M. Sunday. Ask students how an understanding of standard time and the international date line could have prevented this confusion.

DEMONSTRATION: The pole that was set up for the *Motivator* can also serve to demonstrate the time of local noon and, additionally, the direction of true north. Local noon is the time of the shortest shadow. The shortest shadow also points due north. A method of determining approximate north whenever the sun is shining involves pointing the hour hand of a watch at the sun. The point halfway between the hour hand and 12 o'clock is south. Opposite this point is north.

Science Background
In addition to clock time and solar time, astronomers use universal time (UT) and/or Greenwich mean time (GMT). Both indicate clock time at the prime meridian. Navigators on ships keep track of UT, since the difference between universal time and local time can be used to determine longitude at sea. For example, if sun time is two hours earlier than universal time, the ship is at 30°W longitude.

Lesson III: Earth's Revolution

(Topics 9–11)

Teaching Suggestions

This is a good place for another review of the terms *rotation* and *revolution*. Next, move to the evidence for Earth's revolution. The demonstration of parallax may help students to remember one of the pieces of evidence. You may want to refer to seasonal constellation changes (Chapter 21) and emphasize this change as evidence for revolution.

The following points from Topic 11 are also important to emphasize:

■ The hemisphere that leans toward the sun has longer days and warmer temperatures than the hemisphere that leans away from the sun.

■ Decreasing the tilt of Earth's axis would cause seasons to be more moderate, while increasing the tilt would cause seasons to be more severe.

Lesson IV: Seasons on Earth

(Topics 12–16)

Teaching Suggestions

An understanding of seasons causes difficulty for many students. You may have to start with the locations of the equator, the Tropics of Cancer and Capricorn, the Arctic and Antarctic Circles, and the North and South Poles. Discuss the reasons for the location of each of these features. *Interpret and Apply* question 3 in the Chapter 25 Review is a good exercise to check student understanding of this concept.

As a class exercise, you may wish to find the altitude of the sun during the solstices and equinoxes for your latitude. (This exercise is done in the *Critical Thinking* section of the Chapter 25 Review for 43.5° N.) Use the difference between your latitude and the latitude where the sun is at the zenith. For example, at 37° N latitude, you are 13.5° from the Tropic of Cancer (37° − 23.5°=13.5°). Therefore, on June 21 at 37°N, you are 13.5° from where the sun is at zenith at noon. The

altitude of the sun at 37° N on this date is 13.5° below the zenith, or 76.5° above the horizon (90° − 13.5° = 76.5°). Use the same method to calculate the altitude of the sun on the other dates. (For the winter solstice, remember that the latitude south of the Tropic of Capricorn will need to be added to the latitude north of your location to find the total angular distance.)

CHAPTER **25** **LAB** ACTIVITY
Apparent Size of the Sun

■ A student report sheet for this activity can be found in the *Laboratory Investigations* booklet.

Time estimate
35–45 minutes

Process Skills

■ Constructing Tables and Graphs: Procedure 4

■ Analyzing Data: Analysis and Conclusions 1–3, 5, 6

■ Stating a Conclusion: Analysis and Conclusions 4

■ Comparing/Contrasting: Analysis and Conclusions 7

■ Calculating: Analysis and Conclusions 8, 9

Materials

For a class of 24 students, you will need 24 sheets of either English (8 squares per inch) or metric (10 squares per cm) graph paper.

Preparation Hints

The belief that distance from the sun is what causes the seasons turns out to be a firmly-held misconception among students of all ages. In order for students to confront these misconceptions, have a discussion on what causes the seasons before the activity. Write a list of possible causes for seasons on the chalkboard that includes everybody's ideas. After performing the activity, return to this list and again generate a discussion. One interesting point to be made is that if distance from the sun were the cause of the seasons, everyone on Earth would experience the same season at the same time.

Procedural Hints

Students may need help scaling the axes of the graph. In general, the axes should be scaled to fill the space available on the graph paper.

Answers— Procedure

Answers to *Procedure* question 4 can be found on the annotated graph on page 471 of this Teachers Annotated Edition.

Answers—Analysis and Conclusions

1. The object will appear larger when the observer is closer, smaller when the observer is farther away.

2. The sun's apparent diameter is largest in winter. Earth must be closer to the sun during the winter.

3. The sun's apparent diameter is smallest in summer. Earth must be farther from the sun during the summer.

4. According to the answers to questions 1–3, Earth is farther from the sun during the summer and closer during the winter. If distance were a cause of seasons, the opposite relationship should be true.

5. Aphelion is the point in the orbit of a planet at which it is farthest from the sun. According to the graph, aphelion occurs between June 30 and July 10.

6. Perihelion is the point in a planet's orbit at which it is nearest to the sun. According to the graph, perihelion occurs between January 1 and January 10.

7. The answers are consistent with the text. The text lists perihelion as occurring on or about January 2 and aphelion as occurring on or about July 4.

8. average apparent diameter = (32′ 32″ + 31′ 28″)/2 = 32′

9. % variation =
{[32″ - 31′ 28″]/[32′ x (60″ / 1′)]} x 100 = 1.7%
The percent variation is the amount by which Earth's distance varies from the average. Thus, Earth's distance from the sun is 150 000 000 km ± 1.7 %, or 150 000 000 km ± 2 550 000 km. Point out to students that this is a small percent change. Ask them to think about the variation in heating of the atmosphere that occurs throughout the year in their location. Most students will probably conclude that the heating variations are greater than ±1.7%.

Review

1–c, 2–a, 3–d, 4–b, 5–c, 6–b, 7–c, 8–d, 9–a, 10–a, 11–b, 12–d, 13–b, 14–b, 15–d, 16–c, 17–d, 18–b

Interpret and Apply

1. The sun would rise in the west and set in the east, and days would be only 12 hours long instead of 24.

2. The international date line is in the 180° time zone. On the west side of the line, the clock time is 6 hours earlier than our 90° W (Central) belt, but the date is 1 day later. Therefore, at 12:01 A.M. (1 minute past midnight) Saturday at the date line it is 7:01 A.M. Friday Eastern, 6:01 A.M. Friday Central, 5:01 A.M. Friday Mountain, 4:01 A.M. Friday Pacific, 3:01 A.M. Friday Alaska, and 2:01 A.M. Friday Hawaii—Aleutian.

3. All of these circles are determined by axial tilt. Cancer would be at 33.5°N, Capricorn at 33.5°S. Arctic Circle would be 33.5° from the North Pole, or 56.5°N, while Antarctic Circle would be 56.5°S.

4. Increasing the tilt of Earth's axis would tip the Northern Hemisphere more toward the sun in summer and more away from the sun in winter. The longest days would be longer than at present and the shortest days would be shorter.

5. June 21 is the summer solstice. Daylight period increases with latitude north of the equator and decreases with latitude south of the equator. Most locations in the U.S. have more hours of daylight on June 21 than Mexico City or Buenos Aires, but less than Vancouver. On December 21, the situation is reversed.

Critical Thinking

1. 43.5° – 23.5° = 20°

2. 90° – 20° = 70°

3. From Sioux Falls to equator = 43.5°; from equator to Tropic of Capricorn = 23.5°, 43.5° + 23.5° = 67° from Sioux Falls to Tropic of Capricorn

4. 90° – 67° = 23

PLANNING CHART

Topic	Support Material
Lesson I Composition and Structure of the Atmosphere	
1 What Is Weather?	**Content Evaluation:** p. 483 *Topic Review:* 1; p. 496-497 *Chapter Review:* 10
2 Observing the Weather	**Content Evaluation:** p. 483 *Topic Review:* 2; p. 496-497 *Chapter Review:* 3; Interpret and Apply: 1, 2
3 Composition of the Atmosphere	**Content Evaluation:** p. 483 *Topic Review:* 3; p. 496-497 *Chapter Review:* 4
4 Water Vapor, Ozone, and Dust	**Content Evaluation:** p. 483 *Topic Review:* 4; p. 496-497 *Chapter Review:* 12
5 Structure of the Atmosphere	**Content Evaluation:** p. 483 *Topic Review:* 5; p. 496-497 *Chapter Review:* 16; **Transparency 41:** Layers of the Atmosphere
6 The Ionosphere	**Content Evaluation:** p. 483 *Topic Review:* 6; p. 496-497 *Chapter Review:* 1
Lesson II Heating of the Atmosphere	**Laboratory Investigation:** Absorption and Radiation of Heat Energy
7 How Heat Moves	**Content Evaluation:** p. 486 *Topic Review:* 7; p. 496-497 *Chapter Review:* 8, 14, 20; Interpret and Apply: 3
8 The Heat Balance of Earth and Atmosphere	**Content Evaluation:** p. 486 *Topic Review:* 8; p. 496-497 *Chapter Review:* 15
9 Absorption and the Greenhouse Effect	**Content Evaluation:** p. 486 *Topic Review:* 9; p. 496-497 *Chapter Review:* 2, 19
Lesson III How and Why the Temperature Varies	**In-Text Lab Activity:** Temperature Inversion
10 Temperature Drops with Altitude	**Content Evaluation:** p. 490 *Topic Review:* 10; p. 496-497 *Chapter Review:* 9
11 Temperature Inversions	**Content Evaluation:** p. 490 *Topic Review:* 11; p. 496-497 *Chapter Review:* 17; Interpret and Apply: 4

PLANNING CHART (continued)

Topic	Support Material
Lesson III (continued) **12 The Sun's Rays and the Seasons**	**Content Evaluation:** p. 490 *Topic Review:* 12; p. 496-497 *Chapter Review:* 18
13 Warmest and Coldest Hours	**Content Evaluation:** p. 490 *Topic Review:* 13; p. 496-497 *Chapter Review:* 13; Interpret and Apply: 5
14 Warmest and Coldest Months	**Content Evaluation:** p. 490 *Topic Review:* 14; p. 496-497 *Chapter Review:* 15
15 Heating of Land and Water	**Content Evaluation:** p. 490 *Topic Review:* 15; p. 496-497 *Chapter Review:* 6; Interpret and Apply: 2
Lesson IV Measuring Air Temperature	
16 Temperature and Thermometers	**Content Evaluation:** p. 493 *Topic Review:* 16; p. 496-497 *Chapter Review:* 11
17 Temperature Scales	**Content Evaluation:** p. 493 *Topic Review:* 17; p. 496-497 Interpret and Apply: 2
18 Isotherms	**Content Evaluation:** p. 493 *Topic Review:* 18; p. 496-497 *Chapter Review:* 7
19 Why Isotherms Shift	**Content Evaluation:** p. 493 *Topic Review:* 19; p. 496-497 *Chapter Review:* 7
Lab Activity p. 494-495	Temperature Inversion
Chapter Review p. 496-497	Critical Thinking 1-5 **Study Guide:** Vocabulary; Interpreting and Applying
Chapter 26 Assessment Program	**Chapter Tests; Computer Test Bank**

Introducing UNIT SIX

Student Writing

Most students are probably aware of the term *global warming*, but may not know what it means or why it is occurring. Ask your students to each write an essay on what they already know about global warming. Students should be encouraged to write freely and to include questions they may have on this topic. Explain that their essays will not be graded. If necessary, generate a list of student's ideas to be used as a springboard for their essay.

Throughout the course of teaching Unit Six, you may wish to assign readings on the topic of global warming. (See the list of reference books and periodicals for Chapter 31 in Teacher Resources, pages T692–T699.) Further, you and your students can scan newspapers and journals, such as *Science News* and *Discover*, to gather the latest information about global warming.

After finishing Unit Six, return students' original essays to be reread. Start a discussion by asking students to comment on any misconceptions revealed in their original essays. Spark further discussion by asking questions such as—What is global warming? What causes global warming? Is global warming real, or, as some believe, a fabrication based on insufficient scientific evidence? What affect will global warming have on our climate, oceans, and lifestyles? Are problems associated with global warming a problem for our generation or future generations only? What are some solutions? Should industries and/or individuals be willing to make sacrifices to protect Earth from the affects of global warming? Which countries/industries of the world are most responsible for global warming? Depending on the flow of the discussion and the make up of your class, students may end up in a debate about how to deal with the complex issues surrounding global warming. After the class discussion, have each student again write an essay that reflects their new understanding of global warming, its causes and effects. Ask students to include their ideas on how to best solve the problems of global warming.

CHAPTER 26

Motivator

DEMONSTRATION: Perform the following demonstration to show that air takes up space. Fill half of an aquarium tank with water. Float a cork on the water to show the water level plainly. Mark the water level on the cork. Now turn an empty drinking glass over the cork, push the glass straight down into the water, and hold it there. Have the students look at the position of the cork. Was the glass empty? What is the evidence that it is really filled with air? What evidence is there that the air in the glass is compressible?

Lesson I: Composition and Structure of the Atmosphere

(Topics 1–6)

Teaching Suggestions

The first part of this lesson is designed to give the students some tools with which to observe and become familiar with the atmosphere. Discuss the weather on the day of the lesson. Give some examples of sources of local and national weather information (e.g., the television, radio, newspaper weather maps). A videotape of a local weather broadcast would be particularly useful. The better-quality broadcasts often have the AMS (American Meteorological Society) or NWA (National Weather Association) seal of approval. The videotape should provide a weather map discussion, radar precipitation displays, and a satellite film loop of the clouds.

Have students bring in articles about weather topics of current interest. The articles could be about particularly bad storms, El Niño, a heat wave, etc. Post these articles. Use them to relate the topics they are studying to their lives.

Note that many of the concepts, such as pressure falling with height, will be useful when they are discussed later in the unit.

The remainder of the lesson deals with the structure of the atmosphere. Emphasize that the weather takes place in a relatively thin part of the atmosphere, the troposphere.

Science Background

The Antarctic ozone hole. The chlorine atom released when a CFC molecule breaks apart is particularly destructive in the presence of dust particles or ice crystals. The dry, cold air over Antarctica is filled with ice crystals. These pieces of ice provide surfaces on which the chlorine and ozone meet, resulting in the destruction of the ozone molecule. Seasonal wind patterns also isolate the ozone layer over Antarctica, preventing ozone from other areas from "healing" the developing ozone hole. At its peak, the hole extends from 12 to 20 km in altitude and from the South Pole to 70 degrees south. Variable winds keep Arctic air from being sufficiently cold or isolated to form a strong ozone hole. However, *Nimbus-7* satellite data indicate that the Arctic ozone layer thins as much as 6 % during the year.

Layers of the atmosphere: The average temperature of the thermosphere increases with height because the molecules cannot effectively reemit the solar radiation they receive. The temperature variation in the thermosphere is large, exceeding 300°C. Above the thermosphere, meaningful temperatures cannot be measured because the atmosphere is so thin.

There are still two more layers in the atmosphere. These are the exosphere and magnetosphere. The molecules of the atmosphere escape continuously through the exosphere. The magnetosphere is strongly affected by Earth's magnetic field and the solar wind. As if blown by the solar wind, the magnetosphere extends to only 10 Earth radii on Earth's "windward" side, and extends to several times that distance on Earth's "leeward" side.

Lesson II: Heating of the Atmosphere

(Topics 7–9)

Science Background

Heat is a measure of energy of the molecules in a substance. Heat is transferred by conduction, convection, and radiation. Conduction is most efficient in solids and liquids because the molecules are in close contact and can easily transmit energy to one another. However, the molecules in a gas must bump into each other to transmit energy, and the distance between the molecules is large compared to their sizes. In the atmosphere, conduction is important only near solid or liquid boundaries. At distances of over a few millimeters, tiny convection currents take over.

Convection is the result of uneven heating: the warmer (buoyant) gas rises; the cooler (heavier) gas sinks. In the atmosphere's lowest kilometer or so—roughly from the ground to the lowest cloud base—this convection is fairly continuous during the day. The light turbulence an aircraft feels during daytime takeoffs and landings is usually convection. There is no convection when the ground is cooler than the air; however, air can still be mixed by wind. This layer of nearly continuous mixing and turbulence is called the *boundary layer*.

Radiation transmits energy from one place to another by electromagnetic waves. Whether bodies heat readily by solar radiation alone has mainly to do with their ability to reflect visible light. The color of an object is the color of the radiation it reflects. Black bodies absorb all of the visible radiation; that is why we see no color. Similarly, white bodies reflect most of the light, since white is a mixture of all the visible light. This is why dark bodies heat more readily.

Lesson III: How and Why the Temperature Varies

(Topics 10–15)

Teaching Suggestions

This lesson explains vertical and horizontal changes in the temperature of Earth's atmosphere. It begins with the variation of temperature with height. Then the lesson discusses the horizontal and temporal temperature changes that result from varying sun angle and the differences in how land and water heat and cool.

When explaining how a drop in pressure with height causes air to expand, refer to the experience of ear popping. The air inside the eustachian tubes is expanding and has to come out. Ear popping is direct evidence that air pressure changes with height. If a more formal discussion of pressure is desired, refer to Chapter 28.

Science Background

Dry-adiabatic lapse rate and moist-adiabatic lapse rate are discussed more in Chapter 27. Normal lapse rate is very close to the lapse rate of air rising or sinking in clouds. In the air below the cloud base, the average temperature falls off with height at the dry-adiabatic lapse rate. Both of these facts suggest that convection is an important heat-transfer mechanism in the troposphere.

The lapse rate on a given day can be quite different from average, with layers where the temperature stays the same, and layers in which the temperature increases with height. There can be inversions far above the surface (for example, when warm air is being brought in at higher levels). The tropopause is the base of a temperature inversion.

Lesson IV: Measuring Air Temperature

(Topics 16–19)

Teaching Suggestions

The different kinds of thermometers could be drawn, displayed, explained, and/or demonstrated.

Ask the students to use Figure 26.13 to find the Celsius equivalents of some familiar temperatures, such as room temperature, body temperature, and the temperature outside.

The discussion of isotherms provides an excellent opportunity to reinforce the points of the previous lesson. The effect of the sun's angle on the seasons is readily seen on the maps, as is the greater temperature range overland.

Science Background

A good thermometer is not enough to guarantee a good measurement of air temperature. For example, a thermometer exposed to sunlight registers too high because the sunlight is heating the thermometer. People are sometimes careful to note that a temperature is "in the shade." Similarly, a thermometer sheltered from the wind and exposed to the sky can cool by radiation to a temperature colder than that of the air.

To avoid this problem in standard temperature measurements, Weather Service thermometers are put into a white box with louvered sides. One of the sides is a door, about face level, which can be opened to read the thermometer. The box is white to prevent heating by radiation. It has louvers so that the thermometer is exposed to the wind.

CHAPTER **26 LAB** ACTIVITY
Temperature Inversion

■ A student report sheet for this activity can be found in the *Laboratory Investigations* booklet.

Time estimate
50 minutes

Process Skills

■ Constructing Tables and Graphs: Procedure 1, 2, 3
■ Interpreting Diagrams: Analysis and Conclusions 1, 2
■ Comparing/Contrasting: Analysis and Conclusions 3, 5, 6
■ Describing: Analysis and Conclusions 4
■ Predicting: Analysis and Conclusions 7, 8

Procedural Hints
Students may ask why the temperature scales on their graphs start at 15°C rather than 0°C. Students can review graphing skills in Appendix A, page 649.

Answers—Procedure
An annotated graph of *Procedure* steps 1–3 can be found on page 495 of this Teachers Annotated Edition.

Answers—Analysis and Conclusions
1. Temperature decreases as altitude increases.
2. Temperature changes 1°C per 160 meters. The rate at which temperature changes remains the same.
3. The rate of change in Graph 2 is about the same as the rate of change in Graph 1.
4. In Graph 2 above 200 meters, the temperature begins to rise.
5. Graph 1 represents normal conditions; Graph 2 represents temperature inversion. Answers will vary but should include some description of temperature changes being upside down or the opposite of the normal lapse rate.
6. The air above 500 meters is denser than the air from 200 to 500 meters.
7. Air pollutants would be trapped near the surface of the earth by a dense layer of air. Air quality would be much worse than usual during this time.
8. Denver, Colorado; Features of topography, such as mountains, can increase the frequency of temperature inversions by trapping the air.

ANSWERS TO
CHAPTER 26 R E V I E W

Review
1–i, 2–1, 3–d, 4–p, 5–a, 6–m, 7–n, 8–q, 9–t, 10–o, 11–g, 12–s, 13–j, 14–f, 15–h, 16–r, 17–e, 18–c, 19–k, 20–b

Interpret and Apply
1. (a) 39–46 mph (b) 13–18 mph (c) less than 1 mph

2. (a) –22°F (b) –33°F (c) –40°F (d) –30°C; –36°C; –40°C

3. The water cools fastest at the surface, becomes denser, and sinks. This forces warm water up, resulting in convection currents.

4. (a) On cloudy nights the clouds act as blankets that prevent loss of heat by radiation from the lower atmosphere. (b) If the morning sky is cloudy, the ground, and therefore the air below the inversion, heats more slowly.

5. because the sun rises and sets at about the same time every day

Critical Thinking

1. container A
2. container A
3. container B

4. No. Soil absorbs radiant energy better than water does. Water reflects radiation from its surface, so not all of the available energy is absorbed.

5. The smallest daily temperature ranges are over the oceans because the water temperature varies so little. This is because the sun's rays heat a large depth of water; water can mix the heat vertically because it is a fluid. Water needs more energy to change its temperature, and some of the energy is used to evaporate the water.

The largest daily temperature range would be over a dry area with no clouds, such as a desert. There would be no clouds to trap the infrared radiation at night or to reflect away the sunlight during the day. There would be less water vapor in the air to interfere with the surface's radiating to space at night, and less to interfere with the sun's heating the surface during the day.

CHAPTER 27
Evaporation, Condensation, and Precipitation

PLANNING CHART

Topic	Support Material
Lesson I Evaporation and Humidity	
1 States of Water	**Content Evaluation:** p. 502 *Topic Review:* 1; p. 520-521 *Chapter Review:* 1
2 Evaporation	**Content Evaluation:** p. 502 *Topic Review:* 2; p. 520-521 *Chapter Review:* 3
3 Specific Humidity and Capacity	**Content Evaluation:** p. 502 *Topic Review:* 3; p. 520-521 *Chapter Review:* 2
4 Relative Humidity	**Content Evaluation:** p. 502 *Topic Review:* 4; p. 520-521 *Chapter Review:* 2
5 Finding Relative Humidity	**Content Evaluation:** p. 502 *Topic Review:* 5; p. 520-521 *Chapter Review:* 3
Lesson II Forms of Condensation	**In-Text Lab Activity:** Dew Point and Relative Humidity
6 Condensation and Dew Point	**Content Evaluation:** p. 505 *Topic Review:* 6; p. 520-521 *Chapter Review:* 4
7 Condensation Requires Cooling and Nuclei	**Content Evaluation:** p. 505 *Topic Review:* 7; p. 520-521 *Chapter Review:* 5, 6; Interpret and Apply: 1
8 Dew and Frost from Contact	**Content Evaluation:** p. 505 *Topic Review:* 8; p. 520-521 *Chapter Review:* 7
9 Fogs from Radiation and Advection	**Content Evaluation:** p. 505 *Topic Review:* 9; p. 520-521 *Chapter Review:* 8
Lesson III Clouds	
10 The Origin of Clouds	**Content Evaluation:** p. 511 *Topic Review:* 10; p. 520-521 *Chapter Review:* 9; Interpret and Apply: 1
11 Cloud Names and Their Types	**Content Evaluation:** p. 511 *Topic Review:* 11; p. 520-521 *Chapter Review:* 9; Interpret and Apply: 1; **Transparency 42**: Cloud Meanings
12 Dry- and Moist-Adiabatic Lapse Rates	**Content Evaluation:** p. 511 *Topic Review:* 12; p. 520-521 *Chapter Review:* 10, 11

PLANNING CHART (continued)

Topic	Support Material
Lesson III (continued) **13 Clouds with Vertical Development**	**Content Evaluation:** p. 511 *Topic Review:* 13; p. 520-521 *Chapter Review:* 10, 11
14 Cumulus and Cumulonimbus Clouds	**Content Evaluation:** p. 511 *Topic Review:* 14; p. 520-521 *Chapter Review:* 11; Interpret and Apply: 2
15 Layer Clouds	**Content Evaluation:** p. 511 *Topic Review:* 15; p. 520-521 *Chapter Review:* 12; Interpret and Apply: 2
Lesson IV **Precipitation**	**Laboratory Investigation:** Cloud Droplets, Light, and Rainbows
16 How Raindrops Form	**Content Evaluation:** p. 517 *Topic Review:* 16; p. 520-521 *Chapter Review:* 13
17 Forms of Precipitation	**Content Evaluation:** p. 517 *Topic Review:* 17; p. 520-521 *Chapter Review:* 14
18 Measuring Precipitation	**Content Evaluation:** p. 517 *Topic Review:* 18; p. 520-521 *Chapter Review:* 15
19 Where Does It Rain?	**Content Evaluation:** p. 517 *Topic Review:* 19; p. 520-521 *Chapter Review:* 16; Interpret and Apply: 3
20 Where Does It Not Rain?	**Content Evaluation:** p. 517 *Topic Review:* 20; p. 520-521 *Chapter Review:* 16; Interpret and Apply: 3
21 Weather Modification	**Content Evaluation:** p. 517 *Topic Review:* 21; p. 520-521 *Chapter Review:* 17
22 Acid Clouds and Acid Rain	**Content Evaluation:** p. 517 *Topic Review:* 22; p. 520-521 *Chapter Review:* 18; Interpret and Apply: 1
Lab Activity p. 518-519	Dew Point and Relative Humidity
Chapter Review p. 520-521	Critical Thinking 1-4 **Study Guide:** Vocabulary; Interpreting and Applying
Chapter 27 Assessment Program	**Chapter Tests; Computer Test Bank**

CHAPTER 27

Motivator

DEMONSTRATION: Demonstrate that evaporation is a cooling process. Put a little water on a student's wrist and have him or her blow on it. Ask what happens to the water. (It begins to disappear.) How does the wrist feel? (cooler) Repeat the experiment with alcohol. The results should be more noticeable. What is happening? The liquids require energy to evaporate. This energy is supplied by the surroundings, including the body. The chilliness people may feel when they step out of the shower or swimming pool is due to water evaporating from the skin. Evaporation of perspiration from the skin is what cools people off on a hot day or after exercise.

Lesson I: Evaporation and Humidity

(Topics 1–5)

Teaching Suggestions

This lesson includes two important physical concepts. First, evaporation requires heat from the surrounding environment. Therefore, evaporation is a cooling process. Second, warmer air has a greater capacity for water vapor than cooler air.

Constructing a chart such as the one below will help students understand how the differences between wet bulb and dry bulb temperatures can be used to determine relative humidity.

Dry-Bulb Temperature (°C)	10	10	10	10	10
Wet-Bulb Temperature (°C)	10	8	6	4	2
Temperature Difference (°C)	0	2	4	6	8
Relative Humidity (%)	100	77	55	34	15

A second chart can be used to show what happens to the relative humidity when the wet bulb temperature remains constant but the dry bulb temperature increases.

Dry-Bulb Temperature (°C)	10	12	14	16	18
Wet-Bulb Temperature (°C)	10	10	10	10	10
Temperature Difference (°C)	0	2	4	6	8
Relative Humidity (%)	100	78	60	46	34

Science Background

When ice melts, the molecules break free from the crystal lattice of ice and form liquid water. The molecules can freely move past one another, but they are still in close contact and are bound together by intermolecular forces. (These forces are what hold water drops together.) During evaporation, the molecules gain enough energy to leave the water surface and become a gas. Both of these processes require energy.

When there is no phase change, the addition of heat results in a rise in temperature. The terms "heat" and "temperature" are often mistakenly used interchangeably. One calorie (about 4 joules) is the amount of heat needed to raise the temperature of 1 gram of water 1°C. When ice is heated to the melting point of 0°C, the temperature stays constant until 80 calories of heat (334 joules) per gram of water have been added. The energy is used to change the state of water from solid to liquid. It takes even more energy to convert water from a liquid to a gas. When the temperature reaches 100°C, the temperature remains constant until 540 calories (2260 joules) per gram of water have been added.

The maximum amount of water vapor that can be held in the air depends on air temperature, not air density. Warmer air has a greater capacity for water vapor because the water molecules have more energy. Consider the water in a droplet or on a flat surface. The temperature is a measurement of the energy of the molecules. However, not all molecules have the same energy. Instead, there is a range of energy levels. The more energetic molecules evaporate. As the temperature rises, more of the molecules reach the "escape velocity" required to evaporate. Water vapor molecules in the air reenter the water surface as well. At equilibrium, the number of water molecules escaping equals the number of water vapor molecules being recaptured. Equilibrium occurs when the air has reached saturation.

Lesson II: Forms of Condensation

(Topics 6–9)

Teaching Suggestions

Point out the following: (1) At 100 percent relative humidity, the wet-bulb, dry-bulb, and dew-point temperatures are the same. (2) Below 100 percent humidity, the dew point is lower than the wet-bulb reading. (3) The dew point drops with the wet-bulb temperature, but faster. A final note: At a given pressure, the specific humidity alone can be used to determine the dew point. If the temperature increases but the specific humidity remains constant, the dew point also remains constant.

DEMONSTRATION: You can demonstrate the importance of condensation nuclei in the following way. Obtain an empty 2-liter soda bottle and remove the labels. Pour a small quantity of water into the bottle, cap it tightly, and shake it a few times. Squeeze the bottle and then release it suddenly. A cloud will form in the bottle because the compressed air expands suddenly and cools adiabatically below its dew point (Topic 13). Shining a light through the bottle makes the cloud more visible.

Now repeat the demonstration promptly after adding a small amount of smoke from a match or candle to the bottle and capping it tightly. A much denser cloud should form after adding smoke because the smoke provides condensation nuclei.

Lesson III:
Clouds

(Topics 10–15)

Teaching Suggestions
Since some students enjoy identifying clouds, it would be useful to practice daily identification of cloud types. Photos in the text make a good starting place for a visual reference. Many more cloud photos are available on Optical Data's *Living Textbook: Earth Science* videodisc, sides 1 and 2. Correlations to some of these photos appear on the chapter pages of this book. Cloud charts are available from scientific supply catalogs and from How the Weatherworks Educational Weather Services, 1522 Baylor Avenue, Rockville, MD 20850.

Students could record cloud cover using the weather map symbols in Figure 27.11. It would be instructive for students to compare their observations with daily weather maps and satellite images on television broadcasts.

Science Background
Stability and instability of the atmosphere are important concepts to severe-storm forecasters. Experience shows that, provided there is enough wind change with height, the most unstable atmospheres produce the most severe storms. The strength of the updraft is directly related to its buoyancy. So, for example, unstable air is necessary for hail formation.

The weight of falling rain and cooling by its evaporation produce negative buoyancy, resulting in downdraft. The cool, gusty wind that comes with a thunderstorm is usually downdraft air.

Lesson IV:
Precipitation

(Topics 16–22)

Teaching Suggestions
The text can be followed fairly closely to describe the formation and definitions of the different kinds of precipitation. Try to show a rain gauge to the class. Point out that a tin can with straight sides can also make a good rain gauge.

To tie to previous topics and chapters, note the relationship of hail to strong updrafts (instability) and the role of temperature inversions in producing sleet and ice storms.

Topics 19 and 20 apply principles learned earlier to determine areas in which rain can be expected and areas in which rain is unlikely. Stress the relationship of rising air to rain and sinking air to dryness.

Topic 21 also applies principles learned earlier. Note that weather-modification efforts are still in their infancy. It is important to stress the nonscientific problems associated with weather modification. For example, producing rain in one place may prevent rain farther downwind, or some farmers might want rain while the others might not.

The acid-rain problem involves chemistry as well as meteorology. Note that atmospheric chemists lump all of the acid-producing particles falling to Earth as acid deposition. Both wet (rain, snow, etc.) and dry (nitrate or sulfate particles) acid deposition are important. Significant amounts of dry sulfate and nitrate particles fall to the ground and then form acid with groundwater. Have the students watch for articles on the effects of acid rain.

Science Background

Weather modification has been used for more than just rainmaking. Sometimes clouds are overseeded to slow down the growth of precipitation. In overseeding, so many nuclei are introduced that there is not enough water for the droplets to grow rapidly. This overseeding technique has been tried to move rainfall from the windward to the leeward sides of mountains. If the precipitation particles grow slowly enough, they will be blown across the mountains before they fall. Similarly, hail-producing regions of thunderstorms have been overseeded to produce many small hailstones instead of a few large ones. The hope is that either the smaller hail will melt before it hits the ground or the hail will be too small to produce damage. As with rainmaking, scientists are still not sure that overseeding is successful.

CHAPTER 27 LAB ACTIVITY
Dew Point and Relative Humidity

■ A student report sheet for this activity can be found in the *Laboratory Investigations* booklet.

Time estimate
45–50 minutes

Process Skills
■ Observing: Procedure 6
■ Calculate: Procedure 8, 10, 16
■ Analyzing Data: Analysis and Conclusions 1
■ Forming Models: Analysis and Conclusions 2, 3

Procedural Hints
Warn students that they must watch carefully for the first appearance of moisture.

The dew point can occasionally be below 0°C, particularly during the winter. In this case, dew will not form because ice water will not cool below 0°C.

Answers—Analysis and Conclusions
1. Answers will vary. The first method is probably less accurate because the first appearance of dew may be missed.

2. The bottom of the cloud shows that the dew point has been reached.
3. (a) No evaporation is taking place. (b) Relative humidity is 100 percent. (c) Clothes will not dry in air with 100 percent relative humidity.

ANSWERS TO
CHAPTER 27 REVIEW

Review
1–d, 2–b, 3–a, 4–b, 5–c, 6–a, 7–c, 8–c, 9–b, 10–d, 11–b, 12–a, 13–c, 14–b, 15–a, 16–d, 17–d, 18–c

Interpret and Apply
1. (a) Cloudiness is increasing. (b) cirrus (c) Jet contrails provide ice nuclei and water vapor.
2. Nighttime and early-morning air is usually stable; therefore, the condensation level will not be reached. (The exception to this is a foggy night.) Daytime warming by the sun results in unstable air and the possible formation of clouds.
3. The warmer winds of Mississippi carry more water vapor than the colder winds of Maine.

Critical Thinking
table: 500 m, 500 m, 2000 m, 1000 m

1. makes it higher
2. makes it lower
3. From Figure 27.2, a cubic foot of saturated air at 5°C contains about 6 grams of water vapor. A cubic foot of air at 26.5°C with 50% relative humidity contains 11 grams of water vapor.
4. At warmer temperatures, there would be less temperature change with height. At very cold temperatures, when the air holds little water, the moist-adiabatic lapse rate approaches the dry-adiabatic lapse rate.

CHAPTER 28
Atmospheric Pressure and Winds

PLANNING CHART

Topic	Support Material
Lesson I **Air Pressure**	**In-Text Lab Activity:** Recording and Correlating Weather Variables
1 What Is Air Pressure?	**Content Evaluation:** p. 526 *Topic Review:* 1; p. 540-541 *Chapter Review:* 1; Interpret and Apply: 1, 8
2 Measuring Air Pressure	**Content Evaluation:** p. 526 *Topic Review:* 2; p. 540-541 *Chapter Review:* 2
3 Air Pressure Units	**Content Evaluation:** p. 526 *Topic Review:* 3; p. 540-541 *Chapter Review:* 3, 4; Interpret and Apply: 6
4 Why Air Pressure Changes	**Content Evaluation:** p. 526 *Topic Review:* 4; p. 540-541 *Chapter Review:* 5, 6; Interpret and Apply: 9
5 Highs, Lows, and Pressure Gradients	**Content Evaluation:** p. 526 *Topic Review:* 5; p. 540-541 *Chapter Review:* 7
Lesson II **Winds**	**Laboratory Investigation:** The Foucault Pendulum and the Coriolis Effect
6 What Makes the Wind Blow?	**Content Evaluation:** p. 530 *Topic Review:* 6; p. 540-541 *Chapter Review:* 8
7 Local Winds	**Content Evaluation:** p. 530 *Topic Review:* 7; p. 540-541 *Chapter Review:* 9; Interpret and Apply: 4, 5; **Transparency 43:** Sea and Land Breezes
8 The Coriolis Effect	**Content Evaluation:** p. 530 *Topic Review:* 8; p. 540-541 *Chapter Review:* 10 Interpret and Apply: 2, 3, 7; **Transparency 44:** The Coriolis Effect
9 How the Coriolis Effect Changes the Wind	**Content Evaluation:** p. 530 *Topic Review:* 9; p. 540-541 *Chapter Review:* 11; Interpret and Apply: 2, 4, 7
10 Measuring Wind	**Content Evaluation:** p. 530 *Topic Review:* 10; p. 540-541 *Chapter Review:* 12, 13; Interpret and Apply: 6
Lesson III Origin of the World Wind Belt	
11 Winds on a Nonrotating Earth	**Content Evaluation:** p. 534 *Topic Review:* 11; p. 540-541 *Chapter Review:* 14
12 Latitude Winds Cells	**Content Evaluation:** p. 534 *Topic Review:* 12; p. 540-541 *Chapter Review:* 14, 15, 16; Interpret and Apply: 3

PLANNING CHART (continued)

Topic	Support Material
Lesson III (continued) **13 Pressure Belts and Winds**	**Content Evaluation:** p. 534 *Topic Review:* 13; p. 540-541 *Chapter Review:* 17; Interpret and Apply: 3; **Transparency 11:** Prevailing World Winds
14 Weather in the Wind and Pressure Belts	**Content Evaluation:** p. 534 *Topic Review:* 14; p. 540-541 *Chapter Review:* 18
Lesson IV **Winds and Wind Shifts**	
15 Effects of Continents	**Content Evaluation:** p. 537 *Topic Review:* 15; p. 540-541 *Chapter Review:* 19
16 Monsoons	**Content Evaluation:** p. 537 *Topic Review:* 16; p. 540-541 *Chapter Review:* 19
17 Jet Streams	**Content Evaluation:** p. 537 *Topic Review:* 17; p. 540-541 *Chapter Review:* 20
Lab Activity p. 538-539	Recording and Correlating Weather Variables
Chapter Review p. 540-541	Critical Thinking 1-3 **Study Guide:** Vocabulary; Interpreting and Applying
Chapter 28 Assessment Program	**Chapter Tests; Computer Test Bank**

CHAPTER 28

Motivator

DEMONSTRATION: Show that weather changes are related to changes in barometric pressure by recording the barometer reading daily and noting the weather conditions (sunny, rainy, cloudy, etc.). A fall in atmospheric pressure is often followed by cloudy weather, rain, or snow. A rise in pressure often means fair weather. The highest pressures occur with very cold temperatures in the wintertime.

Lesson I: Air Pressure

(Topics 1–5)

Teaching Suggestions
It will probably be difficult for the students to understand that pressure is felt in all directions. This concept is important to understand when discussing the pressure-gradient force later in the chapter. The text explains this concept by noting that pressure is caused by the impact of molecular collisions, which occur from all directions. The high pressures on submarines and divers are familiar examples of pressure acting in all directions.

It must be emphasized that pressure is only a force when it acts on a surface area, such as on the skin of a diver. In the atmosphere, a pressure-gradient force is created by pressure differences over a given area. Ear popping experienced when flying up and down in an airplane is a result of pressure differences.

DEMONSTRATION: The following demonstration shows that air has pressure. You will need a yardstick or other long stick and some sheets of newspaper.

Lay the yardstick on the table so that slightly more than half its length is on the table and push the free part of the yardstick down rapidly. Of course it falls off the table.

Return the yardstick to the table so that slightly over half of it is on the table. Spread out a whole sheet of newspaper so that its center lies over the part of the yardstick on the table. Smooth out the newspaper so that it is in contact with the table. Again, push the free part of the yardstick down vigorously. The yardstick should break or at least strongly resist the downward push because the air pressure on the newspaper keeps the end of the yardstick on the table from rising. (To convince the skeptics that the weight of the newspaper is not important, repeat the experiment with the newspaper folded in half, in quarters, etc.)

Teaching Suggestion
The most important cause of air pressure fluctuations is changing temperatures of the air overhead. This concept can be clarified by watching videos of satellite cloud images. For example, clouds moving from the north bring in cold air at higher levels. In the absence of satellite pictures, students can watch the motions of the clouds overhead. Of course, the layer of air near the ground is important, too! If the wind is out of the northwest and cumulus clouds are also moving in the same direction, a layer of air with a thickness of at least the height of the cloud-base brings in cold temperatures.

The second source of pressure change—increasing humidity—is explained in the text. The phrase "high and dry" is useful for remembering that higher pressure comes with drier air. The students could be reminded that adding water vapor to air in a closed container would increase its pressure. Air in the open atmosphere, however, expands to let in the lighter water vapor molecules. Water vapor causes the weight of the air over a given area—its pressure—to decrease.

Interpretation of isobars and pressure gradients should be straightforward for those who mastered topographic maps, but some students will need a review. Find a weather map showing isobars for some practice in identifying highs, lows, and pressure gradients.

You may wish to subscribe to the National Weather Service 7:00 A.M. weather maps. Write to the National Oceanographic and Atmospheric Administration, Daily Weather Maps, Climate Analysis Center, Room 808

World Weather Building, Washington. Ask for the Daily Weather Maps, weekly series.

Science Background
The pressure of a gas is related to its density and temperature. How does pressure respond to a force such as the weight of the air above? If an additional weight is introduced from above, the gas will compress. When it does, the density (and probably the temperature) becomes greater. The pressure also becomes greater. When the pressure is large enough to equal the force from above, the gas stops compressing. The gas supports the weight from above. In the same way, the air supports the air overhead.

Lesson II: Winds

(Topics 6–10)

Teaching Suggestions
This lesson deals with some basic concepts about how the wind blows. First, the wind blows "down the pressure gradient" from high to low pressure. Second, the stronger (steeper) the pressure gradient, the stronger the wind. Third, the Coriolis effect turns the wind to the right in the Northern Hemisphere and to the left in the Southern Hemisphere.

A good way of thinking about how the pressure-gradient force works is that the air with greater pressure pushes harder than the air with less pressure. The air that pushes the hardest wins out. Also, the flow from high to low pressure can be interpreted as an attempt to make the pressure the same. Perhaps the best way to interpret the pressure-gradient force is to picture it as pointing "downhill" from high to low pressure. By going down the pressure gradient, the air is going "downhill." All three analogies are very useful in that they predict that stronger (steeper) pressure gradients would produce stronger winds.

The upper-level weather maps used by meteorologists are contour maps showing the height of a pressure surface, rather than a map of pressure at a fixed altitude. Note that the pressure gradient is perpendicular to the isobars, or pointing straight downhill.

DEMONSTRATION: Demonstrate how the Coriolis effect works using a turntable, a collapsible globe such as a globe-shaped Japanese lantern, and chalk. Try to draw straight north-south lines on the globe as a student turns it. If the globe is turned counterclockwise looking down from the top (to duplicate Earth's rotation), the chalk lines should always curve toward the right in the Northern Hemisphere.

Students often find it harder to understand why both east and west winds turn right. An effective way to show this is to collapse a globe-shaped Japanese lantern into a disk. Rotate the disk on a turntable, and again try to draw straight lines. This time the lines should start out perpendicular to a radius of the disk to simulate east or west winds. The lines curve to the right on the turntable (assuming it is rotating counterclockwise as viewed from the top). When the Japanese lantern is expanded into a globe, the left-to-right lines (west winds) are seen to curve southward, while the right-to-left lines (east winds) are seen to curve northward.

To demonstrate the Coriolis effect in the Southern Hemisphere, have the students look at the bottom of the globe while it is rotated in the usual sense, pointing out that the rotation is clockwise when looking at the South Pole. This is the opposite of the Northern Hemisphere.

Lesson III: Origin of the World Wind Belts

(Topics 11–14)

Teaching Suggestions
A good way to help the students fully understand this lesson is to help them develop a drawing of the planetary wind belts. Start by drawing the circulation on a nonrotating Earth with no continents. Then, following the text, draw rotating Earth and explain the two Hadley cells between 0 and 30 degrees. The polar cell between the poles and 60 degrees is the next easiest to understand. The third cell, between 30 and 60 degrees, fills in between the two other cells nicely, with upward and downward moving air coinciding and the horizontal motions completing the circulation.

Science Background
The circulation of the air over Earth, also called its general circulation, has been studied since the 1700's. Not surprisingly, the Hadley cell, which is the most well defined of the three circulation cells, was discovered first. Early maps show the winds coming together near the equator.

The cells to the north and south appear in long-term averages. Perhaps the polar high is best defined in the Southern Hemisphere, where the cold Antarctic continent lies over the pole. The coldest temperatures in the Northern Hemisphere are in northeastern Asia.

The middle cell is poorly defined. The pressure and wind fluctuations are mostly related to traveling weather systems (the subject of the next two chapters) and semipermanent highs and lows (dealt with in the next lesson). While texts and reference books agree on the well-defined Hadley cell and polar cells, there are several depictions of the middle cell in earlier references. This is not surprising in view of the poor definition of the middle cell.

Lesson IV: Winds and Wind Shifts

(Topics 15–17)

Teaching Suggestions
The first two topics discuss how the presence of continents complicates global wind patterns. These topics apply principles learned earlier. First, land heats (and cools) faster than water. Second, pressure lowers over warmed surfaces (a warm island, a warm coast, or a warm continent) or rises over a cooled surface. The following information should be discussed based on these principles:

1. The world belts of pressure are broken up into semipermanent highs and lows, with the low-pressure areas over warm regions and the high-pressure areas over cold regions. Therefore, during the summer, low-pressure areas tend to occur over the warmer land and high-pressure areas over the cooler ocean.

2. The highs and lows affect the winds. In summer, the air flowing into the lows goes from sea to land. These winds bring moisture and precipitation.

3. The monsoon over India and Southeast Asia is a particularly strong example of this effect.

Use a simple diagram on the blackboard to explain the Indian monsoon. Review the association of low pressure with converging, rising air and precipitation.

Science Background
The monsoon over India and Southeast Asia is the strongest in the world because of the size of the continent and the fact that these regions are surrounded on three sides by water. The warm temperatures of the Arabian Sea (to the west of India) and the Bay of Bengal (to the east of India) moisten air traveling toward India through high rates of evaporation. This air, lifted over the Indian subcontinent, brings heavy precipitation.

CHAPTER 28 LAB ACTIVITY
Recording and Correlating Weather Variables

■ A student report sheet for this activity can be found in the *Laboratory Investigations* booklet.

Time estimate
10–15 minutes each day for 3 weeks

Process Skills
- Observing: Procedure 10
- Measuring: Procedure 2, 3, 4, 5, 6, 7, 8
- Predicting: Analysis and Conclusions 10
- Determining Cause and Effect: Analysis and Conclusions 3, 4, 6, 7, 8
- Analyzing Data: Analysis and Conclusions 1, 2, 3, 4, 5, 6, 7, 8, 9
- Applying a Strategy: Analysis and Conclusions 9, 10

Materials
If a rain gauge is not available, one can be made from a transparent container with a plastic metric ruler taped to the outside.

Procedural Hints
Review with students how to read the rain gauge and anemometer.

Answers to *Analysis and Conclusions* questions will vary because they are controlled by geographic location, weather oddities, and students' interpretations.

Answers—Analysis and Conclusions
1. North winds bring in cooler air because they come from colder latitudes.
2. South winds bring in warmer air because they come from warmer latitudes.
3. Wind speed increases as air pressure changes. Winds remain light when the air pressure is steady.
4. In general, high pressure is associated with clear weather and low pressure is associated with stormy weather.
5. The state of the sky is not a good indicator of the next day's weather.
6. Nimbostratus and cumulonimbus
7. High humidity occurs with precipitation. Low humidity occurs with clear weather.
8. Decreasing humidity indicates clearing and increasing humidity indicates precipitation.
9. Wind direction, air pressure, relative humidity, and cloud type are most useful.
10. Answers will vary.

ANSWERS TO
CHAPTER 28 REVIEW

Review
1–Air (atmospheric) pressure, 2–barometer; altimeter, 3–lower, 4–isobars, 5–temperature; humidity, 6–more, 7–low-pressure area, 8–steep (strong); strong, 9–sea breeze, 10–Coriolis effect, 11–Surface friction, 12–toward, 13–knots, 14–circulation cells, 15–Hadley cell, 16–polar front, 17–doldrums or intertropical convergence zone (ITCZ), 18–high; low, 19–monsoon, 20–west; east

Interpret and Apply
1. about 0.74 kg/cm²
2. (a) counterclockwise (b) clockwise
3. The diagram should show south easterlies instead of southwesterlies, northwesterlies instead of northeasterlies, etc.
4. sea breeze would penetrate farther inland
5. The sailboats should go out in the early morning with the land breeze and return in the afternoon with the sea breeze.
6. Wind direction and speed are affected by nearby buildings, trees, etc., so measurements must be taken higher above the ground.

7. The circulation of water going down a drain is too small and occurs too quickly to be affected by the Coriolis effect.

8. Both are examples of pressure acting in all directions; both increase with depth.

9. The atmosphere is not a closed container, so the air can expand to let the lighter water vapor molecules in. This makes the weight (and pressure) of the same volume of air less.

Critical Thinking

1. (a) At the surface, low pressure on the warm side toward the sun, high pressure on the cold side away from the sun. Winds would blow from the center of the cold side of Earth to the center of its warm side. (b) At 10 kilometers: high pressure due to increased thickness of air layers below on the warm side; low pressure from decreased thickness of air on the cool side. Winds flow from warm to cold side. Air would rise above the surface low; air would sink above the surface high. Pressure extremes at the centers of the warm and cold sides of the planet.

2. Hadley cell would not extend as far from the equator, polar cell would not extend as far from the poles, both due to faster turning of the wind by the Coriolis effect. More cells between for the same reason. Earth's cloud pattern might look more like that of Jupiter (rotates once every 10 hours), except for the colors.

3. (a) The cloud is buoyant; therefore there is warm air aloft; pressure falls. (b) layer of cold air raises the pressure (c) dying thunderstorm no longer buoyant, due in part to the weight of the heavy rain; pressure rises (d) Pressure falls. The 1-km-thick layer of air near the surface contains more air than the 1-km-thick layer aloft (recall that air thins out with height). The moisture effect also helps lower the pressure.

PLANNING CHART

Topic	Support Material
Lesson I **Air Masses**	**Laboratory Investigation**
1 **Origin of an Air Mass**	**Content Evaluation:** p. 546 *Topic Review:* 1; p. 554-555 *Chapter Review:* 5
2 **Kinds, Sources, and Paths of Air Masses**	**Content Evaluation:** p. 546 *Topic Review:* 2; p. 554-555 *Chapter Review:* 1, 11, 14; Interpret and Apply: 2, 7, 9; **Transparency 45:** Air Mass
3 **Weather in an Air Mass**	**Content Evaluation:** p. 546 *Topic Review:* 3; p. 554-555 *Chapter Review:* 4, 10; Interpret and Apply: 4, 10
4 **Skies in an Air Mass**	**Content Evaluation:** p. 546 *Topic Review:* 4; p. 554-555 *Chapter Review:* 8, 16; Interpret and Apply: 9
5 **Observing an Air Mass**	**Content Evaluation:** p. 546 *Topic Review:* 5; p. 554-555 *Chapter Review:* 15; Interpret and Apply: 3
Lesson II Fronts and the Formation of Lows	**In-Text Lab Activity:** Evaporation and the Windchill Factor
6 **What Is a Front?**	**Content Evaluation:** p. 549 *Topic Review:* 6; p. 554-555 *Chapter Review:* 2; Interpret and Apply: 11
7 **Kinds of Fronts**	**Content Evaluation:** p. 549 *Topic Review:* 7; p. 554-555 *Chapter Review:* 9, 12, 17; Interpret and Apply: 11
8 **How Mid-Latitude Lows Form**	**Content Evaluation:** p. 549 *Topic Review:* 8; p. 554-555 *Chapter Review:* 6, 13; Interpret and Apply: 8; **Transparency 46:** Middle Latitude Lows
Lesson III Weather Associated with Lows, Fronts, and Highs	
9 **Winds and Weather in a Low**	**Content Evaluation:** p. 551 *Topic Review:* 9; p. 554-555 *Chapter Review:* 3
10 **Warm-Front Weather**	**Content Evaluation:** p. 551 *Topic Review:* 10; p. 554-555 *Chapter Review:* 12; Interpret and Apply: 5, 6, 11
11 **Cold-Front Weather**	**Content Evaluation:** p. 551 *Topic Review:* 11; p. 554-555 *Chapter Review:* 17; Interpret and Apply: 5, 6, 11

PLANNING CHART (continued)

Topic	Support Material
Lesson III (continued) **12 Weather in a High**	**Content Evaluation:** p. 551 *Topic Review:* 12; p. 554-555 *Chapter Review:* 7; Interpret and Apply: 1
Lab Activity p. 552-553	Evaporation and the Windchill Factor
Chapter Review p. 554-555	Critical Thinking 1-4 **Study Guide:** Vocabulary; Interpreting and Applying
Chapter 29 Assessment Program	**Chapter Tests; Computer Test Bank**

CHAPTER 29

Motivator
DEMONSTRATION: Show how air masses and fronts affect local weather by studying the temperature patterns on a surface weather map. Locate the fronts and check the temperatures on both sides of the front. Point out the large temperature changes along the fronts. When the front passes through your town, note the temperature changes.

Point out how the temperature changes gradually with distance from the fronts. Regions of uniform temperature and humidity are called *air masses*. As long as an air mass stays over an area, the temperature changes are gradual.

Lesson I:
Air Masses

(Topics 1–5)

Teaching Suggestions
The *Motivator* will be a good introduction to the uniformity of air masses, but students should be made aware of air masses stagnating for long periods of time at their sources. Because air masses stay in one area (the source region) for a long time, they acquire the characteristics of that area's climate. Air masses are uniform, so the source area has to be fairly uniform.

Point out on a wall map of North America where United States air masses originate. The names follow from the location of the source area—c = continental (dry); m = maritime, meaning ocean (moist); P = polar (cold); T = tropical (warm). These terms will appear again in discussions of climate. The heating and cooling processes discussed in Chapter 26 describe how air masses take on the character of their source region.

The weather and clouds in an air mass can be explained in terms of stability and instability and what makes clouds cumuliform or stratiform. Warm air over a cold surface is stable near the surface, forming stratiform clouds. Cold air over a warm surface is unstable near the surface, and cumuliform clouds develop.

Science Background
Air masses adopt the climate of their source regions. Continental polar air masses cool through radiation. Recall that snow reflects sunlight but radiates well in the infrared, so the ground in the source region is quite cold. The air just over the ground is cold and stable. Over time, the layer of stable cold air thickens. The cooling condenses moisture, drying the air out.

Maritime polar air masses match the temperature of the cold ocean waters over which they lie. Evaporation of water from the sea makes them moist, but not as moist as the warmer maritime tropical air masses, since the cold air cannot hold as much water vapor. (A review of Chapter 27 Topic 3, *Specific Humidity and Capacity*, may help here.) Tropical air masses are warmed primarily through convection (aside from conduction right at the water surface). In a tropical maritime air mass, the ocean surface provides much heat and moisture to the air it comes in contact with. Because the water (and therefore the air) is warm, the maritime tropical air mass has more moisture than a maritime polar air mass. Moisture as well as heat is carried up by convection, which forms cumuliform clouds. These moisten the air higher up.

A tropical continental air mass typically forms over a desert area, where hot ground is heated by radiation. Since the desert ground is dry, all of the solar radiation goes to heating the ground and therefore the air.

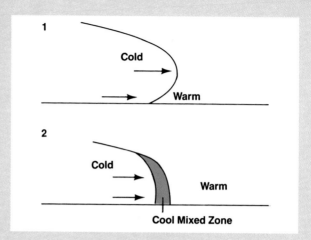

Lesson II:
Fronts and the Formation of Lows

(Topics 6–8)

Teaching Suggestions
The shape of fronts can be illustrated by a few diagrams on the chalkboard. You may wish to review the use of vertical exaggeration to stress specific points. Emphasize that the vertical is exaggerated in all front diagrams. Review the concept of slope, referring to common experiences with stairs and steep mountain roads (a 7 percent grade is 7 in 100).

Chalkboard diagrams are helpful in explaining why cold fronts are sloped more steeply in the lowest few kilometers.

Before discussing the evolution of lows, it might be useful to review the polar front. The discussion of low formation in the text ties the polar front nicely to lows. It also underscores the fact that the polar front is extremely irregular.

Science Background
Cold fronts have a much steeper frontal surface than warm fronts. This is a result of friction. (See Figure 29.7.) An alert reader might notice that at higher levels the cold front should overtake the front at the surface. As shown in the diagram below, this does happen. As soon as it happens, vertical mixing occurs. This mixing creates a zone of intermediate temperature and smoothes out the wind profile.

The frontal slope at higher levels is difficult to explain without resorting to complex mathematics. Basically, the greater the temperature difference across the frontal surface, the more horizontal it tends to be. The tendency for this cold air to sink under the warm air is neutralized by the wind changes with height. Increasing winds with height mean increased Coriolis "force," which pulls air parcels to the right (in the Northern Hemisphere) and keeps the frontal surface at an incline instead of sinking to horizontal. Normally, fronts with strong temperature contrast also have strong wind changes with height.

The theory for the formation of lows or cyclones along the polar front dates from the early twentieth century, but still is a useful qualitative explanation.

Lesson III: Weather Associated with Lows, Fronts, and Highs

(Topics 9–12)

Teaching Suggestions
The first topic expands on winds around lows and elaborates on the presence of precipitation. The importance of heat released by precipitation draws on several earlier concepts, including the association of rising air with condensation, the heat released by condensation, and the effect of heating of the atmosphere (at any level) on the air pressure at the surface.

The next two topics describe and offer some brief explanation of the weather at fronts. Reconstructing the frontal cross sections and associating rising air with clouds is a good device to help the class remember the logic behind the structure of fronts. Slides showing the clouds and weather associated with the approach and passage of warm and cold fronts could reinforce the lesson and relate fronts to everyday experience.

Science Background

Data from radar, special field programs, satellites, and instruments such as wind profilers are providing a detailed picture of fronts. Although basic ideas about fronts still hold true, some new details have emerged. For example, the precipitation of both cold and warm fronts is often organized into discrete bands. The squall line is one well-known example. In addition, increased observations have revealed that some fronts have very small "mixing zones." At the surface, some fronts have virtually no mixing zones at all!

On the other hand, frontal structure can be so disorganized that a single front on the weather map rarely occurs. Squall lines well ahead of the front cool the air significantly and shift the wind, making it hard to know exactly where the front is. If a warm front is "dry," with little cloudiness, the cold air mass beneath can sometimes be warmed enough to destroy the front/temperature inversion over a broad region. The surface front then "jumps" farther to the north and east.

CHAPTER 29 LAB ACTIVITY
Evaporation and the Windchill Factor

■ A student report sheet for this activity can be found in the *Laboratory Investigations* booklet.

Time estimate
40–50 minutes

Process Skills
- Analyzing Data: Analysis and Conclusions 1, 4
- Determining Main Ideas: Analysis and Conclusions 2, 3, 5, 10
- Forming Hypotheses: Analysis and Conclusions 5, 6, 7, 8, 9, 11

Preparation Hints
There should be no breezes in the room from fans or open windows. Make sure that the water, the glycerin, and the alcohol are at room temperature before starting the activity.

Safety

⚠ **CAUTION:** Depending on the arrangement of outlets in your classroom, it may be safer to limit the number of blow dryers to six. In this way, two lab teams could share a single blow dryer.

In step 11, make sure that students have access only to properly labeled containers of water, glycerin, and rubbing alcohol. Under no circumstances should students put chemicals other than water or rubbing alcohol on their skin.

Answers—Analysis and Conclusions

1. Blow drying the water produced a greater temperature change.
2. It made the liquids evaporate at a greater rate. The evaporation removed heat from the thermometer and caused the temperature to fall. Point out to students that the reason wind increases the rate of evaporation is that it replaces the saturated air surrounding the moist surface with drier, nonsaturated air.
3. The liquids did not evaporate at the same rate.
4. The alcohol evaporated the fastest, and the glycerin evaporated the slowest.
5. The cloth holds more liquid than the surface of the bulb alone, allowing more evaporation to take place.
6. If the room temperature varied during the experiment, the varied temperature would affect the accuracy of the results.
7. The temperature would not change because the saturated air would allow no more evaporation.
8. Alcohol feels cooler. Alcohol evaporates rapidly, drawing heat from a feverish patient.
9. By continually blowing the moist air away from the body, wind speeds up the evaporation of perspiration from the skin.
10. Wind can cool your skin below the air temperature. Frostbite can occur, depending on wind speed and air temperature.
11. The car's surface does not produce any moisture. Therefore, no evaporation takes

place, and the car remains at the same temperature as the air.

12. Condensation releases heat to the surroundings. As moisture condenses to form clouds in a low-pressure system, the air is heated, which in turn lowers the pressure further. The increased pressure gradient results in stronger winds.

ANSWERS TO
CHAPTER 29 R E V I E W

Review

1–l, 2–m, 3–p, 4–o, 5–j, 6–i, 7–n, 8–e, 9–q, 10–g, 11–d, 12–k, 13–c, 14–b, 15–a, 16–h, 17–f

Interpret and Apply

1. The clear, dry air favors rapid radiation and cooling (below the dew point) at night.

2. Polar air masses in the Southern Hemisphere originate in south polar regions and move northward toward the equator. Tropical air masses originate in lower latitudes near the equator and move southward with the prevailing northwesterly winds toward the polar regions.

3. As air pressure decreases with altitude, the gas in the balloon expands more and more, stretching the balloon fabric until finally its strength is exceeded and it bursts. The level at which the expansive force of the gas exceeds the strength of the fabric is the maximum height the balloon can reach.

4. During the summer, the contrast in temperatures is the smallest.

5. After a warm front passes, the weather will be warm air-mass weather. After a cold front, there will be cold air-mass weather.

6. Along a steep (cold) front the air rises quickly, forming clouds of vertical development. Horizontally-developing clouds dominate along gently sloping (warm) fronts.

7. The warmer air of the maritime tropical air mass can hold more water vapor.

8. An occluded front forms when one front overtakes another and the two fronts merge.

9. During the winter, it is continuously nighttime in the Arctic. Inversions form at night because the ground cools faster than the air. The air near the ground cools as well, through conduction, mixing, and radiation. The long night allows a strong inversion to form, and the air is stable.

10. (a) The warmer water below warms the lowest layers of air, setting up convection currents, which rapidly warm and moisten the lowest layers of the air mass. (b) As the air mass moves over the mountains, its moisture condenses and falls out as snow. This dries out the air mass. The air mass is also warmer, since the air on the westward side of the mountains cools at only the moist-adiabatic lapse rate, but it warms on the eastward side at the larger dry-adiabatic lapse rate. So, there is a net warming. The clear skies on the east side of the mountains let in sunlight to warm the air even more.

11. (a) The cT air mass is denser, so it slides under the mT air mass. The weather and slope would be much like that of a cold front. (Such fronts do exist. The "dry line" that forms across western Oklahoma and Texas is an example. Strong thunderstorms often originate along the dry line in the spring and summer. Its slope is nearly vertical, however, since the cT air is hotter as well as drier.) (b) A cold front will form as before, but there will be less precipitation, since the air is so dry. Cumulus clouds that form along the front will have high bases and may not grow very far upward.

Critical Thinking

1. three—cold, warm, and stationary

2. (a) purple (b) green (c) The arrows show the wind blowing outward and clockwise around the green areas (highs) and inward and counterclockwise around the purple areas (lows).

3. Winter. The cold front is fairly far to the south, indicating that the polar air masses are pushing southward. In the summer, the cold air would be farther to the north.

4. The stationary front in that area indicates that there was probably a long period of steady precipitation.

CHAPTER 30
Storms and Weather Forecasts

PLANNING CHART

Topic	Support Material
Lesson I Thunderstorms and Tornadoes	
1 How Thunderstorms Form	**Content Evaluation:** p. 560 *Topic Review:* 1; p. 572-573 *Chapter Review:* 1, 2; Interpret and Apply: 5, 7
2 Electricity in a Thunderstorm	**Content Evaluation:** p. 560 *Topic Review:* 2; p. 572-573 *Chapter Review:* 3; Interpret and Apply: 3, 4
3 Lightning Danger and Protection	**Content Evaluation:** p. 560 *Topic Review:* 3; p. 572-573 *Chapter Review:* 4; Interpret and Apply: 4
4 Tornadoes	**Content Evaluation:** p. 560 *Topic Review:* 4; p. 572-573 *Chapter Review:* 5, 6
5 Severe Weather Watches and Warnings	**Content Evaluation:** p. 560 *Topic Review:* 5; p. 572-573 *Chapter Review:* 7
Lesson II Cyclonic Storms	**Laboratory Investigation:** Hurricane Weather
6 Hurricanes	**Content Evaluation:** p. 564 *Topic Review:* 6; p. 572-573 *Chapter Review:* 8, 9; Interpret and Apply: 1, 2, 6
7 Sources and Tracks of Tropical Storms	**Content Evaluation:** p. 564 *Topic Review:* 7; p. 572-573 *Chapter Review:* 10; Interpret and Apply: 2, 6
8 Naming and Forecasting Hurricanes	**Content Evaluation:** p. 564 *Topic Review:* 8; p. 572-573 *Chapter Review:* 11
9 Winter Storms	**Content Evaluation:** p. 564 *Topic Review:* 9; p. 572-573 *Chapter Review:* 12; Interpret and Apply: 8
Lesson III Forecasting and Weather Maps	**In-Text Map Activity:** Reading Weather Maps **In-Text Map Activity:** Forecasting Severe Storms
10 Weather Forecasts in the United States	**Content Evaluation:** p. 569 *Topic Review:* 10; p. 572-573 *Chapter Review:* 13
11 Forecasting with Computers	**Content Evaluation:** p. 569 *Topic Review:* 11; p. 572-573 *Chapter Review:* 14
12 Satellites and Radar in Weather Forecasting	**Content Evaluation:** p. 569 *Topic Review:* 12; p. 572-573 *Chapter Review:* 15, 16, 17, 18

PLANNING CHART (continued)

Topic	Support Material
Lesson III (continued) **13 Making a Surface Weather Map**	**Content Evaluation:** p. 569 *Topic Review:* 13; p. 572-573 *Chapter Review:* 19; **Transparency 47:** Weather Map Symbols
14 The Station Model	**Content Evaluation:** p. 569 *Topic Review:* 14; p. 572-573 *Chapter Review:* 20; **Transparency 14:** Weather Maps (January 28 & 29) **Transparency 15:** Weather Maps (January 30 & 31)
Map Activities p. 570-571	Reading Weather Maps Forecasting Severe Storms
Chapter Review p. 572-573	Critical Thinking 1-5 **Study Guide:** Vocabulary; Interpreting and Applying
Chapter 30 Assessment Program	**Chapter Tests; Computer Test Bank**

CHAPTER 30

Motivator
Collect magazine and newspaper clippings or videotapes about the types of storms most likely to hit your geographic area. Discuss the most relevant or interesting type of storm. Find out how much the students already know about warnings, safety precautions, and so on. Have students share some of their personal experiences with local storms.

A film or a discussion by a local meteorologist from the Weather Service, TV or radio station, university, or local chapter of the American Meteorological Society (AMS) would complement the discussion nicely. The AMS (45 Beacon St., Boston, MA 02108) keeps a list of their local chapters, many of which have members willing to speak at local schools, particularly on storms.

Lesson I:
Thunderstorms and Tornadoes

(Topics 1–5)

Teaching Suggestions
To students fascinated with storms, this chapter is the reward for going through some-times seemingly irrelevant material. Now is the chance to pull it together and show how the material is important to something everyone relates to. For example, in discussing thunderstorms, it can be noted that they occur in maritime tropical air masses, that the release of heat by condensation is important, that thunderstorms form in air unstable through deep layers, and that strong thunderstorms are favored by strong winds (thus the jet stream can be important).

There are some very good films and slide collections of tornadoes and thunderstorms. If you are in an area particularly vulnerable to thunderstorms and tornadoes, this lesson might deserve a little extra emphasis.

Science Background
One of the tools meteorologists use to forecast severe thunderstorms is a measure of stability called the *Lifted Index*. First they predict the afternoon temperature. Then they calculate the temperature of an air parcel rising from the surface to 500 mb (about 5.5 km), if it starts out with this temperature and the measured moisture. They assume the parcel rises dry-adiabatically to the condensation level, and then moist-adiabatically to 500 mb. The calculated temperature of the air parcel is compared to the environmental air at this level. If the air parcel is much warmer than the

environment, the air is unstable enough to contribute to the growth of severe thunderstorms.

Lesson II: Cyclonic Storms

(Topics 6–9)

Teaching Suggestions

Point out that hurricanes and mid-latitude lows are examples of cyclonic storms. They are both low-pressure areas, and the wind flows counterclockwise around them in the Northern Hemisphere. Both have heavy precipitation.

There are important differences between the two, however. Although both get energy from condensation, the main source of energy for mid-latitude lows is the temperature difference across fronts. Hurricanes are more intense, typically have lower central pressures, have stronger winds, have no fronts, and have an eye.

Intense winter lows can have very strong winds, even though the central pressures do not necessarily get that low. This is because the surrounding pressure is so high.

In talking about these systems, again take the opportunity to review some of the concepts from past chapters. You may want to emphasize the type of storm that affects your part of the country, particularly if one has recently occurred. A collection of recent news clippings could be quite useful.

As in the case of tornadoes and severe thunderstorms, snowstorms and hurricanes are excellent topics for visiting speakers. They are also good topics for reports.

If a snowfall occurs at a convenient time, it would be instructive to measure the snow in several places to get a rough snow depth and then to melt down the snow to find out the amount of water that actually fell. On the average, a centimeter of water makes about 10 centimeters of snow. When temperatures are quite cold, "lighter" snows fall with greater depth per unit water content. When temperatures are warmer, heavier, "sticky" snow has lower depths per unit water content.

Science Background

The formation of wintertime lows is favored in two parts of the country—to the east of the Rocky Mountains and along the East Coast. The lows to the east of the Rockies bring snows along a path that usually goes eastward or northeastward across the Great Plains, through the Midwest, and on toward the East.

The snowstorms in eastern Colorado are particularly interesting because the land slopes upward to the west. When lows move across southern Colorado, they bring east winds to the rest of the state. The east winds are forced up the terrain slope. Forced to higher levels, the winds can bring heavy precipitation. This is called "upslope precipitation."

The lows that form and intensify along the East Coast often move northeastward along the coast. Lows often form here because of the contrast between the cold, dry air on the continent and the warm, moist air over the Gulf Stream.

New lows often form associated with "cold-air damming." Cold air gets "trapped" east of the Appalachians. When a warm front tries to move northward, it becomes blocked by the cold air and moves out unchecked over the Atlantic. A new low can form around the resulting "kink" in the front.

Lesson III: Forecasting and Weather Maps

(Topics 10–14)

Teaching Suggestions

This lesson gives some insight into how forecasts are made. Emphasize the importance of both the computer model and the human meteorologist in forecasting. The computer model is designed to predict the larger-scale patterns and give guidance as to probable weather. Forecasters use their experience to "fit in" the weather for their areas given the larger-scale picture. After considerable experience with the collection of numerical models from the National Meteorological Center, meteorologists know of the models' shortcomings and can work around them.

The models are based on the observation times at which rawinsondes provide a three-dimensional picture of the atmosphere. The surface maps at the three-hour intervals provide updates. If the forecaster thinks that the model prediction is poor, he or she can modify the forecast accordingly.

"Model time" is a phrase that may produce some confusion. Model time is very different from real time. A full 24-hour run of a model may take minutes. To be useful, a 24-hour forecast obviously has to be ready before 24 hours have elapsed. In very simple models, one 5- or 10-minute time step will take the computer only seconds of "real time." Complex models take longer.

Science Background

Numerical models are steadily improving. The major limitation to their development is the size and speed of the computers used in forecasting. In the model discussed in the text, there is one point each 100 kilometers in the horizontal and 18 points each kilometer in the vertical at each location. This means that 918 000 points are needed to cover Earth's atmosphere. Ten to twenty numbers are required to describe the atmosphere at each point. This means 9 to 18 million numbers are needed. At least five equations are used in the model, and these are solved every 5 to 10 minutes. These numbers challenge even the largest computers. Increasing the resolution of the model to include important smaller-scale phenomena increases the numbers correspondingly. For example, halving the distance between the points in the horizontal quadruples the number of points in the computer grid. Improving the "physics" of the model to make it more like the atmosphere requires more complex calculations and hence causes more strain on the computer.

The National Weather Service has been evaluating its forecasts since the 1950's. Computer forecasts of the movement of larger weather systems have steadily improved. Forecasts have become more reliable for longer periods. Better radars and faster communications to the public have provided more accurate and timely severe weather watches and warnings. Ironically, improvement in severe-weather warning skills also requires better "verification," that is, public or spotter reports of whatever has been warned against! Forecasts of whether or not it will rain have also improved.

Some forecasts have improved considerably less. For example, local temperature forecasts are not much better than 10 years ago, although large temperature errors are rarer. Also, it remains difficult to forecast actual precipitation amounts. This is unfortunate, because for example, both temperature and amount of precipitation are needed in the prediction of a major snowstorm.

CHAPTER **30** **MAP** ACTIVITY
Reading Weather Maps

■ A student report sheet for this activity can be found in the *Laboratory Investigations* booklet.

Time estimate for performing lab
30–40 minutes

Process Skills
■ Predicting: Analysis and Conclusions 4
■ Interpreting Diagrams: Procedure 3, 4, 5, 7; Analysis and Conclusions 1, 2, 3, 4
■ Determining Cause and Effect: Analysis and Conclusions 3

Answers—Procedure
1. The fourteen cities are Atlanta, GA; Bismarck, ND; Boise, ID; Chicago, IL; Kansas City, MO; Miami, FL; Minneapolis/St. Paul, MN; New York, NY; Oklahoma City, OK; Phoenix, AZ; Portland, OR; Salt Lake City, UT; San Antonio, TX; and San Francisco, CA.
2. The variables are wind speed, wind direction, and percentage of sky cover.
3. The highest temperature was in Miami on January 31 at 61°F. The lowest was in New York City on January 28 at -12°F.
4. The station with the highest wind speed was Salt Lake City at 20 knots on January 28. The wind direction is SE. The station with the lowest wind speed is Boise on January 30. There was no wind.
5. Four stations with 100 percent sky cover were Boise, Salt Lake City, Minneapolis/St. Paul, and Chicago. Four stations with clear skies were Kansas City, Oklahoma City, Atlanta, and Miami.

6. High pressure systems were centered in Idaho and Mississippi. Low pressure systems were centered in Arizona and New Mexico.

7. The front was a cold front. It moved half way between Phoenix and San Antonio.

8. (a) rain (b) snow (c) drizzle

Answers—Analysis and Conclusions

1. The weather systems moved from west to east.

2.

Variable			
	Jan. 29	**Jan. 30**	**Jan. 31**
Temperature °F	32	59	34
Percent Sky Cover	10	100	10
Wind Speed (knots)	1-2	8-12	3-7
Wind Direction	SE	SW	NW

3. A warm front followed by a cold front crossed Atlanta.

4. The temperatures in Miami will decrease because a cold front will pass through.

CHAPTER 30 MAP ACTIVITY
Forecasting Severe Storms

■ A student report sheet for this activity can be found in the *Laboratory Investigations* booklet.

Time estimate
30–40 minutes

Process Skills
■ Predicting: Analysis and Conclusions 2, 3
■ Interpreting Diagrams: Procedure 1, 2, 3; Analysis and Conclusions 1,2 3, 4, 5
■ Determining Cause and Effect: Analysis and Conclusions 1, 4, 5, 6

Preparation
Review with students the weather conditions that lead to the formation of thunderstorms.

Answers—Procedure
1. The weather variables are wind speed, wind direction, cloud cover, temperature, dew point, and precipitation.

2. Indianapolis has a dew point of 43°F and a temperature of 52°F, Louisville has a dew point of 52°F and a temperature of 64°F, and Chattanooga has a dew point of 59°F and a temperature of 70°F.

3. Front A is a cold front moving east. Front B is a warm front moving north. Front C is an occluded front moving north.

Answers—Analysis and Conclusions

1. Winds move counterclockwise around low pressure systems. Therefore the cold front extending south is pushed east and the warm front extending to the east is pushed north.

2. The dew point increases from north to south. Because the wind is coming from the south, moist air should be pushed north, increasing the dew point over Indianapolis.

3. South winds push warmer air from the south. The temperature should also increase due to heat from the sun.

4. Cool, dry air from the west is pushed over warm, moist air from the south, causing unstable conditions.

5. The squall line is located directly over Memphis.

6. Winds from the south cause the lower levels of air to become warmer and more moist. Therefore, there is a larger differential in temperature and dew point between the bottom layer of warm air from the south, and the top layer of cool air from the west.

ANSWERS TO
CHAPTER 30 REVIEW

Review
1–cold, 2–air mass, 3–lightning; electricity, 4–highest, 5–cloud; dust, 6–waterspout, 7–watch; warning, 8–hurricane; eye, 9–storm surges, 10–weaker, 11–65, 12–temperature; moisture, 13–four, 14–model; weather predictions, 15–satellites; radar, 16–satellites, 17–geostationary, 18–wind; precipitation, 19–hour, 20–station model

Interpret and Apply
1. A hurricane is all one air mass.

PLANNING CHART (continued)

Topic	Support Material
Lesson III (continued) **12 Distance from the Oceans**	**Content Evaluation:** p. 585 *Topic Review:* 12; p. 592-593 *Chapter Review:* 11
13 Ocean Currents and Fogs	**Content Evaluation:** p. 585 *Topic Review:* 13; p. 592-593 *Chapter Review:* 12; **Transparency 16:** World Climates
Lesson IV **Climate Change**	
14 Sources of Climate Change	**Content Evaluation:** p. 589 *Topic Review:* 14; p. 592-593 *Chapter Review:* 13
15 Causes of Global Cooling	**Content Evaluation:** p. 589 *Topic Review:* 15; p. 592-593 *Chapter Review:* 14; Interpret and Apply: 1
16 Causes of Global Warming	**Content Evaluation:** p. 589 *Topic Review:* 16; p. 592-593 *Chapter Review:* 15, 16, 17; Interpret and Apply: 2
17 Is Climate Getting Warmer?	**Content Evaluation:** p. 589 *Topic Review:* 17; p. 592-593 *Chapter Review:* 17; Interpret and Apply: 2
Map Activity p. 590-591	World Climates
Chapter Review p. 592-593	Critical Thinking 1-2 **Study Guide:** Vocabulary; Interpreting and Applying
Chapter 31 Assessment Program	**Chapter Tests; Computer Test Bank**

CHAPTER 31

Motivator

Bring a variety of common house plants into the classroom, including ones needing little water, such as cactus, and ones needing a lot of water, such as hibiscus. Have the students water them for a few weeks, noting the differences in the amount of water needed for each plant. Note the differences in the structures of the plants and the environment in which each plant normally lives (hibiscus in moist tropical climates, cactus in semiarid or arid climates, etc.). How are the plants' water needs related to the precipitation of the area in which they normally grow?

Plants are adapted to the climate in which they live. Scientists can use plants to learn about an area's climate, even if no measurements of precipitation or temperature have ever been taken. Animals are also adapted to their environments. Because of this, fossils of past plant and animal life are valuable clues to past climates.

Lesson I: Climate and Climate Controls

(Topics 1–3)

Teaching Suggestions

A general discussion of the characteristics of the local climate would be helpful in giving the students a feel for how climate can be described. The discussion should include the temperature and precipitation statistics of a nearby location, available from the local Weather Service Office or a climate atlas. Use representative data for the same station, collected from newspapers or television, to calculate some average temperatures and temperature ranges. Some slides of local vegetation and a discussion of local land use (timber, crops, cattle, desert) would make an excellent tie-in with the rest of the chapter.

Lesson II: Factors That Control Temperature

(Topics 4–9)

Teaching Suggestions

A wall map of the physical world will be useful in discussing the points in this lesson. Slides showing the vegetation in different climates would also be helpful. Whatever technique is selected, the following points need to be made:

1. Average yearly temperature decreases with increasing latitude.

2. Yearly temperature range increases with increasing latitude.

3. Temperatures decrease with altitude.

4. Oceans have a modifying effect on climate. They keep coastal locations warmer in winter and cooler in summer than continental locations at the same latitude. Water is slow to heat in summer and slow to cool in winter. As a result, marine climates have warm winters and cool summers.

5. Marine climates have small yearly temperature ranges. The largest temperature ranges occur in the continental interiors. Larger continents have larger temperature ranges.

6. The east coasts of continents in mid latitudes do not have marine climates because the prevailing winds come from the continental interiors and bring a continental climate with them.

7. Mountains are temperature barriers.

8. Warm ocean currents raise coastal temperatures, while cold ocean currents lower them.

Lesson III: Factors That Control Rainfall

(Topics 10–13)

Teaching Suggestions

The satellite picture that accompanies Topic 10, Figure 31.4, can be used to point out precipitation areas in the ITCZ and in mid-latitude lows. Frontal precipitation also appears in Figure 29.10. In this infrared picture, the brightness (infrared energy) is related to the temperature. The temperature a cloud top radiates is nearly the same as that of the surrounding air. Since the temperature drops off with height, the colder cloud tops are higher. The clouds with the highest tops are either rainclouds or cirrus.

Lesson IV: Climate Change

(Topics 14–17)

Teaching Suggestions

The study of climate change is one of the most rapidly evolving and multidisciplinary fields in science. The rapid pace of climate study is reflected in the media—numerous articles report new discoveries by scientists and arguments among scientists. Discussions of these articles would be valuable, and with the students background from *Earth Science*, the class is well-equipped to understand the arguments. These articles are important reminders that science is not a set of facts learned long ago, but an evolving set of ideas debated by people today. Articles about the influence of El Niño on weather provides another opportunity to explore scientific discoveries being made today.

Teaching Suggestions

Climate study is particularly well suited to an integrated curriculum. Oral and written histories of a locality reveal local climate trends, which may or may not match global trends. One might be able to detect the warming effects of urbanization from local records. Furthermore, the influence of climate shifts on people and nations provides stimulating material for a class bulletin board or individual student projects. It is valid to ask how humans would need to adjust to climate changes. Famines, for example, show the potentially catastrophic impact of drought exacerbated by overpopulation and political unrest. Finally, a classroom session about steps that could be taken to reduce greenhouse gases would be stimulating. A useful reference would be *50 Simple Things You Can Do to Save the Earth*, Earthworks Press, Berkeley, CA, 96 pp.

Science Background

Changes in the concentration of greenhouse gases in Earth's atmosphere can have a significant effect. The effect of carbon dioxide alone, discussed in the text, is significant; but changes in the other greenhouse gases–CFC's, methane, and nitrous oxide, among others, may be equally important. CFC's are manufactured and have no natural sources. Concentrations of methane and nitrous oxide are supplied by natural sources, and by people. For example, termites produce much of Earth's methane, but rice paddies and cattle also contribute. Some of these gases also come from nitrogen fertilizers and forest fires set to clear land for farming.

Science Background

An important example of the complex interactions involved in studying Earth's climate change is the water cycle, described in Chapter 9, Topic 2. To predict climate change, it is necessarily to know how the cycle changes in response to changes of other variables—for example, temperature. This is important not only because water vapor forms clouds and precipitation, but because water vapor is a greenhouse gas. In addition, water vapor changes are difficult to predict. A little greenhouse heating causes more water to evaporate, and this increase in water vapor causes more heating. This in turn causes more evaporation. The cycle continues until another process forces a new equilibrium. Such a self-reinforcing "vicious cycle" is called a *positive feedback loop*. Ice in the polar regions interacts with solar radiation in much the same way: more cooling causes more ice which causes more reflection which causes more cooling. "Negative feedback loops" would put the brakes on climate change. If climate warming

were to increase the amount of low clouds, these would reflect more solar radiation and slow the warming.

A second important cycle is the carbon cycle, because carbon dioxide and methane are both greenhouse gases. Although this cycle is far from completely understood, we know that plants, animals, bacteria in the soil, and the ocean, produce, absorb, or store carbon. Bogs store carbon, as does limestone, and the fossil fuels coal, oil, and natural gas. The carbon in fossil fuels is released by human activity. Of course, different parts of the carbon cycle take place at different rates. For example, rotting trees or leaves release carbon much more rapidly than a bog, and limestone can store carbon dioxide over geologic time. We need to understand how these elements interact to understand the role carbon dioxide and methane play in future or past climates. All of the other greenhouse gases except for CFC's have such natural cycles.

CHAPTER 31 MAP ACTIVITY
World Climates

■ A student report sheet for this activity can be found in the *Laboratory Investigations* booklet.

Time estimate
80–90 minutes

Process Skills

■ Comparing/Contrasting: Procedure 2, 9, 13

■ Interpreting Diagrams: Procedure 1, 4, 5, 6, 7, 8, 9, 10, 11, 13, 14, 15; Analysis and Conclusions 3

■ Forming Models: Analysis and Conclusions 1

■ Determining Cause and Effect: Procedure 4, 8, 14, 15; Analysis and Conclusions 3

■ Stating a Conclusion: Analysis and Conclusions 2

Preparation

Before starting, have students turn to each map to be used in this activity. You may want to provide, or have students make, three labeled book marks to facilitate locating the maps.

Answers—Procedure

1. Answers to *Procedure* question 1 can be found on the annotated table, page 590 of this Teachers Annotated Edition.

2. No; other factors affect climate besides latitude. Students can compare the differences in climate between cities at the same latitudes, such as Bombay and Mexico City, Houston and Cairo, or Rome and Chicago.

4. 5°N–5°S, wet tropical; 55°N–65°N, subarctic; latitude

5. South America, Africa, and Australia do not extend far enough towards the poles for polar climates to occur.

6. Johannesburg; The climate there is mild and rainy all year while Cape Town has a desert climate.

7. Perth; December is summer in Australia and, in summer, the climate in Perth is hot and dry.

8. Since Asia is a larger continent, its climate is less tempered by oceans. Therefore Yakutsk has greater seasonal temperature variations than Edmonton.

9. The climate in Nairobi is hot all year. St. Petersburg has a change from warm in summer to cold in winter, resulting in a larger temperature range.

10. arid, semiarid, and humid subtropical. Rainfall and humidity must increase from west to east. The pattern can be easily seen in Australia as well as in southern South America and southern Africa. Although the climates cover larger areas and have several interruptions by mountains, the pattern from dry to wet can also be seen from west to east across Asia.

11. The horse latitudes are associated with the dry climates (arid and semiarid) while the doldrums are associated with humid tropical climates (wet and wet-and-dry).

13. arid, semi-arid, subarctic, subpolar, and polar

14. The west coast of Europe (east side of North Atlantic) has a temperate marine climate due to warm air moving inland from the warm Gulf Stream and North Atlantic currents. The east coast of North America (west side of North Atlantic) has polar and subpolar climates because it is washed by cold air from the cold Labrador and East Greenland currents

15. North America (Rockies), South America (Andes), Africa (Ahmar Mountains, not on map), and Asia (Himalayas). Altitude is the significant climate control.

Answers—Analysis and Conclusions

1. Climate zones would occur in horizontal bands parallel to lines of latitude.

2. Monsoons occur in wet-and-dry tropical climates. Since monsoons are seasonal winds that bring rain, areas that experience monsoons alternate between rainy seasons and a dry seasons.

3. The Rocky Mountains protect California from cold Canadian air. There are no similar mountains to protect Florida.

ANSWERS TO
CHAPTER 31 REVIEW

Review

1–d, 2–d, 3–c, 4–b, 5–d, 6–c, 7–b, 8–d, 9–b, 10–b, 11–b, 12–d, 13–d, 14–a, 15–b, 16–d, 17–b

Interpret and Apply

1. Volcano A. Its sulfur dioxide and dust will stay in the atmosphere much longer than those of Volcano B which are mixed down by convection and washed out by rain.

2. Carbon dioxide would probably have more effect because it does not slowly settle out or fall with precipitation, as smoke particles do.

Critical Thinking

1. (a) The West Coast would be the driest because of being on the downwind side of the continent and the downwind side of the coastal mountains. (b) Wyoming would be drier than the East Coast, because of being farther from the ocean than Philadelphia. (c) Philadelphia would be very moist, because of being so close to the ocean on the windward side of the continent.

2. Canada would be at least partially desert because of the descending air in the horse latitudes.

CHAPTER **32**
The Rock Record

PLANNING CHART

Topic	Support Material
Lesson I Reading the Rock Record	**Laboratory Investigation:** Making a Geologic Time Line **In-Text Map Activity:** Interpreting Geologic History
1 Telling Time	**Content Evaluation:** p. 601 *Topic Review:* 1; p. 612-613 *Chapter Review:* 19
2 Finding Age with Relative Time	**Content Evaluation:** p. 601 *Topic Review:* 2; p. 612-613 *Chapter Review:* 1, 16; **Transparency 5:** Geologic Map: Flaming Gorge, UT; **Transparency 48:** Determining Relative Age; **Software:** Mountains and Crustal Movement
3 The Geologic Timetable	**Content Evaluation:** p. 601 *Topic Review:* 3; p. 612-613 *Chapter Review:* 4, 8, 13; **Transparency 49:** Geologic Timetable
Lesson II The Fossil Record	
4 How Fossils Are Formed	**Content Evaluation:** p. 605 *Topic Review:* 4; p. 612-613 *Chapter Review:* 3, 11, 15; Interpret and Apply: 1
5 Fossils as Evidence for Evolution	**Content Evaluation:** p. 605 *Topic Review:* 5; p. 612-613 *Chapter Review:* 7; Interpret and Apply: 1
6 Index Fossils and Key Beds	**Content Evaluation:** p. 605 *Topic Review:* 6; p. 612-613 *Chapter Review:* 5, 9
7 Rock Correlation	**Content Evaluation:** p. 605 *Topic Review:* 7; p. 612-613 *Chapter Review:* 9; Interpret and Apply: 1
8 Other Uses of Fossils	**Content Evaluation:** p. 605 *Topic Review:* 8; p. 612-613 *Chapter Review:* 12
Lesson III Measuring Absolute Time	
9 Tree Rings	**Content Evaluation:** p. 609 *Topic Review:* 9; p. 612-613 *Chapter Review:* 2
10 Varves	**Content Evaluation:** p. 609 *Topic Review:* 10; p. 612-613 *Chapter Review:* 18; Interpret and Apply: 2
11 Radioactive Elements and Absolute Time	**Content Evaluation:** p. 609 *Topic Review:* 11; p. 612-613 *Chapter Review:* 20

PLANNING CHART (continued)

Topic	Support Material
Lesson III (continued) 12 Half-Life	**Content Evaluation:** p. 609 *Topic Review:* 12; p. 612-613 *Chapter Review:* 17; **Software:** Dating and Geologic Time
13 Radiocarbon Dating	**Content Evaluation:** p. 609 *Topic Review:* 13; p. 612-613 *Chapter Review:* 10; Interpret and Apply: 3
14 Other Radiometric Methods	**Content Evaluation:** p. 609 *Topic Review:* 14; p. 612-613 *Chapter Review:* 6, 14; Interpret and Apply: 4
Map Activity p. 610-611	Interpreting Geologic History
Chapter Review p. 612-613	Critical Thinking 1-6 **Study Guide:** Vocabulary; Interpreting and Applying
Chapter 32 Assessment Program	**Chapter Tests; Computer Test Bank**

Introducing UNIT SEVEN

Student Writing

Begin Unit Seven with a brief discussion of the photos on pages 593–594 and the evidence each shows about events in Earth's history. Throughout Unit Seven, students will learn about the techniques used to find the age of rock layers and about the history of Earth as determined from the study of those layers.

Upon completing Unit Seven, students can relate the photos in the Unit Seven introduction (pages 593–594) to the material in the unit by organizing and writing an essay. Listed below is information about each photo. Using this information and the Geologic Timetable (pages 600–601), students can write an essay describing local and global conditions at the time of the fossil's formation. Take the sand dunes as an example. Students can say that the Zion National Park area was above sea level when the sand dunes formed and that at this time the first mammals had not yet developed on Earth. Student essays should reflect an understanding of the processes of fossil preservation and should include examples of conditions at each era, period, or epoch represented.

- *Dinosaur hatching from egg:* Found in Montana; dates to late Cretaceous Period

- *Fossil crinoid:* Found in Indiana; dates to Mississippian Period
- *Yellow crinoid:* Found in the Philippines; Quaternary Period, Holocene Epoch (this is a living organism, not a fossil, but could become one)
- *Ferns and horsetails:* Found in bituminous shale in Pennsylvania; date to Pennsylvanian Period
- *Tracks:* Dinosaur tracks, found in Arizona; Mesozoic Era
- *Ancient sand dunes:* Zion National Park, Utah; oldest layers date to Triassic Period

CHAPTER 32

Motivator

One way to start the chapter and to introduce Lesson I is to ask students to tell when they were born without using dates. For example, a student could say that he or she was born after an older brother but before a younger sister. Or students could relate their birth to events such as the assassination of Martin Luther King (1968), the first astronauts on the moon (1969), Camp David accords between Egypt and Israel (1978), the nuclear accident at Three Mile Island (1979), the eruption of Mount St. Helens

(1980), Sally Ride becoming first U.S. woman in space (1983), opening of the Berlin Wall (1989), and so on. You may have to help with some specific dates like those above. An almanac may help you find other examples.

Lesson I: Reading the Rock Record

(Topics 1–3)

Teaching Suggestions

The illustration which follows can be used with your discussion of Topic 3. The interpretation of the time sequence in the illustration will require application of each of the rules and laws in the topic. Make a copy of the illustration either on the chalkboard or on paper and ask students to put the rock units in the correct order according to their ages and to then explain their reasoning.

Starting with the oldest rock or occurrence, the correct order is:

1. **Shale deposition** (principle of superposition). The granite is not the oldest rock in the diagram because pieces of the shale are included within the granite (law of included fragments).

2. **Granite intrusion.** (The granite also could have come after the deposition of the sandstone or after the deposition of the conglomerate. The only certainty in the sequence is that the granite came after the shale directly above it.)

3. **Sandstone deposition.**

4. **Conglomerate deposition.** The shale/sandstone/conglomerate sequence might also indicate that either the shoreline of the land area that was the source of these sediments was getting closer to this area or that the land area was rising, enabling streams to flow faster and wash larger particles farther from the shore. This sequence goes with sea regression or land uplift.

5. **Fault.** The fault cuts across the granite, shale, sandstone, and conglomerate layers. Therefore the fault must be younger than those rocks (law of cross-cutting relationships).

6. **Basalt.** The intrusion of the basalt cuts across the granite, shale, sandstone,

conglomerate, and across the fault (law of cross-cutting relationships).

7. **Unconformity.** At some time, the layers were tilted and raised above sea level. The intrusion of the basalt could have come after the tilting and uplift, but it definitely occurred before erosion was completed and the area subsided for new deposition. The unconformity is an angular unconformity (see *Science Background*).

8. **Sandstone deposition.** This is the first layer to have been deposited on top of the old erosion surface.

9. **Shale deposition.**

10. **Limestone deposition.** The sandstone/shale/limestone sequence might indicate that the shoreline was moving away from the area of deposition or that the land area from which the sediments came was being worn down. This sequence goes with sea transgression or land subsidence.

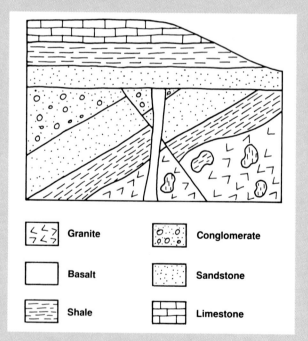

⧼ Granite	⧼ Conglomerate
Basalt	Sandstone
Shale	Limestone

Science Background

Geologic Timetable: The geologic timetable was developed over a long period of time and often through lengthy and sometimes heated debates. A good example is the problem that developed between Adam Sedgwick and Roderick Murchison, two British geologists working in Wales. Sedgwick was mapping the Cambrian while Murchison mapped the

Silurian. As mapping continued, it became apparent that each had mapped a portion of the other's rocks as part of his system. The result was that two former friends feuded for the rest of their lives over the duplicated rocks. A compromise did not occur until years later, when the rocks in question were removed from both systems and given the name Ordovician.

Unconformities: Unconformities fall into three major groups. An *angular unconformity* occurs when one series of rock layers meets another series at an angle— the layers above and below the unconformity are not parallel. A famous example of an angular unconformity occurs in the Grand Canyon of the Colorado River, where flat-lying Paleozoic layers rest on tilted upper Precambrian layers.

ANGULAR UNCONFORMITY

DISCONFORMITY

NONCONFORMITY

No tilting or faulting is involved in a *disconformity*. The layers below the disconformity have been uplifted, eroded, and then have subsided to be buried under other layers. (It is also possible for layers to be removed by submarine erosion.) The layers above and below the disconformity are horizontal and parallel, so this type of unconformity is difficult to

detect. Sometimes disconformities can be detected only by determining the geologic age of each layer. In parts of the Grand Canyon, Mississippian layers rest disconformably upon Cambrian layers— Silurian and Ordovician layers are missing. Both the Mississippian and Cambrian layers are horizontal.

A *nonconformity* occurs when younger sedimentary rocks rest on older crystalline rocks that have been uplifted and eroded. The younger sedimentary rocks were deposited on the erosion surface when the area later subsided. An example occurs in the Granite Gorge of the Grand Canyon, where Cambrian layers rest nonconformably on Precambrian crystalline rocks.

Lesson II: The Fossil Record

(Topics 4–8)

Science Background

The woolly mammoths were preserved by freezing. The most famous is the Berezovka mammoth, named for its discovery on the Berezovka River in Siberia in 1900. The frozen carcass was discovered by a hunter's dog that apparently smelled the raw meat. The Berezovka mammoth is thought to have died 45 000 years ago, when a cliff edge beneath the mammoth collapsed and the animal was buried in dirt. Several of the animal's bones were broken, and partly-chewed food was found in its mouth and on its teeth. The discovery of a complete baby mammoth in 1976 enabled scientists to even analyze mammoth blood. Other mammoths or parts of mammoths have been found in the permafrost of Siberia and Alaska.

Lesson III: Measuring Absolute Time

(Topics 9–14)

Science Background

A major problem in radiometric age dating is that no method measures the time interval between about 50 000 years and one million years ago very well. This interval in Earth's history is particularly important to scientists wishing to study the origin of humans. Recently, several new methods of measuring absolute time in that span have been developed. One of these methods is *thermoluminescence* (TL). This method is based on the light given off when a material previously subjected to natural radioactive bombardment is heated to a high temperature. The bombardment causes some of the electrons to be trapped within the mineral structure or other areas of the rock. Heating the rock releases these trapped particles as a flash of light that can be measured with a photomultiplier. Older rocks give off larger flashes. This method has yielded interesting but controversial dates on flint tools discarded into hearth fires. (The fire resets the flint's "electron clock" to zero. The TL age is therefore a measure of how long ago an early human threw the flint into the fire.)

A second new method of radioactive dating is *electron spin resonance* (ESR). This method also depends upon the natural radioactive bombardment of the material over time. However, ESR measures the number of electrons still trapped in the rock. This means that the measurement can be repeated many times on a given sample (as opposed to TL, which can be done only once). ESR is particularly effective on dating tooth enamel.

Several other techniques for dating are also now available. One is amino acid racemization. This technique utilizes the ratio between two different forms of amino acid preserved in fossil bones. Another technique is fission-track dating. This method uses the tracks made by alpha particles leaving radioactive nuclei during decay. Treating a mineral crystal with acid enables the tracks to be seen with a microscope. Older rocks have more tracks.

CHAPTER 32 MAP ACTIVITY
Interpreting Geologic History

■ A student report sheet for this activity can be found in the *Laboratory Investigations* booklet.

Time estimate
35-35 minutes

Process Skills
■ Interpreting Diagrams: Procedure 1, 2, 6, 9; Analysis and Conclusions 2, 3
■ Calculating: Procedure 3, 4
■ Determining Cause and Effect: Procedure 5, 10, 11; Analysis and Conclusions 1, 4

Answers—Procedure

1. The Green River begins in the Rocky Mountains and is a tributary of the Colorado River.

2. The right side is the north edge; the top edge is east.

3. The map is about 2.5 miles by 2.9 miles. Based upon that data, the area is 7.25 or 7.3 (to the nearest tenth) square miles.

4. From the bottom of the Green River to the peak in the Weber Formation, the total relief is about 1400 ft.

5. The calcareous sandstone is cemented together with calcite while the quartzitic sandstone is cemented with quartz. The Weber and Morgan formations both have calcareous sandstones while the Navajo and Uinta Mountain are quartzitic sandstones. Rocks with calcite cement should bubble in acid.

6. Morgan, Weber, and Park City are Paleozoic; Dinwoody, Moenkopi, Shinarump, Chinle, Navajo, and Carmel are Mesozoic.

7. The Moenkopi is the next younger rock unit; the Park City is next older. You would walk north (or NNW) to reach the younger formation (the Moenkopi) and south (or SSE) to reach the older (the Park City).

8. The Navajo Sandstone is the youngest because it is at the top; law of superposition.

9. The Uinta Mountain Group and the Morgan Formation are in contact with the fault. The fault is younger than either rock unit because it cuts across both; law of cross-cutting relationships.

10. Such surfaces are called unconformities. The Moenkopi was raised above sea level, eroded, and then buried under Shinarump sediments.

11. The Park City Formation forms the rim of the canyon. It must be more resistant to erosion than the units above it.

Answers—Analysis and Conclusions

1. The large sand grains are older than the sandstone; the law of included fragments states that pieces of one rock in another rock must be older.

2. The Morgan at 45° has a steeper dip than the Dinwoody at 19°. This difference is also shown in the cross-section where the Morgan dip increases toward the surface.

3. The two dip in opposite directions. The Uinta Mountain Group has a generally northern dip while the Uinta Fault dips toward the south.

4. The dip of the Park City is nearly horizontal. The unit does not disappear underground until surface elevations rise above it into younger rocks.

ANSWERS TO

CHAPTER 32 REVIEW

Review

1–v, 2–u, 3–e, 4–c, 5–y, 6–s, 7–d, 8–m, 9–g, 10–q, 11–k, 12–j, 13–b, 14–w, 15–t, 16–i, 17–f, 18–x, 19–r, 20–p

Interpret and Apply

1. Archean and Proterozoic rocks rarely contain fossils, the best method of correlation.

2. This is largely a result of the presence in the fall of decaying leaves and other plant material from trees, shrubs, and grasses.

3. No. Although the bone was once part of a living thing, the dinosaur lived too long ago for a measurable amount of C-14 to be left. C-14 cannot be used to date back more than about 100 000 years. The dinosaurs became extinct 65 million years ago.

4. The date will be the time the feldspar formed. Since its formation, the feldspar has been weathered from the bedrock and deposited in the arkose. The time of formation of the arkose could not be determined by this method.

Critical Thinking

1. 50%. The first half-life uses one half of the model circle. Also, one half-life is the time needed for half of the radioactive material to decay.

2. 25%. 75% has decayed.

3. 6 billion years

4. No, only half because each half-life uses up only half of the remaining material.

5. 3 grams. Half of the 24 grams decayed during the first half-life, half of the remainder during the second half-life, and half again during the third. 12 grams + 6 grams + 3 grams = a total of 21 grams. That leaves only 3 grams.

6. 160 grams. Four half-lives means that the amount of material has been cut in half four times. Therefore, there must have been 20 grams at the end of the third half-life, 40 grams at the end of the second half-life, 80 grams at the end of the first half-life, and 160 grams at the start. Or just double 10 four times– 20, 40, 80, 160.

CHAPTER **33**
Precambrian Through Paleozoic

PLANNING CHART

Topic	Support Material
Lesson I **Precambrian Time**	
1 What Is Precambrian Time?	**Content Evaluation:** p. 617 *Topic Review:* 1; p. 626-627 *Chapter Review:* 1
2 Precambrian Life	**Content Evaluation:** p. 617 *Topic Review:* 2; p. 626-627 *Chapter Review:* 2; *Interpret and Apply:* 1
3 Precambrian Rock Record	**Content Evaluation:** p. 617 *Topic Review:* 3; p. 626-627 *Chapter Review:* 3, 4; *Interpret and Apply:* 2
4 Precambrian Mineral Deposits	**Content Evaluation:** p. 617 *Topic Review:* 4; p. 626-627 *Chapter Review:* 5
Lesson II **The Paleozoic Era**	**Laboratory Investigation:** Rock Correlation **In-Text Lab Activity:** Analysis of Brachiopod Fossils
5 Introduction to the Paleozoic Era	**Content Evaluation:** p. 623 *Topic Review:* 5; p. 626-627 *Chapter Review:* 6
6 The Cambrian Period	**Content Evaluation:** p. 623 *Topic Review:* 6; p. 626-627 *Chapter Review:* 7, 8; *Interpret and Apply:* 4
7 The Ordovician Period	**Content Evaluation:** p. 623 *Topic Review:* 7; p. 626-627 *Chapter Review:* 9, 10; *Interpret and Apply:* 3
8 The Silurian Period	**Content Evaluation:** p. 623 *Topic Review:* 8; p. 626-627 *Chapter Review:* 11; *Interpret and Apply:* 1
9 The Devonian Period	**Content Evaluation:** p. 623 *Topic Review:* 9; p. 626-627 *Chapter Review:* 12, 13
10 The Mississippian Period	**Content Evaluation:** p. 623 *Topic Review:* 10; p. 626-627 *Chapter Review:* 14, 15; *Interpret and Apply:* 3
11 The Pennsylvanian Period	**Content Evaluation:** p. 623 *Topic Review:* 11; p. 626-627 *Chapter Review:* 16, 17; *Interpret and Apply:* 1, 4
12 The Permian Period	**Content Evaluation:** p. 623 *Topic Review:* 12; p. 626-627 *Chapter Review:* 18, 19
13 The Close of the Paleozoic Era	**Content Evaluation:** p. 623 *Topic Review:* 13; p. 626-627 *Chapter Review:* 20; *Interpret and Apply:* 5

Topic	Support Material
Lab Activity p. 624-625	Analysis of Brachiopod Fossils
Chapter Review p. 626-627	Critical Thinking 1-7 **Study Guide:** Vocabulary; Interpreting and Applying
Chapter 33 Assessment Program	**Chapter Tests; Computer Test Bank**

CHAPTER 33

Motivator

This motivator is designed to start the chapter and the first lesson as well as to stress an important fact about geologic time. Give each student a metric ruler and a sheet of paper. Then have each student complete the following steps:

1. Draw a line 10 centimeters down the middle of the paper.
2. Label the top of the line *NOW*.
3. Label the bottom of the line *ORIGIN OF EARTH*.
4. Measure 0.1 cm, 0.6 cm, and 1.3 cm down from the *NOW* mark. Mark each location.

When their plots are completed, tell students that their line represents all of geologic time drawn to scale. Ask students which interval on the line is the Precambrian. Have them label that interval. Stress that most of geologic time is Precambrian. Have your students determine the percent of geologic time that is Precambrian. (Since the Precambrian is all but 1.3 centimeters of a 10.0 centimeter line, Precambrian must be all but 13 percent of geologic time, or 87 percent.)

Have students label the other intervals on the line as well. The interval from *NOW* to 0.1 cm is the Cenozoic Era, from 0.1 cm to 0.6 cm is the Mesozoic, and from 0.6 cm to 1.3 cm is the Paleozoic. The Paleozoic Era, the second longest interval on the line, is the topic of Lesson II of this chapter.

If you wish to add Archean and Proterozoic to the drawing, Archean will plot from 5.6 to 8.4 centimeters and Proterozoic from 1.3 to 5.6 centi-

meters. The span from 8.4 to 10.0 centimeters is not Archean because Archean does not start until some evidence of life occurs in the rock record.

Lesson I: Precambrian Time

(Topics 1–4)

Teaching Suggestions

This lesson covers a number of ideas about Precambrian time. Emphasize these important points:

- Precambrian represents most of geologic time.
- Precambrian fossils are not common. Stromatolites are the best example. Stromatolites are still forming today in warm, shallow water areas.
- The Precambrian rock record is difficult to interpret because: 1) Precambrian encompasses such a long interval of time; 2) many Precambrian rocks are severely deformed; and 3) there are no Precambrian index fossils.
- Precambrian rocks can be found in shield areas. These are the exposed parts of cratons— the "backbone" of the continent. Four mountain-building episodes have been identified for the rocks of the Canadian Shield, the latest being the Grenville Orogeny about 1 billion years ago.
- Precambrian rocks contain about half of the world's metallic ore deposits. Important deposits are located in or near: Sudbury, Ontario (nickel); Lake Superior region (iron); Great Bear Lake, Canada (uranium);

Adirondack Mountains (iron, titanium); and South Africa (gold).

Lesson II:
The Paleozoic Era

(Topics 5–13)

Teaching Suggestions

Hands-on exposure to fossils is important for this lesson. If actual Paleozoic fossils are not available, consider purchasing the plastic models that are available from most science suppliers. In many ways, the plastic models are superior to actual samples because they show details clearly and are relatively indestructible.

A good way to start this lesson is by showing fossil bivalves and brachiopods. Ask students for ways in which the two kinds of shells are different. The difference between brachiopod and bivalve shells is a classic question for beginning paleontology students. In brachiopods, each valve is symmetrical on either side of a central axis. However, the two valves of a brachiopod are not symmetrical to each other. The two valves of a bivalve are mirror images of each other, but the single valve is not symmetrical. Be prepared to define *symmetrical*.

After discussing the shells, move to a discussion of the material in the lesson. Although this lesson appears long, try not to spend more than one class period on it. Developing a chart like the one shown below may help to emphasize the important points in a minimum of class time:

Science Background

The names of the other periods of the Paleozoic originated in ways similar to the examples in the text. Ordovician is named for the Ordovices, an ancient tribe that lived in the part of Wales where rocks of this age were first studied . Silurian is named for the Silures, people who lived in the part of England and Wales where these rocks were first studied. Devonian is named for Devonshire, England.

Both brachiopods and bivalves still exist today. However, the brachiopods were far more abundant during the early Paleozoic. Bivalves, on the other hand, have done well throughout geologic time and exist today in considerable abundance and variety.

CHAPTER 33 LAB ACTIVITY
Analysis of Brachiopod Fossils

■ A student report sheet for this activity can be found in the *Laboratory Investigations* booklet.

Time estimate
35–45 minutes

Process Skills
- Constructing Tables and Graphs: Procedure 5
- Analyzing Data: Analysis and Conclusions 1, 2, 4
- Classifying: Analysis and Conclusions 5, 6
- Stating a Conclusion: Analysis and Conclusions 7

Materials
Molded plastic sheets with casts of two kinds of brachiopods are available from science supply houses. These can be used in this activity instead of (or in addition to) the data in Data Table A. Beside ridge number, the length, width, or height of each fossil could be determined and plotted on a variety of graphs. For example,

Period	Important Fossils	Important Events
Cambrian	Trilobites, brachiopods	First abundant fossil record (Burgess shale), first fish
Ordovician	Graptolites	Taconic Orogeny
Silurian	Eurypterids	First land animals; salt and gypsum in northeast
Devonian	Coral reefs	Age of Fishes, first amphibians, first forests
Mississippian	Crinoids, foraminifera	
Pennsylvanian		Coal swamps, first reptiles
Permian		Rock salt, gypsum in west, ice age in Southern Hemisphere; Pangaea forms; many life forms die out

plotting length versus width should yield a scatter graph of points in a cluster. If two different types of plastic sheet are used, two groups of scattered points should result.

Answers—Procedure

Answers to *Procedure* questions 1-3 can be found on the annotated Data Table B on page 625 of this Teachers Annotated Edition.

6. The medians for Population 1 and 2 are 11 and 18 respectively.

Answers—Analysis and Conclusions

1. Both the modes and the medians of Population 1 and 2 are 11 and 18 respectively.
2. There is very little overlap between the two graphs. The modes and medians of the two graphs are also different. One can conclude that the two populations are distinct.
3. Measure the dimensions of the shells—length or width or thickness.
4. The number of ridges most closely matches the number of ridges in Population 1.
5. Because brachiopods with 14 and 15 ridges were found in both populations, one cannot determine to which population these new fossils belong based on the number of ridges.
6. The graph would be skewed to the right.
7. The number of ridges increased over time.

ANSWERS TO

CHAPTER 33 R E V I E W

Review

1–fossil, 2–shallow; not deep, 3–index, 4–shield, 5–Precambrian, 6–America, 7–trilobites, 8–Cambrian, 9–fish, 10–fossil, 11–Silurian, 12–Devonian, 13–east, 14–sea, 15–shells, 16–coal, 17–dragonfly, 18–dry, 19–ice, 20–extinct

Interpret and Apply

1. Coal beds form from trees and other land plant material. Land plants did not evolve until the Paleozoic.
2. Sedimentary rocks are made of bits and pieces of other rocks. The original rock must have been igneous.
3. Basically, graptolites are floaters and can be carried to all parts of the oceans. Crinoids spend most of their lives attached to the seafloor.
4. During the Cambrian, the land surface would have either been barren or covered with an algal mat. There were no advanced land plants.
5. Since almost all of the land areas were joined at the time of Pangaea, land plants and animals could spread throughout the world. In fact, the occurrence of identical animals in the fossil record of Africa and South America is evidence for continental drift (Chapter 13, Topic 4).

Critical Thinking

1. Ordovician
2. Cambrian to Mississippian
3. Neither occurred in Mississippian-age rocks.
4. Mississippian, the only age common to both fossils
5. Silurian, the only period common to both
6. *Actinostroma, Hallopora, Atrypa, Eurypterus, Phacops*
7. Because, according to the text, trilobites are the most abundant fossil of the Cambrian and lived until the Permian. Neither of these trilobites lived over the entire range. Other trilobites must have lived during the other times and are just not listed.

CHAPTER 34
The Mesozoic and Cenozoic Eras

PLANNING CHART

Topic	Support Material
Lesson I **The Mesozoic Era**	**In-Text Lab Activity:** How Big Was That Dinosaur?
1 Highlights of the Mesozoic Era	**Content Evaluation:** p. 633 *Topic Review:* 1; p. 642-643 *Chapter Review:* 1
2 Continent Formation	**Content Evaluation:** p. 633 *Topic Review:* 2; p. 642-643 *Chapter Review:* 2; Interpret and Apply: 1; **Transparency 50:** Formation of Modern Continents
3 The Rise of the Dinosaurs	**Content Evaluation:** p. 633 *Topic Review:* 3; p. 642-643 *Chapter Review:* 3, 4
4 Other Land Animals	**Content Evaluation:** p. 633 *Topic Review:* 4; p. 642-643 *Chapter Review:* 5
5 Marine Life	**Content Evaluation:** p. 633 *Topic Review:* 5; p. 642-643 *Chapter Review:* 6
6 Land Plants	**Content Evaluation:** p. 633 *Topic Review:* 6; p. 642-643 *Chapter Review:* 7
7 The Mesozoic Era Closes	**Content Evaluation:** p. 633 *Topic Review:* 7; p. 642-643 *Chapter Review:* 8; Interpret and Apply: 2
Lesson II **The Cenozoic Era**	**Laboratory Investigation:** Using Fossils
8 Highlights of the Cenozoic Era	**Content Evaluation:** p. 639 *Topic Review:* 8; p. 642-643 *Chapter Review:* 9, 10; Interpret and Apply: 3
9 Crustal Activity in the Cenozoic Era	**Content Evaluation:** p. 639 *Topic Review:* 9; p. 642-643 *Chapter Review:* 11
10 Rise of the Mammals	**Content Evaluation:** p. 639 *Topic Review:* 10; p. 642-643 *Chapter Review:* 12
11 Other Cenozoic Animals	**Content Evaluation:** p. 639 *Topic Review:* 11; p. 642-643 *Chapter Review:* 13
12 Plant Life	**Content Evaluation:** p. 639 *Topic Review:* 12; p. 642-643 *Chapter Review:* 14

PLANNING CHART (continued)

Topic	Support Material
Lesson II (continued) **13 The Rise of Humans**	**Content Evaluation:** p. 639 *Topic Review:* 13; p. 642-643 *Chapter Review:* 15
14 The Past 11 000 Years	**Content Evaluation:** p. 639 *Topic Review:* 14; p. 642-643 *Chapter Review:* 16
Lab Activity p. 640-641	How Big Was That Dinosaur?
Chapter Review p. 642-643	Critical Thinking 1-9 **Study Guide:** Vocabulary; Interpreting and Applying
Chapter 34 Assessment Program	**Chapter Tests; Computer Test Bank**

CHAPTER 34

Motivator

DEMONSTRATION: This demonstration will require some advance preparation, but it shows your students the frustration faced by vertebrate paleontologists in reconstructing skeletons. Collect as many different kinds of bones as possible—chicken, turkey, beef, and so on. The bones should all be separate, clean, and dry. They need not be entire specimens; pieces of bone are fine. Place all of the bones together in a single box.

In class, hold up a bone and ask your students to identify the animal from which it came. Depending on the bone, identifying the animal may be relatively easy. Next, hold up several bones and ask students how they would go about reconstructing a skeleton. This would be extremely difficult, since you have mixed up bones from different animals and probably do not have a complete skeleton of any single animal. Use student comments to point out that vertebrate paleontologists have exactly the same problem when they dig into a rock layer, remove bones, and try to reconstruct skeletons from them. In some cases, an entire skeleton is present, but more often, bones were washed away before the skeleton was buried. In other cases, only a bone or two from an entire animal may have been preserved.

Lesson I: The Mesozoic Era

(Topics 1–7)

Science Background

An example of the problem in matching fossil bones is shown by the first two specimens of *Apatosaurus (or Brontosaurus)* that were found in Wyoming in the 1870's. Both skeletons were headless. Two skulls were finally found— one 6 kilometers away and the other 650 kilometers away. These heads were used to complete the *Apatosaurus* skeletons. Unfortunately the new skulls did not belong to *Apatosaurus.*As a result, the *Apatosaurus* at the Carnegie Museum in Pittsburgh, models made from that skeleton and shipped to other museums around the world, as well as photographs and drawings in books, all showed *Apatosaurus* with the wrong head. Although some scientists in the early 1900's suspected the error, it was not corrected until 1979.

This story as well as many other fascinating dinosaur stories can be found in *The Riddle of the Dinosaur* by John Noble Wilford, New York: Alfred A. Knopf, 1986. The evidence for warm-blooded dinosaurs can be found in *The Dinosaur Heresies* by Robert T. Bakker, New York: William Morrow and Company, Inc., 1986.

The names for the Mesozoic Era are European. The Triassic is so named because the area in Germany where these rocks were first studied has a clear division into three parts. Unfortunately that division is not as clear throughout the rest of the world's Triassic rocks. Jurassic is named for the Iura Alps between France and Switzerland. *Cretaceous* means "chalk" and is named for some rocks known as the chalk formation in England and France. This Cretaceous chalk forms the famous White Cliffs of Dover.

Lesson II:
The Cenozoic Era

(Topics 8–14)

Science Background
The original basis for naming the epochs of the Cenozoic Era was the percentage of mollusks in that epoch compared to the modern mollusk population. The breakdown is as follows:

- Pleistocene– "most recent"– 90 to 100 percent modern species
- Pliocene– "more recent"– 50 to 90 percent modern species
- Miocene– "less recent"– 20 to 40 percent modern species
- Oligocene– "little recent"– 10 to 15 percent modern species
- Eocene– "dawn recent"– 1 to 5 percent modern species
- Paleocene– "ancient recent"– 0 percent modern species

Land bridges were used for animal migration at least two times during the Cenozoic. In the Eocene, North America and Asia were joined by a land bridge between Alaska and Siberia. Two-way species traffic occurred. Horses, originally found only in North America, spread to Asia. Mastodons from Asia moved into North America. Mastodons had earlier spread from Africa to Europe and Asia. In the Pliocene, the Isthmus of Panama formed, connecting North and South America for the first time. The giant armadillo, the giant ground sloth, and the opossum came to North America. Camels,

horses, mastodons, and wild pigs spread to South America. In time, more than 20 mammal families had members on both continents. Horses and camels became extinct in North America in the Pleistocene after the northern land bridge had ceased to exist. Horses were brought back to North America by early Spanish explorers.

The origins of modern humans is constantly being debated. You may wish to have students do some research on this controversial subject. African-American students in particular may be interested in exploring the "mitochondiral Eve" theory, which suggests that the DNA of all modern humans can be traced to one African woman living some 200 000 years ago. A place to start might be the April 1992 issue of *Scientific American* in which two articles on human origins take both sides of the debate.

CHAPTER 34 LAB ACTIVITY
How Big Was That Dinosaur?

■ A student report sheet for this activity can be found in the *Laboratory Investigations* booklet.

Time estimate
60–70 minutes

Process Skills
- Measuring: Procedure 2, 3
- Calculating: Procedure 5, 6, 7, 8, 9, 12, 14
- Analyzing Data: Analysis and Conclusions 1, 2, 3

Materials
Dinosaur models can be purchased from toy stores for under $2.00 per package of about 20 models. Look carefully at the assortment in several packages and select those with the most usable models. Larger models are available from science supply houses and may have been designed using more accurate scales. Remember that the model dinosaur's scales may very well not be the same, even if they come from the same set.

Procedural Hints
Choose how you want to approach the use of the bathroom scale for determining student weights. Remember how self-conscious an

adolescent can be about self-image, etc. Be sensitive. You may find it easier to simply weigh yourself and have your students calculate the number of *teachers* equal to the mass of one dinosaur.

The amount of reading required for this activity is tedious for some students. This is a good lab for the lab group to have a "designated reader"—one person to read the directions aloud to the others.

Answers—Analysis and Conclusions

1. This question is designed to make students think about their final answer. Students who do not arrive at reasonable, logical answers should be encouraged to recheck their measurements and arithmetic.

2. Basically, this question involves two steps: 1) determining the volume of the dinosaur; and 2) determining the volume of the classroom. There are several methods by which the volume of the dinosaur could be found, including using the model's scale or displacing an equal volume of water. The assumption about a dinosaur having a density of 1 g/cm^3 could be used with the dinosaur mass already determined. The volume of the room could be determined by measuring the dimensions and multiplying. Other methods, such as measuring the amount of water needed to fill the room, should also be accepted, even if they are impractical.

3. Scale is the key to this question. Compare the 18 centimeter long *Tyrannosaurus* tooth to the length of a human tooth. Based upon the size of the human mouth, compare the size of the dinosaur's mouth to the size of a human mouth. *Tyrannosaurus* probably could have swallowed a human whole.

Interpret and Apply

1. There would probably be less diversity, more similarity in species. African animals would be essentially the same as South American animals, North American animals essentially the same as Asian animals, and so on.

2. A nuclear war today might well have exactly the same effect on the environment as that theorized from the asteroid impact. Thick clouds would reduce insolation, plants could not grow, animals that eat the plants would die of starvation along with animals that eat other animals.

3. Sea level was lower, so the land was exposed. Presumably the animals merely grazed their way across over several generations.

Critical Thinking

1. Insects and pelecypods (bivalves). Both the insect and pelecypod columns are narrowest in Triassic and gradually widen to the top. The change in the pelecypod column, however, is not as marked as that of the insects.

2. ammonites and sauropods

3. flowering plants

4. sauropods

5. bryozoans

6. Cretaceous

7. brontotheriums, because they appear only in the Tertiary

8. less than half as abundant, perhaps 40 percent

9. Both sauropods and ammonites lived during the Mesozoic. However, sauropods lived on land and ammonites lived in the ocean. Chances are one rock would not contain both fossils.

ANSWERS TO

CHAPTER 34 REVIEW

Review

1–d, 2–a, 3–d, 4–a, 5–c, 6–d, 7–b, 8–a, 9–c, 10–a, 11–d, 12–d, 13–a, 14–a, 15–d, 16–c

Teacher's Notes

Chapter 1

Chapter 2

Chapter 3

Teacher's Notes

Chapter 4

Chapter 5

Chapter 6

Teacher's Notes

Chapter 7

Chapter 8

Chapter 9

Teacher's Notes

Chapter 10

Chapter 11

Chapter 12

Teacher's Notes

Chapter 13

Chapter 14

Chapter 15

Teacher's Notes

Chapter 16

Chapter 17

Chapter 18

Teacher's Notes

Chapter 19

Chapter 20

Chapter 21

Teacher's Notes

Chapter 22

Chapter 23

Chapter 24

Teacher's Notes

Chapter 25

Chapter 26

Chapter 27

Teacher's Notes

Chapter 28

Chapter 29

Chapter 30

Teacher's Notes

Chapter 31

Chapter 32

Chapter 33

Teacher's Notes

Chapter 34